DSS 220 Business Analytics

Saint Joseph's University Decision & System Sciences Department

Australia • Brazil • Japan • Korea • Mexico • Singapore • Spain • United Kingdom • United States

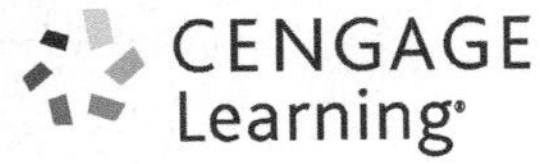

DSS 220 Business Analytics: Saint Joseph's University Decision & System Sciences Department

Quantitative Methods for Business,
Thirteenth edition
David R. Anderson, Dennis J. Sweeney,
Thomas A. Williams, Jeffrey D. Camm,
James J. Cochran, Michael J. Fry, Jeffrey
W. Ohlmann

© 2016, 2013 Cengage Learning. All rights reserved.

Essentials of Business Analytics,
Second Edition
Jeffrey D. Camm, James J. Cochran,
Michael J. Fry, Jeffrey W. Ohlmann,
David R. Anderson, Dennis J. Sweeney,
Thomas A. Williams

© 2017, 2015 Cengage Learning. All rights reserved.

ALL RIGHTS RESERVED. No part of this work covered by the copyright herein may be reproduced or distributed in any form or by any means, except as permitted by U.S. copyright law, without the prior written permission of the copyright owner.

For product information and technology assistance, contact us at
Cengage Learning Customer & Sales Support, 1-800-354-9706
For permission to use material from this text or product,
submit all requests online at **cengage.com/permissions**
Further permissions questions can be emailed to
permissionrequest@cengage.com

This book contains select works from existing Cengage Learning resources and was produced by Cengage Learning Custom Solutions for collegiate use. As such, those adopting and/or contributing to this work are responsible for editorial content accuracy, continuity and completeness.

Compilation © 2016 Cengage Learning

ISBN: 978-1-337-32373-4

Cengage Learning
20 Channel Center Street
Boston, MA 02210
USA

Cengage Learning is a leading provider of customized learning solutions with office locations around the globe, including Singapore, the United Kingdom, Australia, Mexico, Brazil, and Japan. Locate your local office at: **www.international.cengage.com/region.**

Cengage Learning products are represented in Canada by Nelson Education, Ltd.

For your lifelong learning solutions, visit **www.cengage.com/custom.**

Visit our corporate website at **www.cengage.com.**

Brief Contents

From:
Essentials of Business Analytics
Camm | Cochran

From:
Quantitative Methods for Business
Anderson | Sweeney | Wilson

Chapter 7

Linear Regression

CONTENTS

ANALYTICS IN ACTION

Alliance Data Systems*

DALLAS, TEXAS

Alliance Data Systems (ADS) provides transaction processing, credit services, and marketing services for clients in the rapidly growing customer relationship management (CRM) industry. ADS clients are concentrated in four industries: retail, petroleum/convenience stores, utilities, and transportation. In 1983, Alliance began offering end-to-end credit-processing services to the retail, petroleum, and casual dining industries; today the company employs more than 6,500 employees who provide services to clients around the world. Operating more than 140,000 point-of-sale terminals in the United States alone, ADS processes in excess of 2.5 billion transactions annually. The company ranks second in the United States in private-label credit services by representing 49 private label programs with nearly 72 million cardholders. In 2001, ADS made an initial public offering and is now listed on the New York Stock Exchange.

As one of its marketing services, ADS designs direct mail campaigns and promotions. With its database containing information on the spending habits of more than 100 million consumers, ADS can target consumers who are the most likely to benefit from a direct mail promotion. The Analytical Development Group uses regression analysis to build models that measure and predict the responsiveness of consumers to direct market campaigns. Some regression models predict the probability of purchase for individuals receiving a promotion, and others predict the amount spent by consumers who make purchases.

For one campaign, a retail store chain wanted to attract new customers. To predict the effect of the campaign, ADS analysts selected a sample from the consumer database, sent the sampled individuals promotional materials, and then collected transaction data on the consumers' responses. Sample data were collected on the amount of purchases made by the consumers responding to the campaign, as well as on a variety of consumer-specific variables thought to be useful in predicting sales. The consumer-specific variable that contributed most to predicting the amount purchased was the total amount of credit purchases at related stores over the past 39 months. ADS analysts developed an estimated regression equation relating the amount of purchase to the amount spent at related stores:

$$\hat{y} = 26.7 + 0.00205x,$$

where

$\hat{y}$ = predicted amount of purchase
x = amount spent at related stores

Using this equation, we could predict that someone spending $10,000 over the past 39 months at related stores would spend $47.20 when responding to the direct mail promotion. In this chapter, you will learn how to develop this type of estimated regression equation. The final model developed by ADS analysts also included several other variables that increased the predictive power of the preceding equation. Among these variables was the absence or presence of a bank credit card, estimated income, and the average amount spent per trip at a selected store. In this chapter, we will also learn how such additional variables can be incorporated into a multiple regression model.

*The authors are indebted to Philip Clemance, Director of Analytical Development at Alliance Data Systems, for providing this Analytics in Action.

Managerial decisions are often based on the relationship between two or more variables. For example, after considering the relationship between advertising expenditures and sales, a marketing manager might attempt to predict sales for a given level of advertising expenditures. In another case, a public utility might use the relationship between the daily high temperature and the demand for electricity to predict electricity usage on the basis of next month's anticipated daily high temperatures. Sometimes a manager will rely on intuition to judge how two variables are related. However, if data can be obtained, a statistical procedure called **regression analysis** can be used to develop an equation showing how the variables are related.

The statistical methods used in studying the relationship between two variables were first employed by Sir Francis Galton (1822–1911). Galton found that the heights of the sons of unusually tall or unusually short fathers tend to move, or "regress," toward the average height of the male population. Karl Pearson (1857–1936), a disciple of Galton, later confirmed this finding in a sample of 1,078 pairs of fathers and sons.

In regression terminology, the variable being predicted is called the **dependent variable**, or *response*, and the variables being used to predict the value of the dependent variable are called the **independent variables**, or *predictor variables*. For example, in analyzing the effect of advertising expenditures on sales, a marketing manager's desire to predict sales would suggest making sales the dependent variable. Advertising expenditure would be the independent variable used to help predict sales.

In this chapter, we begin by considering **simple linear regression**, in which the relationship between one dependent variable (denoted by y) and one independent variable (denoted by x) is approximated by a straight line. We then extend this concept to higher dimensions by introducing **multiple linear regression** to model the relationship between a dependent variable (y) and two or more independent variables ($x_1, x_2, \ldots, x_q$).

7.1 Simple Linear Regression Model

Butler Trucking Company is an independent trucking company in southern California. A major portion of Butler's business involves deliveries throughout its local area. To develop better work schedules, the managers want to estimate the total daily travel times for their drivers. The managers believe that the total daily travel times (denoted by y) are closely related to the number of miles traveled in making the daily deliveries (denoted by x). Using regression analysis, we can develop an equation showing how the dependent variable y is related to the independent variable x.

Regression Model

In the Butler Trucking Company example, a simple linear regression model hypothesizes that the travel time of a driving assignment (y) is linearly related to the number of miles traveled (x) as follows:

SIMPLE LINEAR REGRESSION MODEL

$$y = \beta_0 + \beta_1 x + \varepsilon \quad \textbf{(7.1)}$$

In equation (7.1), β_0 and β_1 are population parameters that describe the y-intercept and slope of the line relating y and x. The error term ε (Greek letter epsilon) accounts for the variability in y that cannot be explained by the linear relationship between x and y. The simple linear regression model assumes that the error term is a normally distributed random variable with a mean of zero and constant variance for all observations.

Estimated Regression Equation

In practice, the values of the population parameters β_0 and β_1 are not known and must be estimated using sample data. Sample statistics (denoted b_0 and b_1) are computed as estimates of the population parameters β_0 and β_1. Substituting the values of the sample statistics b_0 and b_1 for β_0 and β_1 in equation (7.1) and dropping the error term (because its expected value is zero), we obtain the **estimated regression** for simple linear regression:

ESTIMATED SIMPLE LINEAR REGRESSION EQUATION

$$\hat{y} = b_0 + b_1 x \quad \textbf{(7.2)}$$

The estimation of β_0 and β_1 is a statistical process much like the estimation of the population mean, μ, discussed in Chapter 6. β_0 and β_1 are the unknown parameters of interest, and b_0 and b_1 are the sample statistics used to estimate the parameters.

FIGURE 7.1 The Estimation Process in Simple Linear Regression

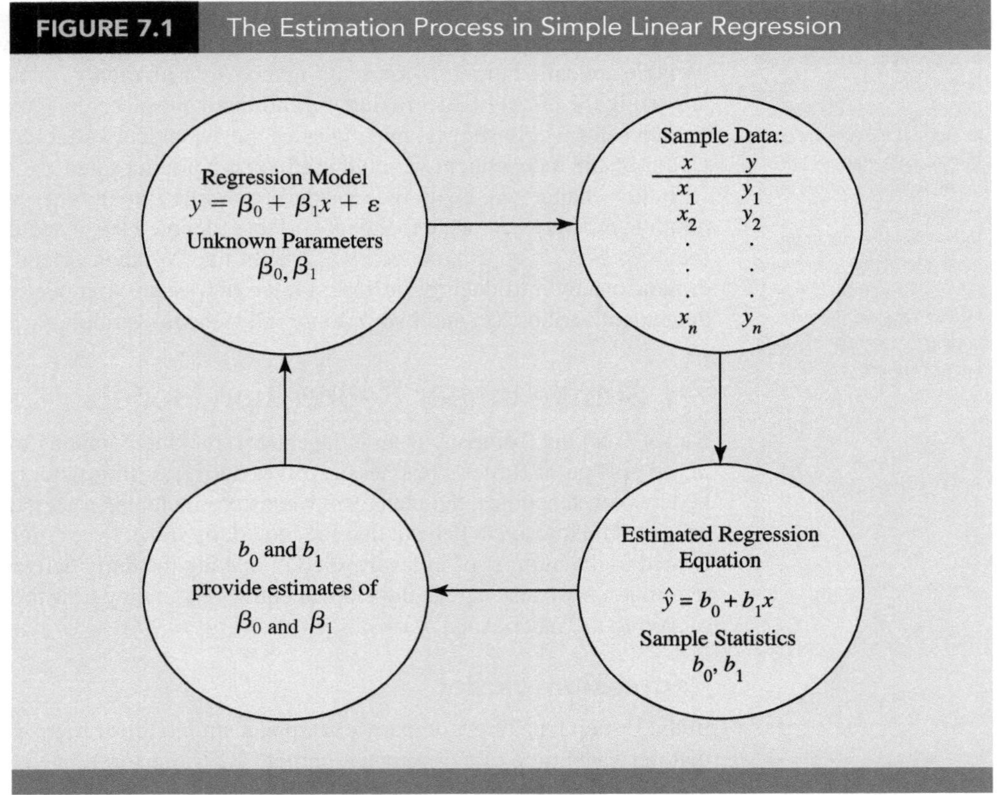

Figure 7.1 provides a summary of the estimation process for simple linear regression. Using equation (7.2), $\hat{y}$ provides an estimate for the mean value of y corresponding to a given value of x.

The graph of the estimated simple linear regression equation is called the *estimated regression line*; b_0 is the estimated y-intercept, and b_1 is the estimated slope. In the next section, we show how the least squares method can be used to compute the values of b_0 and b_1 in the estimated regression equation.

Examples of possible regression lines are shown in Figure 7.2. The regression line in Panel A shows that the estimated mean value of y is related positively to x, with larger values of $\hat{y}$ associated with larger values of x. In Panel B, the estimated mean value of y is related negatively to x, with smaller values of $\hat{y}$ associated with larger values of x. In Panel C, the estimated mean value of y is not related to x; that is, $\hat{y}$ is the same for every value of x.

In general, $\hat{y}$ is the **point estimator** of $E(y|x)$, the mean value of y for a given value of x. Thus, to estimate the mean or expected value of travel time for a driving assignment of 75 miles, Butler trucking would substitute the value of 75 for x in equation (7.2). In some cases, however, Butler Trucking may be more interested in predicting travel time for an upcoming driving assignment of a particular length. For example, suppose Butler Trucking would like to predict travel time for a new 75-mile driving assignment the company is considering. As it turns out, the best predictor of y for a given value of x is also provided by $\hat{y}$. Thus, to predict travel time for a new 75-mile driving assignment, Butler Trucking would also substitute the value of 75 for x in equation (7.3). The value of $\hat{y}$ provides both

A point estimator is a single value used as an estimate of the corresponding population parameter.

FIGURE 7.2 Possible Regression Lines in Simple Linear Regression

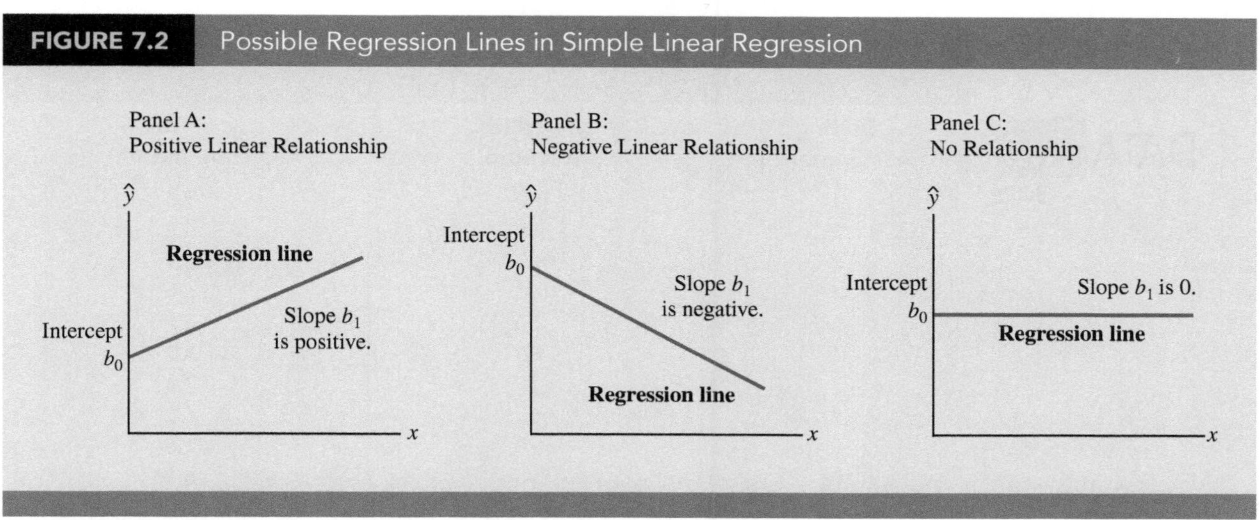

a point estimate of $E(y|x)$ for a given value of x and a prediction of an individual value of y for a given value of x. In most cases, we will refer to $\hat{y}$ simply as the predicted value of y.

7.2 Least Squares Method

The **least squares method** is a procedure for using sample data to find the estimated regression equation. To illustrate the least squares method, suppose data were collected from a sample of 10 Butler Trucking Company driving assignments. For the ith observation or driving assignment in the sample, x_i is the miles traveled and y_i is the travel time (in hours). The values of x_i and y_i for the 10 driving assignments in the sample are summarized in Table 7.1. We see that driving assignment 1, with $x_1 = 100$ and $y_1 = 9.3$, is a driving assignment of 100 miles and a travel time of 9.3 hours. Driving assignment 2, with $x_2 = 50$ and $y_2 = 4.8$, is a driving assignment of 50 miles and a travel time of 4.8 hours. The shortest travel time is for driving assignment 5, which requires 50 miles with a travel time of 4.2 hours.

Figure 7.3 is a scatter chart of the data in Table 7.1. Miles traveled is shown on the horizontal axis, and travel time (in hours) is shown on the vertical axis. Scatter charts for regression analysis are constructed with the independent variable x on the horizontal axis and the dependent variable y on the vertical axis. The scatter chart enables us to observe the data graphically and to draw preliminary conclusions about the possible relationship between the variables.

What preliminary conclusions can be drawn from Figure 7.3? Longer travel times appear to coincide with more miles traveled. In addition, for these data, the relationship between the travel time and miles traveled appears to be approximated by a straight line; indeed, a positive linear relationship is indicated between x and y. We therefore choose the simple linear regression model to represent this relationship. Given that choice, our next task is to use the sample data in Table 7.1 to determine the values of b_0 and b_1 in the estimated simple linear regression equation. For the ith driving assignment, the estimated regression equation provides:

$$\hat{y}_i = b_0 + b_1x_i, \tag{7.3}$$

where

$\hat{y}_i$ = predicted travel time (in hours) for the ith driving assignment
b_0 = the y-intercept of the estimated regression line

TABLE 7.1 Miles Traveled and Travel Time for 10 Butler Trucking Company Driving Assignments

Driving Assignment i	x = Miles Traveled	y = Travel Time (hours)
1	100	9.3
2	50	4.8
3	100	8.9
4	100	6.5
5	50	4.2
6	80	6.2
7	75	7.4
8	65	6.0
9	90	7.6
10	90	6.1

b_1 = the slope of the estimated regression line
x_i = miles traveled for the ith driving assignment

With y_i denoting the observed (actual) travel time for driving assignment i and $\hat{y}_i$ in equation (7.3) representing the predicted travel time for driving assignment i, every driving assignment in the sample will have an observed travel time y_i and a predicted travel time $\hat{y}_i$. For the estimated regression line to provide a good fit to the data, the differences between the observed travel times y_i and the predicted travel times $\hat{y}_i$ should be small.

The least squares method uses the sample data to provide the values of b_0 and b_1 that minimize the sum of the squares of the deviations between the observed values of the

FIGURE 7.3 Scatter Chart of Miles Traveled and Travel Time for Sample of 10 Butler Trucking Company Driving Assignments

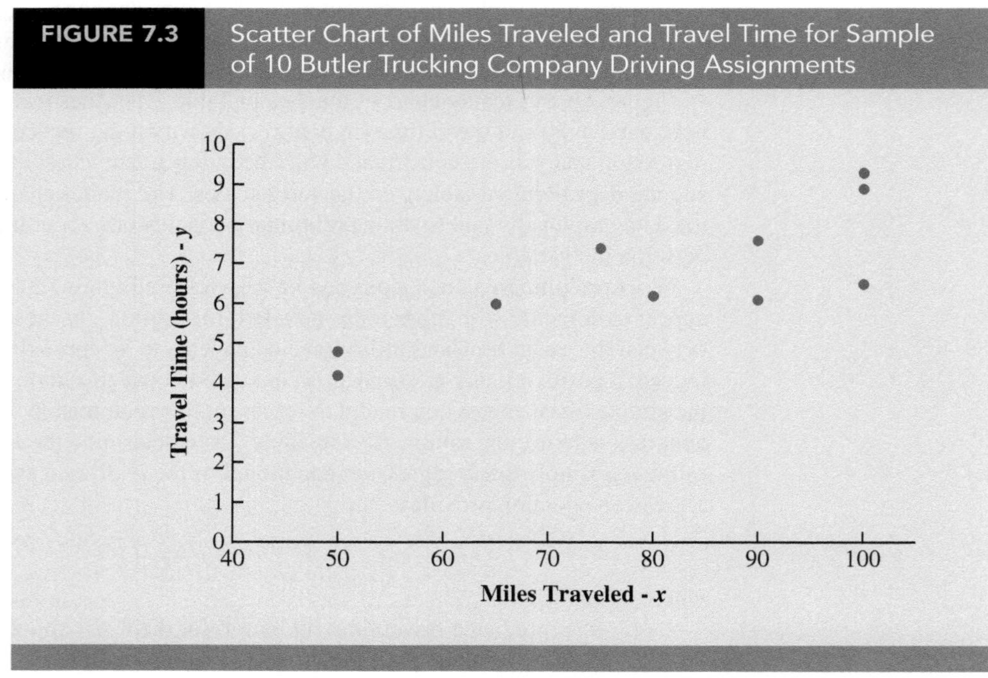

dependent variable y_i and the predicted values of the dependent variable $\hat{y}_i$. The criterion for the least squares method is given by equation (7.4).

LEAST SQUARES EQUATION

$$\min \sum_{i=1}^{n} (y_i - \hat{y}_i)^2 = \min \sum_{i=1}^{n} (y_1 - b_0 - b_1 x_1)^2 \quad \textbf{(7.4)}$$

where

y_i = observed value of the dependent variable for the ith observation
$\hat{y}_i$ = predicted value of the dependent variable for the ith observation
n = total number of observations

This is known as the least squares method for estimating the regression equation.

The error we make using the regression model to estimate the mean value of the dependent variable for the ith observation is often written as $e_i = y_i - \hat{y}_i$ and is referred to as the ith **residual**. Using this notation, equation (7.4) can be rewritten as:

$$\min \sum_{i=1}^{n} e_i^2$$

and we say that we are finding the regression that minimizes the sum of squared errors.

Least Squares Estimates of the Regression Parameters

Although the values of b_0 and b_1 that minimize equation (7.3) can be calculated manually with equations (see note at end of this section), computer software such as Excel or XLMiner is generally used to calculate b_1 and b_0. For the Butler Trucking Company data in Table 7.1, an estimated slope of $b_1 = 0.0678$ and a y-intercept of $b_0 = 1.2739$ minimize the sum of squared errors (in the next section we show how to use Excel to obtain these values). Thus, our estimated simple linear regression model is $\hat{y} = 1.2739 + 0.0678x_1$.

We interpret b_1 and b_0 as we would the y-intercept and slope of any straight line. The slope b_1 is the estimated change in the mean of the dependent variable y that is associated with a one-unit increase in the independent variable x. For the Butler Trucking Company model, we therefore estimate that, if the length of a driving assignment were 1 unit (1 mile) longer, the mean travel time for that driving assignment would be 0.0678 unit (0.0678 hour, or approximately 4 minutes) longer. The y-intercept b_0 is the estimated value of the dependent variable y when the independent variable x is equal to 0. For the Butler Trucking Company model, we estimate that if the driving distance for a driving assignment was 0 units (0 miles), the mean travel time would be 1.2739 units (1.2739 hours, or approximately 76 minutes). Can we find a plausible explanation for this? Perhaps the 76 minutes represent the time needed to prepare, load, and unload the vehicle, which is required for all trips regardless of distance and which therefore does not depend on the distance traveled. However, we must use caution: To estimate the travel time for a driving distance of 0 miles, we have to extend the relationship we have found with simple linear regression well beyond the range of values for driving distance in our sample. Those sample values range from 50 to 100 miles, and this range represents the only values of driving distance for which we have empirical evidence of the relationship between driving distance and our estimated travel time.

It is important to note that the regression model is valid only over the **experimental region**, which is the range of values of the independent variables in the data used to estimate the model. Prediction of the value of the dependent variable outside the experimental region is called **extrapolation** and is risky. Because we have no empirical evidence that the relationship we have found holds true for values of x outside of the range of values of x in

The estimated value of the y-intercept often results from extrapolation.

the data used to estimate the relationship, extrapolation is risky and should be avoided if possible. For Butler Trucking, this means that any prediction outside the travel time for a driving distance less than 50 miles or greater than 100 miles is not a reliable estimate, and so for this model the estimate of β_0 is meaningless. However, if the experimental region for a regression problem includes zero, the y-intercept will have a meaningful interpretation.

We can now also use this model and our known values for miles traveled for a driving assignment (x) to estimate mean travel time in hours. For example, the first driving assignment in Table 7.1 has a value for miles traveled of $x = 100$. We estimate the mean travel time in hours for this driving assignment to be:

The point estimate $\hat{y}$ provided by the regression equation does not give us any information about the precision associated with the prediction. For that we must develop an interval estimate around the point estimate. In the appendix at the end of the chapter, we demonstrate how to generate interval estimates around the point estimates provided by a regression equation.

$$\hat{y}_i = 1.2739 + 0.0678(100) = 8.0539.$$

Since the travel time for this driving assignment was 9.3 hours, this regression estimate would have resulted in a residual of:

$$e_1 = y_1 - \hat{y}_i = 9.3 - 8.0539 = 1.2461.$$

The simple linear regression model underestimated travel time for this driving assignment by 1.2461 hours (approximately 74 minutes). Table 7.2 shows the predicted mean travel times, the residuals, and the squared residuals for all 10 driving assignments in the sample data.

Note in Table 7.2 that:

- The sum of predicted values $\hat{y}_i$ is equal to the sum of the values of the dependent variable y.
- The sum of the residuals e_i is 0.
- The sum of the squared residuals e_i^2 has been minimized.

These three points will always be true for a simple linear regression that is determined by equations (7.6) and (7.7). Figure 7.4 shows the simple linear regression line $\hat{y}_i = 1.2739 + 0.0678x_i$ superimposed on the scatter chart for the Butler Trucking Company data in Table 7.1. This figure, which also highlights the residuals for driving assignment 3 (e_3) and driving assignment 5 (e_5), shows that the regression model underpredicts travel time for some driving assignments (such as driving assignment 3) and overpredicts travel time for others (such as driving assignment 5), but in general appears to fit the data relatively well.

TABLE 7.2 Predicted Travel Time and Residuals for 10 Butler Trucking Company Driving Assignments

Driving Assignment i	x = Miles Traveled	y = Travel Time (hours)	$\hat{y}_i = b_0 + b_1x_i$	$e_i = y_i - \hat{y}_i$	e_i^2
1	100	9.3	8.0565	1.2435	1.5463
2	50	4.8	4.6652	0.1348	0.0182
3	100	8.9	8.0565	0.8435	0.7115
4	100	6.5	8.0565	−1.5565	2.4227
5	50	4.2	4.6652	−0.4652	0.2164
6	80	6.2	6.7000	−0.5000	0.2500
7	75	7.4	6.3609	1.0391	1.0797
8	65	6.0	5.6826	0.3174	0.1007
9	90	7.6	7.3783	0.2217	0.0492
10	90	6.1	7.3783	−1.2783	1.6341
	Totals	67.0	67.0000	0.0000	8.0288

FIGURE 7.4 Scatter Chart of Miles Traveled and Travel Time for Butler Trucking Company Driving Assignments with Regression Line Superimposed

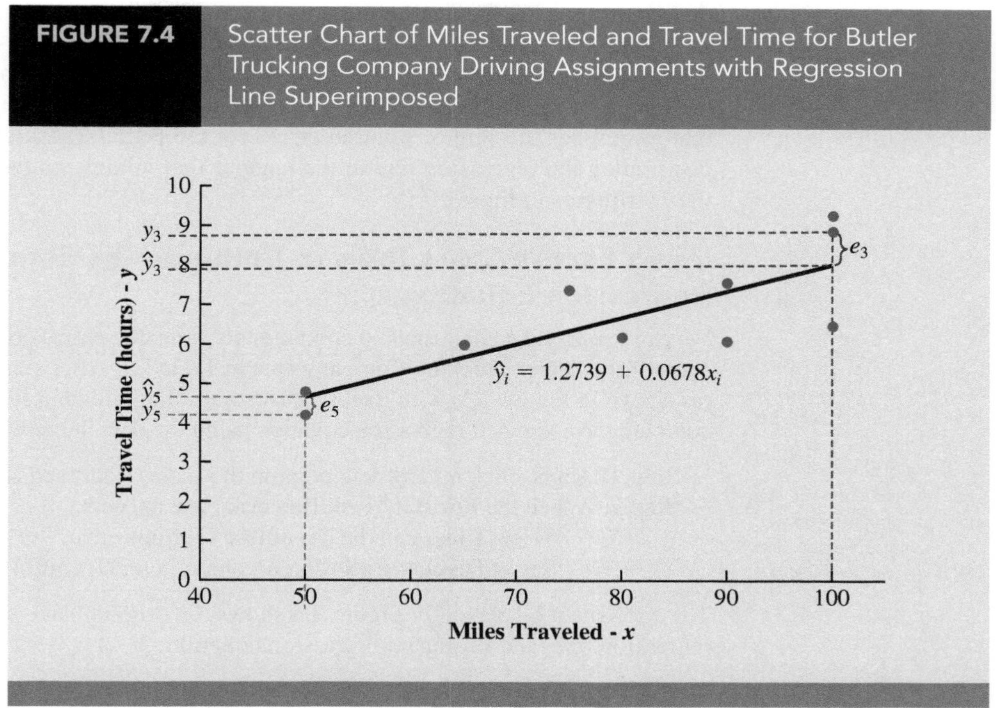

In Figure 7.5, a vertical line is drawn from each point in the scatter chart to the linear regression line. Each of these vertical lines represents the difference between the actual driving time and the driving time we predict using linear regression for one of the assignments in our data. The length of each vertical line is equal to the absolute value of the residual for one of the driving assignments. When we square a residual,

FIGURE 7.5 A Geometric Interpretation of the Least Squares Method

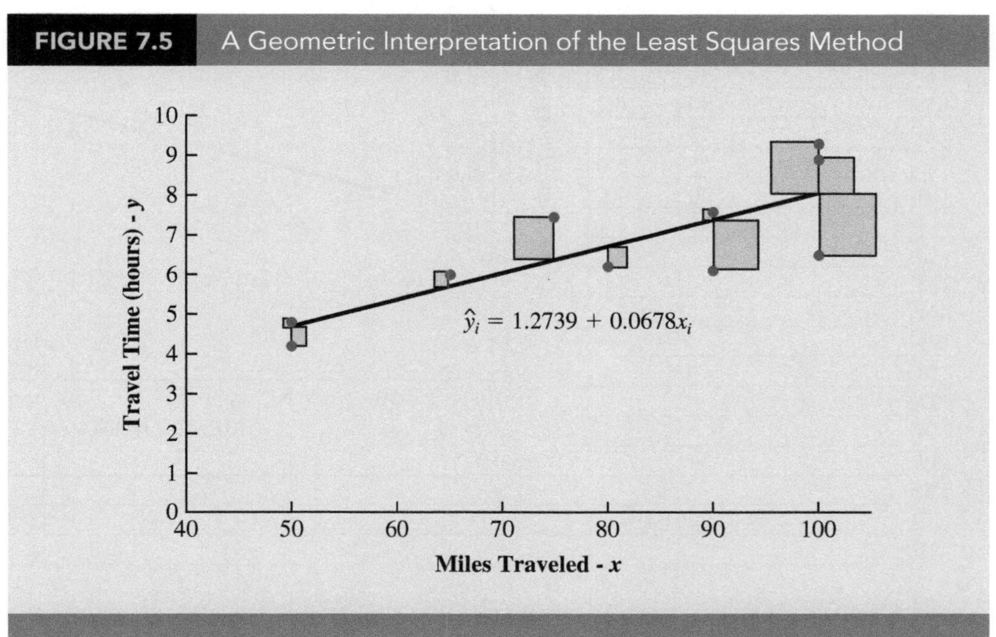

the resulting value is equal to the area of the square with the length of each side equal to the absolute value of the residual. In other words, the square of the residual for driving assignment 4 (e_4), $(-1.5565)^2 = 2.4227$, is the area of a square for which the length of each side is 1.5565. Thus, when we find the linear regression model that minimizes the sum of squared errors for the Butler Trucking example, we are positioning the regression line in the manner that minimizes the sum of the areas of the 10 squares in Figure 7.5.

Using Excel's Chart Tools to Compute the Estimated Regression Equation

We can use Excel's chart tools to compute the estimated regression equation on a scatter chart of the Butler Trucking Company data in Table 7.1. After constructing a scatter chart (as shown in Figure 7.3) with Excel's chart tools, the following steps describe how to compute the estimated regression equation using the data in the worksheet:

Note that Excel uses y instead of $\hat{y}$ to denote the predicted value of the dependent variable and puts the regression equation into slope-intercept form, whereas we use the intercept-slope form that is standard in statistics.

Step 1. Right-click on any data point in the scatter chart and select **Add Trendline . . .**
Step 2. When the **Format Trendline** task pane appears:
Select **Linear** in the **Trendline Options** area
Select **Display Equation on chart** in the **Trendline Options** area

The worksheet displayed in Figure 7.6 shows the original data, scatter chart, estimated regression line, and estimated regression equation.

FIGURE 7.6 Scatter Chart and Estimated Regression Line for Butler Trucking Company

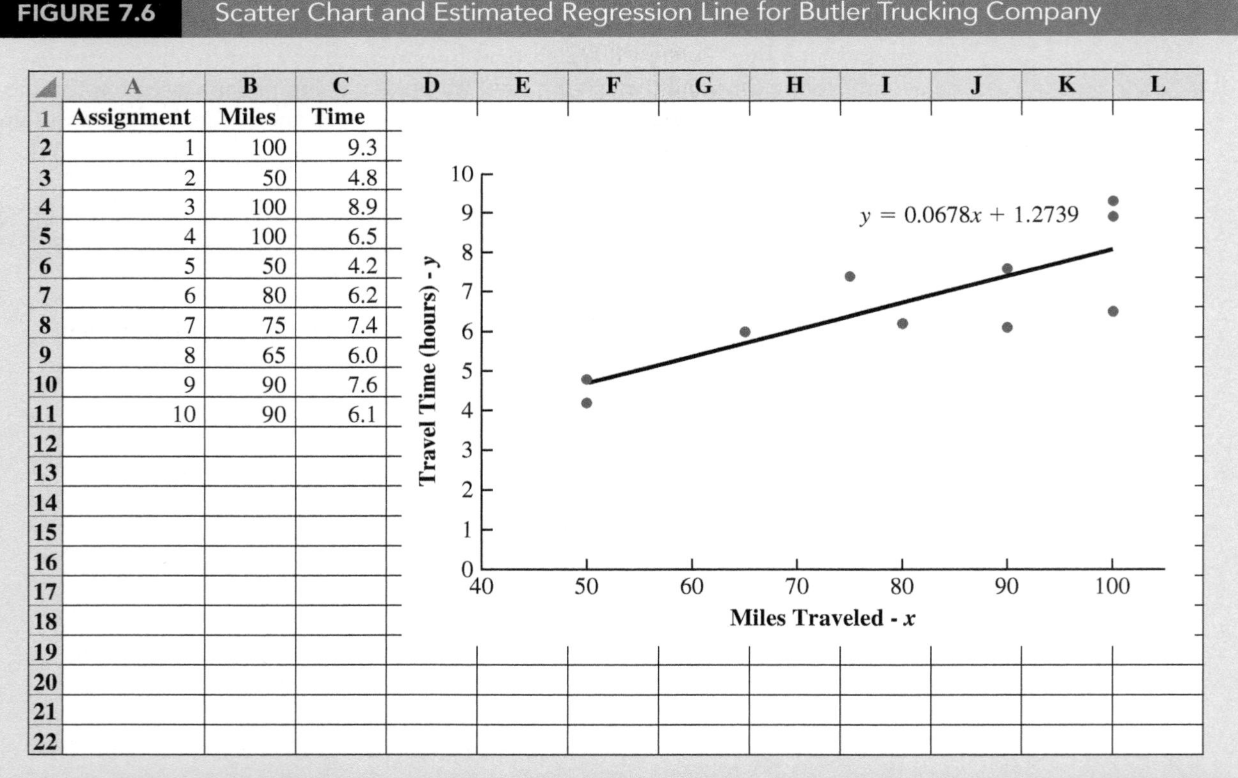

	A	B	C
1	Assignment	Miles	Time
2	1	100	9.3
3	2	50	4.8
4	3	100	8.9
5	4	100	6.5
6	5	50	4.2
7	6	80	6.2
8	7	75	7.4
9	8	65	6.0
10	9	90	7.6
11	10	90	6.1

NOTES + COMMENTS

1. Differential calculus can be used to show that the values of b_0 and b_1 that minimize expression (7.5) are given by:

SLOPE EQUATION

$$b_1 = \frac{\sum_{i=1}^{n}(x_i - \bar{x})(y_i - \bar{y})}{\sum_{i=1}^{n}(x_i - \bar{x})^2}$$

***y*-INTERCEPT EQUATION**

$$b_0 = \bar{y} - b_1\bar{x}$$

where

x_i = value of the independent variable for the ith observation
y_i = value of the dependent variable for the ith observation
$\bar{x}$ = mean value for the independent variable
$\bar{y}$ = mean value for the dependent variable
n = total number of observations

2. Equation 7.5 minimizes the sum of the squared deviations between the observed values of the dependent variable y_i and the predicted values of the dependent variable $\hat{y}_i$. One alternative is to simply minimize the sum of the deviations between the observed values of the dependent variable y_i and the predicted values of the dependent variable $\hat{y}_i$. This is not a viable option because then negative deviations (observations for which the regression forecast exceeds the actual value) and positive deviations (observations for which the regression forecast is less than the actual value) offset each other. Another alternative is to minimize the sum of the absolute value of the deviations between the observed values of the dependent variable y_i and the predicted values of the dependent variable $\hat{y}_i$. It is possible to compute estimated regression parameters that minimize this sum of the absolute value of the deviations, but this approach is more difficult than the least squares approach.

7.3 Assessing the Fit of the Simple Linear Regression Model

For the Butler Trucking Company example, we developed the estimated regression equation $\hat{y}_i = 1.2739 + 0.0678x_i$ to approximate the linear relationship between the miles traveled x and travel time in hours y. We now wish to assess how well the estimated regression equation fits the sample data. We begin by developing the intermediate calculations, referred to as sums of squares.

The Sums of Squares

Recall that we found our estimated regression equation for the Butler Trucking Company example by minimizing the sum of squares of the residuals. This quantity, also known as the *sum of squares due to error*, is denoted by SSE.

SUM OF SQUARES DUE TO ERROR

$$\text{SSE} = \sum_{i=1}^{n}(y_i - \hat{y}_i)^2 \qquad \textbf{(7.5)}$$

The value of SSE is a measure of the error (in the same units as the dependent variable) that results from using the estimated regression equation to predict the values of the dependent variable in the sample.

We have already shown the calculations required to compute the sum of squares due to error for the Butler Trucking Company example in Table 7.2. The squared residual or error for each observation in the data is shown in the last column of that table. After computing and squaring

FIGURE 7.7 The Sample Mean $\bar{y}$ as a Predictor of Travel Time for Butler Trucking Company

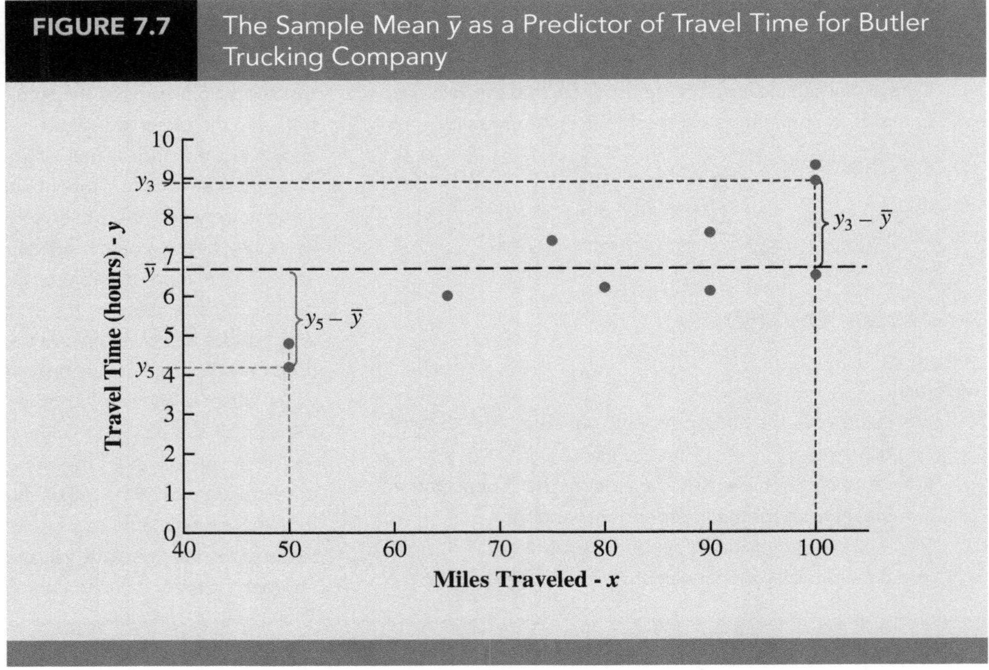

the residuals for each driving assignment in the sample, we sum them to obtain SSE = 8.0288 hours. Thus, SSE = 8.0288 measures the error in using the estimated regression equation $\hat{y}_i = 1.2739 + 0.0678x_i$ to predict travel time for the driving assignments in the sample.

Now suppose we are asked to predict travel time in hours without knowing the miles traveled for a driving assignment. Without knowledge of any related variables, we would use the sample mean $\bar{y}$ as a predictor of travel time for any given driving assignment. To find $\bar{y}$, we divide the sum of the actual driving times y_i from Table 7.2 (67) by the number of observations n in the data (10); this yields $\bar{y} = 6.7$.

Figure 7.7 provides insight on how well we would predict the values of y_i in the Butler Trucking company example using $\bar{y} = 6.7$. From this figure, which again highlights the residuals for driving assignments 3 and 5, we can see that $\bar{y}$ tends to overpredict travel times for driving assignments that have relatively small values for miles traveled (such as driving assignment 5) and tends to underpredict travel times for driving assignments that have relatively large values for miles traveled (such as driving assignment 3).

In Table 7.3 we show the sum of squared deviations obtained by using the sample mean $\bar{y} = 6.7$ to predict the value of travel time in hours for each driving assignment in the sample. For the ith driving assignment in the sample, the difference $y_i - \bar{y}$ provides a measure of the error involved in using $\bar{y}$ to predict travel time for the ith driving assignment. The corresponding sum of squares, called the total sum of squares, is denoted SST.

TOTAL SUM OF SQUARES, SST

$$\text{SST} = \sum_{i=1}^{n} (y_i - \bar{y})^2 \tag{7.6}$$

TABLE 7.3 Calculations for the Sum of Squares Total for the Butler Trucking Simple Linear Regression

Driving Assignment i	x = Miles Traveled	y = Travel Time (hours)	$y_i - \bar{y}$	$(y_i - \bar{y})^2$
1	100	9.3	2.6	6.76
2	50	4.8	−1.9	3.61
3	100	8.9	2.2	4.84
4	100	6.5	−0.2	0.04
5	50	4.2	−2.5	6.25
6	80	6.2	−0.5	0.25
7	75	7.4	0.7	0.49
8	65	6.0	−0.7	0.49
9	90	7.6	0.9	0.81
10	90	6.1	2.6	6.76
	Totals	67.0	0	23.9

The sum at the bottom of the last column in Table 7.3 is the total sum of squares for Butler Trucking Company: SST = 23.9.

Now we put it all together. In Figure 7.8 we show the estimated regression line $\hat{y}_i = 1.2739 + 0.0678x_i$ and the line corresponding to $\bar{y} = 6.7$. Note that the points cluster more closely around the estimated regression line $\hat{y}_i = 1.2739 + 0.0678x_i$ than they do about the horizontal line $\bar{y} = 6.7$. For example, for the third driving assignment in the sample, we see that the error is much larger when $\bar{y} = 6.7$ is used to predict y_3 than when $\hat{y}_3 = 1.2739 + 0.0678\ (100) = 8.0539$ is used. We can think of SST as a measure of

FIGURE 7.8 Deviations About the Estimated Regression Line and the Line $y = \bar{y}$ for the Third Butler Trucking Company Driving Assignment

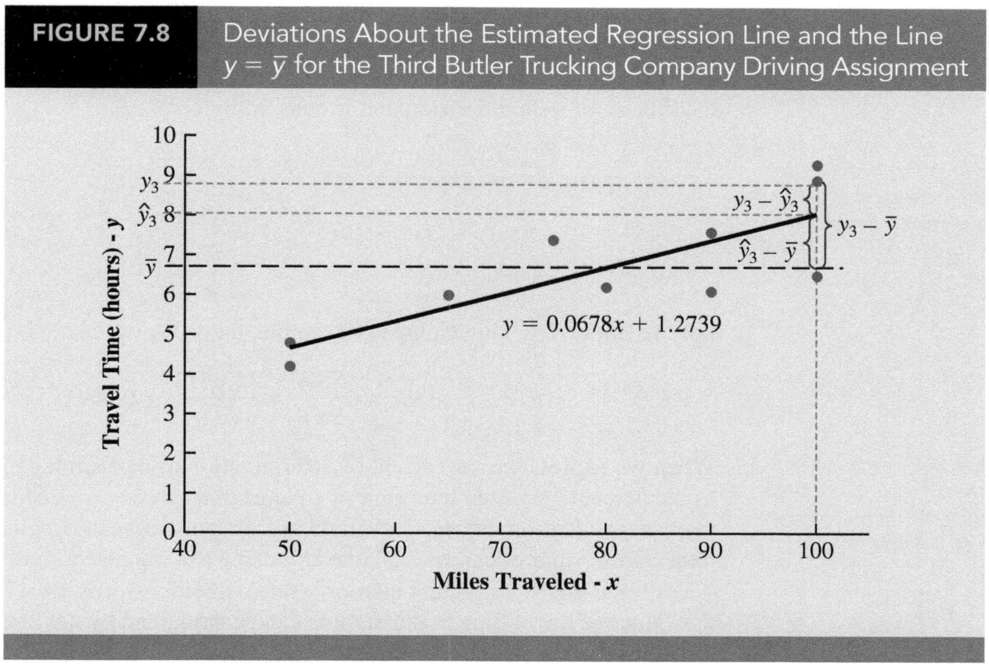

how well the observations cluster about the $\bar{y}$ line and SSE as a measure of how well the observations cluster about the $\hat{y}$ line.

To measure how much the $\hat{y}$ values on the estimated regression line deviate from $\bar{y}$, another sum of squares is computed. This sum of squares, called the *sum of squares due to regression*, is denoted SSR.

SUM OF SQUARES DUE TO REGRESSION, SSR

$$\text{SSR} = \sum_{i=1}^{n} (\hat{y}_i - \bar{y})^2 \tag{7.7}$$

From the preceding discussion, we should expect that SST, SSR, and SSE are related. Indeed, the relationship among these three sums of squares is:

$$\text{SST} = \text{SSR} + \text{SSE}, \tag{7.8}$$

where

SST = total sum of squares
SSR = sum of squares due to regression
SSE = sum of squares due to error

The Coefficient of Determination

Now let us see how the three sums of squares, SST, SSR, and SSE, can be used to provide a measure of the goodness of fit for the estimated regression equation. The estimated regression equation would provide a perfect fit if every value of the dependent variable y_i happened to lie on the estimated regression line. In this case, $y_i - \hat{y}$ would be zero for each observation, resulting in SSE = 0. Because SST = SSR + SSE, we see that for a perfect fit SSR must equal SST, and the ratio (SSR/SST) must equal one. Poorer fits will result in larger values for SSE. Solving for SSE in equation (7.11), we see that SSE = SST − SSR. Hence, the largest value for SSE (and hence the poorest fit) occurs when SSR = 0 and SSE = SST. The ratio SSR/SST, which will take values between zero and one, is used to evaluate the goodness of fit for the estimated regression equation. This ratio is called the **coefficient of determination** and is denoted by r^2.

In simple regression, r^2 is often referred to as the simple coefficient of determination.

COEFFICIENT OF DETERMINATION

$$r^2 = \frac{\text{SSR}}{\text{SST}} \tag{7.9}$$

For the Butler Trucking Company example, the value of the coefficient of determination is:

$$r^2 = \frac{\text{SSR}}{\text{SST}} = \frac{15.8712}{23.9} = 0.6641.$$

The coefficient of determination r^2 is the square of the correlation between the y_i and $\hat{y}_i$, and $0 \le r^2 \le 1$.

When we express the coefficient of determination as a percentage, r^2 can be interpreted as the percentage of the total sum of squares that can be explained by using the estimated regression equation. For Butler Trucking Company, we can conclude that 66.41% of the total sum of squares can be explained by using the estimated regression equation $\hat{y}_i = 1.2739 + 0.0678x_i$ to predict quarterly sales. In other words, 66.41% of the variability in the values of travel time in our sample can be explained by the linear relationship between the miles traveled and travel time.

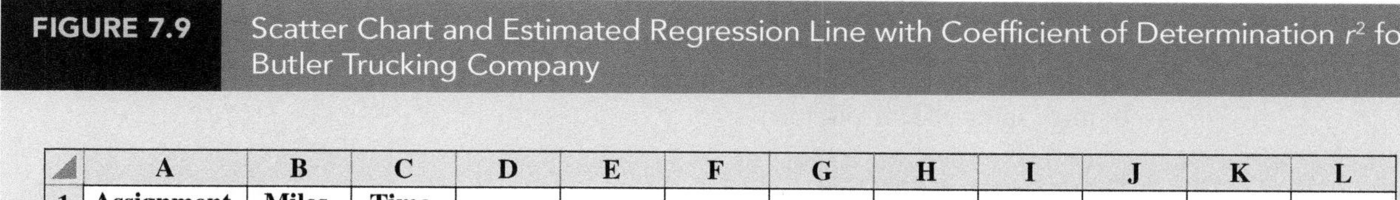

FIGURE 7.9 Scatter Chart and Estimated Regression Line with Coefficient of Determination r^2 for Butler Trucking Company

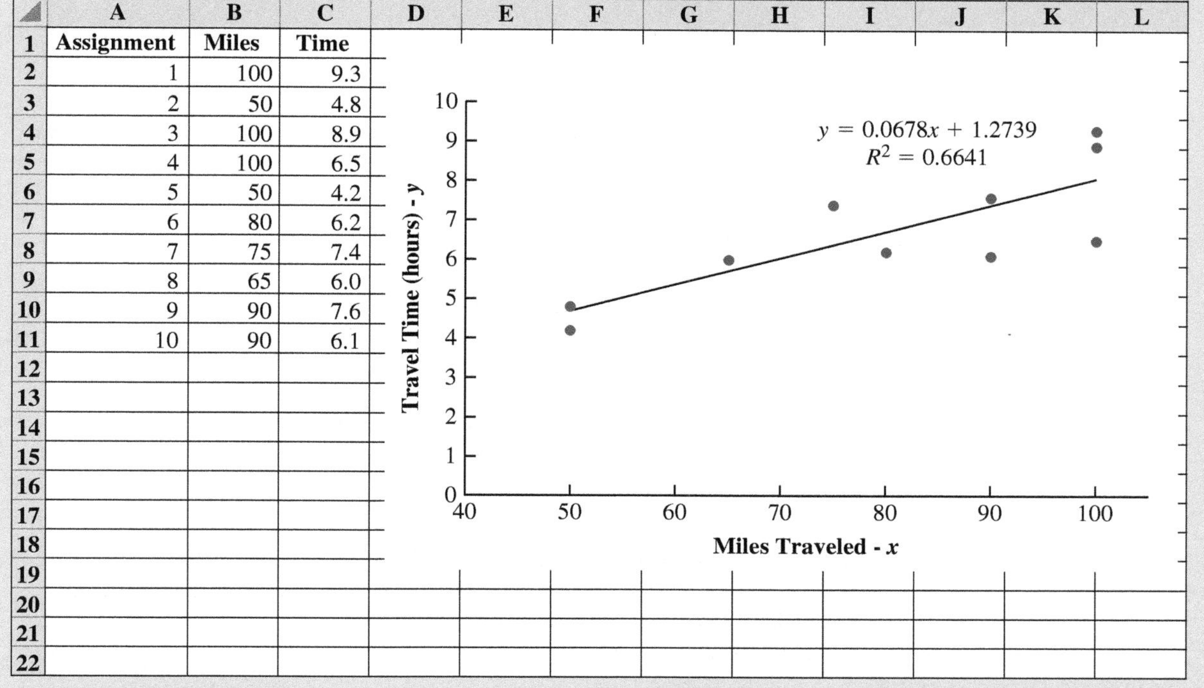

	A	B	C
1	Assignment	Miles	Time
2	1	100	9.3
3	2	50	4.8
4	3	100	8.9
5	4	100	6.5
6	5	50	4.2
7	6	80	6.2
8	7	75	7.4
9	8	65	6.0
10	9	90	7.6
11	10	90	6.1

Using Excel's Chart Tools to Compute the Coefficient of Determination

In Section 7.1 we used Excel's chart tools to construct a scatter chart and compute the estimated regression equation for the Butler Trucking Company data. We will now describe how to compute the coefficient of determination using the scatter chart in Figure 7.3.

Step 1. Right-click on any data point in the scatter chart and select **Add Trendline. . .**
Step 2. When the **Format Trendline** task pane appears:
Select **Display R-squared value on chart** in the **Trendline Options** area

Note that Excel notates the coefficient of determination as R^2.

Figure 7.9 displays the scatter chart, the estimated regression equation, the graph of the estimated regression equation, and the coefficient of determination for the Butler Trucking Company data. We see that $r^2 = 0.6641$.

NOTES + COMMENTS

As a practical matter, for typical data in the social and behavioral sciences, values of r^2 as low as 0.25 are often considered useful. For data in the physical and life sciences, r^2 values of 0.60 or greater are often found; in fact, in some cases, r^2 values greater than 0.90 can be found. In business applications, r^2 values vary greatly, depending on the unique characteristics of each application.

7.4 The Multiple Regression Model

We now extend our discussion to the study of how a dependent variable y is related to two or more independent variables.

Regression Model

The concepts of a regression model and a regression equation introduced in the preceding sections are applicable in the multiple regression case. We will use q to denote the number of independent variables in the regression model. The equation that describes how the dependent variable y is related to the independent variables $x_1, x_2, \ldots, x_q$ and an error term is called the multiple regression model. We begin with the assumption that the multiple regression model takes the following form:

MULTIPLE REGRESSION MODEL

$$y = \beta_0 + \beta_1 x_1 + \beta_2 x_2 + \cdots + \beta_q x_q + \varepsilon \qquad \textbf{(7.10)}$$

In the multiple regression model, $\beta_0, \beta_1, \beta_2, \ldots, \beta_q$ are the parameters and the error term ε is a normally distributed random variable with a mean of zero and a constant variance across all observations. A close examination of this model reveals that y is a linear function of $x_1, x_2, \ldots, x_q$ plus the error term ε. As in simple regression, the error term accounts for the variability in y that cannot be explained by the linear effect of the q independent variables. The interpretation of the y-intercept β_0 in multiple regression is similar to the interpretation in simple regression; in a multiple regression model, β_0 is the mean of the dependent variable y when all of the independent variables $x_1, x_2, \ldots, x_q$ are equal to zero. On the other hand, the interpretation of the slope coefficients $\beta_1, \beta_2, \ldots, \beta_q$ in a multiple regression model differ in a subtle but important way from the interpretation of the slope β_1 in a simple regression model. In a multiple regression model the slope coefficient β_j represents the change in the mean value of the dependent variable y that corresponds to a one-unit increase in the independent variable x_j, *holding the values of all other independent variables in the model constant.* Thus, in a multiple regression model, the slope coefficient β_1 represents the change in the mean value of the dependent variable y that corresponds to a one-unit increase in the independent variable x_1, holding the values of $x_2, x_3, \ldots, x_q$ constant. Similarly, the slope coefficient β_2 represents the change in the mean value of the dependent variable y that corresponds to a one-unit increase in the independent variable x_2, holding the values of $x_1, x_3, \ldots, x_q$ constant.

Estimated Multiple Regression Equation

In practice, the values of the population parameters $\beta_0, \beta_1, \beta_2, \ldots, \beta_q$ are not known and so must be estimated from sample data. A simple random sample is used to compute sample statistics $b_0, b_1, b_2, \ldots, b_q$ that are then used as the point estimators of the parameters $\beta_0, \beta_1, \beta_2, \ldots, \beta_q$. These sample statistics provide the following estimated multiple regression equation.

ESTIMATED MULTIPLE REGRESSION EQUATION

$$\hat{y} = b_0 + b_1 x_1 + b_2 x_2 + \cdots + b_q x_q, \qquad \textbf{(7.11)}$$

where

$$b_0, b_1, b_2, \ldots, b_q = \text{the point estimates of } \beta_0, \beta_1, \beta_2, \ldots, \beta_q$$
$$\hat{y} = \text{estimated mean value of } y \text{ given values for } x_1, \ldots, x_q$$

*If Data Analysis does not appear in your Analysis group, you will have to load the Analysis ToolPak add-in into Excel. To do so, click the **FILE** tab in the Ribbon, and click **Options**. When the **Excel Options** dialog box appears, click **Add-Ins** from the menu. Next to **Manage:**, select **Excel Add-ins**, and click **Go. . .** at the bottom of the dialog box. When the **Add-Ins** dialog box appears, select **Analysis ToolPak** and click **Go.** When the **Add-Ins** dialog box appears, check the box next to **Analysis Toolpak** and click **OK.***

FIGURE 7.11 Data Analysis Tools Box

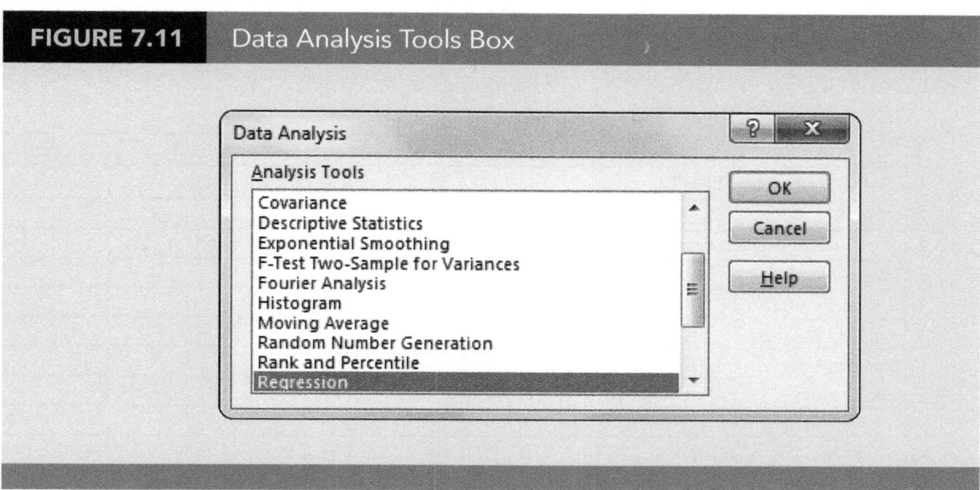

Select **Confidence Level:**
Enter *99* in the **Confidence Level:** box
Select **New Worksheet Ply:**
Click **OK**

In the Excel output shown in Figure 7.13, the label for the independent variable x_1 is Miles (see cell A18), and the label for the independent variable x_2 is Deliveries (see cell A19). The estimated regression equation is:

$$\hat{y} = 0.1273 + 0.0672x_1 + 0.6900x_2 \quad \textbf{(7.13)}$$

FIGURE 7.12 Regression Dialog Box

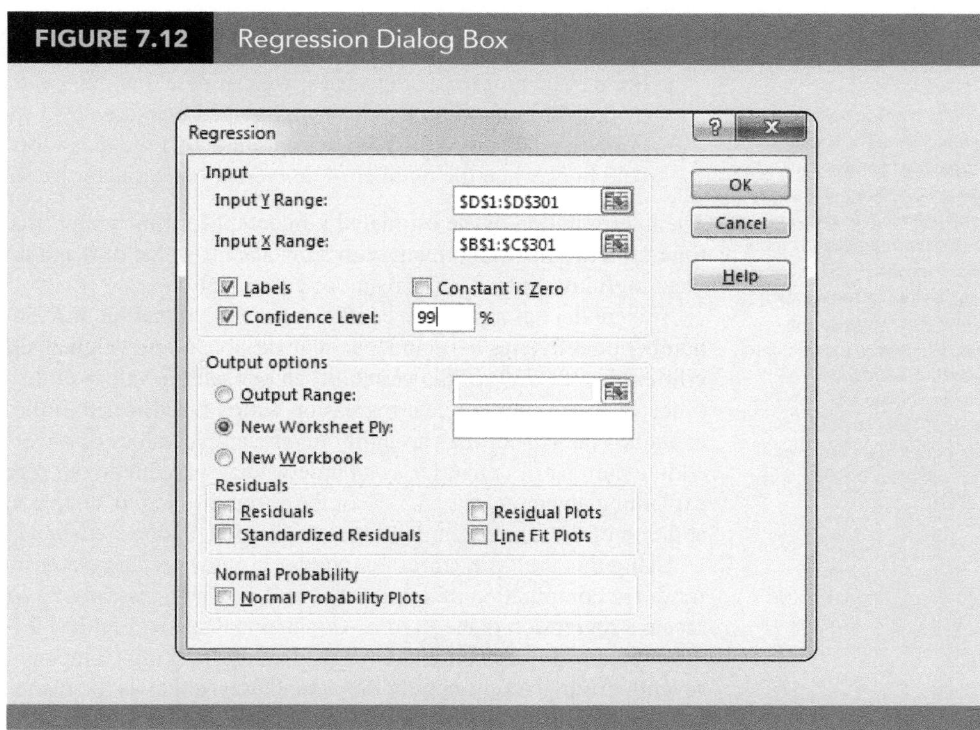

FIGURE 7.13 Excel Regression Output for the Butler Trucking Company with Miles and Deliveries as Independent Variables

	A	B	C	D	E	F	G	H	I
1	SUMMARY OUTPUT								
2									
3	*Regression Statistics*								
4	Multiple R	0.90407397							
5	R Square	0.817349743							
6	Adjusted R Square	0.816119775							
7	Standard Error	0.829967216							
8	Observations	300							
9									
10	ANOVA								
11		*df*	*SS*	*MS*	*F*	*Significance F*			
12	Regression	2	915.5160626	457.7580313	664.5292419	2.2419E-110			
13	Residual	297	204.5871374	0.68884558					
14	Total	299	1120.1032						
15									
16		*Coefficients*	*Standard Error*	*t Stat*	*P-value*	*Lower 95%*	*Upper 95%*	*Lower 99.0%*	*Upper 99.0%*
17	Intercept	0.127337137	0.20520348	0.620540826	0.53537766	−0.276499931	0.531174204	−0.404649592	0.659323866
18	Miles	0.067181742	0.002454979	27.36551071	3.5398E-83	0.062350385	0.072013099	0.06081725	0.073546235
19	Deliveries	0.68999828	0.029521057	23.37308852	2.84826E-69	0.631901326	0.748095234	0.613465414	0.766531147

We interpret this model in the following manner:

- For a fixed number of deliveries, we estimate that the mean travel time will increase by 0.0672 hour when the distance traveled increases by 1 mile.
- For a fixed distance traveled, we estimate that the mean travel time will increase by 0.69 hour when the number of deliveries increases by 1 delivery.

The sum of squares due to error, SSE, cannot become larger (and generally will become smaller) when independent variables are added to a regression model. Because SSR − SST = SSE, the SSR cannot become smaller (and generally becomes larger) when an independent variable is added to a regression model. Thus, R^2 = SSR/SST can never decrease as independent variables are added to the regression model.

The interpretation of the estimated y-intercept for this model (the expected mean travel time for a driving assignment with a distance traveled of 0 and no deliveries) is not meaningful because it is the result of extrapolation.

This model has a multiple coefficient of determination of $R^2 = 0.8173$. By adding the number of deliveries as an independent variable to our original simple linear regression, we now explain 81.73% of the variability in our sample values of the dependent variable, travel time. Since the simple linear regression with miles traveled as the sole independent variable explained 66.41% of the variability in our sample values of travel time, we can see that adding number of deliveries as an independent variable to our regression model resulted in explaining an additional 15.32% of the variability in our sample values of travel time. The addition of the number of deliveries to the model appears to have been worthwhile.

Using this multiple regression model, we now generate an estimated mean value of y for every combination of values of x_1 and x_2. Thus, instead of a regression line, we now create a regression plane in three-dimensional space. Figure 7.14 provides the graph of the estimated regression plane for the Butler Trucking Company example and shows the seventh driving assignment in the data. Observe that as the plane slopes upward to larger values of estimated mean travel time ($\hat{y}$) as either the number of miles traveled (x_1) or

FIGURE 7.14 Graph of the Regression Equation for Multiple Regression Analysis with Two Independent Variables

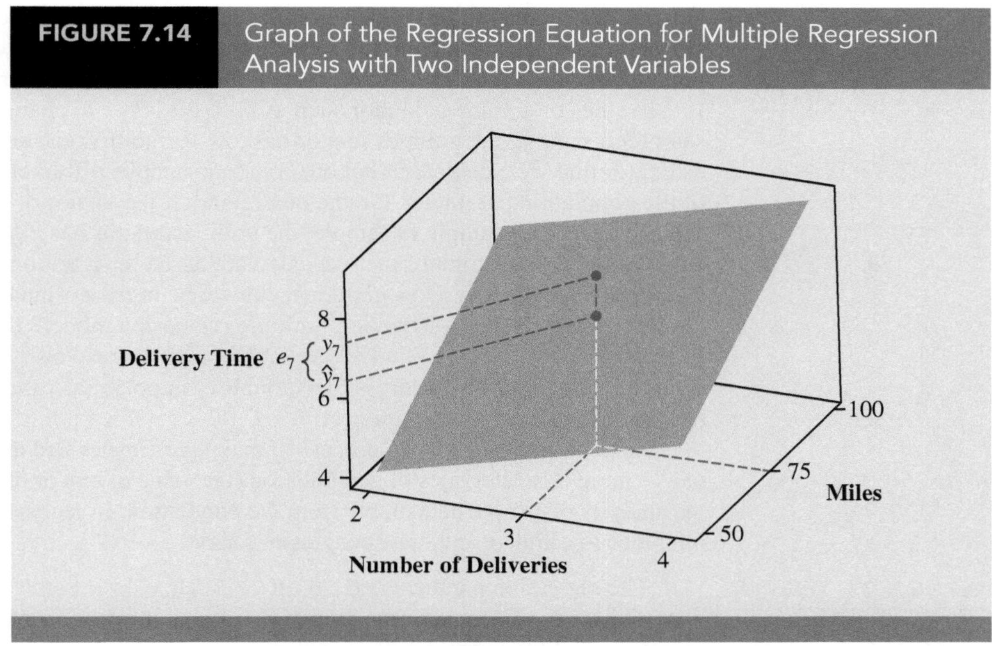

the number of deliveries (x_2) increases. Further, observe that the residual for a driving assignment when $x_1 = 75$ and $x_2 = 3$ is the difference between the observed y value and the estimated mean value of y given $x_1 = 75$ and $x_2 = 3$. Note that in Figure 7.14, the observed value lies above the regression plane, indicating that the regression model underestimates the expected driving time for the seventh driving assignment.

NOTES + COMMENTS

Although we use regression analysis to estimate relationships between independent variables and the dependent variable, it does not provide information on whether these are cause-and-effect relationships. The analyst can conclude that a cause-and-effect relationship exists between an independent variable and the dependent variable only if there is a theoretical justification that the relationship is in fact causal. In the Butler Trucking Company multiple regression, through regression analysis we have found evidence of a relationship between distance traveled and travel time and evidence of a relationship between number of deliveries and travel time. Nonetheless, we cannot conclude from the regression model that changes in distance traveled x_1 cause changes in travel time y, and we cannot conclude that changes in number of deliveries x_2 cause changes in travel time y. The appropriateness of such cause-and-effect conclusions are left to supporting practical justification and to good judgment on the part of the analyst. Based on their practical experience, Butler Trucking's managers felt that increases in distance traveled and number of deliveries were likely causes of increased travel time. However, it is important to realize that the regression model itself provides no information about cause-and-effect relationships.

7.5 Inference and Regression

The statistics $b_0, b_1, b_2, \ldots, b_q$ are point estimators of the population parameters $\beta_0, \beta_1, \beta_2, \ldots, \beta_q$; that is, each of these $q + 1$ estimates is a single value used as an estimate of the corresponding population parameter. Similarly, we use $\hat{y}$ as a point estimator of $E(y \mid x_1, x_2, \ldots, x_q)$, the conditional expectation of y given values of $x_1, x_2, \ldots, x_q$.

However, we must recognize that samples do not replicate the population exactly. Different samples taken from the same population will result in different values of the point estimators $b_0, b_1, b_2, \ldots, b_q$; that is, the point estimators are random variables. If the values of a point estimator such as $b_0, b_1, b_2, \ldots, b_q$ change relatively little from sample to sample, the point estimator has low variability, and so the value of the point estimator that we calculate based on a random sample will likely be a reliable estimate of the population parameter. On the other hand, if the values of a point estimator change dramatically from sample to sample, the point estimator has high variability, and so the value of the point estimator that we calculate based on a random sample will likely be a less reliable estimate. How confident can we be in the estimates b_0, b_1, and b_2 that we developed for the Butler Trucking multiple regression model? Do these estimates have little variation and so are relatively reliable, or do they have so much variation that they have little meaning? We address the variability in potential values of the estimators through use of statistical inference.

Statistical inference is the process of making estimates and drawing conclusions about one or more characteristics of a population (the value of one or more parameters) through the analysis of sample data drawn from the population. In regression, we commonly use inference to estimate and draw conclusions about:

See Chapter 6 for a more thorough treatment of hypothesis testing and confidence intervals.

- The regression parameters $\beta_0, \beta_1, \beta_2, \ldots, \beta_q$.
- The mean value and/or the predicted value of the dependent variable y for specific values of the independent variables $x_1, x_2, \ldots, x_q$.

In our discussion of inference and regression, we will consider both **hypothesis testing** and **interval estimation**.

Conditions Necessary for Valid Inference in the Least Squares Regression Model

In conducting a regression analysis, we begin by making an assumption about the appropriate model for the relationship between the dependent and independent variable(s). For the case of linear regression, the assumed multiple regression model is:

$$y = \beta_0 + \beta_1 x_1 + \beta_2 x_2 + \cdots + \beta_q x_q + \varepsilon.$$

The least squares method is used to develop values for $b_1, b_2, \ldots, b_q$, the estimates of the model parameters $\beta_0, \beta_1, \beta_2, \ldots, \beta_p$, respectively. The resulting estimated multiple regression equation is:

$$\hat{y} = b_0 + b_1 x_1 + b_2 x_2 + \cdots + b_q x_q.$$

Although inference can provide greater understanding of the nature of relationships estimated through regression analysis, our inferences are valid only if the error term ε behaves in a certain way. Specifically, the validity of inferences in regression analysis depends on how well the following two conditions about the error term ε are met:

1. For any given combination of values of the independent variables $x_1, x_2, \ldots, x_q$, the population of potential error terms ε is normally distributed with a mean of 0 and a constant variance.
2. The values of ε are statistically independent.

The practical implication of normally distributed errors with a mean of zero and a constant variation for any given combination of values of $x_1, x_2, \ldots, x_q$ is that the regression estimates are unbiased (i.e., do not tend to over- or underpredict), possess

FIGURE 7.15 Illustration of the Conditions for Valid Inference in Regression

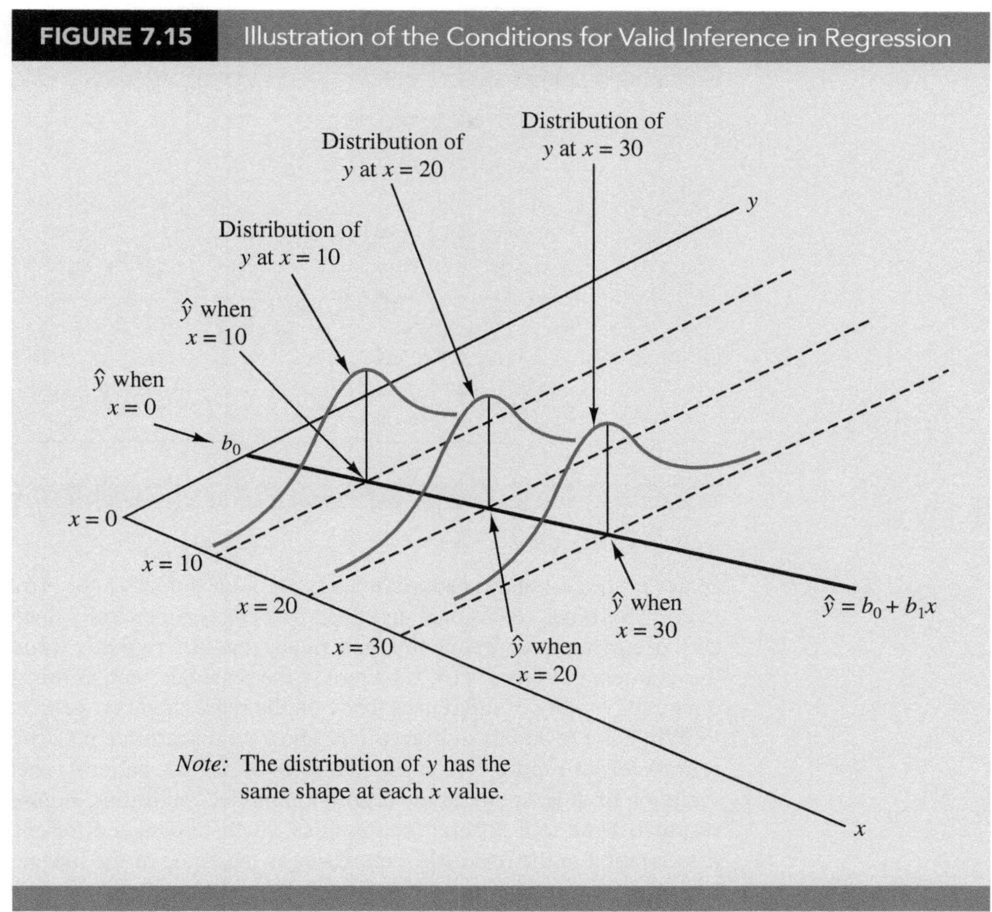

consistent accuracy, and tend to err in small amounts rather than in large amounts. This first condition must be met for statistical inference in regression to be valid. The second condition is generally a concern when we collect data from a single entity over several periods of time and must also be met for statistical inference in regression to be valid in these instances. However, inferences in regression are generally reliable unless there are marked violations of these conditions.

Keep in mind that we are also making an assumption or hypothesis about the form of the relationship between x and y. We assume that a straight line represented by $\beta_0 + \beta_1 x$ is the basis for the relationship between the variables. We must not lose sight of the fact that some other model, for instance $y = \beta_0 + \beta_1 x_1 + \beta_2 x_2 + \varepsilon$, may actually provide a better representation for the underlying population relationship.

Figure 7.15 illustrates these model conditions and their implications for a simple linear regression; note that in this graphical interpretation, the value of $E(y|x)$ changes linearly according to the specific value of x considered, and so the mean error is zero at each value of x. However, regardless of the x value, the error term ε and hence the dependent variable y are normally distributed, each with the same variance.

To evaluate whether the error of an estimated regression equation reasonably meets the two conditions, the sample residuals ($e_i = y_i, - \hat{y}_i$ for observations $i = 1, \ldots n$) need to be analyzed. There are many sophisticated diagnostic procedures for detecting whether the sample errors violate these conditions, but simple scatter charts of the residuals and independent variables are an extremely effective method for assessing whether these conditions are violated. We should review the scatter chart for patterns in the residuals indicating that one or more of the conditions have been violated. At any given value of x, the

FIGURE 7.16 Example of a Random Error Pattern in a Scatter Chart of Residuals and Predicted Values of the Dependent Variable

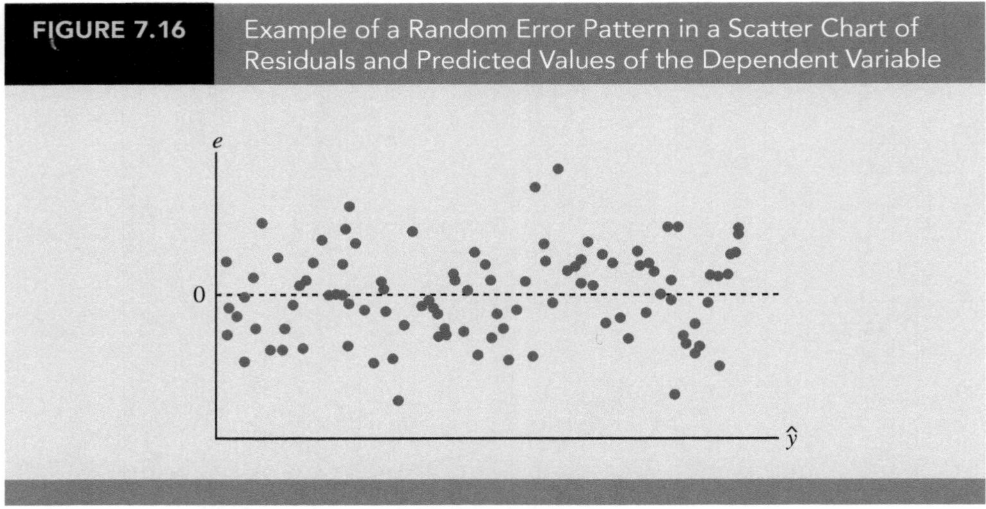

center of the residuals is approximately zero, the spread in the errors is similar to the spread in error for other values of x, and the errors are symmetrically distributed with values near zero occurring more frequently than values that differ greatly from zero. This is shown in the example in Figure 7.16. A pattern in the residuals such as this gives us little reason to doubt the validity of inferences made on the regression that generated the residuals.

While the residuals in Figure 7.16 show no discernible pattern, the residuals in the four panels of Figure 7.17 show examples of distinct patterns, each of which suggests a violation of at least one of the regression model conditions. Figure 7.17 shows plots of residuals from four different regressions, each showing a different pattern. In panel (a), the variation in the residuals e increases as the value of the independent variable x increases, suggesting that the residuals do not have a constant variance. In panel (b), the residuals are positive for small and large values of the independent variable x but are negative for moderate values of the independent variable. This pattern suggests that the linear regression model underpredicts the value of dependent variable for small and large values of the independent variable and overpredicts the value of the dependent variable for intermediate values of the independent variable. In this case, the regression model does not adequately capture the relationship between the independent variable x and the dependent variable y. The residuals in panel (c) are not symmetrically distributed around 0; many of the negative residuals are relatively close to zero, while the relatively few positive residuals tend to be far from zero. This skewness suggests that the residuals are not normally distributed. Finally, the residuals in panel (d) are plotted over time t, which generally serves as an independent variable; that is, an observation is made at each of several (usually equally spaced) points in time. In this case, connected consecutive residuals allow us to see a distinct pattern across every set of four residuals; the second residual is consistently larger than the first and smaller than the third, whereas the fourth residual is consistently the smallest. This pattern, which occurs consistently over each set of four consecutive residuals in the chart in panel (d), suggests that the residuals generated by this model are not independent. A residual pattern such as this generally occurs when we have collected quarterly data and have not captured seasonal effects in the model. In each of these four instances, any inferences based on our regression will likely not be reliable.

Frequently, the residuals do not meet these conditions either because an important independent variable has been omitted from the model or because the functional form of

FIGURE 7.19 Table of the First Several Predicted Values $\hat{y}$ and Residuals e Generated by the Excel Regression Tool

23	RESIDUAL OUTPUT		
24			
25	*Observation*	*Predicted Time*	*Residuals*
26	1	9.605504464	–0.305504464
27	2	5.556419081	–0.756419081
28	3	9.605504464	–0.705504464
29	4	8.225507903	–1.725507903
30	5	4.8664208	–0.6664208
31	6	6.881873062	–0.681873062
32	7	7.235932632	0.164037368
33	8	7.254143492	–1.254143492
34	9	8.243688763	–0.643688763
35	10	7.553690482	–1.453690482
36	11	6.936415641	0.063584359
37	12	7.290505212	–0.290505212
38	13	9.287776613	0.312223387
39	14	5.874146931	0.625853069
40	15	6.954596501	0.245403499
41	16	5.556419081	0.443580919

FIGURE 7.20 Scatter Chart of Predicted Values $\hat{y}$ and Residuals e

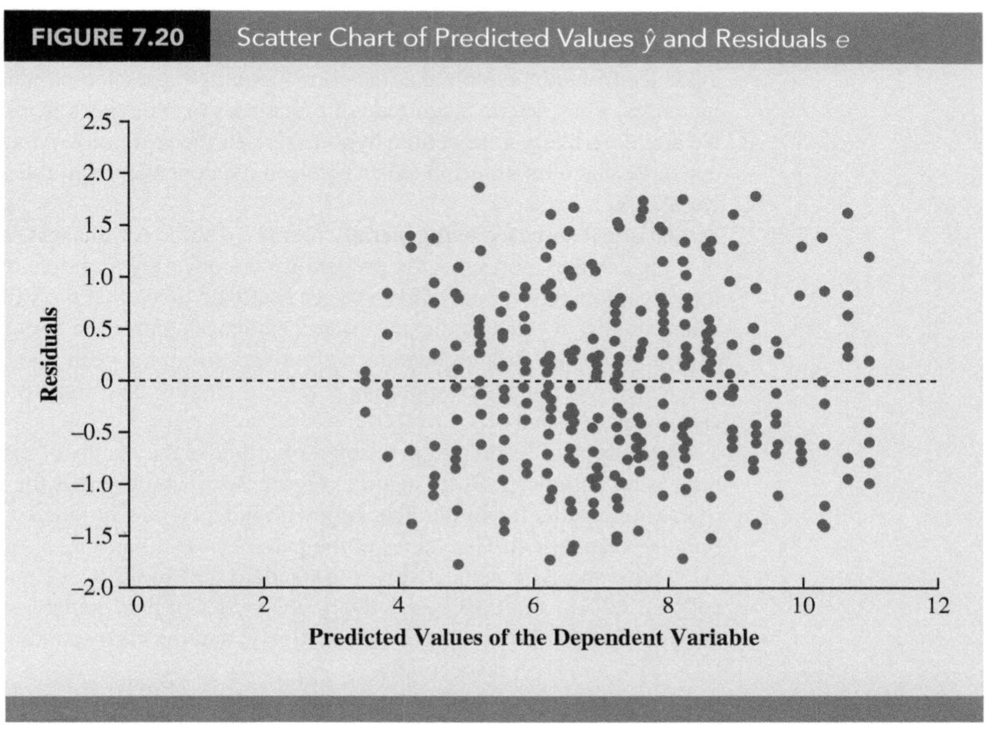

each predicted value of the dependent variable appear to have a mean of zero, to have similar variances, and to be concentrated around zero. This leads us to the same conclusion we reached when looking at the residuals plotted against the independent variables: The residuals provide little evidence that our regression model violates the conditions necessary for reliable inference. We can trust the inferences that we may wish to perform on our regression model.

Testing Individual Regression Parameters

Once we ascertain that our regression model satisfies the conditions necessary for reliable inference reasonably well, we can begin testing hypotheses and building confidence intervals. Specifically, we may then wish to determine whether statistically significant relationships exist between the dependent variable y and each of the independent variables $x_1, x_2, \ldots, x_q$ individually. Note that if a β_j is zero, then the dependent variable y does not change when the independent variable x_j changes, and there is no linear relationship between y and x_j. Alternatively, if a β_j is not zero, there is a linear relationship between the dependent variable y and the independent variable x_j.

See Chapter 6 for a more in-depth discussion of hypothesis testing.

We use a **t test** to test the hypothesis that a regression parameter β_j is zero. The corresponding null and alternative hypotheses are:

$$H_0: \beta = 0$$
$$H_a: \beta \neq 0$$

The test statistic for this t test is:

The standard deviation of b_j is often referred to as the standard error of b_j. Thus, s_{b_j} provides an estimate of the standard error of b_j.

$$t = \frac{b_j}{s_{b_j}}, \tag{7.14}$$

where b_j is the point estimate of the regression parameter β_j and s_{b_j} is the estimated standard deviation of b_j.

As the value of b_j, the point estimate of β_j, deviates from zero in either direction, the evidence from our sample that the corresponding regression parameter β_j is not zero increases. Thus, as the magnitude of t increases (as t deviates from zero in either direction), we are more likely to reject the hypothesis that the regression parameter β_j is zero and so conclude that a relationship exists between the dependent variable y and the independent variable x_j.

Statistical software will generally report a p value for this test statistic; for a given value of t, this p value represents the probability of collecting a sample of the same size from the same population that yields a larger t statistic given that the value of β_j is actually zero. Thus, smaller p values indicate stronger evidence against the hypothesis that the value of β_j is zero (i.e., stronger evidence of a relationship between x_j and y). The hypothesis is rejected when the corresponding p value is smaller than some predetermined level of significance (usually 0.05 or 0.01).

The output of Excel's Regression tool provides the results of the t tests for each regression parameter. Refer again to Figure 7.13, which shows the multiple linear regression results for Butler Trucking with independent variables x_1 (labeled Miles) and x_2 (labeled Deliveries). The values of the parameter estimates b_0, b_1, and b_2 are located in cells B17, B18, and B19, respectively; the standard deviations s_{b_0}, s_{b_1}, and s_{b_2} are contained in cells C17, C18, and C19, respectively; the values of the t statistics for the hypothesis tests are in cells D17, D18, and D19, respectively; and the corresponding p values are in cells E17, E18, and E19, respectively.

Let's use these results to test the hypothesis that β_1 is zero. If we do not reject this hypothesis, we conclude that the mean value of y does not change when the value of x_1 changes, and so there is no relationship between driving time and miles traveled. We see in the Excel output in Figure 7.13 that the statistic for this test is 27.3655 and that the associated p value is 3.5398E-83. This p value tells us that if the value of β_1 is actually zero, the probability we could collect a random sample of 300 observations from the population of Butler Trucking driving assignments that yields a t statistic with an absolute value greater than 27.3655 is practically zero. Such a small probability represents a highly unlikely scenario; thus, the small p value allows us to conclude that a relationship exists between driving time and miles traveled. (The p value is small enough to justify rejecting the hypothesis that $\beta_1 = 0$ for the Butler Trucking multiple regression example at a 0.01 level of significance or even at a far smaller level of significance.) Thus, this p value is sufficiently small to allow us to reject the hypothesis that there is no relationship between driving time and miles traveled at the 0.05 level of significance.

Similarly, we can test the hypothesis that β_2 is zero. If we do not reject this hypothesis, we conclude that the mean value of y does not change when the value of x_2 changes, and so there is no relationship between driving time and number of deliveries. We see in the Excel output in Figure 7.13 that the t statistic for this test is 23.3731 and that the associated p value is 2.84826E-69. This p value tells us that if the value of β_2 is actually zero, the probability we could collect a random sample of 300 observations from the population of Butler Trucking driving assignments that yields a t statistic with an absolute value greater than 23.3731 is practically zero. This is highly unlikely, and so the p value is sufficiently small to allow us to conclude that a relationship exists between driving time and number of deliveries. (The p value is small enough to justify rejecting the hypothesis that $\beta_2 = 0$ for the Butler Trucking multiple regression example at a 0.01 level of significance or even at a far smaller level of significance.) Thus, this p value is sufficiently small to allow us to reject the hypothesis that there is no relationship between driving time and number of deliveries at the 0.05 level of significance.

Finally, we can test the hypothesis that β_0 is zero in a similar fashion. If we do not reject this hypothesis, we conclude that the mean value of y is zero when the values of x_1 and x_2 are both zero, and so there is no driving time when a driving assignment is 0 miles and has 0 deliveries. We see in the Excel output that the t statistic for this test is 0.6205 and the associated p value is 0.5358. This p value tells us that if the value of β_0 is actually zero, the probability we could collect a random sample of 300 observations from the population of Butler Trucking driving assignments that yields a t statistic with an absolute value greater than 0.6205 is 0.5358. Thus, we do not reject the hypothesis that mean driving time is zero when a driving assignment is 0 miles and has 0 deliveries. However, the range of values for the independent variable distance traveled for the Butler Trucking multiple regression is 40 to 100, and the range of values for the independent variable number of deliveries is 1 to 6. Any prediction outside these ranges, such as the y-intercept for this model, is not a reliable estimate, and so a hypothesis test of β_0 is meaningless for this model. However, if the experimental region for a regression problem includes the origin, a hypothesis test of β_0 will be meaningful.

The estimated value of the y-intercept often results from extrapolation.

We can also execute each of these hypothesis tests through confidence intervals. A **confidence interval** for a regression parameter β_i is an estimated interval believed to contain the true value of β_i at some level of confidence. The level of confidence, or **confidence level**, indicates how frequently interval estimates based on samples of the same size taken from the same population using identical sampling techniques will contain the true value of β_i. Thus, when building a 95% confidence interval, we can expect that if we took samples of the same size from the same population using identical sampling

See Chapter 6 for a more in-depth discussion of ***confidence intervals****.*

techniques, the corresponding interval estimates would contain the true value of β_i for 95% of the samples.

Although the confidence intervals for $\beta_0, \beta_1, \beta_2, \ldots, \beta_q$ convey information about the variation in the estimates $b_1, b_2, \ldots, b_q$ that can be expected across repeated samples, they can also be used to test whether each of the regression parameters $\beta_0, \beta_1, \beta_2, \ldots, \beta_q$ is equal to zero in the following manner. To test that β_j is zero (i.e., there is no linear relationship between x_j and y) at some predetermined level of significance (say 0.05), first build a confidence interval at the $(1 - 0.05)100\%$ confidence level. If the resulting confidence interval does not contain zero, we conclude that β_j differs from zero at the predetermined level of significance.

The form of a confidence interval for β_j is as follows:

$$b_j \pm t_{\alpha/2} s_{b_j},$$

where b_j is the point estimate of the regression parameter β_j, s_{b_j} is the estimated standard deviation of b_j, and $t_{\alpha/2}$ is a multiplier term based on the sample size and specified $100(1 - \alpha)\%$ confidence level of the interval. More specifically, $t_{\alpha/2}$ is the t value that provides an area of $\alpha/2$ in the upper tail of a t distribution with $n - 2$ degrees of freedom.

Most software that is capable of regression analysis can also produce these confidence intervals. For example, the output of Excel's Regression tool for Butler Trucking, given in Figure 7.13, provides confidence intervals for β_1 (the slope coefficient associated with the independent variable x_1, labeled Miles) and β_2 (the slope coefficient associated with the independent variable x_2, labeled Deliveries), as well as the y-intercept β_0. The 95% confidence intervals for β_0, β_1, and β_2 are shown in cells F17:G17, F18:G18, and F19:G19, respectively; these 95% confidence intervals are automatically generated. Neither of the 95% confidence intervals for β_1 and β_2 includes zero, so we can conclude that β_1 and β_2 each differ from zero at the 0.05 level of significance. On the other hand, the 95% confidence interval for β_0 does include zero, so we conclude that β_0 does not differ from zero at the 0.05 level of significance. Again note that, for the Butler Trucking example, the estimated y-intercept results from extrapolation, and so the confidence interval for β_0 is meaningless. However, if the experimental region for a regression problem includes the origin, the confidence interval for β_0 will be meaningful.

The Regression tool dialog box offers the user the opportunity to generate confidence intervals for β_0, β_1, and β_2 at a confidence level other than 95%. In this example, we chose to create 99% confidence intervals for β_0, β_1, and β_2, which in Figure 7.13 are given in cells H17:I17, H18:I18, and H19:I19, respectively. Neither of the 99% confidence intervals for β_1 and β_2 includes zero, so we can conclude that β_1 and β_2 each differs from zero at the 0.01 level of significance. On the other hand, the 99% confidence interval for β_0 does include zero, so we conclude that β_0 does not differ from zero at the 0.01 level of significance.

Addressing Nonsignificant Independent Variables

If the data do not support rejection of the hypothesis that a β_j is zero, we conclude that there is no linear relationship between y and x_j. This leads to the question of how to handle the corresponding independent variable. Do we use the model as originally formulated with the nonsignificant independent variable, or do we rerun the regression without the nonsignificant independent variable and use the new result? The approach to be taken depends on a number of factors, but ultimately whatever model we use should have a theoretical basis. If practical experience dictates that the nonsignificant independent variable has a relationship with the dependent variable, the independent variable should be left in the model. On the other hand, if the model sufficiently explains the dependent variable without the nonsignificant independent variable, then we should consider rerunning the regression without the nonsignificant independent variable. Note that it is possible that the estimates of the other regression coefficients and their p values may change considerably when we remove the nonsignificant independent variable from the model.

The appropriate treatment of the inclusion or exclusion of the y-intercept when b_0 is not statistically significant may require special consideration. For example, in the Butler Trucking multiple regression model, recall that the p value for b_0 is 0.5354, suggesting that this estimate of β_0 is not statistically significant. Should we remove the y-intercept from this model because it is not statistically significant? Excel provides functionality to remove the y-intercept from the model by selecting **Constant is zero** in Excel's Regression tool. This will force the y-intercept to go through the origin (when the independent variables $x_1, x_2, \ldots, x_q$ all equal zero, the estimated value of the dependent variable will be zero). However, doing this can substantially alter the estimated slopes in the regression model and result in a less effective regression that yields less accurate predicted values of the dependent variable. The primary purpose of the regression model is to explain or predict values of the dependent variable for values of the independent variables that lie within the experimental region on which the model is based. Therefore, regression through the origin should not be forced unless there are strong *a priori* reasons for believing that the dependent variable is equal to zero when the values of all independent variables in the model are equal to zero. A common business example of regression through the origin is a model for which output in a labor-intensive production process is the dependent variable and hours of labor is the independent variable; because the production process is labor intense, we would expect no output when the value of labor hours is zero.

Multicollinearity

We use the term *independent variable* in regression analysis to refer to any variable used to predict or explain the value of the dependent variable. The term does not mean, however, that the independent variables themselves are independent in any statistical sense. On the contrary, most independent variables in a multiple regression problem are correlated with one another to some degree. For example, in the Butler Trucking example involving the two independent variables x_1 (miles traveled) and x_2 (number of deliveries), we could compute the sample correlation coefficient r_{x_1,x_2} to determine the extent to which these two variables are related. Doing so yields $r_{x_1,x_2} = 0.16$. Thus, we find some degree of linear association between the two independent variables. In multiple regression analysis, **multicollinearity** refers to the correlation among the independent variables.

To gain a better perspective of the potential problems of multicollinearity, let us consider a modification of the Butler Trucking example. Instead of x_2 being the number of deliveries, let x_2 denote the number of gallons of gasoline consumed. Clearly, x_1 (the miles traveled) and x_2 are now related; that is, we know that the number of gallons of gasoline used depends to a large extent on the number of miles traveled. Hence, we would conclude logically that x_1 and x_2 are highly correlated independent variables and that multicollinearity is present in the model. The data for this example are provided in the file *ButlerWithGasConsumption.*

ButlerWithGasConsumption

Using Excel's Regression tool, we obtain the results shown in Figure 7.21 for our multiple regression. When we conduct a t test to determine whether β_1 is equal to zero, we find a p value of 3.1544E-07, and so we reject this hypothesis and conclude that travel time is related to miles traveled. On the other hand, when we conduct a t test to determine whether β_2 is equal to zero, we find a p value of 0.6588, and so we do not reject this hypothesis. Does this mean that travel time is not related to gasoline consumption? Not necessarily.

FIGURE 7.21 Excel Regression Output for the Butler Trucking Company with Miles and Gasoline Consumption as Independent Variables

	A	B	C	D	E	F	G	H	I
1	SUMMARY OUTPUT								
2									
3	*Regression Statistics*								
4	Multiple R	0.69406354							
5	R Square	0.481724198							
6	Adjusted R Square	0.478234125							
7	Standard Error	1.398077545							
8	Observations	300							
9									
10	ANOVA								
11		*df*	*SS*	*MS*	*F*	*Significance F*			
12	Regression	2	539.5808158	269.7904079	138.0269794	4.09542E-43			
13	Residual	297	580.5223842	1.954620822					
14	Total	299	1120.1032						
15									
16		*Coefficients*	*Standard Error*	*t Stat*	*P-value*	*Lower 95%*	*Upper 95%*	*Lower 99.0%*	*Upper 99.0%*
17	Intercept	2.493095385	0.33669895	7.404523781	1.36703E-12	1.830477398	3.155713373	1.620208758	3.365982013
18	Miles	0.074701825	0.014274552	5.233216928	3.15444E-07	0.046609743	0.102793908	0.037695279	0.111708371
19	Gasoline Consumption	–0.067506102	0.152707928	–0.442060235	0.658767336	–0.368032789	0.233020584	–0.463398955	0.328386751

What it probably means in this instance is that, with x_1 already in the model, x_2 does not make a significant marginal contribution to predicting the value of y. This interpretation makes sense within the context of the Butler Trucking example; if we know the miles traveled, we do not gain much new information that would be useful in predicting driving time by also knowing the amount of gasoline consumed. We can see this in the scatter chart in Figure 7.22; miles traveled and gasoline consumed are strongly related.

Note that, even though we rejected the hypothesis that β_1 is equal to zero for this model, the value of the t statistic is much smaller and the p value substantially larger than in the multiple regression model that includes miles driven and number of deliveries as the independent variables. The evidence against the hypothesis that β_1 is equal to zero is weaker in the multiple regression that includes miles driven and gasoline consumed as the independent variables because of the high correlation between these two independent variables.

If any estimated regression parameters $b_1, b_2, \ldots, b_q$ or associated p values change dramatically when a new independent variable is added to the model (or an existing independent variable is removed from the model), multicollinearity is likely present. Looking for changes such as these is sometimes used as a way to detect multicollinearity.

To summarize, in t tests for the significance of individual parameters, the difficulty caused by multicollinearity is that it is possible to conclude that a parameter associated with one of the multicollinear independent variables is not significantly different from zero when the independent variable actually has a strong relationship with the dependent variable. This problem is avoided when there is little correlation among the independent variables.

Statisticians have developed several tests for determining whether multicollinearity is strong enough to cause problems. In addition to the initial understanding of the nature of the relationships between the various pairs of variables that we can gain through scatter charts such as the chart shown in Figure 7.22, correlations between pairs of independent

FIGURE 7.22 Scatter Chart of Miles and Gasoline Consumed for Butler Trucking Company

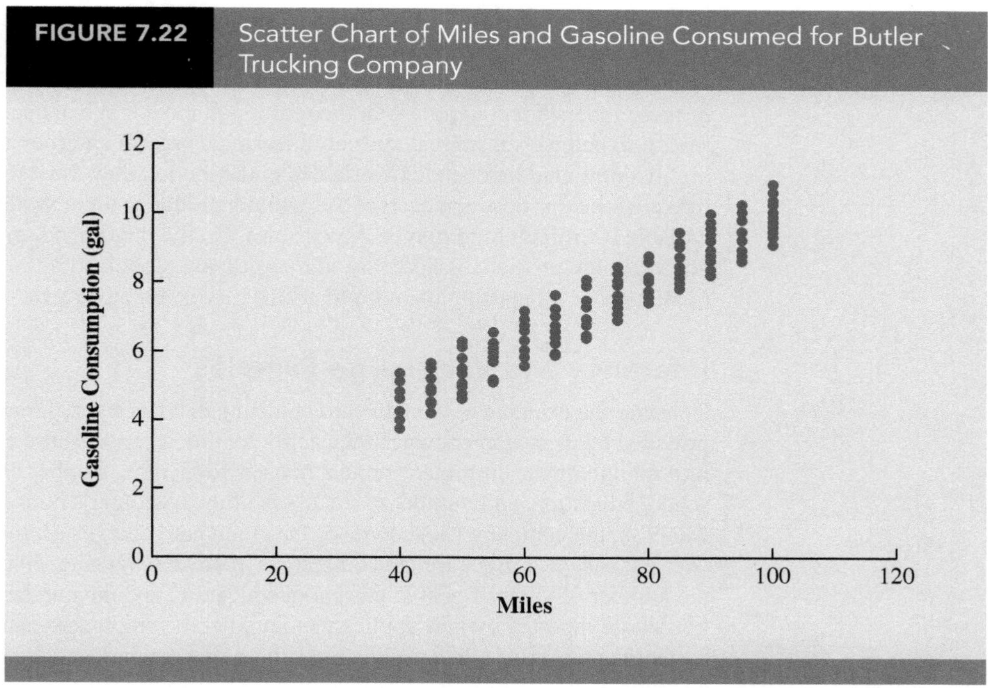

See Chapter 2 for a more in-depth discussion of correlation and how to compute it with Excel.

variables can be used to identify potential problems. According to a common rule-of-thumb test, multicollinearity is a potential problem if the absolute value of the sample correlation coefficient exceeds 0.7 for any two of the independent variables. We can place the Excel function:

=CORREL(B2:B301, C2:C301)

into any empty cell of the file *ButlerWithGasConsumption* to find that the correlation between Miles (in column B) and Gasoline Consumed (in column C) for the sample Butler Trucking data is $r_{\text{Miles, Gasoline Consumed}} = 0.9572$, which supports the conclusion that Miles and Gasoline Consumed are multicollinear. Similarly, by placing the Excel function:

=CORREL(B2:B301, D2:D301)

into any empty cell of the file *ButlerWithGasConsumption* shows that the correlation between Miles (in column B) and Deliveries (in column D) for the sample data is $r_{\text{Miles, Deliveries}} = 0.0258$. This supports the conclusion that Miles and Deliveries are not multicollinear. Other tests for multicollinearity are more advanced and beyond the scope of this text.

The primary consequence of multicollinearity is that it increases the standard deviation of $b_0, b_1, \ldots, b_q$ and predicted values of the dependent variable, and so inference based on these estimates is less precise than it should be. This means that confidence intervals for $\beta_0, \beta_1, \beta_2, \ldots, \beta_q$ and predicted values of the dependent variable are wider than they should be. Thus, we are less likely to reject the hypothesis that an individual parameter b_j is equal to zero than we otherwise would be, and multicollinearity leads us to conclude that an independent variable x_j is not related to the dependent variable y when they in fact are related. In addition, multicollinearity can result in confusing or misleading regression parameters $b_1, b_2, \ldots, b_q$. Therefore, if a primary objective of the regression analysis is inference, to explain the relationship between a dependent variable y and a set of independent variables $x_1, \ldots, x_q$, you should, if possible, avoid including independent variables that are highly correlated in the regression model. For example, when a pair of independent variables is highly correlated it is common to simply include only one of these independent variables in the regression model. When decision makers have reason to believe substantial multicollinearity is present and they choose to retain the highly correlated independent variables in the model, they must realize that separating the relationships between each of the individual independent variables and the dependent variable is difficult (and maybe impossible). On the other hand, multicollinearity does not affect the predictive capability of a regression model, so if the primary objective is prediction or forecasting, then multicollinearity is not a concern.

Inference and Very Large Samples

Consider the example of a credit card company that has a very large database of information provided by its customers when they apply for credit cards. These customer records include information on the customer's annual household income, number of years of post–high school education, and number of members of the customer's household. In a second database, the company has records of the credit card charges accrued by each customer over the past year. Because the company is interested in using annual household income, the number of years of post–high school education, and the number of members of the household reported by new applicants to predict the credit card charges that will be accrued by these applicants, a data analyst links these two databases to create one data set containing all relevant information for a sample of 5,000 customers (these data are available in the file *LargeCredit*).

LargeCredit

The company has decided to apply multiple regression to these data to develop a model for predicting annual credit card charges for its new applicants. The dependent variable in the model is credit card charges accrued by a customer in the data set over the past year (y); the independent variables are the customer's annual household income (x_1), number of members of the household (x_2), and number of years of post–high school education (x_3). Figure 7.23 provides Excel output for the multiple regression model estimated using the data set the company has created.

The model has a coefficient of determination of 0.3635 (see cell B5 in Figure 7.23), indicating that this model explains approximately 36% of the variation in credit card charges accrued by the customers in the sample over the past year. The p value for each test of the individual regression parameters is also very small (see cells E18 through E20), indicating that for each independent variable we can reject the hypothesis of no relationship with the dependent variable. The estimated slopes associated with the dependent variables are all highly significant. The model estimates that:

- For a fixed number of members of the household and number of years of post–high school education, accrued credit card charges increase by \$120.63 when a customer's annual household income increases by \$1,000. This is shown in cell B18 of Figure 7.23.
- For a fixed annual household income and number of years of post–high school education, accrued credit card charges increase by \$533.85 when a customer's household increases by one member. This is shown in cell B19 of Figure 7.23.
- For a fixed annual household income and number of members of the household, accrued credit card charges decrease by \$505.63 when a customer's number of years of post–high school education increases by one year. This is shown in cell B20 of Figure 7.23.

Because the y-intercept is an obvious result of extrapolation (no customer in the data has values of zero for annual household income, number of members of the household, *and*

FIGURE 7.23 Excel Regression Output for Credit Card Company Example

	A	B	C	D	E	F	G	H	I
1	SUMMARY OUTPUT								
2									
3	*Regression Statistics*								
4	Multiple R	0.602946393							
5	R Square	0.363544353							
6	Adjusted R Square	0.363162174							
7	Standard Error	4847.563495							
8	Observations	5000							
9									
10	ANOVA								
11		*df*	*SS*	*MS*	*F*	*Significance F*			
12	Regression	3	67059251577	22353083859	951.2407238	0			
13	Residual	4996	1.174E+11	23498871.84					
14	Total	4999	1.8446E+11						
15									
16		*Coefficients*	*Standard Error*	*t Stat*	*P-value*	*Lower 95%*	*Upper 95%*	*Lower 99.0%*	*Upper 99.0%*
17	Intercept	2051.638735	258.2118129	7.945564971	2.37056E-15	1545.430245	2557.847226	1386.274984	2717.002486
18	Annual Income ($1000)	120.6315397	2.439500895	49.44927054	0	115.8490472	125.4140323	114.3454003	126.9176792
19	Household Size	533.8460243	33.07739782	16.13929932	3.6874E-57	468.9998058	598.6922428	448.6117306	619.080318
20	Years of Post-High School Education	–505.632418	45.54182323	–11.10259498	2.60612E-28	–594.9143812	–416.3504547	–622.9852144	–388.2796215

number of years of post–high school education), the estimated regression parameter b_0 is meaningless.

The small p values associated with a model that is fit on an extremely large sample do not imply that an extremely large sample solves all problems. Virtually all relationships between independent variables and the dependent variable will be statistically significant if the sample size is sufficiently large. That is, if the sample size is very large, there will be little difference in the b_j values generated by different random samples. Because we address the variability in potential values of our estimators through the use of statistical inference, and variability of our estimates b_j essentially disappears as the sample size grows very large, inference is of little use for estimates generated from very large samples. Thus, we generally are not concerned with the conditions a regression model must satisfy in order for inference to be reliable when we use a very large sample. Multicollinearity, on the other hand, can result in confusing or misleading regression parameters $b_1, b_2, \ldots, b_q$ and so is still a concern when we use a large data set to estimate a regression model that is to be used for explanatory purposes.

The phenomenon by which the value of an estimate generally becomes closer to the value of parameter being estimated as the sample size grows is called the Law of Large Numbers.

How much does sample size matter? Table 7.4 provides the regression parameter estimates and the corresponding p values for multiple regression models estimated on the first 50 observations, the second 50 observations, and so on for the *LargeCredit* data. Note that, even though the means of the parameter estimates for the regressions based on 50 observations are similar to the parameter estimates based on the full sample of 5,000 observations, the individual values of the estimated regression parameters in the regressions based on 50 observations show a great deal of variation. In these 10 regressions, the estimated values

TABLE 7.4 Regression Parameter Estimates and the Corresponding *p* values for 10 Multiple Regression Models, Each Estimated on 50 Observations from the *LargeCredit* Data

Observations	b_0	*p* value	b_1	*p* value	b_2	*p* value	b_3	*p* value
1–50	−805.182	0.7814	154.488	1.45E-06	234.664	0.5489	207.828	0.6721
51–100	894.407	0.6796	125.343	2.23E-07	822.675	0.0070	−355.585	0.3553
101–150	−2,191.590	0.4869	155.187	3.56E-07	674.961	0.0501	−25.309	0.9560
151–200	2,294.023	0.3445	114.734	1.26E-04	297.011	0.3700	−537.063	0.2205
201–250	8,994.040	0.0289	103.378	6.89E-04	−489.932	0.2270	−375.601	0.5261
251–300	7,265.471	0.0234	73.207	1.02E-02	−77.874	0.8409	−405.195	0.4060
301–350	2,147.906	0.5236	117.500	1.88E-04	390.447	0.3053	−374.799	0.4696
351–400	−504.532	0.8380	118.926	8.54E-07	798.499	0.0112	45.259	0.9209
401–450	1,587.067	0.5123	81.532	5.06E-04	1,267.041	0.0004	−891.118	0.0359
451–500	−315.945	0.9048	148.860	1.07E-05	1,000.243	0.0053	−974.791	0.0420
Mean	1,936.567		119.316		491.773		−368.637	

of b_0 range from −2,191.590 to 8,994.040, the estimated values of b_1 range from 73.207 to 155.187, the estimated values of b_2 range from −489.932 to 1,267.041, and the estimated values of b_3 range from −974.791 to 207.828. This is reflected in the *p* values corresponding to the parameter estimates in the regressions based on 50 observations, which are substantially larger than the corresponding *p* values in the regression based on 5,000 observations. These results underscore the impact that a very large sample size can have on inference.

For another example, suppose the credit card company also has a separate database of information on shopping and lifestyle characteristics that it has collected from its customers during a recent Internet survey. The data analyst notes in the results in Figure 7.23 that the original regression model fails to explain almost 65% of the variation in credit card charges accrued by the customers in the data set. In an attempt to increase the variation in the dependent variable explained by the model, the data analyst decides to augment the original regression with a new independent variable, number of hours per week spent watching television (which we will designate as x_4). After linking the databases so that all necessary information for each of the 5,000 customers is in a single data set, the analyst runs the new multiple regression and achieves the results shown in Figure 7.24.

The new model has a coefficient of determination of 0.3669 (see cell B5 in Figure 7.24), indicating the addition of number of hours per week spent watching television increased the explained variation in sample values of accrued credit card charges by less than 1%. The estimated regression parameters and associated *p* values for annual household income, number of members of the household, and number of years of post–high school education changed little after introducing into the model the number of hours per week spent watching television.

The estimated regression parameter for number of hours per week spent watching television is 20.44 (see cell B21 in Figure 7.24), suggesting a that 1-hour increase coincides with an increase of $20.44 in credit card charges accrued by each customer over the past year. The *p* value associated with this estimate is 2.3744E-07 (see cell E21 in Figure 7.24), so we can reject the hypothesis that there is no relationship between the number of hours per week spent watching television and credit card charges accrued. However, when the model is based on a very large sample, almost all relationships will be significant whether they are real or not, and statistical significance does not necessarily imply that a relationship is meaningful or useful.

FIGURE 7.24 Excel Regression Output for Credit Card Company Example after Adding Number of Hours per Week Spent Watching Television to the Model

	A	B	C	D	E	F	G	H	I
1	SUMMARY OUTPUT								
2									
3	*Regression Statistics*								
4	Multiple R	0.605753974							
5	R Square	0.366937877							
6	Adjusted R Square	0.36643092							
7	Standard Error	4835.106762							
8	Observations	5000							
9									
10	ANOVA								
11		*df*	*SS*	*MS*	*F*	*Significance F*			
12	Regression	4	67685219598	16921304900	723.8052269	0			
13	Residual	4995	1.16774E+11	23378257.4					
14	Total	4999	1.8446E+11						
15									
16		*Coefficients*	*Standard Error*	*t Stat*	*P-value*	*Lower 95%*	*Upper 95%*	*Lower 99.0%*	*Upper 99.0%*
17	Intercept	1440.385909	283.3464635	5.083479398	3.84109E-07	884.9024443	1995.869374	710.2547892	2170.51703
18	Annual Income ($1000)	120.4937794	2.433377775	49.51708715	0	115.7232906	125.2642681	114.2234176	126.7641412
19	Household Size	538.2043625	33.00314865	16.30766713	2.72804E-58	473.5037019	602.9050231	453.1613886	623.2473364
20	Years of Post-High School Education	-509.7777354	45.43185836	-11.22071062	7.12888E-29	-598.8441236	-420.7113472	-626.8471819	-392.7082889
21	Hours Per Week Watching Television	20.4413308	3.950382611	5.174519234	2.37441E-07	12.69684656	28.18581504	10.26192978	30.62073183

Is it reasonable to expect that the credit card charges accrued by a customer are related to the number of hours per week the consumer watches television? If not, the model that includes number of hours per week the consumer watches television as an independent variable may provide inaccurate or unreliable predictions of the credit card charges that will be accrued by new customers, even though we have found a significant relationship between these two variables. If the model is to be used to predict future amounts of credit charges, then the usefulness of including the number of hours per week the consumer watches television is best evaluated by measuring the accuracy of predictions for observations not included in the sample data used to construct the model. This use of out-of-sample data is common in data-mining applications and is covered in detail in Chapter 9.

NOTES + COMMENTS

1. In multiple regression we can test the null hypothesis that the regression parameters $b_1, b_2, \ldots, b_q$ are all equal to zero (H_0: $\beta_1 = \beta_2 = \cdots = \beta_q = 0$, H_a: at least one $b_j \neq 0$ for $j = 1, \ldots, q$) with an F test based on the F probability distribution. The test statistic generated by the sample data for this test is:

$$F = \frac{SSR/q}{SSE/(n - q - 1)},$$

where SSR and SSE are as defined by equations (7.5) and (7.7), q is the number of independent variables in the regression model, and n is the number of observations in the sample. If the *p* value corresponding to the *F* statistic is smaller than some predetermined level of significance (usually 0.05 or 0.01), this leads us to reject the hypothesis that the values of $b_1, b_2, \ldots, b_q$ are all zero, and we would conclude that there is an overall regression relationship; otherwise, we conclude that there is no overall regression relationship.

The output of Excel's Regression tool provides the results of the *F* test; in Figure 7.13, which shows the multiple linear regression results for Butler Trucking with independent variables x_1 (labeled Miles) and x_2 (labeled Deliveries), the value of the *F* statistic and the corresponding *p* value are in cells E24 and F24, respectively. From the Excel output in Figure 7.13 we see tht the *p* value for the *F* test is essentially 0 (2.2419E-110, or 2.2419 with the decimal moved 110 places to the left). Thus, the *p* value is sufficiently small to allow us to reject the hypothesis that no overall regression relationship exists at the 0.05 level of significance.

2. Finding a significant relationship between an independent variable x_j and a dependent variable *y* in a linear regression does not enable us to conclude that the relationship is linear. We can state only that x_j and *y* are related and that a linear relationship explains a statistically significant portion of the variability in *y* over the range of values for x_j observed in the sample.
3. Note that a review of the correlations of pairs of independent variables is not always sufficient to entirely uncover multicollinearity. The problem is that sometimes one independent variable is highly correlated with some combination of several other independent variables. If you suspect that one independent variable is highly correlated with a combination of several other independent variables, you can use multiple regression to assess whether the sample data support your suspicion. Suppose that your original regression model includes the independent variables $x_1, x_2, \ldots, x_q$ and that you suspect that x_1 is highly correlated with a subset of the other independent variables $x_2, \ldots, x_q$. Estimate the multiple linear regression for which x_1 is now the dependent variable; the subset of the independent variables $x_2, \ldots, x_q$ that you suspect are highly correlated with x_1 are now the independent variables. The coefficient of determination R^2 for this regression provides an estimate of the strength of the relationship between x_1 and the subset of the other independent variables $x_2, \ldots, x_q$ that you suspect are highly correlated with x_1. As a rule of thumb, if the coefficient of determination R^2 for this regression exceeds 0.50, multicollinearity between x_1 and the subset of the other independent variables $x_2, \ldots, x_q$ is a concern.
4. When working with a small number of observations, assessing the conditions necessary for inference to be valid in regression can be extremely difficult. Similarly, when working with a small number of observations, assessing multicollinearity can also be difficult. Under these conditions we generally proceed with inference unless we find strong evidence of a violation of the conditions necessary for inference to be valid in regression or a strong multicollinearity.
5. To determine the independent variables to be included in a regression model when working with an extremely large sample, one can partition the sample into a training set and a validation set. The training set is used to estimate the regression coefficients and the validation set is then used to estimate the accuracy of the model.

7.6 Categorical Independent Variables

Thus far, the examples we have considered have involved quantitative independent variables such as distance traveled and number of deliveries. In many situations, however, we must work with categorical independent variables such as sex (male, female), method of payment (cash, credit card, check), and so on. The purpose of this section is to show how categorical variables are handled in regression analysis. To illustrate the use and interpretation of a categorical independent variable, we will again consider the Butler Trucking Company example.

Butler Trucking Company and Rush Hour

Several of Butler Trucking's driving assignments require the driver to travel on a congested segment of a highway during the afternoon rush hour. Management believes this factor may also contribute substantially to variability in the travel times across driving assignments.

Dummy variables are sometimes referred to as indicator variables.

How do we incorporate information on which driving assignments include travel on a congested segment of a highway during the afternoon rush hour into a regression model?

The previous independent variables we have considered (such as miles traveled and number of deliveries) have been quantitative, but this new variable is categorical and will require us to define a new type of variable called a **dummy variable**. To incorporate a variable that indicates whether a driving assignment included travel on this congested segment of a highway during the afternoon rush hour into a model that currently includes the independent variables miles traveled (x_1) and number of deliveries (x_2), we define the following variable:

$$x_3 = \begin{cases} 0 \text{ if an assignment did not include travel on the congested segment of highway} \\ \text{during afternoon rush hour} \\ 1 \text{ if an assignment included travel on the congested segment of highway} \\ \text{during afternoon rush hour} \end{cases}$$

Once a value of one is input for each of the driving assignments that included travel on a congested segment of a highway during the afternoon rush hour and a value of zero is input for each of the remaining driving assignments in the sample data, the independent variable x_3 can be included in the model. The file *ButlerHighway* includes this dummy variable.

See Chapter 2 for step-by-step descriptions of how to construct charts in Excel.

Will this dummy variable add valuable information to the current Butler Trucking regression model? A review of the residuals produced by the current model may help us make an initial assessment. Using Excel chart tools, we can create a frequency distribution and a histogram of the residuals for driving assignments that included travel on a congested segment of a highway during the afternoon rush hour period. We then create a frequency distribution and a histogram of the residuals for driving assignments that did not include travel on a congested segment of a highway during the afternoon rush hour period. The two histograms are shown in Figure 7.25.

Recall that the residual for the ith observation is $e_i = y_i - \hat{y}_i$, which is the difference between the observed and predicted values of the dependent variable. The histograms in Figure 7.25 show that driving assignments that included travel on a congested segment of a highway during the afternoon rush hour period tend to have positive residuals, which means we are generally underpredicting the travel times for those driving assignments. Conversely, driving assignments that did not include travel on a congested segment of a highway during the afternoon rush hour period tend to have negative residuals, which means we are generally overpredicting the travel times for those driving assignments. These results suggest that the dummy variable could potentially explain a substantial proportion of the variance in travel time that is unexplained by the current model, and so we proceed by adding the dummy variable x_3 to the current Butler Trucking multiple regression model. Using Excel's Regression tool to develop the estimated regression equation, we obtained the Excel output in Figure 7.26. The estimated regression equation is:

ButlerHighway

$$\hat{y} = -0.3302 + 0.0672x_1 + 0.6735x_2 + 0.9980x_3. \tag{7.15}$$

Interpreting the Parameters

After checking to make sure this regression satisfies the conditions for inference and the model does not suffer from serious multicollinearity, we can consider inference on our results. The p values for the t tests of miles traveled (p value = 4.7852E-105), number of deliveries (p value = 6.7480E-87), and the rush hour driving dummy variable (p value = 6.4982E-31) are all extremely small, indicating that each of these independent variables has

FIGURE 7.25 Histograms of the Residuals for Driving Assignments That Included Travel on a Congested Segment of a Highway During the Afternoon Rush Hour and Residuals for Driving Assignments That Did Not

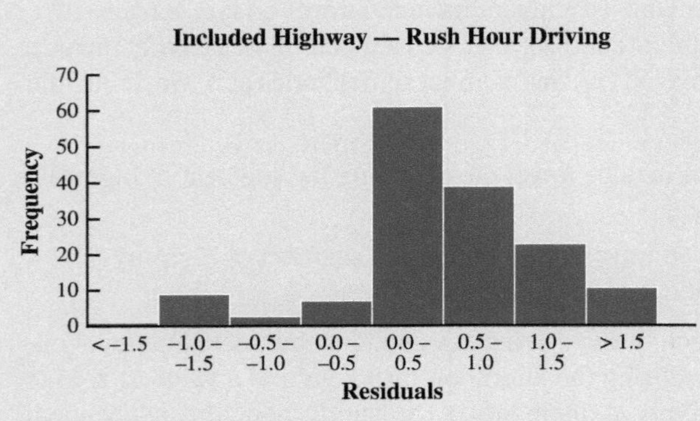

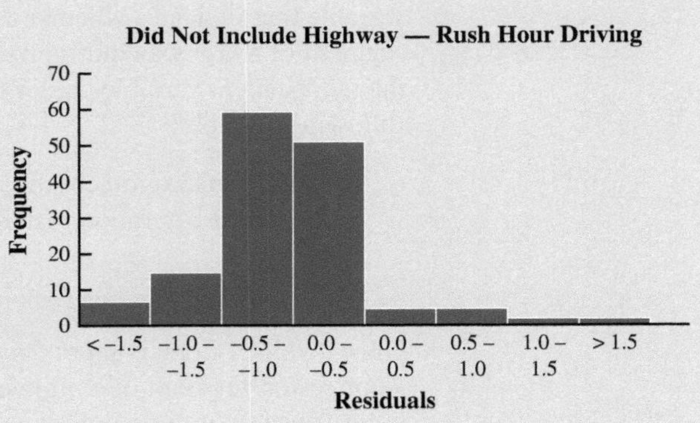

FIGURE 7.26 Excel Data and Output for Butler Trucking with Miles Traveled (x_1), Number of Deliveries (x_2), and the Highway Rush Hour Dummy Variable (x_3) as the Independent Variables

	A	B	C	D	E	F	G	H	I
1	SUMMARY OUTPUT								
2									
3	*Regression Statistics*								
4	Multiple R	0.940107228							
5	R Square	0.8838016							
6	Adjusted R Square	0.882623914							
7	Standard Error	0.663106426							
8	Observations	300							
9									
10	ANOVA								
11		*df*	*SS*	*MS*	*F*	*Significance F*			
12	Regression	3	989.9490008	329.9830003	750.455757	5.7766E−138			
13	Residual	296	130.1541992	0.439710132					
14	Total	299	1120.1032						
15									
16		*Coefficients*	*Standard Error*	*t Stat*	*P-value*	*Lower 95%*	*Upper 95%*	*Lower 99.0%*	*Upper 99.0%*
17	Intercept	−0.330229304	0.167677925	−1.969426232	0.04983651	−0.66022126	−0.000237349	−0.764941128	0.104482519
18	Miles	0.067220302	0.00196142	34.27125147	4.7852E-105	0.063360208	0.071080397	0.062135243	0.072305362
19	Deliveries	0.67351584	0.023619993	28.51465081	6.74797E-87	0.627031441	0.720000239	0.612280051	0.734751629
20	Highway	0.9980033	0.076706582	13.0106605	6.49817E-31	0.847043924	1.148962677	0.799138374	1.196868226

a statistical relationship with travel time. The model estimates that the mean travel time of a driving assignment increases by:

- 0.0672 hour for every increase of 1 mile traveled, holding constant the number of deliveries and whether the driving assignment route requires the driver to travel on the congested segment of a highway during the afternoon rush hour.
- 0.6735 hour for every delivery, holding constant the number of miles traveled and whether the driving assignment route requires the driver to travel on the congested segment of a highway during the afternoon rush hour.
- 0.9980 hour if the driving assignment route requires the driver to travel on the congested segment of a highway during the afternoon rush hour, holding constant the number of miles traveled and the number of deliveries.

In addition, $R^2 = 0.8838$ indicates that the regression model explains approximately 88.4% of the variability in travel time for the driving assignments in the sample. Thus, equation (7.15) should prove helpful in estimating the travel time necessary for the various driving assignments.

To understand how to interpret the regression when a categorical variable is present, let's compare the regression model for the case when $x_3 = 0$ (the driving assignment does not include travel on congested highways) and when $x_3 = 1$ (the driving assignment does include travel on congested highways). In the case that $x_3 = 0$, we have:

$$\begin{aligned}\hat{y} &= -0.3302 + 0.0672x_1 + 0.6735x_2 + 0.9980(0) \\ &= -0.3302 + 0.0672x_1 + 0.6735x_2. \end{aligned} \quad \textbf{(7.16)}$$

In the case that $x_3 = 1$, we have:

$$\begin{aligned}\hat{y} &= -0.3302 + 0.0672x_1 + 0.6735x_2 + 0.9980(1) \\ &= 0.6678 + 0.0672x_1 + 0.6735x_2. \end{aligned} \quad \textbf{(7.17)}$$

Comparing equations (7.16) and (7.17), we see that the mean travel time has the same linear relationship with x_1 and x_2 for both driving assignments that include travel on the congested segment of highway during the afternoon rush hour period and driving assignments that do not. However, the y-intercept is -0.3302 in equation (7.16) and $(-0.3302 + 0.9980)$ in equation (7.17). That is, 0.9980 is the difference between the mean travel time for driving assignments that include travel on the congested segment of highway during the afternoon rush hour and the mean travel time for driving assignments that do not.

In effect, the use of a dummy variable provides two estimated regression equations that can be used to predict the travel time: One that corresponds to driving assignments that include travel on the congested segment of highway during the afternoon rush hour period, and one that corresponds to driving assignments that do not include such travel.

More Complex Categorical Variables

The categorical variable for the Butler Trucking Company example had two levels: (1) driving assignments that include travel on the congested segment of highway during the afternoon rush hour, and (2) driving assignments that do not. As a result, defining a dummy variable with a value of zero indicating a driving assignment that does not include travel on the congested segment of highway during the afternoon rush hour and a value of one indicating a driving assignment that includes such travel was sufficient. However, when a categorical variable has more than two levels, care must be taken in both defining and interpreting the dummy variables. As we will show, if a categorical variable has k levels,

$k - 1$ dummy variables are required, with each dummy variable corresponding to one of the levels of the categorical variable and coded as 0 or 1.

For example, suppose a manufacturer of vending machines organized the sales territories for a particular state into three regions: A, B, and C. The managers want to use regression analysis to help predict the number of vending machines sold per week. With the number of units sold as the dependent variable, they are considering several independent variables (the number of sales personnel, advertising expenditures, etc.). Suppose the managers believe that sales region is also an important factor in predicting the number of units sold. Because sales region is a categorical variable with three levels (A, B, and C), we will need $3 - 1 = 2$ dummy variables to represent the sales region. Selecting Region A to be the "reference" region, each dummy variable can be coded 0 or 1 as follows:

$$x_1 = \begin{cases} 1 \text{ if sales Region B} \\ 0 \text{ otherwise} \end{cases}, \quad x_2 = \begin{cases} 1 \text{ if sales Region C} \\ 0 \text{ otherwise} \end{cases}$$

With this definition, we have the following values of x_1 and x_2:

Region	x_1	x_2
A	0	0
B	1	0
C	0	1

The regression equation relating the estimated mean number of units sold to the dummy variables is written as:

$$\hat{y} = b_0 + b_1x_1 + b_2x_2.$$

Observations corresponding to Region A correspond to $x_1 = 0, x_2 = 0$, so the estimated mean number of units sold in Region A is:

$$\hat{y} = b_0 + b_1(0) + b_2(0) = b_0.$$

Observations corresponding to Region B are coded $x_1 = 1, x_2 = 0$, so the estimated mean number of units sold in Region B is:

$$\hat{y} = b_0 + b_1(1) + b_2(0) = b_0 + b_1.$$

Observations corresponding to Region C are coded $x_1 = 0, x_2 = 1$, so the estimated mean number of units sold in Region C is:

$$\hat{y} = b_0 + b_1(0) + b_2(1) = b_0 + b_2.$$

Thus, b_0 is the estimated mean sales for Region A, b_1 is the estimated difference between the mean number of units sold in Region B and the mean number of units sold in Region A, and b_2 is the estimated difference between the mean number of units sold in Region C and the mean number of units sold in Region A.

Dummy variables are often used to model seasonal effects in sales data. If the data are collected quarterly, we may use three dummy variables defined in the following manner:

$$x_1 = \begin{cases} 1 \text{ if spring;} \\ 0 \text{ otherwise} \end{cases}$$

$$x_2 = \begin{cases} 1 \text{ if summer;} \\ 0 \text{ otherwise} \end{cases}$$

$$x_3 = \begin{cases} 1 \text{ if fall} \\ 0 \text{ otherwise} \end{cases}$$

Two dummy variables were required because sales region is a categorical variable with three levels. But the assignment of $x_1 = 0$ and $x_2 = 0$ to indicate Region A, $x_1 = 1$ and $x_2 = 0$ to indicate Region B, and $x_1 = 0$ and $x_2 = 1$ to indicate Region C was arbitrary. For example, we could have chosen to let $x_1 = 1$ and $x_2 = 0$ indicate Region A, $x_1 = 0$ and $x_2 = 0$ indicate Region B, and $x_1 = 0$ and $x_2 = 1$ indicate Region C. In this case, b_0 is the mean or expected value of sales for Region B, b_1 is the difference between the mean number of units sold in Region A and the mean number of units sold in Region B, and b_2 is the difference between the mean number of units sold in Region C and the mean number of units sold in Region B.

The important point to remember is that when a categorical variable has k levels, $k - 1$ dummy variables are required in the multiple regression analysis. Thus, if the sales region example had a fourth region, labeled D, three dummy variables would be necessary. For example, these three dummy variables could then be coded as follows:

$$x_1 = \begin{cases} 1 \text{ if sales Region B} \\ 0 \text{ otherwise} \end{cases}, \quad x_2 = \begin{cases} 1 \text{ if sales Region C} \\ 0 \text{ otherwise} \end{cases}, \quad x_3 = \begin{cases} 1 \text{ if sales Region D} \\ 0 \text{ otherwise} \end{cases}$$

NOTES + COMMENTS

Detecting multicollinearity when a categorical variable is involved is difficult. The correlation coefficient that we used in Section 7.5 is appropriate only when assessing the relationship between two quantitative variables. However, recall that if any estimated regression parameters $b_1, b_2, \ldots, b_q$ or associated p values change dramatically when a new independent variable is added to the model (or an existing independent variable is removed from the model), multicollinearity is likely present. We can use our understanding of these ramifications of multicollinearity to assess whether there is multicollinearity that involves a dummy variable. We estimate the regression model twice; once with the dummy variable included as an independent variable and once with the dummy variable omitted from the regression model. If we see relatively little change in the estimated regression parameters $b_1, b_2, \ldots, b_q$ or associated p values for the independent variables that have been included in both regression models, we can be confident there is not a strong multicollinearity involving the dummy variable.

7.7 Modeling Nonlinear Relationships

Regression may be used to model more complex types of relationships. To illustrate, let us consider the problem facing Reynolds, Inc., a manufacturer of industrial scales and laboratory equipment. Managers at Reynolds want to investigate the relationship between length of employment of their salespeople and the number of electronic laboratory scales sold. The file *Reynolds* gives the number of scales sold by 15 randomly selected salespeople for the most recent sales period and the number of months each salesperson has been employed by the firm. Figure 7.27, the scatter chart for these data, indicates a possible curvilinear relationship between the length of time employed and the number of units sold.

FIGURE 7.27 Scatter Chart for the Reynolds Example

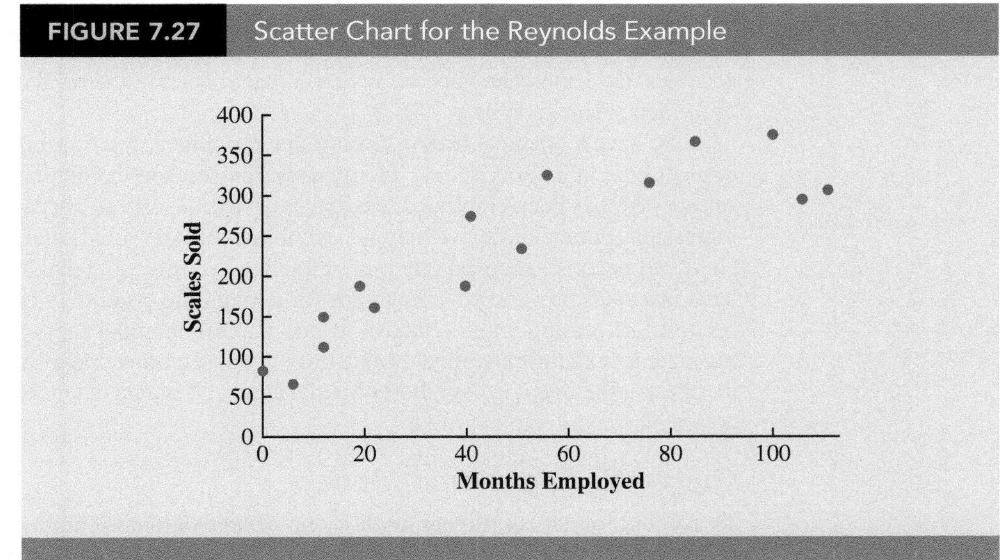

FIGURE 7.28 Excel Regression Output for the Reynolds Example

	A	B	C	D	E	F	G	H	I
1	SUMMARY OUTPUT								
2									
3	*Regression Statistics*								
4	Multiple R	0.888897515							
5	R Square	0.790138792							
6	Adjusted R Square	0.773995622							
7	Standard Error	48.49087146							
8	Observations	15							
9									
10	ANOVA								
11		*df*	*SS*	*MS*	*F*	*Significance F*			
12	Regression	1	115089.1933	115089.1933	48.94570268	9.39543E–06			
13	Residual	13	30567.74	2351.364615					
14	Total	14	145656.9333						
15									
16		*Coefficients*	*Standard Error*	*t Stat*	*P-value*	*Lower 95%*	*Upper 95%*	*Lower 95.0%*	*Upper 95.0%*
17	Intercept	113.7452874	20.81345608	5.464987985	0.000108415	68.78054927	158.7100256	68.78054927	158.7100256
18	Months Employed	2.367463621	0.338396631	6.996120545	9.39543E-06	1.636402146	3.098525095	1.636402146	3.098525095

Before considering how to develop a curvilinear relationship for Reynolds, let us consider the Excel output in Figure 7.28 for a simple linear regression; the estimated regression is:

$$\text{Sales} = 113.7453 + 2.3675 \text{ Months Employed.}$$

The scatter chart of residuals against the independent variable Months Employed would also suggest that a curvilinear relationship may provide a better fit to the data.

The computer output shows that the relationship is significant (p value = 9.3954E-06 in cell E18 of Figure 7.28 for the t test that $\beta_1 = 0$) and that a linear relationship explains a high percentage of the variability in sales ($r^2 = 0.7901$ in cell B5). However, Figure 7.29 reveals a pattern in the scatter chart of residuals against the predicted values of the dependent variable that suggests that a curvilinear relationship may provide a better fit to the data. This becomes more apparent when we review a scatter chart of the residuals and predicted values of the dependent variable.

If we have a practical reason to suspect a curvilinear relationship between number of electronic laboratory scales sold by a salesperson and the number of months the salesperson has been employed, we may wish to consider an alternative to simple linear regression. For example, we may believe that a recently hired salesperson faces a learning curve but becomes increasingly more effective over time and that a salesperson who has been in a sales position with Reynolds for a long time eventually becomes burned out and becomes increasingly less effective. If our regression model supports this theory, Reynolds management can use the model to identify the approximate point in employment when its salespeople begin to lose their effectiveness, and management can plan strategies to counteract salesperson burnout.

Quadratic Regression Models

To account for the curvilinear relationship between months employed and scales sold that is suggested by the scatter chart of residuals against the predicted values of the dependent

FIGURE 7.29 Scatter Chart of the Residuals and Predicted Values of the Dependent Variable for the Reynolds Simple Linear Regression

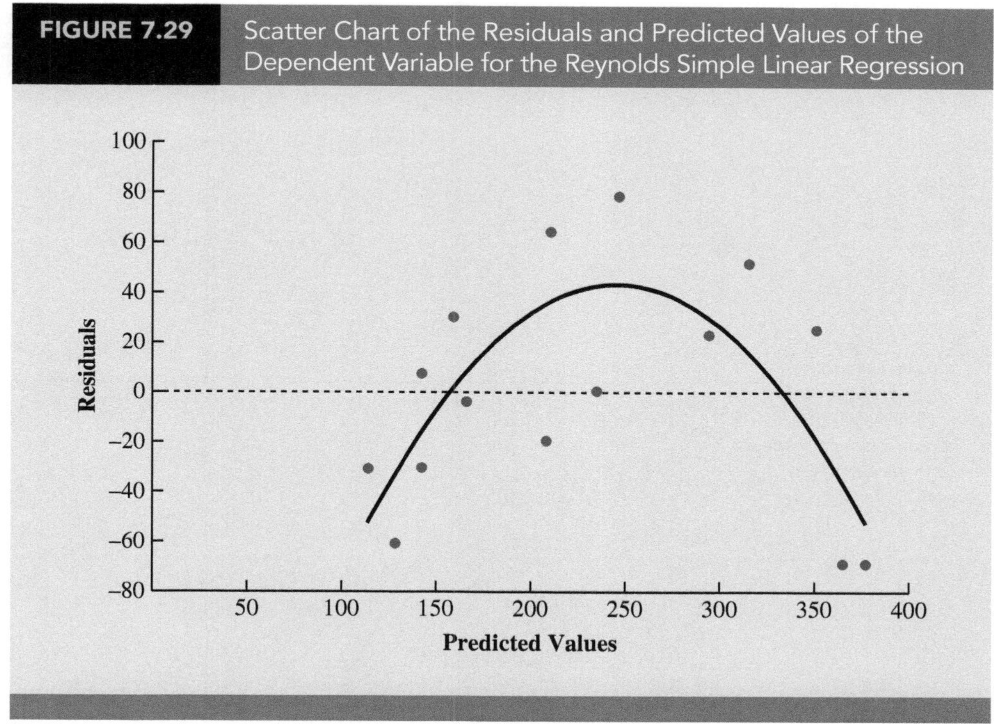

variable, we could include the square of the number of months the salesperson has been employed in the model as a second independent variable:

$$y = b_0 + b_1x_1 + b_2x_1^2 + e. \quad \textbf{(7.18)}$$

As we can see in Figure 7.30, quadratic regression models are flexible and are capable of representing a wide variety of nonlinear relationships between an independent variable and the dependent variable.

To develop an estimated regression equation corresponding to this model, referred to as a **quadratic regression model**, the statistical software package we are using needs the original data as well as the square of the number of months the employee has been with the firm. Figure 7.31 shows the Excel spreadsheet that includes the square of the number of months the employee has been with the firm. To create the variable, which we will call MonthsSq, we create a new column and set each cell in that column equal to the square of the associated value of the variable Months. These values are shown in Column B of Figure 7.31.

The regression output for the model in equation (7.18) is shown in Figure 7.32. The estimated regression equation is:

$$\text{Sales} = 61.4299 + 5.8198 \text{ Months Employed} - 0.0310 \text{ MonthsSq},$$

where MonthsSq is the square of the number of months the salesperson has been employed. Because the value of b_1 (5.8198) is positive, and the value of b_2 (−0.0310) is negative, $\hat{y}$ will initially increase as the number of months the salesperson has been employed increases. As the value of the independent variable Months Employed increases, its squared value increases more rapidly, and eventually $\hat{y}$ will decrease as the number of months the salesperson has been employed increases.

The R^2 of 0.9013 indicates that this regression model explains approximately 90.2% of the variation in Scales Sold for our sample data. The lack of a distinct pattern in the scatter

FIGURE 7.30 Relationships That Can Be Fit with a Quadratic Regression Model

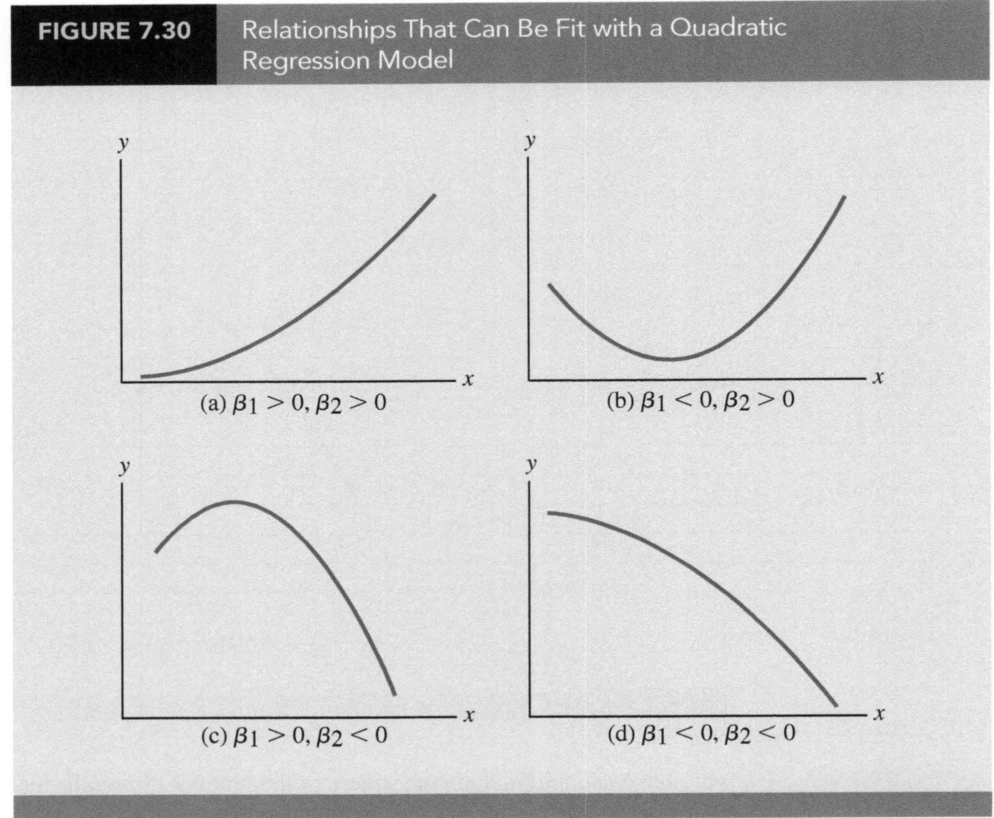

If $\beta_2 > 0$, the function is bowl-shaped relative to the x-axis, it is convex; if $\beta_2 < 0$, the function is mound-shaped relative to the x-axis, it is concave.

FIGURE 7.31 Excel Data for the Reynolds Quadratic Regression Model

	A	B	C
1	Months Employed	MonthsSq	Scales Sold
2	41	1,681	275
3	106	11,236	296
4	76	5,776	317
5	100	10,000	376
6	22	484	162
7	12	144	150
8	85	7,225	367
9	111	12,321	308
10	40	1,600	189
11	51	2,601	235
12	0	0	83
13	12	144	112
14	6	36	67
15	56	3,136	325
16	19	361	189

FIGURE 7.32 Excel Output for the Reynolds Quadratic Regression Model

	A	B	C	D	E	F	G	H	I
1	SUMMARY OUTPUT								
2									
3	*Regression Statistics*								
4	Multiple R	0.949361402							
5	R Square	0.901287072							
6	Adjusted R Square	0.884834917							
7	Standard Error	34.61481184							
8	Observations	15							
9									
10	ANOVA								
11		*df*	*SS*	*MS*	*F*	*Significance F*			
12	Regression	2	131278.711	65639.35548	54.78231208	9.25218E-07			
13	Residual	12	14378.22238	1198.185199					
14	Total	14	145656.9333						
15									
16		*Coefficients*	*Standard Error*	*t Stat*	*P-value*	*Lower 95%*	*Upper 95%*	*Lower 99.0%*	*Upper 99.0%*
17	Intercept	61.42993467	20.57433536	2.985755485	0.011363561	16.60230882	106.2575605	−1.415187222	124.2750566
18	Months Employed	5.819796648	0.969766536	6.001234761	6.20497E-05	3.706856877	7.93273642	2.857606371	8.781986926
19	MonthsSq	−0.031009589	0.008436087	−3.675826286	0.003172962	−0.049390243	−0.012628935	−0.05677795	−0.005241228

The scatter chart of residuals against the independent variable Months Employed would also lead us to this conclusion.

chart of residuals against the predicted values of the dependent variable (Figure 7.33) suggests that the quadratic model fits the data better than the simple linear regression in the Reynolds example.

Although it is difficult to assess from a sample as small as this whether the regression model satisfies the conditions necessary for reliable inference, we see no marked violations of these conditions, so we will proceed with hypothesis tests of the regression parameters β_0, β_1, and β_2 for our quadratic regression model.

From the Excel output for the model in equation (7.18) provided in Figure 7.32, we see that the p values corresponding to the t statistics for Months Employed (6.2050E-05) and MonthsSq (0.0032) are both substantially less than 0.05, and hence we can conclude that adding MonthsSq to the model involving Months is significant. There is a nonlinear relationship between months and sales.

Note that if the estimated regression parameters b_1 and b_2 corresponding to the linear term x and the squared term x^2 are of the same sign, the estimated value of the dependent variable is either increasing over the experimental range of x (when $b_1 > 0$ and $b_2 > 0$) or decreasing over the experimental range of x (when $b_1 < 0$ and $b_2 < 0$). If the estimated regression parameters b_1 and b_2 corresponding to the linear term x and the squared term x^2 have different signs, the estimated value of the dependent variable has a maximum over the experimental range of x (when $b_1 > 0$ and $b_2 < 0$) or a minimum over the experimental range of x (when $b_1 < 0$ and $b_2 > 0$). In these instances, we can find the estimated maximum or minimum over the experimental range of x by finding the value of x at which the estimated value of the dependent variable stops increasing and begins decreasing (when a maximum exists) or stops decreasing and begins increasing (when a minimum exists).

FIGURE 7.33 Scatter Chart of the Residuals and Predicted Values of the Dependent Variable for the Reynolds Quadratic Regression Model

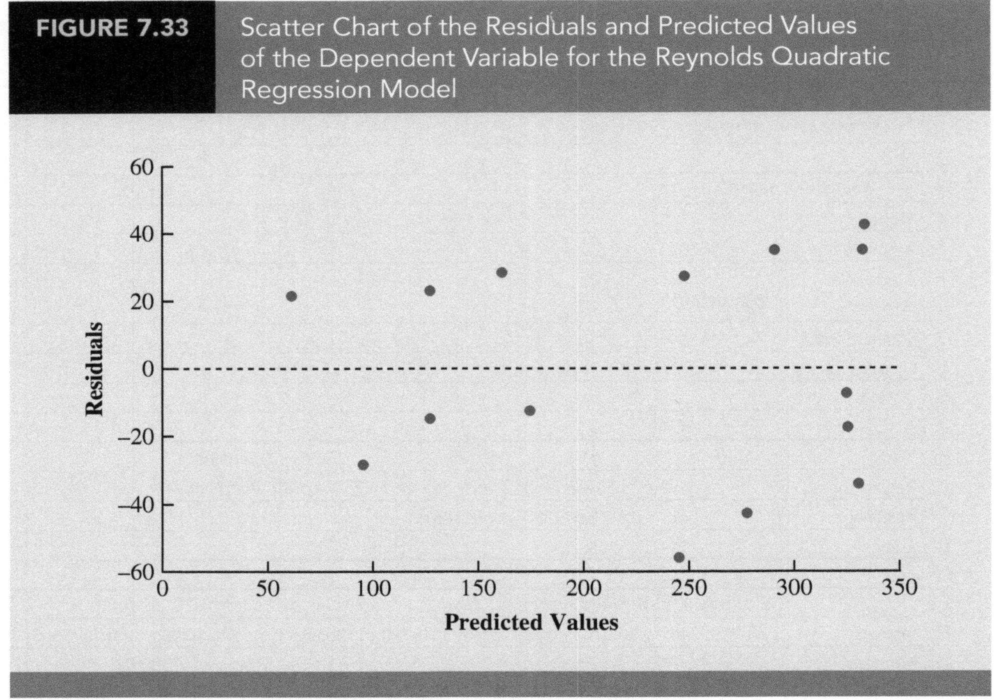

For example, we estimate that when months employed increases by 1 from some value x $(x + 1)$, sales changes by:

$$\begin{aligned} &5.8198\,[(x + 1) - x] - 0.0310\,[(x + 1)^2 - x^2] \\ &= 5.8198\,(x - x + 1) - 0.0310\,(x^2 + 2x + 1 - x^2) \\ &= 5.8198 - 0.0310\,(2x + 1) \\ &= 5.7888 - 0.0620x. \end{aligned}$$

That is, estimated Sales initially increases as Months Employed increases and then eventually decreases as Months Employed increases. Solving this result for x:

$$\begin{aligned} 5.7888 - 0.0620x &= 0 \\ -0.0620x &= -5.7888 \\ x &= \frac{-5.7888}{-0.0620} = 93.3387 \end{aligned}$$

tells us that estimated maximum sales occurs at approximately 93 months (in about seven years nine months). We can then find the estimated maximum value of the dependent variable Sales by substituting this value of x into the estimated regression equation:

In business analytics applications, polynomial regression models of higher than second or third order are rarely used.

$$\text{Sales} = 61.58198 + 5.8198\,(93.3387) - 0.0310\,(93.3387^2) = 334.4909.$$

At approximately 93 months, the maximum estimated sales of approximately 334 scales occurs.

Piecewise Linear Regression Models

A piecewise linear regression model is sometimes referred to as a segment regression or a spline model.

As an alternative to a quadratic regression model, we can recognize that below some value of Months Employed, the relationship between Months Employed and Sales appears to be positive and linear, whereas the relationship between Months Employed and Sales appears to be negative and linear for the remaining observations. A **piecewise linear regression model**

FIGURE 7.34 Possible Position of Knot $x^{(k)}$

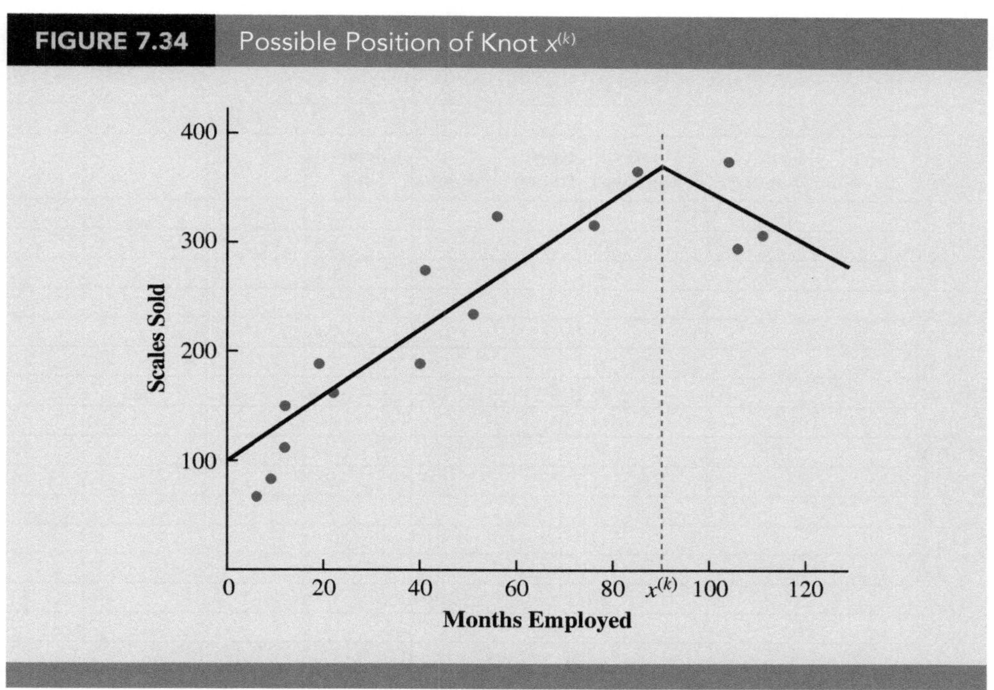

will allow us to fit these relationships as two linear regressions that are joined at the value of Months at which the relationship between Months Employed and Sales changes.

Our first step in fitting a piecewise linear regression model is to identify the value of the independent variable Months Employed at which the relationship between Months Employed and Sales changes; this point is called the **knot**, or *breakpoint*. Although theory should determine this value, analysts often use the sample data to aid in the identification of this point. Figure 7.34 provides the scatter chart for the Reynolds data with an indication of the possible location of the knot, which we have denoted $x^{(k)}$. From this scatter chart, it appears the knot is at approximately 90 months.

Once we have decided on the location of the knot, we define a dummy variable that is equal to zero for any observation for which the value of Months Employed is less than or equal to the value of the knot, and equal to one for any observation for which the value of Months Employed is greater than the value of the knot:

$$x_k = \begin{cases} 0 \text{ if } x_1 \leq x^{(k)} \\ 1 \text{ if } x_1 > x^{(k)} \end{cases} \tag{7.19}$$

where

x_1 = Months

$x^{(k)}$ = the value of the knot (90 months for the Reynolds example)

x_k = the knot dummy variable

We then fit the following regression model:

$$y = b_0 + b_1x_1 + b_2(x_1 - x^{(k)})x_k + e. \tag{7.20}$$

The data and Excel output for the Reynolds piecewise linear regression model are provided in Figure 7.35. Because we placed the knot at $x^{(k)} = 90$, the estimated regression model is

$$\hat{y} = 87.2172 + 3.4094x_1 - 7.8726(x_1 - 90)x_k$$

FIGURE 7.35 Data and Excel Output for the Reynolds Piecewise Linear Regression Model

	A	B	C	D	E	F	G	H	I
1	**Knot Dummy**	**Months Employed**	**Knot Dummy* Months**	**Scales Sold**					
2	0	41	0	275					
3	1	106	16	296					
4	0	76	0	317					
5	1	100	10	376					
6	0	22	0	162					
7	0	12	0	150					
8	0	85	0	367					
9	1	111	21	308					
10	0	40	0	189					
11	0	51	0	235					
12	0	0	0	83					
13	0	12	0	112					
14	0	6	0	67					
15	0	56	0	325					
16	0	19	0	189					
17									
18									
19	SUMMARY OUTPUT								
20									
21	*Regression Statistics*								
22	Multiple R	0.955796127							
23	R Square	0.913546237							
24	Adjusted R Square	0.899137276							
25	Standard Error	32.3941739							
26	Observations	15							
27									
28	ANOVA								
29		*df*	*SS*	*MS*	*F*	*Significance F*			
30	Regression	2	133064.3433	66532.17165	63.4012588	4.17545E-07			
31	Residual	12	12592.59003	1049.382502					
32	Total	14	145656.9333						
33									
34		*Coefficients*	*Standard Error*	*t Stat*	*P-value*	*Lower 95%*	*Upper 95%*	*Lower 99.0%*	*Upper 99.0%*
35	Intercept	87.21724231	15.31062519	5.696517369	9.9677E-05	53.85825572	120.5762289	40.45033153	133.9841531
36	Months Employed	3.409431979	0.338360666	10.07632484	3.2987E-07	2.67220742	4.146656538	2.375895931	4.442968028
37	Knot Dummy* Months	−7.872553259	1.902156543	−4.138751508	0.00137388	−12.01699634	−3.728110179	−13.68276572	−2.062340794

The output shows that the p value corresponding to the t statistic for knot term ($p = 0.0014$) is less than 0.05, and hence we can conclude that adding the knot to the model with Months Employed as the independent variable is significant.

But what does this model mean? For any value of Months less than or equal to 90, the knot term $7.8726(x_1 - 90)x_k$ is zero because the knot dummy variable $x_k = 0$, so the regression model is:

$$\hat{y} = 87.2172 + 3.4094x_1.$$

*The variable Knot Dummy*Months is the product of the corresponding values of Knot Dummy and the difference between Months Employed and the knot value, i.e., C2 = A2 * (B2 − 90) in this Excel spreadsheet.*

For any value of Months Employed greater than 90, the knot term is $-7.87(x_1 - 90)$ because the knot dummy variable $x_k = 1$, so the regression model is:

$$\begin{aligned}\hat{y} &= 87.2172 + 3.4094x_1 - 7.8726(x_1 - 90)\\ &= 87.2172 - 7.8726(-90) + (3.4094 - 7.8726)x_1 = 795.7512 - 4.4632x_1.\end{aligned}$$

Note that if Months Employed is equal to 90, both regressions yield the same value of $\hat{y}$:

$$\hat{y} = 87.2172 + 3.4094(90) = 795.7512 - 4.4632(90) = 394.06.$$

So the two regression segments are joined at the knot.

Multiple knots can be used to fit complex piecewise linear regressions.

The interpretation of this model is similar to the interpretation of the quadratic regression model. A salesperson's sales are expected to increase by 3,409.4 electronic laboratory scales for each month of employment until the salesperson has been employed for 90 months. At that point the salesperson's sales are expected to decrease by 4,463.1 (because 3,409.4 − 7,872.5 = −4,463.1) electronic laboratory scales for each additional month of employment.

Should we use the quadratic regression model or the piecewise linear regression model? These models fit the data equally well, and both have reasonable interpretations, so we cannot differentiate between the models on either of these criteria. Thus, we must consider whether the abrupt change in the relationship between Sales and Months Employed that is suggested by the piecewise linear regression model captures the real relationship between Sales and Months Employed better than the smooth change in the relationship between Sales and Months Employed suggested by the quadratic model.

Interaction Between Independent Variables

Often the relationship between the dependent variable and one independent variable is different at various values of a second independent variable. When this occurs, it is called an **interaction**. If the original data set consists of observations for y and two independent variables x_1 and x_2, we can incorporate an x_1x_2 interaction into the multiple linear regression in the following manner:

$$y = b_0 + b_1x_1 + b_2x_2 + b_3x_1x_2 + e. \quad \textbf{(7.21)}$$

To provide an illustration of interaction and what it means, let us consider the regression study conducted by Tyler Personal Care for one of its new shampoo products. The two factors believed to have the most influence on sales are unit selling price and advertising expenditure. To investigate the effects of these two variables on sales, prices of \$2.00, \$2.50, and \$3.00 were paired with advertising expenditures of \$50,000 and \$100,000 in 24 test markets.

Tyler

The data collected by Tyler are provided in the file *Tyler*. Figure 7.36 shows the sample mean sales for the six price advertising expenditure combinations. Note that the sample mean sales corresponding to a price of \$2.00 and an advertising expenditure of \$50,000 is 461,000 units and that the sample mean sales corresponding to a price of \$2.00 and an advertising expenditure of \$100,000 is 808,000 units. Hence, with price held constant at \$2.00, the difference in mean sales between advertising expenditures of \$50,000 and \$100,000 is 808,000 − 461,000 = 347,000 units. When the price of the product is \$2.50, the difference in mean sales between advertising expenditures of \$50,000 and \$100,000 is 646,000 − 364,000 = 282,000 units. Finally, when the price is \$3.00, the difference in mean sales between advertising expenditures of \$50,000 and \$100,000 is 375,000 − 332,000 = 43,000 units. Clearly, the difference in mean sales between advertising expenditures of \$50,000 and \$100,000 depends on the price of the product. In other words, at higher selling prices, the effect of increased advertising expenditure diminishes. These

FIGURE 7.36 Mean Unit Sales (1,000s) as a Function of Selling Price and Advertising Expenditures

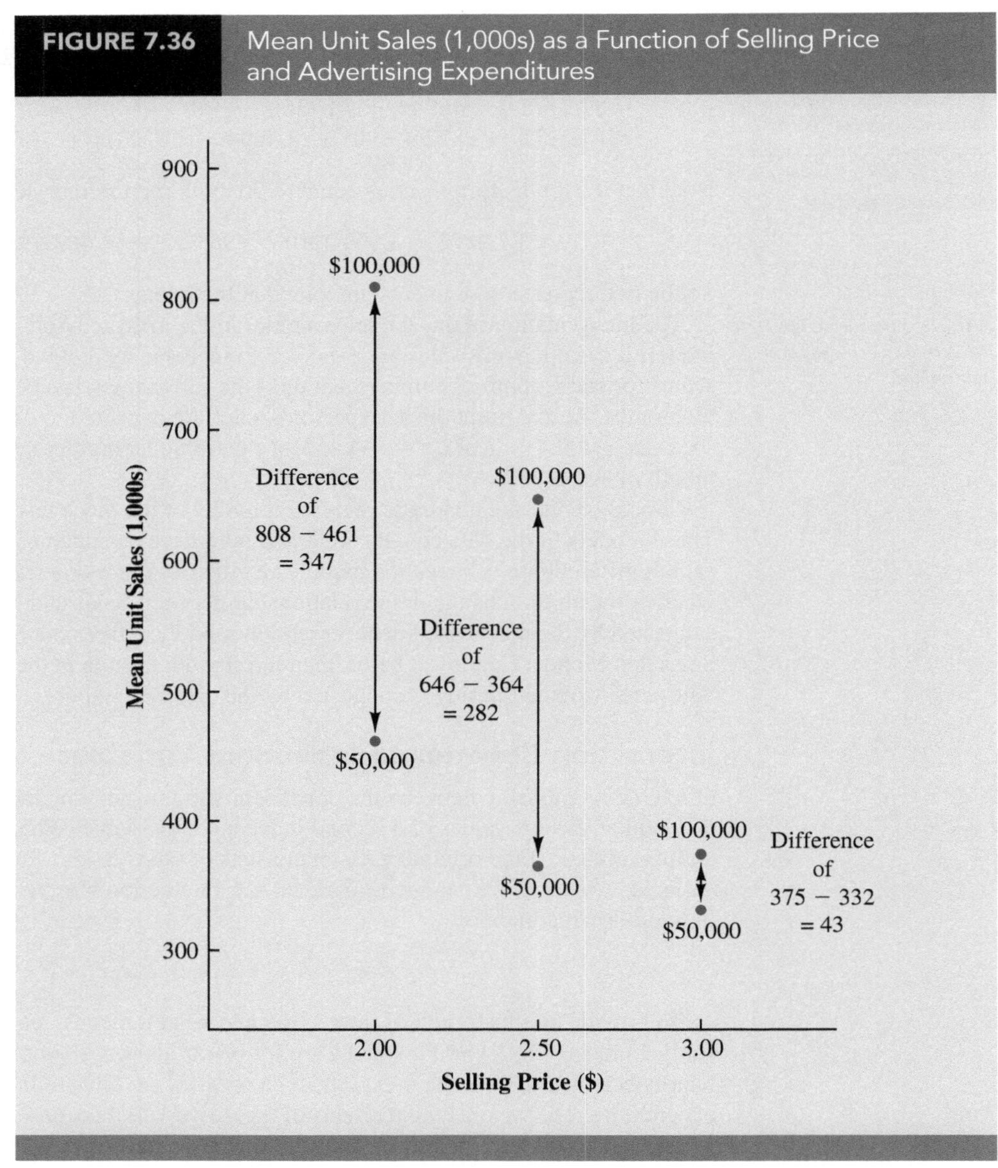

*In the file Tyler, the data for the independent variable Price is in column A, the independent variable Advertising Expenditures is in column B, and the dependent variable Sales is in column D. We created the interaction variable Price*Advertising in column C by entering the function A2*B2 in cell C2, and then copying cell C2 into cells C3 through C25.*

observations provide evidence of interaction between the price and advertising expenditure variables.

When interaction between two variables is present, we cannot study the relationship between one independent variable and the dependent variable y independently of the other variable. In other words, meaningful conclusions can be developed only if we consider the joint relationship that both independent variables have with the dependent variable. To account for the interaction, we use the regression model in equation (7.21), where:

$$y = \text{Unit Sales (1,000s)}$$
$$x_1 = \text{Price (\$)}$$
$$x_2 = \text{Advertising Expenditure (\$1,000s)}$$

FIGURE 7.37 Excel Output for the Tyler Personal Care Linear Regression Model with Interaction

	A	B	C	D	E	F	G	H	I
1	SUMMARY OUTPUT								
2									
3	*Regression Statistics*								
4	Multiple R	0.988993815							
5	R Square	0.978108766							
6	Adjusted R Square	0.974825081							
7	Standard Error	28.17386496							
8	Observations	24							
9									
10	ANOVA								
11		*df*	*SS*	*MS*	*F*	*Significance F*			
12	Regression	3	709316	236438.6667	297.8692	9.25881E-17			
13	Residual	20	15875.33333	793.7666667					
14	Total	23	725191.3333						
15									
16		*Coefficients*	*Standard Error*	*t Stat*	*P-value*	*Lower 95%*	*Upper 95%*	*Lower 99.0%*	*Upper 99.0%*
17	Intercept	–275.8333333	112.8421033	–2.444418575	0.023898351	–511.2178361	–40.44883053	–596.9074508	45.24078413
18	Price	175	44.54679188	3.928453489	0.0008316	82.07702045	267.9229796	48.24924412	301.7507559
19	Advertising Expenditure ($1,000s)	19.68	1.42735225	13.78776683	1.1263E-11	16.70259538	22.65740462	15.61869796	23.74130204
20	Price*Advertising	–6.08	0.563477299	–10.79014187	8.67721E-10	–7.255393049	–4.904606951	–7.683284335	–4.476715665

Note that the regression model in equation (7.21) reflects Tyler's belief that the number of units sold is related to selling price and advertising expenditure (accounted for by the $\beta_1 x_1$ and $\beta_2 x_2$ terms) and an interaction between the two variables (accounted for by the $\beta_3 x_1 x_2$ term).

The Excel output corresponding to the interaction model for the Tyler Personal Care example is provided in Figure 7.37.

The resulting estimated regression equation is:

$$\text{Sales} = -275.8333 + 175 \text{ Price} + 19.68 \text{ Advertising} - 6.08 \text{ Price*Advertising}.$$

Because the p value corresponding to the t test for Price*Advertising is 8.6772E-10, we conclude that interaction is significant. Thus, the regression results show that the relationship between advertising expenditure and sales depends on the price (and the relationship between advertising expenditures and price depends on sales).

Our initial review of these results may alarm us: How can price have a positive estimated regression coefficient? With the exception of luxury goods, we expect sales to decrease as price increases. Although this result appears counterintuitive, we can make sense of this model if we work through the interpretation of the interaction. In other words, the relationship between the independent variable Price and the dependent variable Sales is different at various values of Advertising (and the relationship between the independent variable Advertising and the dependent variable Sales is different at various values of Price).

It becomes easier to see how the predicted value of Sales depends on Price by using the estimated regression model to consider the effect when Price increases by $1:

$$\text{Sales After \$1 Price Increase} = -275.8333 + 175\ (\text{Price} + 1) + 19.68\ \text{Advertising} - 6.08\ (\text{Price} + 1) * \text{Advertising}.$$

Thus,

$$\text{Sales After \$1 Price Increase} - \text{Sales Before \$1 Price Increase} = 175 - 6.08\ \text{Advertising Expenditure}.$$

So the change in the predicted value of the dependent variable that occurs when the independent variable Price increases by $1 depends on how much was spent on advertising.

Consider a concrete example. If Advertising Expenditures is $50,000 when price is $2.00, we estimate sales to be:

$$\text{Sales} = -275.8333 + 175\ (2) + 19.68\ (50) - 6.08\ (2)\ (50) = 450.1667, \text{ or } 450{,}167 \text{ units.}$$

At the same level of Advertising Expenditures ($50,000) when price is $3.00, we estimate sales to be:

$$\text{Sales} = -275.8333 + 175\ (3) + 19.68\ (50) - 6.08\ (3)\ (50) = 321.1667, \text{ or } 321{,}167 \text{ units.}$$

So when Advertising Expenditures is $50,000, a change in price from $2.00 to $3.00 results in a 450,167 − 321,167 = 129,000-unit decrease in estimated sales. However, if Advertising Expenditures is $100,000 when price is $2.00, we estimate sales to be:

$$\text{Sales} = -275.8333 + 175\ (2) + 19.68\ (100) - 6.08\ (2)\ (100) = 826.1667, \text{ or } 826{,}167 \text{ units.}$$

At the same level of Advertising Expenditures ($100,000) when price is $3.00, we estimate sales to be:

$$\text{Sales} = -275.8333 + 175\ (3) + 19.68\ (100) - 6.08\ (3)\ (100) = 393.1667, \text{ or } 393{,}167 \text{ units.}$$

So when Advertising Expenditures is $100,000, a change in price from $2.00 to $3.00 results in a 826,167 − 393,167 = 433,000-unit decrease in estimated sales. When Tyler spends more on advertising, its sales are more sensitive to changes in price. Perhaps at larger Advertising Expenditures, Tyler attracts new customers who have been buying the product from another company and so are more aware of the prices charged for the product by Tyler's competitors.

There is a second and equally valid interpretation of the interaction; it tells us that the relationship between the independent variable Advertising Expenditure and the dependent variable Sales is different at various values of Price. Using the estimated regression model to consider the effect when Advertising Expenditure increases by $1,000:

$$\text{Sales After \$1K Advertising Increase} = -275.8333 + 175\ \text{Price} + 19.68\ (\text{Advertising} + 1) - 6.08\ \text{Price} * (\text{Advertising} + 1).$$

Thus,

$$\text{Sales After \$1K Advertising Increase} - \text{Sales Before \$1K Advertising Increase} = 19.68 - 6.08\ \text{Price}.$$

So the change in the predicted value of the dependent variable that occurs when the independent variable Advertising Expenditure increases by $1,000 depends on the price.

Thus, if Price is \$2.00 when Advertising Expenditures is \$50,000, we estimate sales to be:

Sales $= -275.8333 + 175\,(2) + 19.68\,(50) - 6.08\,(2)\,(50) = 450.1667$, or 450,167 units.

At the same level of Price (\$2.00) when Advertising Expenditures is \$100,000, we estimate sales to be:

Sales $= -275.8333 + 175\,(2) + 19.68\,(100) - 6.08\,(2)\,(100) = 826.1667$, or 826,167 units.

So when Price is \$2.00, a change in Advertising Expenditures from \$50,000 to \$100,000 results in a 826,167 − 450,167 = 376,000-unit increase in estimated sales. However, if Price is \$3.00 when Advertising Expenditures is 50,000, we estimate sales to be:

Sales $= -275.8333 + 175\,(3) + 19.68\,(50) - 6.08\,(3)\,(50) = 321.1667$, or 321,167 units.

At the same level of Price (\$3.00) when Advertising Expenditures is \$100,000, we estimate sales to be:

Sales $= -275.8333 + 175\,(3) + 19.68\,(100) - 6.08\,(3)\,(100) = 393.1667$, or 393,167 units.

So when Price is \$3.00, a change in Advertising Expenditure from \$50,000 to \$100,000 results in a 393,167 − 321,167 = 72,000-unit increase in estimated sales. When the price of Tyler's product is high, its sales are less sensitive to changes in advertising expenditure. Perhaps as Tyler increases its price, it must advertise more to convince potential customers that its product is a good value.

Note that we can combine a quadratic effect with interaction to produce a second-order polynomial model with interaction between the two independent variables. The model obtained is:

$$y = b_0 + b_1x_1 + b_2x_2 + b_3x_1^2 + b_4x_2^2 + b_5x_1x_2 + e. \quad \textbf{(7.22)}$$

This model provides a great deal of flexibility in capturing nonlinear effects.

NOTES + COMMENTS

1. Just as a dummy variable can be used to allow for different y-intercepts for the two groups represented by the dummy, we can use an interaction between a dummy variable and a quantitative independent variable to allow for different relationships between independent and dependent variables for the two groups represented by the dummy. Consider the Butler Trucking example: Travel time is the dependent variable y, miles traveled and number of deliveries are the quantitative independent variables x_1 and x_2, and the dummy variable x_3 differentiates between driving assignments that included travel on a congested segment of a highway and driving assignments that did not. If we believe that the relationship between miles traveled and travel time differs for driving assignments that included travel on a congested segment of a highway and those that did not, we could create a new variable that is the interaction between miles traveled and the dummy variable ($x_4 = x_1{*}x_3$) and estimate the following model:

$$\hat{y} = b_0 + b_1x_1 + b_2x_2 + b_3x_4.$$

If a driving assignment does not include travel on a congested segment of a highway, $x_4 = x_1{*}x_3 = x_1{*}(0) = 0$ and the regression model is:

$$\hat{y} = b_0 + b_1x_1 + b_2x_2.$$

If a driving assignment does include travel on a congested segment of a highway, $x_4 = x_1{*}x_3 = x_1{*}(1) = x_1$ and the regression model is:

$$\hat{y} = b_0 + b_1x_1 + b_2x_2 + b_3x_1(1)$$
$$= b_0 + (b_1 + b_3)x_1 + b_2x_2.$$

So in this regression model b_1 is the estimate of the relationship between miles traveled and travel time for driving assignments that do not include travel on a congested segment of a highway, and $b_1 + b_3$ is the estimate of the relationship between miles traveled and travel time for driving assignments that do include travel on a congested segment of a highway.

2. Multicollinearity can be divided into two types. *Data-based multicollinearity* occurs when separate independent variables that are related are included in the model, whereas *structural multicollinearity* occurs when a new independent variable is created by taking a function of one or more existing independent variables. If we use ratings that consumers give on bread's aroma and taste as independent variables in a model for which the dependent variable is the overall rating of the bread, the multicollinearity that would exist between the aroma and taste ratings is an example of data-based multicollinearity. If we build a quadratic model for which the independent variables are ratings that consumers give on bread's aroma and the square of the ratings that consumers give on bread's aroma, the multicollinearity that would exist is an example of structural multicollinearity.
3. Structural multicollinearity occurs naturally in polynomial regression models and regression models with interactions. You can greatly reduce the structural multicollinearity in a polynomial regression by centering the independent variable x (using $x - \bar{x}$ in place of x). In a regression model with interaction, you can greatly reduce the structural multicollinearity by centering both independent variables that interact. However, quadratic regression models and regression models with interactions are frequently used only for prediction; in these instances centering independent variables is not necessary because we are not concerned with inference.

7.8 Model Fitting

Finding an effective regression model can be challenging. Although we rely on theory to guide us, often we are faced with a large number of potential independent variables from which to choose. In this section we discuss common algorithms for building a regression model and the potential hazards of these and other similar algorithms.

Variable Selection Procedures

When there are many independent variables to consider, special procedures are sometimes employed to select the independent variables to include in the regression model. These variable selection procedures include **backward elimination**, **forward selection**, **stepwise selection**, and the **best subsets** procedure. Given a data set with several possible independent variables, we can use these procedures to identify which independent variables provide a model that best satisfies some criterion. The first four procedures are iterative; at each step of the procedure a single independent variable is added or removed and the new model is evaluated. The process continues until a stopping criterion indicates that the procedure cannot find a superior model. The best subsets procedure is not a one-variable-at-a-time procedure; it evaluates regression models involving different subsets of the independent variables.

The backward elimination procedure begins with the regression model that includes all of the independent variables under consideration. At each step of the procedure, backward elimination considers the removal of an independent variable according to some criterion. For example, if any independent variables currently in the model are not significant at a preselected level of significance, XLMiner removes the least significant of these independent variables from the model. The regression model is then refit with the remaining independent variables and statistical significance is reexamined. The backward elimination procedure stops when all independent variables in the model are significant at a preselected level of significance.

The forward selection procedure begins with none of the independent variables under consideration included in the regression model. At each step of the procedure, forward selection considers the addition of an independent variable according to some criterion. For example, if any independent variables currently not in the model are significant at a preselected level of significance, XLMiner adds the most significant of these independent variables to the model. The regression model is then refit with the additional independent variable and statistical significance is reexamined. The forward selection procedure stops when all of the independent variables not in the model are not significant at a preselected level of significance.

The stepwise procedure requires that the criterion for an independent variable to enter the regression model is more difficult to satisfy than the criterion for an independent variable to be removed from the regression model. This requirement prevents the same independent variable from exiting and then reentering the regression model in the same step.

Similar to the forward selection procedure, the stepwise procedure begins with none of the independent variables under consideration included in the regression model. The analyst establishes both a criterion for allowing independent variables to enter the model and a criterion for allowing independent variables to remain in the model. For example, XLMiner adds the most significant variable and removes the least significant variable at each iteration. In the first step of the procedure, the most significant independent variable is added to the current model if its level of significance satisfies the entering threshold. Each subsequent step involves two intermediate steps. First, the remaining independent variables not in the current model are evaluated, and the most significant one is added to the model if its significance satisfies the entering threshold. Then the independent variables in the resulting model are evaluated, and the least significant variable is removed if its level of significance fails to satisfy the exiting threshold. The procedure stops when no independent variable not currently in the model has a level of significance that satisfies the entering threshold, and no independent variable currently in the model has a level of significance that fails to satisfy the exiting threshold.

XLMiner also provides a sequential replacement algorithm in which, for a given number of independent variables, individual independent variables are sequentially replaced and replacements that improve performance are retained.

In the best subsets procedure, simple linear regressions for each of the independent variables under consideration are generated, and then the multiple regressions with all combinations of two independent variables under consideration are generated, and so on. Once a regression model has been generated for every possible subset of the independent variables under consideration, the entire collection of regression models can be compared and evaluated by the analyst.

Although these algorithms are potentially useful when dealing with a large number of potential independent variables, they do not necessarily provide useful models. Once the procedure terminates, you should deliberate whether the combination of independent variables included in the final regression model makes sense from a practical standpoint and consider whether you can create a more useful regression model with more meaningful interpretation through the addition or removal of independent variables. Use your own judgment and intuition about your data to refine the results of these algorithms.

Overfitting

The objective in building a regression model (or any other type of mathematical model) is to provide the simplest accurate representation of the population. A model that is relatively simple will be easy to understand, interpret, and use, and a model that accurately represents the population will yield meaningful results.

When we base a model on sample data, we must be wary. Sample data generally do not perfectly represent the population from which they are drawn; if we attempt to fit a model too closely to the sample data, we risk capturing behavior that is idiosyncratic to the sample data rather than representative of the population. When the model is too closely fit to sample data and as a result does not accurately reflect the population, the model is said to have been overfit.

The principle of using the simplest meaningful model possible without sacrificing accuracy is referred to as Ockham's razor, the law of parsimony, or the law of economy.

Overfitting generally results from creating an overly complex model to explain idiosyncrasies in the sample data. In regression analysis, this often results from the use of complex functional forms or independent variables that do not have meaningful relationships with the dependent variable. If a model is overfit to the sample data, it will perform better on the sample data used to fit the model than it will on other data from the population. Thus, an overfit model can be misleading with regard to its predictive capability and its interpretation.

Overfitting is a difficult problem to detect and avoid. The following list summarizes one way to avoid overfitting and one way to determine how well a model will may generalize to new data.

- Use only independent variables that you expect to have real and meaningful relationships with the dependent variable.
- Use complex models, such as quadratic models and piecewise linear regression models, only when you have a reasonable expectation that such complexity provides a more accurate depiction of what you are modeling.
- Do not let software dictate your model. Use iterative modeling procedures, such as the stepwise and best-subsets procedures, only for guidance and not to generate your final model. Use your own judgment and intuition about your data and what you are modeling to refine your model.
- If you have access to a sufficient quantity of data, assess your model on data other than the sample data that were used to generate the model (this is referred to as **cross-validation**. The following list contains three possible ways to execute cross-validation.

Validation data sets are sometimes referred to as holdout samples. XLMiner allows the user to easily divide data sets into training and validation sets for use with regression models.

Holdout method: The sample data are randomly divided into mutually exclusive and collectively exhaustive training and validation sets. The **training set** is the data set used to build the candidate models that appear to make practical sense. The **validation set** is the set of data used to compare model performances and ultimately select a model for predicting values of the dependent variable. For example, we might randomly select half of the data for use in developing regression models. We could use these data as our training set to estimate a model or a collection of models that appear to perform well. Then we use the remaining half of the data as a validation set to assess and compare the models' performances and ultimately select the model that minimizes some measure of overall error when applied to the validation set. The advantages of the holdout method are that it is simple and quick. However, results of a holdout sample can vary greatly depending on which observations are randomly selected for the training set, the number of observations in the sample, and the number of observations that are randomly selected for the training and validation sets.

k-fold cross-validation: The sample data set are randomly divided into k equal-sized, mutually exclusive, and collectively exhaustive subsets called folds, and k iterations are executed. For each iteration, a different subset is designated as the validation set and the remaining $k - 1$ subsets are combined and designated as the training set. The model is estimated using the respective training set data and evaluated using the respective validation set. The results of the k iterations are then combined and evaluated. A common choice for the number of folds is $k = 10$. The k-fold cross-validation method is more complex and time consuming than the holdout method, but the results of the k-fold cross-validation method are less sensitive to how the observations are randomly assigned to the training validation sets.

Leave-one-out cross-validation: For a sample of n observations, an iteration consists of estimating the model on $n - 1$ observations and evaluating the model on the single observation that was omitted from the training data. This procedure is repeated for n total iterations so that the model is trained on each possible combination of $n - 1$ observations and evaluated on the single remaining observation in each case.

Observing these guidelines will reduce the risk of overfitting, but one must always be wary of the potential for overfitting when interpreting and assessing a model.

SUMMARY

In this chapter we showed how regression analysis can be used to determine how a dependent variable y is related to an independent variable x. In simple linear regression, the regression model is $y = \beta_0 + \beta_1 x_1 + \varepsilon$. We use sample data and the least squares method to develop the estimated regression equation $\hat{y} = b_0 + b_1 x_1$. In effect, b_0 and b_1 are the sample statistics used to estimate the unknown model parameters.

The coefficient of determination r^2 was presented as a measure of the goodness of fit for the estimated regression equation; it can be interpreted as the proportion of the variation in the sample values of the dependent variable y that can be explained by the estimated regression equation. We then extended our discussion to include multiple independent variables and reviewed how to use Excel to find the estimated multiple regression equation $\hat{y} = b_0 + b_1 x_1 + b_2 x_2 + \cdots + b_q x_q$, and we considered the interpretations of the parameter estimates in multiple regression and the ramifications of multicollinearity.

The assumptions related to the regression model and its associated error term ε were discussed. We reviewed the t test for determining whether there is a statistically significant relationship between the dependent variable and an individual independent variable given the other independent variables in the regression model. We showed how to use Excel to develop confidence interval estimates of the regression parameters $\beta_0, \beta_1, \ldots, \beta_q$, and we discussed the special case of inference with very large samples.

We showed how to incorporate categorical independent variables into a regression model through the use of dummy variables, and we discussed a variety of ways to use multiple regression to fit nonlinear relationships between independent variables and the dependent variable. We concluded with a discussion of various automated procedures for selecting independent variables to include in a regression model and consideration of the problem of overfitting a regression model.

GLOSSARY

Backward elimination An iterative variable selection procedure that starts with a model with all independent variables and considers removing an independent variable at each step.

Best subsets A variable selection procedure that constructs and compares all possible models with up to a specified number of independent variables.

Coefficient of determination A measure of the goodness of fit of the estimated regression equation. It can be interpreted as the proportion of the variability in the dependent variable y that is explained by the estimated regression equation.

Confidence interval An estimate of a population parameter that provides an interval believed to contain the value of the parameter at some level of confidence.

Confidence level An indication of how frequently interval estimates based on samples of the same size taken from the same population using identical sampling techniques will contain the true value of the parameter we are estimating.

Cross-validation Assessment of the performance of a model on data other than the data that were used to generate the model.

Dependent variable The variable that is being predicted or explained. It is denoted by y and is often referred to as the response.

Dummy variable A variable used to model the effect of categorical independent variables in a regression model; generally takes only the value zero or one.

Estimated regression The estimate of the regression equation developed from sample data by using the least squares method. The estimated simple linear regression equation is $\hat{y} = b_0 + b_1 x$, and the estimated multiple linear regression equation is $\hat{y} = b_0 + b_1 x_1 + b_2 x_2 + \cdots + b_q x_q$.

Experimental region The range of values for the independent variables $x_1, x_2, \ldots, x_q$ for the data that are used to estimate the regression model.
Extrapolation Prediction of the mean value of the dependent variable y for values of the independent variables $x_1, x_2, \ldots, x_q$ that are outside the experimental range.
Forward selection an iterative variable selection procedure that starts with a model with no variables and considers adding an independent variable at each step.
Holdout method Method of cross-validation in which sample data are randomly divided into mutually exclusive and collectively exhaustive sets, then one set is used to build the candidate models and the other set is used to compare model performances and ultimately select a model.
Hypothesis testing The process of making a conjecture about the value of a population parameter, collecting sample data that can be used to assess this conjecture, measuring the strength of the evidence against the conjecture that is provided by the sample, and using these results to draw a conclusion about the conjecture.
Independent variable(s) The variable(s) used for predicting or explaining values of the dependent variable. It is denoted by x and is often referred to as the predictor variable.
Interaction The relationship between the dependent variable and one independent variable is different at different values of a second independent variable.
Interval estimation The use of sample data to calculate a range of values that is believed to include the unknown value of a population parameter.
***k*-fold cross validation** Method of cross-validation in which sample data set are randomly divided into k equal sized, mutually exclusive and collectively exhaustive subsets. In each of k iterations, one of the k subsets is used to build a candidate model and the remaining $k - 1$ sets are used evaluate the candidate model.
Knot The prespecified value of the independent variable at which its relationship with the dependent variable changes in a piecewise linear regression model; also called the breakpoint or the joint.
Least squares method A procedure for using sample data to find the estimated regression equation.
Leave-one-out cross validation Method of cross-validation in which candidate models are repeatedly fit using $n - 1$ observations and evaluated with the remaining observation.
Linear regression Regression analysis in which relationships between the independent variables and the dependent variable are approximated by a straight line.
Multicollinearity The degree of correlation among independent variables in a regression model.
Multiple linear regression Regression analysis involving one dependent variable and more than one independent variable.
Overfitting Fitting a model too closely to sample data, resulting in a model that does not accurately reflect the population.
***p* value** The probability that a random sample of the same size collected from the same population using the same procedure will yield stronger evidence against a hypothesis than the evidence in the sample data given that the hypothesis is actually true.
Parameter A measurable factor that defines a characteristic of a population, process, or system.
Piecewise linear regression model Regression model in which one linear relationship between the independent and dependent variables is fit for values of the independent variable below a prespecified value of the independent variable, a different linear relationship between the independent and dependent variables is fit for values of the independent variable above the prespecified value of the independent variable, and the two regressions have the same estimated value of the dependent variable (i.e., are joined) at the prespecified value of the independent variable.
Point estimator A single value used as an estimate of the corresponding population parameter.
Quadratic regression model Regression model in which a nonlinear relationship between the independent and dependent variables is fit by including the independent variable and

the square of the independent variable in the model: $\hat{y} = b_0 + b_1x_1 + b_2x_1^2$; also referred to as a second-order polynomial model.
Random variable The outcome of a random experiment (such as the drawing of a random sample) and so represents an uncertain outcome.
Regression analysis A statistical procedure used to develop an equation showing how the variables are related.
Regression model The equation that describes how the dependent variable y is related to an independent variable x and an error term; the *simple linear regression model* is $y = \beta_0 + \beta_1x_1 + \varepsilon$, and the *multiple linear regression model* is $y = \beta_0 + \beta_1x_1 + \beta_2x_2 + \cdots + \beta_qx_q + \varepsilon$.
Residual The difference between the observed value of the dependent variable and the value predicted using the estimated regression equation; for the ith observation, the ith residual is $y_i - \hat{y}_i$.
Simple linear regression Regression analysis involving one dependent variable and one independent variable.
Statistical inference The process of making estimates and drawing conclusions about one or more characteristics of a population (the value of one or more parameters) through analysis of sample data drawn from the population.
Stepwise selection an iterative variable selection procedure that considers adding an independent variable and removing an independent variable at each step.
***t* test** Statistical test based on the Student's t probability distribution that can be used to test the hypothesis that a regression parameter β_j is zero; if this hypothesis is rejected, we conclude that there is a regression relationship between the jth independent variable and the dependent variable.
Training set The data set used to build the candidate models.
Validation set The data set used to compare model forecasts and ultimately pick a model for predicting values of the dependent variable.

PROBLEMS

1. *Bicycling World*, a magazine devoted to cycling, reviews hundreds of bicycles throughout the year. Its Road-Race category contains reviews of bicycles used by riders primarily interested in racing. One of the most important factors in selecting a bicycle for racing is its weight. The following data show the weight (pounds) and price ($) for ten racing bicycles reviewed by the magazine:

Model	Weight (lb)	Price ($)
Fierro 7B	17.9	2,200
HX 5000	16.2	6,350
Durbin Ultralight	15.0	8,470
Schmidt	16.0	6,300
WSilton Advanced	17.3	4,100
bicyclette vélo	13.2	8,700
Supremo Team	16.3	6,100
XTC Racer	17.2	2,680
D'Onofrio Pro	17.7	3,500
Americana #6	14.2	8,100

a. Develop a scatter chart with weight as the independent variable. What does the scatter chart indicate about the relationship between the weight and price of these bicycles?
b. Use the data to develop an estimated regression equation that could be used to estimate the price for a bicycle, given its weight. What is the estimated regression model?

c. Test whether each of the regression parameters β_0 and β_1 is equal to zero at a 0.05 level of significance. What are the correct interpretations of the estimated regression parameters? Are these interpretations reasonable?
d. How much of the variation in the prices of the bicycles in the sample does the regression model you estimated in part (b) explain?
e. The manufacturers of the D'Onofrio Pro plan to introduce the 15-lb D'Onofrio Elite bicycle later this year. Use the regression model you estimated in part (a) to predict the price of the D'Ononfrio Elite.

2. In a manufacturing process the assembly line speed (feet per minute) was thought to affect the number of defective parts found during the inspection process. To test this theory, managers devised a situation in which the same batch of parts was inspected visually at a variety of line speeds. They collected the following data:

Line Speed (ft/min)	No. of Defective Parts Found
20	21
20	19
40	15
30	16
60	14
40	17

a. Develop a scatter chart with line speed as the independent variable. What does the scatter chart indicate about the relationship between line speed and the number of defective parts found?
b. Use the data to develop an estimated regression equation that could be used to predict the number of defective parts found, given the line speed. What is the estimated regression model?
c. Test whether each of the regression parameters β_0 and β_1 is equal to zero at a 0.01 level of significance. What are the correct interpretations of the estimated regression parameters? Are these interpretations reasonable?
d. How much of the variation in the number of defective parts found for the sample data does the model you estimated in part (b) explain?

3. Jensen Tire & Auto is deciding whether to purchase a maintenance contract for its new computer wheel alignment and balancing machine. Managers feel that maintenance expense should be related to usage, and they collected the following information on weekly usage (hours) and annual maintenance expense (in hundreds of dollars).

Weekly Usage (hours)	Annual Maintenance Expense ($100s)
13	17.0
10	22.0
20	30.0
28	37.0
32	47.0
17	30.5
24	32.5
31	39.0
40	51.5
38	40.0

a. Develop a scatter chart with weekly usage hours as the independent variable. What does the scatter chart indicate about the relationship between weekly usage and annual maintenance expense?
b. Use the data to develop an estimated regression equation that could be used to predict the annual maintenance expense for a given number of hours of weekly usage. What is the estimated regression model?
c. Test whether each of the regression parameters β_0 and β_1 is equal to zero at a 0.05 level of significance. What are the correct interpretations of the estimated regression parameters? Are these interpretations reasonable?
d. How much of the variation in the sample values of annual maintenance expense does the model you estimated in part (b) explain?
e. If the maintenance contract costs $3,000 per year, would you recommend purchasing it? Why or why not?

4. A sociologist was hired by a large city hospital to investigate the relationship between the number of unauthorized days that employees are absent per year and the distance (miles) between home and work for the employees. A sample of 10 employees was chosen, and the following data were collected.

DATA *file*
Absent

Distance to Work (miles)	No. of Days Absent
1	8
3	5
4	8
6	7
8	6
10	3
12	5
14	2
14	4
18	2

a. Develop a scatter chart for these data. Does a linear relationship appear reasonable? Explain.
b. Use the data to develop an estimated regression equation that could be used to predict the number of days absent given the distance to work. What is the estimated regression model?
c. What is the 99% confidence interval for the regression parameter β_1? Based on this interval, what conclusion can you make about the hypotheses that the regression parameter β_1 is equal to zero?
d. What is the 99% confidence interval for the regression parameter β_0? Based on this interval, what conclusion can you make about the hypotheses that the regression parameter β_0 is equal to zero?
e. How much of the variation in the sample values of number of days absent does the model you estimated in part (b) explain?

5. The regional transit authority for a major metropolitan area wants to determine whether there is a relationship between the age of a bus and the annual maintenance cost. A sample of 10 buses resulted in the following data:

AgeCost

Age of Bus (years)	Annual Maintenance Cost ($)
1	350
2	370

(Continued)

Age of Bus (years)	Annual Maintenance Cost ($)
2	480
2	520
2	590
3	550
4	750
4	800
5	790
5	950

a. Develop a scatter chart for these data. What does the scatter chart indicate about the relationship between age of a bus and the annual maintenance cost?
b. Use the data to develop an estimated regression equation that could be used to predict the annual maintenance cost given the age of the bus. What is the estimated regression model?
c. Test whether each of the regression parameters β_0 and β_1 is equal to zero at a 0.05 level of significance. What are the correct interpretations of the estimated regression parameters? Are these interpretations reasonable?
d. How much of the variation in the sample values of annual maintenance cost does the model you estimated in part (b) explain?
e. What do you predict the annual maintenance cost to be for a 3.5-year-old bus?

6. A marketing professor at Givens College is interested in the relationship between hours spent studying and total points earned in a course. Data collected on 156 students who took the course last semester are provided in the file *MktHrsPts*.

a. Develop a scatter chart for these data. What does the scatter chart indicate about the relationship between total points earned and hours spent studying?
b. Develop an estimated regression equation showing how total points earned is related to hours spent studying. What is the estimated regression model?
c. Test whether each of the regression parameters β_0 and β_1 is equal to zero at a 0.01 level of significance. What are the correct interpretations of the estimated regression parameters? Are these interpretations reasonable?
d. How much of the variation in the sample values of total point earned does the model you estimated in part (b) explain?
e. Mark Sweeney spent 95 hours studying. Use the regression model you estimated in part (b) to predict the total points Mark earned.

7. The Dow Jones Industrial Average (DJIA) and the Standard & Poor's 500 (S&P 500) indexes are used as measures of overall movement in the stock market. The DJIA is based on the price movements of 30 large companies; the S&P 500 is an index composed of 500 stocks. Some say the S&P 500 is a better measure of stock market performance because it is broader based. The closing price for the DJIA and the S&P 500 for 15 weeks, beginning with January 6, 2012, follow (*Barron's* web site, April 17, 2012).

Date	DJIA	S&P
January 6	12,360	1,278
January 13	12,422	1,289
January 20	12,720	1,315
January 27	12,660	1,316
February 3	12,862	1,345

February 10	12,801	1,343
February 17	12,950	1,362
February 24	12,983	1,366
March 2	12,978	1,370
March 9	12,922	1,371
March 16	13,233	1,404
March 23	13,081	1,397
March 30	13,212	1,408
April 5	13,060	1,398
April 13	12,850	1,370

a. Develop a scatter chart for these data with DJIA as the independent variable. What does the scatter chart indicate about the relationship between DJIA and S&P 500?
b. Develop an estimated regression equation showing how S&P 500 is related to DJIA. What is the estimated regression model?
c. What is the 95% confidence interval for the regression parameter β_1? Based on this interval, what conclusion can you make about the hypotheses that the regression parameter β_1 is equal to zero?
d. What is the 95% confidence interval for the regression parameter β_0? Based on this interval, what conclusion can you make about the hypotheses that the regression parameter β_0 is equal to zero?
e. How much of the variation in the sample values of S&P 500 does the model estimated in part (b) explain?
f. Suppose that the closing price for the DJIA is 13,500. Estimate the closing price for the S&P 500.
g. Should we be concerned that the DJIA value of 13,500 used to predict the S&P 500 value in part (f) is beyond the range of the DJIA used to develop the estimated regression equation?

8. The Toyota Camry is one of the best-selling cars in North America. The cost of a previously owned Camry depends on many factors, including the model year, mileage, and condition. To investigate the relationship between the car's mileage and the sales price for Camrys, the following data show the mileage and sale price for 19 sales (PriceHub web site, February 24, 2012).

Miles (1,000s)	Price ($1,000s)
22	16.2
29	16.0
36	13.8
47	11.5
63	12.5
77	12.9
73	11.2
87	13.0
92	11.8
101	10.8
110	8.3
28	12.5

(Continued)

Miles (1,000s)	Price ($1,000s)
59	11.1
68	15.0
68	12.2
91	13.0
42	15.6
65	12.7
110	8.3

a. Develop a scatter chart for these data with miles as the independent variable. What does the scatter chart indicate about the relationship between price and miles?
b. Develop an estimated regression equation showing how price is related to miles. What is the estimated regression model?
c. Test whether each of the regression parameters β_0 and β_1 is equal to zero at a 0.01 level of significance. What are the correct interpretations of the estimated regression parameters? Are these interpretations reasonable?
d. How much of the variation in the sample values of price does the model estimated in part (b) explain?
e. For the model estimated in part (b), calculate the predicted price and residual for each automobile in the data. Identify the two automobiles that were the biggest bargains.
f. Suppose that you are considering purchasing a previously owned Camry that has been driven 60,000 miles. Use the estimated regression equation developed in part (b) to predict the price for this car. Is this the price you would offer the seller?

9. Dixie Showtime Movie Theaters, Inc., owns and operates a chain of cinemas in several markets in the southern United States. The owners would like to estimate weekly gross revenue as a function of advertising expenditures. Data for a sample of eight markets for a recent week follow:

Market	Weekly Gross Revenue ($100s)	Television Advertising ($100s)	Newspaper Advertising ($100s)
Mobile	101.3	5.0	1.5
Shreveport	51.9	3.0	3.0
Jackson	74.8	4.0	1.5
Birmingham	126.2	4.3	4.3
Little Rock	137.8	3.6	4.0
Biloxi	101.4	3.5	2.3
New Orleans	237.8	5.0	8.4
Baton Rouge	219.6	6.9	5.8

a. Develop an estimated regression equation with the amount of television advertising as the independent variable. Test for a significant relationship between television advertising and weekly gross revenue at the 0.05 level of significance. What is the interpretation of this relationship?
b. How much of the variation in the sample values of weekly gross revenue does the model in part (a) explain?

c. Develop an estimated regression equation with both television advertising and newspaper advertising as the independent variables. Test whether each of the regression parameters β_0, β_1, and β_2 is equal to zero at a 0.05 level of significance. What are the correct interpretations of the estimated regression parameters? Are these interpretations reasonable?
d. How much of the variation in the sample values of weekly gross revenue does the model in part (c) explain?
e. Given the results in parts (a) and (c), what should your next step be? Explain.
f. What are the managerial implications of these results?

10. *Resorts & Spas,* a magazine devoted to upscale vacations and accommodations, published its Reader's Choice List of the top 20 independent beachfront boutique hotels in the world. The data shown are the scores received by these hotels based on the results from *Resorts & Spas'* annual Readers' Choice Survey. Each score represents the percentage of respondents who rated a hotel as excellent or very good on one of three criteria (comfort, amenities, and in-house dining). An overall score was also reported and used to rank the hotels. The highest ranked hotel, the Muri Beach Odyssey, has an overall score of 94.3, the highest component of which is 97.7 for in-house dining.

Hotel	Overall	Comfort	Amenities	In-House Dining
Muri Beach Odyssey	94.3	94.5	90.8	97.7
Pattaya Resort	92.9	96.6	84.1	96.6
Sojourner's Respite	92.8	99.9	100.0	88.4
Spa Carribe	91.2	88.5	94.7	97.0
Penang Resort and Spa	90.4	95.0	87.8	91.1
Mokihana Hōkele	90.2	92.4	82.0	98.7
Theo's of Cape Town	90.1	95.9	86.2	91.9
Cap d'Agde Resort	89.8	92.5	92.5	88.8
Spirit of Mykonos	89.3	94.6	85.8	90.7
Turismo del Mar	89.1	90.5	83.2	90.4
Hotel Iguana	89.1	90.8	81.9	88.5
Sidi Abdel Rahman Palace	89.0	93.0	93.0	89.6
Sainte-Maxime Quarters	88.6	92.5	78.2	91.2
Rotorua Inn	87.1	93.0	91.6	73.5
Club Lapu-Lapu	87.1	90.9	74.9	89.6
Terracina Retreat	86.5	94.3	78.0	91.5
Hacienda Punta Barco	86.1	95.4	77.3	90.8
Rendezvous Kolocep	86.0	94.8	76.4	91.4
Cabo de Gata Vista	86.0	92.0	72.2	89.2
Sanya Deluxe	85.1	93.4	77.3	91.8

a. Determine the estimated multiple linear regression equation that can be used to predict the overall score given the scores for comfort, amenities, and in-house dining.
b. Use the *t* test to determine the significance of each independent variable. What is the conclusion for each test at the 0.01 level of significance?
c. Remove all independent variables that are not significant at the 0.01 level of significance from the estimated regression equation. What is your recommended estimated regression equation?

11. The American Association of Individual Investors (AAII) On-Line Discount Broker Survey polls members on their experiences with electronic trades handled by discount brokers. As part of the survey, members were asked to rate their satisfaction with the trade price and the speed of execution, as well as provide an overall satisfaction rating. Possible responses (scores) were no opinion (0), unsatisfied (1), somewhat satisfied (2), satisfied (3), and very satisfied (4). For each broker, summary scores were computed by computing a weighted average of the scores provided by each respondent. A portion the survey results follow (AAII web site, February 7, 2012).

Brokerage	Satisfaction with Trade Price	Satisfaction with Speed of Execution	Overall Satisfaction with Electronic Trades
Scottrade, Inc.	3.4	3.4	3.5
Charles Schwab	3.2	3.3	3.4
Fidelity Brokerage Services	3.1	3.4	3.9
TD Ameritrade	2.9	3.6	3.7
E*Trade Financial	2.9	3.2	2.9
(Not listed)	2.5	3.2	2.7
Vanguard Brokerage Services	2.6	3.8	2.8
USAA Brokerage Services	2.4	3.8	3.6
Thinkorswim	2.6	2.6	2.6
Wells Fargo Investments	2.3	2.7	2.3
Interactive Brokers	3.7	4.0	4.0
Zecco.com	2.5	2.5	2.5
Firstrade Securities	3.0	3.0	4.0
Banc of America Investment Services	4.0	1.0	2.0

a. Develop an estimated regression equation using trade price and speed of execution to predict overall satisfaction with the broker. Interpret the coefficient of determination.
b. Use the t test to determine the significance of each independent variable. What are your conclusions at the 0.05 level of significance?
c. Interpret the estimated regression parameters. Are the relationships indicated by these estimates what you would expect?
d. Finger Lakes Investments has developed a new electronic trading system and would like to predict overall customer satisfaction assuming they can provide satisfactory service levels (3) for both trade price and speed of execution. Use the estimated regression equation developed in part (a) to predict overall satisfaction level for Finger Lakes Investments if they can achieve these performance levels.
e. What concerns (if any) do you have with regard to the possible responses the respondents could select on the survey.

12. The National Football League (NFL) records a variety of performance data for individuals and teams. To investigate the importance of passing on the percentage of games won by a team, the following data show the conference (Conf), average number of passing yards per attempt (Yds/Att), the number of interceptions thrown per attempt

(Int/Att), and the percentage of games won (Win%) for a random sample of 16 NFL teams for the 2011 season (NFL web site, February 12, 2012).

Team	Conf	Yds/Att	Int/Att	Win%
Arizona Cardinals	NFC	6.5	0.042	50.0
Atlanta Falcons	NFC	7.1	0.022	62.5
Carolina Panthers	NFC	7.4	0.033	37.5
Cincinnati Bengals	AFC	6.2	0.026	56.3
Detroit Lions	NFC	7.2	0.024	62.5
Green Bay Packers	NFC	8.9	0.014	93.8
Houston Texans	AFC	7.5	0.019	62.5
Indianapolis Colts	AFC	5.6	0.026	12.5
Jacksonville Jaguars	AFC	4.6	0.032	31.3
Minnesota Vikings	NFC	5.8	0.033	18.8
New England Patriots	AFC	8.3	0.020	81.3
New Orleans Saints	NFC	8.1	0.021	81.3
Oakland Raiders	AFC	7.6	0.044	50.0
San Francisco 49ers	NFC	6.5	0.011	81.3
Tennessee Titans	AFC	6.7	0.024	56.3
Washington Redskins	NFC	6.4	0.041	31.3

a. Develop the estimated regression equation that could be used to predict the percentage of games won, given the average number of passing yards per attempt. What proportion of variation in the sample values of proportion of games won does this model explain?

b. Develop the estimated regression equation that could be used to predict the percentage of games won, given the number of interceptions thrown per attempt. What proportion of variation in the sample values of proportion of games won does this model explain?

c. Develop the estimated regression equation that could be used to predict the percentage of games won, given the average number of passing yards per attempt and the number of interceptions thrown per attempt. What proportion of variation in the sample values of proportion of games won does this model explain?

d. The average number of passing yards per attempt for the Kansas City Chiefs during the 2011 season was 6.2, and the team's number of interceptions thrown per attempt was 0.036. Use the estimated regression equation developed in part (c) to predict the percentage of games won by the Kansas City Chiefs during the 2011 season. Compare your prediction to the actual percentage of games won by the Kansas City Chiefs. (*Note:* For the 2011 season, the Kansas City Chiefs' record was 7 wins and 9 losses.)

e. Did the estimated regression equation that uses only the average number of passing yards per attempt as the independent variable to predict the percentage of games won provide a good fit?

13. Johnson Filtration, Inc., provides maintenance service for water filtration systems throughout southern Florida. Customers contact Johnson with requests for maintenance service on their water filtration systems. To estimate the service time and the service cost, Johnson's managers want to predict the repair time necessary for each maintenance request. Hence, repair time in hours is the dependent variable. Repair time is believed to be related to three factors: the number of months since the last

maintenance service, the type of repair problem (mechanical or electrical), and the repairperson who performs the repair (Donna Newton or Bob Jones). Data for a sample of 10 service calls are reported in the following table:

DATA *file* Repair

Repair Time in Hours	Months Since Last Service	Type of Repair	Repairperson
2.9	2	Electrical	Donna Newton
3.0	6	Mechanical	Donna Newton
4.8	8	Electrical	Bob Jones
1.8	3	Mechanical	Donna Newton
2.9	2	Electrical	Donna Newton
4.9	7	Electrical	Bob Jones
4.2	9	Mechanical	Bob Jones
4.8	8	Mechanical	Bob Jones
4.4	4	Electrical	Bob Jones
4.5	6	Electrical	Donna Newton

a. Develop the simple linear regression equation to predict repair time given the number of months since the last maintenance service, and use the results to test the hypothesis that no relationship exists between repair time and the number of months since the last maintenance service at the 0.05 level of significance. What is the interpretation of this relationship? What does the coefficient of determination tell you about this model?
b. Using the simple linear regression model developed in part (a), calculate the predicted repair time and residual for each of the 10 repairs in the data. Sort the data in ascending order by value of the residual. Do you see any pattern in the residuals for the two types of repair? Do you see any pattern in the residuals for the two repairpersons? Do these results suggest any potential modifications to your simple linear regression model? Now create a scatter chart with months since last service on the x-axis and repair time in hours on the y-axis for which the points representing electrical and mechanical repairs are shown in different shapes and/or colors. Create a similar scatter chart of months since last service and repair time in hours for which the points representing repairs by Bob Jones and Donna Newton are shown in different shapes and/or colors, Do these charts and the results of your residual analysis suggest the same potential modifications to your simple linear regression model?
c. Create a new dummy variable that is equal to zero if the type of repair is mechanical and one if the type of repair is electrical. Develop the multiple regression equation to predict repair time, given the number of months since the last maintenance service and the type of repair. What are the interpretations of the estimated regression parameters? What does the coefficient of determination tell you about this model?
d. Create a new dummy variable that is equal to zero if the repairperson is Bob Jones and one if the repairperson is Donna Newton. Develop the multiple regression equation to predict repair time, given the number of months since the last maintenance service and the repairperson. What are the interpretations of the estimated regression parameters? What does the coefficient of determination tell you about this model?
e. Develop the multiple regression equation to predict repair time, given the number of months since the last maintenance service, the type of repair, and the repairperson. What are the interpretations of the estimated regression parameters? What does the coefficient of determination tell you about this model?
f. Which of these models would you use? Why?

14. A study investigated the relationship between audit delay (the length of time from a company's fiscal year-end to the date of the auditor's report) and variables that describe the client and the auditor. Some of the independent variables that were included in this study follow:

Industry	A dummy variable coded 1 if the firm was an industrial company or 0 if the firm was a bank, savings and loan, or insurance company.
Public	A dummy variable coded 1 if the company was traded on an organized exchange or over the counter; otherwise coded 0.
Quality	A measure of overall quality of internal controls, as judged by the auditor, on a 5-point scale ranging from "virtually none" (1) to "excellent" (5).
Finished	A measure ranging from 1 to 4, as judged by the auditor, where 1 indicates "all work performed subsequent to year-end" and 4 indicates "most work performed prior to year-end."

A sample of 40 companies provided the following data:

Delay (Days)	Industry	Public	Quality	Finished
62	0	0	3	1
45	0	1	3	3
54	0	0	2	2
71	0	1	1	2
91	0	0	1	1
62	0	0	4	4
61	0	0	3	2
69	0	1	5	2
80	0	0	1	1
52	0	0	5	3
47	0	0	3	2
65	0	1	2	3
60	0	0	1	3
81	1	0	1	2
73	1	0	2	2
89	1	0	2	1
71	1	0	5	4
76	1	0	2	2
68	1	0	1	2
68	1	0	5	2
86	1	0	2	2
76	1	1	3	1
67	1	0	2	3
57	1	0	4	2
55	1	1	3	2
54	1	0	5	2
69	1	0	3	3
82	1	0	5	1
94	1	0	1	1
74	1	1	5	2
75	1	1	4	3

(Continued)

Delay (Days)	Industry	Public	Quality	Finished
69	1	0	2	2
71	1	0	4	4
79	1	0	5	2
80	1	0	1	4
91	1	0	4	1
92	1	0	1	4
46	1	1	4	3
72	1	0	5	2
85	1	0	5	1

a. Develop the estimated regression equation using all of the independent variables included in the data.
b. How much of the variation in the sample values of delay does this estimated regression equation explain? What other independent variables could you include in this regression model to improve the fit?
c. Test the relationship between each independent variable and the dependent variable at the 0.05 level of significance, and interpret the relationship between each of the independent variables and the dependent variable.
d. On the basis of your observations about the relationships between the dependent variable Delay and the independent variables Quality and Finished, suggest an alternative model for the regression equation developed in part (a) to explain as much of the variability in Delay as possible.

15. The U.S. Department of Energy's Fuel Economy Guide provides fuel efficiency data for cars and trucks. A portion of the data for 311 compact, midsized, and large cars follows. The Class column identifies the size of the car: Compact, Midsize, or Large. The Displacement column shows the engine's displacement in liters. The FuelType column shows whether the car uses premium (P) or regular (R) fuel, and the HwyMPG column shows the fuel efficiency rating for highway driving in terms of miles per gallon. The complete data set is contained in the file *FuelData*:

DATA *file*
FuelData

Car	Class	Displacement	FuelType	HwyMPG
1	Compact	3.1	P	25
2	Compact	3.1	P	25
3	Compact	3.0	P	25
⋮	⋮	⋮	⋮	⋮
161	Midsize	2.4	R	30
162	Midsize	2.0	P	29
⋮	⋮	⋮	⋮	⋮
310	Large	3.0	R	25

a. Develop an estimated regression equation that can be used to predict the fuel efficiency for highway driving given the engine's displacement. Test for significance using the 0.05 level of significance. How much of the variation in the sample values of HwyMPG does this estimated regression equation explain?

b. Create a scatter chart with HwyMPG on the y-axis and displacement on the x-axis for which the points representing compact, midsize, and large automobiles are shown in different shapes and/or colors. What does this chart suggest about the relationship between the class of automobile (compact, midsize, and large) and HwyMPG?
c. Now consider the addition of the dummy variables ClassMidsize and ClassLarge to the simple linear regression model in part (a). The value of ClassMidsize is 1 if the car is a midsize car and 0 otherwise; the value of ClassLarge is 1 if the car is a large car and 0 otherwise. Thus, for a compact car, the value of ClassMidsize and the value of ClassLarge are both 0. Develop the estimated regression equation that can be used to predict the fuel efficiency for highway driving, given the engine's displacement and the dummy variables ClassMidsize and ClassLarge. How much of the variation in the sample values of HwyMPG is explained by this estimated regression equation?
d. Use significance level of 0.05 to determine whether the dummy variables added to the model in part (c) are significant.
e. Consider the addition of the dummy variable FuelPremium, where the value of FuelPremium is 1 if the car uses premium fuel and 0 if the car uses regular fuel. Develop the estimated regression equation that can be used to predict the fuel efficiency for highway driving given the engine's displacement, the dummy variables ClassMidsize and ClassLarge, and the dummy variable FuelPremium. How much of the variation in the sample values of HwyMPG does this estimated regression equation explain?
f. For the estimated regression equation developed in part (e), test for the significance of the relationship between each of the independent variables and the dependent variable using the 0.05 level of significance for each test.

16. A highway department is studying the relationship between traffic flow and speed during rush hour on Highway 193. The data in the file *TrafficFlow* were collected on Highway 193 during 100 recent rush hours.
    a. Develop a scatter chart for these data. What does the scatter chart indicate about the relationship between vehicle speed and traffic flow?
    b. Develop an estimated simple linear regression equation for the data. How much variation in the sample values of traffic flow is explained by this regression model? Use a 0.05 level of significance to test the relationship between vehicle speed and traffic flow. What is the interpretation of this relationship?
    c. Develop an estimated quadratic regression equation for the data. How much variation in the sample values of traffic flow is explained by this regression model? Test the relationship between each of the independent variables and the dependent variable at a 0.05 level of significance. How would you interpret this model? Is this model superior to the model you developed in part (b)?
    d. As an alternative to fitting a second-order model, fit a model using a piecewise linear regression with a single knot. What value of vehicle speed appears to be a good point for the placement of the knot? Does the estimated piecewise linear regression provide a better fit than the estimated quadratic regression developed in part (c)? Explain.
    e. Separate the data into two sets such that one data set contains the observations of vehicle speed less than the value of the knot from part (d) and the other data set contains the observations of vehicle speed greater than or equal to the value of the knot from part (d). Then fit a simple linear regression equation to each data set. How does this pair of regression equations compare to the single piecewise linear regression with the single knot from part (d)? In particular, compare predicted values of traffic flow for values of the speed slightly above and slightly below the knot value from part (d).

f. What other independent variables could you include in your regression model to explain more variation in traffic flow?

17. A sample containing years to maturity and (percent) yield for 40 corporate bonds is contained in the file named *CorporateBonds* (*Barron's*, April 2, 2012).
    a. Develop a scatter chart of the data using years to maturity as the independent variable. Does a simple linear regression model appear to be appropriate?
    b. Develop an estimated quadratic regression equation with years to maturity and squared values of years to maturity as the independent variables. How much variation in the sample values of yield is explained by this regression model? Test the relationship between each of the independent variables and the dependent variable at a 0.05 level of significance. How would you interpret this model?
    c. Create a plot of the linear and quadratic regression lines overlaid on the scatter chart of years to maturity and yield. Does this helps you better understand the difference in how the quadratic regression model and a simple linear regression model fit the sample data? Which model does this chart suggest provides a superior fit to the sample data?
    d. What other independent variables could you include in your regression model to explain more variation in yield?
18. In 2011, home prices and mortgage rates fell so far that in a number of cities the monthly cost of owning a home was less expensive than renting. The following data show the average asking rent for 10 markets and the monthly mortgage on the median priced home (including taxes and insurance) for 10 cites where the average monthly mortgage payment was less than the average asking rent (*The Wall Street Journal*, November 26–27, 2011).

City	Rent ($)	Mortgage ($)
Atlanta	840	539
Chicago	1,062	1,002
Detroit	823	626
Jacksonville	779	711
Las Vegas	796	655
Miami	1,071	977
Minneapolis	953	776
Orlando	851	695
Phoenix	762	651
St. Louis	723	654

    a. Develop a scatter chart for these data, treating the average asking rent as the independent variable. Does a simple linear regression model appear to be appropriate?
    b. Use a simple linear regression model to develop an estimated regression equation to predict the monthly mortgage on the median priced home given the average asking rent. Construct a plot of the residuals against the independent variable rent. Based on this residual plot, does a simple linear regression model appear to be appropriate?
    c. Using a quadratic regression model, develop an estimated regression equation to predict the monthly mortgage on the median-priced home, given the average asking rent.
    d. Do you prefer the estimated regression equation developed in part (a) or part (c)? Create a plot of the linear and quadratic regression lines overlaid on the scatter chart of the monthly mortgage on the median-priced home and the average asking rent to help you assess the two regression equations. Explain your conclusions.

19. A recent 10-year study conducted by a research team at the Great Falls Medical School was conducted to assess how age, systolic blood pressure, and smoking relate to the risk of strokes. Assume that the following data are from a portion of this study. Risk is interpreted as the probability (times 100) that the patient will have a stroke over the next 10-year period. For the smoking variable, define a dummy variable with 1 indicating a smoker and 0 indicating a nonsmoker.

Stroke

Risk	Age	Systolic Blood Pressure	Smoker
12	57	152	No
24	67	163	No
13	58	155	No
56	86	177	Yes
28	59	196	No
51	76	189	Yes
18	56	155	Yes
31	78	120	No
37	80	135	Yes
15	78	98	No
22	71	152	No
36	70	173	Yes
15	67	135	Yes
48	77	209	Yes
15	60	199	No
36	82	119	Yes
8	66	166	No
34	80	125	Yes
3	62	117	No
37	59	207	Yes

a. Develop an estimated multiple regression equation that relates risk of a stroke to the person's age, systolic blood pressure, and whether the person is a smoker.
b. Is smoking a significant factor in the risk of a stroke? Explain. Use a 0.05 level of significance.
c. What is the probability of a stroke over the next 10 years for Art Speen, a 68-year-old smoker who has a systolic blood pressure of 175? What action might the physician recommend for this patient?
d. What other factors could be included in the model as independent variables?

RugglesCollege

20. The Scholastic Aptitude Test (or SAT) is a standardized college entrance test that is used by colleges and universities as a means for making admission decisions. The critical reading and mathematics components of the SAT are reported on a scale from 200 to 800. Several universities believe these scores are strong predictors of an incoming student's potential success, and they use these scores as important inputs when making admission decisions on potential freshman. The file *RugglesCollege* contains freshman year GPA and the critical reading and mathematics SAT scores for a random sample of 200 students who recently completed their freshman year at Ruggles College.
a. Develop an estimated multiple regression equation that includes critical reading and mathematics SAT scores as independent variables. How much variation in freshman GPA is explained by this model? Test whether each of the regression parameters

β_0, β_1, and β_2 is equal to zero at a 0.05 level of significance. What are the correct interpretations of the estimated regression parameters? Are these interpretations reasonable?

b. Using the multiple linear regression model you developed in part (a), what is the predicted freshman GPA of Bobby Engle, a student who has been admitted to Ruggles College with a 660 SAT score on critical reading and at a 630 SAT score on mathematics?

c. The Ruggles College Director of Admissions believes that the relationship between a student's scores on the critical reading component of the SAT and the student's freshman GPA varies with the student's score on the mathematics component of the SAT. Develop an estimated multiple regression equation that includes critical reading and mathematics SAT scores and their interaction as independent variables. How much variation in freshman GPA is explained by this model? Test whether each of the regression parameters β_0, β_1, β_2, and β_3 is equal to zero at a 0.05 level of significance. What are the correct interpretations of the estimated regression parameters? Do these results support the conjecture made by the Ruggles College Director of Admissions?

d. Do you prefer the estimated regression model developed in part (a) or part (c)? Explain.

e. What other factors could be included in the model as independent variables?

ExtendedLargeCredit

21. Consider again the example introduced in Section 7.5 of a credit card company that has a database of information provided by its customers when they apply for credit cards. An analyst has created a multiple regression model for which the dependent variable in the model is credit card charges accrued by a customer in the data set over the past year (y), and the independent variables are the customer's annual household income (x_1), number of members of the household (x_2), and number of years of post–high school education (x_3). Figure 7.23 provides Excel output for a multiple regression model estimated using a data set the company created.

a. Estimate the corresponding simple linear regression with the customer's annual household income as the independent variable and credit card charges accrued by a customer over the past year as the dependent variable. Interpret the estimated relationship between the customer's annual household income and credit card charges accrued over the past year. How much variation in credit card charges accrued by a customer over the past year is explained by this simple linear regression model?

b. Estimate the corresponding simple linear regression with the number of members in the customer's household as the independent variable and credit card charges accrued by a customer over the past year as the dependent variable. Interpret the estimated relationship between the number of members in the customer's household and credit card charges accrued over the past year. How much variation in credit card charges accrued by a customer over the past year is explained by this simple linear regression model?

c. Estimate the corresponding simple linear regression with the customer's number of years of post–high school education as the independent variable and credit card charges accrued by a customer over the past year as the dependent variable. Interpret the estimated relationship between the customer's number of years of post–high school education and credit card charges accrued over the past year. How much variation in credit card charges accrued by a customer over the past year is explained by this simple linear regression model?

d. Recall the multiple regression in Figure 7.23 with credit card charges accrued by a customer over the past year as the dependent variable and customer's annual household income (x_1), number of members of the household (x_2), and number of years of post–high school education (x_3) as the independent variables. Do the estimated slopes differ substantially from the corresponding slopes that were estimated using simple linear regression in parts (a), (b), and (c)? What does this tell you about multicollinearity in the multiple regression model in Figure 7.23?

e. Add the coefficients of determination for the simple linear regression in parts (a), (b), and (c), and compare the result to the coefficient of determination for the multiple regression model in Figure 7.23. What does this tell you about multicollinearity in the multiple regression model in Figure 7.23?

f. Add age, a dummy variable for sex, and a dummy variable for whether a customer has exceeded his or her credit limit in the past 12 months as independent variables to the multiple regression model in Figure 7.23. Code the dummy variable for sex as 1 if the customer is female and 0 if male, and code the dummy variable for whether a customer has exceeded his or her credit limit in the past 12 months as 1 if the customer has exceeded his or her credit limit in the past 12 months and 0 otherwise. Do these variables substantially improve the fit of your model?

CASE PROBLEM ALUMNI GIVING

Alumni donations are an important source of revenue for colleges and universities. If administrators could determine the factors that could lead to increases in the percentage of alumni who make a donation, they might be able to implement policies that could lead to increased revenues. Research shows that students who are more satisfied with their contact with teachers are more likely to graduate. As a result, one might suspect that smaller class sizes and lower student/faculty ratios might lead to a higher percentage of satisfied graduates, which in turn might lead to increases in the percentage of alumni who make a donation. The following table shows data for 48 national universities. The Graduation Rate column is the percentage of students who initially enrolled at the university and graduated. The % of Classes Under 20 column shows the percentages of classes with fewer than 20 students that are offered. The Student/Faculty Ratio column is the number of students enrolled divided by the total number of faculty. Finally, the Alumni Giving Rate column is the percentage of alumni who made a donation to the university.

	State	Graduation Rate	% of Classes Under 20	Student/ Faculty Ratio	Alumni Giving Rate
Boston College	MA	85	39	13	25
Brandeis University	MA	79	68	8	33
Brown University	RI	93	60	8	40
California Institute of Technology	CA	85	65	3	46
Carnegie Mellon University	PA	75	67	10	28
Case Western Reserve Univ.	OH	72	52	8	31
College of William and Mary	VA	89	45	12	27
Columbia University	NY	90	69	7	31
Cornell University	NY	91	72	13	35
Dartmouth College	NH	94	61	10	53
Duke University	NC	92	68	8	45
Emory University	GA	84	65	7	37

(Continued)

	State	Graduation Rate	% of Classes Under 20	Student/ Faculty Ratio	Alumni Giving Rate
Georgetown University	DC	91	54	10	29
Harvard University	MA	97	73	8	46
Johns Hopkins University	MD	89	64	9	27
Lehigh University	PA	81	55	11	40
Massachusetts Institute of Technology	MA	92	65	6	44
New York University	NY	72	63	13	13
Northwestern University	IL	90	66	8	30
Pennsylvania State Univ.	PA	80	32	19	21
Princeton University	NJ	95	68	5	67
Rice University	TX	92	62	8	40
Stanford University	CA	92	69	7	34
Tufts University	MA	87	67	9	29
Tulane University	LA	72	56	12	17
University of California–Berkeley	CA	83	58	17	18
University of California–Davis	CA	74	32	19	7
University of California–Irvine	CA	74	42	20	9
University of California–Los Angeles	CA	78	41	18	13
University of California–San Diego	CA	80	48	19	8
University of California–Santa Barbara	CA	70	45	20	12
University of Chicago	IL	84	65	4	36
University of Florida	FL	67	31	23	19
University of Illinois–Urbana Champaign	IL	77	29	15	23
University of Michigan–Ann Arbor	MI	83	51	15	13
University of North Carolina–Chapel Hill	NC	82	40	16	26
University of Notre Dame	IN	94	53	13	49
University of Pennsylvania	PA	90	65	7	41
University of Rochester	NY	76	63	10	23
University of Southern California	CA	70	53	13	22
University of Texas–Austin	TX	66	39	21	13
University of Virginia	VA	92	44	13	28
University of Washington	WA	70	37	12	12
University of Wisconsin–Madison	WI	73	37	13	13
Vanderbilt University	TN	82	68	9	31
Wake Forest University	NC	82	59	11	38
Washington University–St. Louis	MO	86	73	7	33
Yale University	CT	94	77	7	50

Managerial Report

1. Use methods of descriptive statistics to summarize the data.
2. Develop an estimated simple linear regression model that can be used to predict the alumni giving rate, given the graduation rate. Discuss your findings.
3. Develop an estimated multiple linear regression model that could be used to predict the alumni giving rate using the Graduation Rate, % of Classes Under 20, and Student/Faculty Ratio as independent variables. Discuss your findings.
4. Based on the results in parts (2) and (3), do you believe another regression model may be more appropriate? Estimate this model, and discuss your results.
5. What conclusions and recommendations can you derive from your analysis? What universities are achieving a substantially higher alumni giving rate than would be expected, given their Graduation Rate, % of Classes Under 20, and Student/Faculty Ratio? What universities are achieving a substantially lower alumni giving rate than would be expected, given their Graduation Rate, % of Classes Under 20, and Student/Faculty Ratio? What other independent variables could be included in the model?

Chapter 7 Appendix

Appendix 7.1 Regression with XLMiner

ButlerNewData

To show how XLMiner can be used for regression analysis, we again consider the Butler Trucking Company. The dependent variable is Travel Time (y), and the independent variables are Miles, Gasoline Consumption, and Deliveries. In the file *ButlerNewData*, there are two worksheets. The *Data* worksheet contains 300 observations from past routes. The *NewData* worksheet contains 10 additional observations corresponding to upcoming routes for which we have estimates on the miles driven, gasoline consumption, and number of deliveries. We would like to construct a regression model on the 300 observations in the *Data* worksheet and then use this model to predict the travel time for the 10 new observations in the *NewData* worksheet.

We use the following steps, accompanied by Figure 7.38, to execute a regression analysis for these data in XLMiner:

Step 1. Select any cell in the range of data (any cell in A1:D301)
Step 2. Click the **XLMiner Platform** tab in the Ribbon

FIGURE 7.38 XLMiner Regression Procedure

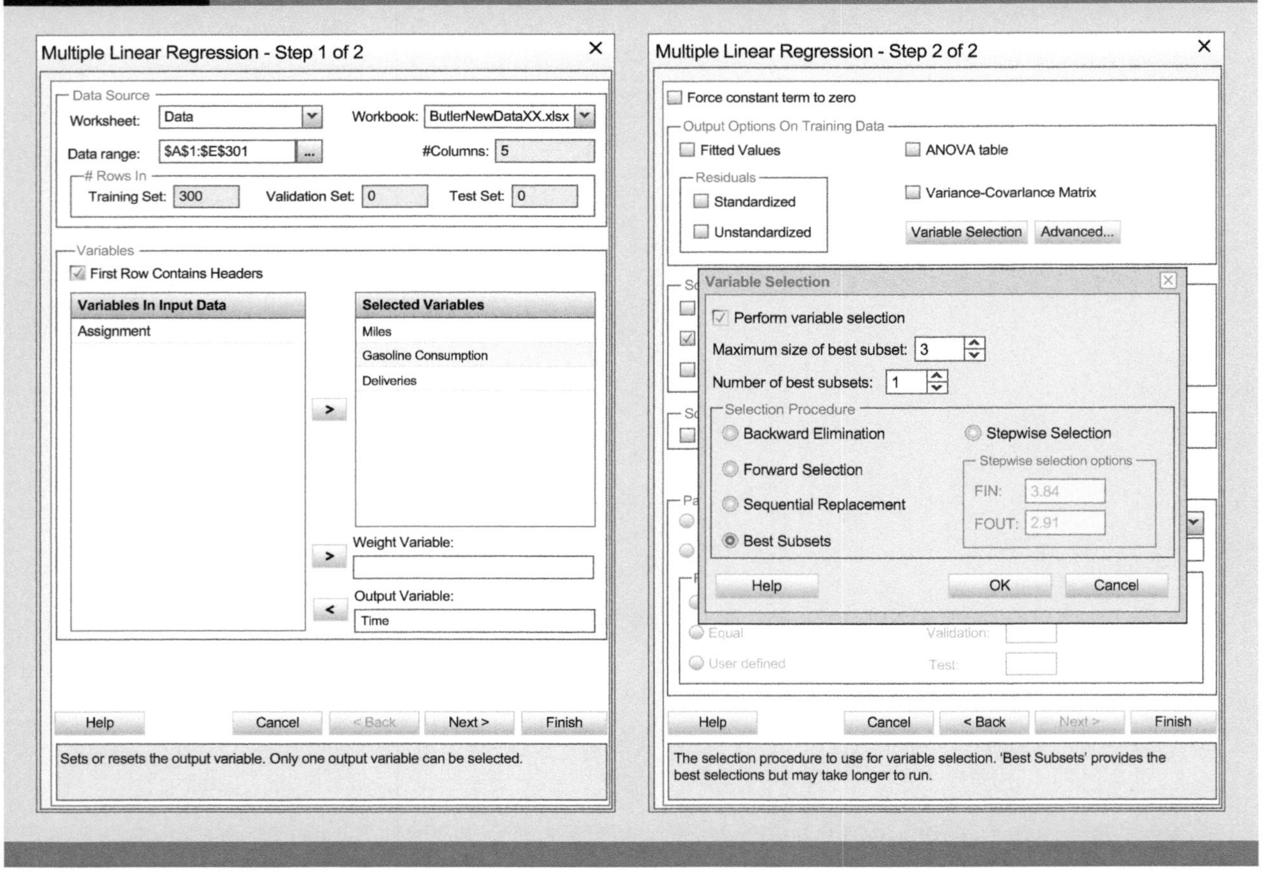

Step 3. Click **Predict** in the **Data Mining** group, and select **Multiple Linear Regression**

Step 4. When the **Multiple Linear Regression–Step 1 of 2** dialog box appears:
In the Data Source area, confirm that the **Worksheet:**, **Workbook:**, and **Data range:** entries correspond to the appropriate data
In the **Variables In Input Data** box of the **Variables** area, select the **Miles**, **Gasoline Consumption**, and **Deliveries** variables, and click the > button to the left of the of the **Selected Variables** box to identify the independent variables
In the **Variables In Input Data** box of the **Variables** area, select **Time** and click the > button to the left of the of the **Output Variable** box to identify the dependent variable
Click **Next** >

Step 5. In the **Multiple Linear Regression–Step 2 of 2** dialog box:
Select **Summary report** in the **Score Training Data** area
In the **Output Options On Training Data** area, select **Variable Selection**
When the **Variable Selection** dialog box appears:
Select **Perform variable selection**
In the **Selection Procedure** area, select **Best Subsets**
Enter *3* in the **Maximum size of best subset:** box
Enter *1* in the **Number of best subsets:** box
Click **OK**
Click **Finish**

This procedure executes best-subsets variable selection by considering all multiple regression models with up to three variables. That is, XLMiner constructs all possible regression models with zero, one, two, and three independent variables (a total of $2^3 = 8$ models), and then outputs the best-fitting model of each respective size.

Figure 7.39 shows a portion of the output from the *MLR_Output* worksheet. The Regression Model table provides model information for the "full" regression model with all possible independent variables and the intercept (constant) term. The Variable Selection table lists the

FIGURE 7.39 XLMiner *MLR_Output* Worksheet

Regression Model

Input Variables	Coefficient	Std. Error	t-Statistic	P-Value	CI Lower	CI Upper	RSS Reduction
Intercept	0.237719	0.221644508	1.072522841	0.284359	-0.198479972	0.673917567	15917
Miles	0.077782	0.008464959	9.188649826	7.21E-18	0.061122415	0.094440676	539.1988
Gasoline Consumption	-0.1185	0.090572642	-1.30828857	0.19179	-0.296743085	0.059752779	0.381967
Deliveries	0.690926	0.029494272	23.42575518	2.25E-69	0.632880552	0.74897064	377.1115

Residual DF	296
R²	0.8184
Adjusted R²	0.816559
Std. Error Estimate	0.828975
RSS	203.4109

Variable Selection

Subset Link	#Coeffs	RSS	Cp	R²	Adjusted R²	Probability	Model 1	2	3	4
Choose Subset	1	1120.1032	1331.9546	0	0	0	Intercept			
Choose Subset	2	580.9044	549.3218	0.4814	0.4796	0	Intercept	Miles		
Choose Subset	3	204.5871	3.7116	0.8173	0.8161	0.1918	Intercept	Miles		Deliveries
Choose Subset	4	203.4109	4	0.8184	0.8166	1	Intercept	Miles	Gasoline Consumption	Deliveries

best-fitting regression model with one coefficient (corresponding to the constant or intercept term), two coefficients (corresponding to the y-intercept term and one independent variable), three coefficients (corresponding to the y-intercept term and two independent variables), and four coefficients (corresponding to the y-intercept term and three independent variables).

As Figure 7.39 shows, the model with the two independent variables Miles and Deliveries has only a slightly lower R^2 than the model with all three independent variables. Furthermore, as the Regression Model table shows, the Gasoline Consumption variable is statistically insignificant in the full regression model ($p = 0.19$) and has a counterintuitively negative effect on travel time (coefficient $= -0.1185$). These observations are due to the multicollinearity between Gasoline Consumption and Miles.

Based on the comparison of the various regression models, the regression model with three coefficients (the y-intercept, Miles, and Deliveries) seems to be the most appropriate. Therefore, we will use this model to predict the travel time for the 10 new observations in the NewData worksheet. We use the following steps to refit this regression model and generate predicted values in XLMiner:

Step 1. Click the link **Choose Subset** in cell C72 of the *MLR_Output* worksheet
Step 2. When the **Multiple Linear Regression–Step 1 of 2** dialog box appears, the confirm that the entries are prepopulated as in Figure 7.40 and click **Next**
Step 3. In the **Multiple Linear Regression–Step 2 of 2** dialog box:
In the **Score New Data** area, select **In Worksheet**
When the **Match Variables in the New Range** dialog box appears:
In the **Data Source** area, enter *NewData* in the **Worksheet:** box and \$A\$1:\$E\$11 in the **Data Range:** box
Confirm that the box next to **First Row Contains Headers** is checked
In the **Variables** area, select **Match By Name**
Click **OK**
Click **Finish**

FIGURE 7.40 Predicting New Observations with XLMiner Regression Procedure

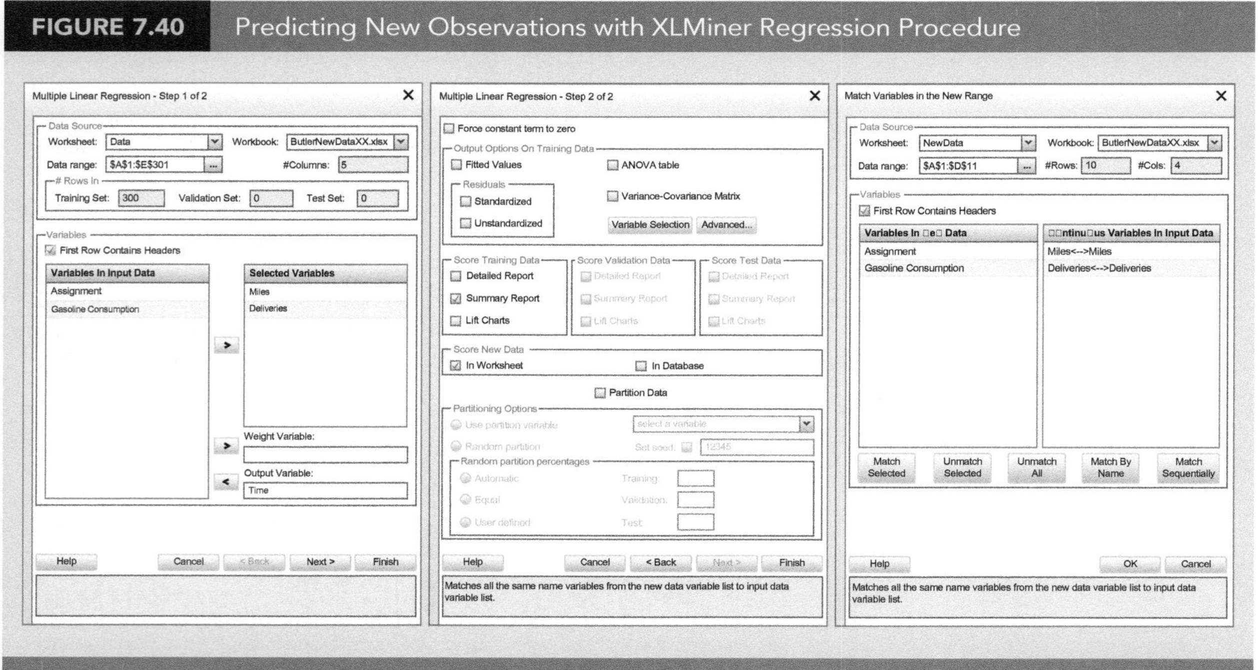

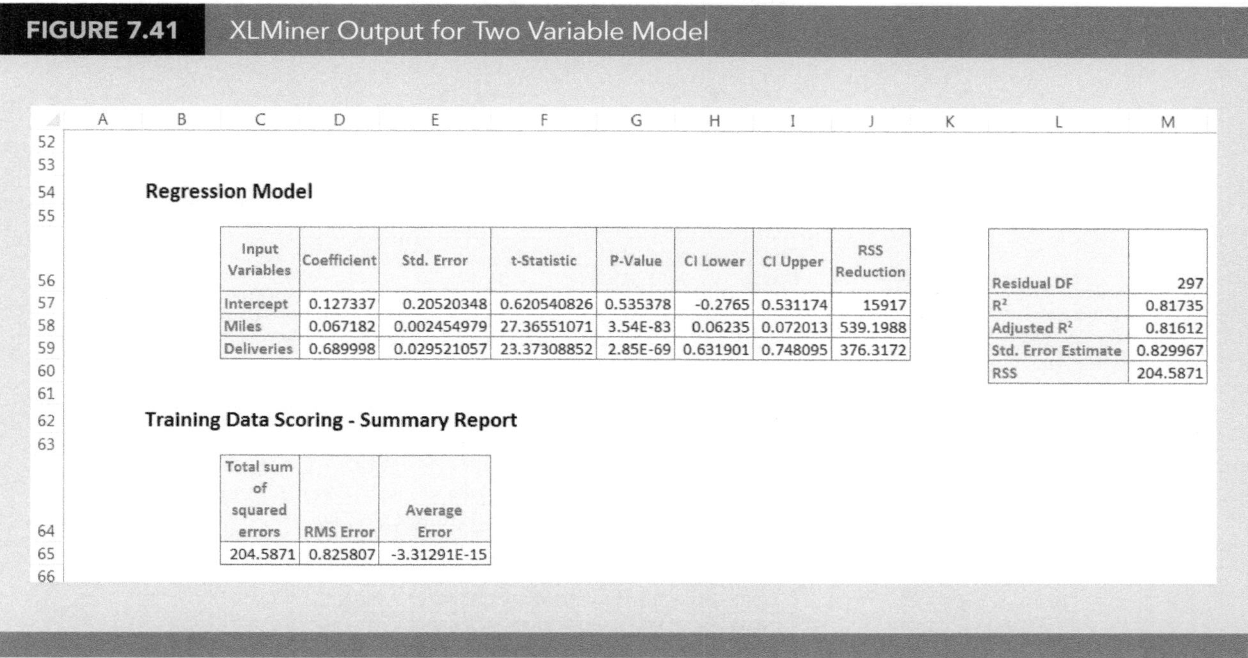

Regression Model

Input Variables	Coefficient	Std. Error	t-Statistic	P-Value	CI Lower	CI Upper	RSS Reduction
Intercept	0.127337	0.20520348	0.620540826	0.535378	-0.2765	0.531174	15917
Miles	0.067182	0.002454979	27.36551071	3.54E-83	0.06235	0.072013	539.1988
Deliveries	0.689998	0.029521057	23.37308852	2.85E-69	0.631901	0.748095	376.3172

Residual DF	297
R^2	0.81735
Adjusted R^2	0.81612
Std. Error Estimate	0.829967
RSS	204.5871

Training Data Scoring - Summary Report

Total sum of squared errors	RMS Error	Average Error
204.5871	0.825807	-3.31291E-15

FIGURE 7.41 XLMiner Output for Two Variable Model

This procedure constructs the regression model to predict travel time using miles driving and deliveries made. Figure 7.41 shows the fit information from the *MLR_Output1* worksheet; the corresponding regression equation is: Time = 0.1273 + 0.0672 Miles + 0.6900 Deliveries. Cells B16:B25 in Figure 7.42 contain the predictions for the travel time for the 10 new observations. For example, the predicted travel time for first observation (Row 16) is given by: Time = 0.1273 + 0.0672 (105) + 0.6900 (3) = 9.25 hours.

As Figure 7.42 shows, XLMiner also produces two types of interval estimates around the point estimate of the travel time for a new observation. Here, the 95% confidence interval is an interval estimate of the mean travel time for a route assignment with the given values of Miles and Deliveries. This is the appropriate interval estimate if we are interested in estimating the mean travel time for all route assignments with given mileage and number of deliveries. This confidence interval estimates the variability in the mean travel time.

Alternatively, the 95% prediction interval is an interval estimate on the prediction of travel time for an individual route assignment with the given values of Miles and Deliveries. This is the appropriate interval estimate if we are interested in predicting the travel time for an individual route assignment with the specified mileage and number of deliveries. This prediction interval estimates the variability inherent in a single route's travel time.

To illustrate, consider the first observation (Row 16) with 105 miles and 3 deliveries. The point estimate for the mean travel time as provided by the regression equation is 9.25 hours. For all 105-mile routes with 3 deliveries, a 95% confidence interval on the mean travel time ranges from 9.06 to 9.44 hours (cells C16 and D16 in Figure 7.42). That is, we are 95% confident that the true population mean travel time for 105-mile routes with 3 deliveries is between 9.06 and 9.44 hours.

Now suppose Butler Trucking is interested in predicting the travel time for an upcoming route assignment covering 105-miles and 3 deliveries. The best prediction for this route's travel time is 9.25 hours, as provided by the regression equation. However, a 95%

FIGURE 7.42 XLMiner Predictions of New Observations

Workbook	ButlerNewData.xlsx
Worksheet	NewData
Range	$A$1:$E$11

Predicted Value	95% Confidence Intervals		95% Prediction Intervals		Miles	Deliveries
	Lower	Upper	Lower	Upper		
9.251415	9.058104	9.444725	7.606654	10.89618	105	3
6.918235	6.80624	7.030229	5.281038	8.555432	60	4
9.959594	9.786808	10.13238	8.317119	11.60207	95	5
7.53551	7.310045	7.760975	5.88666	9.184359	100	1
4.884602	4.707121	5.062082	3.241626	6.527578	40	3
7.571871	7.463385	7.680358	5.934911	9.208832	80	3
7.254143	7.151247	7.35704	5.617544	8.890743	65	4
5.892328	5.768443	6.016212	4.254275	7.530381	55	3
7.889599	7.714556	8.064642	6.246885	9.532314	95	2
8.579597	8.425884	8.733311	6.939019	10.22018	95	3

prediction interval for this travel time prediction ranges from 7.61 to 10.90 hours (cells E16 and F16 in Figure 7.42). That is, we are 95% confident that the travel time for a single 105-mile route with 3 deliveries will be between 7.61 and 10.90 hours.

Note that the 95% prediction interval for the travel time of a single route assignment with 105 miles and 3 deliveries is wider than the 95% confidence interval for the mean travel time of all route assignments with 105 miles and 3 deliveries. The difference reflects the fact that we are able to estimate the mean value of y more precisely than we can predict an individual value of y.

Finally, we point out that the width of the prediction (and confidence) intervals for the regression point estimate are not the same for each observation. Instead, the width of the interval depends on the corresponding values of the independent variables. Confidence intervals and prediction intervals are narrower when the values of the independent variables $x_1, x_2, \ldots,$ are closer to their respective means, $\bar{x}_1, \bar{x}_2, \ldots.$

For the Butler example, Table 7.5 shows the 10 new observations, the predicted travel times from the regression equation, and the corresponding 95% confidence intervals (CI) and prediction intervals (PI). Table 7.5 illustrates the varying width of the confidence and prediction intervals depending on the values of the independent variables Miles and Deliveries. For the 300 observations on which the regression equation model is based, the mean miles for a route assignment is 70.7 miles and the mean number of deliveries for a route assignment is 3.5. Assignment 307 has the mileage (65) and number of deliveries (4) that are closest to these means and correspondingly has the narrowest confidence and prediction intervals. Conversely, Assignment 304 has the widest confidence and prediction intervals because it has the mileage (100) and number of deliveries (1) that are the farthest from the average miles and average number of deliveries.

Table 7.5 Predicted Values and 95% Confidence Interval and Prediction Interval Half Widths for 10 New Observations

Assignment	Miles	Deliveries	Predicted Value	95% CI Half-Width (+/–)	95% PI Half-Width (+/–)
301	105	3	9.25	0.193	1.645
302	60	4	6.92	0.112	1.637
303	95	5	9.96	0.173	1.642
304	100	1	7.54	0.225	1.649
305	40	3	4.88	0.177	1.643
306	80	3	7.57	0.108	1.637
307	65	4	7.25	0.103	1.637
308	55	3	5.89	0.124	1.638
309	95	2	7.89	0.175	1.643
310	95	3	8.58	0.154	1.641
	Avg. Miles = 70.7	Avg. Deliveries = 3.5			

Preface

The purpose of this thirteenth edition, as with previous editions, is to provide undergraduate and graduate students with a conceptual understanding of the role that quantitative methods play in the decision-making process. The text describes the many quantitative methods developed over the years, explains how they work, and shows how the decision maker can apply and interpret them.

This book is applications-oriented and uses our problem scenario approach to gently introduce quantitative material. In each chapter, a problem is described in conjunction with the quantitative procedure being introduced. Development of the quantitative technique or model includes applying it to the problem to generate a solution or recommendation. This approach can help to motivate the student by demonstrating not only how the procedure works, but also how it contributes to the decision-making process.

The mathematical prerequisite for this text is an algebra course. The two chapters on probability and probability distributions will provide the necessary background for the use of probability in subsequent chapters. Throughout the text we use generally accepted notation for the topic being covered. As a result, students who pursue study beyond the level of this text will generally experience little difficulty reading more advanced material. To also assist in further study, a bibliography is included at the end of this book.

CHANGES IN THE THIRTEENTH EDITION

We are very excited about the changes in the thirteenth edition of *Quantitative Methods for Business*, and want to tell you about some of the changes we have made and why.

Updated Chapter 16: Simulation

The most substantial content change in this latest edition involves the coverage of simulation. We maintain an intuitive introduction by continuing to use the concepts of best-, worst-, and base-case scenarios, but we have added a more elaborate treatment of uncertainty by using Microsoft Excel to develop spreadsheet simulation models. Within the chapter, we explain how to construct a spreadsheet simulation model using only native Excel functionality. In the chapter appendix, we describe how an Excel add-in, Analytic Solver Platform, facilitates more sophisticated simulation analyses. This new appendix on Analytic Solver Platform replaces the previous edition's coverage of Crystal Ball, which we no longer pair with our textbook. Nine new problems are introduced, and several others have been updated to reflect the new simulation coverage.

Other Content Changes

A variety of other changes have been made throughout the text in response to user suggestions. The most prominent of these include a new section on variability in project management in Chapter 13, new Appendix A coverage of data tables and Goal Seek functionality in Excel 2013, and adjustment of forecasting notation in Chapter 6. The software previously used to create decision trees in the Chapter 4 appendix, TreePlan, has now been incorporated into the Excel add-in Analytic Solver Platform, and we have updated Chapter 4 accordingly.

New Q.M. in Action, Cases, and Problems

Q.M. in Action is the name of the short summaries that describe how the quantitative methods being covered in the chapter have been used in practice. In this edition, you will find numerous Q.M. in Action vignettes, cases, and homework problems. We have updated many of these Q.M. in Actions to provide more recent examples. In all, we have added 15 new Q.M. in Actions.

The end of each chapter of this book contains cases for students. The cases are more in-depth and often more open-ended than the end-of-chapter homework problems. We have added three new cases to this edition: one on linear programming applications in Chapter 9, one on distribution and network models in Chapter 10, and one on integer programming in Chapter 11. Solutions to all cases are available to instructors.

We have added more than 35 new homework problems to this edition. Many other homework problems have been updated to provide more timely references.

FEATURES AND PEDAGOGY

We continued many of the features that appeared in previous editions. Some of the important ones are noted here.

- Annotations: Annotations that highlight key points and provide additional insights for the student are a continuing feature of this edition. These annotations, which appear in the margins, are designed to provide emphasis and enhance understanding of the terms and concepts presented in the text.
- Notes and Comments: We provide Notes and Comments at the end of many sections to give the student additional insights about the methodology being discussed and its application. These insights include warnings about or limitations of the methodology, recommendations for application, brief descriptions of additional technical considerations, and other matters.
- Self-Test Exercises: Certain exercises are identified as self-test exercises. Completely worked-out solutions for these exercises are provided in Appendix G, entitled Self-Test Solutions and Answers to Even-Numbered Problems, located at the end of the book. Students can attempt the self-test problems and immediately check the solutions to evaluate their understanding of the concepts presented in the chapter. At the request of professors using our textbooks, we now provide the answers to even-numbered problems in this same appendix.
- Q.M. in Action: These articles are presented throughout the text and provide a summary of an application of quantitative methods found in business today. Adaptations of materials from the popular press, academic journals such as *Interfaces*, and write-ups provided by practitioners provide the basis for the applications in this feature.

ANCILLARY LEARNING AND TEACHING MATERIALS

For Students

Print and online resources are available to help the student work more efficiently as well as learn how to use Excel.

- LINGO: The student version of LINGO 14.0 software is available for download at no additional cost to students who purchase a new text, through a link on the student companion site.

- Analytic Solver Platform: An educational version of the latest version of the Analytic Solver Platform software is available at no cost with a new text.

For Instructors

Instructor ancillaries are now provided on the website. Included in this convenient format are the following:

- Solutions Manual: The Solutions Manual, prepared by the authors, includes solutions for all problems in the text.
- Solutions to Case Problems: Also prepared by the authors, it contains solutions to all case problems presented in the text.
- PowerPoint Presentation Slides: Prepared by John Loucks of St. Edwards University, the presentation slides contain a teaching outline that incorporates graphics to help instructors create even more stimulating lectures. The slides may be adapted using PowerPoint software to facilitate classroom use.
- Test Bank: Also prepared by John Loucks, the Test Bank in Microsoft Word files includes multiple choice, true/false, short-answer questions, and problems for each chapter.

Cengage Learning Testing Powered by Cognero is a flexible, online system that allows you to:

- author, edit, and manage test bank content from multiple Cengage Learning solutions
- create multiple test versions in an instant
- deliver tests from your LMS, your classroom, or wherever you want

COURSE OUTLINE FLEXIBILITY

The text provides instructors with substantial flexibility in selecting topics to meet specific course needs. Although many variations are possible, the single-semester and single-quarter outlines that follow are illustrative of the options available.

Suggested One-Semester Course Outline

- Introduction (Chapter 1)
- Probability Concepts (Chapters 2 and 3)
- Decision Analysis (Chapters 4 and 5)
- Forecasting (Chapter 6)
- Linear Programming (Chapters 7, 8, and 9)
- Distribution and Network Models (Chapter 10)
- Integer Linear Programming (Chapter 11)
- Advanced Optimization Applications (Chapter 12)
- Project Scheduling: PERT/CPM (Chapter 13)
- Simulation (Chapter 15)

Suggested One-Quarter Course Outline

- Introduction (Chapter 1)
- Decision Analysis (Chapters 4 and 5)
- Linear Programming (Chapters 7, 8, and 9)
- Distribution and Network Models (Chapter 10)
- Integer Linear Programming (Chapter 11)

Advanced Optimization Applications (Chapter 12)
Project Scheduling: PERT/CPM (Chapter 13)
Simulation (Chapter 15)

Many other possibilities exist for one-term courses, depending on the time available, course objectives, and backgrounds of the students.

ACKNOWLEDGMENTS

We were fortunate in having the thoughts and comments of a number of colleagues as we began work on this thirteenth edition of *Quantitative Methods for Business*. Our appreciation and thanks go to:

Larry Barchett
Ohio Valley University

Stacie A. Bosley
Hamline University

Gregory Chase
West Liberty University

Ali A. Choudry
Embry-Riddle University

Mary Fletcher
Mount Mary University

Edward Gordhammer
Embry-Riddle Aeronautical University

Wendy Keyes
California Baptist University

Kenneth Lawrence
New Jersey Institute of Technology

Holly S. Lutze
Texas Lutheran University

Penina Orenstein
Seton Hall University

Edward R. Sim
Hardin-Simmons University

Rahmat Tavallali
Walsh University

John S. Watters
McKendree University

Susan M. L. Zee
Southeastern Louisiana University

Writing and revising a textbook is a continuing process. We owe a debt to many of our colleagues and friends for their helpful comments and suggestions during the development of earlier editions. Among these are the following:

Ellen Parker Allen
Southern Methodist University

Gopesh Anand
The Ohio State University

Robert L. Armacost
University of Central Florida

Daniel Asera
University of Nevada, Las Vegas

Uttarayan Bagchi
University of Texas at Austin

Stephen Baglione
Saint Leo University

Ardith Baker
Oral Roberts University

Edward Baker
University of Miami

Norman Baker
University of Cincinnati

David Bakuli
Westfield State College

Robert T. Barrett
Francis Marion University

Oded Berman
University of Toronto

Gary Blau
Purdue University

William Bleuel
Pepperdine University

Richard G. Bradford
Avila University

Thomas Bundt
Hillsdale College

Heidi Burgiel
Bridgewater State College

Rodger D. Carlson
Morehead State University

Ying Chien
University of Scranton

Renato Clavijo
Robert Morris University

Ron Craig
Wilfrid Laurier University

Mary M. Danaher
Florida Atlantic University

Stanley Dick
Babson College

Swarna D. Dutt
State University of West Georgia

John Eatman
University of North Carolina–Greensboro

Ronald Ebert
University of Missouri–Columbia

Charlie Edmonson
University of Dayton

Don Edwards
University of South Carolina

Ronald Ehresman
Baldwin-Wallace College

Peter Ellis
Utah State University

Lawrence Ettkin
University of Tennessee at Chattanooga

James Evans
University of Cincinnati

Paul Ewell,
Bridgewater College

Ephrem Eyob
Virginia State University

Michael Ford
Rochester Institute of Technology

Terri Friel
Eastern Kentucky University

Phil Fry
Boise State University

Christian V. Fugar
Dillard University

Robert Garfinkel
University of Connecticut

Alfredo Gomez,
Florida Atlantic University

Bob Gregory
Bellevue University

Leland Gustafson
State University of West Georgia

Joseph Haimowitz
Avila University

Nicholas G. Hall
The Ohio State University

Michael E. Hanna
University of Houston–Clear Lake

John Hanson
University of San Diego

William V. Harper
Otterbein College

Melanie Hatch
Miami University

Harry G. Henderson
Davis & Elkins College

Carl H. Hess
Marymount University

Daniel G. Hotard
Southeastern Louisiana University

David Hott
Florida Institute of Technology

Woodrow W. Hughes
Jr., Converse College

Christine Irujo
Westfield State College

Barry Kadets
Bryant College

Birsen Karpak
Youngstown State University

William C. Keller
Webb Institute of the University of Phoenix

Christos Koulamas
Florida International University

M. S. Krishnamoorthy
Alliant International University

Melvin H. Kuhbander
Sullivan University

Anil Kukreja
Xavier University of Louisiana

Alireza Lari
Fayetteville State University

John Lawrence, Jr.
California State University–Fullerton

Jodey Lingg
City University

John S. Loucks
St. Edwards University

Constantine Loucopoulos
Emporia State University

Donald R. MacRitchie
Framingham State College

Larry Maes
Davenport University

Ka-sing Man
Georgetown University

William G. Marchal
University of Toledo

Barbara J. Mardis
University of Northern Iowa

Kamlesh Mathur
Case Western Reserve University

Joseph Mazzola
Duke University

Timothy McDaniel
Buena Vista University

Patrick McKeown
University of Georgia

Constance McLaren
Indiana State University

Mohammad Meybodi
Indiana University–Kokomo

John R. Miller
Mercer University

Mario Miranda
The Ohio State University

Joe Moffitt
University of Massachusetts

Saeed Mohaghegh
Assumption College

Herbert Moskowitz
Purdue University

Shahriar Mostashari
Campbell University–School of Business

Alan Neebe
University of North Carolina

V. R. Nemani
Trinity College

William C. O'Connor
University of Montana–Western

Donald A. Ostasiewski
Thomas More College

David Pentico
Duquesne University

John E. Powell
University of South Dakota

B. Madhusudan Rao
Bowling Green State University

Handanhal V. Ravinder
University of New Mexico

Avuthu Rami Reddy
University of Wisconsin

Donna Retzlaff-Roberts
University of Memphis

Don R. Robinson
Illinois State University

Richard Rosenthal
Naval Postgraduate School

Kazim Ruhi
University of Maryland

Susan D. Sandblom
Scottsdale Community College

Tom Schmidt
Simpson College

Antoinette Somers
Wayne State University

Rajesh Srivastava
Florida Gulf Coast University

Donald E. Stout, Jr.
Saint Martin's College

Minghe Sun
University of Texas at San Antonio

Christopher S. Tang
University of California–Los Angeles

Giri Kumar Tayi
State University of New York–Albany

Willban Terpening
Gonzaga University

Dothang Truong
Fayetteville State University

Vicente A. Vargas
University of San Diego

William Vasbinder
Becker College

Emre Veral
City University of New York–Baruch

Elizabeth J. Wark
Springfield College

John F. Wellington
Indiana University–Purdue University, Fort Wayne

Robert P. Wells
Becker College

Laura J. White
University of West Florida

Edward P. Winkofsky
University of Cincinnati

Cynthia Woodburn
Pittsburg State University

Neba L J Wu
Eastern Michigan University

Kefeng Xu
University of Texas at San Antonio

Mari Yetimyan
San Jose State University

Our associates from organizations who provided application write-ups made a major contribution to the text. These individuals are cited in a credit line on the associated Q.M. in Action.

We are also indebted to our product manager, Aaron Arnsparger; our marketing manager, Heather Mooney; our senior content developer, Maggie Kubale; our content project manager, Jana Lewis; our media editor, Chris Valentine; and others at Cengage Learning for their counsel and support during the preparation of this text.

David R. Anderson
Dennis J. Sweeney
Thomas A. Williams
Jeffrey D. Camm
James J. Cochran
Michael J. Fry
Jeffrey W. Ohlmann

CHAPTER 6

Time Series Analysis and Forecasting

CONTENTS

The purpose of this chapter is to provide an introduction to time series analysis and forecasting. Suppose we are asked to provide quarterly forecasts of sales for one of our company's products over the coming one-year period. Production schedules, raw materials purchasing, inventory policies, and sales quotas will all be affected by the quarterly forecasts we provide. Consequently, poor forecasts may result in poor planning and increased costs for the company. How should we go about providing the quarterly sales forecasts? Good judgment, intuition, and an awareness of the state of the economy may give us a rough idea or "feeling" of what is likely to happen in the future, but converting that feeling into a number that can be used as next year's sales forecast is challenging. The Q.M. in Action, Forecasting Energy Needs in the Utility Industry, describes the role that forecasting plays in the utility industry.

A forecast is simply a prediction of what will happen in the future. Managers must accept that regardless of the technique used, they will not be able to develop perfect forecasts.

Forecasting methods can be classified as qualitative or quantitative. Qualitative methods generally involve the use of expert judgment to develop forecasts. Such methods are appropriate when historical data on the variable being forecast are either unavailable or not applicable. Quantitative forecasting methods can be used when (1) past information about the variable being forecast is available, (2) the information can be quantified, and (3) it is reasonable to assume that past is prologue (i.e., the pattern of the past will continue into the future). We will focus exclusively on quantitative forecasting methods in this chapter.

If the historical data are restricted to past values of the variable to be forecast, the forecasting procedure is called a *time series method* and the historical data are referred to as a

Q.M. *in* ACTION

*FORECASTING ENERGY NEEDS IN THE UTILITY INDUSTRY**

Duke Energy is a diversified energy company with a portfolio of natural gas and electric businesses and an affiliated real estate company. In 2006, Duke Energy merged with Cinergy of Cincinnati, Ohio, to create one of North America's largest energy companies, with assets totaling more than $70 billion. As a result of this merger the Cincinnati Gas & Electric Company became part of Duke Energy. Today, Duke Energy services over 5.5 million retail electric and gas customers in North Carolina, South Carolina, Ohio, Kentucky, Indiana, and Ontario, Canada.

Forecasting in the utility industry offers some unique perspectives. Because energy is difficult to store, this product must be generated to meet the instantaneous requirements of the customers. Electrical shortages are not just lost sales, but "brownouts" or "blackouts." This situation places an unusual burden on the utility forecaster. On the positive side, the demand for energy and the sale of energy are more predictable than for many other products. Also, unlike the situation in a multiproduct firm, a great amount of forecasting effort and expertise can be concentrated on the two products: gas and electricity.

The largest observed electric demand for any given period, such as an hour, a day, a month, or a year, is defined as the peak load. The forecast of the annual electric peak load guides the timing decision for constructing future generating units, and the financial impact of this decision is great. Obviously, a timing decision that leads to having the unit available no sooner than necessary is crucial.

The energy forecasts are important in other ways also. For example, purchases of coal as fuel for the generating units are based on the forecast levels of energy needed. The revenue from the electric operations of the company is determined from forecasted sales, which in turn enters into the planning of rate changes and external financing. These planning and decision-making processes are among the most important managerial activities in the company. It is imperative that the decision makers have the best forecast information available to assist them in arriving at these decisions.

*Based on information provided by Dr. Richard Evans of Duke Energy.

time series. The objective of time series analysis is to uncover a pattern in the historical data or time series and then extrapolate the pattern into the future; the forecast is based solely on past values of the variable and/or on past forecast errors.

In Section 6.1 we discuss the various kinds of time series that a forecaster might be faced with in practice. These include a constant or horizontal pattern, a trend, a seasonal pattern, both a trend and a seasonal pattern, and a cyclical pattern. In order to build a quantitative forecasting model it is also necessary to have a measurement of forecast accuracy. Different measurements of forecast accuracy, and their respective advantages and disadvantages, are discussed in Section 6.2. In Section 6.3 we consider the simplest case, which is a horizontal or constant pattern. For this pattern, we develop the classical moving average, weighted moving average, and exponential smoothing models. Many time series have a trend, and taking this trend into account is important; in Section 6.4 we provide regression models for finding the best model parameters when a linear trend is present. Finally, in Section 6.5 we show how to incorporate both a trend and seasonality into a forecasting model.

6.1 Time Series Patterns

A **time series** is a sequence of observations on a variable measured at successive points in time or over successive periods of time. The measurements may be taken every hour, day, week, month, or year, or at any other regular interval.[1] The pattern of the data is an important factor in understanding how the time series has behaved in the past. If such behavior can be expected to continue in the future, we can use it to guide us in selecting an appropriate forecasting method.

To identify the underlying pattern in the data, a useful first step is to construct a time series plot. A **time series plot** is a graphical presentation of the relationship between time and the time series variable; time is represented on the horizontal axis and values of the time series variable are shown on the vertical axis. Let us first review some of the common types of data patterns that can be identified when examining a time series plot.

Horizontal Pattern

A horizontal pattern exists when the data fluctuate randomly around a constant mean over time. To illustrate a time series with a horizontal pattern, consider the 12 weeks of data in Table 6.1. These data show the number of gallons of gasoline (in 1000s) sold by a gasoline distributor in Bennington, Vermont, over the past 12 weeks. The average value or mean for this time series is 19.25 or 19,250 gallons per week. Figure 6.1 shows a time series plot for these data. Note how the data fluctuate around the sample mean of 19,250 gallons. Although random variability is present, we would say that these data follow a horizontal pattern.

The term **stationary time series**[2] is used to denote a time series whose statistical properties are independent of time. In particular this means that

1. The process generating the data has a constant mean.
2. The variability of the time series is constant over time.

A time series plot for a stationary time series will always exhibit a horizontal pattern with random fluctuations. However, simply observing a horizontal pattern is not sufficient

[1]We limit our discussion to time series for which the values of the series are recorded at equal intervals. Cases in which the observations are made at unequal intervals are beyond the scope of this text.

[2]For a formal definition of stationarity, see K. Ord and R. Fildes (2012), *Principles of Business Forecasting*. Mason, OH: Cengage Learning, p. 155.

TABLE 6.1 GASOLINE SALES TIME SERIES

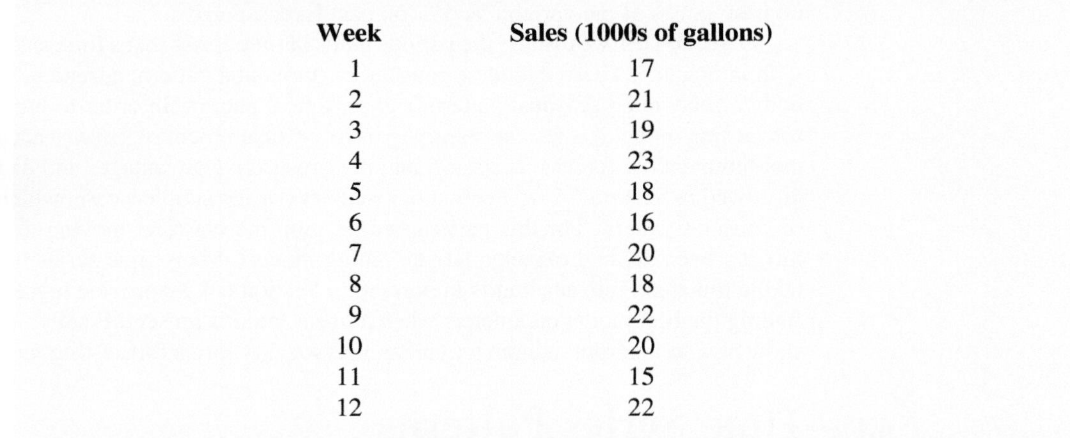

Week	Sales (1000s of gallons)
1	17
2	21
3	19
4	23
5	18
6	16
7	20
8	18
9	22
10	20
11	15
12	22

WEB file
Gasoline

FIGURE 6.1 GASOLINE SALES TIME SERIES PLOT

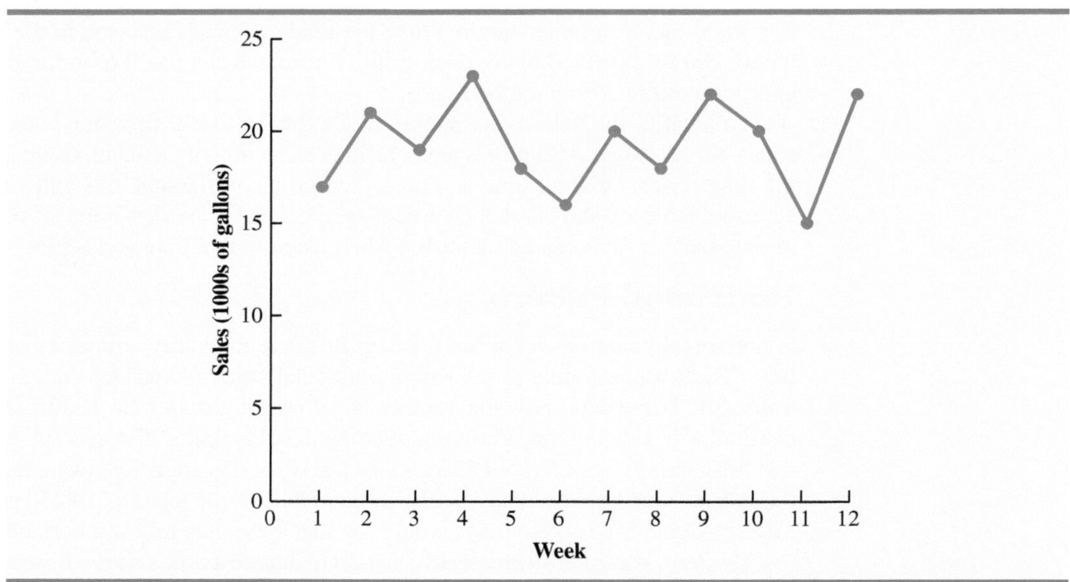

evidence to conclude that the time series is stationary. More advanced texts on forecasting discuss procedures for determining if a time series is stationary and provide methods for transforming a time series that is nonstationary into a stationary series.

Changes in business conditions often result in a time series with a horizontal pattern that shifts to a new level at some point in time. For instance, suppose the gasoline distributor signs a contract with the Vermont Sate Police to provide gasoline for state police cars located in southern Vermont beginning in week 13. With this new contract, the distributor naturally expects to see a substantial increase in weekly sales starting in week 13. Table 6.2 shows the number of gallons of gasoline sold for the original time series and the 10 weeks

TABLE 6.2 GASOLINE SALES TIME SERIES AFTER OBTAINING THE CONTRACT WITH THE VERMONT STATE POLICE

GasolineRevised

Week	Sales (1000s of gallons)	Week	Sales (1000s of gallons)
1	17	12	22
2	21	13	31
3	19	14	34
4	23	15	31
5	18	16	33
6	16	17	28
7	20	18	32
8	18	19	30
9	22	20	29
10	20	21	34
11	15	22	33

after signing the new contract. Figure 6.2 shows the corresponding time series plot. Note the increased level of the time series beginning in week 13. This change in the level of the time series makes it more difficult to choose an appropriate forecasting method. Selecting a forecasting method that adapts well to changes in the level of a time series is an important consideration in many practical applications.

Trend Pattern

Although time series data generally exhibit random fluctuations, a time series may also show gradual shifts or movements to relatively higher or lower values over a longer period

FIGURE 6.2 GASOLINE SALES TIME SERIES PLOT AFTER OBTAINING THE CONTRACT WITH THE VERMONT STATE POLICE

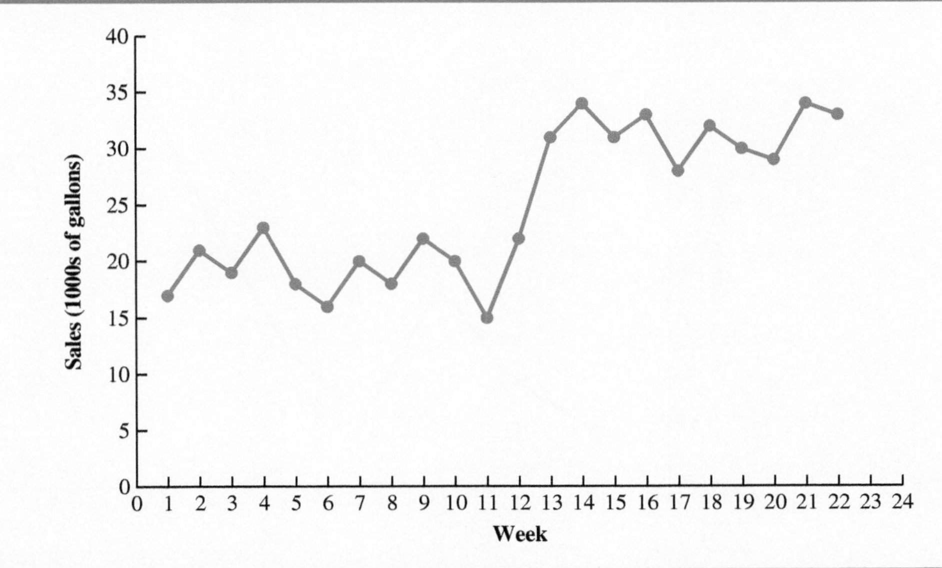

of time. If a time series plot exhibits this type of behavior, we say that a **trend pattern** exists. A trend is usually the result of long-term factors such as population increases or decreases, shifting demographic characteristics of the population, improving technology, and/or changes in consumer preferences.

To illustrate a time series with a linear trend pattern, consider the time series of bicycle sales for a particular manufacturer over the past 10 years, as shown in Table 6.3 and Figure 6.3. Note that 21,600 bicycles were sold in year 1, 22,900 were sold in year 2, and so on. In year 10, the most recent year, 31,400 bicycles were sold. Visual inspection of the time series plot shows some up and down movement over the past 10 years, but the time series seems also to have a systematically increasing or upward trend.

WEB file Bicycle

TABLE 6.3 BICYCLE SALES TIME SERIES

Year	Sales (1000s)
1	21.6
2	22.9
3	25.5
4	21.9
5	23.9
6	27.5
7	31.5
8	29.7
9	28.6
10	31.4

FIGURE 6.3 BICYCLE SALES TIME SERIES PLOT

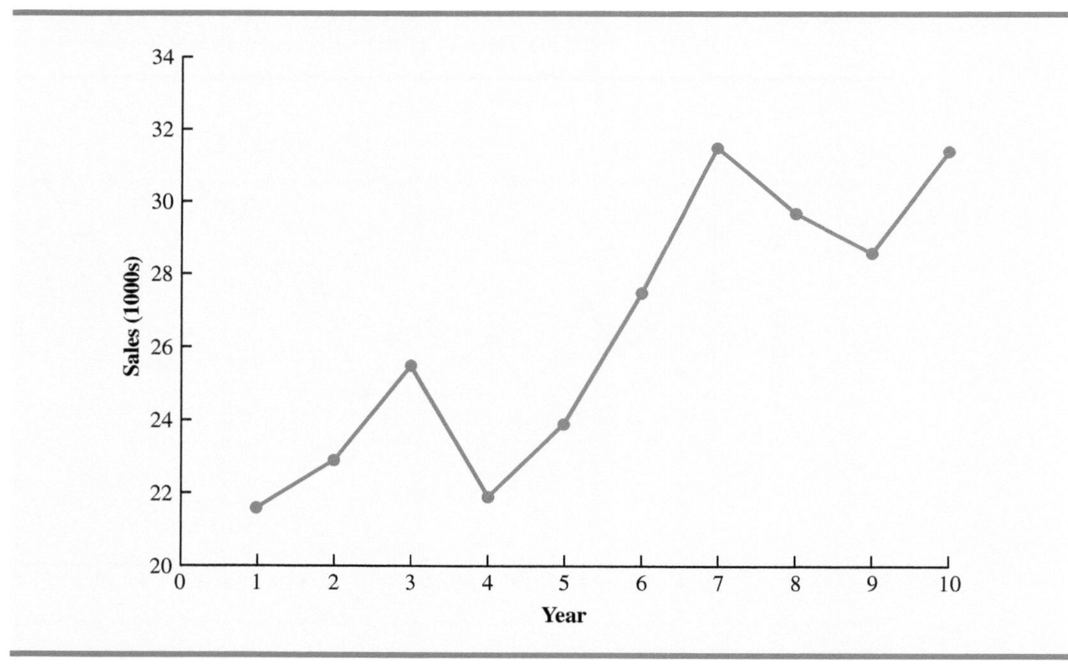

The trend for the bicycle sales time series appears to be linear and increasing over time, but sometimes a trend can be described better by other types of patterns. For instance, the data in Table 6.4 and the corresponding time series plot in Figure 6.4 show the sales revenue for a cholesterol drug since the company won FDA approval for the drug 10 years ago. The time series increases in a nonlinear fashion; that is, the rate of change of revenue does not increase by a constant amount from one year to the next. In fact, the revenue appears to be growing in an exponential fashion. Exponential relationships such as this are appropriate when the percentage change from one period to the next is relatively constant.

Seasonal Pattern

The trend of a time series can be identified by analyzing movements in historical data over multiple years. **Seasonal patterns** are recognized by observing recurring patterns

TABLE 6.4 CHOLESTEROL DRUG REVENUE TIME SERIES ($ MILLIONS)

Cholesterol

Year	Revenue
1	23.1
2	21.3
3	27.4
4	34.6
5	33.8
6	43.2
7	59.5
8	64.4
9	74.2
10	99.3

FIGURE 6.4 CHOLESTEROL DRUG REVENUE TIMES SERIES PLOT ($ MILLIONS)

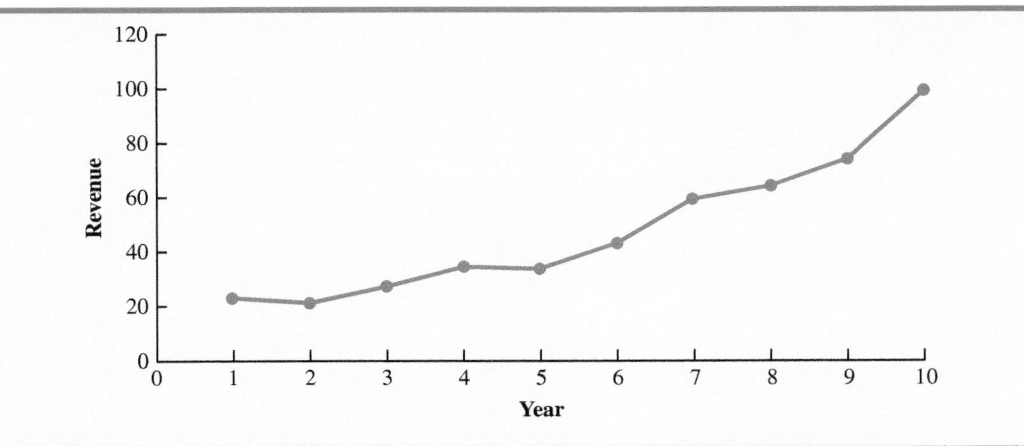

over successive periods of time. For example, a manufacturer of swimming pools expects low sales activity in the fall and winter months, with peak sales in the spring and summer months to occur each year. Manufacturers of snow removal equipment and heavy clothing, however, expect the opposite yearly pattern. Not surprisingly, the pattern for a time series plot that exhibits a recurring pattern over a one-year period due to seasonal influences is called a seasonal pattern. While we generally think of seasonal movement in a time series as occurring within one year, time series data can also exhibit seasonal patterns of less than one year in duration. For example, daily traffic volume shows within-the-day "seasonal" behavior, with peak levels occurring during rush hours, moderate flow during the rest of the day and early evening, and light flow from midnight to early morning. Another example of an industry with sales that exhibit easily discernible seasonal patterns within a day is the restaurant industry.

As an example of a seasonal pattern, consider the number of umbrellas sold at a clothing store over the past five years. Table 6.5 shows the time series and Figure 6.5 shows the corresponding time series plot. The time series plot does not indicate a long-term trend in sales. In fact, unless you look carefully at the data, you might conclude that the data follow a horizontal pattern with random fluctuation. However, closer inspection of the fluctuations in the time series plot reveals a systematic pattern in the data that occurs within each year. That is, the first and third quarters have moderate sales, the second quarter has the highest sales, and the fourth quarter tends to have the lowest sales volume. Thus, we would conclude that a quarterly seasonal pattern is present.

TABLE 6.5 UMBRELLA SALES TIME SERIES

Umbrella

Year	Quarter	Sales
1	1	125
	2	153
	3	106
	4	88
2	1	118
	2	161
	3	133
	4	102
3	1	138
	2	144
	3	113
	4	80
4	1	109
	2	137
	3	125
	4	109
5	1	130
	2	165
	3	128
	4	96

FIGURE 6.5 UMBRELLA SALES TIME SERIES PLOT

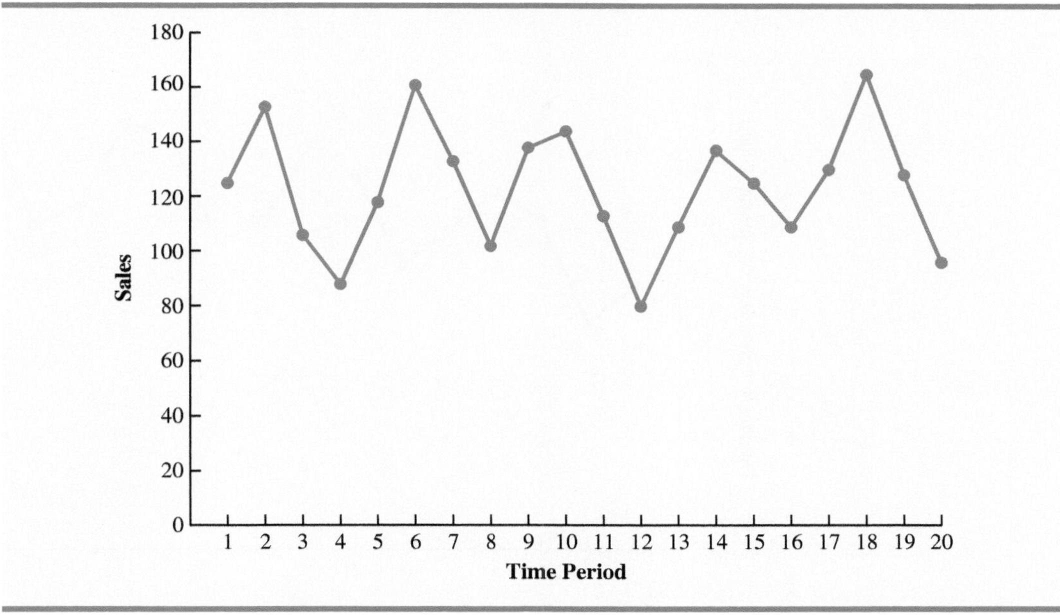

Trend and Seasonal Pattern

Some time series include both a trend and a seasonal pattern. For instance, the data in Table 6.6 and the corresponding time series plot in Figure 6.6 show quarterly television set sales for a particular manufacturer over the past four years. Clearly an increasing trend is

TABLE 6.6 QUARTERLY TELEVISION SET SALES TIME SERIES

Year	Quarter	Sales (1000s)
1	1	4.8
	2	4.1
	3	6.0
	4	6.5
2	1	5.8
	2	5.2
	3	6.8
	4	7.4
3	1	6.0
	2	5.6
	3	7.5
	4	7.8
4	1	6.3
	2	5.9
	3	8.0
	4	8.4

FIGURE 6.6 QUARTERLY TELEVISION SET SALES TIME SERIES PLOT

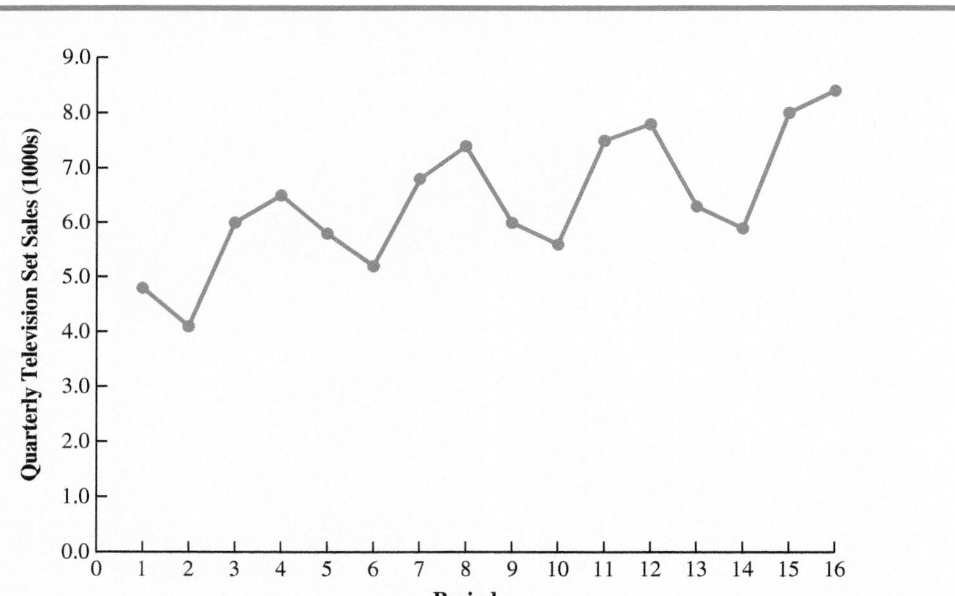

present. However, Figure 6.6 also indicates that sales are lowest in the second quarter of each year and highest in quarters 3 and 4. Thus, we conclude that a seasonal pattern also exists for television sales. In such cases we need to use a forecasting method that is capable of dealing with both trend and seasonality.

Cyclical Pattern

A **cyclical pattern** exists if the time series plot shows an alternating sequence of points below and above the trend line that lasts for more than one year. Many economic time series exhibit cyclical behavior with regular runs of observations below and above the trend line. Often the cyclical component of a time series is due to multiyear business cycles. For example, periods of moderate inflation followed by periods of rapid inflation can lead to a time series that alternates below and above a generally increasing trend line (e.g., a time series for housing costs). Business cycles are extremely difficult, if not impossible, to forecast. As a result, cyclical effects are often combined with long-term trend effects and referred to as trend-cycle effects. In this chapter we do not deal with cyclical effects that may be present in the time series.

Selecting a Forecasting Method

The underlying pattern in the time series is an important factor in selecting a forecasting method. Thus, a time series plot should be one of the first analytic tools employed when trying to determine which forecasting method to use. If we see a horizontal pattern, then we need to select a method appropriate for this type of pattern. Similarly, if we observe a trend in the data, then we need to use a forecasting method that is capable of handling a trend effectively. In the next two sections we illustrate methods for assessing forecast accuracy and consider forecasting models that can be used in situations for which the underlying pattern is horizontal; in other words, no trend or seasonal effects are present. We then consider methods appropriate when trend and/or seasonality are present in the data. The Q.M. in Action, Forecasting Demand for a Broad Product Line of Office Products, describes the considerations made by ACCO Brands when forecasting demand for its consumer and office products.

Q.M. *in* ACTION

*FORECASTING DEMAND FOR A BROAD LINE OF OFFICE PRODUCTS**

ACCO Brands Corporation is one of the world's largest suppliers of branded office and consumer products and print finishing solutions. The company's widely recognized brands include AT-A-GLANCE®, Day-Timer®, Five Star®, GBC®, Hilroy®, Kensington®, Marbig®, Mead®, NOBO, Quartet®, Rexel, Swingline®, Tilibra®, Wilson Jones®, and many others.

Because it produces and markets a wide array of products with a myriad of demand characteristics, ACCO Brands relies heavily on sales forecasts in planning its manufacturing, distribution, and marketing activities. By viewing its relationship in terms of a supply chain, ACCO Brands and its customers (which are generally retail chains) establish close collaborative relationships and consider each other to be valued partners. As a result, ACCO Brands' customers share valuable information and data that serve as inputs into ACCO Brands' forecasting process.

In her role as a forecasting manager for ACCO Brands, Vanessa Baker appreciates the importance of this additional information. "We do separate forecasts of demand for each major customer," said Baker, "and we generally use twenty-four to thirty-six months of history to generate monthly forecasts twelve to eighteen months into the future. While trends are important, several of our major product lines, including school, planning and organizing, and decorative calendars, are heavily seasonal, and seasonal sales make up the bulk of our annual volume."

Daniel Marks, one of several account-level strategic forecast managers for ACCO Brands, adds,

> The supply chain process includes the total lead time from identifying opportunities to making or procuring the product to getting the product on the shelves to align with the forecasted demand; this can potentially take several months, so the accuracy of our forecasts is critical throughout each step of the supply chain. Adding to this challenge is the risk of obsolescence. We sell many dated items, such as planners and calendars, which have a natural, built-in obsolescence. In addition, many of our products feature designs that are fashion-conscious or contain pop culture images, and these products can also become obsolete very quickly as tastes and popularity change. An overly optimistic forecast for these products can be very costly, but an overly pessimistic forecast can result in lost sales potential and give our competitors an opportunity to take market share from us.

In addition to looking at trends, seasonal components, and cyclical patterns, Baker and Marks must contend with several other factors. Baker notes, "We have to adjust our forecasts for upcoming promotions by our customers." Marks agrees and adds:

> We also have to go beyond just forecasting consumer demand; we must consider the retailer's specific needs in our order forecasts, such as what type of display will be used and how many units of a product must be on display to satisfy their presentation requirements. Current inventory is another factor—if a customer is carrying either too much or too little inventory, that will affect their future orders, and we need to reflect that in our forecasts. Will the product have a short life because it is tied to a cultural fad? What are the retailer's marketing and markdown strategies? Our knowledge of the environments in which our supply chain partners are competing helps us to forecast demand more accurately, and that reduces waste and makes our customers, as well as ACCO Brands, far more profitable.

*The authors are indebted to Vanessa Baker and Daniel Marks of ACCO Brands for providing input for this Q.M. in Action.

6.2 Forecast Accuracy

In this section we begin by developing forecasts for the gasoline time series shown in Table 6.1 using the simplest of all the forecasting methods, an approach that uses the most recent week's sales volume as the forecast for the next week. For instance, the distributor sold 17,000 gallons of gasoline in week 1; this value is used as the forecast for week 2. Next, we use 21, the actual value of sales in week 2, as the forecast for week 3, and so on. The forecasts obtained for the historical data using this method are shown in Table 6.7 in the column labeled Forecast. Because of its simplicity, this method is often referred to as a naïve forecasting method.

How accurate are the forecasts obtained using this naïve forecasting method? To answer this question we will introduce several measures of forecast accuracy. These measures are used to determine how well a particular forecasting method is able to reproduce the time series data that are already available. By selecting the method that is most accurate for the data already known, we hope to increase the likelihood that we will obtain more accurate forecasts for future time periods.

The key concept associated with measuring forecast accuracy is **forecast error**. If we denote Y_t and $\hat{Y}_t$ as the actual and forecasted values of the time series for period t, respectively, the forecasting error for period t is

$$e_t = Y_t - \hat{Y}_t \tag{6.1}$$

That is, the forecast error for time period t is the difference between the actual and the forecasted values for period t.

TABLE 6.7 COMPUTING FORECASTS AND MEASURES OF FORECAST ACCURACY USING THE MOST RECENT VALUE AS THE FORECAST FOR THE NEXT PERIOD

Week	Time Series Value	Forecast	Forecast Error	Absolute Value of Forecast Error	Squared Forecast Error	Percentage Error	Absolute Value of Percentage Error
1	17						
2	21	17	4	4	16	19.05	19.05
3	19	21	−2	2	4	−10.53	10.53
4	23	19	4	4	16	17.39	17.39
5	18	23	−5	5	25	−27.78	27.78
6	16	18	−2	2	4	−12.50	12.50
7	20	16	4	4	16	20.00	20.00
8	18	20	−2	2	4	−11.11	11.11
9	22	18	4	4	16	18.18	18.18
10	20	22	−2	2	4	−10.00	10.00
11	15	20	−5	5	25	−33.33	33.33
12	22	15	7	7	49	31.82	31.82
		Totals	5	41	179	1.19	211.69

For instance, because the distributor actually sold 21,000 gallons of gasoline in week 2 and the forecast, using the sales volume in week 1, was 17,000 gallons, the forecast error in week 2 is

$$\text{Forecast Error in week 2} = e_2 = Y_2 - \hat{Y}_2 = 21 - 17 = 4$$

The fact that the forecast error is positive indicates that in week 2 the forecasting method underestimated the actual value of sales. Next we use 21, the actual value of sales in week 2, as the forecast for week 3. Since the actual value of sales in week 3 is 19, the forecast error for week 3 is $e_3 = 19 - 21 = -2$. In this case, the negative forecast error indicates the forecast overestimated the actual value for week 3. Thus, the forecast error may be positive or negative, depending on whether the forecast is too low or too high. A complete summary of the forecast errors for this naïve forecasting method is shown in Table 6.7 in the column labeled Forecast Error. It is important to note that because we are using a past value of the time series to produce a forecast for period t, we do not have sufficient data to produce a naïve forecast for the first week of this time series.

A simple measure of forecast accuracy is the mean or average of the forecast errors. If we have n periods in our time series and k is the number of periods at the beginning of the time series for which we cannot produce a naïve forecast, the mean forecast error (MFE) is

$$\text{MFE} = \frac{\sum_{t=k+1}^{n} e_t}{n - k} \tag{6.2}$$

Table 6.7 shows that the sum of the forecast errors for the gasoline sales time series is 5; thus, the mean or average error is $5/11 = 0.45$. Because we do not have sufficient data to produce a naïve forecast for the first week of this time series, we must adjust our calculations in both the numerator and denominator accordingly. This is common in forecasting; we often use k past periods from the time series to produce forecasts, and so we frequently cannot produce forecasts for the first k periods. In those instances the summation in the numerator starts at the first value of t for which we have produced a forecast (so we begin the summation at $t = k + 1$), and the denominator (which is the number of periods in our time series for which we are able to produce a forecast) will also reflect these circumstances. In the gasoline example, although the time series consists of 12 values, to compute the mean error we divided the sum of the forecast errors by 11 because there are only 11 forecast errors (we cannot generate forecast sales for the first week using this naïve forecasting method).

Also note that in the gasoline time series, the mean forecast error is positive, which implies that the method is generally underforecasting; in other words, the observed values tend to be greater than the forecasted values. Because positive and negative forecast errors tend to offset one another, the mean error is likely to be small; thus, the mean error is not a very useful measure of forecast accuracy.

The **mean absolute error**, denoted MAE, is a measure of forecast accuracy that avoids the problem of positive and negative forecast errors offsetting one another. As you might expect given its name, MAE is the average of the absolute values of the forecast errors:

$$\text{MAE} = \frac{\sum_{t=k+1}^{n} |e_t|}{n - k} \tag{6.3}$$

This is also referred to as the mean absolute deviation or MAD. Table 6.7 shows that the sum of the absolute values of the forecast errors is 41; thus

$$\text{MAE} = \text{average of the absolute value of forecast errors} = \frac{41}{11} = 3.73$$

Another measure that avoids the problem of positive and negative errors offsetting each other is obtained by computing the average of the squared forecast errors. This measure of forecast accuracy, referred to as the **mean squared error**, is denoted MSE:

$$\text{MSE} = \frac{\sum_{t=k+1}^{n} e_t^2}{n-k} \tag{6.4}$$

From Table 6.7, the sum of the squared errors is 179; hence,

$$\text{MSE} = \text{average of the sum of squared forecast errors} = \frac{179}{11} = 16.27$$

The size of MAE and MSE depends upon the scale of the data. As a result, it is difficult to make comparisons for different time intervals (such as comparing a method of forecasting monthly gasoline sales to a method of forecasting weekly sales) or to make comparisons across different time series (such as monthly sales of gasoline and monthly sales of oil filters). To make comparisons such as these we need to work with relative or percentage error measures. The **mean absolute percentage error**, denoted MAPE, is such a measure. To compute MAPE we must first compute the percentage error for each forecast:

$$\left(\frac{e_t}{Y_t}\right)100$$

For example, the percentage error corresponding to the forecast of 17 in week 2 is computed by dividing the forecast error in week 2 by the actual value in week 2 and multiplying the result by 100. For week 2 the percentage error is computed as follows:

$$\text{Percentage error for week 2} = \left(\frac{e_2}{Y_2}\right)100 = \left(\frac{4}{21}\right)100 = 19.05\%$$

Thus, the forecast error for week 2 is 19.05% of the observed value in week 2. A complete summary of the percentage errors is shown in Table 6.7 in the column labeled Percentage Error. In the next column, we show the absolute value of the percentage error. Finally, we find the MAPE, which is calculated as:

$$\text{MAPE} = \frac{\sum_{t=k+1}^{n} \left|\left(\frac{e_t}{Y_t}\right)100\right|}{n-k} \tag{6.5}$$

Table 6.7 shows that the sum of the absolute values of the percentage errors is 211.69; thus

$$\begin{aligned}\text{MAPE} &= \text{average of the absolute value of percentage forecast errors}\\ &= \frac{211.69}{11} = 19.24\%\end{aligned}$$

In summary, using the naïve (most recent observation) forecasting method, we obtained the following measures of forecast accuracy:

$$\text{MAE} = 3.73$$
$$\text{MSE} = 16.27$$
$$\text{MAPE} = 19.24\%$$

Try Problem 1 for practice in computing measures of forecast accuracy.

These measures of forecast accuracy simply measure how well the forecasting method is able to forecast historical values of the time series. Now, suppose we want to forecast sales for a future time period, such as week 13. In this case the forecast for week 13 is 22, the actual value of the time series in week 12. Is this an accurate estimate of sales for week 13? Unfortunately there is no way to address the issue of accuracy associated with forecasts for future time periods. However, if we select a forecasting method that works well for the historical data, and we have reason to believe the historical pattern will continue into the future, we should obtain forecasts that will ultimately be shown to be accurate.

Before closing this section, let us consider another method for forecasting the gasoline sales time series in Table 6.1. Suppose we use the average of all the historical data available as the forecast for the next period. We begin by developing a forecast for week 2. Since there is only one historical value available prior to week 2, the forecast for week 2 is just the time series value in week 1; thus, the forecast for week 2 is 17,000 gallons of gasoline. To compute the forecast for week 3, we take the average of the sales values in weeks 1 and 2. Thus,

$$\hat{Y}_3 = \frac{17 + 21}{2} = 19$$

Similarly, the forecast for week 4 is

$$\hat{Y}_4 = \frac{17 + 21 + 19}{3} = 19$$

The forecasts obtained using this method for the gasoline time series are shown in Table 6.8 in the column labeled Forecast. Using the results shown in Table 6.8, we obtained the following values of MAE, MSE, and MAPE:

$$\text{MAE} = \frac{26.81}{11} = 2.44$$

$$\text{MSE} = \frac{89.07}{11} = 8.10$$

$$\text{MAPE} = \frac{141.34}{11} = 12.85\%$$

We can now compare the accuracy of the two forecasting methods we have considered in this section by comparing the values of MAE, MSE, and MAPE for each method.

	Naïve Method	Average of Past Values
MAE	3.73	2.44
MSE	16.27	8.10
MAPE	19.24%	12.85%

TABLE 6.8 COMPUTING FORECASTS AND MEASURES OF FORECAST ACCURACY USING THE AVERAGE OF ALL THE HISTORICAL DATA AS THE FORECAST FOR THE NEXT PERIOD

Week	Time Series Value	Forecast	Forecast Error	Absolute Value of Forecast Error	Squared Forecast Error	Percentage Error	Absolute Value of Percentage Error
1	17						
2	21	17.00	4.00	4.00	16.00	19.05	19.05
3	19	19.00	0.00	0.00	0.00	0.00	0.00
4	23	19.00	4.00	4.00	16.00	17.39	17.39
5	18	20.00	−2.00	2.00	4.00	−11.11	11.11
6	16	19.60	−3.60	3.60	12.96	−22.50	22.50
7	20	19.00	1.00	1.00	1.00	5.00	5.00
8	18	19.14	−1.14	1.14	1.31	−6.35	6.35
9	22	19.00	3.00	3.00	9.00	13.64	13.64
10	20	19.33	0.67	0.67	0.44	3.33	3.33
11	15	19.40	−4.40	4.40	19.36	−29.33	29.33
12	22	19.00	3.00	3.00	9.00	13.64	13.64
		Totals	4.52	26.81	89.07	2.75	141.34

For each of these measures, the average of past values provides more accurate forecasts than using the most recent observation as the forecast for the next period. In general, if the underlying time series is stationary, the average of all the historical data will provide the most accurate forecasts.

Evaluating different forecasts based on historical accuracy is only helpful if historical patterns continue into the future. As we noted in Section 6.1, the 12 observations of Table 6.1 comprise a stationary time series. In Section 6.1 we mentioned that changes in business conditions often result in a time series that is not stationary. We discussed a situation in which the gasoline distributor signed a contract with the Vermont State Police to provide gasoline for state police cars located in southern Vermont. Table 6.2 shows the number of gallons of gasoline sold for the original time series and the 10 weeks after signing the new contract, and Figure 6.2 shows the corresponding time series plot. Note the change in level in week 13 for the resulting time series. When a shift to a new level such as this occurs, it takes several periods for the forecasting method that uses the average of all the historical data to adjust to the new level of the time series. However, in this case the simple naïve method adjusts very rapidly to the change in level because it uses only the most recent observation available as the forecast.

Measures of forecast accuracy are important factors in comparing different forecasting methods, but we have to be careful to not rely too heavily upon them. Good judgment and knowledge about business conditions that might affect the value of the variable to be forecast also have to be considered carefully when selecting a method. Historical forecast accuracy is not the sole consideration, especially if the pattern exhibited by the time series is likely to change in the future.

In the next section we will introduce more sophisticated methods for developing forecasts for a time series that exhibits a horizontal pattern. Using the measures of forecast accuracy developed here, we will be able to assess whether such methods provide more accurate forecasts than we obtained using the simple approaches illustrated in this section. The methods that we will introduce also have the advantage that they adapt well to situations in which the time series changes to a new level. The ability of a forecasting method to adapt quickly to changes in level is an important consideration, especially in short-term forecasting situations.

6.3 Moving Averages and Exponential Smoothing

In this section we discuss three forecasting methods that are appropriate for a time series with a horizontal pattern: moving averages, weighted moving averages, and exponential smoothing. These methods are also capable of adapting well to changes in the level of a horizontal pattern such as what we saw with the extended gasoline sales time series (Table 6.2 and Figure 6.2). However, without modification they are not appropriate when considerable trend, cyclical, or seasonal effects are present. Because the objective of each of these methods is to "smooth out" random fluctuations in the time series, they are referred to as smoothing methods. These methods are easy to use and generally provide a high level of accuracy for short-range forecasts, such as a forecast for the next time period.

Moving Averages

The moving averages method uses the average of the most recent k data values in the time series as the forecast for the next period. Mathematically, a **moving average** forecast of order k is as follows:

$$\hat{Y}_{t+1} = \frac{\Sigma(\text{most recent } k \text{ data values})}{k} = \frac{\sum_{i=t-k+1}^{t} Y_i}{k} = \frac{Y_{t-k+1} + \cdots + Y_{t-1} + Y_t}{k} \tag{6.6}$$

where

$\hat{Y}_{t+1}$ = forecast of the time series for period $t + 1$
Y_i = actual value of the time series in period i
k = number of periods of time series data used to generate the forecast

The term *moving* is used because every time a new observation becomes available for the time series, it replaces the oldest observation in the equation and a new average is computed. Thus, the periods over which the average is calculated change, or move, with each ensuing period.

To illustrate the moving averages method, let us return to the original 12 weeks of gasoline sales data in Table 6.1 and Figure 6.1. The time series plot in Figure 6.1 indicates that the gasoline sales time series has a horizontal pattern. Thus, the smoothing methods of this section are applicable.

To use moving averages to forecast a time series, we must first select the order k, or number of time series values to be included in the moving average. If only the most recent values of the time series are considered relevant, a small value of k is preferred. If a greater number of past values are considered relevant, then we generally opt for a larger value of k. As mentioned earlier, a time series with a horizontal pattern can shift to a new level over time. A moving average will adapt to the new level of the series and resume providing good forecasts in k periods. Thus a smaller value of k will track shifts in a time series more quickly (the naïve approach discussed earlier is actually a moving average for $k = 1$). On the other hand, larger values of k will be more effective in smoothing out random fluctuations. Thus, managerial judgment based on an understanding of the behavior of a time series is helpful in choosing an appropriate value of k.

To illustrate how moving averages can be used to forecast gasoline sales, we will use a three-week moving average ($k = 3$). We begin by computing the forecast of sales in week 4 using the average of the time series values in weeks 1 to 3.

$$\hat{Y}_4 = \text{average of weeks 1 to 3} = \frac{17 + 21 + 19}{3} = 19$$

Thus, the moving average forecast of sales in week 4 is 19 or 19,000 gallons of gasoline. Because the actual value observed in week 4 is 23, the forecast error in week 4 is $e_4 = 23 - 19 = 4$.

We next compute the forecast of sales in week 5 by averaging the time series values in weeks 2–4.

$$\hat{Y}_5 = \text{average of weeks 2 to 4} = \frac{21 + 19 + 23}{3} = 21$$

Hence, the forecast of sales in week 5 is 21 and the error associated with this forecast is $e_5 = 18 - 21 = -3$. A complete summary of the three-week moving average forecasts for the gasoline sales time series is provided in Table 6.9. Figure 6.7 shows the original time series plot and the three-week moving average forecasts. Note how the graph of the moving average forecasts has tended to smooth out the random fluctuations in the time series.

TABLE 6.9 SUMMARY OF THREE-WEEK MOVING AVERAGE CALCULATIONS

Week	Time Series Value	Forecast	Forecast Error	Absolute Value of Forecast Error	Squared Forecast Error	Percentage Error	Absolute Value of Percentage Error
1	17						
2	21						
3	19						
4	23	19	4	4	16	17.39	17.39
5	18	21	−3	3	9	−16.67	16.67
6	16	20	−4	4	16	−25.00	25.00
7	20	19	1	1	1	5.00	5.00
8	18	18	0	0	0	0.00	0.00
9	22	18	4	4	16	18.18	18.18
10	20	20	0	0	0	0.00	0.00
11	15	20	−5	5	25	−33.33	33.33
12	22	19	3	3	9	13.64	13.64
		Totals	0	24	92	−20.79	129.21

FIGURE 6.7 GASOLINE SALES TIME SERIES PLOT AND THREE-WEEK MOVING AERAGE FORECASTS

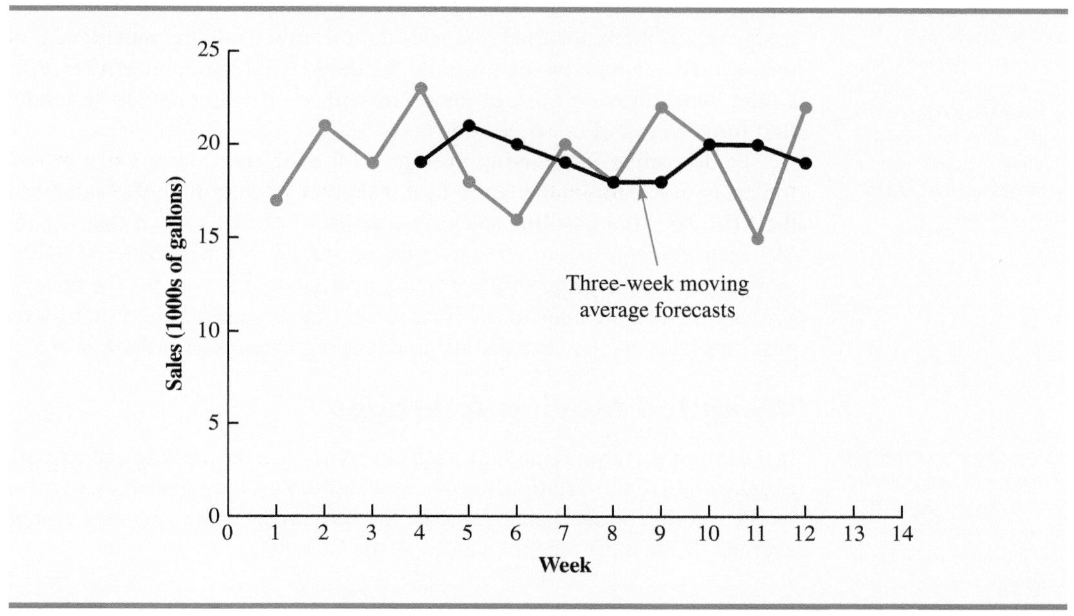

Can you now use moving averages to develop forecasts? Try Problem 7.

To forecast sales in week 13, the next time period in the future, we simply compute the average of the time series values in weeks 10, 11, and 12.

$$\hat{Y}_{13} = \text{average of weeks 10 to 12} = \frac{20 + 15 + 22}{3} = 19$$

Thus, the forecast for week 13 is 19 or 19,000 gallons of gasoline.

Forecast Accuracy In Section 6.2 we discussed three measures of forecast accuracy: mean absolute error (MAE); mean squared error (MSE); and mean absolute percentage error (MAPE). Using the three-week moving average calculations in Table 6.9, the values for these three measures of forecast accuracy are

$$\text{MAE} = \frac{\sum_{t=4}^{12} |e_t|}{12 - 3} = \frac{24}{9} = 2.67$$

$$\text{MSE} = \frac{\sum_{t=4}^{12} e_t^2}{12 - 3} = \frac{92}{9} = 10.22$$

$$\text{MAPE} = \frac{\sum_{t=4}^{12} \left| \left(\frac{e_t}{Y_t} \right) 100 \right|}{12 - 3} = \frac{129.21}{9} = 14.36\%$$

In situations where you need to compare forecasting methods for different time periods, such as comparing a forecast of weekly sales to a forecast of monthly sales, relative measures such as MAPE are preferred.

In Section 6.2 we showed that using the most recent observation as the forecast for the next week (a moving average of order $k = 1$) resulted in values of MAE = 3.73, MSE = 16.27, and MAPE = 19.24%. Thus, in each case the three-week moving average approach has provided more accurate forecasts than simply using the most recent observation as the forecast. Also note how the formulas for the MAE, MSE, and MAPE reflect that our use of a three-week moving average leaves us with insufficient data to generate forecasts for the first three weeks of our time series.

To determine if a moving average with a different order k can provide more accurate forecasts, we recommend using trial and error to determine the value of k that minimizes the MSE. For the gasoline sales time series, it can be shown that the minimum value of MSE corresponds to a moving average of order $k = 6$ with MSE = 6.79. If we are willing to assume that the order of the moving average that is best for the historical data will also be best for future values of the time series, the most accurate moving average forecasts of gasoline sales can be obtained using a moving average of order $k = 6$.

Weighted Moving Averages

A moving average forecast of order k is just a special case of the weighted moving averages method in which each weight is equal to 1/k; for example, a moving average forecast of order k = 3 is just a special case of the weighted moving averages method in which each weight is equal to $\frac{1}{3}$.

In the moving averages method, each observation in the moving average calculation receives equal weight. One variation, known as **weighted moving averages**, involves selecting a different weight for each data value in the moving average and then computing a weighted average of the most recent k values as the forecast.

$$\hat{Y}_{t+1} = w_t Y_t + w_{t-1} Y_{t-1} + \cdots + w_{t-k+1} Y_{t-k+1} \qquad \textbf{(6.7)}$$

where

$\hat{Y}_{t+1}$ = forecast of the time series for period $t + 1$
Y_t = actual value of the time series in period t
w_t = weight applied to the actual time series value for period t
k = number of periods of time series data used to generate the forecast

Generally the most recent observation receives the largest weight, and the weight decreases with the relative age of the data values. Let us use the gasoline sales time series in Table 6.1 to illustrate the computation of a weighted three-week moving average. We will assign a weight of $w_t = \frac{3}{6}$ to the most recent observation, a weight of $w_{t-1} = \frac{2}{6}$ to the second most recent observation, and a weight of $w_{t-2} = \frac{1}{6}$ to the third most recent observation. Using this weighted average, our forecast for week 4 is computed as follows:

$$\text{Forecast for week 4} = \frac{1}{6}(17) + \frac{2}{6}(21) = \frac{3}{6}(19) = 19.33$$

Use Problem 8 to practice using weighted moving averages to produce forecasts.

Note that the sum of the weights is equal to 1 for the weighted moving average method.

Forecast Accuracy To use the weighted moving averages method, we must first select the number of data values to be included in the weighted moving average and then choose weights for each of these data values. In general, if we believe that the recent past is a better predictor of the future than the distant past, larger weights should be given to the more recent observations. However, when the time series is highly variable, selecting approximately equal weights for the data values may be preferable. The only requirements in selecting the weights are that they be nonnegative and that their sum must equal 1. To determine whether one particular combination of number of data values and weights provides a more accurate forecast than another combination, we recommend using MSE as the measure of forecast accuracy. That is, if we assume that the combination that is best for the past will also be best for the future, we would use the combination of number of data values and weights that minimized MSE for the historical time series to forecast the next value in the time series.

Exponential Smoothing

Exponential smoothing also uses a weighted average of past time series values as a forecast; it is a special case of the weighted moving averages method in which we select only one weight—the weight for the most recent observation. The weights for the other data values are computed automatically and become smaller as the observations move farther into the past. The exponential smoothing model follows.

$$\hat{Y}_{t+1} = \alpha Y_t + (1 - \alpha)\hat{Y}_t \quad (6.8)$$

where

$\hat{Y}_{t+1}$ = forecast of the time series for period $t + 1$
Y_t = actual value of the time series in period t
$\hat{Y}_t$ = forecast of the time series for period t
α = smoothing constant ($0 \le \alpha \le 1$)

There are several exponential smoothing procedures. Because it has a single smoothing constant α, the method presented here is often referred to as single exponential smoothing.

Equation (6.8) shows that the forecast for period $t + 1$ is a weighted average of the actual value in period t and the forecast for period t. The weight given to the actual value in period t is the smoothing constant α and the weight given to the forecast in period t is $1 - \alpha$. It turns out that the exponential smoothing forecast for any period is actually a weighted average of *all the previous actual values* of the time series. Let us illustrate by working with a time series involving only three periods of data: Y_1, Y_2, and Y_3.

To initiate the calculations, we let $\hat{Y}_1$ equal the actual value of the time series in period 1; that is, $\hat{Y}_1 = Y_1$. Hence, the forecast for period 2 is

$$\begin{aligned}\hat{Y}_2 &= \alpha Y_1 + (1 - \alpha)\hat{Y}_1 \\ &= \alpha Y_1 + (1 - \alpha)Y_1 \\ &= Y_1\end{aligned}$$

We see that the exponential smoothing forecast for period 2 is equal to the actual value of the time series in period 1.

The forecast for period 3 is

$$\hat{Y}_3 = \alpha Y_2 + (1 - \alpha)\hat{Y}_2 = \alpha Y_2 + (1 - \alpha)Y_1$$

Finally, substituting this expression for $\hat{Y}_3$ into the expression for $\hat{Y}_4$, we obtain

$$\begin{aligned}\hat{Y}_4 &= \alpha Y_3 + (1 - \alpha)\hat{Y}_3 \\ &= \alpha Y_3 + (1 - \alpha)[\alpha Y_2 + (1 - \alpha)Y_1] \\ &= \alpha Y_3 + \alpha(1 - \alpha)Y_2 + (1 - \alpha)^2 Y_1\end{aligned}$$

The term exponential smoothing *comes from the exponential nature of the weighting scheme for the historical values.*

We now see that $\hat{Y}_4$ is a weighted average of the first three time series values. The sum of the coefficients, or weights, for Y_1, Y_2, and Y_3 equals 1. A similar argument can be made to show that, in general, any forecast $\hat{Y}_{t+1}$ is a weighted average of all the t previous time series values.

Despite the fact that exponential smoothing provides a forecast that is a weighted average of all past observations, all past data do not need to be retained to compute the forecast for the next period. In fact, equation (6.8) shows that once the value for the smoothing constant α is selected, only two pieces of information are needed to compute the forecast for period $t + 1$: Y_t, the actual value of the time series in period t; and $\hat{Y}_t$, the forecast for period t.

To illustrate the exponential smoothing approach to forecasting, let us again consider the gasoline sales time series in Table 6.1 and Figure 6.1. As indicated previously, to initialize the calculations we set the exponential smoothing forecast for period 2 equal to the actual value of the time series in period 1. Thus, with $Y_1 = 17$, we set $\hat{Y}_2 = 17$ to initiate the computations. Referring to the time series data in Table 6.1, we find an actual time series value in period 2 of $Y_2 = 21$. Thus, in period 2 we have a forecast error of $e_2 = 21 - 17 = 4$.

Continuing with the exponential smoothing computations using a smoothing constant of $\alpha = 0.2$, we obtain the following forecast for period 3.

$$\hat{Y}_3 = 0.2Y_2 + 0.8\hat{Y}_2 = 0.2(21) + 0.8(17) = 17.8$$

Once the actual time series value in period 3, $Y_3 = 19$, is known, we can generate a forecast for period 4 as follows.

$$\hat{Y}_4 = 0.2Y_3 + 0.8\hat{Y}_3 = 0.2(19) + 0.8(17.8) = 18.04$$

Continuing the exponential smoothing calculations, we obtain the weekly forecast values shown in Table 6.10. Note that we have not shown an exponential smoothing forecast or a forecast error for week 1 because no forecast was made (we used actual sales for week 1 as the forecasted sales for week 2 to initialize the exponential smoothing process). For week 12, we have $Y_{12} = 22$ and $\hat{Y}_{12} = 18.48$. We can we use this information to generate a forecast for week 13.

$$\hat{Y}_{13} = 0.2Y_{12} + 0.8\hat{Y}_{12} = 0.2(22) + 0.8(18.48) = 19.18$$

TABLE 6.10 SUMMARY OF THE EXPONENTIAL SMOOTHING FORECASTS AND FORECAST ERRORS FOR THE GASOLINE SALES TIME SERIES WITH SMOOTHING CONSTANT $\alpha = 0.2$

Week	Time Series Value	Forecast	Forecast Error	Squared Forecast Error
1	17			
2	21	17.00	4.00	16.00
3	19	17.80	1.20	1.44
4	23	18.04	4.96	24.60
5	18	19.03	−1.03	1.06
6	16	18.83	−2.83	8.01
7	20	18.26	1.74	3.03
8	18	18.61	−0.61	0.37
9	22	18.49	3.51	12.32
10	20	19.19	0.81	0.66
11	15	19.35	−4.35	18.92
12	22	18.48	3.52	12.39
		Totals	10.92	98.80

FIGURE 6.8 ACTUAL AND FORECAST GASOLINE TIME SERIES WITH SMOOTHING CONSTANT $\alpha = 0.2$

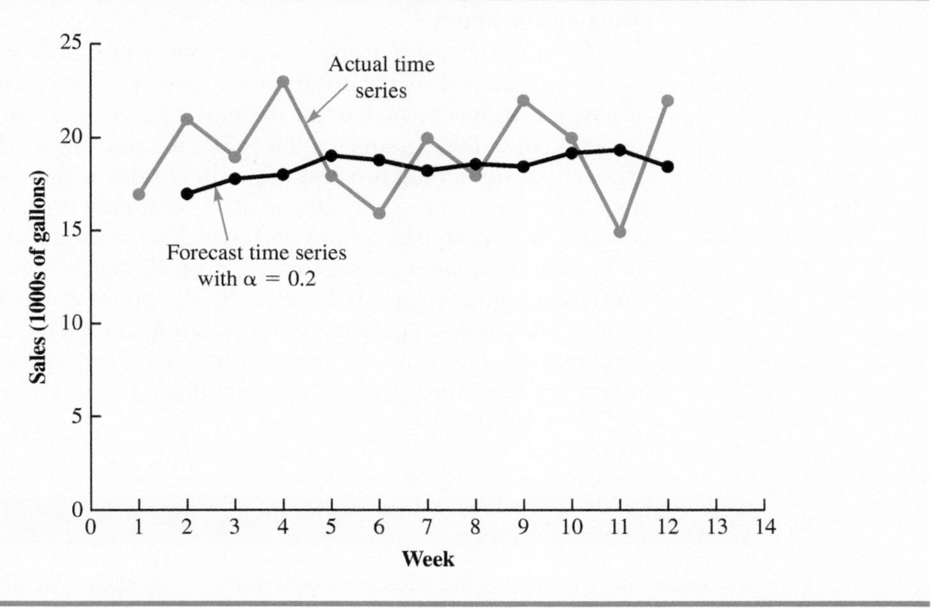

Try Problem 9 for practice using exponential smoothing to produce forecasts.

Thus, the exponential smoothing forecast of the amount sold in week 13 is 19.18, or 19,180 gallons of gasoline. With this forecast, the firm can make plans and decisions accordingly.

Figure 6.8 shows the time series plot of the actual and forecast time series values. Note in particular how the forecasts "smooth out" the irregular or random fluctuations in the time series.

Forecast Accuracy In the preceding exponential smoothing calculations, we used a smoothing constant of $\alpha = 0.2$. Although any value of α between 0 and 1 is acceptable, some values will yield more accurate forecasts than others. Insight into choosing a good value for α can be obtained by rewriting the basic exponential smoothing model as follows.

$$\begin{aligned} \hat{Y}_{t+1} &= \alpha Y_t + (1 - \alpha)\hat{Y}_t \\ \hat{Y}_{t+1} &= \alpha Y_t + \hat{Y}_t - \alpha \hat{Y}_t \\ \hat{Y}_{t+1} &= \hat{Y}_t + \alpha(Y_t - \hat{Y}_t) = \hat{Y}_t + \alpha e_t \end{aligned} \tag{6.9}$$

Thus, the new forecast $\hat{Y}_{t+1}$ is equal to the previous forecast $\hat{Y}_t$ plus an adjustment, which is the smoothing constant α times the most recent forecast error, $e_t = Y_t - \hat{Y}_t$. That is, the forecast in period $t + 1$ is obtained by adjusting the forecast in period t by a fraction of the forecast error from period t. If the time series contains substantial random variability, a small value of the smoothing constant is preferred. The reason for this choice is that if much of the forecast error is due to random variability, we do not want to overreact and adjust the forecasts too quickly. For a time series with relatively little random variability, a forecast error is more likely to represent a real change in the level of the series. Thus, larger values of the smoothing constant provide the advantage of quickly adjusting the forecasts to changes in the time series; this allows the forecasts to react more quickly to changing conditions.

The criterion we will use to determine a desirable value for the smoothing constant α is the same as the criterion we proposed for determining the order or number of periods of data to include in the moving averages calculation. That is, we choose the value of α that minimizes the MSE. A summary of the MSE calculations for the exponential smoothing forecast of gasoline sales with $\alpha = 0.2$ is shown in Table 6.10. Note that there is one less squared error term than the number of time periods; this is because we had no past values with which to make a forecast for period 1. The value of the sum of squared forecast errors is 98.80; hence MSE = 98.80/11 = 8.98. Would a different value of α provide better results in terms of a lower MSE value? Trial and error is often used to determine if a different smoothing constant α can provide more accurate forecasts, but we can avoid trial and error and determine the value of α that minimizes MSE through the use of nonlinear optimization as discussed in Chapter 12 (see Exercise 12.19).

NOTES AND COMMENTS

1. Spreadsheet packages are effective tools for implementing exponential smoothing. With the time series data and the forecasting formulas in a spreadsheet as shown in Table 6.10, you can use the MAE, MSE, and MAPE to evaluate different values of the smoothing constant α.
2. We presented the moving average, weighted moving average, and exponential smoothing methods in the context of a stationary time series. These methods can also be used to forecast a nonstationary time series that shifts in level but exhibits no trend or seasonality. Moving averages with small values of k adapt more quickly than moving averages with larger values of k. Weighted moving averages that place relatively large weights on the most recent values adapt more quickly than weighted moving averages that place relatively equal weights on the k time series values used in calculating the forecast. Exponential smoothing models with smoothing constants closer to 1 adapt more quickly than models with smaller values of the smoothing constant.

Linear Trend Projection

In this section we present forecasting methods that are appropriate for time series exhibiting trend patterns. Here we show how **regression analysis** may be used to forecast a time series with a linear trend. In Section 6.1 we used the bicycle sales time series in Table 6.3 and Figure 6.3 to illustrate a time series with a trend pattern. Let us now use this time series to illustrate how regression analysis can be used to forecast a time series with a linear trend. The data for the bicycle time series are repeated in Table 6.11 and Figure 6.9.

Although the time series plot in Figure 6.9 shows some up and down movement over the past 10 years, we might agree that the linear trend line shown in Figure 6.10 provides a reasonable approximation of the long-run movement in the series. We can use regression analysis to develop such a linear trend line for the bicycle sales time series.

In regression analysis we use known values of variables to estimate the relationship between one variable (called the **dependent variable**) and one or more other related

TABLE 6.11 BICYCLE SALES TIME SERIES

WEB file

Bicycle

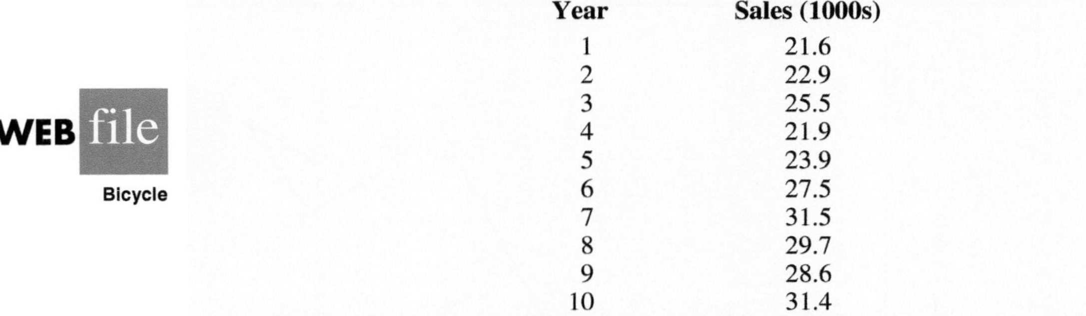

Year	Sales (1000s)
1	21.6
2	22.9
3	25.5
4	21.9
5	23.9
6	27.5
7	31.5
8	29.7
9	28.6
10	31.4

FIGURE 6.9 BICYCLE SALES TIME SERIES PLOT

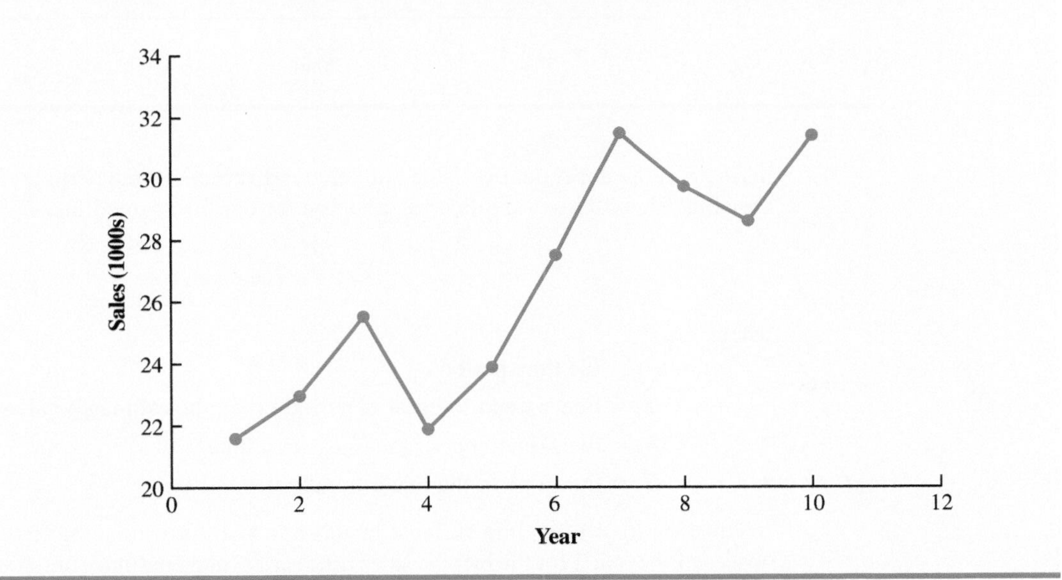

variables (called independent variables). This relationship is usually found in a manner that minimizes the sum of squared errors (and so also minimizes the MSE). With this relationship we can then use values of the independent variables to estimate the associated value of the dependent variable. When we estimate a linear relationship between the dependent variable (which is usually denoted as y) and a single independent variable (which is usually denoted as x), this is referred to as **simple linear regression**. Estimating the relationship between the dependent variable and a single independent variable requires that we find the values of parameters b_0 and b_1 for the straight line $y = b_0 + b_1x$.

Because our use of simple linear regression analysis yields the linear relationship between the independent variable and the dependent variable that minimizes the MSE, we can use this approach to find a best-fitting line to a set of data that exhibits a linear trend. In finding a linear trend, the variable to be forecasted (Y_t, the actual value of the time series in

FIGURE 6.10 TREND REPRESENTED BY A LINEAR FUNCTION FOR THE BICYCLE SALES TIME SERIES

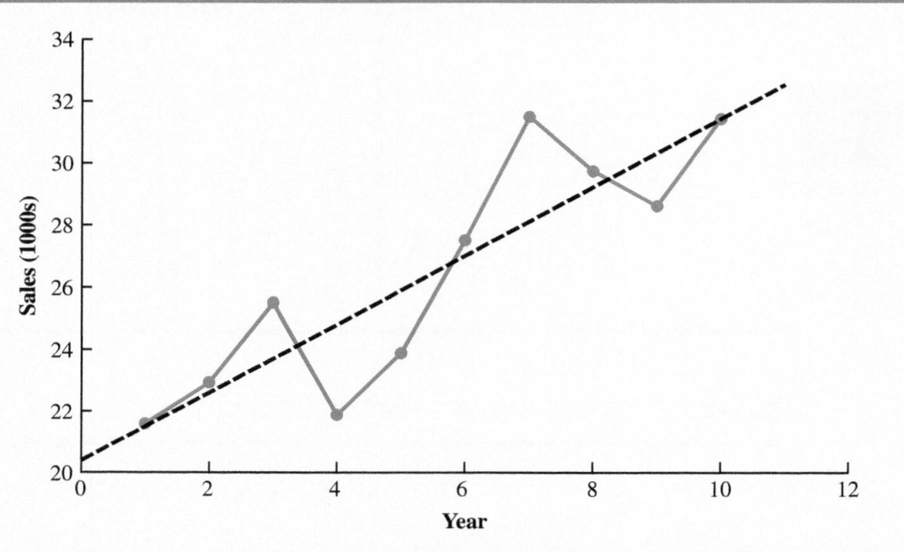

period t) is the dependent variable and the trend variable (time period t) is the independent variable. We will use the following notation for our linear trendline.

$$\hat{Y}_t = b_0 + b_1 t \tag{6.10}$$

where

t = the time period

$\hat{Y}_t$ = linear trend forecast in period t (i.e., the estimated value of Y_t in period t)

b_0 = the Y-intercept of the linear trendline

b_1 = the slope of the linear trendline

In equation (6.10) the time variable begins at $t = 1$ corresponding to the first time series observation (year 1 for the bicycle sales time series) and continues until $t = n$ corresponding to the most recent time series observation (year 10 for the bicycle sales time series). Thus, for the bicycle sales time series $t = 1$ corresponds to the oldest time series value and $t = 10$ corresponds to the most recent year. Calculus may be used to show that the equations given below for b_0 and b_1 yield the line that minimizes the MSE. The equations for computing the values of b_0 and b_1 are

$$b_1 = \frac{\sum_{t=1}^{n} tY_t - \sum_{t=1}^{n} t \sum_{t=1}^{n} Y_t \Big/ n}{\sum_{t=1}^{n} t^2 - \left(\sum_{t=1}^{n} t\right)^2 \Big/ n} \tag{6.11}$$

$$b_0 = \overline{Y} - b_1 \bar{t} \tag{6.12}$$

where

$$t = \text{the time period}$$
$$Y_t = \text{actual value of the time series in period } t$$
$$n = \text{number of periods in the time series}$$
$$\overline{Y} = \text{average value of the time series; that is, } \overline{Y} = \sum_{t=1}^{n} Y_t \Big/ n$$
$$\bar{t} = \text{mean value of } t\text{; that is, } \bar{t} = \sum_{t=1}^{n} t \Big/ n$$

Let us calculate b_0 and b_1 for the bicycle data in Table 6.11; the intermediate summary calculations necessary for computing the values of b_0 and b_1 are

	t	Y_t	tY_t	t^2
	1	21.6	21.6	1
	2	22.9	45.8	4
	3	25.5	76.5	9
	4	21.9	87.6	16
	5	23.9	119.5	25
	6	27.5	165.0	36
	7	31.5	220.5	49
	8	29.7	237.6	64
	9	28.6	257.4	81
	10	31.4	314.0	100
Totals	55	264.5	1545.5	385

And the final calculations of the values of b_0 and b_1 are

$$\bar{t} = \frac{55}{10} = 5.5$$

$$\overline{Y} = \frac{264.5}{10} = 26.45$$

$$b_1 = \frac{1545.5 - (55)(264.5)/10}{385 - 55^2/10} = 1.10$$
$$b_0 = 26.45 - 1.10(5.5) = 20.40$$

Problem 20 provides additional practice in using regression analysis to estimate the linear trend in a time series data set.

Therefore,

$$\hat{Y}_t = 20.4 + 1.1t \tag{6.13}$$

is the regression equation for the linear trend component for the bicycle sales time series.

The slope of 1.1 in this trend equation indicates that over the past 10 years, the firm has experienced an average growth in sales of about 1100 units per year. If we assume that the past 10-year trend in sales is a good indicator for the future, we can use equation (6.13) to project the trend component of the time series. For example, substituting $t = 11$ into equation (6.13) yields next year's trend projection, $\hat{Y}_{11}$:

$$\hat{Y}_{11} = 20.4 + 1.1(11) = 32.5$$

Thus, the linear trend model yields a sales forecast of 32,500 bicycles for the next year.

TABLE 6.12 SUMMARY OF THE LINEAR TREND FORECASTS AND FORECAST ERRORS FOR THE BICYCLE SALES TIME SERIES

Week	Sales (1000s) Y_t	Forecast $\hat{Y}_t$	Forecast Error	Squared Forecast Error
1	21.6	21.5	0.1	0.01
2	22.9	22.6	0.3	0.09
3	25.5	23.7	1.8	3.24
4	21.9	24.8	−2.9	8.41
5	23.9	25.9	−2.0	4.00
6	27.5	27.0	0.5	0.25
7	31.5	28.1	3.4	11.56
8	29.7	29.2	0.5	0.25
9	28.6	30.3	−1.7	2.89
10	31.4	31.4	0.0	0.00
			Total	30.70

Table 6.12 shows the computation of the minimized sum of squared errors for the bicycle sales time series. As previously noted, minimizing sum of squared errors also minimizes the commonly used measure of accuracy, MSE. For the bicycle sales time series,

$$\text{MSE} = \frac{\sum_{t=1}^{n} e_t^2}{n} = \frac{30.7}{10} = 3.07$$

Note that in this example we are not using past values of the time series to produce forecasts, and so $k = 0$; that is, we can produce a forecast for each period of the time series and so do not have to adjust our calculations of the MAE, MSE, or MAPE for k.

We can also use the trendline to forecast sales farther into the future. For instance, using Equation (6.13), we develop annual forecasts for two and three years into the future as follows:

$$\hat{Y}_{12} = 20.4 + 1.1(12) = 33.6$$
$$\hat{Y}_{13} = 20.4 + 1.1(13) = 34.7$$

Note that the forecasted value increases by 1100 bicycles in each year.

NOTES AND COMMENTS

1. Statistical packages such as Minitab and SAS, as well as Excel, have routines to perform regression analysis. Regression analysis minimizes the sum of squared error and under certain assumptions it also allows the analyst to make statistical statements about the parameters and the forecasts.
2. While the use of a linear function to model the trend is common, some time series exhibit a curvilinear (nonlinear) trend. More advanced texts discuss how to develop nonlinear models such as quadratic models and exponential models for these more complex relationships.

In this section we used simple linear regression to estimate the relationship between the dependent variable (Y_t, the actual value of the time series in period t) and a single independent variable (the trend variable t). However, some regression models include several independent variables. When we estimate a linear relationship between the dependent variable and more than one independent variable, this is referred to as multiple linear regression. In the next section we will apply multiple linear regression to time series that include seasonal effects and to time series that include both seasonal effects and a linear trend.

Seasonality

In this section we show how to develop forecasts for a time series that has a seasonal pattern. To the extent that seasonality exists, we need to incorporate it into our forecasting models to ensure accurate forecasts. We begin the section by considering a seasonal time series with no trend and then discuss how to model seasonality with a linear trend.

Seasonality Without Trend

Let us consider again the data from Table 6.5, the number of umbrellas sold at a clothing store over the past five years. We repeat the data here in Table 6.13, and Figure 6.11 again shows the corresponding time series plot. The time series plot does not indicate any long-term trend in sales. In fact, unless you look carefully at the data, you might conclude that the data follow a horizontal pattern with random fluctuation and that single exponential smoothing could be used to forecast sales. However, closer inspection of the time series plot reveals a pattern in the fluctuations. That is, the first and third quarters have moderate sales, the second quarter the highest sales, and the fourth quarter tends to be the lowest quarter in terms of sales volume. Thus, we conclude that a quarterly seasonal pattern is present.

We can model a time series with a seasonal pattern by treating the season as a categorical variable. **Categorical variables** are data used to categorize observations of data. When

TABLE 6.13 UMBRELLA SALES TIME SERIES

Umbrella

Year	Quarter	Sales
1	1	125
	2	153
	3	106
	4	88
2	1	118
	2	161
	3	133
	4	102
3	1	138
	2	144
	3	113
	4	80
4	1	109
	2	137
	3	125
	4	109
5	1	130
	2	165
	3	128
	4	96

FIGURE 6.11 UMBRELLA SALES TIME SERIES PLOT

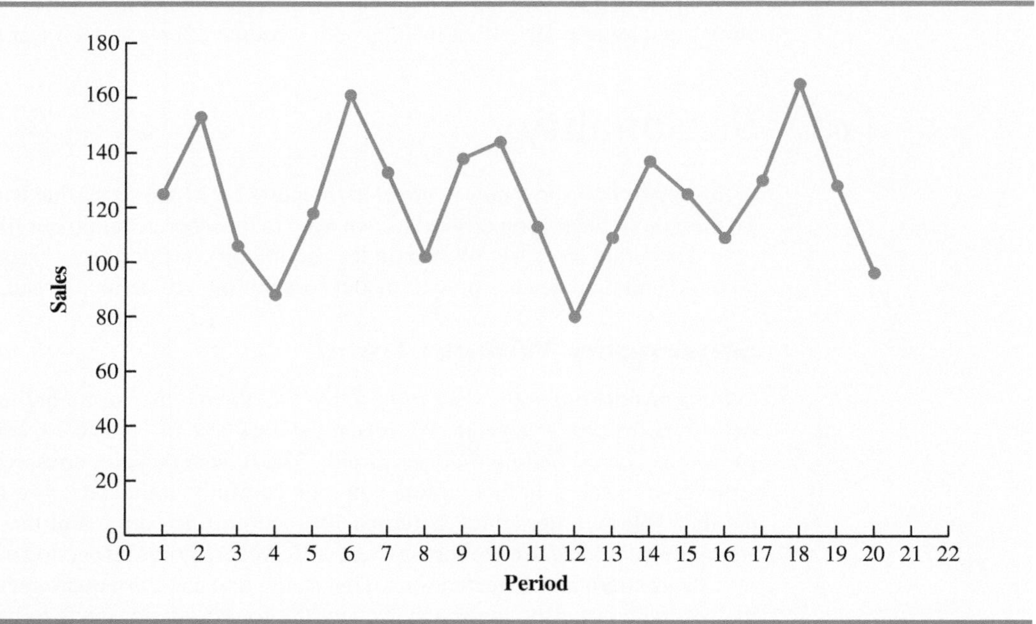

a categorical variable has k levels, $k - 1$ dummy variables (sometimes called 0-1 variables) are required. So if there are four seasons, we need three dummy variables. For instance, in the umbrella sales time series, the quarter to which each observation corresponds is treated as a season; it is a categorical variable with four levels: Quarter 1, Quarter 2, Quarter 3, and Quarter 4. Thus, to model the seasonal effects in the umbrella time series we need $4 - 1 = 3$ dummy variables. The three dummy variables can be coded as follows:

$$\text{Qtr1}_t = \begin{cases} 1 & \text{if period } t \text{ is a Quarter 1} \\ 0 & \text{otherwise} \end{cases}$$

$$\text{Qtr2}_t = \begin{cases} 1 & \text{if period } t \text{ is a Quarter 2} \\ 0 & \text{otherwise} \end{cases}$$

$$\text{Qtr3}_t = \begin{cases} 1 & \text{if period } t \text{ is a Quarter 3} \\ 0 & \text{otherwise} \end{cases}$$

Using F_t to denote the forecasted value of sales for period t, the general form of the equation relating the number of umbrellas sold to the quarter the sales take place follows.

$$\hat{Y}_t = b_0 + b_1 \text{Qtr1}_t + b_2 \text{Qtr2}_t + b_3 \text{Qtr3}_t \qquad \textbf{(6.14)}$$

Note that we have numbered the observations in Table 6.14 as periods 1 to 20. For example, year 3, quarter 3 is observation 11.

Note that the fourth quarter will be denoted by a setting of all three dummy variables to 0. Table 6.14 shows the umbrella sales time series with the coded values of the dummy variables shown. We can use a multiple linear regression model to find the values of b_0, b_1, b_2, and b_3 that minimize the sum of squared errors. For this regression model Y_t is the dependent variable and the quarterly dummy variables Qtr1_t, Qtr2_t, and Qtr3_t are the independent variables.

TABLE 6.14 UMBRELLA SALES TIME SERIES WITH DUMMY VARIABLES

Period	Year	Quarter	Qtr1	Qtr2	Qtr3	Sales
1	1	1	1	0	0	125
2		2	0	1	0	153
3		3	0	0	1	106
4		4	0	0	0	88
5	2	1	1	0	0	118
6		2	0	1	0	161
7		3	0	0	1	133
8		4	0	0	0	102
9	3	1	1	0	0	138
10		2	0	1	0	144
11		3	0	0	1	113
12		4	0	0	0	80
13	4	1	1	0	0	109
14		2	0	1	0	137
15		3	0	0	1	125
16		4	0	0	0	109
17	5	1	1	0	0	130
18		2	0	1	0	165
19		3	0	0	1	128
20		4	0	0	0	96

Using the data in Table 6.14 and regression analysis, we obtain the following equation:

$$\hat{Y}_t = 95.0 + 29.0\text{ Qtr1}_t + 57.0\text{ Qtr2}_t + 26.0\text{ Qtr3}_t \tag{6.15}$$

we can use Equation (6.15) to forecast quarterly sales for next year.

For practice using categorical variables to estimate seasonal effects, try Problem 24.

Quarter 1: Sales $= 95.0 + 29.0(1) + 57.0(0) + 26.0(0) = 124$

Quarter 2: Sales $= 95.0 + 29.0(0) + 57.0(1) + 26.0(0) = 152$

Quarter 3: Sales $= 95.0 + 29.0(0) + 57.0(0) + 26.0(1) = 121$

Quarter 4: Sales $= 95.0 + 29.0(0) + 57.0(0) + 26.0(0) = 95$

It is interesting to note that we could have obtained the quarterly forecasts for next year by simply computing the average number of umbrellas sold in each quarter, as shown in the following table.

Year	Quarter 1	Quarter 2	Quarter 3	Quarter 4
1	125	153	106	88
2	118	161	133	102
3	138	144	113	80
4	109	137	125	109
5	130	165	128	96
Average	124	152	121	95

Nonetheless, for more complex problem situations, such as dealing with a time series that has both trend and seasonal effects, this simple averaging approach will not work.

Seasonality with Trend

We now consider situations for which the time series contains both a seasonal effect and a linear trend by showing how to forecast the quarterly television set sales time series introduced in Section 6.1. The data for the television set time series are shown in Table 6.15. The time series plot in Figure 6.12 indicates that sales are lowest in the second quarter of each year and increase in quarters 3 and 4. Thus, we conclude that a seasonal pattern exists for television set sales. However, the time series also has an upward linear trend that will need to be accounted for in order to develop accurate forecasts of quarterly sales. This is easily done by combining the dummy variable approach for handling seasonality with the approach we discussed in Section 6.4 for handling a linear trend.

The general form of the regression equation for modeling both the quarterly seasonal effects and the linear trend in the television set time series is:

$$\hat{Y}_t = b_0 + b_1\text{Qtr1}_t + b_2\text{Qtr2}_t + b_3\text{Qtr3}_t + b_4 t \qquad (6.16)$$

where

$\hat{Y}_t$ = forecast of sales in period t
Qtr1_t = 1 if time period t corresponds to the first quarter of the year; 0, otherwise
Qtr2_t = 1 if time period t corresponds to the second quarter of the year; 0, otherwise
Qtr3_t = 1 if time period t corresponds to the third quarter of the year; 0, otherwise
t = time period

TABLE 6.15 TELEVISION SET SALES TIME SERIES

TVSales

Year	Quarter	Sales (1000s)
1	1	4.8
	2	4.1
	3	6.0
	4	6.5
2	1	5.8
	2	5.2
	3	6.8
	4	7.4
3	1	6.0
	2	5.6
	3	7.5
	4	7.8
4	1	6.3
	2	5.9
	3	8.0
	4	8.4

FIGURE 6.12 TELEVISION SET SALES TIME SERIES PLOT

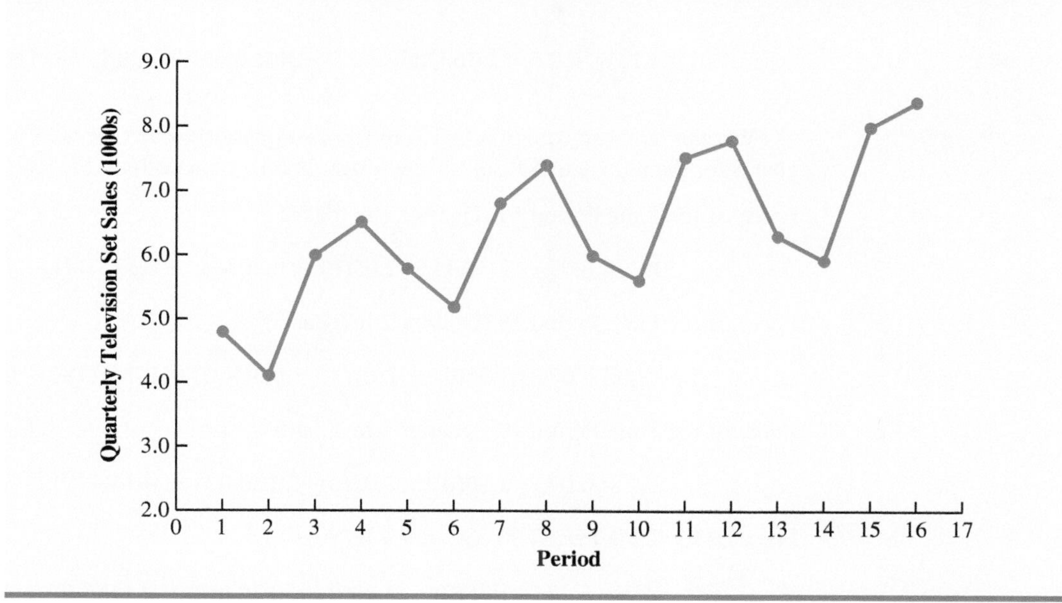

For this regression model Y_t is the dependent variable and the quarterly dummy variables Qtr1_t, Qtr2_t, and Qtr3_t and the time period t are the independent variables.

Table 6.16 shows the revised television set sales time series that includes the coded values of the dummy variables and the time period t. Using the data in Table 6.16 with the

TABLE 6.16 TELEVISION SET SALES TIME SERIES WITH DUMMY VARIABLES AND TIME PERIOD

Period	Year	Quarter	Qtr1	Qtr2	Qtr3	Sales (1000s)
1	1	1	1	0	0	4.8
2		2	0	1	0	4.1
3		3	0	0	1	6.0
4		4	0	0	0	6.5
5	2	1	1	0	0	5.8
6		2	0	1	0	5.2
7		3	0	0	1	6.8
8		4	0	0	0	7.4
9	3	1	1	0	0	6.0
10		2	0	1	0	5.6
11		3	0	0	1	7.5
12		4	0	0	0	7.8
13	4	1	1	0	0	6.3
14		2	0	1	0	5.9
15		3	0	0	1	8.0
16		4	0	0	0	8.4

regression model that includes both the seasonal and trend components, we obtain the following equation that minimizes our sum of squared errors:

$$\hat{Y}_t = 6.07 - 1.36 \text{ Qtr1}_t - 2.03 \text{ Qtr2}_t - 0.304 \text{ Qtr3}_t + 0.146t \quad \textbf{(6.17)}$$

We can now use equation (6.17) to forecast quarterly sales for next year. Next year is year 5 for the television set sales time series; that is, time periods 17, 18, 19, and 20.

Forecast for Time Period 17 (Quarter 1 in Year 5)

$$\hat{Y}_{17} = 6.07 - 1.36(1) - 2.03(0) - 0.304(0) + 0.146(17) = 7.19$$

Forecast for Time Period 18 (Quarter 2 in Year 5)

$$\hat{Y}_{18} = 6.07 - 1.36(0) - 2.03(1) - 0.304(0) + 0.146(18) = 6.67$$

Forecast for Time Period 19 (Quarter 3 in Year 5)

$$\hat{Y}_{19} = 6.07 - 1.36(0) - 2.03(0) - 0.304(1) + 0.146(19) = 8.54$$

Forecast for Time Period 20 (Quarter 4 in Year 5)

$$\hat{Y}_{20} = 6.07 - 1.36(0) - 2.03(0) - 0.304(0) + 0.146(20) = 8.99$$

Thus, accounting for the seasonal effects and the linear trend in television set sales, the estimates of quarterly sales in year 5 are 7190, 6670, 8540, and 8990.

The dummy variables in the equation actually provide four equations, one for each quarter. For instance, if time period t corresponds to quarter 1, the estimate of quarterly sales is

$$\text{Quarter 1: Sales} = 6.07 - 1.36(1) - 2.03(0) - 0.304(0) + 0.146t = 4.71 + 0.146t$$

Similarly, if time period t corresponds to quarters 2, 3, and 4, the estimates of quarterly sales are:

$$\text{Quarter 2: Sales} = 6.07 - 1.36(0) - 2.03(1) - 0.304(0) + 0.146t = 4.04 + 0.146t$$
$$\text{Quarter 3: Sales} = 6.07 - 1.36(0) - 2.03(0) - 0.304(1) + 0.146t = 5.77 + 0.146t$$
$$\text{Quarter 4: Sales} = 6.07 - 1.36(0) - 2.03(0) - 0.304(0) + 0.146t = 6.07 + 0.146t$$

Problem 28 provides another example of using regression analysis to forecast time series data with both trend and seasonal effects.

The slope of the trend line for each quarterly forecast equation is 0.146, indicating a consistent growth in sales of about 146 sets per quarter. The only difference in the four equations is that they have different intercepts.

Models Based on Monthly Data

In the preceding television set sales example, we showed how dummy variables can be used to account for the quarterly seasonal effects in the time series. Because there were four levels for the categorical variable season, three dummy variables were required. However,

Whenever a categorical variable such as season has k levels, k − 1 dummy variables are required.

many businesses use monthly rather than quarterly forecasts. For monthly data, season is a categorical variable with 12 levels, and thus 12 − 1 = 11 dummy variables are required. For example, the 11 dummy variables could be coded as follows:

$$\text{Month1} = \begin{cases} 1 & \text{if January} \\ 0 & \text{otherwise} \end{cases}$$

$$\text{Month2} = \begin{cases} 1 & \text{if February} \\ 0 & \text{otherwise} \end{cases}$$

$$\vdots$$

$$\text{Month1} = \begin{cases} 1 & \text{if November} \\ 0 & \text{otherwise} \end{cases}$$

Other than this change, the approach for handling seasonality remains the same.

Summary

This chapter provided an introduction to basic methods of time series analysis and forecasting. We first showed that the underlying pattern in the time series can often be identified by constructing a time series plot. Several types of data patterns can be distinguished, including a horizontal pattern, a trend pattern, and a seasonal pattern. The forecasting methods we have discussed are based on which of these patterns are present in the time series.

We also discussed that the accuracy of the method is an important factor in determining which forecasting method to use. We considered three measures of forecast accuracy: mean absolute error (MAE), mean squared error (MSE), and mean absolute percentage error (MAPE). Each of these measures is designed to determine how well a particular forecasting method is able to reproduce the time series data that are already available. By selecting the method that is most accurate for the data already known, we hope to increase the likelihood that we will obtain more accurate forecasts for future time periods.

For a time series with a horizontal pattern, we showed how moving averages, weighted moving averages, and exponential smoothing can be used to develop a forecast. The moving averages method consists of computing an average of past data values and then using that average as the forecast for the next period. In the weighted moving average and exponential smoothing methods, weighted averages of past time series values are used to compute forecasts. These methods also adapt well to a horizontal pattern that shifts to a different level and then resumes a horizontal pattern.

For time series that have only a long-term linear trend, we showed how regression analysis can be used to make trend projections. For a time series with a seasonal pattern, we showed how dummy variables and regression analysis can be used to develop an equation with seasonal effects. We then extended the approach to include situations where the time series contains both a seasonal and a linear trend effect by showing how to combine the dummy variable approach for handling seasonality with the approach for handling a linear trend.

Glossary

Categorical (dummy) variable A variable used to categorize observations of data. Used when modeling a time series with a seasonal pattern.
Cyclical pattern A cyclical pattern exists if the time series plot shows an alternating sequence of points below and above the trend line lasting more than one year.
Dependent variable The variable that is being predicted or explained in a regression analysis.
Exponential smoothing A forecasting method that uses a weighted average of past time series values as the forecast; it is a special case of the weighted moving averages method in which we select only one weight—the weight for the most recent observation.
Forecast error The difference between the actual time series value and the forecast.
Independent variable A variable used to predict or explain values of the dependent variable in regression analysis.
Mean absolute error (MAE) The average of the absolute values of the forecast errors.
Mean absolute percentage error (MAPE) The average of the absolute values of the percentage forecast errors.
Mean squared error (MSE) The average of the sum of squared forecast errors.
Moving averages A forecasting method that uses the average of the k most recent data values in the time series as the forecast for the next period.
Regression analysis A procedure for estimating values of a dependent variable given the values of one or more independent variables in a manner that minimizes the sum of the squared errors.
Seasonal pattern A seasonal pattern exists if the time series plot exhibits a repeating pattern over successive periods.
Smoothing constant A parameter of the exponential smoothing model that provides the weight given to the most recent time series value in the calculation of the forecast value.
Stationary time series A time series whose statistical properties are independent of time. For a stationary time series, the process generating the data has a constant mean and the variability of the time series is constant over time.
Time series A sequence of observations on a variable measured at successive points in time or over successive periods of time.
Time series plot A graphical presentation of the relationship between time and the time series variable. Time is shown on the horizontal axis and the time series values are shown on the verical axis.
Trend pattern A trend pattern exists if the time series plot shows gradual shifts or movements to relatively higher or lower values over a longer period of time.
Weighted moving averages A forecasting method that involves selecting a different weight for the k most recent data values values in the time series and then computing a weighted average of the of the values. The sum of the weights must equal one.

Problems

1. Consider the following time series data.

Week	1	2	3	4	5	6
Value	18	13	16	11	17	14

Using the naïve method (most recent value) as the forecast for the next week, compute the following measures of forecast accuracy.

a. Mean absolute error
b. Mean squared error
c. Mean absolute percentage error
d. What is the forecast for week 7?

2. Refer to the time series data in Exercise 1. Using the average of all the historical data as a forecast for the next period, compute the following measures of forecast accuracy:
   a. Mean absolute error
   b. Mean squared error
   c. Mean absolute percentage error
   d. What is the forecast for week 7?

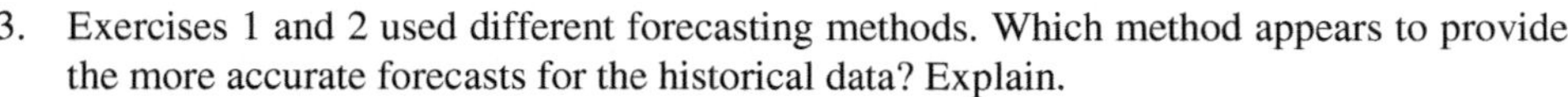

3. Exercises 1 and 2 used different forecasting methods. Which method appears to provide the more accurate forecasts for the historical data? Explain.

4. Consider the following time series data.

Month	1	2	3	4	5	6	7
Value	24	13	20	12	19	23	15

   a. Compute MSE using the most recent value as the forecast for the next period. What is the forecast for month 8?
   b. Compute MSE using the average of all the data available as the forecast for the next period. What is the forecast for month 8?
   c. Which method appears to provide the better forecast?

5. Consider the following time series data.

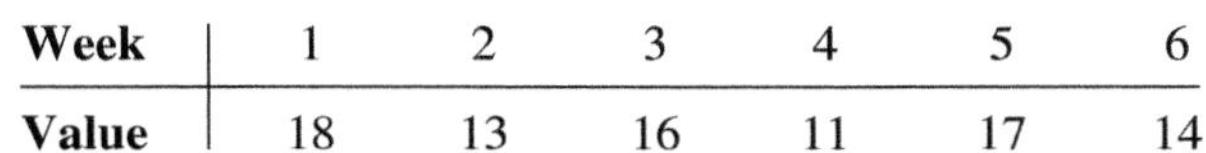

Week	1	2	3	4	5	6
Value	18	13	16	11	17	14

   a. Construct a time series plot. What type of pattern exists in the data?
   b. Develop a three-week moving average for this time series. Compute MSE and a forecast for week 7.
   c. Use $\alpha = 0.2$ to compute the exponential smoothing values for the time series. Compute MSE and a forecast for week 7.
   d. Compare the three-week moving average forecast with the exponential smoothing forecast using $\alpha = 0.2$. Which appears to provide the better forecast based on MSE? Explain.
   e. Use trial and error to find a value of the exponential smoothing coefficient α that results in a smaller MSE than what you calculated for $\alpha = 0.2$.

6. Consider the following time series data.

Month	1	2	3	4	5	6	7
Value	24	13	20	12	19	23	15

   a. Construct a time series plot. What type of pattern exists in the data?
   b. Develop a three-week moving average for this time series. Compute MSE and a forecast for week 8.
   c. Use $\alpha = 0.2$ to compute the exponential smoothing values for the time series. Compute MSE and a forecast for week 8.
   d. Compare the three-week moving average forecast with the exponential smoothing forecast using $\alpha = 0.2$. Which appears to provide the better forecast based on MSE?
   e. Use trial and error to find a value of the exponential smoothing coefficient α that results in a smaller MSE than what you calculated for $\alpha = 0.2$.

7. Refer to the gasoline sales time series data in Table 6.1.
   a. Compute four-week and five-week moving averages for the time series.
   b. Compute the MSE for the four-week and five-week moving average forecasts.
   c. What appears to be the best number of weeks of past data (three, four, or five) to use in the moving average computation? Recall that MSE for the three-week moving average is 10.22.

8. Refer again to the gasoline sales time series data in Table 6.1.
   a. Using a weight of 1/2 for the most recent observation, 1/3 for the second most recent, and 1/6 for third most recent, compute a three-week weighted moving average for the time series.
   b. Compute the MSE for the weighted moving average in part (a). Do you prefer this weighted moving average to the unweighted moving average? Remember that the MSE for the unweighted moving average is 10.22.
   c. Suppose you are allowed to choose any weights as long as they sum to 1. Could you always find a set of weights that would make the MSE smaller for a weighted moving average than for an unweighted moving average? Why or why not?

9. With the gasoline time series data from Table 6.1, show the exponential smoothing forecasts using $\alpha = 0.1$.
   a. Applying the MSE measure of forecast accuracy, would you prefer a smoothing constant of $\alpha = 0.1$ or $\alpha = 0.2$ for the gasoline sales time series?
   b. Are the results the same if you apply MAE as the measure of accuracy?
   c. What are the results if MAPE is used?

10. With a smoothing constant of $\alpha = 0.2$, equation (6.8) shows that the forecast for week 13 of the gasoline sales data from Table 6.1 is given by $\hat{Y}_{13} = 0.2Y_{12} + 0.8\hat{Y}_{12}$. However, the forecast for week 12 is given by $\hat{Y}_{12} = 0.2Y_{11} + 0.8\hat{Y}_{11}$. Thus, we could combine these two results to show that the forecast for week 13 can be written

$$\hat{Y}_{13} = 0.2Y_{12} + 0.8(0.2Y_{11} + 0.8\hat{Y}_{11}) = 0.2Y_{12} + 0.16Y_{11} + 0.64\hat{Y}_{11}$$

   a. Making use of the fact that $\hat{Y}_{11} = 0.2Y_{10} + 0.8\hat{Y}_{10}$ (and similarly for $\hat{Y}_{10}$ and $\hat{Y}_9$), continue to expand the expression for $\hat{Y}_{13}$ until it is written in terms of the past data values Y_{12}, Y_{11}, Y_{10}, Y_9, Y_8, and the forecast for period 8.
   b. Refer to the coefficients or weights for the past values Y_{12}, Y_{11}, Y_{10}, Y_9, and Y_8. What observation can you make about how exponential smoothing weights past data values in arriving at new forecasts? Compare this weighting pattern with the weighting pattern of the moving averages method.

11. For the Hawkins Company, the monthly percentages of all shipments received on time over the past 12 months are 80, 82, 84, 83, 83, 84, 85, 84, 82, 83, 84, and 83.
   a. Construct a time series plot. What type of pattern exists in the data?
   b. Compare a three-month moving average forecast with an exponential smoothing forecast for $\alpha = 0.2$. Which provides the better forecasts using MSE as the measure of model accuracy?
   c. What is the forecast for next month?

12. Corporate triple A bond interest rates for 12 consecutive months follow.

9.5 9.3 9.4 9.6 9.8 9.7 9.8 10.5 9.9 9.7 9.6 9.6

   a. Construct a time series plot. What type of pattern exists in the data?
   b. Develop three-month and four-month moving averages for this time series. Does the three-month or four-month moving average provide the better forecasts based on MSE? Explain.
   c. What is the moving average forecast for the next month?

13. The values of Alabama building contracts (in millions of dollars) for a 12-month period follow.

240 350 230 260 280 320 220 310 240 310 240 230

a. Construct a time series plot. What type of pattern exists in the data?
b. Compare a three-month moving average forecast with an exponential smoothing forecast. Use $\alpha = 0.2$. Which provides the better forecasts based on MSE?
c. What is the forecast for the next month?

14. The following time series shows the sales of a particular product over the past 12 months.

Month	Sales	Month	Sales
1	105	7	145
2	135	8	140
3	120	9	100
4	105	10	80
5	90	11	100
6	120	12	110

a. Construct a time series plot. What type of pattern exists in the data?
b. Use $\alpha = 0.3$ to compute the exponential smoothing values for the time series.
c. Use trial and error to find a value of the exponential smoothing coefficient α that results in a relatively small MSE.

CFI

15. Ten weeks of data on the Commodity Futures Index are 7.35, 7.40, 7.55, 7.56, 7.60, 7.52, 7.52, 7.70, 7.62, and 7.55.
a. Construct a time series plot. What type of pattern exists in the data?
b. Use trial and error to find a value of the exponential smoothing coefficient α that results in a relatively small MSE.

SuperBowlRatings

16. Since its inception in 1967, the Super Bowl has been one of the most watched events on U.S. television every year. The number of U.S. households that tuned in for each Super Bowl, reported by Nielsen.com, is provided in the data set SuperBowlRatings.
a. Construct a time series plot for the data. What type of pattern exists in the data? Discuss some of the patterns that may have resulted in the pattern exhibited in the time series plot of the data.
b. Given the pattern of the time series plot developed in part (a), do you think the forecasting methods discussed in this chapter are appropriate to develop forecasts for this time series? Explain.
c. Use simple linear regression analysis to find the parameters for the line that minimizes MSE for this time series.

17. Consider the following time series.

t	1	2	3	4	5
Y_t	6	11	9	14	15

a. Construct a time series plot. What type of pattern exists in the data?
b. Use simple linear regression analysis to find the parameters for the line that minimizes MSE for this time series.
c. What is the forecast for $t = 6$?

Portfolio

18. The following table reports the percentage of stocks in a portfolio for the nine previous quarters.

Year	Quarter	Stock%
1	1	29.8
1	2	31.0
1	3	29.9
1	4	30.1
2	1	32.2
2	2	31.5
2	3	32.0
2	4	31.9
3	1	30.0

a. Construct a time series plot. What type of pattern exists in the data?
b. Use trial and error to find a value of the exponential smoothing coefficient α that results in a relatively small MSE.
c. Using the exponential smoothing model you developed in part (b), what is the forecast of the percentage of stocks in a typical portfolio for the second quarter of year 3?

19. Consider the following time series.

t	1	2	3	4	5	6	7
Y_t	120	110	100	96	94	92	88

a. Construct a time series plot. What type of pattern exists in the data?
b. Use simple linear regression analysis to find the parameters for the line that minimizes MSE for this time series.
c. What is the forecast for $t = 8$?

20. Because of high tuition costs at state and private universities, enrollments at community colleges have increased dramatically in recent years. The following data show the enrollment (in thousands) for Jefferson Community College for the nine most recent years.

JeffersonEnrollment

Year	Enrollment (1000s)
1	6.5
2	8.1
3	8.4
4	10.2
5	12.5
6	13.3
7	13.7
8	17.2
9	18.1

a. Construct a time series plot. What type of pattern exists in the data?
b. Use simple linear regression analysis to find the parameters for the line that minimizes MSE for this time series.
c. What is the forecast for next year?

AdultSmokers

21. The Centers for Disease Control and Prevention Office on Smoking and Health (OSH) is the lead federal agency responsible for comprehensive tobacco prevention and control. OSH was established in 1965 to reduce the death and disease caused by tobacco use and exposure to secondhand smoke. One of the many responsibilities of the OSH is to collect

data on tobacco use. The following data show the percentage of U.S. adults who were users of tobacco for a recent 11-year period (http://www.cdc.gov/tobacco/data_statistics/tables/trends/cig_smoking/index.htm).

Year	Percentage of Adults Who Smoke
1	22.8
2	22.5
3	21.6
4	20.9
5	20.9
6	20.8
7	19.8
8	20.6
9	20.6
10	19.3
11	18.9

a. Construct a time series plot. What type of pattern exists in the data?
b. Use simple linear regression to find the parameters for the line that minimizes MSE for this time series.
c. One of OSH's goals is to cut the percentage of U.S. adults who were users of tobacco to 12% or less within nine years of the last year of these data. Does your regression model from part (b) suggest that OSH is on target to meet this goal? If not, use your model from part (b) to estimate the number of years that must pass after these data have been collected before OSH will achieve this goal.

22. The president of a small manufacturing firm is concerned about the continual increase in manufacturing costs over the past several years. The following figures provide a time series of the cost per unit for the firm's leading product over the past eight years.

Year	Cost/Unit ($)	Year	Cost/Unit ($)
1	20.00	5	26.60
2	24.50	6	30.00
3	28.20	7	31.00
4	27.50	8	36.00

a. Construct a time series plot. What type of pattern exists in the data?
b. Use simple linear regression analysis to find the parameters for the line that minimizes MSE for this time series.
c. What is the average cost increase that the firm has been realizing per year?
d. Compute an estimate of the cost/unit for next year.

Exercise

23. The medical community unanimously agrees on the health benefits of regular exercise, but are adults listening? During each of the past 15 years, a polling organization has surveyed Americans about their exercise habits. In the most recent of these polls, slightly over half of all American adults reported that they exercise for 30 or more minutes at least three times per week. The following data show the percentages of adults who reported that they exercise for 30 or more minutes at least three times per week during each of the 15 years of this study.

Year	Percentage of Adults Who Reported That They Exercise for 30 or More Minutes at Least Three Times per Week
1	41.0
2	44.9
3	47.1
4	45.7
5	46.6
6	44.5
7	47.6
8	49.8
9	48.1
10	48.9
11	49.9
12	52.1
13	50.6
14	54.6
15	52.4

a. Construct a time series plot. Does a linear trend appear to be present?
b. Use simple linear regression to find the parameters for the line that minimizes MSE for this time series.
c. Use the trend equation from part (b) to forecast the percentage of adults next year (year 16 of the study) who will report that they exercise for 30 or more minutes at least three times per week.
d. Would you feel comfortable using the trend equation from part (b) to forecast the percentage of adults three years from now (year 18 of the study) who will report that they exercise for 30 or more minutes at least three times per week?

24. Consider the following time series.

Quarter	Year 1	Year 2	Year 3
1	71	68	62
2	49	41	51
3	58	60	53
4	78	81	72

a. Construct a time series plot. What type of pattern exists in the data?
b. Use a multiple linear regression model with dummy variables as follows to develop an equation to account for seasonal effects in the data. Qtr1 = 1 if Quarter 1, 0 otherwise; Qtr2 = 1 if Quarter 2, 0 otherwise; Qtr3 = 1 if Quarter 3, 0 otherwise.
c. Compute the quarterly forecasts for next year.

25. Consider the following time series data.

Quarter	Year 1	Year 2	Year 3
1	4	6	7
2	2	3	6
3	3	5	6
4	5	7	8

a. Construct a time series plot. What type of pattern exists in the data?
b. Use a multiple regression model with dummy variables as follows to develop an equation to account for seasonal effects in the data. Qtr1 = 1 if Quarter 1, 0 otherwise; Qtr2 = 1 if Quarter 2, 0 otherwise; Qtr3 = 1 if Quarter 3, 0 otherwise.
c. Compute the quarterly forecasts for next year.

TextbookSales

26. The quarterly sales data (number of copies sold) for a college textbook over the past three years follow.

Quarter	Year 1	Year 2	Year 3
1	1690	1800	1850
2	940	900	1100
3	2625	2900	2930
4	2500	2360	2615

a. Construct a time series plot. What type of pattern exists in the data?
b. Use a regression model with dummy variables as follows to develop an equation to account for seasonal effects in the data. Qtr1 = 1 if Quarter 1, 0 otherwise; Qtr2 = 1 if Quarter 2, 0 otherwise; Qtr3 = 1 if Quarter 3, 0 otherwise.
c. Compute the quarterly forecasts for next year.
d. Let $t = 1$ to refer to the observation in quarter 1 of year 1; $t = 2$ to refer to the observation in quarter 2 of year 1; . . . ; and $t = 12$ to refer to the observation in quarter 4 of year 3. Using the dummy variables defined in part (b) and also using t, develop an equation to account for seasonal effects and any linear trend in the time series. Based upon the seasonal effects in the data and linear trend, compute the quarterly forecasts for next year.

Pollution

27. Air pollution control specialists in southern California monitor the amount of ozone, carbon dioxide, and nitrogen dioxide in the air on an hourly basis. The hourly time series data exhibit seasonality, with the levels of pollutants showing patterns that vary over the hours in the day. On July 15, 16, and 17, the following levels of nitrogen dioxide were observed for the 12 hours from 6:00 A.M. to 6:00 P.M.

July 15:	25	28	35	50	60	60	40	35	30	25	25	20
July 16:	28	30	35	48	60	65	50	40	35	25	20	20
July 17:	35	42	45	70	72	75	60	45	40	25	25	25

a. Construct a time series plot. What type of pattern exists in the data?
b. Use a multiple linear regression model with dummy variables as follows to develop an equation to account for seasonal effects in the data:

Hour1 = 1 if the reading was made between 6:00 A.M. and 7:00 A.M.; 0 otherwise

Hour2 = 1 if the reading was made between 7:00 A.M. and 8:00 A.M.; 0 otherwise

⋮

Hour11 = 1 if the reading was made between 4:00 P.M. and 5:00 P.M.; 0 otherwise

Note that when the values of the 11 dummy variables are equal to 0, the observation corresponds to the 5:00 P.M. to 6:00 P.M. hour.

c. Using the equation developed in part (b), compute estimates of the levels of nitrogen dioxide for July 18.
d. Let $t = 1$ to refer to the observation in hour 1 on July 15; $t = 2$ to refer to the observation in hour 2 of July 15; . . . ; and $t = 36$ to refer to the observation in hour 12 of July 17. Using the dummy variables defined in part (b) and t, develop an equation to

account for seasonal effects and any linear trend in the time series. Based upon the seasonal effects in the data and linear trend, compute estimates of the levels of nitrogen dioxide for July 18.

SouthShore

28. South Shore Construction builds permanent docks and seawalls along the southern shore of Long Island, New York. Although the firm has been in business only five years, revenue has increased from $308,000 in the first year of operation to $1,084,000 in the most recent year. The following data show the quarterly sales revenue in thousands of dollars.

Quarter	Year 1	Year 2	Year 3	Year 4	Year 5
1	20	37	75	92	176
2	100	136	155	202	282
3	175	245	326	384	445
4	13	26	48	82	181

a. Construct a time series plot. What type of pattern exists in the data?
b. Use a multiple regression model with dummy variables as follows to develop an equation to account for seasonal effects in the data. Qtr1 = 1 if Quarter 1, 0 otherwise; Qtr2 = 1 if Quarter 2, 0 otherwise; Qtr3 = 1 if Quarter 3, 0 otherwise.
c. Let Period = 1 to refer to the observation in quarter 1 of year 1; Period = 2 to refer to the observation in quarter 2 of year 1; . . . and Period = 20 to refer to the observation in quarter 4 of year 5. Using the dummy variables defined in part (b) and Period, develop an equation to account for seasonal effects and any linear trend in the time series. Based upon the seasonal effects in the data and linear trend, compute estimates of quarterly sales for year 6.

Case Problem 1 Forecasting Food and Beverage Sales

The Vintage Restaurant, on Captiva Island near Fort Myers, Florida, is owned and operated by Karen Payne. The restaurant just completed its third year of operation. During that time, Karen sought to establish a reputation for the restaurant as a high-quality dining establishment that specializes in fresh seafood. Through the efforts of Karen and her staff, her restaurant has become one of the best and fastest-growing restaurants on the island.

To better plan for future growth of the restaurant, Karen needs to develop a system that will enable her to forecast food and beverage sales by month for up to one year in advance. Table 6.17 shows the value of food and beverage sales ($1000s) for the first three years of operation.

Managerial Report

Perform an analysis of the sales data for the Vintage Restaurant. Prepare a report for Karen that summarizes your findings, forecasts, and recommendations. Include the following:

1. A time series plot. Comment on the underlying pattern in the time series.
2. Using the dummy variable approach, forecast sales for January through December of the fourth year.

Assume that January sales for the fourth year turn out to be $295,000. What was your forecast error? If this error is large, Karen may be puzzled about the difference between your forecast and the actual sales value. What can you do to resolve her uncertainty in the forecasting procedure?

TABLE 6.17 FOOD AND BEVERAGE SALES FOR THE VINTAGE RESTAURANT ($1000s)

Month	First Year	Second Year	Third Year
January	242	263	282
February	235	238	255
March	232	247	265
April	178	193	205
May	184	193	210
June	140	149	160
July	145	157	166
August	152	161	174
September	110	122	126
October	130	130	148
November	152	167	173
December	206	230	235

Case Problem 2 Forecasting Lost Sales

The Carlson Department Store suffered heavy damage when a hurricane struck on August 31. The store was closed for four months (September through December), and Carlson is now involved in a dispute with its insurance company about the amount of lost sales during the time the store was closed. Two key issues must be resolved: (1) the amount of sales Carlson would have made if the hurricane had not struck and (2) whether Carlson is entitled to any compensation for excess sales due to increased business activity after the storm. More than $8 billion in federal disaster relief and insurance money came into the county, resulting in increased sales at department stores and numerous other businesses.

Table 6.18 gives Carlson's sales data for the 48 months preceding the storm. Table 6.19 reports total sales for the 48 months preceding the storm for all department stores in the county, as well as the total sales in the county for the four months the Carlson Department Store was closed. Carlson's managers asked you to analyze these data and develop

TABLE 6.18 SALES FOR CARLSON DEPARTMENT STORE ($ MILLIONS)

Month	Year 1	Year 2	Year 3	Year 4	Year 5
January		1.45	2.31	2.31	2.56
February		1.80	1.89	1.99	2.28
March		2.03	2.02	2.42	2.69
April		1.99	2.23	2.45	2.48
May		2.32	2.39	2.57	2.73
June		2.20	2.14	2.42	2.37
July		2.13	2.27	2.40	2.31
August		2.43	2.21	2.50	2.23
September	1.71	1.90	1.89	2.09	
October	1.90	2.13	2.29	2.54	
November	2.74	2.56	2.83	2.97	
December	4.20	4.16	4.04	4.35	

TABLE 6.19 DEPARTMENT STORE SALES FOR THE COUNTY ($ MILLIONS)

CountySales

Month	Year 1	Year 2	Year 3	Year 4	Year 5
January		46.80	46.80	43.80	48.00
February		48.00	48.60	45.60	51.60
March		60.00	59.40	57.60	57.60
April		57.60	58.20	53.40	58.20
May		61.80	60.60	56.40	60.00
June		58.20	55.20	52.80	57.00
July		56.40	51.00	54.00	57.60
August		63.00	58.80	60.60	61.80
September	55.80	57.60	49.80	47.40	69.00
October	56.40	53.40	54.60	54.60	75.00
November	71.40	71.40	65.40	67.80	85.20
December	117.60	114.00	102.00	100.20	121.80

estimates of the lost sales at the Carlson Department Store for the months of September through December. They also asked you to determine whether a case can be made for excess storm-related sales during the same period. If such a case can be made, Carlson is entitled to compensation for excess sales it would have earned in addition to ordinary sales.

Managerial Report

Prepare a report for the managers of the Carlson Department Store that summarizes your findings, forecasts, and recommendations. Include the following:

1. An estimate of sales for Carlson Department Store had there been no hurricane
2. An estimate of countywide department store sales had there been no hurricane
3. An estimate of lost sales for the Carlson Department Store for September through December

In addition, use the countywide actual department stores sales for September through December and the estimate in part (2) to make a case for or against excess storm-related sales.

Appendix 6.1 Forecasting with Excel Data Analysis Tools

In this appendix we show how Excel can be used to develop forecasts using three forecasting methods: moving averages, exponential smoothing, and trend projection. We also show how to use Excel Solver for least-squares fitting of models to data.

Moving Averages

To show how Excel can be used to develop forecasts using the moving averages method, we develop a forecast for the gasoline sales time series in Table 6.1 and Figure 6.1. We assume that the user has entered the week in rows 2 through 13 of column A and the sales data for the 12 weeks into worksheet rows 2 through 13 of column B (as in Figure 6.13).

FIGURE 6.13 GASOLINE SALES DATA IN EXCEL ARRANGED TO USE THE MOVING AVERAGES FUNCTION TO DEVELOP FORECASTS

	A	B
1	Week	Sales (1000s of gallons)
2	1	17
3	2	21
4	3	19
5	4	23
6	5	18
7	6	16
8	7	20
9	8	18
10	9	22
11	10	20
12	11	15
13	12	22

The following steps can be used to produce a three-week moving average.

*If the **Data Analysis** option does not appear in the **Analysis** group, you will have to include the Add-In in Excel. To do so, click on the **File** tab, then click **Options**, and then **Add-Ins**. Click **Go** next to the **Excel Add-Ins** drop-down box. Click the box next to **Analysis ToolPak** and click **OK**.*

Step 1. Select the **Data** tab

Step 2. From the **Analysis** group select the **Data Analysis** option

Step 3. When the **Data Analysis** dialog box appears, choose **Moving Average** and click **OK**

Step 4. When the **Moving Average** dialog box appears:
Enter B2:B13 in the **Input Range** box
Enter 3 in the **Interval** box
Enter C2 in the **Output Range** box
Click **OK**

Once you have completed this step (as shown in Figure 6.14), the three-week moving average forecasts will appear in column C of the worksheet as in Figure 6.15. Note that forecasts for periods of other lengths can be computed easily by entering a different value in the **Interval** box.

FIGURE 6.14 EXCEL MOVING AVERAGE DIALOGUE BOX FOR A 3-PERIOD MOVING AVERAGE

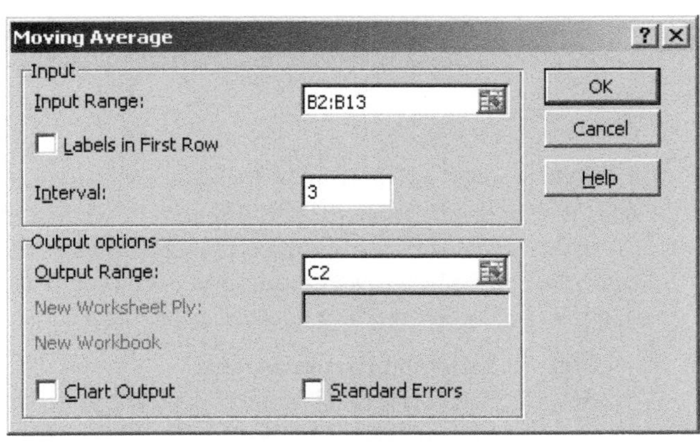

FIGURE 6.15 GASOLINE SALES DATA AND OUTPUT OF MOVING AVERAGES FUNCTION IN EXCEL

	A	B	C
1	Week	Sales (1000s of gallons)	F_t
2	1	17	#N/A
3	2	21	#N/A
4	3	19	19
5	4	23	21
6	5	18	20
7	6	16	19
8	7	20	18
9	8	18	18
10	9	22	20
11	10	20	20
12	11	15	19
13	12	22	19

Exponential Smoothing

To show how Excel can be used for exponential smoothing, we again develop a forecast for the gasoline sales time series in Table 6.1 and Figure 6.1. We assume that the user has entered the week in rows 2 through 13 of column A and the sales data for the 12 weeks into worksheet rows 2 through 13 of column B (as in Figure 6.13), and that the smoothing constant is $\alpha = 0.2$. The following steps can be used to produce a forecast.

Step 1. Select the **Data** tab
Step 2. From the **Analysis** group select the **Data Analysis** option
Step 3. When the **Data Analysis** dialog box appears, choose **Exponential Smoothing** and click **OK**
Step 4. When the **Exponential Smoothing** dialog box appears:
Enter B2:B13 in the **Input Range** box
Enter 0.8 in the **Damping factor** box
Enter C2 in the **Output Range** box
Click **OK**

Once you have completed this step (as shown in Figure 6.16), the exponential smoothing forecasts will appear in column C of the worksheet (as in Figure 6.17). Note that the value we entered in the **Damping factor** box is $1 - \alpha$; forecasts for other smoothing constants can be computed easily by entering a different value for $1 - \alpha$ in the **Damping factor** box.

Trend Projection

To show how Excel can be used for trend projection, we develop a forecast for the bicycle sales time series in Table 6.3 and Figure 6.3. We assume that the user has entered the year (1–10) for each observation into worksheet rows 2 through 11 of column A and the sales values into worksheet rows 2 through 11 of column B as shown in Figure 6.18. The following steps can be used to produce a forecast for year 11 by trend projection.

Step 1. Select the **Formulas** tab
Step 2. Select two cells in the row where you want the regression coefficients b_1 and b_0 to appear (for this example, choose D1 and E1)

FIGURE 6.16 EXCEL EXPONENTIAL SMOOTHING DIALOGUE BOX FOR $\alpha = 0.20$

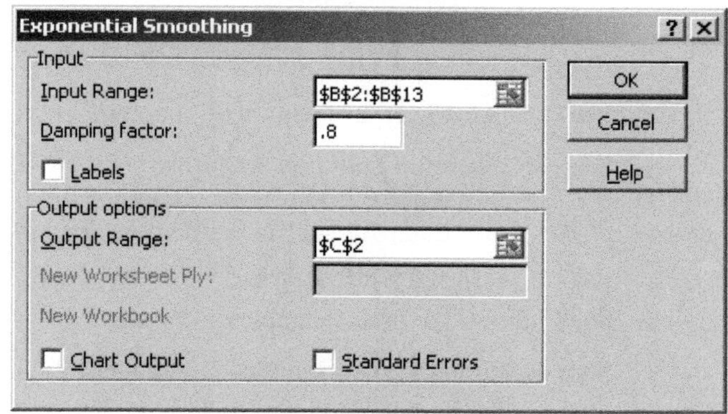

FIGURE 6.17 GASOLINE SALES DATA AND OUTPUT OF EXPONENTIAL SMOOTHING FUNCTION IN EXCEL

	A	B	C
1	Week	Sales (1000s of gallons)	F_t
2	1	17	#N/A
3	2	21	17
4	3	19	17.8
5	4	23	18.04
6	5	18	19.032
7	6	16	18.8256
8	7	20	18.26048
9	8	18	18.60838
10	9	22	18.48671
11	10	20	19.18937
12	11	15	19.35149
13	12	22	18.48119

FIGURE 6.18 BICYCLE SALES DATA IN EXCEL ARRANGED TO USE THE LINEST FUNCTION TO FIND THE LINEAR TREND

	A	B
1	Year	Sales (1000s)
2	1	21.6
3	2	22.9
4	3	25.5
5	4	21.9
6	5	23.9
7	6	27.5
8	7	31.5
9	8	29.7
10	9	28.6
11	10	31.4

Step 3. Click on the **Insert Function** key
Step 4. When the **Insert Function** dialog box appears:
Choose **Statistical** in the **Or select a category** box
Choose **LINEST** in the **Select a function** box
Click **OK**

See Figure 6.19 for an example of this step.

Step 5. When the **Function Arguments** dialog box appears:
Enter B2:B11 in the **Known_y's** box
Enter A2:A11 in the **Known_x's** box
Click **OK**

See Figure 6.20 for an example of this step.

Step 6. Hit the F2 key and then simultaneously hit the Shift, Control, and Enter keys (Shift + Control + Enter) to create an array that contains the values of the regression coefficients b_1 and b_0

At this point you have generated the regression coefficients b_1 and b_0 in the two cells you originally selected in step 1. It is important to note that cell D1 contains b_1 and cell E1 contains b_0.

To generate a forecast, in a blank cell, multiply the value of the independent variable t by b_1 and add the value of b_0 to this product. For example, if you wish to use this linear trend model to generate a forecast for year 11 and the value of b_1 is in cell D1 and the value of b_0 is in cell E1, then enter =11*D1+E1 in a blank cell. The forecast for year 11, in this case 32.5, will appear in the blank cell in which you enter this formula.

FIGURE 6.19 EXCEL INSERT FUNCTION DIALOGUE BOX FOR THE FINDING THE TREND LINE USING THE LINEST FUNCTION IN EXCEL

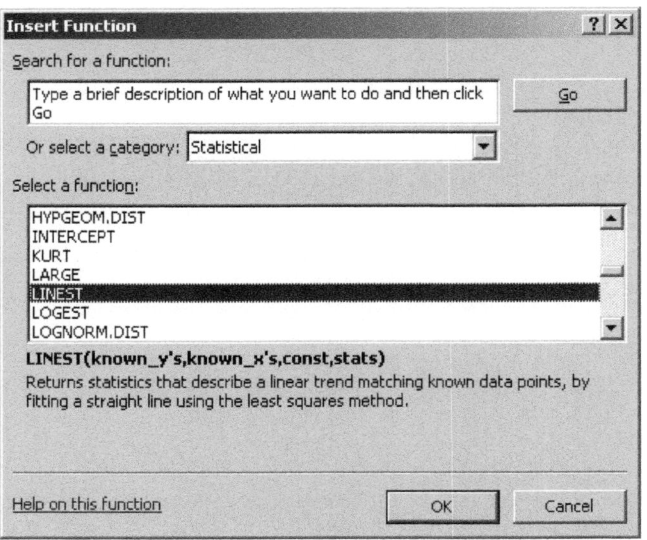

FIGURE 6.20 EXCEL FUNCTION ARGUMENTS DIALOGUE BOX FOR THE FINDING THE TREND LINE USING THE LINEST FUNCTION IN EXCEL

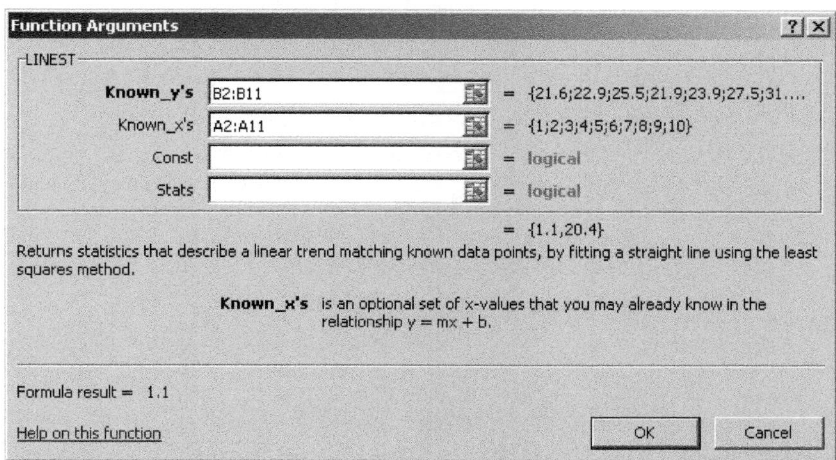

Models with Seasonality and No Trend

To show how Excel can be used to fit models with seasonality, we develop a forecast for the umbrella sales time series in Table 6.13 and Figure 6.11. We assume that the user has entered the year (1–5) for each observation into worksheet rows 3 through 22 of column A; the values for the quarter in worksheet rows 3 through 22 of column B; the values for the quarterly dummy variables $Qtr1_t$, $Qtr2_t$, and $Qtr3_t$ in worksheet rows 3 through 22 of columns C, D, and E, respectively; and the sales values into worksheet rows 3 through 22 of column F. The following steps can be used to produce a forecast for year 11 by trend projection as shown in Figure 6.21.

Step 1. Select the **Formulas** tab

Step 2. Select four cells in the row where you want the regression coefficients b_3, b_2, b_1, and b_0 to appear (for this example, choose G1:J1)

Step 3. Click on the **Insert Function** key

Step 4. When the **Insert Function** dialog box appears:
Choose **Statistical** in the **Or select a category** box
Choose **LINEST** in the **Select a function** box
Click **OK**

Step 5. When the **Function Arguments** dialog box appears:
Enter F3:F22 in the **Known_y's** box
Enter C3:E22 in the **Known_x's** box
Click **OK**

See Figure 6.22 for an example of this step.

Step 6. Hit the F2 key and then simultaneously hit the Shift, Control, and Enter keys (Shift + Control + Enter) to create an array that contains the values of the regression coefficients b_3, b_2, b_1, and b_0

FIGURE 6.21 UMBRELLA SALES DATA IN EXCEL ARRANGED TO USE THE LINEST FUNCTION TO FIND THE SEASONAL COMPONENTS

	A	B	C	D	E	F
1				Dummy Variables		
2	Year	Quarter	Quarter 1	Quarter 2	Quarter 3	Y_t
3	1	1	1	0	0	125
4	1	2	0	1	0	153
5	1	3	0	0	1	106
6	1	4	0	0	0	88
7	2	1	1	0	0	118
8	2	2	0	1	0	161
9	2	3	0	0	1	133
10	2	4	0	0	0	102
11	3	1	1	0	0	138
12	3	2	0	1	0	144
13	3	3	0	0	1	113
14	3	4	0	0	0	80
15	4	1	1	0	0	109
16	4	2	0	1	0	137
17	4	3	0	0	1	125
18	4	4	0	0	0	109
19	5	1	1	0	0	130
20	5	2	0	1	0	165
21	5	3	0	0	1	128
22	5	4	0	0	0	96
23						

FIGURE 6.22 EXCEL FUNCTION ARGUMENTS DIALOGUE BOX FOR FINDING THE SEASONAL COMPONENTS USING THE LINEST FUNCTION IN EXCEL

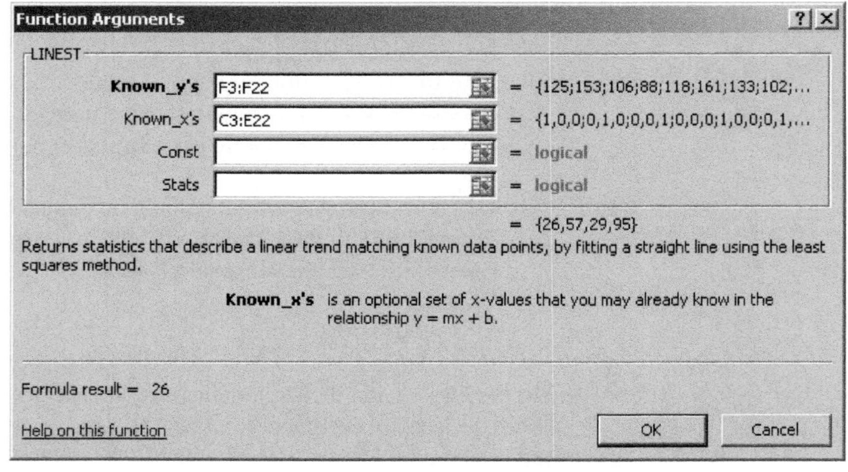

At this point you have generated the regression coefficients b_3, b_2, b_1, and b_0 in cells G1:J1 selected in step 1. It is important to note that the first cell you selected contains b_3, the second cell you selected contains b_2, the third cell you selected contains b_1, and the fourth cell you selected contains b_0 (i.e., if you selected cells G1:J1 in step 1, the value of b_1 will be in cell G1, the value of b_2 will be in H1, the value of b_1 will be in I1, and the value of b_0 will be in cell J1).

To generate a forecast, in a blank cell, add together b_0 and the product of b_1 and $Qtr1_t$, the product of b_2 and $Qtr2_t$, and the product of b_3 and $Qtr3_t$. For example, if you wish to use this linear trend model to generate a forecast for the first quarter of next year and the value of b_3 is in cell G1, the value of b_2 is in cell H1, the value of b_1 is in cell I1, and the value of b_0 is in cell J1, then enter =1*G1+0*H1+0*I1+J1 in a blank cell. The forecast for the first quarter of next year, in this case 124.0, will appear in the blank cell in which you enter this formula.

Models with Seasonality and Linear Trend

To show how Excel can be used to fit models with seasonality and a linear trend, we develop a forecast for the umbrella set time series in Table 6.13 and Figure 6.11. We assume that the user has entered the year (1–5) for each observation into worksheet rows 3 through 22 of column A; the values for the quarter in worksheet rows 3 through 22 of column B; the values for the quarterly dummy variables $Qtr1_t$, $Qtr2_t$, and $Qtr3_t$ into worksheet rows 3 through 22 of columns C, D, and E, respectively; the values of period t into worksheet rows 3 through 22 of column F; and the sales values into worksheet rows 3 through 22 of column G. The following steps can be used to produce a forecast for year 11 by trend projection as shown in Figure 6.23.

FIGURE 6.23 UMBRELLA TIME SERIES DATA IN EXCEL ARRANGED TO USE THE LINEST FUNCTION TO FIND BOTH THE SEASONAL COMPONENTS AND TREND COMPONENT

	A	B	C	D	E	F	G
1				Dummy Variables			
2	Year	Quarter	Quarter 1	Quarter 2	Quarter 3	t	Y_t
3	1	1	1	0	0	1	125
4	1	2	0	1	0	2	153
5	1	3	0	0	1	3	106
6	1	4	0	0	0	4	88
7	2	1	1	0	0	5	118
8	2	2	0	1	0	6	161
9	2	3	0	0	1	7	133
10	2	4	0	0	0	8	102
11	3	1	1	0	0	9	138
12	3	2	0	1	0	10	144
13	3	3	0	0	1	11	113
14	3	4	0	0	0	12	80
15	4	1	1	0	0	13	109
16	4	2	0	1	0	14	137
17	4	3	0	0	1	15	125
18	4	4	0	0	0	16	109
19	5	1	1	0	0	17	130
20	5	2	0	1	0	18	165
21	5	3	0	0	1	19	128
22	5	4	0	0	0	20	96
23							

Step 1. Select the **Formulas** tab

Step 2. Select five cells in the row where you want the regression coefficients b_4, b_3, b_2, b_1, and b_0 to appear for this example; choose H1:L1

Step 3. Click on the **Insert Function** key

Step 4. When the **Insert Function** dialog box appears:

Choose **Statistical** in the **Or select a category** box

Choose **LINEST** in the **Select a function** box

Click **OK**

Step 5. When the **Function Arguments** dialog box appears:

Enter G3:G22 in the **Known_y's** box

Enter C3:F22 in the **Known_x's** box

Click **OK**

Step 6. Hit the F2 key and then simultaneously hit the Shift, Control, and Enter keys (Shift + Control + Enter) to create an array that contains the values of the regression coefficients b_4, b_3, b_2, b_1, and b_0

At this point you have generated the regression coefficients b_4, b_3, b_2, b_1, and b_0 in cells H1:L1 selected in step 1. It is important to note that the first cell you selected contains b_4, the second cell you selected contains b_3, the third cell you selected contains b_2, the fourth cell you selected contains b_1, and the fifth cell you selected contains b_0 (i.e., if you selected cells H1:L1 in step 1, the value of b_4 will be in cell H1, the value of b_1 will be in cell I1, the value of b_2 will be in J1, the value of b_1 will be in K1, and the value of b_0 will be in cell L1).

To generate a forecast, in a blank cell, add together b_0 and the product of b_1 and Qtr1$_t$, the product of b_2 and Qtr2$_t$, the product of b_3 and Qtr3$_t$, and the product of b_4 and t. For example, if you wish to use this linear trend model to generate a forecast for the first quarter of year 5 and the value of b_4 is in cell H1, the value of b_3 is in cell I1, the value of b_2 is in cell J1, the value of b_1 is in cell K1, and the value of b_0 is in cell L1, then enter =17*H1+ 1*I1+0*J1+0*K1+L1 in a blank cell. The forecast for the first quarter of next year, in this case 7.19, will appear in the blank cell in which you enter this formula.

CHAPTER 7

Introduction to Linear Programming

CONTENTS

Linear programming is a problem-solving approach developed to help managers make decisions. Numerous applications of linear programming can be found in today's competitive business environment. For instance, IBM uses linear programming to perform capacity planning and to make capacity investment decisions for its semiconductor manufacturing operations. GE Capital uses linear programming to help determine optimal lease structuring. Marathon Oil Company uses linear programming for gasoline blending and to evaluate the economics of a new terminal or pipeline. The Q.M. in Action, Timber Harvesting Model at MeadWestvaco Corporation, provides another example of the use of linear programming. Later in the chapter another Q.M. in Action illustrates how IBM uses linear programming and other quantitative methods to plan and operate its semiconductor supply chain.

To illustrate some of the properties that all linear programming problems have in common, consider the following typical applications:

1. A manufacturer wants to develop a production schedule and an inventory policy that will satisfy sales demand in future periods. Ideally, the schedule and policy will enable the company to satisfy demand and at the same time *minimize* the total production and inventory costs.
2. A financial analyst must select an investment portfolio from a variety of stock and bond investment alternatives. The analyst would like to establish the portfolio that *maximizes* the return on investment.
3. A marketing manager wants to determine how best to allocate a fixed advertising budget among alternative advertising media such as radio, television, newspaper, and magazine. The manager would like to determine the media mix that *maximizes* advertising effectiveness.
4. A company has warehouses in a number of locations. Given specific customer demands, the company would like to determine how much each warehouse should ship to each customer so that total transportation costs are *minimized.*

These examples are only a few of the situations in which linear programming has been used successfully, but they illustrate the diversity of linear programming applications. A close scrutiny reveals one basic property they all have in common. In each example, we were concerned with *maximizing* or *minimizing* some quantity. In example 1, the manufacturer wanted to minimize costs; in example 2, the financial analyst wanted to maximize return on investment; in example 3, the marketing manager wanted to maximize advertising effectiveness; and in example 4, the company wanted to minimize total transportation costs. In all linear programming problems, the maximization or minimization of some quantity is the objective.

Q.M. *in* ACTION

*TIMBER HARVESTING MODEL AT MEADWESTVACO CORPORATION**

MeadWestvaco Corporation is a major producer of premium papers for periodicals, books, commercial printing, and business forms. The company also produces pulp and lumber, designs and manufactures packaging systems for beverage and other consumables markets, and is a world leader in the production of coated board and shipping containers. Quantitative analyses at MeadWestvaco are developed and implemented by the company's Decision Analysis Department. The department assists decision makers by providing them with analytical tools of quantitative methods as well as personal analysis and recommendations.

*Based on information provided by Dr. Edward P. Winkofsky of MeadWestvaco Corporation.

(*continued*)

MeadWestvaco uses quantitative models to assist with the long-range management of the company's timberland. Through the use of large-scale linear programs, timber harvesting plans are developed to cover a substantial time horizon. These models consider wood market conditions, mill pulpwood requirements, harvesting capacities, and general forest management principles. Within these constraints, the model arrives at an optimal harvesting and purchasing schedule based on discounted cash flow. Alternative schedules reflect changes in the various assumptions concerning forest growth, wood availability, and general economic conditions.

Quantitative methods are also used in the development of the inputs for the linear programming models. Timber prices and supplies as well as mill requirements must be forecast over the time horizon, and advanced sampling techniques are used to evaluate land holdings and to project forest growth. The harvest schedule is then developed using quantitative methods.

Linear programming was initially referred to as "programming in a linear structure." In 1948, Tjalling Koopmans suggested to George Dantzig that the name was much too long: Koopman's suggestion was to shorten it to linear programming. George Dantzig agreed, and the field we now know as linear programming was named.

All linear programming problems also have a second property: restrictions or **constraints** that limit the degree to which the objective can be pursued. In the first example, the manufacturer is restricted by constraints requiring product demand to be satisfied and by the constraints limiting production capacity. The financial analyst's portfolio problem is constrained by the total amount of investment funds available and the maximum amounts that can be invested in each stock or bond. The marketing manager's media selection decision is constrained by a fixed advertising budget and the availability of the various media. In the transportation problem, the minimum-cost shipping schedule is constrained by the supply of product available at each warehouse. Thus, constraints are another general feature of every linear programming problem.

7.1 A Simple Maximization Problem

RMC, Inc., is a small firm that produces a variety of chemical-based products. In a particular production process, three raw materials are used to produce two products: a fuel additive and a solvent base. The fuel additive is sold to oil companies and is used in the production of gasoline and related fuels. The solvent base is sold to a variety of chemical firms and is used in both home and industrial cleaning products. The three raw materials are blended to form the fuel additive and solvent base as indicated in Table 7.1, which shows that a ton of fuel additive is a mixture of 0.4 tons of material 1 and 0.6 tons of material 3. A ton of solvent base is a mixture of 0.5 tons of material 1, 0.2 tons of material 2, and 0.3 tons of material 3.

TABLE 7.1 MATERIAL REQUIREMENTS PER TON FOR THE RMC PROBLEM

	Product	
	Fuel Additive	**Solvent Base**
Material 1	0.4	0.5
Material 2		0.2
Material 3	0.6	0.3

0.6 tons of material 3 is used in each ton of fuel additive

RMC's production is constrained by a limited availability of the three raw materials. For the current production period, RMC has available the following quantities of each raw material:

Material	Amount Available for Production
Material 1	20 tons
Material 2	5 tons
Material 3	21 tons

It is important to understand that we are maximizing profit contribution, not profit. Overhead and other shared costs must be deducted before arriving at a profit figure.

Because of spoilage and the nature of the production process, any materials not used for current production are useless and must be discarded.

The accounting department analyzed the production figures, assigned all relevant costs, and arrived at prices for both products that will result in a profit contribution[1] of $40 for every ton of fuel additive produced and $30 for every ton of solvent base produced. Let us now use linear programming to determine the number of tons of fuel additive and the number of tons of solvent base to produce in order to maximize total profit contribution.

Problem Formulation

Problem formulation is the process of translating a verbal statement of a problem into a mathematical statement. The mathematical statement of the problem is referred to as a **mathematical model**. Developing an appropriate mathematical model is an art that can only be mastered with practice and experience. Even though every problem has at least some unique features, most problems also have many common or similar features. As a result, some general guidelines for developing a mathematical model can be helpful. We will illustrate these guidelines by developing a mathematical model for the RMC problem.

Understand the Problem Thoroughly The RMC problem is relatively easy to understand. RMC wants to determine how much of each product to produce in order to maximize the total contribution to profit. The number of tons available for the three materials that are required to produce the two products will limit the number of tons of each product that can be produced. More complex problems will require more work in order to understand the problem. However, understanding the problem thoroughly is the first step in developing any mathematical model.

Describe the Objective RMC's objective is to maximize the total contribution to profit.

Describe Each Constraint Three constraints limit the number of tons of fuel additive and the number of tons of solvent base that can be produced.

Constraint 1: The number of tons of material 1 used must be less than or equal to the 20 tons available.

Constraint 2: The number of tons of material 2 used must be less than or equal to the 5 tons available.

Constraint 3: The number of tons of material 3 used must be less than or equal to the 21 tons available.

---

[1]From an accounting perspective, profit contribution is more correctly described as the contribution margin per ton; overhead and other shared costs have not been allocated to the fuel additive and solvent base costs.

Define the Decision Variables The decision variables are the controllable inputs in the problem. For the RMC problem the two decision variables are (1) the number of tons of fuel additive produced, and (2) the number of tons of solvent base produced. In developing the mathematical model for the RMC problem, we will use the following notation for the decision variables:

$$F = \text{number of tons of fuel additive}$$
$$S = \text{number of tons of solvent base}$$

Write the Objective in Terms of the Decision Variables RMC's profit contribution comes from the production of F tons of fuel additive and S tons of solvent base. Because RMC makes \$40 for every ton of fuel additive produced and \$30 for every ton of solvent base produced, the company will make \$40F from the production of the fuel additive and \$30S from the production of the solvent base. Thus,

$$\text{Total profit contribution} = 40F + 30S$$

Because the objective—maximize total profit contribution—is a function of the decision variables F and S, we refer to $40F + 30S$ as the objective function. Using "Max" as an abbreviation for maximize, we can write RMC's objective as follows:

$$\text{Max } 40F + 30S \tag{7.1}$$

Write the Constraints in Terms of the Decision Variables

Constraint 1:

$$\text{Tons of material 1 used} \leq \text{Tons of material 1 available}$$

Every ton of fuel additive that RMC produces will use 0.4 tons of material 1. Thus, $0.4F$ tons of material 1 is used to produce F tons of fuel additive. Similarly, every ton of solvent base that RMC produces will use 0.5 tons of material 1. Thus, $0.5S$ tons of material 1 is used to produce S tons of solvent base. Therefore, the number of tons of material 1 used to produce F tons of fuel additive and S tons of solvent base is

$$\text{Tons of material 1 used} = 0.4F + 0.5S$$

Because 20 tons of material 1 are available for use in production, the mathematical statement of constraint 1 is

$$0.4F + 0.5S \leq 20 \tag{7.2}$$

Constraint 2:

$$\text{Tons of material 2 used} \leq \text{Tons of material 2 available}$$

Fuel additive does not use material 2. However, every ton of solvent base that RMC produces will use 0.2 tons of material 2. Thus, $0.2S$ tons of material 2 is used to produce S tons of solvent base. Therefore, the number of tons of material 2 used to produce F tons of fuel additive and S tons of solvent base is

$$\text{Tons of material 2 used} = 0.2S$$

Because 5 tons of material 2 are available for production, the mathematical statement of constraint 2 is

$$0.2S \le 5 \tag{7.3}$$

Constraint 3:

Tons of material 3 used $\le$ Tons of material 3 available

Every ton of fuel additive RMC produces will use 0.6 tons of material 3. Thus, $0.6F$ tons of material 1 is used to produce F tons of fuel additive. Similarly, every ton of solvent base RMC produces will use 0.3 tons of material 3. Thus, $0.3S$ tons of material 1 is used to produce S tons of solvent base. Therefore, the number of tons of material 3 used to produce F tons of fuel additive and S tons of solvent base is

$$\text{Tons of material 3 used} = 0.6F + 0.3S$$

Because 21 tons of material 3 are available for production, the mathematical statement of constraint 3 is

$$0.6F + 0.3S \le 21 \tag{7.4}$$

Add the Nonnegativity Constraints RMC cannot produce a negative number of tons of fuel additive or a negative number of tons of solvent base. Therefore, **nonnegativity constraints** must be added to prevent the decision variables F and S from having negative values. These nonnegativity constraints are

$$F \ge 0 \text{ and } S \ge 0$$

Nonnegativity constraints are a general feature of many linear programming problems and may be written in the abbreviated form:

$$F, S \ge 0 \tag{7.5}$$

Mathematical Model for the RMC Problem

Problem formulation is now complete. We have succeeded in translating the verbal statement of the RMC problem into the following mathematical model:

$$\begin{aligned}
&\text{Max } 40F + 30S \\
&\text{Subject to (s.t.)} \\
&\qquad 0.4F + 0.5S \le 20 \quad \text{Material 1} \\
&\qquad\qquad\quad 0.2S \le \ \ 5 \quad \text{Material 2} \\
&\qquad 0.6F + 0.3S \le 21 \quad \text{Material 3} \\
&\qquad F, S \ge 0
\end{aligned}$$

Our job now is to find the product mix (i.e., the combination of F and S) that satisfies all the constraints and, at the same time, yields a maximum value for the objective function. Once these values of F and S are calculated, we will have found the optimal solution to the problem.

This mathematical model of the RMC problem is a **linear program**. The RMC problem has an objective and constraints that, as we said earlier, are common properties of all *linear* programs. But what is the special feature of this mathematical model that makes it a linear program? The special feature that makes it a linear program is that the objective function and all constraint functions (the left-hand sides of the constraint inequalities) are linear functions of the decision variables.

Mathematical functions in which each variable appears in a separate term and is raised to the first power are called **linear functions**. The objective function ($40F + 30S$) is linear because each decision variable appears in a separate term and has an exponent of 1. The amount of material 1 used ($0.4F + 0.5S$) is also a linear function of the decision variables for the same reason. Similarly, the functions on the left-hand side of the material 2 and material 3 constraint inequalities (the constraint functions) are also linear functions. Thus, the mathematical formulation is referred to as a linear program.

Try Problem 1 to test your ability to recognize the types of mathematical relationships that can be found in a linear program.

Linear *programming* has nothing to do with computer programming. The use of the word *programming* here means "choosing a course of action." Linear programming involves choosing a course of action when the mathematical model of the problem contains only linear functions.

NOTES AND COMMENTS

1. The three assumptions necessary for a linear programming model to be appropriate are proportionality, additivity, and divisibility. *Proportionality* means that the contribution to the objective function and the amount of resources used in each constraint are proportional to the value of each decision variable. *Additivity* means that the value of the objective function and the total resources used can be found by summing the objective function contribution and the resources used for all decision variables. *Divisibility* means that the decision variables are continuous. The divisibility assumption plus the nonnegativity constraints mean that decision variables can take on any value greater than or equal to zero.
2. Quantitative analysts formulate and solve a variety of mathematical models that contain an objective function and a set of constraints. Models of this type are referred to as *mathematical programming models.* Linear programming models are a special type of mathematical programming model in that the objective function and all constraint functions are linear.

7.2 Graphical Solution Procedure

A linear programming problem involving only two decision variables can be solved using a graphical solution procedure. Let us begin the graphical solution procedure by developing a graph that displays the possible solutions (F and S values) for the RMC problem. The graph in Figure 7.1 has values of F on the horizontal axis and values of S on the vertical axis. Any point on the graph can be identified by its F and S values, which indicate the position of the point along the horizontal and vertical axes, respectively. Thus, every point on the graph corresponds to a possible solution. The solution of $F = 0$ and $S = 0$ is referred to as the origin. Because both F and S must be nonnegative, the graph in Figure 7.1 only displays solutions where $F \geq 0$ and $S \geq 0$.

Earlier we determined that the inequality representing the material 1 constraint was

$$0.4F + 0.5S \leq 20$$

To show all solutions that satisfy this relationship, we start by graphing the line corresponding to the equation

$$0.4F + 0.5S = 20$$

FIGURE 7.1 GRAPH SHOWING TWO SOLUTIONS FOR THE TWO-VARIABLE RMC PROBLEM

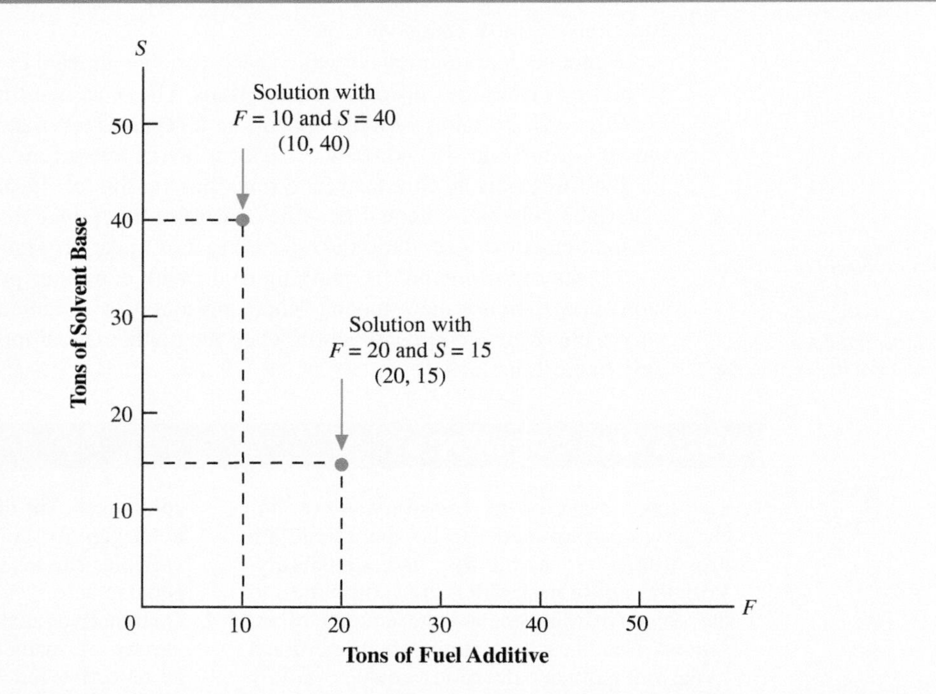

We graph this equation by identifying two points that satisfy this equation and then drawing a line through the points. Setting $F = 0$ and solving for S gives $0.5S = 20$, or $S = 40$; hence the solution ($F = 0$, $S = 40$) satisfies the preceding equation. To find a second solution satisfying this equation, we set $S = 0$ and solve for F. Doing so, we obtain $0.4F = 20$, or $F = 50$. Thus, a second solution satisfying the equation is ($F = 50$, $S = 0$). With these two points, we can now graph the line. This line, called the *material 1 constraint line,* is shown in Figure 7.2.

Recall that the inequality representing the material 1 constraint is

$$0.4F + 0.5S \leq 20$$

Can you identify all the solutions that satisfy this constraint? First, note that any point on the line $0.4F + 0.5S = 20$ must satisfy the constraint. But where are the solutions satisfying $0.4F + 0.5S < 20$? Consider two solutions ($F = 10$, $S = 10$) and ($F = 40$, $S = 30$). Figure 7.2 shows that the first solution is on the same side of the constraint line as the origin while the second solution is on the side of the constraint line opposite of the origin. Which of these solutions satisfies the material 1 constraint? For ($F = 10$, $S = 10$) we have

$$0.4F + 0.5S = 0.4(10) + 0.5(10) = 9$$

Because 9 tons is less than the 20 tons of material 1 available, the $F = 10$, $S = 10$ solution satisfies the constraint. For $F = 40$ and $S = 30$ we have

$$0.4F + 0.5S = 0.4(40) + 0.5(30) = 31$$

FIGURE 7.2 MATERIAL 1 CONSTRAINT LINE

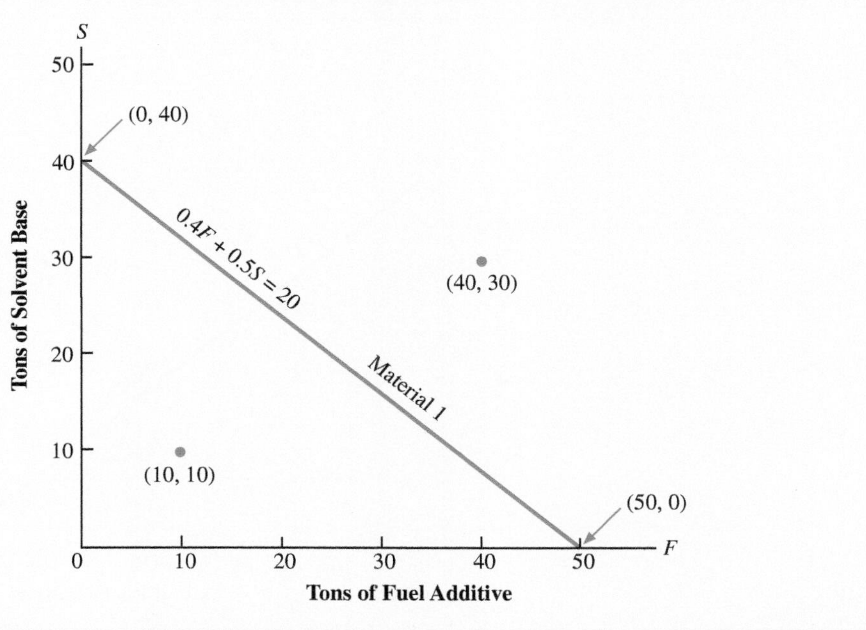

The 31 tons is greater than the 20 tons available, so the $F = 40$, $S = 30$ solution does not satisfy the constraint.

You should now be able to graph a constraint line and find the solution points that satisfy the constraint. Try Problem 2.

If a particular solution satisfies the constraint, all other solutions on the same side of the constraint line will also satisfy the constraint. If a particular solution does not satisfy the constraint, all other solutions on the same side of the constraint line will not satisfy the constraint. Thus, you need to evaluate only one solution to determine which side of a constraint line provides solutions that will satisfy the constraint. The shaded area in Figure 7.3 shows all the solutions that satisfy the material 1 constraint.

Next let us identify all solutions that satisfy the material 2 constraint:

$$0.2S \leq 5$$

We start by drawing the constraint line corresponding to the equation $0.2S = 5$. Because this equation is equivalent to the equation $S = 25$, we simply draw a line whose S value is 25 for every value of F; this line is parallel to and 25 units above the horizontal axis. Figure 7.4 shows the line corresponding to the material 2 constraint. Following the approach we used for the material 1 constraint, we realize that only solutions on or below the line will satisfy the material 2 constraint. Thus, in Figure 7.4 the shaded area corresponds to the solutions that satisfy the material 2 constraint.

Similarly, we can determine the solutions that satisfy the material 3 constraint. Figure 7.5 shows the result. For practice, try to graph the feasible solutions that satisfy the material 3 constraint and determine whether your result agrees with that shown in Figure 7.5.

We now have three separate graphs showing the solutions that satisfy each of the three constraints. In a linear programming problem, we need to identify the solutions that satisfy

FIGURE 7.3 SOLUTIONS THAT SATISFY THE MATERIAL 1 CONSTRAINT

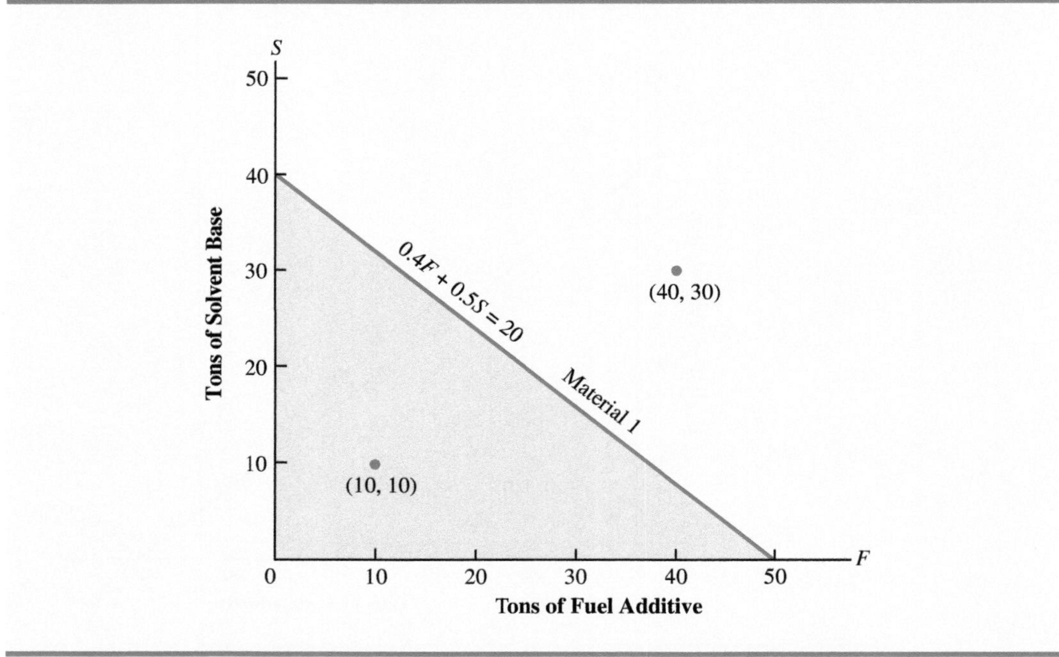

FIGURE 7.4 SOLUTIONS THAT SATISFY THE MATERIAL 2 CONSTRAINT

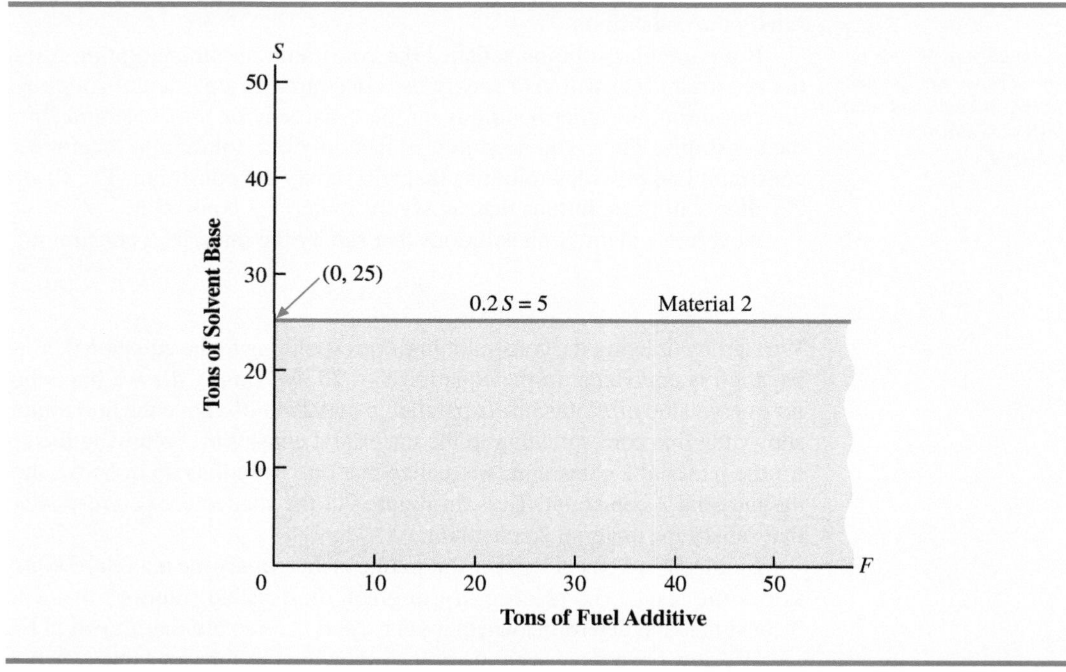

FIGURE 7.5 SOLUTIONS THAT SATISFY THE MATERIAL 3 CONSTRAINT

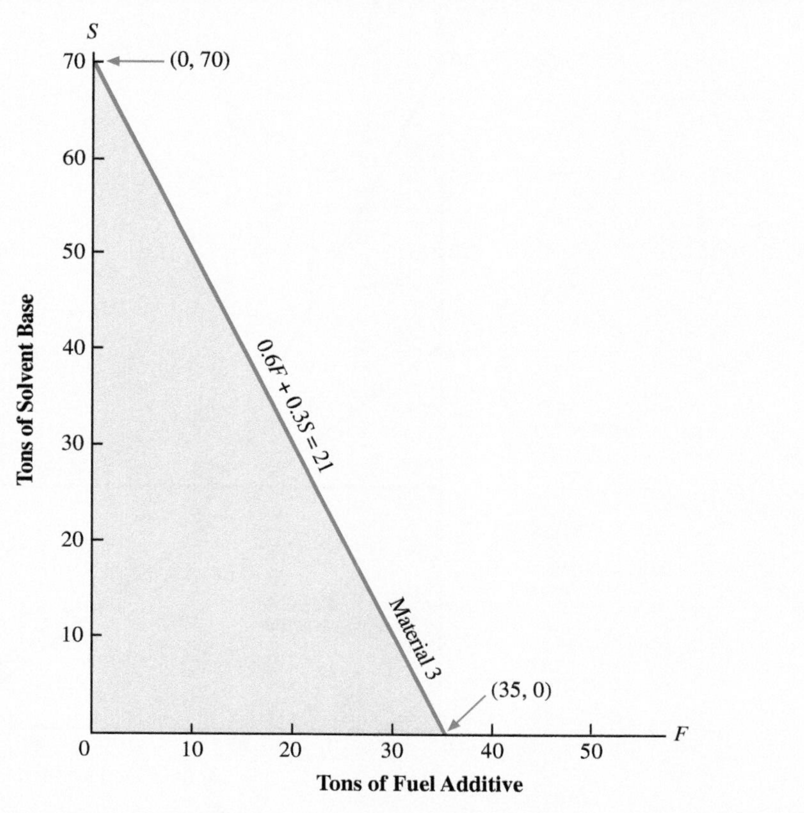

all the constraints *simultaneously*. To find these solutions, we can draw the three constraints on one graph and observe the region containing the points that do in fact satisfy all the constraints simultaneously.

The graphs in Figures 7.3, 7.4, and 7.5 can be superimposed to obtain one graph with all three constraints. Figure 7.6 shows this combined constraint graph. The shaded region in this figure includes every solution point that satisfies all the constraints simultaneously. Because solutions that satisfy all the constraints simultaneously are termed **feasible solutions**, the shaded region is called the *feasible solution region,* or simply the **feasible region**. Any point on the boundary of the feasible region, or within the feasible region, is a *feasible solution point* for the linear programming problem.

Can you now find the feasible region given several constraints? Try Problem 7.

Now that we have identified the feasible region, we are ready to proceed with the graphical solution method and find the optimal solution to the RMC problem. Recall that the optimal solution for a linear programming problem is the feasible solution that provides the best possible value of the objective function. Let us start the optimizing step of the graphical solution procedure by redrawing the feasible region on a separate graph. Figure 7.7 shows the graph.

One approach to finding the optimal solution would be to evaluate the objective function for each feasible solution; the optimal solution would then be the one yielding the

FIGURE 7.6 FEASIBLE REGION FOR THE RMC PROBLEM

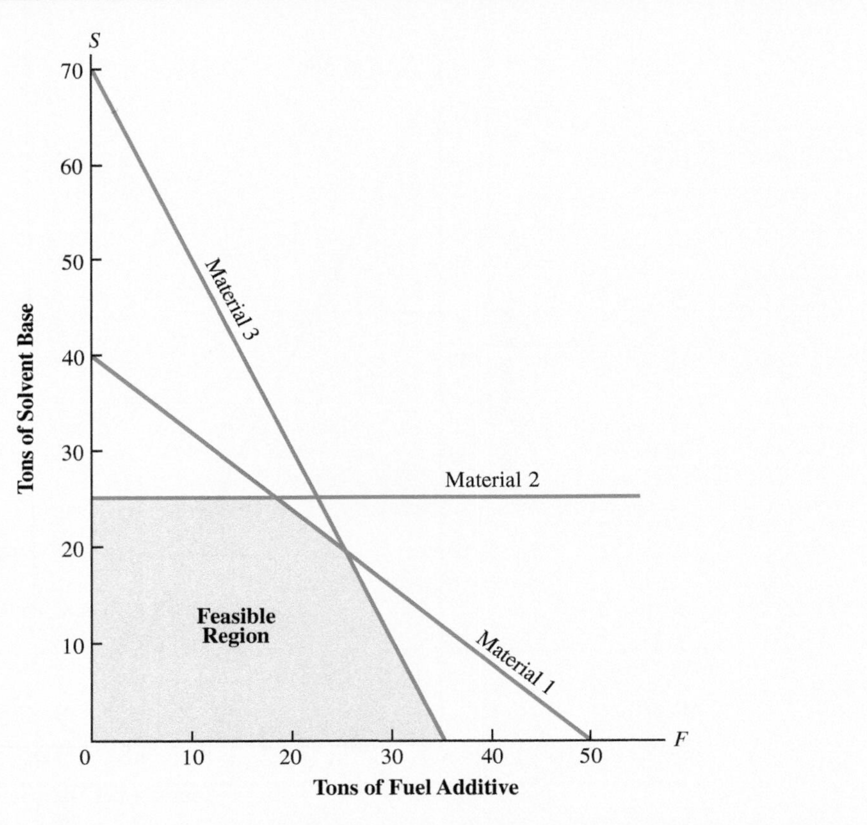

largest value. The difficulty with this approach is that the infinite number of feasible solutions makes evaluating all feasible solutions impossible. Hence, this trial-and-error procedure cannot be used to identify the optimal solution.

Rather than trying to compute the profit contribution for each feasible solution, we select an arbitrary value for profit contribution and identify all the feasible solutions that yield the selected value. For example, what feasible solutions provide a profit contribution of \$240? These solutions are given by the values of F and S in the feasible region that will make the objective function

$$40F + 30S = 240$$

This expression is simply the equation of a line. Thus all feasible solutions (F, S) yielding a profit contribution of \$240 must be on the line. We learned earlier in this section how to graph a constraint line. The procedure for graphing the profit or objective function line is the same. Letting $F = 0$, we see that S must be 8; thus the solution point $(F = 0, S = 8)$ is on the line. Similarly, by letting $S = 0$ we see that the solution point $(F = 6, S = 0)$ is also on the line. Drawing the line through these two points identifies all the solutions that have a profit contribution of \$240. A graph of this profit line is presented in Figure 7.8. The graph shows that an infinite number of feasible production combinations will provide a \$240 profit contribution.

FIGURE 7.7 FEASIBLE REGION FOR THE RMC PROBLEM

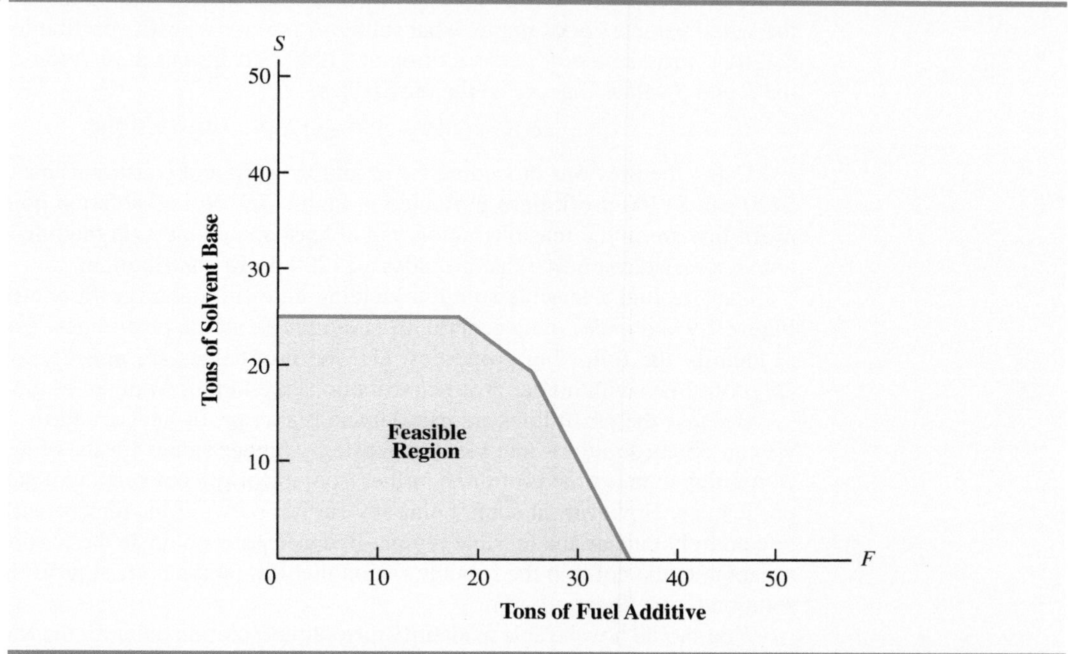

FIGURE 7.8 \$240 PROFIT LINE FOR THE RMC PROBLEM

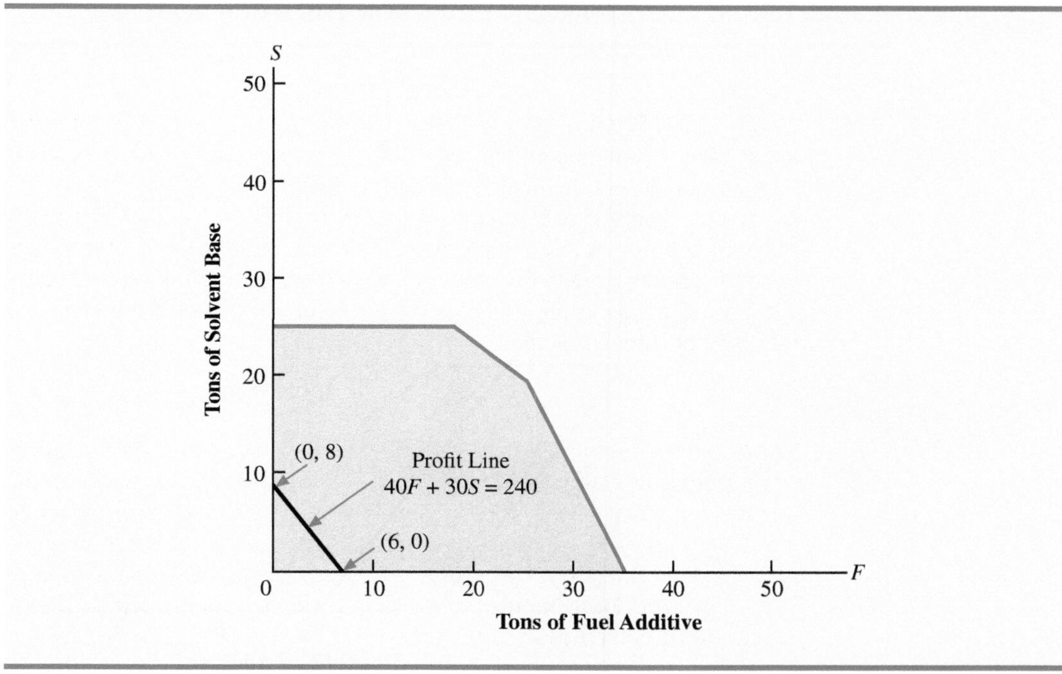

The objective is to find the feasible solution yielding the highest profit contribution, so we proceed by selecting higher profit contributions and finding the solutions that yield the stated values. For example, what solutions provide a profit contribution of \$720? What solutions provide a profit contribution of \$1200? To answer these questions, we must find the F and S values that are on the profit lines:

$$40F + 30S = 720 \text{ and } 40F + 30S = 1200$$

Using the previous procedure for graphing profit and constraint lines, we graphed the \$720 and \$1200 profit lines presented in Figure 7.9. Not all solution points on the \$1200 profit line are in the feasible region, but at least some points on the line are; thus, we can obtain a feasible solution that provides a \$1200 profit contribution.

Can we find a feasible solution yielding an even higher profit contribution? Look at Figure 7.9 and make some general observations about the profit lines. You should be able to identify the following properties: (1) The profit lines are *parallel* to each other, and (2) profit lines with higher profit contributions are farther from the origin.

Because the profit lines are parallel and higher profit lines are farther from the origin, we can obtain solutions that yield increasingly higher values for the objective function by continuing to move the profit line farther from the origin but keeping it parallel to the other profit lines. However, at some point any further outward movement will place the profit line entirely outside the feasible region. Because points outside the feasible region are unacceptable, the point in the feasible region that lies on the highest profit line is an optimal solution to the linear program.

You should now be able to identify the optimal solution point for the RMC problem. Use a ruler and move the profit line as far from the origin as you can. What is the last point in the feasible region? This point, which is the optimal solution, is shown graphically in Figure 7.10. The optimal values for the decision variables are the F and S values at this point.

FIGURE 7.9 SELECTED PROFIT LINES FOR THE RMC PROBLEM

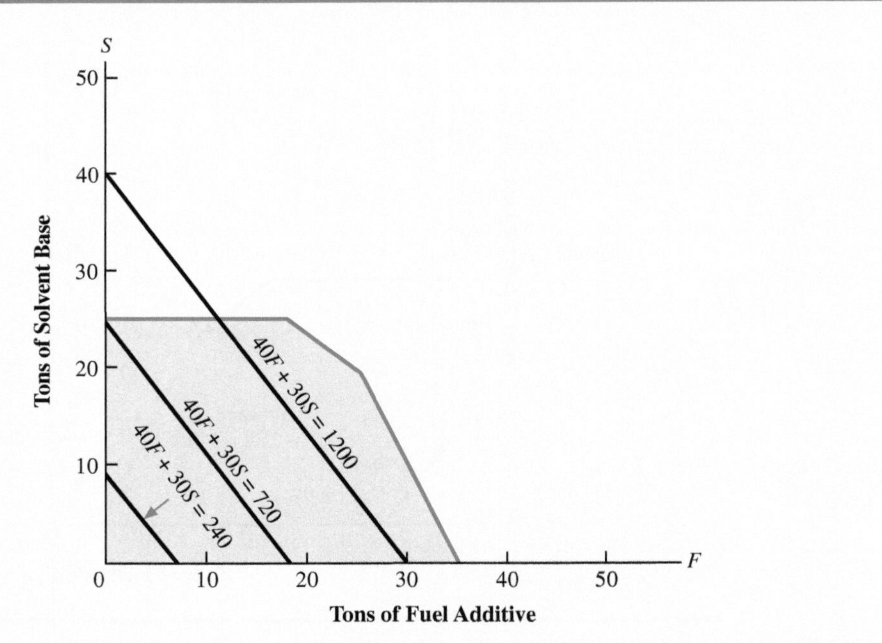

FIGURE 7.10 OPTIMAL SOLUTION FOR THE RMC PROBLEM

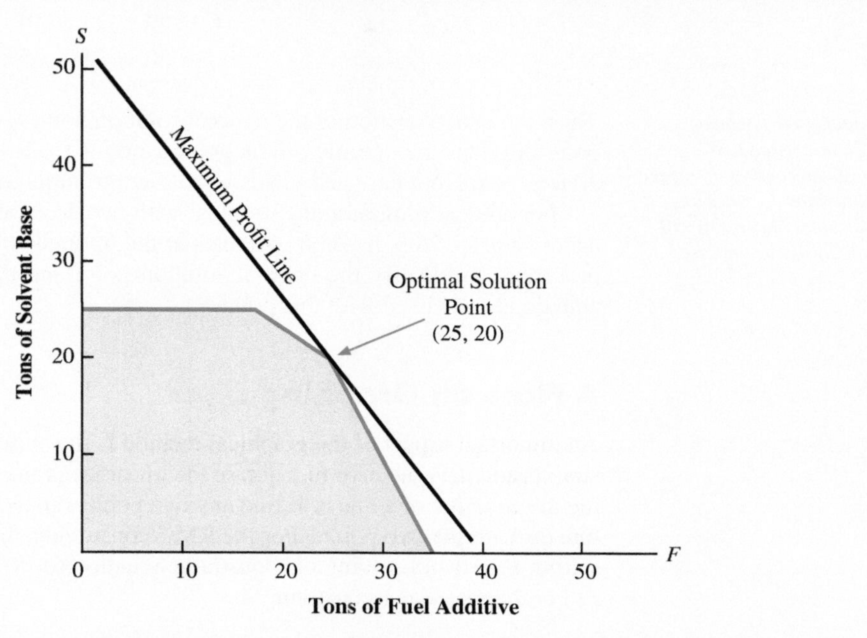

Depending on the accuracy of your graph, you may or may not be able to determine the exact optimal values of F and S directly from the graph. However, refer to Figure 7.6 and note that the optimal solution point for the RMC example is at the *intersection* of the material 1 and material 3 constraint lines. That is, the optimal solution is on both the material 1 constraint line,

$$0.4F + 0.5S = 20 \tag{7.6}$$

and the material 3 constraint line,

$$0.6F + 0.3S = 21 \tag{7.7}$$

Thus, the values of the decision variables F and S must satisfy both equations (7.6) and (7.7) simultaneously. Using (7.6) and solving for F gives

$$0.4F = 20 - 0.5S$$

or

$$F = 50 - 1.25S \tag{7.8}$$

Substituting this expression for F into equation (7.7) and solving for S yields

$$\begin{aligned} 0.6(50 - 1.25S) + 0.3S &= 21 \\ 30 - 0.75S + 0.3S &= 21 \\ -0.45S &= -9 \\ S &= 20 \end{aligned}$$

Substituting $S = 20$ in equation (7.8) and solving for F provides

$$\begin{aligned} F &= 50 - 1.25(20) \\ &= 50 - 25 = 25 \end{aligned}$$

Although the optimal solution to the RMC problem consists of integer values for the decision variables, this result will not always be the case.

Thus, the exact location of the optimal solution point is $F = 25$ and $S = 20$. This solution point provides the optimal production quantities for RMC at 25 tons of fuel additive and 20 tons of solvent base and yields a profit contribution of $40(25) + 30(20) = \$1600$.

For a linear programming problem with two decision variables, you can determine the exact values of the decision variables at the optimal solution by first using the graphical procedure to identify the optimal solution point and then solving the two simultaneous equations associated with this point.

A Note on Graphing Lines

An important aspect of the graphical method is the ability to graph lines showing the constraints and the objective function of the linear program. The procedure we used for graphing the equation of a line is to find any two points satisfying the equation and then draw the line through the two points. For the RMC constraints, the two points were easily found by setting $F = 0$ and solving the constraint equation for S. Then we set $S = 0$ and solved for F. For the material 1 constraint line

$$0.4F + 0.5S = 20$$

this procedure identified the two points ($F = 0$, $S = 40$) and ($F = 50$, $S = 0$). The material 1 constraint line was then graphed by drawing a line through these two points.

Try Problem 10 to test your ability to use the graphical solution procedure to identify the optimal solution and find the exact values of the decision variables at the optimal solution.

All constraints and objective function lines in two-variable linear programs can be graphed if two points on the line can be identified. However, finding the two points on the line is not always as easy as shown in the RMC problem. For example, suppose a company manufactures two models of a tablet computer: the Professional (P) and the Assistant (A). Management needs 50 units of the Professional model for its own sales force and expects sales of the remaining Professionals to be less than or equal to 50% of the sales of the Assistant. A constraint enforcing this requirement is

$$P - 50 \le 0.5A$$

or

$$P - 0.5A \le 50$$

Using the equality form of the constraint and setting $P = 0$, we find that the point ($P = 0$, $A = -100$) is on the constraint line. Setting $A = 0$, we find a second point ($P = 50$, $A = 0$) on the constraint line. If we have drawn only the nonnegative ($P \ge 0$, $A \ge 0$) portion of the graph, the first point ($P = 0$, $A = -100$) cannot be plotted because $A = -100$ is not on the graph. Whenever we have two points on the line, but one or both of the points cannot be plotted in the nonnegative portion of the graph, the simplest approach is to enlarge the graph. In this example, the point ($P = 0$, $A = -100$) can be plotted by extending the graph to include the negative A axis. Once both points satisfying the constraint equation have been located, the line can be drawn. The constraint line and the solutions that satisfy the constraint $P - 0.5A \le 50$ are shown in Figure 7.11.

FIGURE 7.11 SOLUTIONS THAT SATISFY THE CONSTRAINT $P - 0.5A \leq 50$

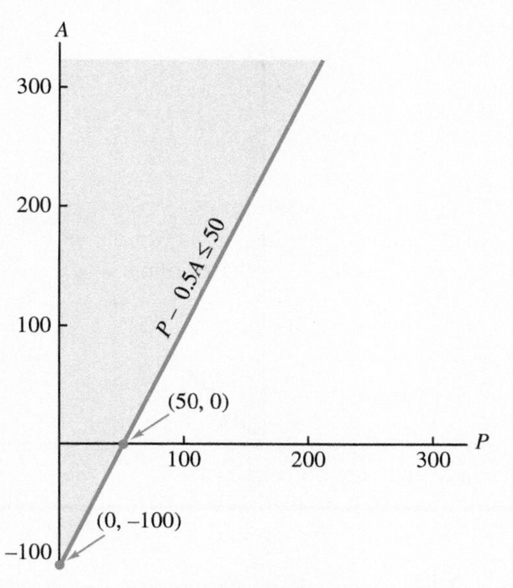

As another example, consider a problem involving two decision variables, R and T. Suppose that the number of units of R produced has to be at least equal to the number of units of T produced. A constraint enforcing this requirement is

$$R \geq T$$

or

$$R - T \geq 0$$

Can you graph a constraint line when the origin is on the constraint line? Try Problem 5.

To find all solutions satisfying the constraint as an equality, we first set $R = 0$ and solve for T. This result shows that the origin ($T = 0$, $R = 0$) is on the constraint line. Setting $T = 0$ and solving for R provides the same point. However, we can obtain a second point on the line by setting T equal to any value other than zero and then solving for R. For instance, setting $T = 100$ and solving for R, we find that the point ($T = 100$, $R = 100$) is on the line. With the two points ($R = 0$, $T = 0$) and ($R = 100$, $T = 100$), the constraint line $R - T = 0$ and the solutions that satisfy the constraint $R - T \geq 0$ can be plotted as shown in Figure 7.12.

Summary of the Graphical Solution Procedure for Maximization Problems

For additional practice in using the graphical solution procedure, try Problem 24.

As we have seen, the graphical solution procedure is a method for solving two-variable linear programming problems such as the RMC problem. The steps of the graphical solution procedure for a maximization problem are summarized here:

1. Prepare a graph for each constraint that shows the solutions that satisfy the constraint.
2. Determine the feasible region by identifying the solutions that satisfy all the constraints simultaneously.

FIGURE 7.12 FEASIBLE SOLUTIONS FOR THE CONSTRAINT $R - T \geq 0$

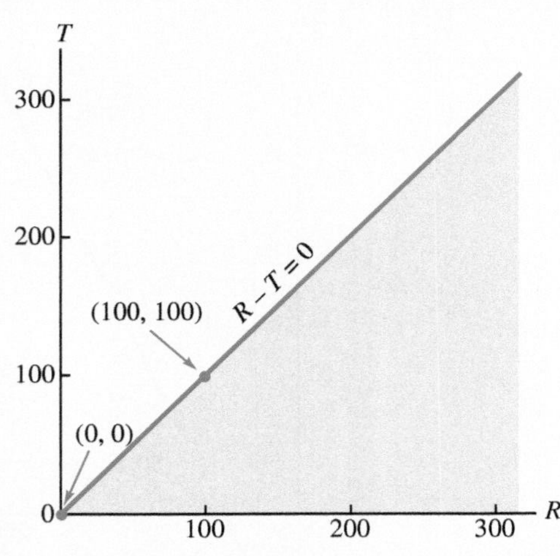

3. Draw an objective function line showing the values of the decision variables that yield a specified value of the objective function.
4. Move parallel objective function lines toward larger objective function values until further movement would take the line completely outside the feasible region.
5. Any feasible solution on the objective function line with the largest value is an optimal solution.

Slack Variables

In addition to the optimal solution and its associated profit contribution, the RMC managers will want information about the production requirements for the three materials. We can determine this information by substituting the optimal solution values ($F = 25$, $S = 20$) into the constraints of the linear program.

Constraint	Tons Required for $F = 25$, $S = 20$ Tons	Tons Available	Unused Tons
Material 1	$0.4(25) + 0.5(20) = 20$	20	0
Material 2	$0.2(20) = 4$	5	1
Material 3	$0.6(25) + 0.3(20) = 21$	21	0

Thus, the optimal solution tells management that the production of 25 tons of fuel additive and 20 tons of solvent base will require all available material 1 and material 3 but only 4 of the 5 tons of material 2. The 1 ton of unused material 2 is referred to as *slack.* In linear programming terminology, any unused or idle capacity for a $\leq$ constraint is referred to as the *slack associated with the constraint.* Thus, the material 2 constraint has a slack of 1 ton.

Can you identify the slack associated with a constraint? Try Problem 24, part (e).

Often variables, called **slack variables**, are added to the formulation of a linear programming problem to represent the slack, or unused capacity, associated with a constraint. Unused capacity makes no contribution to profit, so slack variables have coefficients of zero in the objective function. More generally, slack variables represent the difference between the right-hand side and the left-hand side of a ≤ constraint. After the addition of three slack variables, denoted S_1, S_2, and S_3, the mathematical model of the RMC problem becomes

$$\begin{aligned}
\text{Max} \quad & 40F + 30S + 0S_1 + 0S_2 + 0S_3 \\
\text{s.t.} \quad & \\
& 0.4F + 0.5S + 1S_1 \qquad\qquad\qquad = 20 \\
& \qquad\quad 0.2S \qquad\quad + 1S_2 \qquad\quad = 5 \\
& 0.6F + 0.3S \qquad\qquad\qquad + 1S_3 = 21 \\
& F, S, S_1, S_2, S_3 \geq 0
\end{aligned}$$

Can you write a linear program in standard form? Try Problem 18.

Whenever a linear program is written in a form with all the constraints expressed as equalities, it is said to be written in **standard form**.

Referring to the standard form of the RMC problem, we see that at the optimal solution ($F = 25$, $S = 20$) the values for the slack variables are

Constraint	Value of Slack Variable
Material 1	$S_1 = 0$
Material 2	$S_2 = 1$
Material 3	$S_3 = 0$

Could we have used the graphical analysis to provide some of the previous information? The answer is yes. By finding the optimal solution in Figure 7.6, we see that the material 1 constraint and the material 3 constraint restrict, or *bind*, the feasible region at this point. Thus, the optimal solution requires the use of all of these two resources. In other words, the graph shows that at the optimal solution material 1 and material 3 will have zero slack. But, because the material 2 constraint is not binding the feasible region at the optimal solution, we can expect some slack for this resource.

Finally, some linear programs may have one or more constraints that do not affect the feasible region; that is, the feasible region remains the same whether or not the constraint is included in the problem. Because such a constraint does not affect the feasible region, it is called a **redundant constraint**. Redundant constraints can be dropped from the problem without having any effect on the optimal solution. However, in most linear programming problems redundant constraints are not discarded because they are not immediately recognizable as being redundant. The RMC problem had no redundant constraints because each constraint had an effect on the feasible region.

NOTES AND COMMENTS

1. In the standard form representation of a linear program, the objective function coefficients for the slack variables are zero. This condition implies that slack variables, which represent unused resources, do not affect the value of the objective function. However, in some applications, some or all of the unused resources can be sold and contribute to profit. In such cases the corresponding slack variables become decision variables representing the amount of resources to be sold. For each of these variables, a nonzero coefficient in the objective function would reflect the profit associated with selling a unit of the corresponding resource.
2. Redundant constraints do not affect the feasible region; as a result they can be removed from a linear programming model without affecting the optimal solution. However, if the linear programming model is to be resolved later, changes in some of the data might change a previously redundant constraint into a binding constraint. Thus, we recommend keeping all constraints in the linear programming model even though one or more of the constraints may be redundant.

7.3 Extreme Points and the Optimal Solution

Suppose that the profit contribution for 1 ton of solvent base increases from \$30 to \$60 while the profit contribution for 1 ton of fuel additive and all the constraints remain unchanged. The complete linear programming model of this new problem is identical to the mathematical model in Section 7.2, except for the revised objective function:

$$\text{Max } 40F + 60S$$

How does this change in the objective function affect the optimal solution to the RMC problem? Figure 7.13 shows the graphical solution of the RMC problem with the revised objective function. Note that because the constraints do not change, the feasible region remains unchanged. However, the profit lines must be altered to reflect the new objective function.

By moving the profit line in a parallel manner away from the origin, we find the optimal solution as shown in Figure 7.13. The values of the decision variables at this point are $F = 18.75$ and $S = 25$. The increased profit for the solvent base caused a change in the optimal solution. In fact, as you might suspect, we cut back the production of the lower profit fuel additive and increase the production of the higher profit solvent base.

What do you notice about the location of the optimal solutions in the linear programming problems that we solved thus far? Look closely at the graphical solutions in Figures 7.10 and 7.13. An important observation that you should be able to make is that the optimal solutions occur at one of the vertices, or "corners," of the feasible region. In linear programming terminology these vertices are referred to as the **extreme points** of the feasible region.

FIGURE 7.13 OPTIMAL SOLUTION FOR THE RMC PROBLEM WITH AN OBJECTIVE FUNCTION OF $40F + 60S$

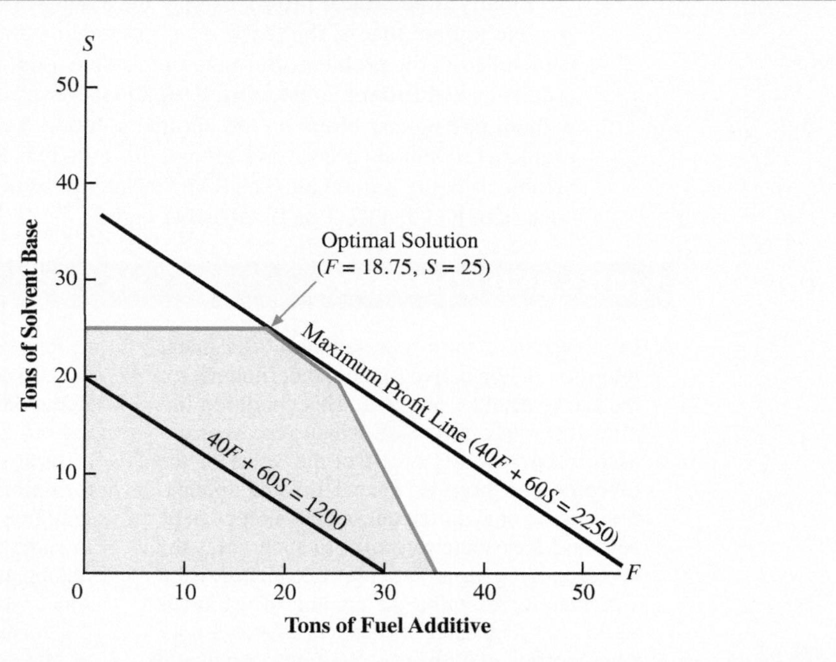

FIGURE 7.14 THE FIVE EXTREME POINTS OF THE FEASIBLE REGION FOR THE RMC PROBLEM

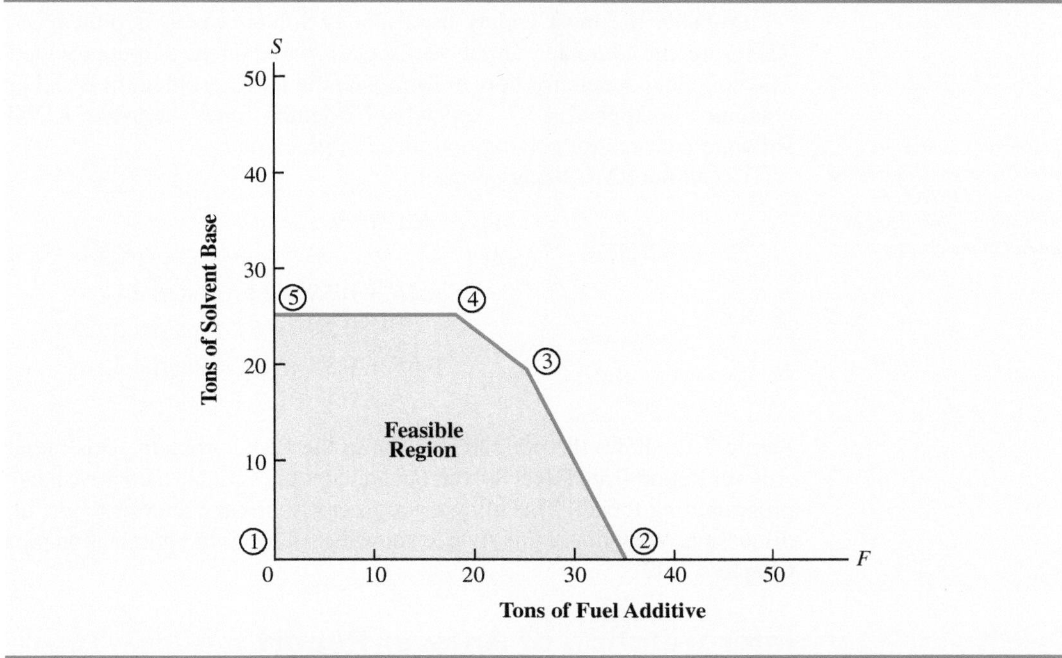

Thus, the RMC has five vertices or five extreme points (Figure 7.14). We can now state our observation about the location of optimal solutions:[2]

> The optimal solution to a linear programming problem can be found at an extreme point of the feasible region for the problem.

For additional practice in identifying the extreme points of the feasible region and determining the optimal solution by computing and comparing the objective function value at each extreme point, try Problem 13.

This property means that, if you are looking for the optimal solution to a linear programming problem, you do not have to evaluate all feasible solution points. In fact, you have to consider *only* the feasible solutions that occur at the extreme points of the feasible region. Thus, for the RMC problem, instead of computing and comparing the profit for all feasible solutions, we can find the optimal solution by evaluating the five extreme-point solutions and selecting the one that provides the highest profit. Actually, the graphical solution procedure is nothing more than a convenient way of identifying an optimal extreme point for two-variable problems.

7.4 Computer Solution of the RMC Problem

Computer programs designed to solve linear programming problems are widely available. After a short period of familiarization with the specific features of the program, most users can solve linear programming problems with few difficulties. Problems involving thousands of variables and thousands of constraints are now routinely solved with computer packages. Some of the leading commercial packages include CPLEX, LINGO, MOSEK, Gurobi,

[2]In Section 7.6 we show that two special cases (infeasibility and unboundedness) in linear programming have no optimal solution. The observation stated does not apply to these cases.

Excel Solver, and Analytic Solver Platform for Excel. Packages are also available for free download. A good example is Clp (COIN-OR linear programming) available from the COIN-OR organization at *http://www.coin-or.org*.

Probably the most widely used tool is Solver, which is built into Microsoft Excel. Therefore, the computer output we discuss is based on the output provided by Excel Solver. The complete details for how to formulate the RMC problem in Excel and use Solver are contained in Appendix 7.1. Appendix 7.2 demonstrates the use of LINGO, a stand-alone software package for solving optimization problems.

Instructions on how to solve linear programs using Excel and LINGO are provided in appendixes at the end of the chapter.

Recall the RMC linear program:

$$\begin{aligned} \text{Max} \quad & 40F + 30S \\ \text{s.t.} \quad & \\ & 0.4F + 0.5S \le 20 \quad \text{Material 1} \\ & 0.2S \le 5 \quad \text{Material 2} \\ & 0.6F + 0.3S \le 21 \quad \text{Material 3} \\ & F, S \ge 0 \end{aligned}$$

Figure 7.15 shows the optimal solution to the RMC problem. This output is based on the Answer Report from Excel Solver, but includes the variable names we have used in our linear programming model. This allows you to easily link the answer report to the model under discussion. We will use this style to show the solutions to optimization problems throughout Chapters 7–12.

Interpretation of Answer Report

Let us look more closely at the answer report in Figure 7.15 and interpret the computer solution provided for the RMC problem. First, note the number 1600.000 in the Objective Cells (Max) section, which appears in the Final Value column to the right of objective function value, Maximize Total Profit. This number indicates that the optimal solution to this problem will provide a profit of $1600. Directly below the objective function value are the values of

FIGURE 7.15 ANSWER REPORT FOR THE RMC PROBLEM

RMC

Objective Cells (Max)

Name	Original Value	Final Value
Maximize Total Profit	0.000	1600.000

Variable Cells

Model Variable	Name	Original Value	Final Value	Integer
F	Tons Produced Fuel Additive	0.000	25.000	Contin
S	Tons Produced Solvent Base	0.000	20.000	Contin

Constraints

Constraint Number	Name	Cell Value	Status	Slack
1	Material 1 Amount Used	20.000	Binding	0.000
2	Material 2 Amount Used	4.000	Not Binding	1.000
3	Material 3 Amount Used	21.000	Binding	0.000

the decision variables at the optimal solution. These are shown as the Final Value column of the Variable Cells section in the answer report. Thus, we have $F = 25$ tons of fuel additive and $S = 20$ tons of solvent base as the optimal production quantities. We will discuss the meaning of the Integer column in the Variable Cells section in Chapter 11.

The Constraints section of the answer report provides information about the status of the constraints. Recall that the RMC problem had three less-than-or-equal-to constraints corresponding to the tons available for each of the three raw materials. The information shown in the Slack column provides the value of the slack variable for each of the three constraints. This information is summarized as follows:

Constraint Number	Constraint Name	Value of Slack Variable
1	Material 1 Amount Used	0
2	Material 2 Amount Used	1
3	Material 3 Amount Used	0

Thus, we see that the binding constraints (the Material 1 Amount Used and Material 3 Amount Used constraints) have zero slack at the optimal solution. The Material 2 Amount Used constraint has 1 ton of slack, or unused capacity.

7.5 A Simple Minimization Problem

M&D Chemicals produces two products that are sold as raw materials to companies manufacturing bath soaps and laundry detergents. Based on an analysis of current inventory levels and potential demand for the coming month, M&D's management has specified that the combined production for products A and B must total at least 350 gallons. Separately, a major customer's order for 125 gallons of product A must also be satisfied. Product A requires 2 hours of processing time per gallon while product B requires 1 hour of processing time per gallon, and for the coming month, 600 hours of processing time are available. M&D's objective is to satisfy these requirements at a minimum total production cost. Production costs are \$2 per gallon for product A and \$3 per gallon for product B.

To find the minimum-cost production schedule, we will formulate the M&D Chemicals problem as a linear program. Following a procedure similar to the one used for the RMC problem, we first define the decision variables and the objective function for the problem. Let

$$A = \text{number of gallons of product A}$$
$$B = \text{number of gallons of product B}$$

Because the production costs are \$2 per gallon for product A and \$3 per gallon for product B, the objective function that corresponds to the minimization of the total production cost can be written as

$$\text{Min } 2A + 3B$$

Next, consider the constraints placed on the M&D Chemicals problem. To satisfy the major customer's demand for 125 gallons of product A, we know A must be at least 125. Thus, we write the constraint

$$1A \geq 125$$

Because the combined production for both products must total at least 350 gallons, we can write the constraint

$$1A + 1B \geq 350$$

Finally, the limitation on available processing time of 600 hours means that we need to add the constraint

$$2A + 1B \leq 600$$

After adding the nonnegativity constraints ($A, B \geq 0$), we have the following linear program for the M&D Chemicals problem:

$$\begin{aligned}
\text{Max} \quad & 2A + 3B \\
\text{s.t.} \quad & \\
& 1A \geq 125 && \text{Demand for product A} \\
& 1A + 1B \geq 350 && \text{Total production} \\
& 2A + 1B \leq 600 && \text{Processing time} \\
& A, B \geq 0
\end{aligned}$$

Because the linear programming model has only two decision variables, the graphical solution procedure can be used to find the optimal production quantities. The graphical method for this problem, just as in the RMC problem, requires us to first graph the constraint lines to find the feasible region. By graphing each constraint line separately and then checking points on either side of the constraint line, the solutions that satisfy each constraint can be identified. By combining the solutions that satisfy each constraint on the same graph, we obtain the feasible region shown in Figure 7.16.

FIGURE 7.16 FEASIBLE REGION FOR THE M&D CHEMICALS PROBLEM

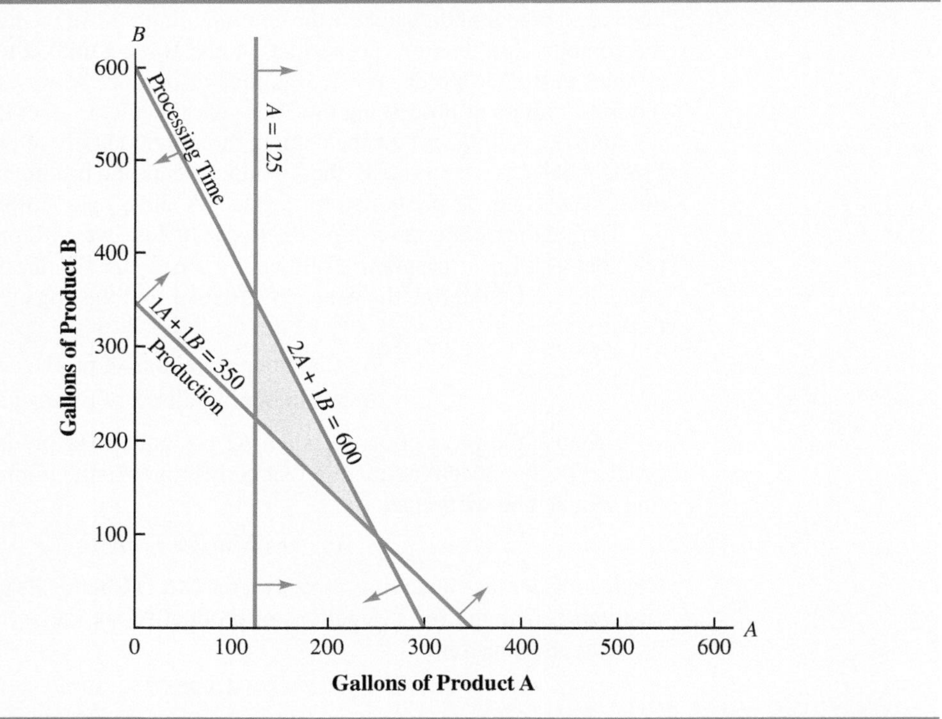

FIGURE 7.17 GRAPHICAL SOLUTION FOR THE M&D CHEMICALS PROBLEM

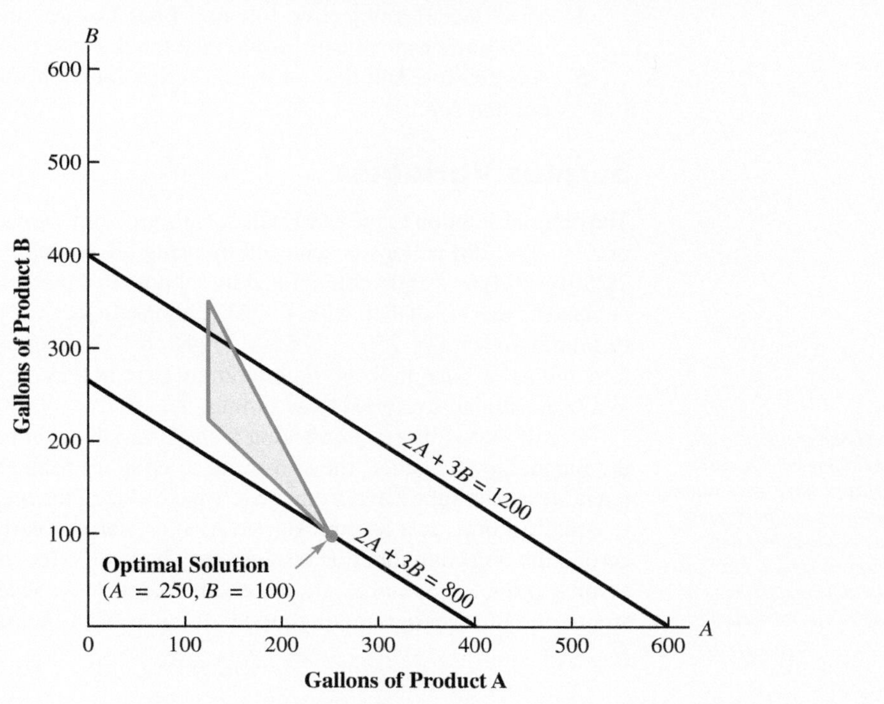

To find the minimum-cost solution, we now draw the objective function line corresponding to a particular total cost value. For example, we might start by drawing the line $2A + 3B = 1200$. This line is shown in Figure 7.17. Clearly some points in the feasible region would provide a total cost of \$1200. To find the values of A and B that provide smaller total cost values, we move the objective function line in a lower left direction until, if we moved it any farther, it would be entirely outside the feasible region. Note that the objective function line $2A + 3B = 800$ intersects the feasible region at the extreme point $A = 250$ and $B = 100$. This extreme point provides the minimum-cost solution with an objective function value of 800. From Figures 7.16 and 7.17, we can see that the total production constraint and the processing time constraint are binding. Just as in every linear programming problem, the optimal solution occurs at an extreme point of the feasible region.

Summary of the Graphical Solution Procedure for Minimization Problems

Can you use the graphical solution procedure to determine the optimal solution for a minimization problem? Try Problem 31.

The steps of the graphical solution procedure for a minimization problem are summarized here:

1. Prepare a graph for each constraint that shows the solutions that satisfy the constraint.
2. Determine the feasible region by identifying the solutions that satisfy all the constraints simultaneously.

3. Draw an objective function line showing the values of the decision variables that yield a specified value of the objective function.
4. Move parallel objective function lines toward smaller objective function values until further movement would take the line completely outside the feasible region.
5. Any feasible solution on the objective function line with the smallest value is an optimal solution.

Surplus Variables

The optimal solution to the M&D Chemicals problem shows that the desired total production of $A + B = 350$ gallons is achieved by using all available processing time of $2A + 1B = 2(250) + 1(100) = 600$ hours. In addition, note that the constraint requiring that product A demand be met is satisfied with $A = 250$ gallons. In fact, the production of product A exceeds its minimum level by $250 - 125 = 125$ gallons. This excess production for product A is referred to as *surplus.* In linear programming terminology, any excess quantity corresponding to a $\geq$ constraint is referred to as surplus.

Excel Solver refers to all nonbinding constraints as having positive slack values regardless of whether they are $\geq$ or $\leq$ constraints. However, we will use "surplus" when referring to a nonbinding $\geq$ constraint.

Recall that with a $\leq$ constraint, a slack variable can be added to the left-hand side of the inequality to convert the constraint to equality form. With a $\geq$ constraint, a **surplus variable** can be subtracted from the left-hand side of the inequality to convert the constraint to equality form. Just as with slack variables, surplus variables are given a coefficient of zero in the objective function because they have no effect on its value. After including two surplus variables, S_1 and S_2, for the $\geq$ constraints and one slack variable, S_3, for the $\leq$ constraint, the linear programming model of the M&D Chemicals problem becomes

$$
\begin{aligned}
\text{Min}\quad & 2A + 3B + 0S_1 + 0S_2 + 0S_3 \\
\text{s.t.}\quad & \\
& 1A \quad - 1S_1 \quad = 125 \\
& 1A + 1B \quad - 1S_2 \quad = 350 \\
& 2A + 1B \quad + 1S_3 = 600 \\
& A, B, S_1, S_2, S_3 \geq 0
\end{aligned}
$$

Try Problem 35 to test your ability to use slack and surplus variables to write a linear program in standard form.

All the constraints are now equalities. Hence, the preceding formulation is the standard form representation of the M&D Chemicals problem. At the optimal solution of $A = 250$ and $B = 100$, the values of the surplus and slack variables are as follows:

Constraint	Value of Surplus or Slack Variable
Demand for product A	$S_1 = 125$
Total production	$S_2 = 0$
Processing time	$S_3 = 0$

Refer to Figures 7.16 and 7.17. Note that the zero surplus and slack variables are associated with the constraints that are binding at the optimal solution—that is, the total production and processing time constraints. The surplus of 125 units is associated with the nonbinding constraint on the demand for product A.

In the RMC problem all the constraints were of the $\leq$ type, and in the M&D Chemicals problem the constraints were a mixture of $\geq$ and $\leq$ types. The number and types of constraints encountered in a particular linear programming problem depend on the specific conditions existing in the problem. Linear programming problems may have some $\leq$ constraints, some $\geq$ constraints, and some $=$ constraints. For an equality constraint, feasible solutions must lie directly on the constraint line.

Try Problem 34 to practice solving a linear program with all three constraint forms.

An example of a linear program with two decision variables, G and H, and all three constraint forms is given here:

$$\begin{aligned} \text{Min} \quad & 2G + 2H \\ \text{s.t.} \quad & \\ & 1G + 3H \le 12 \\ & 3G + 1H \ge 13 \\ & 1G - 1H = 3 \\ & G, H \ge 0 \end{aligned}$$

The standard-form representation of this problem is

$$\begin{aligned} \text{Min} \quad & 2G + 2H + 0S_1 + 0S_2 \\ \text{s.t.} \quad & \\ & 1G + 3H + 1S_1 = 12 \\ & 3G + 1H - 1S_2 = 13 \\ & 1G - 1H = 3 \\ & G, H, S_1, S_2 \ge 0 \end{aligned}$$

The standard form requires a slack variable for the $\le$ constraint and a surplus variable for the $\ge$ constraint. However, neither a slack nor a surplus variable is required for the third constraint because it is already in equality form.

When solving linear programs graphically, it is not necessary to write the problem in its standard form. Nevertheless, it is helpful to be able to compute the values of the slack and surplus variables and understand what they mean. A final point: The standard form of the linear programming problem is equivalent to the original formulation of the problem. That is, the optimal solution to any linear programming problem is the same as the optimal solution to the standard form of the problem. The standard form does not change the basic problem; it only changes how we write the constraints for the problem.

Computer Solution of the M&D Chemicals Problem

The answer report for the M&D Chemicals Problem is presented in Figure 7.18. The answer report shows that the minimum-cost solution yields an objective function value of $800.

FIGURE 7.18 ANSWER REPORT FOR THE M&D CHEMICALS PROBLEM

M&D

Objective Cells (Min)

Name	Original Value	Final Value
Minimize Total Cost Product A	0.000	800.000

Variable Cells

Model Variable	Name	Original Value	Final Value	Integer
A	Gallons Produced Product A	0.000	250.000	Contin
B	Gallons Produced Product B	0.000	100.000	Contin

Constraints

Constraint Number	Name	Cell Value	Status	Slack
1	Demand for Product A	250.000	Not Binding	125.000
2	Total Production	350.000	Binding	0.000
3	Processing Time	600.000	Binding	0.000

The values of the decision variables show that 250 gallons of product A and 100 gallons of product B provide the minimum-cost solution.

The Slack column in the Constraints section of the answer report shows that the $\geq$ constraint corresponding to the demand for product A (see constraint 1) has a value of 125 units. Excel uses "slack" when referring to nonbinding $\geq$ or $\leq$ constraints. However, since this is a $\geq$ constraint, it tells us that production of product A in the optimal solution exceeds demand by 125 gallons. In other words, the demand for product A (constraint 1) has a surplus value of 125 units. The slack values are zero for the total production requirement (constraint 2) and the processing time limitation (constraint 3), which indicates that these constraints are binding at the optimal solution.

7.6 Special Cases

In this section we discuss three special situations that can arise when we attempt to solve linear programming problems.

Alternative Optimal Solutions

From our discussion of the graphical solution procedure, we know that optimal solutions can be found at the extreme points of the feasible region. Now let us consider the special case where the optimal objective function line coincides with one of the binding constraint lines. It can lead to **alternative optimal solutions**, whereby more than one solution provides the optimal value for the objective function.

To illustrate the case of alternative optimal solutions, we return to the RMC problem. However, let us assume that the profit contribution for the solvent base (S) has increased to \$50. The revised objective function is $40F + 50S$. Figure 7.19 shows the graphical solution to this problem. Note that the optimal solution still occurs at an extreme point. In fact, it occurs at two extreme points: extreme point ③ ($F = 25, S = 20$) and extreme point ④ ($F = 18.75, S = 25$).

The objective function values at these two extreme points are identical; that is,

$$40F + 50S = 40(25) + 50(20) = 2000$$

and

$$40F + 50S = 40(18.75) + 50(25) = 2000$$

Furthermore, any point on the line connecting the two optimal extreme points also provides an optimal solution. For example, the solution point ($F = 21.875, S = 22.5$), which is halfway between the two extreme points, also provides the optimal objective function value of

$$40F + 50S = 40(21.875) + 50(22.5) = 2000$$

A linear programming problem with alternative optimal solutions is generally a good situation for the manager or decision maker. It means that several combinations of the decision variables are optimal and that the manager can select the most desirable optimal solution. Unfortunately, determining whether a problem has alternative optimal solutions is not a simple matter.

Infeasibility

Infeasibility means that no solution to the linear programming problem satisfies all constraints, including the nonnegativity constraints. Graphically, infeasibility means that a feasible region does not exist; that is, no points satisfy all constraint equations and

FIGURE 7.19 OPTIMAL SOLUTIONS FOR THE RMC PROBLEM WITH AN OBJECTIVE FUNCTION OF $40F + 50S$

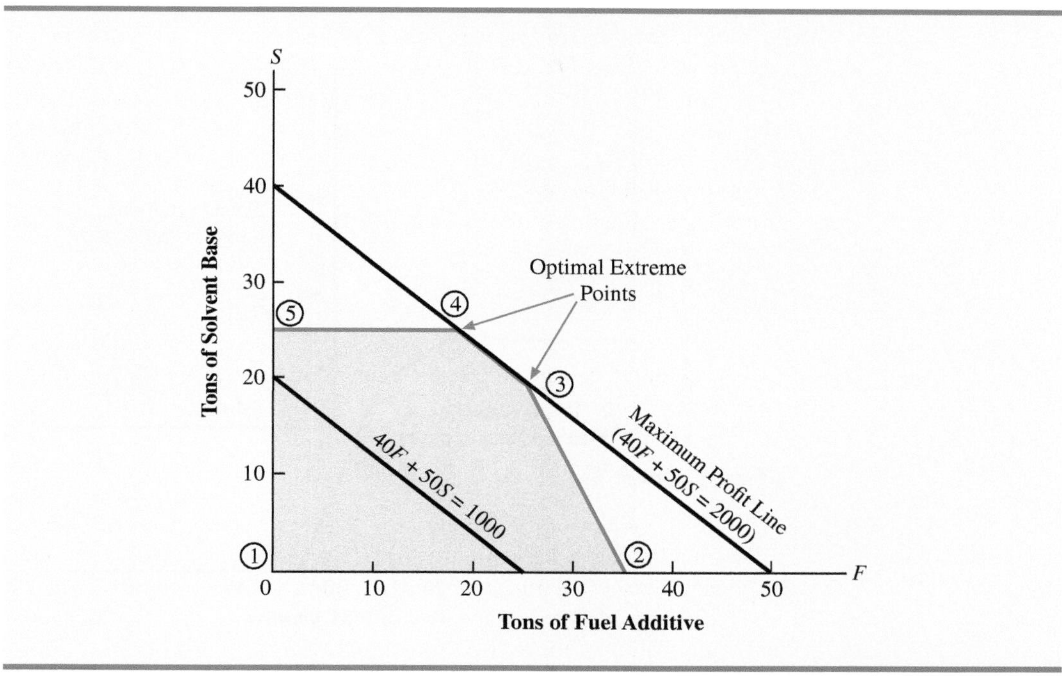

nonnegativity conditions simultaneously. To illustrate this situation, let us return to the problem facing RMC.

Problems with no feasible solution do arise in practice, most often because management's expectations are too high or because too many restrictions have been placed on the problem.

Suppose that management specified that at least 30 tons of fuel additive and at least 15 tons of solvent base must be produced. Figure 7.20 shows the graph of the solution region that reflects these requirements. The shaded area in the lower left-hand portion of the graph depicts those points satisfying the less-than-or-equal-to constraints on the amount of materials available. The shaded area in the upper right-hand portion depicts those points satisfying the minimum production requirements of 30 tons of fuel additive and 15 tons of solvent base. But none of the points satisfy both sets of constraints. Thus, if management imposes these minimum production requirements, no feasible solution to the linear programming problem is possible.

How should we interpret this infeasibility in terms of the current problem? First, we should tell management that, for the available amounts of the three materials, producing 30 tons of fuel additive and 15 tons of solvent base isn't possible. Moreover, we can tell management exactly how much more of each material is needed.

Material	**Minimum Tons Required for $F = 30, S = 15$**	**Tons Available**	**Additional Tons Required**
Material 1	$0.4(30) + 0.5(15) = 19.5$	20	—
Material 2	$0.2(15) = 3$	5	—
Material 3	$0.6(30) + 0.3(15) = 22.5$	21	1.5

FIGURE 7.20 NO FEASIBLE REGION FOR THE RMC PROBLEM WITH MINIMUM PRODUCTION REQUIREMENTS

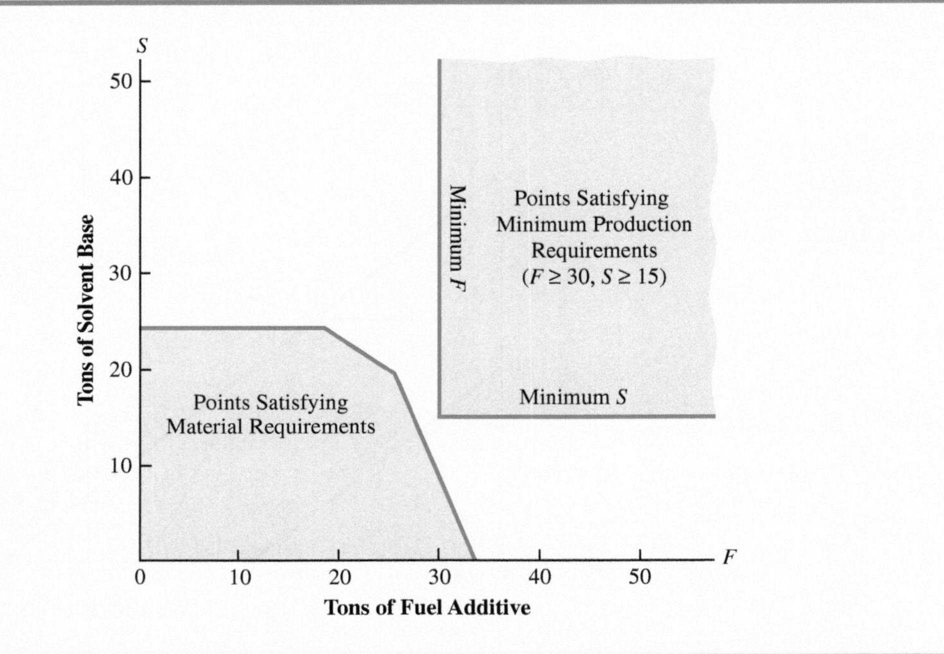

Thus, RMC has a sufficient supply of materials 1 and 2 but will need 1.5 additional tons of material 3 to meet management's production requirements of 30 tons of fuel additive and 15 tons of solvent base. If, after reviewing the preceding analysis, management still wants this level of production for the two products, RMC will have to obtain the additional 1.5 tons of material 3.

Often, many possibilities are available for corrective management action, once we discover the lack of a feasible solution. The important thing to realize is that linear programming analysis can help determine whether management's plans are feasible. By analyzing the problem using linear programming, we are often able to point out infeasible conditions and initiate corrective action.

Whenever you attempt to solve a problem that is infeasible using Excel Solver, you will obtain a message that says "Solver could not find a feasible solution." In this case, you know that no solution to the linear programming problem will satisfy all constraints. Careful inspection of your formulation is necessary to identify why the problem is infeasible. In some situations the only reasonable approach is to drop one or more constraints and resolve the problem. If you are able to find an optimal solution for this revised problem, you will know that the constraint(s) that were omitted are causing the problem to be infeasible.

Unbounded

The solution to a maximization linear programming problem is **unbounded** if the value of the solution may be made infinitely large without violating any of the constraints; for a minimization problem, the solution is unbounded if the value may be made infinitely small. This condition might be termed *managerial utopia*; for example, if this condition were to occur in a profit maximization problem, the manager could achieve an unlimited profit.

However, in linear programming models of real problems, the occurrence of an unbounded solution means that the problem has been improperly formulated. We know it is not possible to increase profits indefinitely. Therefore, we must conclude that if a profit maximization problem results in an unbounded solution, the mathematical model doesn't represent the real-world problem sufficiently. Usually, an unbounded problem results from the inadvertent omission of a constraint during problem formulation.

As an illustration, consider the following linear program with two decision variables, X and Y:

$$\begin{aligned} \text{Max} \quad & 20X + 10Y \\ \text{s.t.} \quad & \\ & 1X \geq 2 \\ & 1Y \leq 5 \\ & X, Y \geq 0 \end{aligned}$$

In Figure 7.21 we graphed the feasible region associated with this problem. Note that we can only indicate part of the feasible region because the feasible region extends indefinitely in the direction of the X-axis. Looking at the objective function lines in Figure 7.21, we see that the solution to this problem may be made as large as we desire. No matter what solution we pick, we will always be able to reach some feasible solution with a larger value. Thus, we say that the solution to this linear program is *unbounded.*

FIGURE 7.21 EXAMPLE OF AN UNBOUNDED PROBLEM

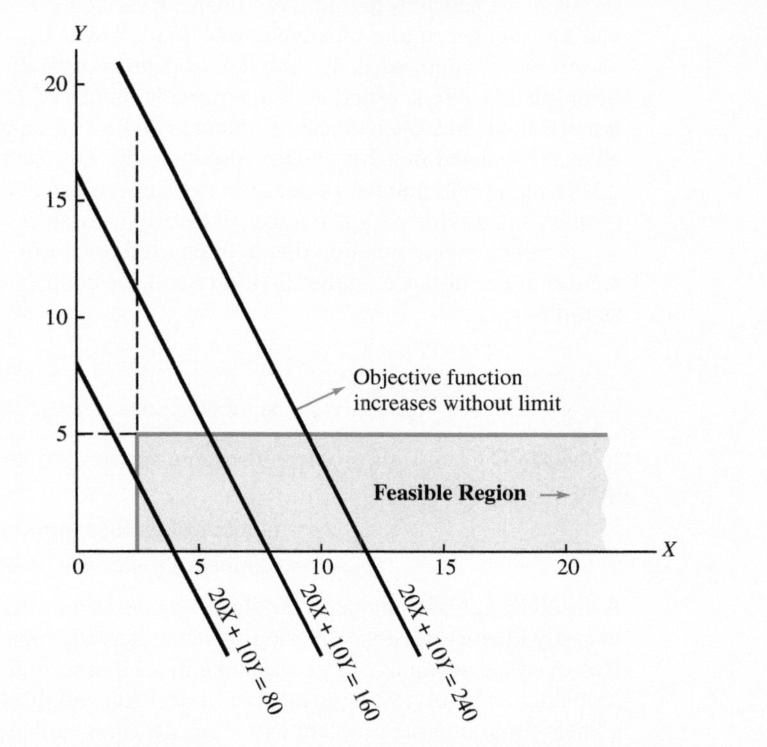

Can you recognize whether a linear program involves alternative optimal solutions, infeasibility, or is unbounded? Try Problems 42 and 43.

Whenever you attempt to solve a problem that is unbounded using Excel Solver, you will obtain a message that says, "The Objective Cell values do not converge." Because unbounded solutions cannot occur in real problems, the first thing you should do is to review your model to determine whether you have incorrectly formulated the problem.

NOTES AND COMMENTS

1. Infeasibility is independent of the objective function. It exists because the constraints are so restrictive that they allow no feasible region for the linear programming model. Thus, when you encounter infeasibility, making changes in the coefficients of the objective function will not help; the problem will remain infeasible.
2. The occurrence of an unbounded solution is often the result of a missing constraint. However, a change in the objective function may cause a previously unbounded problem to become bounded with an optimal solution. For example, the graph in Figure 7.21 shows an unbounded solution for the objective function Max $20X + 10Y$. However, changing the objective function to Max $-20X - 10Y$ will provide the optimal solution $X = 2$ and $Y = 0$ even though no changes have been made in the constraints.

7.7 General Linear Programming Notation

In this chapter we showed how to formulate mathematical models for the RMC and M&D Chemicals linear programming problems. To formulate a mathematical model of the RMC problem, we began by defining two decision variables: F = number of tons of fuel additive, and S = number of tons of solvent base. In the M&D Chemicals problem, the two decision variables were defined as A = number of gallons of product A, and B = number of gallons of product B. We selected decision variable names of F and S in the RMC problem and A and B in the M&D Chemicals problem to make it easier to recall what these decision variables represented in the problem. Although this approach works well for linear programs involving a small number of decision variables, it can become difficult when dealing with problems involving a large number of decision variables.

A more general notation that is often used for linear programs uses the letter x with a subscript. For instance, in the RMC problem, we could have defined the decision variables as follows:

$$x_1 = \text{number of tons of fuel additive}$$
$$x_2 = \text{number of tons of solvent base}$$

In the M&D Chemicals problem, the same variable names would be used, but their definitions would change:

$$x_1 = \text{number of gallons of product A}$$
$$x_2 = \text{number of gallons of product B}$$

A disadvantage of using general notation for decision variables is that we are no longer able to easily identify what the decision variables actually represent in the mathematical model. However, the advantage of general notation is that formulating a mathematical model for a problem that involves a large number of decision variables is much easier. For instance, for a linear programming problem with three decision variables, we would use variable names of x_1, x_2, and x_3; for a problem with four decision variables, we would use variable names of

x_1, x_2, x_3, and x_4; and so on. Clearly, if a problem involved 1000 decision variables, trying to identify 1000 unique names would be difficult. However, using the general linear programming notation, the decision variables would be defined as $x_1, x_2, x_3, \ldots, x_{1000}$.

To illustrate the graphical solution procedure for a linear program written using general linear programming notation, consider the following mathematical model for a maximization problem involving two decision variables:

$$\begin{aligned} \text{Max} \quad & 3x_1 + 2x_2 \\ \text{s.t.} \quad & \\ & 2x_1 + 2x_2 \leq 8 \\ & 1x_1 + 0.5x_2 \leq 3 \\ & x_1, x_2 \geq 0 \end{aligned}$$

We must first develop a graph that displays the possible solutions (x_1 and x_2 values) for the problem. The usual convention is to plot values of x_1 along the horizontal axis and values of x_2 along the vertical axis. Figure 7.22 shows the graphical solution for this two-variable

FIGURE 7.22 GRAPHICAL SOLUTION OF A TWO-VARIABLE LINEAR PROGRAM WITH GENERAL NOTATION

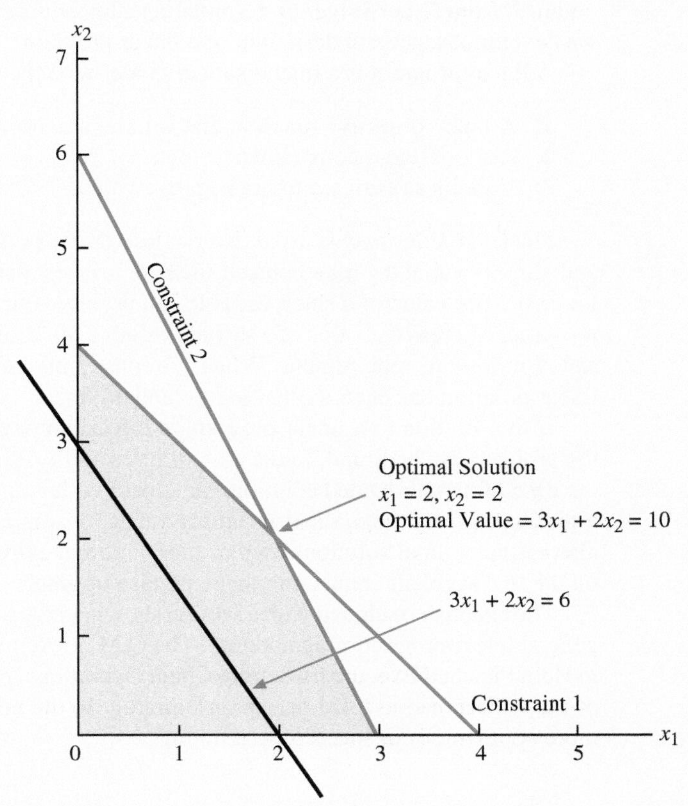

problem. Note that for this problem the optimal solution is $x_1 = 2$ and $x_2 = 2$, with an objective function value of 10.

Using general linear programming notation, we can write the standard form of the preceding problem as follows:

$$
\begin{aligned}
\text{Max} \quad & 3x_1 + 2x_2 + 0s_1 + 0s_2 \\
\text{s.t.} \quad & \\
& 2x_1 + 2x_2 + 1s_1 \qquad = 8 \\
& 1x_1 + 0.5x_2 + \qquad 1s_2 = 3 \\
& x_1, x_2, s_1, s_2 \geq 0
\end{aligned}
$$

Thus, at the optimal solution $x_1 = 2$ and $x_2 = 2$, the values of the slack variables are $s_1 = s_2 = 0$.

Summary

We formulated linear programming models for the RMC maximization problem and the M&D Chemicals minimization problem. For both problems we showed how a graphical solution procedure can be used to identify an optimal solution. To demonstrate how to interpret linear program solutions, we introduced answer reports similar to the output obtained from Excel Solver. In formulating a linear programming model of these problems, we developed a general definition of a linear program.

A linear program is a mathematical model with the following qualities:

1. A linear objective function that is to be maximized or minimized
2. A set of linear constraints
3. Variables restricted to nonnegative values

Slack variables may be used to write less-than-or-equal-to constraints in equality form, and surplus variables may be used to write greater-than-or-equal-to constraints in equality form. The value of a slack variable can usually be interpreted as the amount of unused resource, whereas the value of a surplus variable indicates the amount over and above some stated minimum requirement. When all constraints have been written as equalities, the linear program has been written in its standard form.

If the solution to a linear program is infeasible or unbounded, no optimal solution to the problem can be found. In the case of infeasibility, no feasible solutions are possible. In the case of an unbounded solution, the objective function can be made infinitely large for a maximization problem and infinitely small for a minimization problem. In the case of alternative optimal solutions, two or more optimal extreme points exist, and all the points on the line segment connecting them are also optimal.

The chapter concluded with a section showing how to write a mathematical model using general linear programming notation. The Q.M. in Action, IBM Uses Linear Programming to Help Plan and Execute Its Supply Chain Operations, provides just one of many examples of the widespread use of linear programming. In the next two chapters we will see many more applications of linear programming.

Q.M. *in* ACTION

*IBM USES LINEAR PROGRAMMING TO HELP PLAN AND EXECUTE ITS SUPPLY CHAIN OPERATIONS**

A semiconductor technically refers to the material, usually silicon, used to build integrated circuits that become the main building components for electronic devices. But in casual usage, semiconductor manufacturing refers to the design and production of the actual integrated circuit that performs the calculations necessary to power your computers, smartphones, tablets, and virtually every other electronic device with which you are familiar.

Semiconductor supply chains are very complex because they typically stretch across the globe and include many different suppliers, manufacturers, distributors, and customers. Hundreds of operations are required to produce semiconductors, and lead times are often very long. To produce a finished semiconductor, the three-dimensional circuits must be deposited onto the base layer of semiconductive material through a process of deposition, photolithography, etching, and ion implantation. The circuits must then be thoroughly tested and packaged for shipment to customers. Small deviations in the manufacturing process result in different quality (speed) of devices. These different devices can sometimes be used as a substitute in times of shortages. For instance, if there are no medium-speed devices available for a certain manufacturing step, a high-speed device can be used instead, but a medium-speed device cannot be substituted for a high-speed device. This creates a multitude of different possible flows through the supply chain that must be constantly managed.

IBM has been producing semiconductors for more than 50 years. IBM manufactures semiconductors in Asia and in North America, and they distribute them around the world. IBM has been using quantitative methods for many years to plan and execute its supply chain strategies. IBM's Central Planning Engine (CPE) is the set of tools the company uses to manage its supply chain activities for semiconductors. The CPE uses a combination of quantitative methods, including linear programming. The model constraints include limitations on production capacities, raw material availabilities, lead time delays, and demand requirements. There are also constraints to enforce the substitution possibilities for certain devices. While many different problem-solving methods are used in the CPE, linear programing is used in several different steps, including the allocation of production capacity to devices based on available capacities and materials.

IBM uses the CPE to perform both long-term strategic planning and short-term operational execution for its semiconductor supply chain. Because of the clever use of specific quantitative methods, these complex calculations can be completed in just a few hours. These fast solution times allow IBM to run several different possible scenarios in a single day and implement sensitivity analysis to understand possible risks in its supply chain. IBM credits the use of the CPE to increasing on-time deliveries by 15% and reducing inventory by 25 to 30%.

*Based on Alfred Degbotse, Brian T. Denton, Kenneth Fordyce, R. John Milne, Robert Orzell, Chi-Tai Wang, "IBM Blends Heuristics and Optimization to Plan Its Semiconductor Supply Chain," *Interfaces*, 2012, 1–12.

Glossary

Alternative optimal solutions The case in which more than one solution provides the optimal value for the objective function.

Constraint An equation or inequality that rules out certain combinations of decision variables as feasible solutions.

Decision variable A controllable input for a linear programming model.

Extreme point Graphically speaking, extreme points are the feasible solution points occurring at the vertices, or "corners," of the feasible region. With two-variable problems, extreme points are determined by the intersection of the constraint lines.
Feasible region The set of all feasible solutions.
Feasible solution A solution that satisfies all the constraints simultaneously.
Infeasibility The situation in which no solution to the linear programming problem satisfies all the constraints.
Linear functions Mathematical expressions in which the variables appear in separate terms and are raised to the first power.
Linear program A mathematical model with a linear objective function, a set of linear constraints, and nonnegative variables.
Mathematical model A representation of a problem where the objective and all constraint conditions are described by mathematical expressions.
Nonnegativity constraints A set of constraints that requires all variables to be nonnegative.
Objective function The expression that defines the quantity to be maximized or minimized in a linear programming model.
Problem formulation The process of translating a verbal statement of a problem into a mathematical statement called the *mathematical model.*
Redundant constraint A constraint that does not affect the feasible region. If a constraint is redundant, it can be removed from the problem without affecting the feasible region.
Slack variable A variable added to the left-hand side of a less-than-or-equal-to constraint to convert the constraint into an equality. The value of this variable can usually be interpreted as the amount of unused resource.
Standard form A linear program in which all the constraints are written as equalities. The optimal solution of the standard form of a linear program is the same as the optimal solution of the original formulation of the linear program.
Surplus variable A variable subtracted from the left-hand side of a greater-than-or-equal-to constraint to convert the constraint into an equality. The value of this variable can usually be interpreted as the amount over and above some required minimum level.
Unbounded The situation in which the value of the solution may be made infinitely large in a maximization linear programming problem or infinitely small in a minimization problem without violating any of the constraints.

Problems

1. Which of the following mathematical relationships could be found in a linear programming model, and which could not? For the relationships that are unacceptable for linear programs, state why.
   a. $-1A + 2B \leq 70$
   b. $2A - 2B = 50$
   c. $1A - 2B^2 \leq 10$
   d. $3\sqrt{A} + 2B \geq 15$
   e. $1A + 1B = 6$
   f. $2A + 5B + 1AB \leq 25$

2. Find the solutions that satisfy the following constraints:
   a. $4A + 2B \leq 16$
   b. $4A + 2B \geq 16$
   c. $4A + 2B = 16$

3. Show a separate graph of the constraint lines and the solutions that satisfy each of the following constraints:
   a. $3A + 2B \leq 18$
   b. $12A + 8B \geq 480$
   c. $5A + 10B = 200$
4. Show a separate graph of the constraint lines and the solutions that satisfy each of the following constraints:
   a. $3A - 4B \geq 60$
   b. $-6A + 5B \leq 60$
   c. $5A - 2B \leq 0$
5. Show a separate graph of the constraint lines and the solutions that satisfy each of the following constraints:
   a. $A \geq 0.25\ (A + B)$
   b. $B \leq 0.10\ (A + B)$
   c. $A \leq 0.50\ (A + B)$

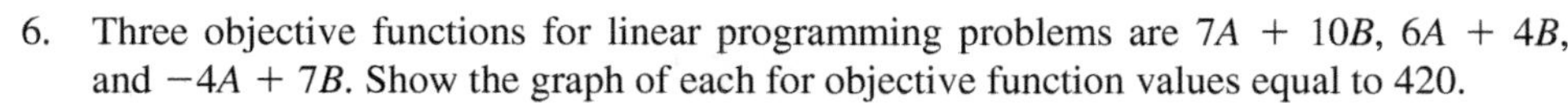

6. Three objective functions for linear programming problems are $7A + 10B$, $6A + 4B$, and $-4A + 7B$. Show the graph of each for objective function values equal to 420.

7. Identify the feasible region for the following set of constraints:

$$\begin{aligned} 0.5A + 0.25B &\geq 30 \\ 1A + \quad 5B &\geq 250 \\ 0.25A + \quad 0.5B &\leq 50 \\ A, B &\geq 0 \end{aligned}$$

8. Identify the feasible region for the following set of constraints:

$$\begin{aligned} 2A - \quad 1B &\leq 0 \\ -1A + 1.5B &\leq 200 \\ A, B &\geq 0 \end{aligned}$$

9. Identify the feasible region for the following set of constraints:

$$\begin{aligned} 3A - 2B &\geq 0 \\ 2A - 1B &\leq 200 \\ 1A \qquad &\leq 150 \\ A, B &\geq 0 \end{aligned}$$

SELF test

10. For the linear program

$$\begin{aligned} \text{Max} \quad & 2A + 3B \\ \text{s.t.} \quad & \\ & 1A + 2B \leq 6 \\ & 5A + 3B \leq 15 \\ & A, B \geq 0 \end{aligned}$$

find the optimal solution using the graphical solution procedure. What is the value of the objective function at the optimal solution?

11. Solve the following linear program using the graphical solution procedure:

$$\begin{aligned} \text{Max} \quad & 5A + 5B \\ \text{s.t.} \quad & \\ & 1A \qquad \leq 100 \\ & \qquad 1B \leq 80 \\ & 2A + 4B \leq 400 \\ & A, B \geq 0 \end{aligned}$$

12. Consider the following linear programming problem:

$$\begin{aligned} \text{Max} \quad & 3A + 3B \\ \text{s.t.} \quad & \\ & 2A + 4B \le 12 \\ & 6A + 4B \le 24 \\ & A, B \ge 0 \end{aligned}$$

   a. Find the optimal solution using the graphical solution procedure.
   b. If the objective function is changed to $2A + 6B$, what is the optimal solution?
   c. How many extreme points are there? What are the values of A and B at each extreme point?

13. Consider the following linear program:

$$\begin{aligned} \text{Max} \quad & 1A + 2B \\ \text{s.t.} \quad & \\ & 1A \le 5 \\ & 1B \le 5 \\ & 2A + 2B = 12 \\ & A, B \ge 0 \end{aligned}$$

   a. Show the feasible region.
   b. What are the extreme points of the feasible region?
   c. Find the optimal solution using the graphical procedure.

14. Par, Inc., is a small manufacturer of golf equipment and supplies. Par's distributor believes a market exists for both a medium-priced golf bag, referred to as a standard model, and a high-priced golf bag, referred to as a deluxe model. The distributor is so confident of the market that, if Par can make the bags at a competitive price, the distributor will purchase all the bags that Par can manufacture over the next three months. A careful analysis of the manufacturing requirements resulted in the following table, which shows the production time requirements for the four required manufacturing operations and the accounting department's estimate of the profit contribution per bag:

	Production Time (hours)				
Product	**Cutting and Dyeing**	**Sewing**	**Finishing**	**Inspection and Packaging**	**Profit per Bag**
Standard	$^7/_{10}$	$^1/_2$	1	$^1/_{10}$	\$10
Deluxe	1	$^5/_6$	$^2/_3$	$^1/_4$	\$ 9

The director of manufacturing estimates that 630 hours of cutting and dyeing time, 600 hours of sewing time, 708 hours of finishing time, and 135 hours of inspection and packaging time will be available for the production of golf bags during the next three months.

   a. If the company wants to maximize total profit contribution, how many bags of each model should it manufacture?
   b. What profit contribution can Par earn on those production quantities?
   c. How many hours of production time will be scheduled for each operation?
   d. What is the slack time in each operation?

15. Suppose that Par's management (Problem 14) encounters the following situations:
    a. The accounting department revises its estimate of the profit contribution for the deluxe bag to \$18 per bag.
    b. A new low-cost material is available for the standard bag, and the profit contribution per standard bag can be increased to \$20 per bag. (Assume that the profit contribution of the deluxe bag is the original \$9 value.)
    c. New sewing equipment is available that would increase the sewing operation capacity to 750 hours. (Assume that $10A + 9B$ is the appropriate objective function.)

    If each of these situations is encountered separately, what is the optimal solution and the total profit contribution?
16. Refer to the feasible region for Par, Inc., in Problem 14.
    a. Develop an objective function that will make extreme point (0, 540) the optimal extreme point.
    b. What is the optimal solution for the objective function you selected in part (a)?
    c. What are the values of the slack variables associated with this solution?

17. Write the following linear program in standard form:

$$\begin{aligned} \text{Max} \quad & 5A + 2B \\ \text{s.t.} \quad & \\ & 1A - 2B \le 420 \\ & 2A + 3B \le 610 \\ & 6A - 1B \le 125 \\ & A, B \ge 0 \end{aligned}$$

18. For the linear program

$$\begin{aligned} \text{Max} \quad & 4A + 1B \\ \text{s.t.} \quad & \\ & 10A + 2B \le 30 \\ & 3A + 2B \le 12 \\ & 2A + 2B \le 10 \\ & A, B \ge 0 \end{aligned}$$

    a. Write this problem in standard form.
    b. Solve the problem using the graphical solution procedure.
    c. What are the values of the three slack variables at the optimal solution?
19. Given the linear program

$$\begin{aligned} \text{Max} \quad & 3A + 4B \\ \text{s.t.} \quad & \\ & -1A + 2B \le 8 \\ & 1A + 2B \le 12 \\ & 2A + 1B \le 16 \\ & A, B \ge 0 \end{aligned}$$

    a. Write the problem in standard form.
    b. Solve the problem using the graphical solution procedure.
    c. What are the values of the three slack variables at the optimal solution?

20. For the linear program

$$\begin{aligned} \text{Max} \quad & 3A + 2B \\ \text{s.t.} \quad & \\ & A + B \geq 4 \\ & 3A + 4B \leq 24 \\ & A \geq 2 \\ & A - B \leq 0 \\ & A, B \geq 0 \end{aligned}$$

a. Write the problem in standard form.
b. Solve the problem.
c. What are the values of the slack and surplus variables at the optimal solution?

21. Consider the following linear program:

$$\begin{aligned} \text{Max} \quad & 2A + 3B \\ \text{s.t.} \quad & \\ & 5A + 5B \leq 400 \quad \text{Constraint 1} \\ & -1A + 1B \leq 10 \quad \text{Constraint 2} \\ & 1A + 3B \geq 90 \quad \text{Constraint 3} \\ & A, B \geq 0 \end{aligned}$$

Figure 7.23 shows a graph of the constraint lines.

a. Place a number (1, 2, or 3) next to each constraint line to identify which constraint it represents.
b. Shade in the feasible region on the graph.
c. Identify the optimal extreme point. What is the optimal solution?
d. Which constraints are binding? Explain.
e. How much slack or surplus is associated with the nonbinding constraint?

FIGURE 7.23 GRAPH OF THE CONSTRAINT LINES FOR EXERCISE 21

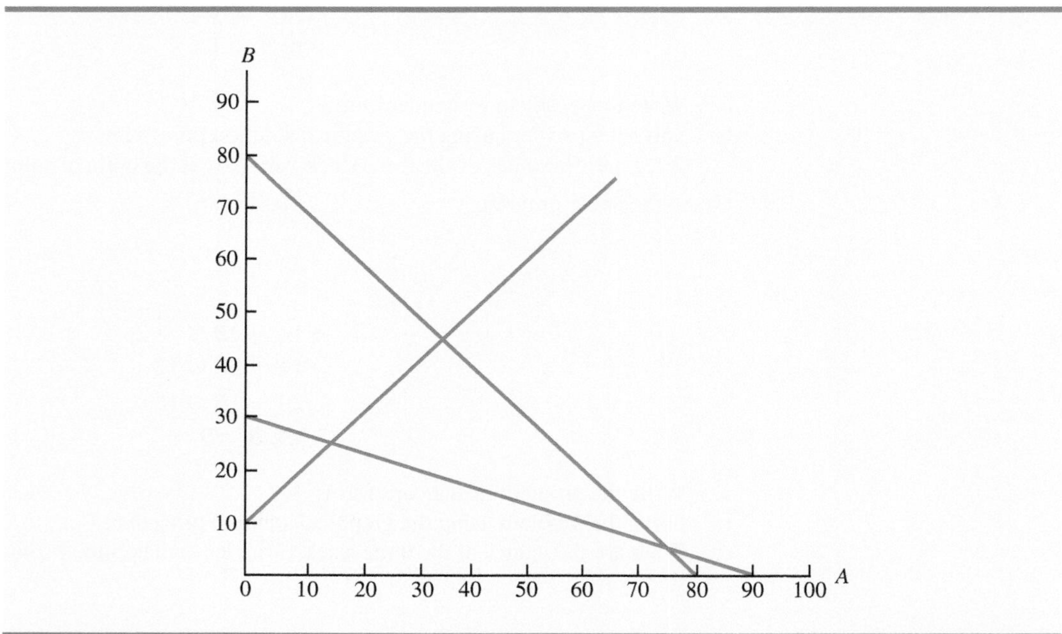

22. Reiser Sports Products wants to determine the number of All-Pro (A) and College (C) footballs to produce in order to maximize profit over the next four-week planning horizon. Constraints affecting the production quantities are the production capacities in three departments: cutting and dyeing; sewing; and inspection and packaging. For the four-week planning period, 340 hours of cutting and dyeing time, 420 hours of sewing time, and 200 hours of inspection and packaging time are available. All-Pro footballs provide a profit of \$5 per unit and College footballs provide a profit of \$4 per unit. The linear programming model with production times expressed in minutes is as follows:

$$
\begin{aligned}
&\text{Max} \quad 5A + 4C \\
&\text{s.t.} \\
&\qquad 12A + 6C \leq 20{,}400 \quad \text{Cutting and dyeing} \\
&\qquad 9A + 15C \leq 25{,}200 \quad \text{Sewing} \\
&\qquad 6A + 6C \leq 12{,}000 \quad \text{Inspection and packaging} \\
&\qquad A, C \geq 0
\end{aligned}
$$

A portion of the graphical solution to the Reiser problem is shown in Figure 7.24.

a. Shade the feasible region for this problem.

b. Determine the coordinates of each extreme point and the corresponding profit. Which extreme point generates the highest profit?

FIGURE 7.24 PORTION OF THE GRAPHICAL SOLUTION FOR EXERCISE 22

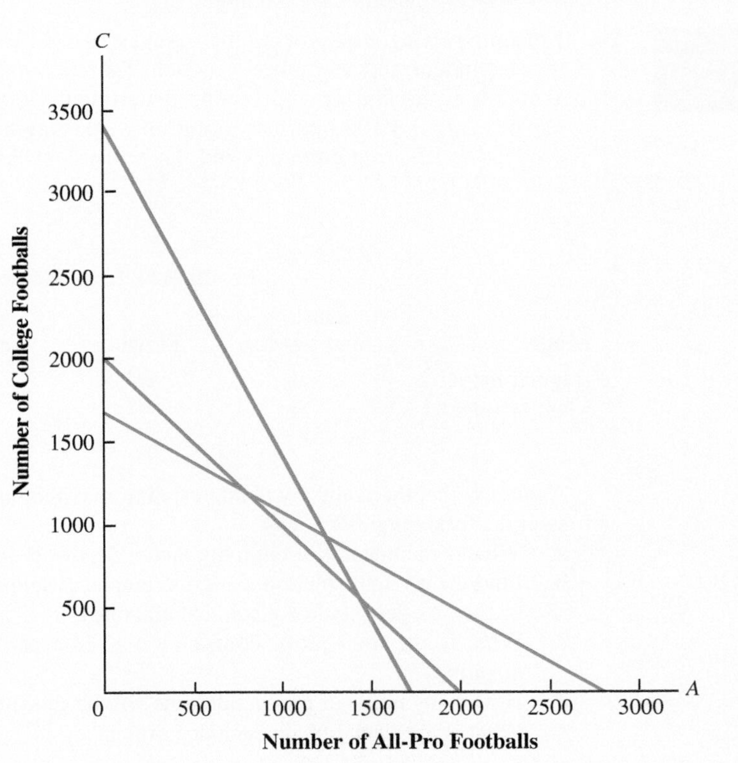

c. Draw the profit line corresponding to a profit of \$4000. Move the profit line as far from the origin as you can in order to determine which extreme point will provide the optimal solution. Compare your answer with the approach you used in part (b).
d. Which constraints are binding? Explain.
e. Suppose that the values of the objective function coefficients are \$4 for each All-Pro model produced and \$5 for each College model. Use the graphical solution procedure to determine the new optimal solution and the corresponding value of profit.

23. Embassy Motorcycles (EM) manufacturers two lightweight motorcycles designed for easy handling and safety. The EZ-Rider model has a new engine and a low profile that make it easy to balance. The Lady-Sport model is slightly larger, uses a more traditional engine, and is specifically designed to appeal to women riders. Embassy produces the engines for both models at its Des Moines, Iowa, plant. Each EZ-Rider engine requires 6 hours of manufacturing time and each Lady-Sport engine requires 3 hours of manufacturing time. The Des Moines plant has 2100 hours of engine manufacturing time available for the next production period. Embassy's motorcycle frame supplier can supply as many EZ-Rider frames as needed. However, the Lady-Sport frame is more complex and the supplier can only provide up to 280 Lady-Sport frames for the next production period. Final assembly and testing requires 2 hours for each EZ-Rider model and 2.5 hours for each Lady-Sport model. A maximum of 1000 hours of assembly and testing time are available for the next production period. The company's accounting department projects a profit contribution of \$2400 for each EZ-Rider produced and \$1800 for each Lady-Sport produced.
    a. Formulate a linear programming model that can be used to determine the number of units of each model that should be produced in order to maximize the total contribution to profit.
    b. Solve the problem graphically. What is the optimal solution?
    c. Which constraints are binding?

24. Kelson Sporting Equipment, Inc., makes two different types of baseball gloves: a regular model and a catcher's model. The firm has 900 hours of production time available in its cutting and sewing department, 300 hours available in its finishing department, and 100 hours available in its packaging and shipping department. The production time requirements and the profit contribution per glove are given in the following table:

	Production Time (hours)			
Model	Cutting and Sewing	Finishing	Packaging and Shipping	Profit/Glove
Regular model	1	$^1/_2$	$^1/_8$	\$5
Catcher's model	$^3/_2$	$^1/_3$	$^1/_4$	\$8

Assuming that the company is interested in maximizing the total profit contribution, answer the following:
    a. What is the linear programming model for this problem?
    b. Find the optimal solution using the graphical solution procedure. How many gloves of each model should Kelson manufacture?
    c. What is the total profit contribution Kelson can earn with the given production quantities?
    d. How many hours of production time will be scheduled in each department?
    e. What is the slack time in each department?

25. George Johnson recently inherited a large sum of money; he wants to use a portion of this money to set up a trust fund for his two children. The trust fund has two investment options: (1) a bond fund and (2) a stock fund. The projected returns over the life of the investments are 6% for the bond fund and 10% for the stock fund. Whatever portion of the inheritance George finally decides to commit to the trust fund, he wants to invest at least 30% of that amount in the bond fund. In addition, he wants to select a mix that will enable him to obtain a total return of at least 7.5%.
    a. Formulate a linear programming model that can be used to determine the percentage that should be allocated to each of the possible investment alternatives.
    b. Solve the problem using the graphical solution procedure.

26. The Sea Wharf Restaurant would like to determine the best way to allocate a monthly advertising budget of $1000 between newspaper advertising and radio advertising. Management decided that at least 25% of the budget must be spent on each type of media, and that the amount of money spent on local newspaper advertising must be at least twice the amount spent on radio advertising. A marketing consultant developed an index that measures audience exposure per dollar of advertising on a scale from 0 to 100, with higher values implying greater audience exposure. If the value of the index for local newspaper advertising is 50 and the value of the index for spot radio advertising is 80, how should the restaurant allocate its advertising budget in order to maximize the value of total audience exposure?
    a. Formulate a linear programming model that can be used to determine how the restaurant should allocate its advertising budget in order to maximize the value of total audience exposure.
    b. Solve the problem using the graphical solution procedure.

27. Blair & Rosen, Inc. (B&R) is a brokerage firm that specializes in investment portfolios designed to meet the specific risk tolerances of its clients. A client who contacted B&R this past week has a maximum of $50,000 to invest. B&R's investment advisor decides to recommend a portfolio consisting of two investment funds: an Internet fund and a Blue Chip fund. The Internet fund has a projected annual return of 12%, while the Blue Chip fund has a projected annual return of 9%. The investment advisor requires that at most $35,000 of the client's funds should be invested in the Internet fund. B&R services include a risk rating for each investment alternative. The Internet fund, which is the more risky of the two investment alternatives, has a risk rating of 6 per thousand dollars invested. The Blue Chip fund has a risk rating of 4 per thousand dollars invested. For example, if $10,000 is invested in each of the two investment funds, B&R's risk rating for the portfolio would be $6(10) + 4(10) = 100$. Finally, B&R developed a questionnaire to measure each client's risk tolerance. Based on the responses, each client is classified as a conservative, moderate, or aggressive investor. Suppose that the questionnaire results classified the current client as a moderate investor. B&R recommends that a client who is a moderate investor limit his or her portfolio to a maximum risk rating of 240.
    a. What is the recommended investment portfolio for this client? What is the annual return for the portfolio?
    b. Suppose that a second client with $50,000 to invest has been classified as an aggressive investor. B&R recommends that the maximum portfolio risk rating for an aggressive investor is 320. What is the recommended investment portfolio for this aggressive investor? Discuss what happens to the portfolio under the aggressive investor strategy.
    c. Suppose that a third client with $50,000 to invest has been classified as a conservative investor. B&R recommends that the maximum portfolio risk rating for a conservative investor is 160. Develop the recommended investment portfolio for the conservative investor. Discuss the interpretation of the slack variable for the total investment fund constraint.

28. Tom's, Inc., produces various Mexican food products and sells them to Western Foods, a chain of grocery stores located in Texas and New Mexico. Tom's, Inc., makes two salsa products: Western Foods Salsa and Mexico City Salsa. Essentially, the two products have different blends of whole tomatoes, tomato sauce, and tomato paste. The Western Foods Salsa is a blend of 50% whole tomatoes, 30% tomato sauce, and 20% tomato paste. The Mexico City Salsa, which has a thicker and chunkier consistency, consists of 70% whole tomatoes, 10% tomato sauce, and 20% tomato paste. Each jar of salsa produced weighs 10 ounces. For the current production period, Tom's, Inc., can purchase up to 280 pounds of whole tomatoes, 130 pounds of tomato sauce, and 100 pounds of tomato paste; the price per pound for these ingredients is \$0.96, \$0.64, and \$0.56, respectively. The cost of the spices and the other ingredients is approximately \$0.10 per jar. Tom's, Inc., buys empty glass jars for \$0.02 each, and labeling and filling costs are estimated to be \$0.03 for each jar of salsa produced. Tom's contract with Western Foods results in sales revenue of \$1.64 for each jar of Western Foods Salsa and \$1.93 for each jar of Mexico City Salsa.
    a. Develop a linear programming model that will enable Tom's to determine the mix of salsa products that will maximize the total profit contribution.
    b. Find the optimal solution.
29. AutoIgnite produces electronic ignition systems for automobiles at a plant in Cleveland, Ohio. Each ignition system is assembled from two components produced at AutoIgnite's plants in Buffalo, New York, and Dayton, Ohio. The Buffalo plant can produce 2000 units of component 1, 1000 units of component 2, or any combination of the two components each day. For instance, 60% of Buffalo's production time could be used to produce component 1 and 40% of Buffalo's production time could be used to produce component 2; in this case, the Buffalo plant would be able to produce 0.6(2000) = 1200 units of component 1 each day and 0.4(1000) = 400 units of component 2 each day. The Dayton plant can produce 600 units of component 1, 1400 units of component 2, or any combination of the two components each day. At the end of each day, the component production at Buffalo and Dayton is sent to Cleveland for assembly of the ignition systems on the following workday.
    a. Formulate a linear programming model that can be used to develop a daily production schedule for the Buffalo and Dayton plants that will maximize daily production of ignition systems at Cleveland.
    b. Find the optimal solution.
30. A financial advisor at Diehl Investments identified two companies that are likely candidates for a takeover in the near future. Eastern Cable is a leading manufacturer of flexible cable systems used in the construction industry, and ComSwitch is a new firm specializing in digital switching systems. Eastern Cable is currently trading for \$40 per share, and ComSwitch is currently trading for \$25 per share. If the takeovers occur, the financial advisor estimates that the price of Eastern Cable will go to \$55 per share and ComSwitch will go to \$43 per share. At this point in time, the financial advisor has identified ComSwitch as the higher-risk alternative. Assume that a client indicated a willingness to invest a maximum of \$50,000 in the two companies. The client wants to invest at least \$15,000 in Eastern Cable and at least \$10,000 in ComSwitch. Because of the higher risk associated with ComSwitch, the financial advisor has recommended that at most \$25,000 should be invested in ComSwitch.
    a. Formulate a linear programming model that can be used to determine the number of shares of Eastern Cable and the number of shares of ComSwitch that will meet the investment constraints and maximize the total return for the investment.
    b. Graph the feasible region.
    c. Determine the coordinates of each extreme point.
    d. Find the optimal solution.

31. Consider the following linear program:

$$\begin{aligned} \text{Min} \quad & 3A + 4B \\ \text{s.t.} \quad & \\ & 1A + 3B \geq 6 \\ & 1A + 1B \geq 4 \\ & A, B \geq 0 \end{aligned}$$

Identify the feasible region and find the optimal solution using the graphical solution procedure. What is the value of the objective function?

32. Identify the three extreme-point solutions for the M&D Chemicals problem (see Section 7.5). Identify the value of the objective function and the values of the slack and surplus variables at each extreme point.

33. Consider the following linear programming problem:

$$\begin{aligned} \text{Min} \quad & A + 2B \\ \text{s.t.} \quad & \\ & A + 4B \leq 21 \\ & 2A + B \geq 7 \\ & 3A + 1.5B \leq 21 \\ & -2A + 6B \geq 0 \\ & A, B \geq 0 \end{aligned}$$

a. Find the optimal solution using the graphical solution procedure and the value of the objective function.
b. Determine the amount of slack or surplus for each constraint.
c. Suppose the objective function is changed to max $5A + 2B$. Find the optimal solution and the value of the objective function.

SELF test

34. Consider the following linear program:

$$\begin{aligned} \text{Min} \quad & 2A + 2B \\ \text{s.t.} \quad & \\ & 1A + 3B \leq 12 \\ & 3A + 1B \geq 13 \\ & 1A - 1B = 3 \\ & A, B \geq 0 \end{aligned}$$

a. Show the feasible region.
b. What are the extreme points of the feasible region?
c. Find the optimal solution using the graphical solution procedure.

35. For the linear program

$$\begin{aligned} \text{Min} \quad & 6A + 4B \\ \text{s.t.} \quad & \\ & 2A + 1B \geq 12 \\ & 1A + 1B \geq 10 \\ & 1B \leq 4 \\ & A, B \geq 0 \end{aligned}$$

a. Write the problem in standard form.
b. Solve the problem using the graphical solution procedure.
c. What are the values of the slack and surplus variables?

36. As part of a quality improvement initiative, Consolidated Electronics employees complete a three-day training program on team building and a two-day training program on problem solving. The manager of quality improvement has requested that at least 8 training programs on team building and at least 10 training programs on problem solving be offered during the next six months. In addition, senior-level management has specified that at least 25 training programs must be offered during this period. Consolidated Electronics uses a consultant to teach the training programs. During the next quarter, the consultant has 84 days of training time available. Each training program on team building costs \$10,000 and each training program on problem solving costs \$8000.
    a. Formulate a linear programming model that can be used to determine the number of training programs on team building and the number of training programs on problem solving that should be offered in order to minimize total cost.
    b. Graph the feasible region.
    c. Determine the coordinates of each extreme point.
    d. Solve for the minimum-cost solution.

37. The New England Cheese Company produces two cheese spreads by blending mild cheddar cheese with extra sharp cheddar cheese. The cheese spreads are packaged in 12-ounce containers, which are then sold to distributors throughout the Northeast. The Regular blend contains 80% mild cheddar and 20% extra sharp, and the Zesty blend contains 60% mild cheddar and 40% extra sharp. This year, a local dairy cooperative offered to provide up to 8100 pounds of mild cheddar cheese for \$1.20 per pound and up to 3000 pounds of extra sharp cheddar cheese for \$1.40 per pound. The cost to blend and package the cheese spreads, excluding the cost of the cheese, is \$0.20 per container. If each container of Regular is sold for \$1.95 and each container of Zesty is sold for \$2.20, how many containers of Regular and Zesty should New England Cheese produce?

38. Applied Technology, Inc. (ATI) produces bicycle frames using two fiberglass materials that improve the strength-to-weight ratio of the frames. The cost of the standard-grade material is \$7.50 per yard and the cost of the professional-grade material is \$9.00 per yard. The standard- and professional-grade materials contain different amounts of fiberglass, carbon fiber, and Kevlar, as shown in the following table:

	Standard Grade	Professional Grade
Fiberglass	84%	58%
Carbon fiber	10%	30%
Kevlar	6%	12%

ATI signed a contract with a bicycle manufacturer to produce a new frame with a carbon fiber content of at least 20% and a Kevlar content of not greater than 10%. To meet the required weight specification, a total of 30 yards of material must be used for each frame.
    a. Formulate a linear program to determine the number of yards of each grade of fiberglass material that ATI should use in each frame in order to minimize total cost. Define the decision variables and indicate the purpose of each constraint.
    b. Use the graphical solution procedure to determine the feasible region. What are the coordinates of the extreme points?
    c. Compute the total cost at each extreme point. What is the optimal solution?

d. The distributor of the fiberglass material is currently overstocked with the professional-grade material. To reduce inventory, the distributor offered ATI the opportunity to purchase the professional-grade material for \$8 per yard. Will the optimal solution change?

e. Suppose that the distributor further lowers the price of the professional-grade material to \$7.40 per yard. Will the optimal solution change? What effect would an even lower price for the professional-grade material have on the optimal solution? Explain.

39. Innis Investments manages funds for a number of companies and wealthy clients. The investment strategy is tailored to each client's needs. For a new client, Innis has been authorized to invest up to \$1.2 million in two investment funds: a stock fund and a money market fund. Each unit of the stock fund costs \$50 and provides an annual rate of return of 10%; each unit of the money market fund costs \$100 and provides an annual rate of return of 4%.

    The client wants to minimize risk subject to the requirement that the annual income from the investment be at least \$60,000. According to Innis's risk measurement system, each unit invested in the stock fund has a risk index of 8, and each unit invested in the money market fund has a risk index of 3; the higher risk index associated with the stock fund simply indicates that it is the riskier investment. Innis's client also specifies that at least \$300,000 be invested in the money market fund.

    a. Determine how many units of each fund Innis should purchase for the client to minimize the total risk index for the portfolio.
    b. How much annual income will this investment strategy generate?
    c. Suppose the client desires to maximize annual return. How should the funds be invested?

40. Eastern Chemicals produces two types of lubricating fluids used in industrial manufacturing. Both products cost Eastern Chemicals \$1 per gallon to produce. Based on an analysis of current inventory levels and outstanding orders for the next month, Eastern Chemicals' management specified that at least 30 gallons of product 1 and at least 20 gallons of product 2 must be produced during the next two weeks. Management also stated that an existing inventory of highly perishable raw material required in the production of both fluids must be used within the next two weeks. The current inventory of the perishable raw material is 80 pounds. Although more of this raw material can be ordered if necessary, any of the current inventory that is not used within the next two weeks will spoil—hence, the management requirement that at least 80 pounds be used in the next two weeks. Furthermore, it is known that product 1 requires 1 pound of this perishable raw material per gallon and product 2 requires 2 pounds of the raw material per gallon. Because Eastern Chemicals' objective is to keep its production costs at the minimum possible level, the firm's management is looking for a minimum-cost production plan that uses all the 80 pounds of perishable raw material and provides at least 30 gallons of product 1 and at least 20 gallons of product 2. What is the minimum-cost solution?

41. Southern Oil Company produces two grades of gasoline: regular and premium. The profit contributions are \$0.30 per gallon for regular gasoline and \$0.50 per gallon for premium gasoline. Each gallon of regular gasoline contains 0.3 gallons of grade A crude oil and each gallon of premium gasoline contains 0.6 gallons of grade A crude oil. For the next production period, Southern has 18,000 gallons of grade A crude oil available. The refinery used to produce the gasolines has a production capacity of 50,000 gallons for the next production period. Southern Oil's distributors have indicated that demand for the premium gasoline for the next production period will be at most 20,000 gallons.

    a. Formulate a linear programming model that can be used to determine the number of gallons of regular gasoline and the number of gallons of premium gasoline that should be produced in order to maximize total profit contribution.

b. What is the optimal solution?
c. What are the values and interpretations of the slack variables?
d. What are the binding constraints?

SELF test

42. Does the following linear program involve infeasibility, unbounded, and/or alternative optimal solutions? Explain.

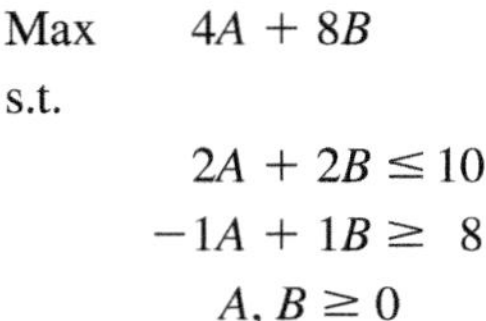

$$
\begin{aligned}
\text{Max} \quad & 4A + 8B \\
\text{s.t.} \quad & \\
& 2A + 2B \leq 10 \\
& -1A + 1B \geq 8 \\
& A, B \geq 0
\end{aligned}
$$

SELF test

43. Does the following linear program involve infeasibility, unbounded, and/or alternative optimal solutions? Explain.

$$
\begin{aligned}
\text{Max} \quad & 1A + 1B \\
\text{s.t.} \quad & \\
& 8A + 6B \geq 24 \\
& 2B \geq 4 \\
& A, B \geq 0
\end{aligned}
$$

44. Consider the following linear program:

$$
\begin{aligned}
\text{Max} \quad & 1A + 1B \\
\text{s.t.} \quad & \\
& 5A + 3B \leq 15 \\
& 3A + 5B \leq 15 \\
& A, B \geq 0
\end{aligned}
$$

a. What is the optimal solution for this problem?
b. Suppose that the objective function is changed to $1A + 2B$. Find the new optimal solution.

45. Consider the following linear program:

$$
\begin{aligned}
\text{Max} \quad & 1A - 2B \\
\text{s.t.} \quad & \\
& -4A + 3B \leq 3 \\
& 1A - 1B \leq 3 \\
& A, B \geq 0
\end{aligned}
$$

a. Graph the feasible region for the problem.
b. Is the feasible region unbounded? Explain.
c. Find the optimal solution.
d. Does an unbounded feasible region imply that the optimal solution to the linear program will be unbounded?

46. The manager of a small independent grocery store is trying to determine the best use of her shelf space for soft drinks. The store carries national and generic brands and currently has 200 square feet of shelf space available. The manager wants to allocate at least 60% of the space to the national brands and, regardless of the profitability, allocate at least 10%

of the space to the generic brands. How many square feet of space should the manager allocate to the national brands and the generic brands under the following circumstances?

a. The national brands are more profitable than the generic brands.
b. Both brands are equally profitable.
c. The generic brand is more profitable than the national brand.

47. Discuss what happens to the M&D Chemicals problem (see Section 7.5) if the cost per gallon for product A is increased to $3.00 per gallon. What would you recommend? Explain.

48. For the M&D Chemicals problem in Section 7.5, discuss the effect of management's requiring total production of 500 gallons for the two products. List two or three actions M&D should consider to correct the situation you encounter.

49. PharmaPlus operates a chain of 30 pharmacies. The pharmacies are staffed by licensed pharmacists and pharmacy technicians. The company currently employs 85 full-time-equivalent pharmacists (combination of full time and part time) and 175 full-time-equivalent technicians. Each spring management reviews current staffing levels and makes hiring plans for the year. A recent forecast of the prescription load for the next year shows that at least 250 full-time-equivalent employees (pharmacists and technicians) will be required to staff the pharmacies. The personnel department expects 10 pharmacists and 30 technicians to leave over the next year. To accommodate the expected attrition and prepare for future growth, management states that at least 15 new pharmacists must be hired. In addition, PharmaPlus's new service quality guidelines specify no more than two technicians per licensed pharmacist. The average salary for licensed pharmacists is $40 per hour and the average salary for technicians is $10 per hour.

 a. Determine a minimum-cost staffing plan for PharmaPlus. How many pharmacists and technicians are needed?
 b. Given current staffing levels and expected attrition, how many new hires (if any) must be made to reach the level recommended in part (a)? What will be the impact on the payroll?

50. Expedition Outfitters manufactures a variety of specialty clothing for hiking, skiing, and mountain climbing. The company has decided to begin production on two new parkas designed for use in extremely cold weather: the Mount Everest Parka and the Rocky Mountain Parka. Expedition's manufacturing plant has 120 hours of cutting time and 120 hours of sewing time available for producing these two parkas. Each Mount Everest Parka requires 30 minutes of cutting time and 45 minutes of sewing time, and each Rocky Mountain Parka requires 20 minutes of cutting time and 15 minutes of sewing time. The labor and material cost is $150 for each Mount Everest Parka and $50 for each Rocky Mountain Parka, and the retail prices through the firm's mail order catalog are $250 for the Mount Everest Parka and $200 for the Rocky Mountain Parka. Because management believes that the Mount Everest Parka is a unique coat that will enhance the image of the firm, management specified that at least 20% of the total production must consist of this model. Assuming that Expedition Outfitters can sell as many coats of each type as it can produce, how many units of each model should it manufacture to maximize the total profit contribution?

51. English Motors, Ltd. (EML), developed a new four-wheel-drive sport utility vehicle. As part of the marketing campaign, EML produced a digitally recorded sales presentation to send to both owners of current EML four-wheel-drive vehicles as well as to owners of four-wheel-drive sport utility vehicles offered by competitors; EML refers to these two target markets as the current customer market and the new customer market. Individuals who receive the new promotion will also receive a coupon for a test drive of the new EML model for one weekend. A key factor in the success of the new promotion is the response rate, the percentage of individuals who receive the new promotion and test drive the new

model. EML estimates that the response rate for the current customer market is 25% and the response rate for the new customer market is 20%. For the customers who test drive the new model, the sales rate is the percentage of individuals who make a purchase. Marketing research studies indicate that the sales rate is 12% for the current customer market and 20% for the new customer market. The cost for each promotion, excluding the test drive costs, is \$4 for each promotion sent to the current customer market and \$6 for each promotion sent to the new customer market. Management also specified that a minimum of 30,000 current customers should test drive the new model and a minimum of 10,000 new customers should test drive the new model. In addition, the number of current customers who test drive the new vehicle must be at least twice the number of new customers who test drive the new vehicle. If the marketing budget, excluding test drive costs, is \$1.2 million, how many promotions should be sent to each group of customers in order to maximize total sales?

52. Creative Sports Design (CSD) manufactures a standard-size tennis racquet and an oversize tennis racquet. The firm's racquets are extremely light due to the use of a magnesium-graphite alloy that was invented by the firm's founder. Each standard-size racquet uses 0.125 kilograms of the alloy and each oversize racquet uses 0.4 kilograms; over the next two-week production period, only 80 kilograms of the alloy are available. Each standard-size racquet uses 10 minutes of manufacturing time and each oversize racquet uses 12 minutes. The profit contributions are \$10 for each standard-size racquet and \$15 for each oversize racquet, and 40 hours of manufacturing time are available each week. Management specified that at least 20% of the total production must be the standard-size racquet. How many racquets of each type should CSD manufacture over the next two weeks to maximize the total profit contribution? Assume that because of the unique nature of its products, CSD can sell as many racquets as it can produce.

53. Management of High Tech Services (HTS) would like to develop a model that will help allocate its technicians' time between service calls to regular contract customers and new customers. A maximum of 80 hours of technician time is available over the two-week planning period. To satisfy cash flow requirements, at least \$800 in revenue (per technician) must be generated during the two-week period. Technician time for regular customers generates \$25 per hour. However, technician time for new customers only generates an average of \$8 per hour because in many cases a new customer contact does not provide billable services. To ensure that new customer contacts are being maintained, the technician time spent on new customer contacts must be at least 60% of the time spent on regular customer contacts. Given these revenue and policy requirements, HTS would like to determine how to allocate technician time between regular customers and new customers so that the total number of customers contacted during the two-week period will be maximized. Technicians require an average of 50 minutes for each regular customer contact and 1 hour for each new customer contact.
    a. Develop a linear programming model that will enable HTS to allocate technician time between regular customers and new customers.
    b. Find the optimal solution.

54. Jackson Hole Manufacturing is a small manufacturer of plastic products used in the automotive and computer industries. One of its major contracts is with a large computer company and involves the production of plastic printer cases for the computer company's portable printers. The printer cases are produced on two injection molding machines. The M-100 machine has a production capacity of 25 printer cases per hour, and the M-200 machine has a production capacity of 40 cases per hour. Both machines use the same chemical material to produce the printer cases; the M-100 uses 40 pounds of the raw material per hour and the M-200 uses 50 pounds per hour. The computer company asked

Jackson Hole to produce as many of the cases during the upcoming week as possible; it will pay \$18 for each case Jackson Hole can deliver. However, next week is a regularly scheduled vacation period for most of Jackson Hole's production employees; during this time, annual maintenance is performed for all equipment in the plant. Because of the downtime for maintenance, the M-100 will be available for no more than 15 hours, and the M-200 will be available for no more than 10 hours. However, because of the high set-up cost involved with both machines, management requires that, if production is scheduled on either machine, the machine must be operated for at least 5 hours. The supplier of the chemical material used in the production process informed Jackson Hole that a maximum of 1000 pounds of the chemical material will be available for next week's production; the cost for this raw material is \$6 per pound. In addition to the raw material cost, Jackson Hole estimates that the hourly costs of operating the M-100 and the M-200 are \$50 and \$75, respectively.

a. Formulate a linear programming model that can be used to maximize the contribution to profit.
b. Find the optimal solution.

55. Xpress Technologies offers complete web design, programming, implementation, and hosting services for customers. Xpress prices their services by the project and categorizes each customer request into one of three possible project categories: simple HTML design, requires Java/Flash coding, requires secure transaction capabilities. Xpress charges \$3000 for each simple HTML design project, \$5000 for each Java/Flash coding project, and \$8000 for each project requiring secure transaction capabilities. Xpress has two types of employees that it assigns to these projects: graphic designers who make \$32/hour and programmers who make \$36/hour. The company currently has two graphic designers and four programmers; each employee can work up to a total of 40 hours per week. Xpress estimates that a simple HTML project will require 2 hours from the graphic designers and 4 hours from the programmers; projects requiring Java/Flash coding require 5 hours from the graphic designers and 6 hours from the programmers; projects requiring secure transaction capabilities require 7 hours from the graphic designers and 12 hours from the programmers. Xpress currently has requests for eight simple HTML projects, six Java/Flash projects, and seven projects requiring secure transaction capabilities.

   a. Develop a linear program that will help Xpress Technologies to choose which of the projects to accept for the coming week to maximize profits.
   b. Find the optimal solution.

Case Problem 1 Workload Balancing

Digital Imaging (DI) produces color printers for both the professional and consumer markets. The DI consumer division recently introduced two new color printers. The DI-910 model can produce a $4'' \times 6''$ borderless color print in approximately 37 seconds. The more sophisticated and faster DI-950 can even produce a $13'' \times 19''$ borderless color print. Financial projections show profit contributions of \$42 for each DI-910 and \$87 for each DI-950.

The printers are assembled, tested, and packaged at DI's plant located in New Bern, North Carolina. This plant is highly automated and uses two manufacturing lines to produce the printers. Line 1 performs the assembly operation with times of 3 minutes per DI-910 printer and 6 minutes per DI-950 printer. Line 2 performs both the testing and packaging operations. Times are 4 minutes per DI-910 printer and 2 minutes per DI-950 printer. The shorter time for the DI-950 printer is a result of its faster print speed. Both manufacturing lines are in operation one 8-hour shift per day.

Managerial Report

Perform an analysis for Digital Imaging in order to determine how many units of each printer to produce. Prepare a report to DI's president presenting your findings and recommendations. Include (but do not limit your discussion to) a consideration of the following:

1. The recommended number of units of each printer to produce to maximize the total contribution to profit for an 8-hour shift. What reasons might management have for not implementing your recommendation?
2. Suppose that management also states that the number of DI-910 printers produced must be at least as great as the number of DI-950 units produced. Assuming that the objective is to maximize the total contribution to profit for an 8-hour shift, how many units of each printer should be produced?
3. Does the solution you developed in part (2) balance the total time spent on line 1 and the total time spent on line 2? Why might this balance or lack of it be a concern to management?
4. Management requested an expansion of the model in part (2) that would provide a better balance between the total time on line 1 and the total time on line 2. Management wants to limit the difference between the total time on line 1 and the total time on line 2 to 30 minutes or less. If the objective is still to maximize the total contribution to profit, how many units of each printer should be produced? What effect does this workload balancing have on total profit in part (2)?
5. Suppose that in part (1) management specified the objective of maximizing the total number of printers produced each shift rather than total profit contribution. With this objective, how many units of each printer should be produced per shift? What effect does this objective have on total profit and workload balancing?

For each solution that you develop, include a copy of your linear programming model and graphical solution in the appendix to your report.

Case Problem 2 Production Strategy

Better Fitness, Inc. (BFI), manufactures exercise equipment at its plant in Freeport, Long Island. It recently designed two universal weight machines for the home exercise market. Both machines use BFI-patented technology that provides the user with an extremely wide range of motion capability for each type of exercise performed. Until now, such capabilities have been available only on expensive weight machines used primarily by physical therapists.

At a recent trade show, demonstrations of the machines resulted in significant dealer interest. In fact, the number of orders that BFI received at the trade show far exceeded its manufacturing capabilities for the current production period. As a result, management decided to begin production of the two machines. The two machines, which BFI named the BodyPlus 100 and the BodyPlus 200, require different amounts of resources to produce.

The BodyPlus 100 consists of a frame unit, a press station, and a pec-dec station. Each frame produced uses 4 hours of machining and welding time and 2 hours of painting and finishing time. Each press station requires 2 hours of machining and welding time and 1 hour of painting and finishing time, and each pec-dec station uses 2 hours of machining and welding time and 2 hours of painting and finishing time. In addition, 2 hours are spent assembling, testing, and packaging each BodyPlus 100. The raw material costs are \$450 for each frame, \$300 for each press station, and \$250 for each pec-dec station; packaging costs are estimated to be \$50 per unit.

The BodyPlus 200 consists of a frame unit, a press station, a pec-dec station, and a leg-press station. Each frame produced uses 5 hours of machining and welding time and 4 hours of painting and finishing time. Each press station requires 3 hours of machining and welding time and 2 hours of painting and finishing time, each pec-dec station uses 2 hours of machining and welding time and 2 hours of painting and finishing time, and each leg-press station requires 2 hours of machining and welding time and 2 hours of painting and finishing time. In addition, 2 hours are spent assembling, testing, and packaging each BodyPlus 200. The raw material costs are $650 for each frame, $400 for each press station, $250 for each pec-dec station, and $200 for each leg-press station; packaging costs are estimated to be $75 per unit.

For the next production period, management estimates that 600 hours of machining and welding time; 450 hours of painting and finishing time; and 140 hours of assembly, testing, and packaging time will be available. Current labor costs are $20 per hour for machining and welding time; $15 per hour for painting and finishing time; and $12 per hour for assembly, testing, and packaging time. The market in which the two machines must compete suggests a retail price of $2400 for the BodyPlus 100 and $3500 for the BodyPlus 200, although some flexibility may be available to BFI because of the unique capabilities of the new machines. Authorized BFI dealers can purchase machines for 70% of the suggested retail price.

BFI's president believes that the unique capabilities of the BodyPlus 200 can help position BFI as one of the leaders in high-end exercise equipment. Consequently, she states that the number of units of the BodyPlus 200 produced must be at least 25% of the total production.

Managerial Report

Analyze the production problem at Better Fitness, Inc., and prepare a report for BFI's president presenting your findings and recommendations. Include (but do not limit your discussion to) a consideration of the following items:

1. The recommended number of BodyPlus 100 and BodyPlus 200 machines to produce
2. The effect on profits of the requirement that the number of units of the BodyPlus 200 produced must be at least 25% of the total production
3. Where efforts should be expended in order to increase contribution to profits

Include a copy of your linear programming model and graphical solution in an appendix to your report.

Case Problem 3 Hart Venture Capital

Hart Venture Capital (HVC) specializes in providing venture capital for software development and Internet applications. Currently HVC has two investment opportunities: (1) Security Systems, a firm that needs additional capital to develop an Internet security software package, and (2) Market Analysis, a market research company that needs additional capital to develop a software package for conducting customer satisfaction surveys. In exchange for Security Systems stock, the firm asked HVC to provide $600,000 in year 1, $600,000 in year 2, and $250,000 in year 3 over the coming three-year period. In exchange for Market Analysis stock, the firm asked HVC to provide $500,000 in year 1, $350,000 in year 2, and $400,000 in year 3 over the same three-year period. HVC believes that both investment opportunities are worth pursuing. However, because of other investments, HVC is willing to commit at most $800,000 for both projects in the first year, at most $700,000 in the second year, and $500,000 in the third year.

HVC's financial analysis team reviewed both projects and recommended that the company's objective should be to maximize the net present value of the total investment in Security Systems and Market Analysis. The net present value takes into account the estimated value of the stock at the end of the three-year period as well as the capital outflows that are necessary during each of the three years. Using an 8% rate of return, HVC's financial analysis team estimates that 100% funding of the Security Systems project has a net present value of $1,800,000, and 100% funding of the Market Analysis project has a net present value of $1,600,000.

HVC has the option to fund any percentage of the Security Systems and Market Analysis projects. For example, if HVC decides to fund 40% of the Security Systems project, investments of 0.40($600,000) = $240,000 would be required in year 1, 0.40($600,000) = $240,000 would be required in year 2, and 0.40($250,000) = $100,000 would be required in year 3. In this case, the net present value of the Security Systems project would be 0.40($1,800,000) = $720,000. The investment amounts and the net present value for partial funding of the Market Analysis project would be computed in the same manner.

Managerial Report

Perform an analysis of HVC's investment problem and prepare a report that presents your findings and recommendations. Be sure to include information on the following:

1. The recommended percentage of each project that HVC should fund and the net present value of the total investment
2. A capital allocation plan for Security Systems and Market Analysis for the coming three-year period and the total HVC investment each year
3. The effect, if any, on the recommended percentage of each project that HVC should fund if HVC is willing to commit an additional $100,000 during the first year
4. A capital allocation plan if an additional $100,000 is made available
5. Your recommendation as to whether HVC should commit the additional $100,000 in the first year

Provide model details and relevant computer output in a report appendix.

Appendix 7.1 Solving Linear Programs with Excel Solver

In this appendix we will use an Excel worksheet to solve the RMC linear programming problem. We will enter the problem data for the RMC problem in the top part of the worksheet and develop the linear programming model in the bottom part of the worksheet. Note that Appendix A contains much more detail on how to formulate models in Excel.

Formulation

Whenever we formulate a worksheet model of a linear program, we perform the following steps:

Step 1. Enter the problem data in the top part of the worksheet
Step 2. Specify cell locations for the decision variables
Step 3. Select a cell and enter a formula for computing the value of the objective function
Step 4. Select a cell and enter a formula for computing the left-hand side of each constraint
Step 5. Select a cell and enter a formula for computing the right-hand side of each constraint

The formula worksheet that we developed for the RMC problem using these five steps is shown in Figure 7.25. Let us review each of the preceding steps as they apply to the RMC problem.

Step 1. Enter the problem data in the top part of the worksheet
Cells B5 to C7 show the material requirements per ton of each product.
Cells B8 and C8 show the profit contribution per ton for the two products.
Cells D5 to D7 show the maximum amounts available for each of the three materials.

FIGURE 7.25 EXCEL FORMULA WORKSHEET FOR THE RMC PROBLEM

RMC

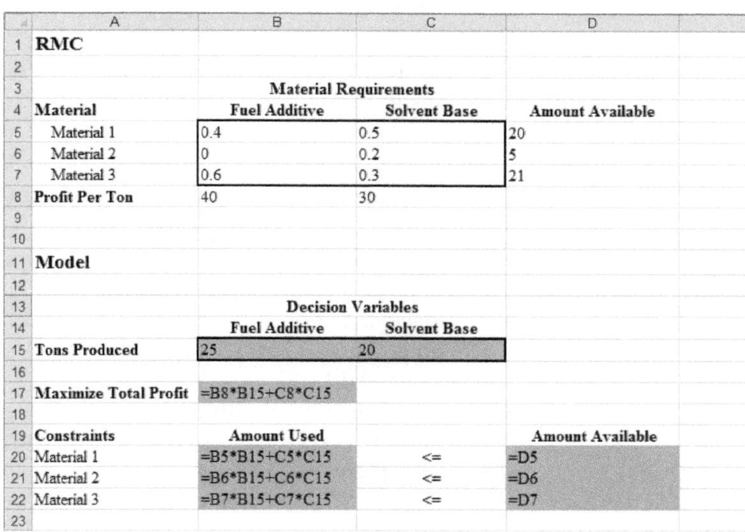

	A	B	C	D
1	**RMC**			
2				
3		**Material Requirements**		
4	**Material**	**Fuel Additive**	**Solvent Base**	**Amount Available**
5	Material 1	0.4	0.5	20
6	Material 2	0	0.2	5
7	Material 3	0.6	0.3	21
8	**Profit Per Ton**	40	30	
9				
10				
11	**Model**			
12				
13		**Decision Variables**		
14		**Fuel Additive**	**Solvent Base**	
15	**Tons Produced**	25	20	
16				
17	**Maximize Total Profit**	=B8*B15+C8*C15		
18				
19	**Constraints**	**Amount Used**		**Amount Available**
20	Material 1	=B5*B15+C5*C15	<=	=D5
21	Material 2	=B6*B15+C6*C15	<=	=D6
22	Material 3	=B7*B15+C7*C15	<=	=D7
23				

Step 2. Specify cell locations for the decision variables
Cell B15 will contain the number of tons of fuel additive produced, and Cell C15 will contain the number of tons of solvent base produced.

Step 3. Select a cell and enter a formula for computing the value of the objective function
Cell B17: =B8*B15+C8*C15

Step 4. Select a cell and enter a formula for computing the left-hand side of each constraint. With three constraints, we have
Cell B20: =B5*B15+C5*C15
Cell B21: =C6*C15
Cell B22: =B7*B15+C7*C15

Step 5. Select a cell and enter a formula for computing the right-hand side of each constraint. With three constraints, we have
Cell D20: =D5
Cell D21: =D6
Cell D22: =D7

Note that descriptive labels make the model section of the worksheet easier to read and understand. For example, we added "Fuel Additive," "Solvent Base," and "Tons Produced" in rows 14 and 15 so that the values of the decision variables appearing in Cells B15 and C15 can be easily interpreted. In addition, we entered "Maximize Total Profit" in Cell A17 to indicate that the value of the objective function appearing in Cell B17 is the maximum profit contribution. In the constraint section of the worksheet we added the constraint names as well as the "<=" symbols to show the relationship that exists between the left-hand side and the right-hand side of each constraint. Although these descriptive labels are not necessary to use Excel Solver to find a solution to the RMC problem, the labels make it easier for the user to understand and interpret the optimal solution.

Excel Solver Solution

Excel contains an add-in known as Solver that can be used to solve many different types of optimization problems, including linear programs. Excel Solver, developed by Frontline Systems, can be used to solve all of the linear programming problems presented in this text.

The following steps describe how Excel Solver can be used to obtain the optimal solution to the RMC problem:

The Excel add-in Analytic Solver Platform (ASP), which is used in Chapter 16 of this textbook for simulation problems, can also be used to solve linear programs. ASP uses more sophisticated algorithms for solving optimization problems and can solve larger problems than Excel Solver. However, since all optimization problems in this textbook can be solved using Excel Solver, we do not specifically discuss the use of ASP for use in optimization.

Step 1. Select the **Data** tab from the Ribbon

Step 2. Select **Solver** from the **Analysis** Group (see Figure 7.25, where the Analysis Group and Data tab are displayed in the Ribbon)

Step 3. When the **Solver Parameters** dialog box appears (see Figure 7.26):
Enter *B17* into the **Set Objective** box
Select the **To: Max** option
Enter *B15:C15* into the **By Changing Variable Cells** box
Select **Add**

Step 4. When the **Add Constraint** dialog box appears:
Enter *B20:B22* in the **Cell Reference** box
Select **<=**
Enter *D20:D22* in the **Constraint** box
Click **OK**

Step 5. When the **Solver Parameters** dialog box reappears:
Click the checkbox for **Make Unconstrained Variables Non-negative**

Step 6. In the **Select a Solving Method** dropdown menu
Select **Simplex LP**

FIGURE 7.26 EXCEL SOLVER PARAMETERS DIALOG BOX FOR THE RMC PROBLEM

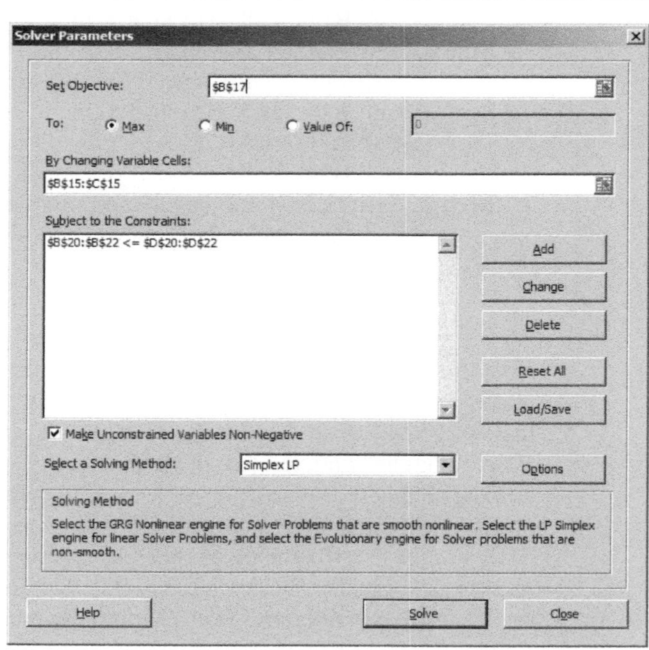

Step 7. Click **Solve**
Step 8. When the **Solver Results** dialog box appears:
Select **Keep Solver Solution**
Click **OK**

The Excel Answer Report that is similar to Figure 7.15 is generated from the ***Solver Results*** *dialog box. This is created by clicking on* ***Answer*** *in the* ***Reports*** *group before clicking* ***OK*** *in step 7. We will discuss the Sensitivity Report in Chapter 8.*

Figure 7.26 shows the completed Excel Solver Parameters dialog box, and Figure 7.27 shows the optimal solution in the worksheet. The optimal solution of 25 tons of fuel additive and 20 tons of solvent base is the same as we obtained using the graphical solution procedure. Solver also has an option to provide sensitivity analysis information. We discuss sensitivity analysis in Chapter 8.

In step 5 we selected the **Make Unconstrained Variables Non-negative** option in the **Solver Parameters** dialog box to avoid having to enter nonnegativity constraints for the decision variables. In general, whenever we want to solve a linear programming model in which the decision variables are all restricted to be nonnegative, we will select this option. In addition, in step 4 we entered all three less-than-or-equal-to constraints simultaneously by entering *B20:B22* into the **Cell Reference** box, selecting **<=**, and entering *D20:D22* into the **Constraint** box. Alternatively, we could have entered the three constraints one at a time.

The Solver Add-In should be found under the **Data** tab on the Excel Ribbon. If it does not appear here, you will have to add it by following the steps shown below.

Step 1. Select the **File** tab from the Ribbon
Step 2. Select **Options** from the **File** menu
Step 3. When the **Excel Options** dialog box appears, choose **Add-Ins**
Step 4. Click **Go** next to **Manage: Excel Add-ins**
Step 5. When the **Add-Ins** dialog box appears, select the checkbox for the **Solver Add-in**

FIGURE 7.27 EXCEL SOLVER SOLUTION FOR THE RMC PROBLEM

	A	B	C	D	E
1	**RMC**				
2					
3		**Material Requirements**			
4	**Material**	**Fuel Additive**	**Solvent Base**	**Amount Available**	
5	Material 1	0.4	0.5	20	
6	Material 2	0	0.2	5	
7	Material 3	0.6	0.3	21	
8	**Profit Per Ton**	40	30		
9					
10					
11	**Model**				
12					
13		**Decision Variables**			
14		**Fuel Additive**	**Solvent Base**		
15	**Tons Produced**	25	20		
16					
17	**Maximize Total Profit**	1600			
18					
19	**Constraints**	**Amount Used**		**Amount Available**	
20	Material 1	20	<=	20	
21	Material 2	4	<=	5	
22	Material 3	21	<=	21	
23					

Appendix 7.2 Solving Linear Programs with LINGO

In this appendix we describe how to use LINGO to solve the RMC problem. When you start LINGO, two windows are immediately displayed. The outer, or mainframe, window contains all the command menus and the command toolbar. The smaller window is the model window; this window is used to enter and edit the linear programming model you want to solve.

As with any model, it is good to document your LINGO model with comments. A comment in a LINGO model begins with an exclamation point and ends with a semicolon. If desired, a comment can span multiple lines.

The first item we enter is a comment describing the objective function. Recall that the objective function for the RMC problem is to maximize profit. Hence we enter the following comment:

```
! MAXIMIZE PROFIT;
```

For the latest information on LINGO software see http://www.lindo.com.

Next we press the Enter key and then type the objective function. The objective function for the RMC problem is Max $40F + 30S$. Thus, in the second line of the LINGO model window, we enter the following expression:

```
MAX = 40*F + 30*S;
```

Note that in LINGO the symbol * is used to denote multiplication and that the objective function, like a comment, ends with a semicolon. In general, each mathematical expression (objective function and constraints) in LINGO is terminated with a semicolon.

Next, we press the Enter key to move to a new line. The first constraint in the RMC problem is $0.4F + 0.5S \leq 20$, for material 1. Thus, in the third and fourth lines of the LINGO model window, we enter the following expressions:

```
!MATERIAL 1 CONSTRAINT;
0.4*F + 0.5*S <= 20;
```

Note that LINGO interprets the <= symbol as ≤. Alternatively, we could enter < instead of <=. As was the case when entering the objective function, a semicolon is required at the end of the first constraint. Pressing the Enter key moves us to a new line, and we continue the process by entering the remaining comments and constraints as shown here:

```
!MATERIAL 2 CONSTRAINT;
0.2*S <= 5;
!MATERIAL 3 CONSTRAINT;
0.6*F + 0.3*S <= 21;
```

The model window will now appear as follows:

```
!MAXIMIZE PROFIT;
MAX = 40*F + 30*S;
!MATERIAL 1 CONSTRAINT;
0.4*F + 0.5*S <=20;
!MATERIAL 2 CONSTRAINT;
0.2*S <= 5;
!MATERIAL 3 CONSTRAINT;
0.6*F + 0.3*S <= 21;
```

If you make an error in entering the model, you can correct it at any time by simply positioning the cursor where you made the error and entering the necessary correction.

FIGURE 7.28 SOLUTION TO THE RMC PROBLEM USING LINGO

```
Global optimal solution found.
Objective value:                                1600.000
Infeasibilities:                                0.000000
Total solver interations:                              2
Elapsed runtime seconds:                            0.04

Model Class:                                          LP

Total variables:                  2
Nonlinear variables:              0
Integer variables:                0

Total constraints:                4
Nonlinear constraints:            0

Total nonzeros:                   7
Nonlinear nonzeros:               0

                        Variable           Value        Reduced Cost
                               F        25.00000            0.000000
                               S        20.00000            0.000000

                             Row    Slack or Surplus      Dual Price
                               1        1600.000            1.000000
                               2        0.000000            33.33333
                               3        1.000000            0.000000
                               4        0.000000            44.44444
```

To solve the model, select the **Solve** command from the **LINGO** menu or press the **Solve** button on the toolbar at the top of the mainframe window. LINGO will begin the solution process by determining whether the model conforms to all syntax requirements. If the LINGO model doesn't pass these tests, you will be informed by an error message. If LINGO does not find any errors in the model input, it will begin to solve the model. As part of the solution process, LINGO displays a **Solver Status** window that allows you to monitor the progress of the solver. LINGO displays the solution in a new window titled "Solution Report." The output that appears in the **Solution Report** window for the RMC problem is shown in Figure 7.28.

The first part of the output shown in Figure 7.28 indicates that an optimal solution has been found and that the value of the objective function is 1600. We see that the optimal solution is $F = 25$ and $S = 20$, and that the slack variables for the three constraints (rows 2–4) are 0, 1, and 0. We will discuss the use of the information in the Reduced Cost column and the Dual Price column in Chapter 8 where we discuss the topic of sensitivity analysis.

CHAPTER 8

Linear Programming: Sensitivity Analysis and Interpretation of Solution

CONTENTS

Sensitivity analysis is the study of how changes in the coefficients of a linear programming problem affect the optimal solution. Using sensitivity analysis, we can answer questions such as the following:

1. How will a change in an *objective function coefficient* affect the optimal solution?
2. How will a change in a *right-hand-side value* for a constraint affect the optimal solution?

Because sensitivity analysis is concerned with how these changes affect the optimal solution, sensitivity analysis does not begin until the optimal solution to the original linear programming problem has been obtained. For this reason, sensitivity analysis is sometimes referred to as *postoptimality analysis.*

Our approach to sensitivity analysis parallels the approach used to introduce linear programming in Chapter 7. We introduce sensitivity analysis by using the graphical method for a linear programming problem with two decision variables. Then, we show how Excel Solver can be used to provide more complete sensitivity analysis information. Finally, we extend the discussion of problem formulation started in Chapter 7 by formulating and solving three larger linear programming problems. In discussing the solution for each of these problems, we focus on managerial interpretation of the optimal solution and sensitivity analysis information.

Sensitivity analysis and the interpretation of the optimal solution are important aspects of applying linear programming. The Q.M. in Action, Optimizing Refinery Operations at Chevron Using Linear Programming, explains how Chevron uses linear programing–based tools and sensitivity analysis to improve their oil refinery operations. Later in the chapter other Q.M. in Action features illustrate how Performance Analysis Corporation uses sensitivity analysis as part of an evaluation model for a chain of fast-food outlets, how GE Plastics (now part of the Saudi Basic Industries Corporation) uses a linear programming model involving thousands of variables and constraints to determine optimal production quantities, how Kimpton Hotels uses a linear program to set prices and room availability on Priceline, and how Duncan Industries Limited's linear programming model for tea distribution convinced management of the benefits of using quantitative analysis techniques to support the decision-making process.

Q.M. *in* ACTION

OPTIMIZING REFINERY OPERATIONS AT CHEVRON USING LINEAR PROGRAMMING

Chevron is a worldwide energy company with operations in more than 180 countries. Chevron has business units that operate in almost all aspects of energy exploration and production, including oil and gas, geothermal, solar, wind, and others. Chevron's oil and gas business requires refineries to take input crude oil and transform the crude oil into products such as gasoline and lubricants that are sold to downstream operations. The processes required to transform crude oil to useable products are complex and involve many different decisions that impact the cost and overall quality of the output products.

Chevron has developed a linear programming–based tool to assist with many of its tactical and strategic decisions related to its refining operations. The decisions that are made based on the linear programming tool output include which crude oils to buy for input, which products to manufacture as output, and how to best operate the refinery. There are many complicating factors in these decisions, such as the fact that crude oils purchased from different areas all have slightly different characteristics

(*continued*)

Based on T. Kutz, M. Davis, R. Creek, N. Kenaston, C. Stenstrom, and M. Connor, "Optimizing Chevron's Refineries," *Interfaces* 44, no. 1 (January/February 2014), 39–54.

that require differing refining operations, which therefore makes them best suited for different output products. Further, prices for output products are often volatile and must be considered when deciding which products to refine.

Chevron first started using linear programs to assist with its decision making in refinery operations in the 1950s. Through the following decades, the company continued to update and expand its linear program–based tools to include additional complexities and exploit advances in computing power. Currently, Chevron uses a linear program–based tool at each of its seven refineries. The tool includes a spreadsheet interface to allow for ease of use in a familiar software environment.

One of the biggest benefits to the linear program–based tools is that they allow Chevron to consider a multitude of possible scenarios through sensitivity analysis. Because prices for gasoline, lubricants, and other output products change often, Chevron can use sensitivity analysis to evaluate the effects of changes on output product prices to its refinery decisions on which input crude oils to purchase and which output products to process.

Chevron believes that the results of its quantitative methods–based tools, including the linear program models, add more than $1 billion per year in overall benefits. In particular, Chevron estimates that using their tools to optimize their choice of crude oil inputs and choosing the best set of output products to refine generates more than $600 million per year in additional earnings and another $400 million per year of benefits through more efficient use of capital.

8.1 Introduction to Sensitivity Analysis

Sensitivity analysis is important to decision makers because real-world problems exist in a changing environment. Prices of raw materials change, product demands change, production capacities change, stock prices change, and so on. If a linear programming model has been used in such an environment, we can expect some of the coefficients in the model to change over time. As a result, we will want to determine how these changes affect the optimal solution. Sensitivity analysis provides information needed to respond to such changes without requiring a complete solution of a revised linear program.

Recall the RMC problem introduced in Chapter 7. RMC wanted to determine the number of tons of fuel additive (F) and the number of tons of solvent base (S) to produce in order to maximize the total profit contribution for the two products. Three raw material constraints limit the amounts of the two products that can be produced. The RMC linear programming model is restated here:

$$
\begin{aligned}
\text{Max} \quad & 40F + 30S \\
\text{s.t.} \quad & \\
& 0.4F + 0.5 \leq 20 \quad \text{Material 1} \\
& 0.2S \leq 5 \quad \text{Material 2} \\
& 0.6F + 0.3S \leq 21 \quad \text{Material 3} \\
& F, S \geq 0
\end{aligned}
$$

The optimal solution, $F = 25$ tons and $S = 20$ tons, provided a maximum profit contribution of $1600.

The optimal solution was based on profit contributions of $40 per ton for the fuel additive and $30 per ton for the solvent base. However, suppose that we later learn that a price reduction causes the profit contribution for the fuel additive to fall from $40 to $30 per ton. Sensitivity analysis can be used to determine whether producing 25 tons of fuel additive and 20 tons of solvent base is still best. If it is, solving a modified linear programming problem with $30F + 30S$ as the new objective function is not necessary.

Sensitivity analysis can also be used to determine which coefficients in a linear programming model are crucial. For example, suppose that management believes that the \$30 per ton profit contribution for the solvent base is only a rough estimate of the profit contribution that will actually be obtained. If sensitivity analysis shows that 25 tons of fuel additive and 20 tons of solvent base will be the optimal solution as long as the profit contribution for the solvent base is between \$20 and \$50, management should feel comfortable with the \$30 per ton estimate and the recommended production quantities. However, if sensitivity analysis shows that 25 tons of fuel additive and 20 tons of solvent base will be the optimal solution only if the profit contribution for the solvent base is between \$29.90 and \$30.20 per ton, management may want to review the accuracy of the \$30 per ton estimate.

Another aspect of sensitivity analysis concerns changes in the right-hand-side values of the constraints. Recall that in the RMC problem the optimal solution used all available material 1 and material 3. What would happen to the optimal solution and total profit contribution if RMC could obtain additional quantities of either of these resources? Sensitivity analysis can help determine how much each added ton of material is worth and how many tons can be added before diminishing returns set in.

8.2 Objective Function Coefficients

Let us begin sensitivity analysis by using the graphical solution procedure to demonstrate how a change in an objective function coefficient can affect the optimal solution to a linear programming problem. We begin with the graphical solution to the original RMC problem shown in Figure 8.1. The feasible region is shaded. The objective function $40F + 30S$ takes on its maximum value at the extreme point $F = 25$ and $S = 20$. Thus, $F = 25$ and $S = 20$ is the optimal solution and $40(25) + 30(20) = 1600$ is the value of the optimal solution.

FIGURE 8.1 OPTIMAL SOLUTION TO THE ORIGINAL RMC PROBLEM

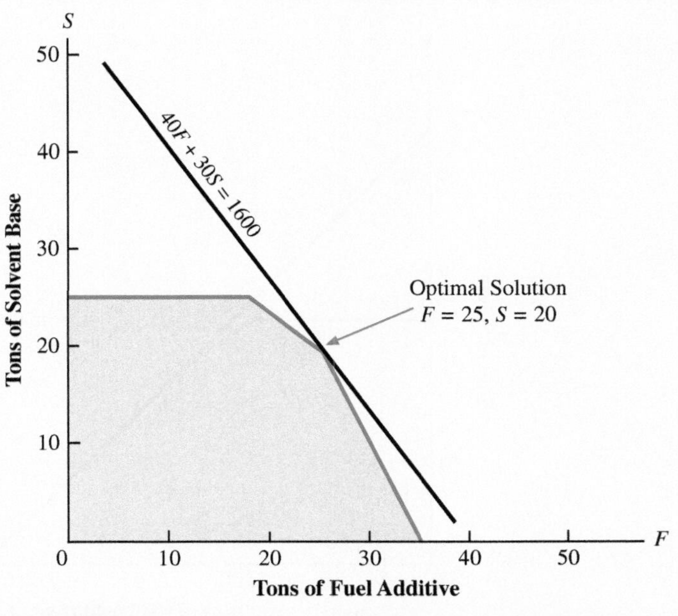

Now suppose RMC learns that a price reduction in the fuel additive has reduced its profit contribution to \$30 per ton. With this reduction, RMC's management may question the desirability of maintaining the original optimal solution of $F = 25$ tons and $S = 20$ tons. Perhaps a different solution is now optimal. The RMC linear program with the revised objective function is as follows:

$$
\begin{aligned}
\text{Max} \quad & 30F + 30S \\
\text{s.t.} \quad & \\
& 0.4F + 0.5S \le 20 \quad \text{Material 1} \\
& 0.2S \le 5 \quad \text{Material 2} \\
& 0.6F + 0.3S \le 21 \quad \text{Material 3} \\
& F, S \ge 0
\end{aligned}
$$

Note that only the objective function has changed. Because the constraints have not changed, the feasible region for the revised RMC problem remains the same as the original problem. The graphical solution to the RMC problem with the objective function $30F + 30S$ is shown in Figure 8.2. Note that the extreme point providing the optimal solution is still $F = 25$ and $S = 20$. Thus, although the total profit contribution decreased to $30(25) + 30(20) = 1350$, the decrease in the profit contribution for the fuel additive from \$40 per ton to \$30 per ton does not change the optimal solution $F = 25$ and $S = 20$.

Now let us suppose that a further price reduction causes the profit contribution for the fuel additive to be reduced to \$20 per ton. Is $F = 25$ and $S = 20$ still the optimal solution? Figure 8.3 shows the graphical solution to the RMC problem with the objective function revised to $20F + 30S$. The extreme point providing the optimal solution is now $F = 18.75$

FIGURE 8.2 REVISED OPTIMAL SOLUTION WITH THE RMC OBJECTIVE FUNCTION $30F + 30S$

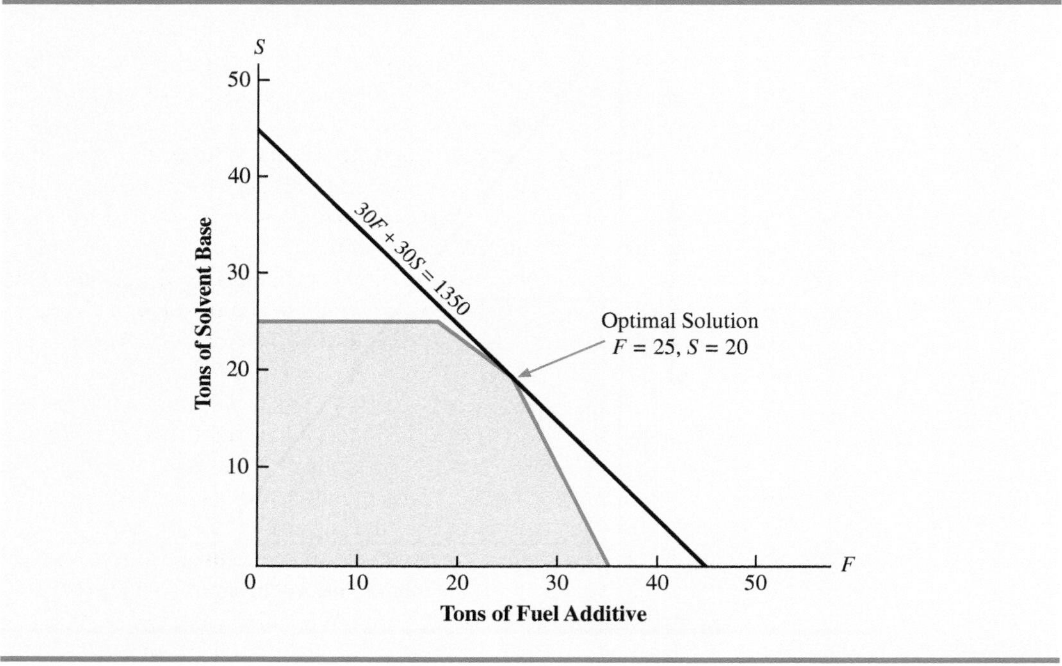

FIGURE 8.3 REVISED OPTIMAL SOLUTION WITH THE RMC OBJECTIVE FUNCTION $20F + 30S$

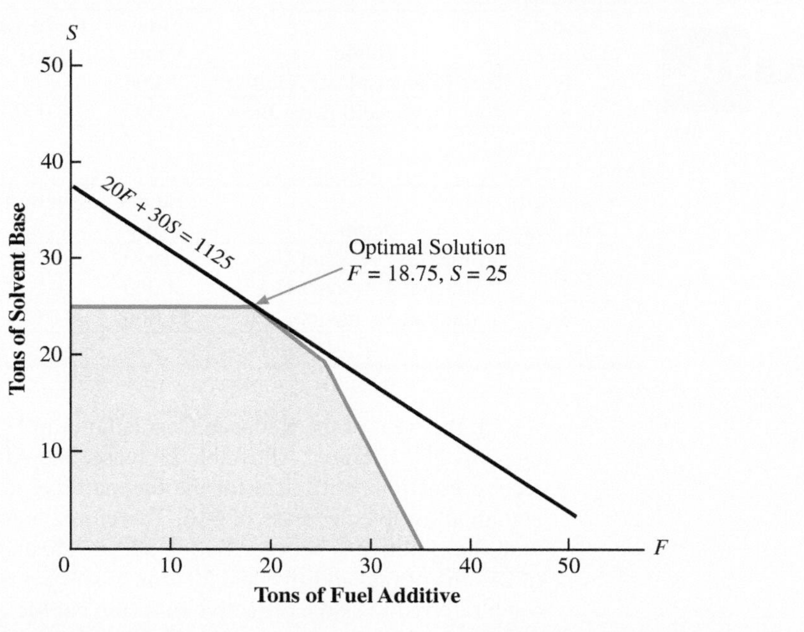

and $S = 25$. The total profit contribution decreased to $20(18.75) + 30(25) = 1125$. However, in this case, we see that decreasing the profit contribution for the fuel additive to $20 per ton changes the optimal solution. The solution $F = 25$ tons and $S = 20$ tons is no longer optimal. The solution $F = 18.75$ and $S = 25$ now provides the optimal production quantities for RMC.

The graphical solution is used here to help the reader visualize how changes to an objective function coefficient may or may not change the optimal solution.

What do we learn from the graphical solutions in Figures 8.1, 8.2, and 8.3? Changing one objective function coefficient changes the slope of the objective function line but leaves the feasible region unchanged. If the change in the objective function coefficient is small, the extreme point that provided the optimal solution to the original problem may still provide the optimal solution. However, if the change in the objective function coefficient is large enough, a different extreme point will provide a new optimal solution.

Computer solutions typically provide sensitivity analysis information.

Fortunately, computer packages such as Excel can easily provide sensitivity analysis information about the objective function coefficients for the original RMC linear programming problem. You do not have to reformulate and re-solve the linear programming problem to obtain the sensitivity analysis information. Appendix 8.1 explains how to generate a Sensitivity Report using Excel Solver. A sensitivity report similar to the output provided by Excel for the original RMC linear programming problem is shown in Figure 8.4. In addition to all of the Excel Solver Sensitivity Report information, the report in Figure 8.4 also shows the variables we used in our model. This allows you to easily link the sensitivity report to the model under discussion. We shall use this style of sensitivity report throughout this chapter.

In the Variable Cells section of the sensitivity report, the column labeled Final Value contains the optimal values of the decision variables. For the RMC problem the optimal solution is to produce 25 tons of fuel additive and 20 tons of solvent base. Associated with each decision variable is a reduced cost. We will discuss reduced costs in more detail after introducing the concept of shadow prices later in this chapter.

FIGURE 8.4 SENSITIVITY REPORT FOR THE RMC PROBLEM

WEB file

RMC

Variable Cells

Model Variable	Name	Final Value	Reduced Cost	Objective Coefficient	Allowable Increase	Allowable Decrease
F	Tons Produced Fuel Additive	25.000	0.000	40.000	20.000	16.000
S	Tons Produced Solvent Base	20.000	0.000	30.000	20.000	10.000

Constraints

Constraint Number	Name	Final Value	Shadow Price	Constraint R.H. Side	Allowable Increase	Allowable Decrease
1	Material 1 Amount Used	20.000	33.333	20.000	1.500	6.000
2	Material 2 Amount Used	4.000	0.000	5.000	1E+30	1.000
3	Material 3 Amount Used	21.000	44.444	21.000	9.000	2.250

To the right of the Reduced Cost column in Figure 8.4, we find three columns labeled Objective Coefficient, Allowable Increase, and Allowable Decrease. For example, the objective function coefficient for the fuel additive is \$40, with an allowable increase of \$20 and an allowable decrease of \$16. Therefore, as long as the profit contribution associated with fuel additive is between \$40 + \$20 = \$60 and \$40 − \$16 = \$24, the optimal solution of 25 tons of fuel additive and 20 tons of solvent base will not change. The value of \$20 is often referred to as the **objective function coefficient allowable increase**, and the value of \$16 is the **objective function coefficient allowable decrease**. The range between \$24 and \$60 is referred to as the **objective coefficient range** or **range of optimality** for the fuel additive variable. If the profit contribution for the fuel additive is outside this range, a different extreme point and a different solution will become optimal.

The objective function coefficient for the solvent base variable is \$30. The allowable decrease of \$10 and allowable increase of \$20 for the solvent base variable show that the optimal solution will not change so long as the profit contribution for solvent base is between \$30 + \$20 = \$50 and \$30 − \$10 = \$20.

NOTES AND COMMENTS

1. The sensitivity analysis information provided for the objective function coefficients is based on the assumption that *only one objective function coefficient changes at a time* and that all other aspects of the original problem remain unchanged. Thus, an objective coefficient range is only applicable for changes to a single objective coefficient. We examine this issue in more depth in Section 8.4.

8.3 Right-Hand Sides

Let us expand the discussion of sensitivity analysis by considering how a change in the right-hand side of a constraint affects the feasible region and the optimal solution to a linear programming problem. As with sensitivity analysis for the objective function coefficients, we consider what happens when we make *one change at a time*. For example, suppose that in the RMC problem an additional 4.5 tons of material 3 becomes available. In this case, the right-hand side of the third constraint increases from 21 tons to 25.5 tons. The revised RMC linear programming model is as follows:

$$\begin{aligned} \text{Max} \quad & 40F + 30S \\ \text{s.t.} \quad & \\ & 0.4F + 0.5S \le 20 \quad \text{Material 1} \\ & 0.2S \le 5 \quad \text{Material 2} \\ & 0.6F + 0.3S \le 25.5 \quad \text{Material 3} \\ & F, S \ge 0 \end{aligned}$$

Sensitivity analysis for right-hand sides is based on the assumption that only one right-hand side changes at a time. All other aspects of the problem are assumed to be as stated in the original problem.

The graphical solution to this problem is shown in Figure 8.5. Note how the feasible region expands because of the additional 4.5 tons of material 3. Application of the graphical solution procedure shows that the extreme point $F = 37.5$ tons and $S = 10$ tons is the new optimal solution. The value of the optimal solution is $40(37.5) + 30(10) = \$1800$. Recall that the optimal solution to the original RMC problem was $F = 25$ tons and $S = 20$ tons and the value of the optimal solution was \$1600. Thus, the additional 4.5 tons of material 3 in the revised problem provides a new optimal solution and increases the value of the optimal solution by $\$1800 - \$1600 = \$200$. On a per-ton basis, the additional 4.5 tons of material 3 increases the value of the optimal solution at the rate of $\$200/4.5 = \$44.44$ per ton.

Shadow prices often provide the economic information that helps make decisions about acquiring additional resources.

The **shadow price** is the change in the optimal objective function value per unit increase in the right-hand side of a constraint. Hence, the shadow price for the material 3 constraint is \$44.44 per ton. In other words, if we increase the right-hand side of the material 3 constraint by 1 ton, the value of the optimal solution will increase by \$44.44. Conversely, if we decrease the right-hand side of the material 3 constraint by 1 ton, the value of the optimal solution will decrease by \$44.44.

FIGURE 8.5 GRAPHICAL SOLUTION TO THE RMC PROBLEM WITH MATERIAL 3 CONSTRAINT $0.6F + 0.5S \le 24.5$

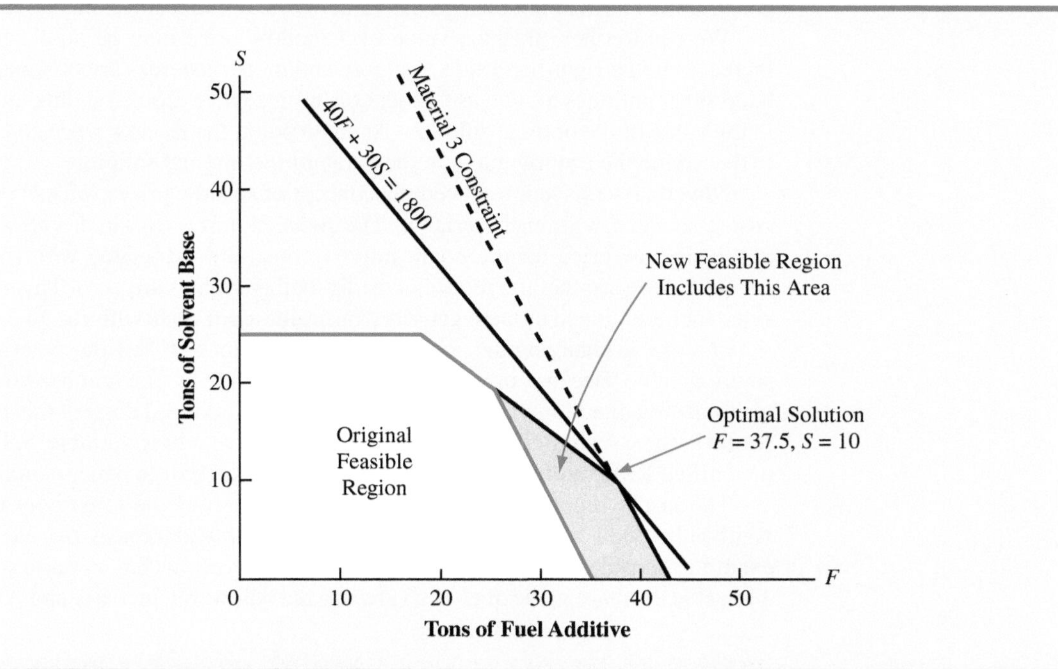

Fortunately, the sensitivity report for the original linear programming problem provides the shadow prices for all the constraints. *You do not have to reformulate and re-solve the linear programming problem to obtain the shadow price information.* The sensitivity report for the original RMC linear programming problem is shown in Figure 8.4.

Examine the Constraints section of the sensitivity report. The entries in the Final Value column indicate the number of tons of each material used in the optimal solution. Thus, RMC will use 20 tons of material 1, 4 tons of material 2, and 21 tons of material 3 in order to produce the optimal solution of 25 tons of fuel additive and 20 tons of solvent base.

The values in the Constraint R.H. Side column are the right-hand sides of the constraints for the RMC problem. The differences between the entries in the Constraint R.H. Side column and the Final Value column provide the values of the slack variables for the RMC problem. Thus, there are $20 - 20 = 0$ tons of slack for material 1, $5 - 4 = 1$ ton of slack for material 2, and $21 - 21 = 0$ tons of slack for material 3.

The column labeled Shadow Price provides the following information:

Computer solutions typically provide the shadow price for each constraint.

Constraint	Shadow Price
Material 1 Amount Used	\$33.33
Material 2 Amount Used	\$ 0.00
Material 3 Amount Used	\$44.44

Note that the shadow price for material 3, \$44.44 per ton, agrees with the calculations we made using the graphical solution procedure. We also observe that the shadow price for the material 1 constraint indicates that the value of the optimal solution will increase at the rate of \$33.33 per ton of material 1. Finally, note that the shadow price for the material 2 constraint is \$0.00. The optimal solution to the RMC problem shows that material 2 has a slack of 1 ton. Thus, at the optimal solution, 1 ton of material 2 is unused. The shadow price of \$0.00 tells us that additional tons of material 2 will simply add to the amount of slack for constraint 2 and will not change the value of the optimal solution.

We caution here that the value of a shadow price may be applicable only for small increases in the right-hand side. As more and more resources are obtained and as the right-hand side continues to increase, other constraints will become binding and limit the change in the value of the optimal solution. At some point, the shadow price can no longer be used to determine the improvement in the value of the optimal solution.

Now that we have introduced the concept of shadow prices, we can define the **reduced cost** associated with each variable. The reduced cost associated with a variable is equal to the shadow price for the nonnegativity constraint associated with the variable.[1] From Figure 8.4 we see that the reduced cost for both variables are zero. This makes sense. Consider fuel additive. The nonegativity constraint associated with the fuel additive variable, F, is $F \geq 0$, so changing the nonnegativity constraint to $F \geq 1$ has no effect on the optimal solution value. Because increasing the right-hand side by one unit has no effect on the optimal objective function value, the shadow price (i.e., reduced cost) of this nonnegativity constraint is zero. A similar argument applies to the solvent base variable, S. Later we introduce a modified RMC problem that has a nonzero reduced cost to better explain this concept.

The last two columns in the Constraints section of the sensitivity report contain the **right-hand side allowable increase** and **allowable decrease** for each constraint. For example, consider the material 1 constraint with an allowable increase value of 1.5 and an allowable decrease value of 6. The values in the Allowable Increase and Allowable Decrease

[1]We also note that, if the value of a variable in an optimal solution is equal to the upper bound of the variable, then the reduced cost will be the shadow price of this upper-bound constraint.

The range of feasibility is also sometimes referred to as the right-hand-side range.

columns indicate that the shadow price of \$33.33 is applicable for increases up to $20 + 1.5 = 21.5$ tons and decreases down to $20 - 6 = 14$ tons. The values between 14 tons and 21.5 tons are often referred to as the **range of feasibility** for the material 1 constraint.

Note that unlike the objective function coefficient ranges, it is not true that the optimal solution will not change if you stay within the range of feasibility. The range of feasibility only implies that the same set of binding constraints will remain binding and hence that the shadow price will accurately predict what will happen to the optimal objective function value as the right-hand side is changed.

Similar to sensitivity analysis for objective function coefficients, the sensitivity analysis for right-hand sides of constraints assumes that only one constraint right-hand side changes at a time.

In summary, the range of feasibility information provides the limits where the shadow prices are applicable. For changes outside the range, the problem must be re-solved to find the new shadow price. Note that the sensitivity analysis information for right-hand sides of constraints is only applicable for changes to a single right-hand side. If two or more right-hand sides of constraints change at the same time, it is easiest to re-solve the problem to see the effect of these changes. This issue is discussed in more detail in Section 8.4.

The Q.M. in Action, Evaluating Efficiency at Performance Analysis Corporation, illustrates the use of shadow prices as part of an evaluation model for a chain of fast-food outlets. This type of model will be studied in more detail in the next chapter when we discuss an application referred to as *data envelopment analysis.*

Q.M. *in* ACTION

*EVALUATING EFFICIENCY AT PERFORMANCE ANALYSIS CORPORATION**

Performance Analysis Corporation specializes in the use of quantitative models to design more efficient and effective operations for a wide variety of chain stores. One such application uses linear programming methodology to provide an evaluation model for a chain of fast-food outlets.

According to the concept of Pareto optimality, a restaurant in a given chain is relatively inefficient if other restaurants in the same chain exhibit the following characteristics:

1. Operate in the same or worse environment
2. Produce at least the same level of *all* outputs
3. Utilize no more of *any* resource and *less* of at least one of the resources

To determine which of the restaurants are Pareto inefficient, Performance Analysis Corporation developed and solved a linear programming model. Model constraints involve requirements concerning the minimum acceptable levels of output and conditions imposed by uncontrollable elements in the environment, and the objective function calls for the minimization of the resources necessary to produce the output. Solving the model produces the following output for each restaurant:

1. A score that assesses the level of so-called relative technical efficiency achieved by the particular restaurant over the time period in question.
2. The reduction in controllable resources or the increase of outputs over the time period in question needed for an inefficient restaurant to be rated as efficient.
3. A peer group of other restaurants with which each restaurant can be compared in the future.

Sensitivity analysis provides important managerial information. For example, for each constraint concerning a minimum acceptable output level, the shadow price tells the manager how much one more unit of output would increase the efficiency measure.

The analysis typically identifies 40% to 50% of the restaurants as underperforming, given the previously stated conditions concerning the inputs available and outputs produced. Performance Analysis Corporation finds that if all the relative inefficiencies identified are eliminated simultaneously, corporate profits typically increase approximately 5% to 10%. This increase is truly substantial given the large scale of operations involved.

*Based on information provided by Richard C. Morey of Performance Analysis Corporation.

NOTES AND COMMENTS

1. Some texts and computer programs use the term *dual value* or *dual price* instead of *shadow price*. Often the meaning of these terms is identical to the definition given here for shadow price. However, you must be careful to understand exactly what is meant by the term being used.

Cautionary Note on the Interpretation of Shadow Prices

As stated previously, the shadow price is the change in the value of the optimal solution per unit increase in the right-hand side of a constraint. When the right-hand side of the constraint represents the amount of a resource available, the shadow price is often interpreted as the maximum amount one should be willing to pay for one additional unit of the resource. However, such an interpretation is not always correct. To see why, we need to understand the difference between sunk and relevant costs. A **sunk cost** is one that is not affected by the decision made. It will be incurred no matter what values the decision variables assume. A **relevant cost** is one that depends on the decision made. The amount of a relevant cost will vary depending on the values of the decision variables.

Let us reconsider the RMC problem. The amount of material 1 available is 20 tons. The cost of material 1 is a sunk cost if it must be paid regardless of the number of tons of fuel additive and solvent base produced. It would be a relevant cost if RMC only had to pay for the number of tons of material 1 actually used to produce fuel additive and solvent base. All relevant costs should be included in the objective function of a linear program. Sunk costs should not be included in the objective function. For RMC we have been assuming that the company has already paid for materials 1, 2, and 3. Therefore, the cost of the raw materials for RMC is a sunk cost and has not been included in the objective function.

When the cost of a resource is *sunk*, the shadow price can be interpreted as the maximum amount the company should be willing to pay for one additional unit of the resource. When the cost of a resource used is relevant, the shadow price can be interpreted as the amount by which the value of the resource exceeds its cost. Thus, when the resource cost is relevant, the shadow price can be interpreted as the maximum premium over the normal cost that the company should be willing to pay for one unit of the resource.

Only relevant costs should be included in the objective function.

NOTES AND COMMENTS

1. Most computer software packages for solving linear programs provide the optimal solution, shadow price information, the objective coefficient ranges, and the ranges of feasibility. The labels used for these ranges may vary, but the meaning is usually the same as what we have described here.
2. We defined the shadow price as the change in the optimal objective function value per unit increase in a right-hand side of a constraint. The negative of the shadow price gives the change in the optimal objective function value per unit decrease in the right-hand side.
3. Whenever one of the right-hand sides is at an endpoint of its range, the shadow price only provides one-sided information. In this case, the shadow price only predicts the change in the optimal value of the objective function for changes toward the interior of the range.
4. A condition called *degeneracy* can cause a subtle difference in how we interpret changes in the objective function coefficients beyond the endpoints of the objective coefficient range. Degeneracy occurs when the shadow price equals zero for one of the binding constraints. Degeneracy does not affect the interpretation of changes toward the

interior of the objective coefficient range. However, when degeneracy is present, changes beyond the endpoints of the range do not necessarily mean a different solution will be optimal. From a practical point of view, changes beyond the endpoints of the range necessitate resolving the problem.

5. Managers are frequently called on to provide an economic justification for new technology. Often the new technology is developed, or purchased, in order to conserve resources. The shadow price can be helpful in such cases because it can be used to determine the savings attributable to the new technology by showing the savings per unit of resource conserved.

8.4 Limitations of Classical Sensitivity Analysis

As we have seen, classical sensitivity analysis can provide useful information on the sensitivity of the solution to changes in the model input data. However, classical sensitivity analysis does have its limitations. In this section we discuss three such limitations: simultaneous changes in input data, changes in constraint coefficients, and nonintuitive shadow prices. We give examples of these three cases and discuss how to deal effectively with these through re-solving the model with changes. In fact, in our experience, it is rarely the case that one solves a model once and makes a recommendation. More often than not, a series of models are solved using a variety of input data sets before a final plan is adopted. With improved algorithms and more powerful computers, solving multiple runs of a model is extremely cost- and time-effective.

Simultaneous Changes

Classical sensitivity analysis is based on the assumption that only one coefficient changes; it is assumed that all other coefficients will remain as stated in the original problem. Thus, the range analysis for the objective function coefficients and the constraint right-hand sides is only applicable for changes in a single coefficient. In many cases, however, we are interested in what would happen if two or more coefficients are changed simultaneously. The easiest way to examine the effect of simultaneous changes is to rerun the model. Computer solution methods such as Excel Solver make rerunning the model easy and fast for many applications.

Consider again the original RMC problem. Suppose RMC's accounting department reviews both the price and cost data for the two products. As a result, the profit contribution for the fuel additive is increased to \$48 per ton and the profit contribution for the solvent base is decreased to \$27 per ton. Figure 8.6 shows the answer report for this revised problem. The total profit has increased to \$48(25) + \$27(20) = \$1740, but the optimal solution of 25 tons of fuel additive and 20 tons of solvent base has not changed.

Now suppose that the profit contribution for fuel additive is increased again to \$55 per ton and the profit contribution for the solvent base remains at \$27 per ton. If RMC produces 25 tons of fuel additive and 20 tons of solvent base, this will generate a profit of \$55(25) + \$27(20) = \$1915. However, the answer report in Figure 8.7 shows that if we re-solve this problem with the new profit contribution values, the optimal solution changes. The optimal solution is to produce 35 tons of fuel additive and zero tons of solvent base. This optimal solution results in a profit of \$55(35) + \$27(0) = \$1925.

Sensitivity analysis for the right-hand side of constraints has a similar limitation. The right-hand-side sensitivity analysis information is based on the assumption that only one right-hand side changes at a time. If two or more right-hand sides change simultaneously, the easiest way to observe the effect of these changes is to re-solve the model.

FIGURE 8.6 ANSWER REPORT FOR RMC PROBLEM WITH CHANGE IN PROFITS PER TON FOR FUEL ADDITIVE TO $48 AND SOLVENT BASE TO $27

Objective Cell (Max)

Name	Original Value	Final Value
Maximize Total Profit	0.000	1740.000

Variable Cells

Model Variable	Name	Original Value	Final Value	Integer
A	Tons Produced Fuel Additive	0.000	25.000	Contin
B	Tons Produced Solvent Base	0.000	20.000	Contin

Constraints

Constraint Number	Name	Cell Value	Status	Slack
1	Material 1 Amount Used	20.000	Binding	0.000
2	Material 2 Amount Used	4.000	Not Binding	1.000
3	Material 3 Amount Used	21.000	Binding	0.000

FIGURE 8.7 ANSWER REPORT FOR THE RMC PROBLEM WITH ADDITIONAL INCREASE IN PROFIT PER TON FOR FUEL ADDITIVE TO $55

Objective Cell (Max)

Name	Original Value	Final Value
Maximize Total Profit	0.000	1925.000

Variable Cells

Model Variable	Name	Original Value	Final Value	Integer
A	Tons Produced Fuel Additive	0.000	35.000	Contin
B	Tons Produced Solvent Base	0.000	0.000	Contin

Constraints

Constraint Number	Name	Cell Value	Status	Slack
1	Material 1 Amount Used	14.000	Not Binding	6.000
2	Material 2 Amount Used	0.000	Not Binding	5.000
3	Material 3 Amount Used	21.000	Binding	0.000

Changes in Constraint Coefficients

Classical sensitivity analysis provides no information about changes resulting from a change in the coefficient of a variable in a constraint. We return to the RMC problem to illustrate this idea.

Suppose RMC is considering a different blending formula such that a ton of fuel additive uses 0.5 tons of material 1 instead of 0.4 tons. The constraint for material 1 would then change to

$$0.5F + 0.5S \leq 20$$

Even though this is a single change in a coefficient in the model, there is no way to tell from classical sensitivity analysis what impact the change in the coefficient of F will have on the

FIGURE 8.8 ANSWER REPORT FOR THE RMC PROBLEM WITH CHANGES TO CONSTRAINT COEFFICIENTS

Objective Cell (Max)

Name	Original Value	Final Value
Maximize Total Profit	0.000	1500.000

Variable Cells

Model Variable	Name	Original Value	Final Value	Integer
A	Tons Produced Fuel Additive	0.000	30.000	Contin
B	Tons Produced Solvent Base	0.000	10.000	Contin

Constraints

Constraint Number	Name	Cell Value	Status	Slack
1	Material 1 Amount Used	20.000	Binding	0.000
2	Material 2 Amount Used	2.000	Not Binding	3.000
3	Material 3 Amount Used	21.000	Binding	0.000

solution. Instead, we must simply change the coefficient and rerun the model. The answer report appears in Figure 8.8. Note that it is optimal to produce 30 tons of fuel additive and 10 tons of solvent base. The optimal profit has also changed from \$1600 to \$40(30) + \$30(10) = \$1500. Changing to this new blending formula will cost RMC \$1600 − \$1500 = \$100.

Nonintuitive Shadow Prices

Constraints with variables naturally on both the left-hand and right-hand sides often lead to shadow prices that have a nonintuitve explanation. To illustrate such a case and how we may deal with it, let us again reconsider the RMC problem.

Suppose that after reviewing the solution to the original RMC problem (sensitivity report shown in Figure 8.4), management decides that it is concerned with solutions requiring greater production of fuel additive than solvent base. Management believes that the profit generated per ton of fuel additive could decrease in the future, so it is more comfortable producing a greater amount of solvent base than fuel additive. If management wants to specify that RMC produces at least as much solvent base as fuel additive, then we must add the constraint

$$S \geq F$$

This new constraint will require RMC to produce at least as many tons of solvent base as fuel additive. The sensitivity report generated from resolving this problem with the new constraint is shown in Figure 8.9. This shows that it is optimal to produce 22.222 tons of fuel additive and 22.222 tons of solvent base. The total profit using this optimal solution is \$40(22.222) + \$30(22.222) = \$1556.

Let us consider the shadow price for the Min Solvent Base Required constraint. The shadow price of −8.89 indicates that a one-unit increase in the right-hand side of the Min Solvent Base Required constraint will lower profits by \$8.89. Thus, what the shadow price is really telling us is what will happen to the value of the optimal solution if the constraint is changed to

$$S \geq F + 1$$

FIGURE 8.9 SENSITIVITY REPORT FOR RMC PROBLEM WITH ADDITIONAL CONSTRAINT FOR MINIMUM SOLVENT BASE PRODUCTION REQUIRED

Variable Cells

Model Variable	Name	Final Value	Reduced Cost	Objective Coefficient	Allowable Increase	Allowable Decrease
F	Tons Produced Fuel Additive	22.222	0.000	40.000	1E+30	16.000
S	Tons Produced Solvent Base	22.222	0.000	30.000	20.000	70.000

Constraints

Constraint Number	Name	Final Value	Shadow Price	Constraint R.H. Side	Allowable Increase	Allowable Decrease
1	Material 1 Amount Used	20.000	77.778	20.000	1.000	20.000
2	Material 2 Amount Used	4.444	0.000	5.000	1E+30	0.556
3	Material 3 Amount Used	20.000	0.000	21.000	1E+30	1.000
4	Min Solvent Base Required	22.222	−8.889	0.000	6.250	5.000

The interpretation for this shadow price of -8.89 is correctly stated as follows: If we are forced to produce 1 ton more of solvent base over and above the amount of fuel additive produced, total profits will decrease by \$8.89. Conversely, if we relax the requirement by 1 ton ($S \geq F - 1$), total profits will increase by \$8.89.

We might instead be more interested in what happens if we change the coefficient on F. For instance, what if management required RMC to produce an amount of solvent base that is at least 110% of the amount of fuel additive produce? In other words, the constraint would change to

$$S \geq 1.1F$$

The shadow price does *not* tell us what will happen in this case. Because we have changed the coefficient of F from 1.0 to 1.1, this is the same as the case discussed in the previous section: a change in the constraint coefficient. Since there is no way to get this information from classical sensitivity analysis, we need to re-solve the problem using the constraint $S \geq 1.1F$. To test the sensitivity of the solution to changes in the minimum required percentage of solvent base required, we can re-solve the model replacing the coefficient of F with any percentage of interest.

To get a feel for how the required percentage impacts total profit, we solved versions of this model varying the percentage from 100% to 200% in increments of 10%. In other words, we varied the coefficient of F from 1.0 to 2.0 in increments of 0.1. The impact of changing this percentage is shown in Figure 8.10, and the results are shown in Table 8.1.

What have we learned from this analysis? Notice from Figure 8.10 that the slope of the graph becomes steeper for values larger than 130%. This indicates that there is a shift in the rate of deterioration in profit starting at 130%. Table 8.1 shows why this is the case. For all percentages larger than 130%, we produce 25 tons of solvent base. We are unable to produce additional solvent base due to the material 2 constraint. This is because the left-hand side of the material 2 constraint $0.2(25) = 5$, which is equal to the right-hand side. Thus, the material 2 constraint is binding whenever we produce 25 tons of material 2.

FIGURE 8.10 PROFIT FOR VARIOUS VALUES OF REQUIRED SOLVENT BASE AS A PERCENTAGE OF FUEL ADDITIVE PRODUCED

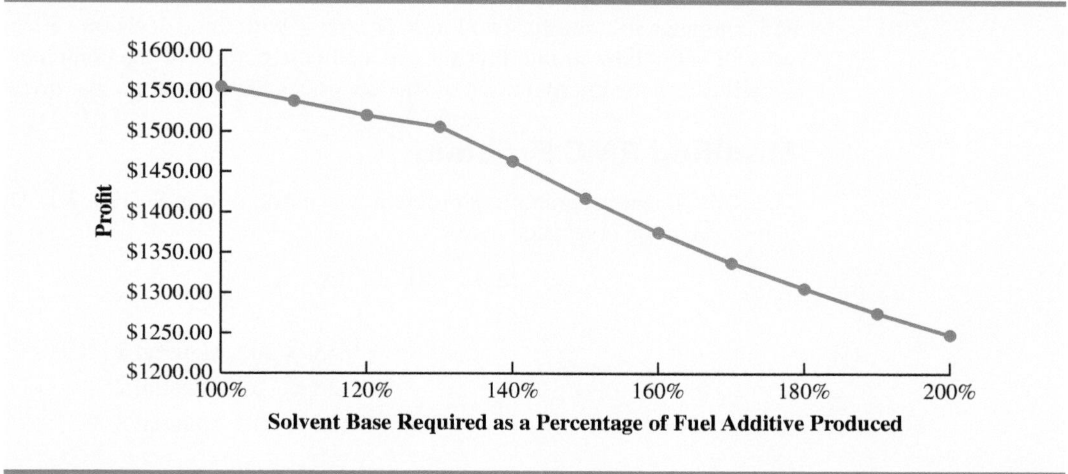

TABLE 8.1 SOLUTIONS FOR VARIOUS VALUES OF MINIMUM REQUIRED PRODUCTION OF SOLVENT BASE AS A PERCENTAGE OF FUEL ADDITIVE PRODUCED

Percent	Profit	Fuel Additive	Solvent Base
100%	$1556.00	22.222	22.222
110%	$1537.00	21.053	23.158
120%	$1520.00	20.000	24.000
130%	$1505.00	19.048	24.762
140%	$1464.00	17.857	25.000
150%	$1417.00	16.667	25.000
160%	$1375.00	15.625	25.000
170%	$1338.00	14.706	25.000
180%	$1306.00	13.889	25.000
190%	$1275.00	13.158	25.000
200%	$1250.00	12.500	25.000

Management now knows that minimum percentage requirements between 100% and 130% result in modest profit losses. Minimum percentage requirements greater than 130% result in greater profit losses. Greater minimum percentage requirements will result in more significant profit losses because we are unable to produce more than 25 tons of solvent base due to the material 2 constraint.

8.5 More Than Two Decision Variables

The graphical solution procedure is useful only for linear programs involving two decision variables. In practice, the problems solved using linear programming usually involve large numbers of variables and constraints. For instance, the Q.M. in Action, Determining

Optimal Production Quantities at GE Plastics, describes how a linear programming model with 3100 variables and 1100 constraints was solved in less than 10 seconds to determine the optimal production quantities at GE Plastics. In this section we discuss the formulation and computer solution for two linear programs with three decision variables. In doing so, we will show how to interpret the reduced-cost portion of the computer output and will also illustrate the interpretation of shadow prices for constraints that involve percentages.

Modified RMC Problem

The RMC linear programming problem was introduced in Section 7.1. The original problem formulation is restated here:

$$\begin{aligned} \text{Max} \quad & 40F + 30S \\ \text{s.t.} \quad & \\ & 0.4F + 0.5S \le 20 \quad \text{Material 1} \\ & \qquad\quad 0.2S \le 5 \quad \text{Material 2} \\ & 0.6F + 0.3S \le 21 \quad \text{Material 3} \\ & F, S \ge 0 \end{aligned}$$

Suppose that management also is considering producing a carpet cleaning fluid. Estimates are that each ton of carpet cleaning fluid will require 0.6 tons of material 1, 0.1 tons of material 2, and 0.3 tons of material 3. Because of the unique capabilities of the new product, RMC's management believes that the company will realize a profit contribution of \$50 for each ton of carpet cleaning fluid produced during the current production period.

Let us consider the modifications in the original linear programming model that are needed to incorporate the effect of this additional decision variable. We let C denote the number of tons of carpet cleaning fluid produced. After adding C to the objective

Q.M. *in* ACTION

*DETERMINING OPTIMAL PRODUCTION QUANTITIES AT GE PLASTICS**

GE Plastics (GEP) is a \$5 billion global materials supplier of plastics and raw materials to many industries (e.g., automotive, computer, and medical equipment). GEP has plants all over the globe. In the past, GEP followed a pole-centric manufacturing approach wherein each product was manufactured in the geographic area (Americas, Europe, or Pacific) where it was to be delivered. When many of GEP's customers started shifting their manufacturing operations to the Pacific, a geographic imbalance was created between GEP's capacity and demand in the form of overcapacity in the Americas and undercapacity in the Pacific.

Recognizing that a pole-centric approach was no longer effective, GEP adopted a global approach to its manufacturing operations. Initial work focused on the high-performance polymers (HPP) division. Using a linear programming model, GEP was able to determine the optimal production quantities at each HPP plant to maximize the total contribution margin for the division. The model included demand constraints, manufacturing capacity constraints, and constraints that modeled the flow of materials produced at resin plants to the finishing plants and on to warehouses in three geographical regions (Americas, Europe, and Pacific). The mathematical model for a one-year problem has 3100 variables and 1100 constraints and can be solved in less than 10 seconds. The new system proved successful at the HPP division, and other GE Plastics divisions are adapting it for their supply chain planning.

In 2007, GEP was acquired by the Saudi Basic Industries Corporation (SABIC), the largest company in the Middle East and one of the largest companies in the world.

*Based on R. Tyagi, P. Kalish, and K. Akbay, "GE Plastics Optimizes the Two-Echelon Global Fulfillment Network at Its High-Performance Polymers Division," *Interfaces* (September/October 2004): 359–366.

FIGURE 8.11 SENSITIVITY REPORT FOR MODIFIED RMC PROBLEM

WEB file

ModifiedRMC

Variable Cells

Model Variable	Name	Final Value	Reduced Cost	Objective Coefficient	Allowable Increase	Allowable Decrease
F	Tons Produced Fuel Additive	27.500	0.000	40.000	60.000	6.667
S	Tons Produced Solvent Base	0.000	−12.500	30.000	12.500	1E+30
C	Tons Produced Carpet Cleaning Fluid	15.000	0.000	50.000	10.000	16.667

Constraints

Constraint Number	Name	Final Value	Shadow Price	Constraint R.H. Side	Allowable Increase	Allowable Decrease
1	Material 1 Amount Used	20.000	75.000	20.000	14.000	6.000
2	Material 2 Amount Used	1.500	0.000	5.000	1E+30	3.500
3	Material 3 Amount Used	21.000	16.667	21.000	9.000	11.000

function and to each of the three constraints, we obtain the linear program for the modified problem:

$$\begin{aligned}
\text{Max} \quad & 40F + 30S + 50C \\
\text{s.t.} \quad & \\
& 0.4F + 0.5S + 0.6C \le 20 \quad \text{Material 1} \\
& \qquad\quad 0.2S + 0.1C \le 5 \quad \text{Material 2} \\
& 0.6F + 0.3S + 0.3C \le 21 \quad \text{Material 3} \\
& \qquad F, S, C \ge 0
\end{aligned}$$

Figure 8.11 shows the sensitivity report for this solution to the modified RMC problem. The optimal solution calls for the production of 27.5 tons of fuel additive, 0 tons of solvent base, and 15 tons of carpet cleaning fluid. The value of the optimal solution is \$40(27.5) + \$30(0) + \$50(15) = \$1850.

Note the information contained in the Reduced Costs column of the Variable Cells section. Recall that reduced costs are the shadow prices of the corresponding nonnegativity constraints. As Figure 8.11 shows, the reduced costs for fuel additive and carpet cleaning fluid variables are zero because increasing the right-hand side of these nonnegativity constraints would not change the optimal objective function value. However, the reduced cost for the solvent base decision variable is −12.50. This means that the shadow price for the nonnegativity constraint associated with the solvent base decision variable is −12.50. The interpretation for this value is that if the nonnegativity constraint, $S \ge 0$, was changed to $S \ge 1$, the optimal objective function value would decrease by \$12.50. In other words, if we forced the production of at least 1 ton of solvent base, the profit for the optimal solution would decrease by \$12.50.[2]

Figure 8.11 also shows that the shadow prices for material 1 amount used and material 3 amount used are 75.000 and 16.667, respectively, indicating that these two constraints are binding in the optimal solution. Thus, each additional ton of material 1 would increase the value of the optimal solution by \$75 and each additional ton of material 3 would increase the value of the optimal solution by \$16.67.

[2]Another interpretation for this is that if we "reduce the cost" of the objective function coefficient for solvent base by −12.50 [i.e., change the profit contribution from solvent base to \$30 − (−\$12.50) = \$42.50], then there is an optimal solution where we produce a nonzero amount of solvent base.

Bluegrass Farms Problem

To provide additional practice in formulating and interpreting the computer solution for linear programs involving more than two decision variables, we consider a minimization problem involving three decision variables. Bluegrass Farms, located in Lexington, Kentucky, has been experimenting with a special diet for its racehorses. The feed components available for the diet are a standard horse feed product, an enriched oat product, and a new vitamin and mineral feed additive. The nutritional values in units per pound and the costs for the three feed components are summarized in Table 8.2; for example, each pound of the standard feed component contains 0.8 units of ingredient A, 1 unit of ingredient B, and 0.1 units of ingredient C. The minimum daily diet requirements for each horse are 3 units of ingredient A, 6 units of ingredient B, and 4 units of ingredient C. In addition, to control the weight of the horses, the total daily feed for a horse should not exceed 6 pounds. Bluegrass Farms would like to determine the minimum-cost mix that will satisfy the daily diet requirements.

To formulate a linear programming model for the Bluegrass Farms problem, we introduce three decision variables:

S = number of pounds of the standard horse feed product

E = number of pounds of the enriched oat product

A = number of pounds of the vitamin and mineral feed additive

Using the data in Table 8.2, the objective function that will minimize the total cost associated with the daily feed can be written as follows:

$$\text{Min } 0.25S + 0.5E + 3A$$

Because the minimum daily requirement for ingredient A is 3 units, we obtain the constraint

$$0.8S + 0.2E \geq 3$$

The constraint for ingredient B is

$$1.0S + 1.5E + 3.0A \geq 6$$

and the constraint for ingredient C is

$$0.1S + 0.6E + 2.0A \geq 4$$

Finally, the constraint that restricts the mix to at most 6 pounds is

$$S + E + A \leq 6$$

TABLE 8.2 NUTRITIONAL VALUE AND COST DATA FOR THE BLUEGRASS FARMS PROBLEM

Feed Component	Standard	Enriched Oat	Additive
Ingredient A	0.8	0.2	0.0
Ingredient B	1.0	1.5	3.0
Ingredient C	0.1	0.6	2.0
Cost per pound	$0.25	$0.50	$3.00

Combining all the constraints with the nonnegativity requirements enables us to write the complete linear programming model for the Bluegrass Farms problem as follows:

$$
\begin{array}{llll}
\text{Min} & 0.25S + 0.50E + 3A & & \\
\text{s.t.} & & & \\
 & 0.8S + 0.2E & \geq 3 & \text{Ingredient A} \\
 & 1.0S + 1.5E + 3.0A & \geq 6 & \text{Ingredient B} \\
 & 0.1S + 0.6E + 2.0A & \geq 4 & \text{Ingredient C} \\
 & S + E + A & \leq 6 & \text{Weight} \\
 & S, E, A \geq 0 & &
\end{array}
$$

The sensitivity report for the Bluegrass Farms problem is shown in Figure 8.12. After rounding, we see that the optimal solution calls for a daily diet consisting of 3.51 pounds of the standard horse feed product, 0.95 pounds of the enriched oat product, and 1.54 pounds of the vitamin and mineral feed additive. Thus, with feed component costs of \$0.25, \$0.50, and \$3.00, the total cost of the optimal diet is

3.51 pounds @ \$0.25 per pound = \$0.88
0.95 pound @ \$0.50 per pound = \$0.47
1.54 pounds @ \$3.00 per pound = \$4.62
Total cost = \$5.97

Looking at the Constraints section of the sensitivity report, we see that the final value for the Ingredient B LHS constraint is 9.554 and the right-hand side of this constraint is 6. Because this constraint is a greater-than-or-equal-to constraint, 3.554 is the surplus; the optimal solution exceeds the minimum daily diet requirement for ingredient B (6 units) by 3.554 units. Because the final values for the ingredient A and ingredient C constraints are

FIGURE 8.12 SENSITIVITY REPORT FOR THE BLUEGRASS FARMS PROBLEM

WEB file

Bluegrass

Variable Cells

Model Variable	Name	Final Value	Reduced Cost	Objective Coefficient	Allowable Increase	Allowable Decrease
S	Number of Pounds Standard	3.514	0.000	0.250	1E+30	0.643
E	Number of Pounds Enriched Oat	0.946	0.000	0.500	0.425	1E+30
A	Number of Pounds Additive	1.541	0.000	3.000	1E+30	1.478

Constraints

Constraint Number	Name	Final Value	Shadow Price	Constraint R.H. Side	Allowable Increase	Allowable Decrease
1	Ingredient A	3.000	1.216	3.000	0.368	1.857
2	Ingredient B	9.554	0.000	6.000	3.554	1E+30
3	Ingredient C	4.000	1.959	4.000	0.875	1.900
4	Weight	6.000	−0.919	6.000	2.478	0.437

equal to the right-hand sides for these constraints, we see that the optimal diet just meets the minimum requirements for ingredients A and C. The final value for the weight constraint is equal to the right-hand side (6 pounds). This tells us that this constraint has a slack value of zero, which means that the optimal solution provides a total daily feed weight of 6 pounds.

The shadow price (after rounding) for ingredient A is 1.22. Thus, increasing the right-hand side of the ingredient A constraint by one unit will cause the solution value to increase by $1.22. Conversely, it is also correct to conclude that a decrease of one unit in the right-hand side of the ingredient A constraint will decrease the total cost by $1.22. Looking at the Allowable Increase and Allowable Decrease columns in the Constraints section of the sensitivity report, we see that these interpretations are correct as long as the right-hand side of the ingredient A constraint is between $3 - 1.857 = 1.143$ and $3 + 0.368 = 3.368$.

Suppose that the Bluegrass management is willing to reconsider its position regarding the maximum weight of the daily diet. The shadow price of -0.92 (after rounding) for the weight constraint shows that a one-unit increase in the right-hand side of constraint 4 will reduce total cost by $0.92. The Allowable Increase column in the sensitivity report shows that this interpretation is correct for increases in the right-hand side up to a maximum of $6 + 2.478 = 8.478$ pounds. Thus, the effect of increasing the right-hand side of the weight constraint from 6 to 8 pounds is a decrease in the total daily cost of $2 \times \$0.92$, or $1.84. Keep in mind that if this change were made, the feasible region would change, and we would obtain a new optimal solution.

Next we look at the Variable Cells section of the sensitivity report. The Allowable Decrease column shows a lower limit of $0.25 - 0.643 = -0.393$ for the objective function coefficient associated with the standard horse feed product variable, S. Clearly, in a real problem, the objective function coefficient of S (the cost of the standard horse feed product) cannot take on a negative value. So, from a practical point of view, we can think of the lower limit for the objective function coefficient of S as being zero. We can thus conclude that no matter how much the cost of the standard mix were to decrease, the optimal solution would not change. Even if Bluegrass Farms could obtain the standard horse feed product for free, the optimal solution would still specify a daily diet of 3.51 pounds of the standard horse feed product, 0.95 pounds of the enriched oat product, and 1.54 pounds of the vitamin and mineral feed additive. However, any decrease in the per-unit cost of the standard feed would result in a decrease in the total cost for the optimal daily diet.

Note from Figure 8.12 that the allowable increases for the objective function coefficients associated with standard horse feed product and additive are shown as 1E+30. This is the same notation as is used in Excel's Sensitivity Report; it means that these objective function coefficients have no upper limit. Even if the cost of additive were to increase, for example, from $3.00 to $13.00 per pound, the optimal solution would not change; the total cost of the solution, however, would increase by $10 (the amount of the increase) $\times$ 1.541, or $15.41. You must always keep in mind that the interpretations we make using classical sensitivity analysis information are only appropriate if all other coefficients in the problem do not change. To consider simultaneous changes, we must re-solve the problem.

Linear programming has been successfully applied to a variety of applications. The Q.M. in Action, Kimpton Hotels Uses Optimization for Setting Prices on Priceline, provides an example from the hotel industry. The Q.M. in Action discusses how Kimpton Hotels uses linear programming and, specifically, the value of shadow prices, to set prices of rooms sold through Priceline.

Q.M. *in* ACTION

*KIMPTON HOTELS USES OPTIMIZATION FOR SETTING PRICES ON PRICELINE**

How to price rooms to maximize revenue is a problem faced by all hotels. If prices are set too low, demand will be higher, but total revenue may be lower than what would have been generated if the customer's willingness to pay was known. If the price is too high, demand may drop, resulting in empty rooms and lost revenue. Revenue management, sometimes called yield management, attempts to determine prices to charge and how many rooms to offer at each price so as to maximize revenue.

Kimpton Hotels owns over 50 boutique four-star hotels in the United States and Canada. Most of Kimpton's customers are business travelers who generally book later and are often willing to pay more than leisure travelers. The shorter lead time of business travelers presents a challenge for Kimpton, since it has less time to react by adjusting its prices when demand does not materialize.

Priceline.com is an Internet site that allows the user to specify the area he or she would like to visit, the dates of the visit, and the level of the hotel (three-star, four-star, etc.) and to make a bid price for a room. Priceline searches a list of participating hotels for a hotel that matches the criteria specified by the user. This is known as opaque marketing because the hotel name is revealed to the user only when a match is found, at which point the user is committed. This opaqueness is important for the hotel, because it allows the hotel to segment the market and offer different prices without diluting its regularly posted prices.

Kimpton participates in the Priceline bidding process and has to submit prices and how many rooms are available at each price level over a specified set of dates. Using historical data, Kimpton predicts future demand and uses a technique known as dynamic programming to set prices. A linear program is then used to determine the number of rooms to offer at each price level. In particular, the shadow price on a room availability constraint is utilized to assess whether or not to offer another room at a given price in a given period. Since implementing this new optimization-based approach, rooms sold via Priceline have increased 11% and the average price for the rooms has increased by nearly 4%.

*Based on C. Anderson, "Setting Prices on Priceline," *Interfaces* 39, no. 4 (July/August 2009): 307–315.

8.6 Electronic Communications Problem

The Electronic Communications problem is a maximization problem involving four decision variables, two less-than-or-equal-to constraints, one equality constraint, and one greater-than-or-equal-to constraint. We will use this problem to provide a summary of the process of formulating a mathematical model, using Excel to obtain an optimal solution, and interpreting the solution and sensitivity report information. In the next chapter we will continue to illustrate how linear programming can be applied by showing additional examples from the areas of marketing, finance, and production management.

Electronic Communications manufactures portable radio systems that can be used for two-way communications. The company's new product, which has a range of up to 25 miles, is suitable for use in a variety of business and personal applications. The distribution channels for the new radio are as follows:

1. Marine equipment distributors
2. Business equipment distributors
3. National chain of retail stores
4. Direct mail

Because of differing distribution and promotional costs, the profitability of the product will vary with the distribution channel. In addition, the advertising cost and the personal sales

TABLE 8.3 PROFIT, ADVERTISING COST, AND PERSONAL SALES TIME DATA FOR THE ELECTRONIC COMMUNICATIONS PROBLEM

Distribution Channel	Profit per Unit Sold	Advertising Cost per Unit Sold	Personal Sales Effort per Unit Sold
Marine distributors	$90	$10	2 hours
Business distributors	$84	$ 8	3 hours
National retail stores	$70	$ 9	3 hours
Direct mail	$60	$15	None

effort required will vary with the distribution channel. Table 8.3 summarizes the contribution to profit, advertising cost, and personal sales effort data for the Electronic Communications problem. The firm set the advertising budget at $5000. A maximum of 1800 hours of sales force time is available for allocation to the sales effort. Management also decided to produce exactly 600 units for the current production period. Finally, an ongoing contract with a national chain of retail stores requires that at least 150 units be distributed through this distribution channel.

Electronic Communications is now faced with the problem of determining the number of units that should be produced for each of the distribution channels in order to maximize the total contribution to profit. In addition to determining how many units should be allocated to each of the four distribution channels, Electronic Communications must also determine how to allocate the advertising budget and sales force effort to each of the four distribution channels.

Problem Formulation

We will now write the objective function and the constraints for the Electronic Communications problem. We begin with the objective function.

Objective function: Maximize profit

Four constraints are needed to account for the following restrictions: (1) a limited advertising budget, (2) limited sales force availability, (3) a production requirement, and (4) a retail stores distribution requirement.

Constraint 1 Advertising expenditure $\leq$ Budget

Constraint 2 Sales time used $\leq$ Time available

Constraint 3 Radios produced $=$ Management requirement

Constraint 4 Retail distribution $\geq$ Contract requirement

These expressions provide descriptions of the objective function and the constraints. We are now ready to define the decision variables that will represent the decisions the manager must make. For the Electronic Communications problem, we introduce the following four decision variables:

M = the number of units produced for the marine equipment distribution channel

B = the number of units produced for the business equipment distribution channel

R = the number of units produced for the national retail chain distribution channel

D = the number of units produced for the direct mail distribution channel

Using the data in Table 8.3, we can write the objective function for maximizing the total contribution to profit associated with the radios as follows:

$$\text{Max } 90M + 84B + 70R + 60D$$

Let us now develop a mathematical statement of the constraints for the problem. For the advertising budget of $5000, the constraint that limits the amount of advertising expenditure can be written as follows:

$$10M + 8B + 9R + 15D \leq 5000$$

Similarly, with sales time limited to 1800 hours, we obtain the constraint

$$2M + 3B + 3R \leq 1800$$

Management's decision to produce exactly 600 units during the current production period is expressed as

$$M + B + R + D = 600$$

Finally, to account for the fact that the number of units distributed by the national chain of retail stores must be at least 150, we add the constraint

$$R \geq 150$$

Combining all of the constraints with the nonnegativity requirements enables us to write the complete linear programming model for the Electronic Communications problem as follows:

$$
\begin{array}{llr}
\text{Max} & 90M + 84B + 70R + 60D & \\
\text{s.t.} & & \\
& 10M + 8B + 9R + 15D \leq 5000 & \text{Advertising budget} \\
& 2M + 3B + 3R \leq 1800 & \text{Sales force availability} \\
& M + B + R + D = 600 & \text{Production level} \\
& R \geq 150 & \text{Retail stores requirement} \\
& M, B, R, D \geq 0 &
\end{array}
$$

Solution and Interpretation

Figure 8.13 shows the sensitivity report for the Electronic Communications problem. The optimal decisions are to produce 25 units for the marine distribution channel ($M = 25$), 425 units for the business equipment distribution channel ($B = 425$), 150 units for the retail chain distribution channel ($R = 150$), and no units for the direct mail distribution channel ($D = 0$). The optimal solution to the problem will provide a profit of \$90(25) + \$84(425) + \$70(150) + \$60(0) = \$48,450. Consider the information contained in the Reduced Cost

FIGURE 8.13 SENSITIVITY REPORT FOR THE ELECTRONIC COMMUNICATIONS PROBLEM

WEB file Electronic

Variable Cells

Model Variable	Name	Final Value	Reduced Cost	Objective Coefficient	Allowable Increase	Allowable Decrease
M	Number of Units Produced Marine	25.000	0.000	90.000	1E+30	6.000
B	Number of Units Produced Business	425.000	0.000	84.000	6.000	34.000
R	Number of Units Produced Retail	150.000	0.000	70.000	17.000	1E+30
D	Number of Units Produced Direct Mail	0.000	−45.000	60.000	45.000	1E+30

Constraints

Constraint Number	Name	Final Value	Shadow Price	Constraint R.H. Side	Allowable Increase	Allowable Decrease
1	Advertising Budget	5000.000	3.000	5000.000	850.000	50.000
2	Sales Force Availability	1775.000	0.000	1800.000	1E+30	25.000
3	Production Level	600.000	60.000	600.000	3.571	85.000
4	Retail Stores Requirement	150.000	−17.000	150.000	50.000	150.000

column of the Variable Cells section of the sensitivity report in Figure 8.13. Recall that the reduced cost of a variable is the shadow price of the corresponding nonnegativity constraint. As the sensitivity analysis shows, the first three reduced costs are zero because the corresponding decision variables already have positive values in the optimal solution. However, the reduced cost of −45 for Number of Units Produced Direct Mail (D) tells us that profit will decrease by \$45 for every unit produced for the direct mail channel. Stated another way, the objective function coefficient associated with D would have to be reduced by at least −\$45 per unit [i.e., the profit contribution would have to be at least \$60 − (−\$45) = \$105 per unit] before it would be profitable to use the direct mail distribution channel.

Next consider the Constraints section of the sensitivity report in Figure 8.13. The advertising budget constraint has a final value equal to the constraint right-hand side, indicating that the entire budget of \$5000 has been used. The corresponding shadow price of 3 tells us that an additional dollar added to the advertising budget will increase the profit by \$3. Thus, the possibility of increasing the advertising budget should be seriously considered by the firm. Comparing the final value to the right-hand-side value for the sales force availability, we see that this constraint has a slack value of 1800 − 1725 = 25 hours. In other words, the allocated 1800 hours of sales time are adequate to distribute the radios produced, and 25 hours of sales time will remain unused. Because the production level constraint is an equality constraint, it is expected that the final value will equal the right-hand side for this constraint. However, the shadow price of 60 associated with this constraint shows that if the firm were to consider increasing the production level for the radios, the value of the objective function, or profit, would increase at the rate of \$60 per radio produced. Finally, the final value is equal to the right-hand side for the retail stores requirement constraint shows that this constraint is binding. The negative shadow price indicates that increasing the commitment from 150 to 151 units will actually decrease the profit by \$17. Thus, Electronic Communications may want to consider reducing its commitment to the retail store distribution channel. A *decrease* in the commitment will actually increase profit at the rate of \$17 per unit.

We now consider the Allowable Increase and Allowable Decrease columns from the Variable Cells section of the sensitivity report shown in Figure 8.13. The allowable increases and decreases for the objective function coefficients are

Name	Objective Coefficient	Allowable Increase	Allowable Decrease
Units Produced Marine	90.000	Infinite	6.000
Units Produced Business	84.000	6.000	34.000
Units Produced Retail	70.000	17.000	Infinite
Units Produced Direct Mail	60.000	45.000	Infinite

The current solution, or strategy, remains optimal, provided that the objective function coefficients do not increase or decrease by more than the allowed amounts. Note in particular the range associated with the direct mail distribution channel coefficient. This information is consistent with the earlier observation for the Reduced Cost portion of the output. In both instances, we see that the per-unit profit would have to increase to $\$60 + \$45 = \$105$ before the direct mail distribution channel could be in the optimal solution with a positive value.

Finally, the sensitivity analysis for the allowable increases and decreases of the right-hand side of the constraints can be taken from Figure 8.13 as follows:

Name	Constraint R.H. Side	Allowable Increase	Allowable Decrease
Advertising Budget	5000.000	850.000	50.000
Sales Force Availability	1800.000	Infinite	25.000
Production Level	600.000	3.571	85.000
Retail Stores Requirement	150.000	50.000	150.000

Several interpretations of these right-hand-side ranges are possible. In particular, recall that the shadow price for the advertising budget enabled us to conclude that each \$1 increase in the budget would improve the profit by \$3. The current advertising budget is \$5000. The allowable increase on the advertising budget is \$850 and this implies that there is value in increasing the budget up to an advertising budget of \$5850. Increases above this level would not necessarily be beneficial. Also note that the shadow price of -17 for the retail stores requirement suggested the desirability of reducing this commitment. The allowable decrease for this constraint is 150, and this implies that the commitment could be reduced to zero and the value of the reduction would be at the rate of \$17 per unit.

Again, the *sensitivity analysis* provided by computer software packages for linear programming problems considers only *one change at a time*, with all other coefficients of the problem remaining as originally specified. As mentioned earlier, simultaneous changes are best handled by re-solving the problem.

Finally, recall that the complete solution to the Electronic Communications problem requested information not only on the number of units to be distributed over each channel, but also on the allocation of the advertising budget and the sales force effort to each distribution channel. Because the optimal solution is $M = 25$, $B = 425$, $R = 150$, and $D = 0$, we can simply evaluate each term in a given constraint to determine how much of the constraint

TABLE 8.4 PROFIT-MAXIMIZING STRATEGY FOR THE ELECTRONIC COMMUNICATIONS PROBLEM

Distribution Channel	Volume	Advertising Allocation	Sales Force Allocation (hours)
Marine distributors	25	\$ 250	50
Business distributors	425	3400	1275
National retail stores	150	1350	450
Direct mail	0	0	0
Totals	600	\$5000	1775
Projected total profit = \$48,450			

resource is allocated to each distribution channel. For example, the advertising budget constraint of

$$10M + 8B + 9R + 15D \leq 5000$$

shows that $10M = 10(25) = \$250$, $8B = 8(425) = \$3400$, $9R = 9(150) = \$1350$, and $15D = 15(0) = \$0$. Thus, the advertising budget allocations are, respectively, \$250, \$3400, \$1350, and \$0 for each of the four distribution channels. Making similar calculations for the sales force constraint results in the managerial summary of the Electronic Communications optimal solution, as shown in Table 8.4.

Summary

We began the chapter with a discussion of sensitivity analysis, the study of how changes in the coefficients of a linear program affect the optimal solution. First, we showed how a graphical method can be used to determine how a change in one of the objective function coefficients or a change in the right-hand-side value for a constraint will affect the optimal solution to the problem. Because graphical sensitivity analysis is limited to linear programs with two decision variables, we showed how to use a computer software package such as Excel Solver to produce a sensitivity report containing the same information.

We continued our discussion of problem formulation, sensitivity analysis, and the interpretation of the solution by introducing modifications of the RMC problem. We also discussed several limitations of classical sensitivity analysis, including issues related to simultaneous changes, changes in constraint coefficients, and nonintuitive shadow prices. Then, in order to provide additional practice in formulating and interpreting the solution for linear programs involving more than two decision variables, we introduced the Bluegrass Farms problem, a minimization problem involving three decision variables. In the last section we summarized all the work to date using the Electronic Communications problem, a maximization problem with four decision variables: two less-than-or-equal-to constraints, one equality constraint, and one greater-than-or-equal-to constraint.

The Q.M. in Action, Tea Production and Distribution at Duncan Industries Limited, illustrates the diversity of problem situations in which linear programming can be applied and the importance of sensitivity analysis. In the next chapter we will see many more applications of linear programming.

Q.M. *in* ACTION

*TEA PRODUCTION AND DISTRIBUTION AT DUNCAN INDUSTRIES LIMITED**

In India, one of the largest tea producers in the world, approximately $1 billion of tea packets and loose tea are sold. Duncan Industries Limited (DIL), the third largest producer of tea in the Indian tea market, sells about $37.5 million of tea, almost all of which is sold in packets.

DIL has 16 tea gardens, 3 blending units, 6 packing units, and 22 depots. Tea from the gardens is sent to blending units, which then mix various grades of tea to produce blends such as Sargam, Double Diamond, and Runglee Rungliot. The blended tea is transported to packing units, where it is placed in packets of different sizes and shapes to produce about 120 different product lines. For example, one line is Sargam tea packed in 500-gram cartons, another line is Double Diamond packed in 100-gram polythene pouches, and so on. The tea is then shipped to the depots that supply 11,500 distributors, through whom the needs of approximately 325,000 retailers are satisfied.

For the coming month, sales managers provide estimates of the demand for each line of tea at each depot. Using these estimates, a team of senior managers would determine the amounts of loose tea of each blend to ship to each packing unit, the quantity of each line of tea to be packed at each packing unit, and the amounts of packed tea of each line to be transported from each packing unit to the various depots. This process requires two to three days each month and often results in stock-outs of lines in demand at specific depots.

Consequently, a linear programming model involving approximately 7000 decision variables and 1500 constraints was developed to minimize the company's freight cost while satisfying demand, supply, and all operational constraints. The model was tested on past data and showed that stock-outs could be prevented at little or no additional cost. Moreover, the model was able to provide management with the ability to perform various what-if types of exercises, convincing managers of the potential benefits of using management science techniques to support the decision-making process.

*Based on Nilotpal Chakravarti, "Tea Company Steeped in OR," *OR/MS Today* (April 2000).

Glossary

Objective coefficient range (range of optimality) The range of values over which an objective function coefficient may vary without causing any change in the values of the decision variables in the optimal solution.

Objective function coefficient allowable increase (decrease) The allowable increase (decrease) of an objective function coefficient is the amount the coefficient may increase (decrease) without causing any change in the values of the decision variables in the optimal solution. The allowable increase/decrease for the objective function coefficients can be used to calculate the range of optimality.

Range of feasibility The range of values over which the shadow price is applicable.

Reduced cost If a variable is at its lower bound of zero, the reduced cost is equal to the shadow price of the nonnegativity constraint for that variable. In general, if a variable is at its lower or upper bound, the reduced cost is the shadow price for that simple lower or upper bound constraint.

Relevant cost A cost that depends upon the decision made. The amount of a relevant cost will vary depending on the values of the decision variables.

Right-hand-side allowable increase (decrease) The allowable increase (decrease) of the right-hand side of a constraint is the amount the right-hand side may increase (decrease) without causing any change in the shadow price for that constraint. The allowable increase and decrease for the right-hand side can be used to calculate the range of feasibility for that constraint.

Sensitivity analysis The study of how changes in the coefficients of a linear programming problem affect the optimal solution.

Shadow price The change in the optimal objective function value per unit increase in the right-hand side of a constraint.

Sunk cost A cost that is not affected by the decision made. It will be incurred no matter what values the decision variables assume.

Problems

1. Consider the following linear program:

$$\begin{aligned} \text{Max} \quad & 3A + 2B \\ \text{s.t.} \quad & \\ & 1A + 1B \le 10 \\ & 3A + 1B \le 24 \\ & 1A + 2B \le 16 \\ & A, B \ge 0 \end{aligned}$$

   a. Use the graphical solution procedure to find the optimal solution.
   b. Assume that the objective function coefficient for A changes from 3 to 5. Does the optimal solution change? Use the graphical solution procedure to find the new optimal solution.
   c. Assume that the objective function coefficient for A remains 3, but the objective function coefficient for B changes from 2 to 4. Does the optimal solution change? Use the graphical solution procedure to find the new optimal solution.
   d. The sensitivity report for the linear program in part (a) provides the following objective coefficient range information:

Variable	Objective Coefficient	Allowable Increase	Allowable Decrease
A	3.000	3.000	1.000
B	2.000	1.000	1.000

   Use this objective coefficient range information to answer parts (b) and (c).

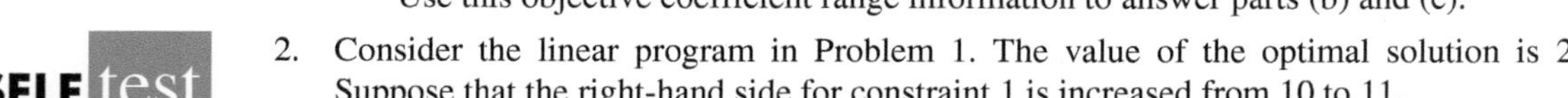

2. Consider the linear program in Problem 1. The value of the optimal solution is 27. Suppose that the right-hand side for constraint 1 is increased from 10 to 11.
   a. Use the graphical solution procedure to find the new optimal solution.
   b. Use the solution to part (a) to determine the shadow price for constraint 1.
   c. The sensitivity report for the linear program in Problem 1 provides the following right-hand-side range information:

Constraint	Constraint R.H. Side	Allowable Increase	Allowable Decrease
1	10.000	1.200	2.000
2	24.000	6.000	6.000
3	16.000	Infinite	3.000

   What does the right-hand-side range information for constraint 1 tell you about the shadow price for constraint 1?

d. The shadow price for constraint 2 is 0.5. Using this shadow price and the right-hand-side range information in part (c), what conclusion can you draw about the effect of changes to the right-hand side of constraint 2?

3. Consider the following linear program:

$$\begin{aligned} \text{Min} \quad & 8X + 12Y \\ \text{s.t.} \quad & \\ & 1X + 3Y \geq 9 \\ & 2X + 2Y \geq 10 \\ & 6X + 2Y \geq 18 \\ & X, Y \geq 0 \end{aligned}$$

a. Use the graphical solution procedure to find the optimal solution.
b. Assume that the objective function coefficient for X changes from 8 to 6. Does the optimal solution change? Use the graphical solution procedure to find the new optimal solution.
c. Assume that the objective function coefficient for X remains 8, but the objective function coefficient for Y changes from 12 to 6. Does the optimal solution change? Use the graphical solution procedure to find the new optimal solution.
d. The sensitivity report for the linear program in part (a) provides the following objective coefficient range information:

Variable	Objective Coefficient	Allowable Increase	Allowable Decrease
X	8.000	4.000	4.000
Y	12.000	12.000	4.000

How would this objective coefficient range information help you answer parts (b) and (c) prior to resolving the problem?

4. Consider the linear program in Problem 3. The value of the optimal solution is 48. Suppose that the right-hand side for constraint 1 is increased from 9 to 10.
a. Use the graphical solution procedure to find the new optimal solution.
b. Use the solution to part (a) to determine the shadow price for constraint 1.
c. The sensitivity report for the linear program in Problem 3 provides the following right-hand-side range information:

Constraint	Constraint R.H. Side	Allowable Increase	Allowable Decrease
1	9.000	2.000	4.000
2	10.000	8.000	1.000
3	18.000	4.000	Infinite

What does the right-hand-side range information for constraint 1 tell you about the shadow price for constraint 1?

d. The shadow price for constraint 2 is 3. Using this shadow price and the right-hand-side range information in part (c), what conclusion can be drawn about the effect of changes to the right-hand side of constraint 2?

5. Refer to the Kelson Sporting Equipment problem (Chapter 7, Problem 24). Letting

R = number of regular gloves
C = number of catcher's mitts

leads to the following formulation:

$$\begin{aligned} \text{Max} \quad & 5R + 8C \\ \text{s.t.} \quad & \\ & R + \tfrac{3}{2}C \leq 900 \quad \text{Cutting and sewing} \\ & \tfrac{1}{2}R + \tfrac{1}{3}C \leq 300 \quad \text{Finishing} \\ & \tfrac{1}{8}R + \tfrac{1}{4}C \leq 100 \quad \text{Packaging and shipping} \\ & R, C \geq 0 \end{aligned}$$

The sensitivity report is shown in Figure 8.14.
a. What is the optimal solution, and what is the value of the total profit contribution?
b. Which constraints are binding?
c. What are the shadow prices for the resources? Interpret each.
d. If overtime can be scheduled in one of the departments, where would you recommend doing so?

6. Refer to the sensitivity information for the Kelson Sporting Equipment problem in Figure 8.14 (see Problem 5).
a. Determine the objective coefficient ranges.
b. Interpret the ranges in part (a).
c. Interpret the right-hand-side ranges.
d. How much will the value of the optimal solution improve if 20 extra hours of packaging and shipping time are made available?

7. Investment Advisors, Inc., is a brokerage firm that manages stock portfolios for a number of clients. A particular portfolio consists of U shares of U.S. Oil and H shares of Huber Steel. The annual return for U.S. Oil is \$3 per share and the annual return for

FIGURE 8.14 SENSITIVITY REPORT FOR THE KELSON SPORTING EQUIPMENT PROBLEM

Variable Cells

Model Variable	Name	Final Value	Reduced Cost	Objective Coefficient	Allowable Increase	Allowable Decrease
R	Gloves Standard	500.000	0.000	5.000	7.000	1.000
C	Gloves Deluxe	150.000	0.000	8.000	2.000	4.667

Constraints

Constraint Number	Name	Final Value	Shadow Price	Constraint R.H. Side	Allowable Increase	Allowable Decrease
1	Cutting and Dyeing Hours Used	725.000	0.000	900.000	1E+30	175.000
2	Finishing Hours Used	300.000	3.000	300.000	100.000	166.667
3	Packaging and Shipping Hours Used	100.000	28.000	100.000	35.000	25.000

Huber Steel is \$5 per share. U.S. Oil sells for \$25 per share and Huber Steel sells for \$50 per share. The portfolio has \$80,000 to be invested. The portfolio risk index (0.50 per share of U.S. Oil and 0.25 per share for Huber Steel) has a maximum of 700. In addition, the portfolio is limited to a maximum of 1000 shares of U.S. Oil. The linear programming formulation that will maximize the total annual return of the portfolio is as follows:

$$
\begin{array}{llll}
\text{Max} & 3U + 5H & & \text{Maximize total annual return} \\
\text{s.t.} & & & \\
& 25U + 50H \leq 80{,}000 & & \text{Funds available} \\
& 0.50U + 0.25H \leq 700 & & \text{Risk maximum} \\
& 1U \leq 1000 & & \text{U.S. Oil maximum} \\
& U, H \geq 0 & &
\end{array}
$$

The sensitivity report for this problem is shown in Figure 8.15.

a. What is the optimal solution, and what is the value of the total annual return?
b. Which constraints are binding? What is your interpretation of these constraints in terms of the problem?
c. What are the shadow prices for the constraints? Interpret each.
d. Would it be beneficial to increase the maximum amount invested in U.S. Oil? Why or why not?

8. Refer to Figure 8.15, which shows the sensitivity report for Problem 7.
   a. How much would the return for U.S. Oil have to increase before it would be beneficial to increase the investment in this stock?
   b. How much would the return for Huber Steel have to decrease before it would be beneficial to reduce the investment in this stock?
   c. How much would the total annual return be reduced if the U.S. Oil maximum were reduced to 900 shares?

9. Recall the Tom's, Inc., problem (Chapter 7, Problem 28). Letting

$$W = \text{jars of Western Foods Salsa}$$
$$M = \text{jars of Mexico City Salsa}$$

FIGURE 8.15 SENSITIVITY REPORT FOR THE INVESTMENT ADVISORS PROBLEM

Variable Cells

Model Variable	Name	Final Value	Reduced Cost	Objective Coefficient	Allowable Increase	Allowable Decrease
U	U.S. Oil	800.000	0.000	3.000	7.000	0.500
H	Huber	1200.000	0.000	5.000	1.000	3.500

Constraints

Constraint Number	Name	Final Value	Shadow Price	Constraint R.H. Side	Allowable Increase	Allowable Decrease
1	Funds available	80000.000	0.093	80000.000	60000.000	15000.000
2	Risk maximum	700.000	1.333	700.000	75.000	300.000
3	U.S. Oil maximum	800.000	0.000	1000.000	1E+30	200.000

FIGURE 8.16 SENSITIVITY REPORT FOR THE TOM'S INC., PROBLEM

Variable Cells

Model Variable	Name	Final Value	Reduced Cost	Objective Coefficient	Allowable Increase	Allowable Decrease
W	Western Foods Salsa	560.000	0.000	1.000	0.250	0.107
M	Mexico City Salsa	240.000	0.000	1.250	0.150	0.250

Constraints

Constraint Number	Name	Final Value	Shadow Price	Constraint R.H. Side	Allowable Increase	Allowable Decrease
1	Whole tomatoes	4480.000	0.125	4480.000	1120.000	160.000
2	Tomato sauce	1920.000	0.000	2080.000	1E+30	160.000
3	Tomato paste	1600.000	0.188	1600.000	40.000	320.000

leads to the formulation:

$$
\begin{aligned}
\text{Max} \quad & 1W + 1.25M \\
\text{s.t.} \quad & \\
& 5W + 7M \leq 4480 \quad \text{Whole tomatoes} \\
& 3W + 1M \leq 2080 \quad \text{Tomato sauce} \\
& 2W + 2M \leq 1600 \quad \text{Tomato paste} \\
& W, M \geq 0
\end{aligned}
$$

The sensitivity report is shown in Figure 8.16.

a. What is the optimal solution, and what are the optimal production quantities?
b. Specify the objective coefficient ranges.
c. What are the shadow prices for each constraint? Interpret each.
d. Identify each of the right-hand-side ranges.

10. Recall the Innis Investments problem (Chapter 7, Problem 39). Letting

$$
\begin{aligned}
S &= \text{units purchased in the stock fund} \\
M &= \text{units purchased in the money market fund}
\end{aligned}
$$

leads to the following formulation:

$$
\begin{aligned}
\text{Min} \quad & 8S + 3M \\
\text{s.t.} \quad & \\
& 50S + 100M \leq 1{,}200{,}000 \quad \text{Funds available} \\
& 5S + 4M \geq 60{,}000 \quad \text{Annual income} \\
& M \geq 3{,}000 \quad \text{Units in money market} \\
& S, M \geq 0
\end{aligned}
$$

The sensitivity report is shown in Figure 8.17.

a. What is the optimal solution, and what is the minimum total risk?
b. Specify the objective coefficient ranges.
c. How much annual income will be earned by the portfolio?
d. What is the rate of return for the portfolio?
e. What is the shadow price for the funds available constraint?
f. What is the marginal rate of return on extra funds added to the portfolio?

FIGURE 8.17 SENSITIVITY REPORT FOR THE INNIS INVESTMENTS PROBLEM

Variable Cells

Model Variable	Name	Final Value	Reduced Cost	Objective Coefficient	Allowable Increase	Allowable Decrease
S	Units in Stock Fund	4000.000	0.000	8.000	1E+30	4.250
M	Units in Money Market Fund	10000.000	0.000	3.000	3.400	1E+30

Constraints

Constraint Number	Name	Final Value	Shadow Price	Constraint R.H. Side	Allowable Increase	Allowable Decrease
1	Funds Available	1200000.000	−0.057	1200000.000	300000.000	420000.000
2	Annual Income	60000.000	2.167	60000.000	42000.000	12000.000
3	Units in Money Market	10000.000	0.000	3000.000	7000.000	1E+30

11. Refer to Problem 10 and the sensitivity report shown in Figure 8.17.
    a. Suppose the risk index for the stock fund (the objective function coefficient for S) increases from its current value of 8 to 12. How does the optimal solution change, if at all?
    b. Suppose the risk index for the money market fund (the objective function coefficient for M) increases from its current value of 3 to 3.5. How does the optimal solution change, if at all?
    c. Suppose the objective function coefficient for S increases to 12 and the objective function coefficient for M increases to 3.5. Can you determine how the optimal solution will change using the information in Figure 8.17?

12. Quality Air Conditioning manufactures three home air conditioners: an economy model, a standard model, and a deluxe model. The profits per unit are \$63, \$95, and \$135, respectively. The production requirements per unit are as follows:

	Number of Fans	Number of Cooling Coils	Manufacturing Time (hours)
Economy	1	1	8
Standard	1	2	12
Deluxe	1	4	14

For the coming production period, the company has 200 fan motors, 320 cooling coils, and 2400 hours of manufacturing time available. How many economy models (E), standard models (S), and deluxe models (D) should the company produce in order to maximize profit? The linear programming model for the problem is as follows.

$$
\begin{aligned}
\text{Max} \quad & 63E + 95S + 135D \\
\text{s.t.} \quad & \\
& 1E + 1S + 1D \leq 200 \quad \text{Fan motors} \\
& 1E + 2S + 4D \leq 320 \quad \text{Cooling coils} \\
& 8E + 12S + 14D \leq 2400 \quad \text{Manufacturing time} \\
& E, S, D \geq 0
\end{aligned}
$$

FIGURE 8.18 SENSITIVITY REPORT FOR THE QUALITY AIR CONDITIONING PROBLEM

Variable Cells

Model Variable	Name	Final Value	Reduced Cost	Objective Coefficient	Allowable Increase	Allowable Decrease
E	Economy Models	80.000	0.000	63.000	12.000	15.500
S	Standard Models	120.000	0.000	95.000	31.000	8.000
D	Deluxe Models	0.000	−24.000	135.000	24.000	1E+30

Constraints

Constraint Number	Name	Final Value	Shadow Price	Constraint R.H. Side	Allowable Increase	Allowable Decrease
1	Fan Motors	200.000	31.000	200.000	80.000	40.000
2	Cooling Coils	320.000	32.000	320.000	80.000	120.000
3	Manufacturing Time	2080.000	0.000	2400.000	1E+30	320.000

The sensitivity report is shown in Figure 8.18.

a. What is the optimal solution, and what is the value of the objective function?
b. Which constraints are binding?
c. Which constraint shows extra capacity? How much?
d. If the profit for the deluxe model were increased to $150 per unit, would the optimal solution change? Use the information in Figure 8.18 to answer this question.

13. Refer to the sensitivity report in Figure 8.18.
    a. Identify the range of optimality for each objective function coefficient.
    b. Suppose the profit for the economy model is increased by $6 per unit, the profit for the standard model is decreased by $2 per unit, and the profit for the deluxe model is increased by $4 per unit. What will the new optimal solution be?
    c. Identify the range of feasibility for the right-hand-side values.
    d. If the number of fan motors available for production is increased by 100, will the shadow price for that constraint change? Explain.

14. Digital Controls, Inc. (DCI) manufactures two models of a radar gun used by police to monitor the speed of automobiles. Model A has an accuracy of plus or minus 1 mile per hour, whereas the smaller model B has an accuracy of plus or minus 3 miles per hour. For the next week, the company has orders for 100 units of model A and 150 units of model B. Although DCI purchases all the electronic components used in both models, the plastic cases for both models are manufactured at a DCI plant in Newark, New Jersey. Each model A case requires 4 minutes of injection-molding time and 6 minutes of assembly time. Each model B case requires 3 minutes of injection-molding time and 8 minutes of assembly time. For next week the Newark plant has 600 minutes of injection-molding time available and 1080 minutes of assembly time available. The manufacturing cost is $10 per case for model A and $6 per case for model B. Depending upon demand and the time available at the Newark plant, DCI occasionally purchases cases for one or both models from an outside supplier in order to fill customer orders that could not be filled otherwise. The purchase cost is $14 for each model A case and $9 for each model B case. Management wants to develop a minimum cost plan that will determine how many cases of each model should be produced at the Newark plant and how many cases of each model should be purchased. The following decision variables were used to formulate a linear programming model for this problem:

AM = number of cases of model A manufactured
BM = number of cases of model B manufactured
AP = number of cases of model A purchased
BP = number of cases of model B purchased

The linear programming model that can be used to solve this problem is as follows:

$$\begin{aligned}
\text{Min} \quad & 10AM + 6BM + 14AP + 9BP \\
\text{s.t.} \quad & \\
& 1AM + \quad + 1AP + \quad = 100 \quad \text{Demand for model A} \\
& \quad 1BM + \quad 1BP = 150 \quad \text{Demand for model B} \\
& 4AM + 3BM \leq 600 \quad \text{Injection molding time} \\
& 6AM + 8BM \leq 1080 \quad \text{Assembly time} \\
& AM, BM, AP, BP \geq 0
\end{aligned}$$

The sensitivity report is shown in Figure 8.19.

a. What is the optimal solution and what is the optimal value of the objective function?
b. Which constraints are binding?
c. What are the shadow prices? Interpret each.
d. If you could change the right-hand side of one constraint by one unit, which one would you choose? Why?

15. Refer to the sensitivity report for Problem 14 in Figure 8.19.
    a. Interpret the ranges of optimality for the objective function coefficients.
    b. Suppose that the manufacturing cost increases to \$11.20 per case for model A. What is the new optimal solution?
    c. Suppose that the manufacturing cost increases to \$11.20 per case for model A and the manufacturing cost for model B decreases to \$5 per unit. Would the optimal solution change?

FIGURE 8.19 SENSITIVITY REPORT FOR THE DIGITAL CONTROLS, INC., PROBLEM

Variable Cells

Model Variable	Name	Final Value	Reduced Cost	Objective Coefficient	Allowable Increase	Allowable Decrease
AM	Models A Manufactured	100.000	0.000	10.000	1.750	1E+30
BM	Models B Manufactured	60.000	0.000	6.000	3.000	2.333
AP	Models A Purchased	0.000	1.750	14.000	1E+30	1.750
BP	Models B Purchased	90.000	0.000	9.000	2.333	3.000

Constraints

Constraint Number	Name	Final Value	Shadow Price	Constraint R.H. Side	Allowable Increase	Allowable Decrease
1	Demand for model A	100.000	12.250	100.000	11.429	100.000
2	Demand for model B	150.000	9.000	150.000	1E+30	90.000
3	Injection molding time	580.000	0.000	600.000	1E+30	20.000
4	Assembly time	1080.000	−0.375	1080.000	53.333	480.000

16. Tucker Inc. produces high-quality suits and sport coats for men. Each suit requires 1.2 hours of cutting time and 0.7 hours of sewing time, uses 6 yards of material, and provides a profit contribution of $190. Each sport coat requires 0.8 hours of cutting time and 0.6 hours of sewing time, uses 4 yards of material, and provides a profit contribution of $150. For the coming week, 200 hours of cutting time, 180 hours of sewing time, and 1200 yards of fabric material are available. Additional cutting and sewing time can be obtained by scheduling overtime for these operations. Each hour of overtime for the cutting operation increases the hourly cost by $15, and each hour of overtime for the sewing operation increases the hourly cost by $10. A maximum of 100 hours of overtime can be scheduled. Marketing requirements specify a minimum production of 100 suits and 75 sport coats. Let

$$S = \text{number of suits produced}$$
$$SC = \text{number of sport coats produced}$$
$$D1 = \text{hours of overtime for the cutting operation}$$
$$D2 = \text{hours of overtime for the sewing operation}$$

The sensitivity report is shown in Figure 8.20.

a. What is the optimal solution, and what is the total profit? What is the plan for the use of overtime?
b. A price increase for suits is being considered that would result in a profit contribution of $210 per suit. If this price increase is undertaken, how will the optimal solution change?
c. Discuss the need for additional material during the coming week. If a rush order for material can be placed at the usual price plus an extra $8 per yard for handling, would you recommend that the company consider placing a rush order for material? What is the maximum price Tucker would be willing to pay for an additional yard of material? How many additional yards of material should Tucker consider ordering?
d. Suppose the minimum production requirement for suits is lowered to 75. Would this change help or hurt profit? Explain.

FIGURE 8.20 SENSITIVITY REPORT FOR THE TUCKER INC. PROBLEM

Variable Cells

Model Variable	Name	Final Value	Reduced Cost	Objective Coefficient	Allowable Increase	Allowable Decrease
S	Suits Produced	100.000	0.000	190.000	35.000	1E+30
SC	Coats Produced	150.000	0.000	150.000	1E+30	23.333
D1	Overtime for Cutting	40.000	0.000	−15.000	15.000	172.500
D2	Overtime for Sewing	0.000	−10.000	−10.000	10.000	1E+30

Constraints

Constraint Number	Name	Final Value	Shadow Price	Constraint R.H. Side	Allowable Increase	Allowable Decrease
1	Cutting time	200.000	15.000	200.000	40.000	60.000
2	Sewing time	160.000	0.000	180.000	1E+30	20.000
3	Material	1200.000	34.500	1200.000	133.333	200.000
4	Overtime	40.000	0.000	100.000	1E+30	60.000
5	Suit minimum	100.000	−35.000	100.000	50.000	100.000
6	Sport coat minimum	150.000	0.000	75.000	75.000	1E+30

17. The Porsche Club of America sponsors driver education events that provide high-performance driving instruction on actual racetracks. Because safety is a primary consideration at such events, many owners elect to install roll bars in their cars. Deegan Industries manufactures two types of roll bars for Porsches. Model DRB is bolted to the car using existing holes in the car's frame. Model DRW is a heavier roll bar that must be welded to the car's frame. Model DRB requires 20 pounds of a special high-alloy steel, 40 minutes of manufacturing time, and 60 minutes of assembly time. Model DRW requires 25 pounds of the special high-alloy steel, 100 minutes of manufacturing time, and 40 minutes of assembly time. Deegan's steel supplier indicated that at most 40,000 pounds of the high-alloy steel will be available next quarter. In addition, Deegan estimates that 2000 hours of manufacturing time and 1600 hours of assembly time will be available next quarter. The profit contributions are $200 per unit for model DRB and $280 per unit for model DRW. The linear programming model for this problem is as follows:

$$\text{Max} \quad 200DRB + 280DRW$$

s.t.

$$\begin{aligned} 20DRB + 25DRW &\le 40{,}000 && \text{Steel available} \\ 40DRB + 100DRW &\le 120{,}000 && \text{Manufacturing minutes} \\ 60DRB + 40DRW &\le 96{,}000 && \text{Assembly minutes} \\ DRB, DRW &\ge 0 \end{aligned}$$

The sensitivity report is shown in Figure 8.21.

a. What are the optimal solution and the total profit contribution?
b. Another supplier offered to provide Deegan Industries with an additional 500 pounds of the steel alloy at $2 per pound. Should Deegan purchase the additional pounds of the steel alloy? Explain.
c. Deegan is considering using overtime to increase the available assembly time. What would you advise Deegan to do regarding this option? Explain.
d. Because of increased competition, Deegan is considering reducing the price of model DRB such that the new contribution to profit is $175 per unit. How would this change in price affect the optimal solution? Explain.
e. If the available manufacturing time is increased by 500 hours, will the shadow price for the manufacturing time constraint change? Explain.

FIGURE 8.21 SENSITIVITY REPORT FOR THE DEEGAN INDUSTRIES PROBLEM

Variable Cells

Model Variable	Name	Final Value	Reduced Cost	Objective Coefficient	Allowable Increase	Allowable Decrease
DRB	Model DRB	1000.000	0.000	200.000	24.000	88.000
DRW	Model DRW	800.000	0.000	280.000	220.000	30.000

Constraints

Constraint Number	Name	Final Value	Shadow Price	Constraint R.H. Side	Allowable Increase	Allowable Decrease
1	Steel available	40000.000	8.800	40000.000	909.091	10000.000
2	Manufacturing minutes	120000.000	0.600	120000.000	40000.000	5714.286
3	Assembly minutes	92000.000	0.000	96000.000	1E+30	4000.000

18. Davison Electronics manufactures two models of LCD televisions, identified as model A and model B. Each model has its lowest possible production cost when produced on Davison's new production line. However, the new production line does not have the capacity to handle the total production of both models. As a result, at least some of the production must be routed to a higher-cost, old production line. The following table shows the minimum production requirements for next month, the production line capacities in units per month, and the production cost per unit for each production line:

	Production Cost per Unit		Minimum Production
Model	New Line	Old Line	Requirements
A	$30	$50	50,000
B	$25	$40	70,000
Production Line Capacity	80,000	60,000	

Let

AN = Units of model A produced on the new production line

AO = Units of model A produced on the old production line

BN = Units of model B produced on the new production line

BO = Units of model B produced on the old production line

Davison's objective is to determine the minimum cost production plan. The sensitivity report is shown in Figure 8.22.

a. Formulate the linear programming model for this problem using the following four constraints:

Constraint 1: Minimum production for model A
Constraint 2: Minimum production for model B

FIGURE 8.22 SENSITIVITY REPORT FOR THE DAVISON ELECTRONICS PROBLEM

Variable Cells

Model Variable	Name	Final Value	Reduced Cost	Objective Coefficient	Allowable Increase	Allowable Decrease
AN	Model A Produced on New Line	50000.000	0.000	30.000	5.000	1E+30
AO	Model A Produced on Old Line	0.000	5.000	50.000	1E+30	5.000
BN	Model B Produced on New Line	30000.000	0.000	25.000	15.000	5.000
BO	Model B Produced on Old Line	40000.000	0.000	40.000	5.000	15.000

Constraints

Constraint Number	Name	Final Value	Shadow Price	Constraint R.H. Side	Allowable Increase	Allowable Decrease
1	Min production for A	50000.000	45.000	50000.000	20000.000	40000.000
2	Min production for B	70000.000	40.000	70000.000	20000.000	40000.000
3	Capacity of new production line	80000.000	−15.000	80000.000	40000.000	20000.000
4	Capacity of old production line	40000.000	0.000	60000.000	1E+30	20000.000

Constraint 3: Capacity of the new production line
Constraint 4: Capacity of the old production line

b. Using the sensitivity analysis information in Figure 8.22, what is the optimal solution and what is the total production cost associated with this solution?
c. Which constraints are binding? Explain.
d. The production manager noted that the only constraint with a negative shadow price is the constraint on the capacity of the new production line. The manager's interpretation of the shadow price was that a one-unit increase in the right-hand side of this constraint would actually increase the total production cost by $15 per unit. Do you agree with this interpretation? Would an increase in capacity for the new production line be desirable? Explain.
e. Would you recommend increasing the capacity of the old production line? Explain.
f. The production cost for model A on the old production line is $50 per unit. How much would this cost have to change to make it worthwhile to produce model A on the old production line? Explain.
g. Suppose that the minimum production requirement for model B is reduced from 70,000 units to 60,000 units. What effect would this change have on the total production cost? Explain.

19. Better Products, Inc., manufactures three products on two machines. In a typical week, 40 hours are available on each machine. The profit contribution and production time in hours per unit are as follows:

Category	Product 1	Product 2	Product 3
Profit/unit	$30	$50	$20
Machine 1 time/unit	0.5	2.0	0.75
Machine 2 time/unit	1.0	1.0	0.5

Two operators are required for machine 1; thus, 2 hours of labor must be scheduled for each hour of machine 1 time. Only one operator is required for machine 2. A maximum of 100 labor-hours is available for assignment to the machines during the coming week. Other production requirements are that product 1 cannot account for more than 50% of the units produced and that product 3 must account for at least 20% of the units produced.

a. How many units of each product should be produced to maximize the total profit contribution? What is the projected weekly profit associated with your solution?
b. How many hours of production time will be scheduled on each machine?
c. What is the value of an additional hour of labor?
d. Assume that labor capacity can be increased to 120 hours. Would you be interested in using the additional 20 hours available for this resource? Develop the optimal product mix, assuming that the extra hours are made available.

20. Adirondack Savings Bank (ASB) has $1 million in new funds that must be allocated to home loans, personal loans, and automobile loans. The annual rates of return for the three types of loans are 7% for home loans, 12% for personal loans, and 9% for automobile loans. The bank's planning committee has decided that at least 40% of the new funds must be allocated to home loans. In addition, the planning committee has specified that the amount allocated to personal loans cannot exceed 60% of the amount allocated to automobile loans.

a. Formulate a linear programming model that can be used to determine the amount of funds ASB should allocate to each type of loan in order to maximize the total annual return for the new funds.

b. How much should be allocated to each type of loan? What is the total annual return? What is the annual percentage return?
c. If the interest rate on home loans increased to 9%, would the amount allocated to each type of loan change? Explain.
d. Suppose the total amount of new funds available was increased by $10,000. What effect would this have on the total annual return? Explain.
e. Assume that ASB has the original $1 million in new funds available and that the planning committee has agreed to relax the requirement that at least 40% of the new funds must be allocated to home loans by 1%. How much would the annual return change? How much would the annual percentage return change?

21. Round Tree Manor is a hotel that provides two types of rooms with three rental classes: Super Saver, Deluxe, and Business. The profit per night for each type of room and rental class is as follows:

		Rental Class		
		Super Saver	**Deluxe**	**Business**
Room	Type I	$30	$35	—
	Type II	$20	$30	$40

Type I rooms do not have dedicated work desks and are not available for the Business rental class.

Round Tree's management makes a forecast of the demand by rental class for each night in the future. A linear programming model developed to maximize profit is used to determine how many reservations to accept for each rental class. The demand forecast for a particular night is 130 rentals in the Super Saver class, 60 rentals in the Deluxe class, and 50 rentals in the Business class. Round Tree has 100 Type I rooms and 120 Type II rooms.

a. Use linear programming to determine how many reservations to accept in each rental class and how the reservations should be allocated to room types. Is the demand by any rental class not satisfied? Explain.
b. How many reservations can be accommodated in each rental class?
c. Management is considering offering a free breakfast to anyone upgrading from a Super Saver reservation to Deluxe class. If the cost of the breakfast to Round Tree is $5, should this incentive be offered?
d. With a little work, an unused office area could be converted to a rental room. If the conversion cost is the same for both types of rooms, would you recommend converting the office to a Type I or a Type II room? Why?
e. Could the linear programming model be modified to plan for the allocation of rental demand for the next night? What information would be needed and how would the model change?

22. Industrial Designs has been awarded a contract to design a label for a new wine produced by Lake View Winery. The company estimates that 150 hours will be required to complete the project. The firm's three graphic designers available for assignment to this project are Lisa, a senior designer and team leader; David, a senior designer; and Sarah, a junior designer. Because Lisa has worked on several projects for Lake View Winery, management specified that Lisa must be assigned at least 40% of the total number of hours assigned to the two senior designers. To provide label-designing experience for Sarah, Sarah must be assigned at least 15% of the total project time. However, the number of hours assigned to Sarah must not exceed 25% of the total number of hours assigned to the two senior

designers. Due to other project commitments, Lisa has a maximum of 50 hours available to work on this project. Hourly wage rates are $30 for Lisa, $25 for David, and $18 for Sarah.

a. Formulate a linear program that can be used to determine the number of hours each graphic designer should be assigned to the project in order to minimize total cost.
b. How many hours should each graphic designer be assigned to the project? What is the total cost?
c. Suppose Lisa could be assigned more than 50 hours. What effect would this have on the optimal solution? Explain.
d. If Sarah were not required to work a minimum number of hours on this project, would the optimal solution change? Explain.

23. Vollmer Manufacturing makes three components for sale to refrigeration companies. The components are processed on two machines: a shaper and a grinder. The times (in minutes) required on each machine are as follows:

	Machine	
Component	**Shaper**	**Grinder**
1	6	4
2	4	5
3	4	2

The shaper is available for 120 hours, and the grinder is available for 110 hours. No more than 200 units of component 3 can be sold, but up to 1000 units of each of the other components can be sold. In fact, the company already has orders for 600 units of component 1 that must be satisfied. The profit contributions for components 1, 2, and 3 are $8, $6, and $9, respectively.

a. Formulate and solve for the recommended production quantities.
b. What are the objective coefficient ranges for the three components? Interpret these ranges for company management.
c. What are the right-hand-side ranges? Interpret these ranges for company management.
d. If more time could be made available on the grinder, how much would it be worth?
e. If more units of component 3 can be sold by reducing the sales price by $4, should the company reduce the price?

24. National Insurance Associates carries an investment portfolio of stocks, bonds, and other investment alternatives. Currently $200,000 of funds are available and must be considered for new investment opportunities. The four stock options National is considering and the relevant financial data are as follows:

	Stock			
	A	**B**	**C**	**D**
Price per share	$100	$50	$80	$40
Annual rate of return	0.12	0.08	0.06	0.10
Risk measure per dollar invested	0.10	0.07	0.05	0.08

The risk measure indicates the relative uncertainty associated with the stock in terms of its realizing the projected annual return; higher values indicate greater risk. The risk measures are provided by the firm's top financial advisor.

National's top management has stipulated the following investment guidelines: The annual rate of return for the portfolio must be at least 9%, and no one stock can account for more than 50% of the total dollar investment.

a. Use linear programming to develop an investment portfolio that minimizes risk.
b. What are the objective coefficient ranges for the four variables? Interpret these ranges.
c. Suppose that the firm decides that the annual rate of return must be at least 10%. What does the shadow price associated with this constraint indicate about the change in risk that would occur from this increased rate of return?

25. Georgia Cabinets manufactures kitchen cabinets that are sold to local dealers throughout the Southeast. Because of a large backlog of orders for oak and cherry cabinets, the company decided to contract with three smaller cabinetmakers to do the final finishing operation. For the three cabinetmakers, the number of hours required to complete all the oak cabinets, the number of hours required to complete all the cherry cabinets, the number of hours available for the final finishing operation, and the cost per hour to perform the work are shown here:

	Cabinetmaker 1	**Cabinetmaker 2**	**Cabinetmaker 3**
Hours required to complete all the oak cabinets	50	42	30
Hours required to complete all the cherry cabinets	60	48	35
Hours available	40	30	35
Cost per hour	\$36	\$42	\$55

For example, Cabinetmaker 1 estimates that it will take 50 hours to complete all the oak cabinets and 60 hours to complete all the cherry cabinets. However, Cabinetmaker 1 only has 40 hours available for the final finishing operation. Thus, Cabinetmaker 1 can only complete 40/50 = 0.80, or 80%, of the oak cabinets if it worked only on oak cabinets. Similarly, Cabinetmaker 1 can only complete 40/60 = 0.67, or 67%, of the cherry cabinets if it worked only on cherry cabinets.

a. Formulate a linear programming model that can be used to determine the percentage of the oak cabinets and the percentage of the cherry cabinets that should be given to each of the three cabinetmakers in order to minimize the total cost of completing both projects.
b. Solve the model formulated in part (a). What percentage of the oak cabinets and what percentage of the cherry cabinets should be assigned to each cabinetmaker? What is the total cost of completing both projects?
c. If Cabinetmaker 1 has additional hours available, would the optimal solution change? Explain.
d. If Cabinetmaker 2 has additional hours available, would the optimal solution change? Explain.
e. Suppose Cabinetmaker 2 reduced its cost to \$38 per hour. What effect would this change have on the optimal solution? Explain.

26. Benson Electronics manufactures three components used to produce cell phones and other communication devices. In a given production period, demand for the three components may exceed Benson's manufacturing capacity. In this case, the company meets demand by purchasing the components from another manufacturer at an increased cost per unit.

Benson's manufacturing cost per unit and purchasing cost per unit for the three components are as follows:

Source	Component 1	Component 2	Component 3
Manufacture	\$4.50	\$5.00	\$2.75
Purchase	\$6.50	\$8.80	\$7.00

Manufacturing times in minutes per unit for Benson's three departments are as follows:

Department	Component 1	Component 2	Component 3
Production	2	3	4
Assembly	1	1.5	3
Testing & Packaging	1.5	2	5

For instance, each unit of component 1 that Benson manufactures requires 2 minutes of production time, 1 minute of assembly time, and 1.5 minutes of testing and packaging time. For the next production period, Benson has capacities of 360 hours in the production department, 250 hours in the assembly department, and 300 hours in the testing and packaging department.

a. Formulate a linear programming model that can be used to determine how many units of each component to manufacture and how many units of each component to purchase. Assume that component demands that must be satisfied are 6000 units for component 1, 4000 units for component 2, and 3500 units for component 3. The objective is to minimize the total manufacturing and purchasing costs.
b. What is the optimal solution? How many units of each component should be manufactured and how many units of each component should be purchased?
c. Which departments are limiting Benson's manufacturing quantities? Use the shadow price to determine the value of an *extra hour* in each of these departments.
d. Suppose that Benson had to obtain one additional unit of component 2. Discuss what the shadow price for the component 2 constraint tells us about the cost to obtain the additional unit.

27. Cranberries can be harvested using either a "wet" method or a "dry" method. Dry-harvested cranberries can be sold at a premium, while wet-harvested cranberries are used mainly for cranberry juice and bring in less revenue. Fresh Made Cranberry Cooperative must decide how much of its cranberry crop should be harvested wet and how much should be dry harvested. Fresh Made has 5000 barrels of cranberries that can be harvested using either the wet or dry method. Dry cranberries are sold for \$32.50 per barrel and wet cranberries are sold for \$17.50 per barrel. Once harvested, cranberries must be processed through several operations before they can be sold. Both wet and dry cranberries must go through dechaffing and cleaning operations. The dechaffing and the cleaning operations can each be run 24 hours per day for the 6-week season (for a total of 1008 hours). Each barrel of dry cranberries requires 0.18 hours in the dechaffing operation and 0.32 hours in the cleaning operation. Wet cranberries require 0.04 hours in the dechaffing operation and 0.10 hours in the cleaning operation. Wet cranberries must also go through a drying process. The drying process can also be operated 24 hours per day for the 6-week season, and each barrel of wet cranberries must be dried for 0.22 hours.

a. Develop a linear program that Fresh Made can use to determine the optimal amount of cranberries to dry harvest and wet harvest.
b. Solve the linear program in part (a). How many barrels should be dry harvested? How many barrels should be wet harvested?

c. Suppose that Fresh Made can increase its dechaffing capacity by using an outside firm for this operation. Fresh Made will still use its own dechaffing operation as much as possible, but it can purchase additional capacity from this outside firm for $500 per hour. Should Fresh Made purchase additional dechaffing capacity? Why or why not?
d. Interpret the shadow price for the constraint corresponding to the cleaning operation. How would you explain the meaning of this shadow price to management?

28. The Pfeiffer Company manages approximately $15 million for clients. For each client, Pfeiffer chooses a mix of three investment vehicles: a growth stock fund, an income fund, and a money market fund. Each client has different investment objectives and different tolerances for risk. To accommodate these differences, Pfeiffer places limits on the percentage of each portfolio that may be invested in the three funds and assigns a portfolio risk index to each client.

    Here's how the system works for Dennis Hartmann, one of Pfeiffer's clients. Based on an evaluation of Hartmann's risk tolerance, Pfeiffer has assigned Hartmann's portfolio a risk index of 0.05. Furthermore, to maintain diversity, the fraction of Hartmann's portfolio invested in the growth and income funds must be at least 10% for each, and at least 20% must be in the money market fund.

    The risk ratings for the growth, income, and money market funds are 0.10, 0.05, and 0.01, respectively. A portfolio risk index is computed as a weighted average of the risk ratings for the three funds, where the weights are the fraction of the portfolio invested in each of the funds. Hartmann has given Pfeiffer $300,000 to manage. Pfeiffer is currently forecasting a yield of 20% on the growth fund, 10% on the income fund, and 6% on the money market fund.

    a. Develop a linear programming model to select the best mix of investments for Hartmann's portfolio.
    b. Solve the model you developed in part (a).
    c. How much may the yields on the three funds vary before it will be necessary for Pfeiffer to modify Hartmann's portfolio?
    d. If Hartmann were more risk tolerant, how much of a yield increase could he expect? For instance, what if his portfolio risk index is increased to 0.06?
    e. If Pfeiffer revised the yield estimate for the growth fund downward to 0.10, how would you recommend modifying Hartmann's portfolio?
    f. What information must Pfeiffer maintain on each client in order to use this system to manage client portfolios?
    g. On a weekly basis Pfeiffer revises the yield estimates for the three funds. Suppose Pfeiffer has 50 clients. Describe how you would envision Pfeiffer making weekly modifications in each client's portfolio and allocating the total funds managed among the three investment funds.

29. La Jolla Beverage Products is considering producing a wine cooler that would be a blend of a white wine, a rosé wine, and fruit juice. To meet taste specifications, the wine cooler must consist of at least 50% white wine, at least 20% and no more than 30% rosé, and exactly 20% fruit juice. La Jolla purchases the wine from local wineries and the fruit juice from a processing plant in San Francisco. For the current production period, 10,000 gallons of white wine and 8000 gallons of rosé wine can be purchased; an unlimited amount of fruit juice can be ordered. The costs for the wine are $1.00 per gallon for the white and $1.50 per gallon for the rosé; the fruit juice can be purchased for $0.50 per gallon. La Jolla Beverage Products can sell all of the wine cooler it can produce for $2.50 per gallon.

    a. Is the cost of the wine and fruit juice a sunk cost or a relevant cost in this situation? Explain.
    b. Formulate a linear program to determine the blend of the three ingredients that will maximize the total profit contribution. Solve the linear program to determine the number of gallons of each ingredient La Jolla should purchase and the total profit contribution it will realize from this blend.

c. If La Jolla could obtain additional amounts of the white wine, should it do so? If so, how much should it be willing to pay for each additional gallon, and how many additional gallons would it want to purchase?
d. If La Jolla Beverage Products could obtain additional amounts of the rosé wine, should it do so? If so, how much should it be willing to pay for each additional gallon, and how many additional gallons would it want to purchase?
e. Interpret the shadow price for the constraint corresponding to the requirement that the wine cooler must contain at least 50% white wine. What is your advice to management given this shadow price?
f. Interpret the shadow price for the constraint corresponding to the requirement that the wine cooler must contain exactly 20% fruit juice. What is your advice to management given this shadow price?

30. The program manager for Channel 10 would like to determine the best way to allocate the time for the 11:00–11:30 evening news broadcast. Specifically, she would like to determine the number of minutes of broadcast time to devote to local news, national news, weather, and sports. Over the 30-minute broadcast, 10 minutes are set aside for advertising. The station's broadcast policy states that at least 15% of the time available should be devoted to local news coverage; the time devoted to the combination of local news and national news must be at least 50% of the total broadcast time; the time devoted to the weather segment must be less than or equal to the time devoted to the sports segment; the time devoted to the sports segment should be no longer than the total time spent on the local and national news; and at least 20% of the time should be devoted to the weather segment. The production costs per minute are \$300 for local news, \$200 for national news, \$100 for weather, and \$100 for sports.
    a. Formulate and solve a linear program that can determine how the 20 available minutes should be used to minimize the total cost of producing the program.
    b. Interpret the shadow price for the constraint corresponding to the available time. What advice would you give the station manager given this shadow price?
    c. Interpret the shadow price for the constraint corresponding to the requirement that at least 15% of the available time should be devoted to local coverage. What advice would you give the station manager given this shadow price?
    d. Interpret the shadow price for the constraint corresponding to the requirement that the time devoted to the local and the national news must be at least 50% of the total broadcast time. What advice would you give the station manager given this shadow price?
    e. Interpret the shadow price for the constraint corresponding to the requirement that the time devoted to the weather segment must be less than or equal to the time devoted to the sports segment. What advice would you give the station manager given this shadow price?

31. Gulf Coast Electronics is ready to award contracts to suppliers for providing reservoir capacitors for use in its electronic devices. For the past several years, Gulf Coast Electronics has relied on two suppliers for its reservoir capacitors: Able Controls and Lyshenko Industries. A new firm, Boston Components, inquired into the possibility of providing a portion of the reservoir capacitors needed by Gulf Coast. The quality of products provided by Lyshenko Industries has been extremely high; in fact, only 0.5% of the capacitors provided by Lyshenko had to be discarded because of quality problems. Able Controls has also had a high quality level historically, producing an average of only 1% unacceptable capacitors. Because Gulf Coast Electronics has had no experience with Boston Components, it estimated Boston's defective rate to be 10%. Gulf Coast would like to determine how many reservoir capacitors should be ordered from each firm to obtain 75,000 acceptable-quality capacitors to use in its electronic devices. To ensure that Boston Components will receive some of the contract, management specified that the volume of reservoir capacitors awarded to Boston Components must be at least 10% of the volume given to Able Controls. In addition, the total volume assigned to Boston

Components, Able Controls, and Lyshenko Industries should not exceed 30,000, 50,000, and 50,000 capacitors, respectively. Because of the long-term relationship with Lyshenko Industries, management also specified that at least 30,000 capacitors should be ordered from Lyshenko. The cost per capacitor is $2.45 for Boston Components, $2.50 for Able Controls, and $2.75 for Lyshenko Industries.

a. Formulate and solve a linear program for determining how many reservoir capacitors should be from each supplier to minimize the total cost of obtaining 75,000 acceptable-quality reservoir capacitors.
b. Suppose that the quality level for Boston Components is much better than estimated. What effect, if any, would this quality level have?
c. Suppose that management is willing to reconsider its requirement that at least 30,000 capacitors must be ordered from Lyshenko Industries. What effect, if any, would this consideration have?

32. PartsTech, Inc., a manufacturer of rechargeable batteries for phones, cameras, and other personal electronic devices, signed a contract with an electronics company to produce three different lithium-ion battery packs for a new line of smartphones. The contract calls for the following:

Battery Pack	Production Quantity
PT-100	200,000
PT-200	100,000
PT-300	150,000

PartsTech can manufacture the battery packs at manufacturing plants located in the Philippines and Mexico. The unit cost of the battery packs differs at the two plants because of differences in production equipment and wage rates. The unit costs for each battery pack at each manufacturing plant are as follows:

	Plant	
Product	Philippines	Mexico
PT-100	$0.95	$0.98
PT-200	$0.98	$1.06
PT-300	$1.34	$1.15

The PT-100 and PT-200 battery packs are produced using similar production equipment available at both plants. However, each plant has a limited capacity for the total number of PT-100 and PT-200 battery packs produced. The combined PT-100 and PT-200 production capacities are 175,000 units at the Philippines plant and 160,000 units at the Mexico plant. The PT-300 production capacities are 75,000 units at the Philippines plant and 100,000 units at the Mexico plant. The cost of shipping from the Philippines plant is $0.18 per unit, and the cost of shipping from the Mexico plant is $0.10 per unit.

a. Develop a linear program that PartsTech can use to determine how many units of each battery pack to produce at each plant in order to minimize the total production and shipping cost associated with the new contract.
b. Solve the linear program developed in part (a) to determine the optimal production plan.
c. Use sensitivity analysis to determine how much the production and/or shipping cost per unit would have to change in order to produce additional units of the PT-100 in the Philippines plant.
d. Use sensitivity analysis to determine how much the production and/or shipping cost per unit would have to change in order to produce additional units of the PT-200 in the Mexico plant.

Case Problem 1 Product Mix

TJ, Inc., makes three nut mixes for sale to grocery chains located in the Southeast. The three mixes, referred to as the Regular Mix, the Deluxe Mix, and the Holiday Mix, are made by mixing different percentages of five types of nuts.

In preparation for the fall season, TJ, Inc., purchased the following shipments of nuts at the prices shown:

Type of Nut	Shipment Amount (pounds)	Cost per Shipment
Almond	6000	$7500
Brazil	7500	$7125
Filbert	7500	$6750
Pecan	6000	$7200
Walnut	7500	$7875

The Regular Mix consists of 15% almonds, 25% Brazil nuts, 25% filberts, 10% pecans, and 25% walnuts. The Deluxe Mix consists of 20% of each type of nut, and the Holiday Mix consists of 25% almonds, 15% Brazil nuts, 15% filberts, 25% pecans, and 20% walnuts.

An accountant at TJ, Inc., analyzed the cost of packaging materials, sales price per pound, and so forth, and determined that the profit contribution per pound is $1.65 for the Regular Mix, $2.00 for the Deluxe Mix, and $2.25 for the Holiday Mix. These figures do not include the cost of specific types of nuts in the different mixes because that cost can vary greatly in the commodity markets.

Customer orders already received are summarized here:

Type of Mix	Orders (pounds)
Regular	10,000
Deluxe	3,000
Holiday	5,000

Because demand is running high, TJ, Inc., expects to receive many more orders than can be satisfied.

TJ, Inc., is committed to using the available nuts to maximize profit over the fall season; nuts not used will be given to the Free Store. Even if it is not profitable to do so, the president of TJ, Inc., indicated that the orders already received must be satisfied.

Managerial Report

Perform an analysis of the TJ, Inc. product mix problem. Prepare a summary report of your findings for TJ, Inc.'s president. Be sure to include information and analysis on the following:

1. The cost per pound of the nuts included in the Regular, Deluxe, and Holiday mixes
2. The optimal product mix and the total profit contribution
3. Recommendations regarding how the total profit contribution can be increased if additional quantities of nuts can be purchased
4. A recommendation as to whether TJ, Inc., should purchase an additional 1000 pounds of almonds for $1000 from a supplier who overbought
5. Recommendations on how profit contribution could be increased (if at all) if TJ, Inc., does not satisfy all existing orders

Case Problem 2 Investment Strategy

J. D. Williams, Inc., is an investment advisory firm that manages more than $120 million in funds for its numerous clients. The company uses an asset allocation model that recommends the portion of each client's portfolio to be invested in a growth stock fund, an income fund, and a money market fund. To maintain diversity in each client's portfolio, the firm places limits on the percentage of each portfolio that may be invested in each of the three funds. General guidelines indicate that the amount invested in the growth fund must be between 20% and 40% of the total portfolio value. Similar percentages for the other two funds stipulate that between 20% and 50% of the total portfolio value must be in the income fund and at least 30% of the total portfolio value must be in the money market fund.

In addition, the company attempts to assess the risk tolerance of each client and adjust the portfolio to meet the needs of the individual investor. For example, Williams just contracted with a new client who has $800,000 to invest. Based on an evaluation of the client's risk tolerance, Williams assigned a maximum risk index of 0.05 for the client. The firm's risk indicators show the risk of the growth fund at 0.10, the income fund at 0.07, and the money market fund at 0.01. An overall portfolio risk index is computed as a weighted average of the risk rating for the three funds, where the weights are the fraction of the client's portfolio invested in each of the funds.

Additionally, Williams is currently forecasting annual yields of 18% for the growth fund, 12.5% for the income fund, and 7.5% for the money market fund. Based on the information provided, how should the new client be advised to allocate the $800,000 among the growth, income, and money market funds? Develop a linear programming model that will provide the maximum yield for the portfolio. Use your model to develop a managerial report.

Managerial Report

1. Recommend how much of the $800,000 should be invested in each of the three funds. What is the annual yield you anticipate for the investment recommendation?
2. Assume that the client's risk index could be increased to 0.055. How much would the yield increase, and how would the investment recommendation change?
3. Refer again to the original situation, where the client's risk index was assessed to be 0.05. How would your investment recommendation change if the annual yield for the growth fund were revised downward to 16% or even to 14%?
4. Assume that the client expressed some concern about having too much money in the growth fund. How would the original recommendation change if the amount invested in the growth fund is not allowed to exceed the amount invested in the income fund?
5. The asset allocation model you developed may be useful in modifying the portfolios for all of the firm's clients whenever the anticipated yields for the three funds are periodically revised. What is your recommendation as to whether use of this model is possible?

Case Problem 3 Truck Leasing Strategy

Reep Construction recently won a contract for the excavation and site preparation of a new rest area on Interstate Highway 5 in California. In preparing his bid for the job, Bob Reep, founder and president of Reep Construction, estimated that it would take four months to perform the work and that 10, 12, 14, and 8 trucks would be needed in months 1 through 4, respectively.

The firm currently has 20 trucks of the type needed to perform the work on the new project. These trucks were obtained last year when Bob signed a long-term lease with CalState Leasing. Although most of these trucks are currently being used on existing jobs, Bob estimates that one truck will be available for use on the new project in month 1, two trucks will be available in month 2, three trucks will be available in month 3, and one truck will be available in month 4. Thus, to complete the project, Bob will have to lease additional trucks.

The long-term leasing contract with CalState charges a monthly cost of $600 per truck. Reep Construction pays its truck drivers $20 an hour, and daily fuel costs are approximately $100 per truck. All maintenance costs are paid by CalState Leasing. For planning purposes, Bob estimates that each truck used on the new project will be operating eight hours a day, five days a week for approximately four weeks each month.

Bob does not believe that current business conditions justify committing the firm to additional long-term leases. In discussing the short-term leasing possibilities with CalState Leasing, Bob learned that he can obtain short-term leases of one to four months. Short-term leases differ from long-term leases in that the short-term leasing plans include the cost of both a truck and a driver. Maintenance costs for short-term leases also are paid by CalState Leasing. The following costs for each of the four months cover the lease of a truck and driver:

Length of Lease	Cost per Month
1	$4000
2	$3700
3	$3225
4	$3040

Bob Reep would like to acquire a lease that minimizes the cost of meeting the monthly trucking requirements for his new project, but he also takes great pride in the fact that his company has never laid off employees. Bob is committed to maintaining his no-layoff policy; that is, he will use his own drivers even if costs are higher.

Managerial Report

Perform an analysis of Reep Construction's leasing problem and prepare a report for Bob Reep that summarizes your findings. Be sure to include information on, and analysis of, the following items:

1. The optimal leasing plan
2. The costs associated with the optimal leasing plan
3. The cost for Reep Construction to maintain its current policy of no layoffs

Appendix 8.1 Sensitivity Analysis with Excel Solver

In Appendix 7.1 we showed how Excel Solver can be used to solve a linear program by using it to solve the RMC problem. We used reports similar to Excel's Answer Report in Chapter 7, but these reports do not contain the sensitivity analysis information discussed in this chapter. Let us now see how Excel Solver can be used to provide sensitivity analysis information.

When Excel Solver has found the optimal solution to a linear program, the **Solver Results** dialog box (see Figure 8.23) will appear on the screen. If only the solution is desired, simply

FIGURE 8.23 EXCEL SOLVER RESULTS DIALOG BOX TO PRODUCE SENSITIVITY REPORT

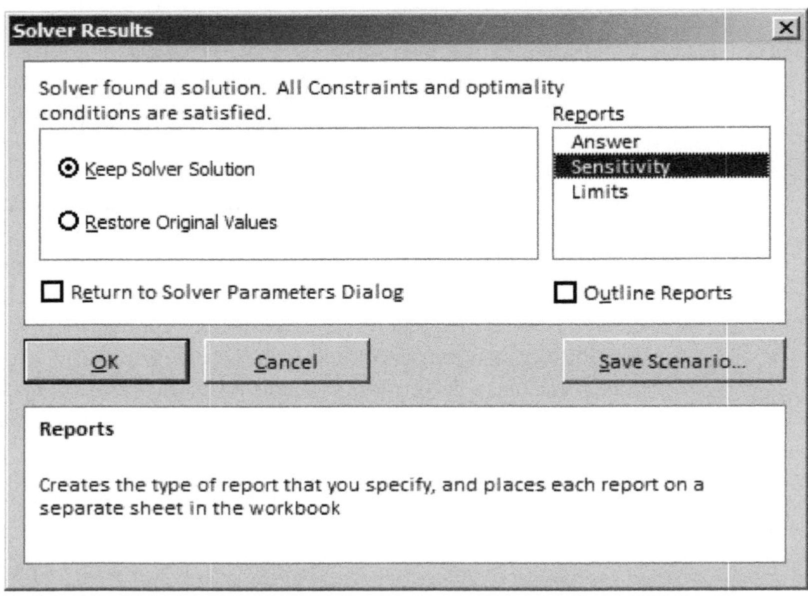

click **OK**. To obtain the optimal solution and the sensitivity analysis output, you must select **Sensitivity** in the **Reports** box before clicking **OK**; the Sensitivity Report is created on another worksheet in the same Excel workbook. Following this procedure for the RMC problem, we obtained the optimal solution shown in Figure 8.24. Figure 8.25 shows the Sensitivity Report as generated by Excel Solver. Note that there are no columns for Model Variables or Constraint Numbers as shown in the reports in Chapter 8. The Cell columns in Figure 8.25 correspond to the location of the decision variables and constraints in the Excel model (Figure 8.24).

Appendix 8.2 Sensitivity Analysis with LINGO

In Appendix 7.2 we showed how LINGO can be used to solve a linear program by using it to solve the RMC problem. A copy of the Solution Report is shown in Figure 8.26. As we discussed previously, the value of the objective function is 1600, the optimal solution is $F = 25$ and $S = 20$, and the values of the slack variables corresponding to the three constraints (rows 2–4) are 0.0, 1.0, and 0.0. Now, let us consider the information in the Reduced Cost column and the Dual Price column.

LINGO always takes the absolute value of the reduced cost.

For the RMC problem, the reduced costs for both decision variables are zero because both variables are at a positive value. LINGO reports a *dual price* rather than a shadow price. For a maximization problem, the dual price and shadow price are identical. For a minimization problem, the dual price is equal to the negative of the shadow price. When interpreting the LINGO output for a minimization problem, multiply the dual prices by -1, treat the resulting number as a shadow price, and interpret the number as described in Section 8.3. The nonzero dual prices of 33.3333 for constraint 1 (material 1 constraint in row 2) and 44.4444

FIGURE 8.24 EXCEL SOLUTION FOR THE RMC PROBLEM

RMC

	A	B	C	D	E
1	**RMC**				
2					
3		**Material Requirements**			
4	**Material**	**Fuel Additive**	**Solvent Base**	**Amount Available**	
5	Material 1	0.4	0.5	20	
6	Material 2	0	0.2	5	
7	Material 3	0.6	0.3	21	
8	**Profit Per Ton**	40	30		
9					
10					
11	**Model**				
12					
13		**Decision Variables**			
14		**Fuel Additive**	**Solvent Base**		
15	**Tons Produced**	25	20		
16					
17	**Maximize Total Profit**	1600			
18					
19	**Constraints**	**Amount Used**		**Amount Available**	
20	Material 1	20	<=	20	
21	Material 2	4	<=	5	
22	Material 3	21	<=	21	
23					

FIGURE 8.25 EXCEL SOLVER SENSITIVITY REPORT FOR THE RMC PROBLEM

Adjustable Cells

Cell	Name	Final Value	Reduced Cost	Objective Coefficient	Allowable Increase	Allowable Decrease
$B$15	Tons Produced Fuel Additive	25.000	0.000	40.000	20.000	16.000
$C$15	Tons Produced Solvent Base	20.000	0.000	30.000	20.000	10.000

Constraints

Cell	Name	Final Value	Shadow Price	Constraint R.H. Side	Allowable Increase	Allowable Decrease
$B$20	Material 1 Amount Used	20.000	33.333	20.000	1.500	6.000
$B$21	Material 2 Amount Used	4.000	0.000	5.000	1E+30	1.000
$B$22	Material 3 Amount Used	21.000	44.444	21.000	9.000	2.250

for constraint 3 (material 3 constraint in row 4) tell us that an additional ton of material 1 increases the value of the optimal solution by $33.33 and an additional ton of material 3 increases the value of the optimal solution by $44.44.

FIGURE 8.26 LINGO SOLUTION REPORT FOR THE RMC PROBLEM

```
Global optimal solution found.        1600.000
Objective value:                             2
Total solver iterations:

Model Title: RMC CORPORATION

     Variable              Value              Reduced Cost
  --------------     ---------------     -----------------
            F               25.00000               0.00000
            S               20.00000               0.00000

          Row          Slack/Surplus          Dual Price
  --------------     ---------------     -----------------
            1             1600.00000               1.00000
            2                0.00000              33.33333
            3                1.00000               0.00000
            4                0.00000              44.44444
```

Next, let us consider how LINGO can be used to compute the range of optimality for each objective function coefficient and the range of feasibility for each of the dual prices. By default, range computations are not enabled in LINGO. To enable range computations, perform the following steps:

Step 1. Choose the **LINGO** menu
Step 2. Select **Options**
Step 3. When the **LINGO Options** dialog box appears:
Select the **General Solver** tab
Choose **Prices & Ranges** in the **Dual Computations:** box
Click **Apply**
Click **OK**

You will now have to re-solve the RMC problem in order for LINGO to perform the range computations. After re-solving the problem, close or minimize the **Solution Report** window. To display the range information, select the **Range** command from the **LINGO** menu. LINGO displays the range information in a new window titled **Range Report**. The output that appears in the Range Report window for the RMC problem is shown in Figure 8.27.

We will use the information in the Objective Coefficient Ranges: section of the range report to compute the range of optimality for the objective function coefficients. For example, the current objective function coefficient for F (fuel additive) is 40. Note that the corresponding allowable increase is 20.0 and the corresponding allowable decrease is 16.0. Thus the range of optimality for the contribution to profit for F, the objective function coefficient for F, is $40.0 - 16.0 = 24.0$ to $40.0 + 20.0 = 60.0$. Using PF to denote the contribution to profit for fuel additive, the range of optimality for PF is $24.0 \leq PF \leq 60.0$. Similarly, with an allowable increase of 20.0 and an allowable decrease of 10.0, the range of optimality for PS, the profit contribution for solvent is $20.0 \leq PS \leq 50.0$.

FIGURE 8.27 LINGO RANGE REPORT FOR THE RMC PROBLEM

```
Ranges in which the basis is unchanged:

OBJECTIVE COEFFICIENT RANGES

                        Current         Allowable        Allowable
   Variable           Coefficient        Increase         Decrease
 ------------      ---------------   -------------    --------------
        F              40.00000         20.00000         16.00000
        S              30.00000         20.00000         10.00000

RIGHTHAND SIDE RANGES

                        Current         Allowable        Allowable
   Row                    RHS            Increase         Decrease
 ------------      ---------------   -------------    -------------
        2              20.00000          1.50000          6.00000
        3               5.00000         INFINITY          1.00000
        4              21.00000          9.00000          2.25000
```

To compute the range of feasibility for each dual price, we will use the information in the Righthand Side Ranges section of the Range Report. For example, the current right-hand-side value for material 1 constraint (row 2) is 20, the allowable increase is 1.5, and the allowable decrease is 6.0. Because the dual price for this constraint is 33.33 (shown in the LINGO Solution Report), we can conclude that an additional ton will increase the objective function by \$33.33 per ton. From the range information given, we see that after rounding, the dual price of \$33.33 is valid for increases up to $20.0 + 1.5 = 21.5$ and decreases to $20.0 - 6.0 = 14.0$. Thus, the range of feasibility for material 1 is 14.0 to 21.5. The ranges of feasibility for the other constraints can be determined in a similar manner.

CHAPTER 9

Linear Programming Applications in Marketing, Finance, and Operations Management

CONTENTS

Linear programming has proven to be one of the most successful quantitative approaches to decision making. Applications have been reported in almost every industry. These applications include production scheduling, media selection, financial planning, capital budgeting, supply chain design, product mix, staffing, and blending.

The Q.M. in Action, A Marketing Planning Model at Marathon Oil Company, provides an example of the use of linear programming by showing how Marathon uses a large-scale linear programming model to solve a wide variety of planning problems. Later in the chapter, other Q.M. in Action features illustrate how General Electric uses linear programming for deciding on investments in solar energy; how Jeppesen Sanderson uses linear programming to optimize production of flight manuals; and how the Kellogg Company uses a large-scale linear programming model to integrate production, distribution, and inventory planning.

In this chapter we present a variety of applications from the traditional business areas of marketing, finance, and operations management. Modeling, computer solution, and interpretation of output are emphasized. A mathematical model is developed for each problem studied, and solutions obtained using Excel Solver are presented for most of the applications. In the chapter appendix we illustrate the use of Excel Solver by solving a financial planning problem.

Q.M. *in* ACTION

*A MARKETING PLANNING MODEL AT MARATHON OIL COMPANY**

Marathon Oil Company has four refineries within the United States, operates 50 light product terminals, and has product demand at more than 95 locations. The Supply and Transportation Division faces the problem of determining which refinery should supply which terminal and, at the same time, determining which products should be transported via pipeline, barge, or tanker to minimize cost. Product demand must be satisfied, and the supply capability of each refinery must not be exceeded. To help solve this difficult problem, Marathon Oil developed a marketing planning model.

The marketing planning model is a large-scale linear programming model that takes into account sales not only at Marathon product terminals but also at all exchange locations. An exchange contract is an agreement with other oil product marketers that involves exchanging or trading Marathon's products for theirs at different locations. All pipelines, barges, and tankers within Marathon's marketing area are also represented in the linear programming model. The objective of the model is to minimize the cost of meeting a given demand structure, taking into account sales price, pipeline tariffs, exchange contract costs, product demand, terminal operating costs, refining costs, and product purchases.

The marketing planning model is used to solve a wide variety of planning problems that vary from evaluating gasoline blending economics to analyzing the economics of a new terminal or pipeline. With daily sales of about 10 million gallons of refined light product, a savings of even one-thousandth of a cent per gallon can result in significant long-term savings. At the same time, what may appear to be a savings in one area, such as refining or transportation, may actually add to overall costs when the effects are fully realized throughout the system. The marketing planning model allows a simultaneous examination of this total effect.

*Based on information provided by Robert W. Wernert at Marathon Oil Company, Findlay, Ohio.

9.1 Marketing Applications

Applications of linear programming in marketing are numerous. In this section we discuss applications in media selection and marketing research.

Media Selection

Online advertising includes search engine marketing, website banner advertisements, mobile-device ads and email marketing.

Media selection applications of linear programming are designed to help marketing managers allocate a fixed advertising budget to various advertising media. Potential media include newspapers, magazines, radio, television, direct mail, and online. In these applications, the objective is to maximize reach, frequency, and quality of exposure. Restrictions on the allowable allocation usually arise during consideration of company policy, contract requirements, and media availability. In the application that follows, we illustrate how a media selection problem might be formulated and solved using a linear programming model.

Relax-and-Enjoy Lake Development Corporation is developing a lakeside community at a privately owned lake. The primary market for the lakeside lots and homes includes all middle- and upper-income families within approximately 100 miles of the development. Relax-and-Enjoy employed the advertising firm of Boone, Phillips, and Jackson (BP&J) to design the promotional campaign.

After considering possible advertising media and the market to be covered, BP&J recommended that the first month's advertising be restricted to five media. At the end of the month, BP&J will then reevaluate its strategy based on the month's results. BP&J collected data on the number of potential customers reached, the cost per advertisement, the maximum number of times each medium is available, and the exposure quality rating for each of the five media. The quality rating is measured in terms of an exposure quality unit, a measure of the relative value of one advertisement in each of the media. This measure, based on BP&J's experience in the advertising business, takes into account factors such as audience demographics (age, income, and education of the audience reached), image presented, and quality of the advertisement. The information collected is presented in Table 9.1.

TABLE 9.1 ADVERTISING MEDIA ALTERNATIVES FOR THE RELAX-AND-ENJOY LAKE DEVELOPMENT CORPORATION

Advertising Media	Number of Potential Customers Reached	Cost ($) per Advertisement	Maximum Times Available per Month*	Exposure Quality Units
1. Daytime TV (1 min), station WKLA	1000	1500	15	65
2. Evening TV (30 sec), station WKLA	2000	3000	10	90
3. Website advertisement (banner ad)	1500	400	25	40
4. Sunday newspaper magazine (½ page color), *The Sunday Press*	2500	1000	4	60
5. Radio, 8:00 A.M. or 5:00 P.M. news (30 sec), station KNOP	300	100	30	20

*The maximum number of times the medium is available is either the maximum number of times the advertising medium occurs (e.g., four Sundays per month) or the maximum number of times BP&J recommends that the medium be used.

In Section 7.1 we provided some general guidelines for modeling linear programming problems. You may want to review Section 7.1 before proceeding with the linear programming applications in this chapter.

Relax-and-Enjoy provided BP&J with an advertising budget of \$30,000 for the first month's campaign. In addition, Relax-and-Enjoy imposed the following restrictions on how BP&J may allocate these funds: At least 10 television commercials must be used, at least 50,000 potential customers must be reached, and no more than \$18,000 may be spent on television advertisements. What advertising media selection plan should be recommended?

The decision to be made is how many times to use each medium. We begin by defining the decision variables:

$$\begin{aligned} DTV &= \text{number of times daytime TV is used} \\ ETV &= \text{number of times evening TV is used} \\ W &= \text{number of times website banner ads are used} \\ SN &= \text{number of times Sunday newspaper is used} \\ R &= \text{number of times radio is used} \end{aligned}$$

The data on quality of exposure in Table 9.1 show that each daytime TV (DTV) advertisement is rated at 65 exposure quality units. Thus, an advertising plan with DTV advertisements will provide a total of $65DTV$ exposure quality units. Continuing with the data in Table 9.1, we find evening TV (ETV) rated at 90 exposure quality units, website banner ads (W) rated at 40 exposure quality units, Sunday newspaper (SN) rated at 60 exposure quality units, and radio (R) rated at 20 exposure quality units. With the objective of maximizing the total exposure quality units for the overall media selection plan, the objective function becomes

$$\text{Max} \quad 65DTV + 90ETV + 40W + 60SN + 20R \qquad \text{Exposure quality}$$

We now formulate the constraints for the model from the information given:

$$\begin{array}{llllll} DTV & & & & & \leq 15 \\ & ETV & & & & \leq 10 \\ & & W & & & \leq 25 \\ & & & SN & & \leq 4 \\ & & & & R & \leq 30 \end{array} \Bigg\} \text{Availability of media}$$

$$\begin{array}{lllll} 1500DTV + 3000ETV + 400W + 1000SN + 100R & \leq 30{,}000 & \text{Budget} \\ DTV + ETV & \geq 10 & \multirow{2}{*}{\} Television restrictions} \\ 1500DTV + 3000ETV & \leq 18{,}000 & \\ 1000DTV + 2000ETV + 1500W + 2500SN + 300R & \geq 50{,}000 & \text{Customers reached} \\ DTV, ETV, W, SN, R \geq 0 & & \end{array}$$

Care must be taken to ensure the linear programming model accurately reflects the real problem. Always review your formulation thoroughly before attempting to solve the model.

Problem 1 provides practice at formulating a similar media selection model.

The optimal solution to this five-variable, nine-constraint linear programming model is shown in Figure 9.1; a summary is presented in Table 9.2.

The optimal solution calls for advertisements to be distributed among daytime TV, websites, Sunday newspaper, and radio. The maximum number of exposure quality units is $65(10) + 90(0) + 40(25) + 60(2) + 20(30) = 2370$, and the total number of customers reached is 61,500. Note that in the constraint section the simple bound constraints on the availability of media are not listed. However, for each variable at its bound, the Reduced Cost gives the shadow price for that constraint. So, for example, the reduced cost of 65 for evening TV indicates that forcing the use of this type of ad would actually drop exposure quality by 65 points. On the other hand, allowing another website banner ad (26 instead of a limit of 25) would increase exposure quality by 16 units. Note that the budget constraint has a shadow price of 0.060. Therefore, a \$1.00 increase in the advertising budget will lead

FIGURE 9.1 SENSITIVITY REPORT FOR THE RELAX-AND-ENJOY LAKE DEVELOPMENT CORPORATION PROBLEM

Relax

Variable Cells

Model Variable	Name	Final Value	Reduced Cost	Objective Coefficient	Allowable Increase	Allowable Decrease
DTV	Ads Placed DTV	10.000	0.000	65.000	25.000	65.000
EVT	Ads Placed ETV	0.000	−65.000	90.000	65.000	1E+30
W	Ads Placed W	25.000	16.000	40.000	1E+30	16.000
SN	Ads Placed SN	2.000	0.000	60.000	40.000	16.667
R	Ads Placed R	30.000	14.000	20.000	1E+30	14.000

Constraints

Constraint Number	Name	Final Value	Shadow Price	Constraint R.H. Side	Allowable Increase	Allowable Decrease
1	Budget	30000.000	0.060	30000.000	2000.000	2000.000
2	Num TV Ads	10.000	−25.000	10.000	1.333	1.333
3	TV Budget	15000.000	0.000	18000.000	1E+30	3000.000
4	Customers Reached	61500.000	0.000	50000.000	11500.000	1E+30

More complex media selection models may include considerations such as the reduced exposure quality value for repeat media usage, cost discounts for repeat media usage, audience overlap by different media, and/or timing recommendations for the advertisements.

to an increase of 0.06 exposure quality units. The shadow price of −25.000 for the number of TV ads indicates that reducing the number of required television commercials by 1 will increase the exposure quality of the advertising plan by 25 units. Thus, Relax-and-Enjoy should consider reducing the requirement of having at least 10 television commercials.

A possible shortcoming of this model is that, even if the exposure quality measure were not subject to error, it offers no guarantee that maximization of total exposure quality will lead to a maximization of profit or of sales (a common surrogate for profit). However, this issue is not a shortcoming of linear programming; rather, it is a shortcoming of the use of exposure quality as a criterion. If we could directly measure the effect of an advertisement on profit, we could use total profit as the objective to be maximized.

TABLE 9.2 ADVERTISING PLAN FOR THE RELAX-AND-ENJOY LAKE DEVELOPMENT CORPORATION

Media	Frequency	Budget
Daytime TV	10	$15,000
Websites	25	10,000
Sunday newspaper	2	2,000
Radio	30	3,000
		$30,000

Exposure quality units = 2370
Total customers reached = 61,500

NOTES AND COMMENTS

1. The media selection model required subjective evaluations of the exposure quality for the media alternatives. Marketing managers may have substantial data concerning exposure quality, but the final coefficients used in the objective function may also include considerations based primarily on managerial judgment.
2. The media selection model presented in this section uses exposure quality as the objective function and places a constraint on the number of

customers reached. An alternative formulation of this problem would be to use the number of customers reached as the objective function and add a constraint indicating the minimum total exposure quality required for the media plan.

Marketing Research

An organization conducts marketing research to learn about consumer characteristics, attitudes, and preferences. Marketing research firms that specialize in providing such information often do the actual research for client organizations. Typical services offered by a marketing research firm include designing the study, conducting market surveys, analyzing the data collected, and providing summary reports and recommendations for the client. In the research design phase, targets or quotas may be established for the number and types of respondents to be surveyed. The marketing research firm's objective is to conduct the survey so as to meet the client's needs at a minimum cost.

Market Survey, Inc. (MSI) specializes in evaluating consumer reaction to new products, services, and advertising campaigns. A client firm requested MSI's assistance in ascertaining consumer reaction to a recently marketed household product. During meetings with the client, MSI agreed to conduct door-to-door personal interviews to obtain responses from households with children and households without children. In addition, MSI agreed to conduct both day and evening interviews. Specifically, the client's contract called for MSI to conduct 1000 interviews under the following quota guidelines:

1. Interview at least 400 households with children.
2. Interview at least 400 households without children.
3. The total number of households interviewed during the evening must be at least as great as the number of households interviewed during the day.
4. At least 40% of the interviews for households with children must be conducted during the evening.
5. At least 60% of the interviews for households without children must be conducted during the evening.

Because the interviews for households with children take additional interviewer time and because evening interviewers are paid more than daytime interviewers, the cost varies with the type of interview. Based on previous research studies, estimates of the interview costs are as follows:

	Interview Cost	
Household	**Day**	**Evening**
Children	$20	$25
No children	$18	$20

What is the household, time-of-day interview plan that will satisfy the contract requirements at a minimum total interviewing cost?

In formulating the linear programming model for the MSI problem, we utilize the following decision-variable notation:

DC = the number of daytime interviews of households with children

EC = the number of evening interviews of households with children

DNC = the number of daytime interviews of households without children

ENC = the number of evening interviews of households without children

We begin the linear programming model formulation by using the cost-per-interview data to develop the objective function:

$$\text{Min} \quad 20DC + 25EC + 18DNC + 20ENC$$

The constraint requiring a total of 1000 interviews is

$$DC + EC + DNC + ENC = 1000$$

The five specifications concerning the types of interviews are as follows:

- Households with children:

$$DC + EC \geq 400$$

- Households without children:

$$DNC + ENC \geq 400$$

- At least as many evening interviews as day interviews:

$$EC + ENC \geq DC + DNC$$

The usual format for linear programming model formulation places all decision variables on the left side of the inequality and a constant (possibly zero) on the right side. Thus, we rewrite this constraint as

$$-DC + EC - DNC + ENC \geq 0$$

- At least 40% of interviews of households with children during the evening:

$$EC \geq 0.4(DC + EC) \quad \text{or} \quad -0.4DC + 0.6EC \geq 0$$

- At least 60% of interviews of households without children during the evening:

$$ENC \geq 0.6(DNC + ENC) \quad \text{or} \quad -0.6DNC + 0.4ENC \geq 0$$

When we add the nonnegativity requirements, the four-variable and six-constraint linear programming model becomes

$$
\begin{array}{lrrrrlll}
\text{Min} & 20DC + & 25EC + & 18DNC + & 20ENC & & & \\
\text{s.t.} & & & & & & & \\
& DC + & EC + & DNC + & ENC & = & 1000 & \text{Total interviews} \\
& DC + & EC & & & \geq & 400 & \text{Households with children} \\
& & & DNC + & ENC & \geq & 400 & \text{Households without children} \\
& -DC + & EC - & DNC + & ENC & \geq & 0 & \text{Evening interviews} \\
& -0.4DC + & 0.6EC & & & \geq & 0 & \text{Evening interviews in households with children} \\
& & & -0.6DNC + & 0.4ENC & \geq & 0 & \text{Evening interviews in households without children} \\
& \multicolumn{4}{l}{DC, EC, DNC, ENC \geq 0} & & &
\end{array}
$$

The sensitivity report based on Excel Solver is shown in Figure 9.2. The solution reveals that the minimum cost of 20(240) + 25(160) + 18(240) + 20(360) = \$20,320 occurs with the following interview schedule:

Market

	Number of Interviews		
Household	Day	Evening	Totals
Children	240	160	400
No children	240	360	600
Totals	480	520	1000

Hence, 480 interviews will be scheduled during the day and 520 during the evening. Households with children will be covered by 400 interviews, and households without children will be covered by 600 interviews.

Selected sensitivity analysis information from Figure 9.2 shows a shadow price of 19.200 for the Total Interviews constraint. This indicates that the total interviewing cost will increase by $19.20 if the number of interviews is increased from 1000 to 1001. Thus, $19.20 is the incremental cost of obtaining additional interviews. It also is the savings that could be realized by reducing the number of interviews from 1000 to 999.

In this solution, exactly 400 households with children are interviewed and we exceed the minimum requirement on households without children by 200 (600 versus the minimum requirement of 400). The shadow price of 5.000 for the fifth constraint indicates that if one more household (with children) than the minimum requirement must be interviewed during the evening, the total interviewing cost will go up by $5.00. Similarly, the sixth constraint shows that requiring one more household (without children) to be interviewed during the evening will increase costs by $2.00.

FIGURE 9.2 SENSITIVITY REPORT FOR THE MARKET SURVEY PROBLEM

Variable Cells

Model Variable	Name	Final Value	Reduced Cost	Objective Coefficient	Allowable Increase	Allowable Decrease
DC	Children Day	240.000	0.000	20.000	5.000	4.667
EC	Children Evening	160.000	0.000	25.000	1E+30	5.000
DNC	No Children Day	240.000	0.000	18.000	2.000	1E+30
ENC	No Children Evening	360.000	0.000	20.000	4.667	2.000

Constraints

Constraint Number	Name	Final Value	Shadow Price	Constraint R.H. Side	Allowable Increase	Allowable Decrease
1	Total Interviews	1000.000	19.200	1000.000	1E+30	200.000
2	Children	400.000	2.800	400.000	100.000	400.000
3	No Children	600.000	0.000	400.000	200.000	1E+30
4	Eve. Interviews	520.000	0.000	0.000	40.000	1E+30
5	Eve. Children	160.000	5.000	0.000	240.000	20.000
6	Eve. No Children	360.000	2.000	0.000	240.000	20.000

9.2 Financial Applications

In finance, linear programming can be applied in problem situations involving capital budgeting, make-or-buy decisions, asset allocation, portfolio selection, financial planning, and many more. In this section we describe a portfolio selection problem and a problem involving funding of an early retirement program.

Portfolio Selection

Portfolio selection problems involve situations in which a financial manager must select specific investments—for example, stocks and bonds—from a variety of investment alternatives. Managers of mutual funds, credit unions, insurance companies, and banks frequently encounter this type of problem. The objective function for portfolio selection problems usually is maximization of expected return or minimization of risk. The constraints usually reflect restrictions on the type of permissible investments, state laws, company policy, maximum permissible risk, and so on. Problems of this type have been formulated and solved using a variety of mathematical programming techniques. In this section we formulate and solve a portfolio selection problem as a linear program.

Consider the case of Welte Mutual Funds, Inc., located in New York City. Welte just obtained $100,000 by converting industrial bonds to cash and is now looking for other investment opportunities for these funds. Based on Welte's current investments, the firm's top financial analyst recommends that all new investments be made in the oil industry, in the steel industry, or in government bonds. Specifically, the analyst identified five investment opportunities and projected their annual rates of return. The investments and rates of return are shown in Table 9.3.

Management of Welte imposed the following investment guidelines:

1. Neither industry (oil or steel) should receive more than $50,000.
2. Government bonds should be at least 25% of the steel industry investments.
3. The investment in Pacific Oil, the high-return but high-risk investment, cannot be more than 60% of the total oil industry investment.

What portfolio recommendations—investments and amounts—should be made for the available $100,000? Given the objective of maximizing projected return subject to the budgetary and managerially imposed constraints, we can answer this question by formulating and solving a linear programming model of the problem. The solution will provide investment recommendations for the management of Welte Mutual Funds.

TABLE 9.3 INVESTMENT OPPORTUNITIES FOR WELTE MUTUAL FUNDS

Investment	Projected Rate of Return (%)
Atlantic Oil	7.3
Pacific Oil	10.3
Midwest Steel	6.4
Huber Steel	7.5
Government bonds	4.5

Let

$$
\begin{aligned}
A &= \text{dollars invested in Atlantic Oil} \\
P &= \text{dollars invested in Pacific Oil} \\
M &= \text{dollars invested in Midwest Steel} \\
H &= \text{dollars invested in Huber Steel} \\
G &= \text{dollars invested in government bonds}
\end{aligned}
$$

Using the projected rates of return shown in Table 9.3, we write the objective function for maximizing the total return for the portfolio as

$$\text{Max} \quad 0.073A + 0.103P + 0.064M + 0.075H + 0.045G$$

The constraint specifying investment of the available $100,000 is

$$A + P + M + H + G = 100{,}000$$

The requirements that neither the oil nor the steel industry should receive more than $50,000 are

$$
\begin{aligned}
A + P &\le 50{,}000 \\
M + H &\le 50{,}000
\end{aligned}
$$

The requirement that government bonds be at least 25% of the steel industry investment is expressed as

$$G \ge 0.25(M + H) \qquad \text{or} \qquad -0.25M - 0.25H + G \ge 0$$

Finally, the constraint that Pacific Oil cannot be more than 60% of the total oil industry investment is

$$P \le 0.60(A + P) \qquad \text{or} \qquad -0.60A + 0.40P \le 0$$

By adding the nonnegativity restrictions, we obtain the complete linear programming model for the Welte Mutual Funds investment problem:

$$
\begin{array}{llllllll}
\text{Max} & 0.073A + 0.103P + 0.064M + 0.075H + 0.045G & & & & & & \\
\text{s.t.} & & & & & & & \\
& A\ + & P\ + & M\ + & H\ + & G = & 100{,}000 & \text{Available funds} \\
& A\ + & P & & & \le & 50{,}000 & \text{Oil industry maximum} \\
& & & M\ + & H & \le & 50{,}000 & \text{Steel industry maximum} \\
& & & -\ 0.25M\ - & 0.25H\ + & G \ge & 0 & \text{Government bonds minimum} \\
& -0.6A\ + & 0.4P & & & \le & 0 & \text{Pacific Oil restriction} \\
& A, P, M, H, G \ge 0 & & & & & &
\end{array}
$$

The sensitivity report based on Excel Solver for this linear program is shown in Figure 9.3. Table 9.4 shows how the funds are allocated among the securities. Note that the optimal solution indicates that the portfolio should be diversified among all the investment opportunities except

FIGURE 9.3 SENSITIVITY REPORT FOR THE WELTE MUTUAL FUNDS PROBLEM

WEB file

Welte

Variable Cells

Model Variable	Name	Final Value	Reduced Cost	Objective Coefficient	Allowable Increase	Allowable Decrease
A	Atlantic Oil Amount Invested	20000.000	0.000	0.073	0.030	0.055
P	Pacific Oil Amount Invested	30000.000	0.000	0.103	1E+30	0.030
M	Midwest Steel Amount Invested	0.000	−0.011	0.064	0.011	1E+30
H	Huber Steel Amount Invested	40000.000	0.000	0.075	0.0275	0.011
G	Gov't Bonds Amount Invested	10000.000	0.000	0.045	0.030	1E+30

Constraints

Constraint Number	Name	Final Value	Shadow Price	Constraint R.H. Side	Allowable Increase	Allowable Decrease
1	Avl. Funds	100000.000	0.069	100000.000	12500.000	50000.000
2	Oil Max	50000.000	0.022	50000.000	50000.000	12500.000
3	Steel Max	40000.000	0.000	50000.000	1E+30	10000.000
4	Gov't Bonds	10000.000	−0.024	0.000	50000.000	12500.000
5	Pacific Oil	30000.000	0.030	0.000	20000.000	30000.000

Midwest Steel. The projected annual return for this portfolio is 0.073(20000) + 0.103(30000) + 0.064(0) + 0.075(40000) + 0.045(10000) = \$8000, which is an overall return of 8%.

The optimal solution shows the shadow price for the third constraint is zero. The reason is that the steel industry maximum constraint is not binding; increases in the steel industry limit of \$50,000 will not improve the value of the optimal solution. Indeed, the final value for the left hand side of the third constraint shows that the current steel industry investment is \$10,000 below its limit of \$50,000. The shadow prices for the other constraints are non-zero, indicating that these constraints are binding.

The shadow price of 0.069 for the first constraint shows that the optimal value of objective function can be increased by 0.069 if one more dollar can be made available for the portfolio investment. If more funds can be obtained at a cost of less than 6.9%, management should consider obtaining them. However, if a return in excess of 6.9% can be obtained by investing funds elsewhere (other than in these five securities), management should question the wisdom of investing the entire \$100,000 in this portfolio.

TABLE 9.4 OPTIMAL PORTFOLIO SELECTION FOR WELTE MUTUAL FUNDS

Investment	Amount	Expected Annual Return
Atlantic Oil	\$ 20,000	\$1460
Pacific Oil	30,000	3090
Huber Steel	40,000	3000
Government bonds	10,000	450
Totals	\$100,000	\$8000

Expected annual return of \$8000
Overall rate of return = 8%

The shadow price for the available funds constraint provides information on the rate of return from additional investment funds.

Similar interpretations can be given to the other shadow prices. Note that the shadow price for the government bonds constraint is −0.024. This result indicates that increasing the value on the right-hand side of the constraint by one unit can be expected to decrease the value of the optimal solution by 0.024. In terms of the optimal portfolio, then, if Welte invests one more dollar in government bonds (beyond the minimum requirement), the total return will decrease by \$0.024. To see why this decrease occurs, note again from the shadow price for the first constraint that the marginal return on the funds invested in the portfolio is 6.9% (the average return is 8%). The rate of return on government bonds is 4.5%. Thus, the cost of investing one more dollar in government bonds is the difference between the marginal return on the portfolio and the marginal return on government bonds: 6.9% − 4.5% = 2.4%.

Note that the optimal solution shows that Midwest Steel should not be included in the portfolio ($M = 0$). The associated reduced cost for M of −0.011 tells us that the objective function value will decrease by 0.011 for every dollar we invest in Midwest Steel. Stated differently, the coefficient for Midwest Steel would have to increase by 0.011 before considering the Midwest Steel investment alternative would be advisable. With such an increase the Midwest Steel return would be 0.064 + 0.011 = 0.075, making this investment just as desirable as the currently used Huber Steel investment alternative.

Finally, a simple modification of the Welte linear programming model permits us to determine the fraction of available funds invested in each security. That is, we divide each of the right-hand-side values by 100,000. Then the optimal values for the variables will give the fraction of funds that should be invested in each security for a portfolio of any size.

NOTES AND COMMENTS

1. The optimal solution to the Welte Mutual Funds problem indicates that \$20,000 is to be spent on the Atlantic Oil stock. If Atlantic Oil sells for \$75 per share, we would have to purchase exactly 266⅔ shares in order to spend exactly \$20,000. The difficulty of purchasing fractional shares can be handled by purchasing the largest possible integer number of shares with the allotted funds (e.g., 266 shares of Atlantic Oil). This approach guarantees that the budget constraint will not be violated. This approach, of course, introduces the possibility that the solution will no longer be optimal, but the danger is slight if a large number of securities are involved. In cases where the analyst believes that the decision variables *must* have integer values, the problem must be formulated as an integer linear programming model. Integer linear programming is the topic of Chapter 11.
2. Financial portfolio theory stresses obtaining a proper balance between risk and return. In the Welte problem, we explicitly considered return in the objective function. Risk is controlled by choosing constraints that ensure diversity among oil and steel stocks and a balance between government bonds and the steel industry investment.

Financial Planning

Linear programming has been used for a variety of investment planning applications. The Q.M. in Action, General Electric Uses Linear Programming for Solar Energy Investment Decisions, describes how linear programming is used to guide GE's investment in solar energy.

Q.M. *in* ACTION

*GENERAL ELECTRIC USES LINEAR PROGRAMMING FOR SOLAR ENERGY INVESTMENT DECISIONS**

With growing concerns about the environment and our ability to continue to utilize limited nonrenewable sources for energy, companies have begun to place much more emphasis on renewable forms of energy. Water, wind, and solar energy are renewable forms of energy that have become the focus of considerable investment by companies.

General Electric (GE) has products in a variety of areas within the energy sector. One such area of interest to GE is solar energy. Solar energy is a relatively new concept with rapidly changing technologies; for example, solar cells and solar power systems. Solar cells can convert sunlight directly into electricity. Concentrating solar power systems focus a larger area of sunlight into a small beam that can be used as a heat source for conventional power generation. Solar cells can be placed on rooftops and hence can be used by both commercial and residential customers, whereas solar power systems are mostly used in commercial settings. In recent years, GE has invested in several solar cell technologies.

Uncertainties in technology development, costs, and demand for solar energy make determining the appropriate amount of production capacity in which to invest a difficult problem. GE uses a set of decision support tools to solve this problem. A detailed descriptive analytical model is used to estimate the cost of newly developed or proposed solar cells. Statistical models developed for new product introductions are used to estimate annual solar demand 10 to 15 years into the future. Finally, the cost and demand estimates are used in a multiperiod linear program to determine the best production capacity investment plan.

The linear program finds an optimal expansion plan by taking into account inventory, capacity, production, and budget constraints. Because of the high level of uncertainty, the linear program is solved over multiple future scenarios. A solution to each individual scenario is found and evaluated in the other scenarios to assess the risk associated with that plan. GE planning analysts have used these tools to support management's strategic investment decisions in the solar energy sector.

*Based on B. G. Thomas and S. Bollapragada, "General Electric Uses an Integrated Framework for Product Costing, Demand Forecasting and Capacity Planning for New Photovoltaic Technology Products," *Interfaces* 40, no. 5 (September/October 2010): 353–367.

Hewlitt Corporation established an early retirement program as part of its corporate restructuring. At the close of the voluntary sign-up period, 68 employees had elected early retirement. As a result of these early retirements, the company incurs the following obligations over the next eight years:

Year	1	2	3	4	5	6	7	8
Cash Requirement	430	210	222	231	240	195	225	255

The cash requirements (in thousands of dollars) are due at the beginning of each year.

The corporate treasurer must determine how much money must be set aside today to meet the eight yearly financial obligations as they come due. The financing plan for the retirement program includes investments in government bonds as well as savings. The investments in government bonds are limited to three choices:

Bond	Price	Rate (%)	Years to Maturity
1	$1150	8.875	5
2	1000	5.500	6
3	1350	11.750	7

The government bonds have a par value of $1000, which means that even with different prices each bond pays $1000 at maturity. The rates shown are based on the par value. For purposes of planning, the treasurer assumed that any funds not invested in bonds will be placed in savings and earn interest at an annual rate of 4%.

We define the decision variables as follows:

F = total dollars required to meet the retirement plan's eight-year obligation
B_1 = units of bond 1 purchased at the beginning of year 1
B_2 = units of bond 2 purchased at the beginning of year 1
B_3 = units of bond 3 purchased at the beginning of year 1
S_i = amount placed in savings at the beginning of year i for $i = 1, \ldots, 8$

The objective function is to minimize the total dollars needed to meet the retirement plan's eight-year obligation, or

$$\text{Min} \quad F$$

A key feature of this type of financial planning problem is that a constraint must be formulated for each year of the planning horizon. In general, each constraint takes the form

$$\begin{pmatrix}\text{Funds available at}\\ \text{the beginning of the year}\end{pmatrix} - \begin{pmatrix}\text{Funds invested in bonds}\\ \text{and placed in savings}\end{pmatrix} = \begin{pmatrix}\text{Cash obligation for}\\ \text{the current year}\end{pmatrix}$$

The funds available at the beginning of year 1 are given by F. With a current price of \$1150 for bond 1 and investments expressed in thousands of dollars, the total investment for B_1 units of bond 1 would be $1.15B_1$. Similarly, the total investment in bonds 2 and 3 would be $1B_2$ and $1.35B_3$, respectively. The investment in savings for year 1 is S_1. Using these results and the first-year obligation of 430, we obtain the constraint for year 1:

$$F - 1.15B_1 - 1B_2 - 1.35B_3 - S_1 = 430 \quad \text{Year 1}$$

Investments in bonds can take place only in this first year, and the bonds will be held until maturity.

The funds available at the beginning of year 2 include the investment returns of 8.875% on the par value of bond 1, 5.5% on the par value of bond 2, 11.75% on the par value of bond 3, and 4% on savings. The new amount to be invested in savings for year 2 is S_2. With an obligation of 210, the constraint for year 2 is

$$0.08875B_1 + 0.055B_2 + 0.1175B_3 + 1.04S_1 - S_2 = 210 \quad \text{Year 2}$$

Similarly, the constraints for years 3 to 8 are

$$\begin{aligned}
0.08875B_1 + 0.055B_2 + 0.1175B_3 + 1.04S_2 - S_3 &= 222 \quad \text{Year 3}\\
0.08875B_1 + 0.055B_2 + 0.1175B_3 + 1.04S_3 - S_4 &= 231 \quad \text{Year 4}\\
0.08875B_1 + 0.055B_2 + 0.1175B_3 + 1.04S_4 - S_5 &= 240 \quad \text{Year 5}\\
1.08875B_1 + 0.055B_2 + 0.1175B_3 + 1.04S_5 - S_6 &= 195 \quad \text{Year 6}\\
1.055B_2 + 0.1175B_3 + 1.04S_6 - S_7 &= 225 \quad \text{Year 7}\\
1.1175B_3 + 1.04S_7 - S_8 &= 255 \quad \text{Year 8}
\end{aligned}$$

We do not consider future investments in bonds because the future price of bonds depends on interest rates and cannot be known in advance.

Note that the constraint for year 6 shows that funds available from bond 1 are $1.08875B_1$. The coefficient of 1.08875 reflects the fact that bond 1 matures at the end of year 5. As a result, the par value plus the interest from bond 1 during year 5 is available at the beginning of year 6. Also, because bond 1 matures in year 5 and becomes available for use at the beginning of year 6, the variable B_1 does not appear in the constraints for years 7 and 8. Note the similar interpretation for bond 2, which matures at the end of year 6 and has the

FIGURE 9.4 SENSITIVITY REPORT FOR THE HEWLITT CORPORATION CASH REQUIREMENTS PROBLEM

Hewlitt

Variable Cells

Model Variable	Name	Final Value	Reduced Cost	Objective Coefficient	Allowable Increase	Allowable Decrease
F	Dollars Needed	1728.794	0.000	1.000	1E+30	1.000
B1	Bond 1 - Year 1	144.988	0.000	0.000	0.067	0.013
B2	Bond 2 - Year 2	187.856	0.000	0.000	0.013	0.020
B3	Bond 3 - Year 3	228.188	0.000	0.000	0.023	0.750
S1	Savings Year 1	636.148	0.000	0.000	0.110	0.055
S2	Savings Year 2	501.606	0.000	0.000	0.143	0.057
S3	Savings Year 3	349.682	0.000	0.000	0.211	0.059
S4	Savings Year 4	182.681	0.000	0.000	0.414	0.061
S5	Savings Year 5	0.000	0.064	0.000	1E+30	0.064
S6	Savings Year 6	0.000	0.013	0.000	1E+30	0.013
S7	Savings Year 7	0.000	0.021	0.000	1E+30	0.021
S8	Savings Year 8	0.000	0.671	0.000	1E+30	0.671

Constraints

Constraint Number	Name	Final Value	Shadow Price	Constraint R.H. Side	Allowable Increase	Allowable Decrease
1	Year 1 Flow	430.000	1.000	430.000	1E+30	1728.794
2	Year 2 Flow	210.000	0.962	210.000	1E+30	661.594
3	Year 3 Flow	222.000	0.925	222.000	1E+30	521.670
4	Year 4 Flow	231.000	0.889	231.000	1E+30	363.669
5	Year 5 Flow	240.000	0.855	240.000	1E+30	189.988
6	Year 6 Flow	195.000	0.760	195.000	2149.928	157.856
7	Year 7 Flow	225.000	0.719	225.000	3027.962	198.188
8	Year 8 Flow	255.000	0.671	255.000	1583.882	255.000

par value plus interest available at the beginning of year 7. In addition, bond 3 matures at the end of year 7 and has the par value plus interest available at the beginning of year 8.

Finally, note that a variable S_8 appears in the constraint for year 8. The retirement fund obligation will be completed at the beginning of year 8, so we anticipate that S_8 will be zero and no funds will be put into savings. However, the formulation includes S_8 in the event that the bond income plus interest from the savings in year 7 exceed the 255 cash requirement for year 8. Thus, S_8 is a surplus variable that shows any funds remaining after the eight-year cash requirements have been satisfied.

The optimal solution and sensitivity report based on Excel Solver is shown in Figure 9.4. With an objective function value of $F = 1728.794$, the total investment required to meet the retirement plan's eight-year obligation is $1,728,794. Using the current prices of $1150, $1000, and $1350 for each of the bonds, respectively, we can summarize the initial investments in the three bonds as follows:

Bond	Units Purchased	Investment Amount
1	$B_1 = 144.988$	$1150(144.988) = $166,736
2	$B_2 = 187.856$	$1000(187.856) = $187,856
3	$B_3 = 228.188$	$1350(228.188) = $308,054

The solution also shows that \$636,148 (see S_1) will be placed in savings at the beginning of the first year. By starting with \$1,728,794, the company can make the specified bond and savings investments and have enough left over to meet the retirement program's first-year cash requirement of \$430,000.

The optimal solution in Figure 9.4 shows that the decision variables S_1, S_2, S_3, and S_4 all are greater than zero, indicating that investments in savings are required in each of the first four years. However, interest from the bonds plus the bond maturity incomes will be sufficient to cover the retirement program's cash requirements in years 5 through 8.

In this application, the shadow price can be thought of as the present value of each dollar in the cash requirement. For example, each dollar that must be paid in year 8 has a present value of \$0.671.

The shadow prices have an interesting interpretation in this application. Each right-hand-side value corresponds to the payment that must be made in that year. Note that the shadow prices are positive, indicating that increasing the requirements in any year causes the needed cash to increase. However, *reducing* the payment in any year would be beneficial because the total funds required for the retirement program's obligation would be less. Note that the shadow prices show that reductions in required funds are more beneficial in the early years, with decreasing benefits in subsequent years. As a result, Hewlitt would benefit by reducing cash requirements in the early years even if it had to make equivalently larger cash payments in later years.

NOTES AND COMMENTS

1. The optimal solution for the Hewlitt Corporation problem shows fractional numbers of government bonds at 144.988, 187.856, and 228.188 units, respectively. However, fractional bond units usually are not available. If we were conservative and rounded up to 145, 188, and 229 units, respectively, the total funds required for the eight-year retirement program obligation would be approximately \$1254 more than the total funds indicated by the objective function. Because of the magnitude of the funds involved, rounding up probably would provide a workable solution. If an optimal integer solution were required, the methods of integer linear programming covered in Chapter 11 would have to be used.
2. We implicitly assumed that interest from the government bonds is paid annually. Investments such as treasury notes actually provide interest payments every six months. In such cases, the model can be reformulated using six-month periods, with interest and/or cash payments occurring every six months.

9.3 Operations Management Applications

Linear programming applications developed for production and operations management include scheduling, staffing, inventory control, and capacity planning. In this section we describe examples of make-or-buy decisions, production scheduling, and workforce assignments.

A Make-or-Buy Decision

We illustrate the use of a linear programming model to determine how much of each of several component parts a company should manufacture and how much it should purchase from an outside supplier. Such a decision is referred to as a make-or-buy decision.

The Janders Company markets various business and engineering products. Currently, Janders is preparing to introduce two new calculators: one for the business market, called the Financial Manager, and one for the engineering market, called the Technician. Each calculator has three components: a base, an electronic cartridge, and a faceplate or top. The same base is used for both calculators, but the cartridges and tops are different. All

TABLE 9.5 MANUFACTURING COSTS AND PURCHASE PRICES FOR JANDERS CALCULATOR COMPONENTS

	Cost per Unit	
Component	**Manufacture (regular time)**	**Purchase**
Base	\$0.50	\$0.60
Financial cartridge	\$3.75	\$4.00
Technician cartridge	\$3.30	\$3.90
Financial top	\$0.60	\$0.65
Technician top	\$0.75	\$0.78

components can be manufactured by the company or purchased from outside suppliers. The manufacturing costs and purchase prices for the components are summarized in Table 9.5.

Company forecasters indicate that 3000 Financial Manager calculators and 2000 Technician calculators will be needed. However, manufacturing capacity is limited. The company has 200 hours of regular manufacturing time and 50 hours of overtime that can be scheduled for the calculators. Overtime involves a premium at the additional cost of \$9 per hour. Table 9.6 shows manufacturing times (in minutes) for the components.

The problem for Janders is to determine how many units of each component to manufacture and how many units of each component to purchase. We define the decision variables as follows:

BM = number of bases manufactured
BP = number of bases purchased
FCM = number of Financial cartridges manufactured
FCP = number of Financial cartridges purchased
TCM = number of Technician cartridges manufactured
TCP = number of Technician cartridges purchased
FTM = number of Financial tops manufactured
FTP = number of Financial tops purchased
TTM = number of Technician tops manufactured
TTP = number of Technician tops purchased

One additional decision variable is needed to determine the hours of overtime that must be scheduled:

OT = number of hours of overtime to be scheduled

TABLE 9.6 MANUFACTURING TIMES IN MINUTES PER UNIT FOR JANDERS CALCULATOR COMPONENTS

Component	Manufacturing Time
Base	1.0
Financial cartridge	3.0
Technician cartridge	2.5
Financial top	1.0
Technician top	1.5

The objective function is to minimize the total cost, including manufacturing costs, purchase costs, and overtime costs. Using the cost-per-unit data in Table 9.5 and the overtime premium cost rate of \$9 per hour, we write the objective function as

$$\text{Min} \quad 0.5BM + 0.6BP + 3.75FCM + 4FCP + 3.3TCM + 3.9TCP + 0.6FTM + 0.65FTP + 0.75TTM + 0.78TTP + 9OT$$

The first five constraints specify the number of each component needed to satisfy the demand for 3000 Financial Manager calculators and 2000 Technician calculators. A total of 5000 base components are needed, with the number of other components depending on the demand for the particular calculator. The five demand constraints are

$$\begin{aligned} BM + BP &= 5000 \quad \text{Bases} \\ FCM + FCP &= 3000 \quad \text{Financial cartridges} \\ TCM + TCP &= 2000 \quad \text{Technician cartridges} \\ FTM + FTP &= 3000 \quad \text{Financial tops} \\ TTM + TTP &= 2000 \quad \text{Technician tops} \end{aligned}$$

Two constraints are needed to guarantee that manufacturing capacities for regular time and overtime cannot be exceeded. The first constraint limits overtime capacity to 50 hours, or

$$OT \leq 50$$

The second constraint states that the total manufacturing time required for all components must be less than or equal to the total manufacturing capacity, including regular time plus overtime. The manufacturing times for the components are expressed in minutes, so we state the total manufacturing capacity constraint in minutes, with the 200 hours of regular time capacity becoming $60(200) = 12{,}000$ minutes. The actual overtime required is unknown at this point, so we write the overtime as $60OT$ minutes. Using the manufacturing times from Table 9.6, we have

$$BM + 3FCM + 2.5TCM + FTM + 1.5TTM \leq 12{,}000 + 60OT$$

Moving the decision variable for overtime to the left-hand side of the constraint provides the manufacturing capacity constraint:

$$BM + 3FCM + 2.5TCM + FTM + 1.5TTM - 60OT \leq 12{,}000$$

The complete formulation of the Janders make-or-buy problem with all decision variables greater than or equal to zero is

$$\begin{aligned} \text{Min} \quad & 0.5BM + 0.6BP + 3.75FCM + 4FCP + 3.3TCM + 3.9TCP \\ & + 0.6FTM + 0.65FTP + 0.75TTM + 0.78TTP + 9OT \\ \text{s.t.} & \\ & BM + BP = 5000 \quad \text{Bases} \\ & FCM + FCP = 3000 \quad \text{Financial cartridges} \\ & TCM + TCP = 2000 \quad \text{Technician cartridges} \\ & FTM + FTP = 3000 \quad \text{Financial tops} \\ & TTM + TTP = 2000 \quad \text{Technician tops} \\ & OT \leq 50 \quad \text{Overtime hours} \\ & BM + 3FCM + 2.5TCM + FTM + 1.5TTM - 60OT \leq 12{,}000 \quad \text{Manufacturing capacity} \end{aligned}$$

FIGURE 9.5 SENSITIVITY REPORT FOR THE JANDERS MAKE-OR-BUY PROBLEM

WEB file

Janders

Variable Cells

Model Variable	Name	Final Value	Reduced Cost	Objective Coefficient	Allowable Increase	Allowable Decrease
BM	Base Make	5000.000	0.000	0.500	0.017	1E+30
BP	Base Purchase	0.000	0.017	0.600	1E+30	0.017
FCM	Fin. Cart. Make	666.667	0.000	3.750	0.100	0.050
FCP	Fin. Cart. Purchase	2333.333	0.000	4.000	0.050	0.100
TCM	Tech. Cart. Make	2000.000	0.000	3.300	0.392	1E+30
TCP	Tech. Cart. Purchase	0.000	0.392	3.900	1E+30	0.392
FTM	Fin. Top Make	0.000	0.033	0.600	1E+30	0.033
FTP	Fin. Top Purchase	3000.000	0.000	0.650	0.033	1E+30
TTM	Tech. Top Make	0.000	0.095	0.750	1E+30	0.095
TTP	Tech. Top Purchase	2000.000	0.000	0.780	0.095	1E+30
OT	Overtime Used	0.000	4.000	9.000	1E+30	4.000

Constraints

Constraint Number	Name	Final Value	Shadow Price	Constraint R.H. Side	Allowable Increase	Allowable Decrease
1	Base Available	5000.0000	0.583	5000.000	2000.000	5000.000
2	Fin. Cart. Available	3000.0000	4.000	3000.000	1E+30	2333.333
3	Tech. Cart. Available	2000.0000	3.508	2000.000	800.000	2000.000
4	Fin. Top Available	3000.0000	0.650	3000.000	1E+30	3000.000
5	Tech. Top Available	2000.0000	0.780	2000.000	1E+30	2000.000
6	Overtime Time Used	0.0000	0.000	0.000	1E+30	50.000
7	Mfg. Time Time Used	12000.0000	−0.083	0.000	7000.000	2000.000

Since we cannot produce or purchase fractional amounts, in reality we would likely purchase 2334 units and produce 666 units of the Financial Manager catridges.

The sensitivity report based on Excel Solver for this 11-variable, 7-constraint linear program is shown in Figure 9.5. The optimal solution indicates that all 5000 bases (*BM*), 666.67 Financial Manager cartridges (*FCM*), and 2000 Technician cartridges (*TCM*) should be manufactured. The remaining 2333.333 Financial Manager cartridges (*FCP*), all the Financial Manager tops (*FTP*), and all Technician tops (*TTP*) should be purchased. No overtime manufacturing is necessary. This plan results in a total cost of 0.5(5000) + 0.6(0) + 3.75(666.67) + 4(2333.333) + 3.3(2000) + 3.9(0) + 0.6(0) + 0.65(3000) + 0.75(0) + 0.78(2000) + 9(0) = \$24,443.33.

The same units of measure must be used for both the left-hand side and right-hand side of the constraint. In this case, minutes are used.

Sensitivity analysis provides some additional information about the unused overtime capacity. The Reduced Costs column shows that the overtime (*OT*) premium would have to decrease by \$4 per hour before overtime production should be considered. That is, if the overtime premium is \$9 − \$4 = \$5 or less, Janders may want to replace some of the purchased components with components manufactured on overtime.

The shadow price for the manufacturing capacity constraint time (constraint 7) is −0.083. This price indicates that an additional hour of manufacturing capacity is worth \$0.083 per minute or (\$0.083)(60) = \$5 per hour. The right-hand-side range for constraint 7 shows that this conclusion is valid until the amount of regular time increases to 19,000 minutes, or 316.7 hours.

Sensitivity analysis also indicates that a change in prices charged by the outside suppliers can affect the optimal solution. For instance, the objective coefficient range for *BP* is 0.600 − 0.017 = 0.583 to no upper limit. If the purchase price for bases remains at \$0.583

or more, the number of bases purchased (*BP*) will remain at zero. However, if the purchase price drops below \$0.583, Janders should begin to purchase rather than manufacture the base component. Similar sensitivity analysis conclusions about the purchase price ranges can be drawn for the other components.

NOTES AND COMMENTS

1. The proper interpretation of the shadow price for manufacturing capacity (constraint 7) in the Janders problem is that an additional hour of manufacturing capacity is worth (\$0.083)(60) = \$5 per hour. Thus, the company should be willing to pay a premium of \$5 per hour over and above the current regular time cost per hour, which is already included in the manufacturing cost of the product. Thus, if the regular time cost is \$18 per hour, Janders should be willing to pay up to \$18 + \$5 = \$23 per hour to obtain additional labor capacity.

Production Scheduling

One of the most important applications of linear programming deals with multiperiod planning such as production scheduling. The solution to a production scheduling problem enables the manager to establish an efficient low-cost production schedule for one or more products over several time periods (weeks or months). Essentially, a production scheduling problem can be viewed as a product-mix problem for each of several periods in the future. The manager must determine the production levels that will allow the company to meet product demand requirements, given limitations on production capacity, labor capacity, and storage space, while minimizing total production costs.

One advantage of using linear programming for production scheduling problems is that they recur. A production schedule must be established for the current month, then again for the next month, for the month after that, and so on. When looking at the problem each month, the production manager will find that, although demand for the products has changed, production times, production capacities, storage space limitations, and so on are roughly the same. Thus, the production manager is basically re-solving the same problem handled in previous months, and a general linear programming model of the production scheduling procedure may be frequently applied. Once the model has been formulated, the manager can simply supply the data—demand, capacities, and so on—for the given production period and use the linear programming model repeatedly to develop the production schedule. The Q.M. in Action, Optimizing Production of Flight Manuals at Jeppesen Sanderson, Inc., describes how linear programming is used to minimize the cost of producing weekly revisions to flight manuals.

Q.M. *in* ACTION

*OPTIMIZING PRODUCTION OF FLIGHT MANUALS AT JEPPESEN SANDERSON, INC.**

Jeppesen Sanderson, Inc., manufactures and distributes flight manuals that contain safety information to more than 300,000 pilots and 4000 airlines. Every week Jeppesen mails between 5 and 30 million pages of chart revisions to 200,000 customers worldwide and receives about 1500 new orders each week. In the late 1990s, its customer service deteriorated as its existing production and supporting systems failed to keep up with this level of activity. To meet customer service goals, Jeppesen turned to optimization-based decision support tools for production planning.

(continued)

*Based on E. Katok, W. Tarantino, and R. Tiedman, "Improving Performance and Flexibility at Jeppesen: The World's Leading Aviation-Information Company," *Interfaces* (January/February 2001): 7–29.

Jeppesen developed a large-scale linear program called Scheduler to minimize the cost of producing the weekly revisions. Model constraints included capacity constraints and numerous internal business rules. The model includes 250,000 variables and 40,000–50,000 constraints. Immediately after introducing the model, Jeppesen established a new record for the number of consecutive weeks with 100% on-time revisions. Scheduler decreased tardiness of revisions from approximately 9% to 3% and dramatically improved customer satisfaction. Even more importantly, Scheduler provided a model of the production system for Jeppesen to use in strategic economic analysis. Overall, the use of optimization techniques at Jeppesen resulted in cost reductions of nearly 10% and a 24% increase in profit.

Let us consider the case of the Bollinger Electronics Company, which produces two different electronic components for a major airplane engine manufacturer. The airplane engine manufacturer notifies the Bollinger sales office each quarter of its monthly requirements for components for each of the next three months. The monthly requirements for the components may vary considerably depending on the type of engine the airplane engine manufacturer is producing. The order shown in Table 9.7 has just been received for the next three-month period.

After the order is processed, a demand statement is sent to the production control department. The production control department must then develop a three-month production plan for the components. In arriving at the desired schedule, the production manager will want to identify the following:

1. Total production cost
2. Inventory holding cost
3. Change-in-production-level costs

In the remainder of this section, we show how to formulate a linear programming model of the production and inventory process for Bollinger Electronics to minimize the total cost.

To develop the model, we let x_{im} denote the production volume in units for product i in month m. Here $i = 1, 2$, and $m = 1, 2, 3$; $i = 1$ refers to component 322A, $i = 2$ refers to component 802B, $m = 1$ refers to April, $m = 2$ refers to May, and $m = 3$ refers to June. The purpose of the double subscript is to provide a more descriptive notation. We could simply use x_6 to represent the number of units of product 2 produced in month 3, but x_{23} is more descriptive, identifying directly the product and month represented by the variable.

If component 322A costs $20 per unit produced and component 802B costs $10 per unit produced, the total production cost part of the objective function is

$$\text{Total production cost} = 20x_{11} + 20x_{12} + 20x_{13} + 10x_{21} + 10x_{22} + 10x_{23}$$

Because the production cost per unit is the same each month, we don't need to include the production costs in the objective function; that is, regardless of the production schedule selected, the total production cost will remain the same. In other words, production costs are not relevant costs for the production scheduling decision under consideration. In cases in which the production cost per unit is expected to change each month, the variable

TABLE 9.7 THREE-MONTH DEMAND SCHEDULE FOR BOLLINGER ELECTRONICS COMPANY

Component	April	May	June
322A	1000	3000	5000
802B	1000	500	3000

production costs per unit per month must be included in the objective function. The solution for the Bollinger Electronics problem will be the same regardless of whether these costs are included; therefore, we included them so that the value of the linear programming objective function will include all the costs associated with the problem.

To incorporate the relevant inventory holding costs into the model, we let s_{im} denote the inventory level for product i at the end of month m. Bollinger determined that on a monthly basis, inventory holding costs are 1.5% of the cost of the product; that is, (0.015)($20) = $0.30 per unit for component 322A and (0.015)($10) = $0.15 per unit for component 802B. A common assumption made in using the linear programming approach to production scheduling is that monthly ending inventories are an acceptable approximation to the average inventory levels throughout the month. Making this assumption, we write the inventory holding cost portion of the objective function as

$$\text{Inventory holding cost} = 0.30s_{11} + 0.30s_{12} + 0.30s_{13} + 0.15s_{21} + 0.15s_{22} + 0.15s_{23}$$

To incorporate the costs of fluctuations in production levels from month to month, we need to define two additional variables:

$$I_m = \text{increase in the total production level necessary during month } m$$
$$D_m = \text{decrease in the total production level necessary during month } m$$

After estimating the effects of employee layoffs, turnovers, reassignment training costs, and other costs associated with fluctuating production levels, Bollinger estimates that the cost associated with increasing the production level for any month is $0.50 per unit increase. A similar cost associated with decreasing the production level for any month is $0.20 per unit. Thus, we write the third portion of the objective function as

$$\begin{aligned}\text{Change-in production-level costs} = {} & 0.50I_1 + 0.50I_2 + 0.50I_3 \\ & + 0.20D_1 + 0.20D_2 + 0.20D_3\end{aligned}$$

Note that the cost associated with changes in production level is a function of the change in the total number of units produced in month m compared to the total number of units produced in month $m - 1$. In other production scheduling applications, fluctuations in production level might be measured in terms of machine-hours or labor-hours required rather than in terms of the total number of units produced.

Combining all three costs, the complete objective function becomes

$$\begin{aligned}\text{Min} \quad & 20x_{11} + 20x_{12} + 20x_{13} + 10x_{21} + 10x_{22} + 10x_{23} + 0.30s_{11} \\ & + 0.30s_{12} + 0.30s_{13} + 0.15s_{21} + 0.15s_{22} + 0.15s_{23} + 0.50I_1 \\ & + 0.50I_2 + 0.50I_3 + 0.20D_1 + 0.20D_2 + 0.20D_3\end{aligned}$$

We now consider the constraints. First, we must guarantee that the schedule meets customer demand. Because the units shipped can come from the current month's production or from inventory carried over from previous months, the demand requirement takes the form

$$\begin{pmatrix}\text{Ending}\\\text{inventory}\\\text{from previous}\\\text{month}\end{pmatrix} + \begin{pmatrix}\text{Current}\\\text{production}\end{pmatrix} - \begin{pmatrix}\text{Ending}\\\text{inventory}\\\text{for this}\\\text{month}\end{pmatrix} = \begin{pmatrix}\text{This month's}\\\text{demand}\end{pmatrix}$$

Suppose that the inventories at the beginning of the three-month scheduling period were 500 units for component 322A and 200 units for component 802B. The demand for both products in the first month (April) was 1000 units, so the constraints for meeting demand in the first month become

$$500 + x_{11} - s_{11} = 1000$$
$$200 + x_{21} - s_{21} = 1000$$

Moving the constants to the right-hand side, we have

$$x_{11} - s_{11} = 500$$
$$x_{21} - s_{21} = 800$$

Similarly, we need demand constraints for both products in the second and third months. We write them as follows:

Month 2

$$s_{11} + x_{12} - s_{12} = 3000$$
$$s_{21} + x_{22} - s_{22} = 500$$

Month 3

$$s_{12} + x_{13} - s_{13} = 5000$$
$$s_{22} + x_{23} - s_{23} = 3000$$

If the company specifies a minimum inventory level at the end of the three-month period of at least 400 units of component 322A and at least 200 units of component 802B, we can add the constraints

$$s_{13} \geq 400$$
$$s_{23} \geq 200$$

Suppose that we have the additional information on machine, labor, and storage capacity shown in Table 9.8. Machine, labor, and storage space requirements are given in Table 9.9. To reflect these limitations, the following constraints are necessary:

TABLE 9.8 MACHINE, LABOR, AND STORAGE CAPACITIES FOR BOLLINGER ELECTRONICS

Month	Machine Capacity (hours)	Labor Capacity (hours)	Storage Capacity (square feet)
April	400	300	10,000
May	500	300	10,000
June	600	300	10,000

TABLE 9.9 MACHINE, LABOR, AND STORAGE REQUIREMENTS FOR COMPONENTS 322A AND 802B

Component	Machine (hours/unit)	Labor (hours/unit)	Storage (square feet/unit)
322A	0.10	0.05	2
802B	0.08	0.07	3

Machine Capacity

$$\begin{aligned} 0.10x_{11} + 0.08x_{21} &\le 400 \quad \text{Month 1} \\ 0.10x_{12} + 0.08x_{22} &\le 500 \quad \text{Month 2} \\ 0.10x_{13} + 0.08x_{23} &\le 600 \quad \text{Month 3} \end{aligned}$$

Labor Capacity

$$\begin{aligned} 0.05x_{11} + 0.07x_{21} &\le 300 \quad \text{Month 1} \\ 0.05x_{12} + 0.07x_{22} &\le 300 \quad \text{Month 2} \\ 0.05x_{13} + 0.07x_{23} &\le 300 \quad \text{Month 3} \end{aligned}$$

Storage Capacity

$$\begin{aligned} 2s_{11} + 3s_{21} &\le 10{,}000 \quad \text{Month 1} \\ 2s_{12} + 3s_{22} &\le 10{,}000 \quad \text{Month 2} \\ 2s_{13} + 3s_{23} &\le 10{,}000 \quad \text{Month 3} \end{aligned}$$

One final set of constraints must be added to guarantee that I_m and D_m will reflect the increase or decrease in the total production level for month m. Suppose that the production levels for March, the month before the start of the current production scheduling period, had been 1500 units of component 322A and 1000 units of component 802B for a total production level of $1500 + 1000 = 2500$ units. We can find the amount of the change in production for April from the relationship

$$\text{April production} - \text{March production} = \text{Change}$$

Using the April production variables, x_{11} and x_{21}, and the March production of 2500 units, we have

$$(x_{11} + x_{21}) - 2500 = \text{Change}$$

Note that the change can be positive or negative. A positive change reflects an increase in the total production level, and a negative change reflects a decrease in the total production level. We can use the increase in production for April, I_1, and the decrease in production for April, D_1, to specify the constraint for the change in total production for the month of April:

$$(x_{11} + x_{21}) - 2500 = I_1 - D_1$$

Of course, we cannot have an increase in production and a decrease in production during the same one-month period; thus, either I_1 or D_1 will be zero. If April requires 3000 units of production, $I_1 = 500$ and $D_1 = 0$. If April requires 2200 units of production, $I_1 = 0$ and $D_1 = 300$. This approach of denoting the change in production level as the difference between two nonnegative variables, I_1 and D_1, permits both positive and negative changes in the total production level. If a single variable (say, c_m) had been used to represent the change in production level, only positive changes would be possible because of the nonnegativity requirement.

Using the same approach in May and June (always subtracting the previous month's total production from the current month's total production), we obtain the constraints for the second and third months of the production scheduling period:

$$(x_{12} + x_{22}) - (x_{11} + x_{21}) = I_2 - D_2$$
$$(x_{13} + x_{23}) - (x_{12} + x_{22}) = I_3 - D_3$$

Placing the variables on the left-hand side and the constants on the right-hand side yields the complete set of what are commonly referred to as production-smoothing constraints:

$$\begin{aligned} x_{11} + x_{21} \qquad\qquad\qquad\qquad\qquad - I_1 + D_1 &= 2500 \\ -x_{11} - x_{21} + x_{12} + x_{22} \qquad\qquad - I_2 + D_2 &= 0 \\ -x_{12} - x_{22} + x_{13} + x_{23} - I_3 + D_3 &= 0 \end{aligned}$$

The initially small, two-product, three-month scheduling problem has now developed into an 18-variable, 20-constraint linear programming problem. Note that in this problem we were concerned only with one type of machine process, one type of labor, and one type of storage area. Actual production scheduling problems usually involve several machine types, several labor grades, and/or several storage areas, requiring large-scale linear programs. For instance, a problem involving 100 products over a 12-month period could have more than 1000 variables and constraints.

Problem 19 involves a production scheduling application with labor-smoothing constraints.

Figure 9.6 shows the optimal solution to the Bollinger Electronics production scheduling problem. Table 9.10 contains a portion of the managerial report based on the optimal solution.

Consider the monthly variation in the production and inventory schedule shown in Table 9.10. Recall that the inventory cost for component 802B is one-half the inventory

TABLE 9.10 MINIMUM COST PRODUCTION SCHEDULE INFORMATION FOR THE BOLLINGER ELECTRONICS PROBLEM

Activity	**April**	**May**	**June**
Production			
Component 322A	500	3200	5200
Component 802B	2500	2000	0
Totals	3000	5200	5200
Ending inventory			
Component 322A	0	200	400
Component 802B	1700	3200	200
Machine usage			
Scheduled hours	250	480	520
Slack capacity hours	150	20	80
Labor usage			
Scheduled hours	200	300	260
Slack capacity hours	100	0	40
Storage usage			
Scheduled storage	5100	10,000	1400
Slack capacity	4900	0	8600
Total production, inventory, and production-smoothing cost = $225,295			

FIGURE 9.6 SENSITIVITY REPORT FOR THE BOLLINGER ELECTRONICS PROBLEM

WEB file

Bollinger

Variable Cells

Model Variable	Name	Final Value	Reduced Cost	Objective Coefficient	Allowable Increase	Allowable Decrease
X11	322A April Production	500.000	0.000	20.000	1E+30	0.172
X12	322A May Production	3200.000	0.000	20.000	0.093	0.100
X13	322A June Production	5200.000	0.000	20.000	0.100	0.093
S11	322A April Ending Inv	0.000	0.172	0.300	1E+30	0.172
S12	322A May Ending Inv	200.000	0.000	0.300	0.093	0.100
S13	322A June Ending Inv	400.000	0.000	0.300	1E+30	20.728
X21	802B April Production	2500.000	0.000	10.000	0.130	0.050
X22	802B May Production	2000.000	0.000	10.000	0.050	0.130
X23	802B June Production	0.000	0.128	10.000	1E+30	0.128
S21	802B April Ending Inv	1700.000	0.000	0.150	0.130	0.050
S22	802B May Ending Inv	3200.000	0.000	0.150	0.128	10.450
S23	802B June Ending Inv	200.000	0.000	0.150	1E+30	10.450
I1	Increase April	500.000	0.000	0.500	0.130	0.050
I2	Increase May	2200.000	0.000	0.500	0.033	0.192
I3	Increase June	0.000	0.072	0.500	1E+30	0.072
D1	Decrease April	0.000	0.700	0.200	1E+30	0.700
D2	Decrease May	0.000	0.700	0.200	1E+30	0.700
D3	Decrease June	0.000	0.628	0.200	1E+30	0.628

Constraints

Constraint Number	Name	Final Value	Shadow Price	Constraint R.H. Side	Allowable Increase	Allowable Decrease
1	322A/April Balance Equation	1000.000	20.000	1000.000	1500.000	500.000
2	802B/April Balance Equation	1000.000	10.000	1000.000	1428.571	500.000
3	322A/May Balance Equation	3000.000	20.128	3000.000	600.000	0.000
4	802B/May Balance Equation	500.000	10.150	500.000	1428.571	500.000
5	322A/June Balance Equation	5000.000	20.428	5000.000	0.000	257.143
6	802B/June Balance Equation	3000.000	10.300	3000.000	0.000	500.000
7	322A Ending Inventory	400.000	20.728	400.000	0.000	257.143
8	802B Ending Inventory	200.000	10.450	200.000	0.000	200.000
9	Mach/Apr Used	250.000	0.000	400.000	1E+30	150.000
10	Mach/May Used	480.000	0.000	500.000	1E+30	20.000
11	Mach/June Used	520.000	0.000	600.000	1E+30	80.000
12	Labor/Apr Used	200.000	0.000	300.000	1E+30	100.000
13	Labor/May Used	300.000	−1.111	300.000	18.000	1.00044E-13
14	Labor/June Used	260.000	0.000	300.000	1E+30	40.000
15	Storage/Apr Used	5100.000	0.000	10000.000	1E+30	4900.000
16	Storage/May Used	10000.000	0.000	10000.000	1E+30	0.000
17	Storage/June Used	1400.000	0.000	10000.000	1E+30	8600.000
18	April Difference	500.000	−0.500	0.000	500.000	1E+30
19	May Difference	2200.000	−0.500	0.000	2200.000	1E+30
20	June Difference	0.000	−0.428	0.000	257.143	0.000

Linear programming models for production scheduling are often very large. Thousands of decision variables and constraints are necessary when the problem involves numerous products, machines, and time periods. Data collection for large-scale models can be more time-consuming than either the formulation of the model or the development of the computer solution.

cost for component 322A. Therefore, as might be expected, component 802B is produced heavily in the first month (April) and then held in inventory for the demand that will occur in future months. Component 322A tends to be produced when needed, and only small amounts are carried in inventory.

The costs of increasing and decreasing the total production volume tend to smooth the monthly variations. In fact, the minimum-cost schedule calls for a 500-unit increase in total production in April and a 2200-unit increase in total production in May. The May production level of 5200 units is then maintained during June.

The machine usage section of the report shows ample machine capacity in all three months. However, labor capacity is at full utilization in the month of May (see constraint 13 in Figure 9.6). The shadow price shows that an additional hour of labor capacity in May will decrease the optimal cost by approximately \$1.11.

A linear programming model of a two-product, three-month production system can provide valuable information in terms of identifying a minimum-cost production schedule. In larger production systems, where the number of variables and constraints is too large to track manually, linear programming models can provide a significant advantage in developing cost-saving production schedules. The Q.M. in Action, Optimizing Production, Inventory, and Distribution at the Kellogg Company, illustrates the use of a large-scale multiperiod linear program for production planning and distribution.

Q.M. *in* ACTION

*OPTIMIZING PRODUCTION, INVENTORY, AND DISTRIBUTION AT THE KELLOGG COMPANY**

The Kellogg Company is the largest cereal producer in the world and a leading producer of convenience foods, such as Kellogg's Pop-Tarts and Nutri-Grain cereal bars. Kellogg produces more than 40 different cereals at plants in 19 countries, on six continents. The company markets its products in more than 160 countries and employs more than 15,600 people in its worldwide organization. In the cereal business alone, Kellogg coordinates the production of about 80 products using a total of approximately 90 production lines and 180 packaging lines.

Kellogg has a long history of using linear programming for production planning and distribution. The Kellogg Planning System (KPS) is a large-scale, multiperiod linear program. The operational version of KPS makes production, packaging, inventory, and distribution decisions on a weekly basis. The primary objective of the system is to minimize the total cost of meeting estimated demand; to deal with constraints involving processing line capacities and packaging line capacities; and to satisfy safety stock requirements.

A tactical version of KPS helps to establish plant budgets and make capacity-expansion and consolidation decisions on a monthly basis. The tactical version was recently used to guide a consolidation of production capacity that resulted in projected savings of \$35 to \$40 million per year. Because of the success Kellogg has had using KPS in its North American operations, the company is now introducing KPS into Latin America and is studying the development of a global KPS model.

*Based on G. Brown, J. Keegan, B. Vigus, and K. Wood, "The Kellogg Company Optimizes Production, Inventory, and Distribution," *Interfaces* (November/December 2001): 1–15.

Workforce Assignment

Workforce assignment problems frequently occur when production managers must make decisions involving staffing requirements for a given planning period. Workforce assignments often have some flexibility, and at least some personnel can be assigned to more than one department or work center. Such is the case when employees have been cross-trained on two or more jobs or, for instance, when sales personnel can be transferred between stores.

In the following application, we show how linear programming can be used to determine not only an optimal product mix, but also an optimal workforce assignment.

McCormick Manufacturing Company produces two products with contributions to profit per unit of \$10 and \$9, respectively. The labor requirements per unit produced and the total hours of labor available from personnel assigned to each of four departments are shown in Table 9.11. Assuming that the number of hours available in each department is fixed, we can formulate McCormick's problem as a standard product-mix linear program with the following decision variables:

$$P_1 = \text{units of product 1}$$
$$P_2 = \text{units of product 2}$$

The linear program is

$$\begin{aligned}
\text{Max} \quad & 10P_1 + 9P_2 \\
\text{s.t.} \quad & \\
& 0.65P_1 + 0.95P_2 \leq 6500 \\
& 0.45P_1 + 0.85P_2 \leq 6000 \\
& 1.00P_1 + 0.70P_2 \leq 7000 \\
& 0.15P_1 + 0.30P_2 \leq 1400 \\
& P_1 P_2 \geq 0
\end{aligned}$$

The answer report to the linear programming model is shown in Figure 9.7. The product mix calls for approximately 5744 units of product 1, 1795 units of product 2, and a total profit of \$73,590. With this optimal solution, departments 3 and 4 are operating at capacity, and departments 1 and 2 have a slack of approximately 1062 and 1890 hours, respectively. We would anticipate that the product mix would change and that the total profit would increase if the workforce assignment could be revised so that the slack, or unused hours, in departments 1 and 2 could be transferred to the departments currently working at capacity. However, the production manager may be uncertain as to how the workforce should be reallocated among the four departments. Let us expand the linear programming model to include decision variables that will help determine the optimal workforce assignment in addition to the profit-maximizing product mix.

TABLE 9.11 DEPARTMENTAL LABOR-HOURS PER UNIT AND TOTAL HOURS AVAILABLE FOR THE MCCORMICK MANUFACTURING COMPANY

	Labor-Hours per Unit		
Department	Product 1	Product 2	Total Hours Available
1	0.65	0.95	6500
2	0.45	0.85	6000
3	1.00	0.70	7000
4	0.15	0.30	1400

FIGURE 9.7 ANSWER REPORT FOR THE McCORMICK MANUFACTURING COMPANY PROBLEM WITH NO WORKFORCE TRANSFERS PERMITTED

WEB file

McCormick

Objective Cell (Max)

Name	Original Value	Final Value
Max Profit	0.000	73589.744

Variable Cells

Model Variable	Name	Original Value	Final Value	Integer
P1	Product 1	0.000	5743.590	Contin
P2	Product 2	0.000	1794.872	Contin

Constraints

Constraint Number	Name	Cell Value	Status	Slack
1	Dept 1 Hours	5438.462	Not Binding	1061.538
2	Dept 2 Hours	4110.256	Not Binding	1889.744
3	Dept 3 Hours	7000.000	Binding	0.000
4	Dept 4 Hours	1400.000	Binding	0.000

Suppose that McCormick has a cross-training program that enables some employees to be transferred between departments. By taking advantage of the cross-training skills, a limited number of employees and labor-hours may be transferred from one department to another. For example, suppose that the cross-training permits transfers as shown in Table 9.12. Row 1 of this table shows that some employees assigned to department 1 have cross-training skills that permit them to be transferred to department 2 or 3. The right-hand column shows that, for the current production planning period, a maximum of 400 hours can be transferred from department 1. Similar cross-training transfer capabilities and capacities are shown for departments 2, 3, and 4.

The right-hand sides are now treated as decision variables.

When workforce assignments are flexible, we do not automatically know how many hours of labor should be assigned to or be transferred from each department. We need to add decision variables to the linear programming model to account for such changes.

b_i = the labor-hours allocated to department i for i = 1, 2, 3, and 4

t_{ij} = the labor-hours transferred from department i to department j

TABLE 9.12 CROSS-TRAINING ABILITY AND CAPACITY INFORMATION

From Department	Cross-Training Transfers Permitted to Department 1	2	3	4	Maximum Hours Transferable
1	—	yes	yes	—	400
2	—	—	yes	yes	800
3	—	—	—	yes	100
4	yes	yes	—	—	200

With the addition of decision variables b_1, b_2, b_3, and b_4, we write the capacity restrictions for the four departments as follows:

$$\begin{aligned} 0.65P_1 + 0.95P_2 &\le b_1 \\ 0.45P_1 + 0.85P_2 &\le b_2 \\ 1.00P_1 + 0.70P_2 &\le b_3 \\ 0.15P_1 + 0.30P_2 &\le b_4 \end{aligned}$$

Because b_1, b_2, b_3, and b_4 are now decision variables, we follow the standard practice of placing these variables on the left side of the inequalities, and the first four constraints of the linear programming model become

$$\begin{aligned} 0.65P_1 + 0.95P_2 - b_1 \qquad\qquad\qquad &\le 0 \\ 0.45P_1 + 0.85P_2 \qquad - b_2 \qquad\qquad &\le 0 \\ 1.00P_1 + 0.70P_2 \qquad\qquad - b_3 \qquad &\le 0 \\ 0.15P_1 + 0.30P_2 \qquad\qquad\qquad - b_4 &\le 0 \end{aligned}$$

The labor-hours ultimately allocated to each department must be determined by a series of labor balance equations, or constraints, that include the number of hours initially assigned to each department plus the number of hours transferred into the department minus the number of hours transferred out of the department. Using department 1 as an example, we determine the workforce allocation as follows:

$$b_1 = \begin{pmatrix} \text{Hours} \\ \text{initially in} \\ \text{department 1} \end{pmatrix} + \begin{pmatrix} \text{Hours} \\ \text{transferred into} \\ \text{department 1} \end{pmatrix} - \begin{pmatrix} \text{Hours} \\ \text{transferred out of} \\ \text{department 1} \end{pmatrix}$$

Table 9.11 shows 6500 hours initially assigned to department 1. We use the transfer decision variables t_{i1} to denote transfers into department 1 and t_{1j} to denote transfers from department 1. Table 9.12 shows that the cross-training capabilities involving department 1 are restricted to transfers from department 4 (variable t_{41}) and transfers to either department 2 or department 3 (variables t_{12} and t_{13}). Thus, we can express the total workforce allocation for department 1 as

$$b_1 = 6500 + t_{41} - t_{12} - t_{13}$$

Moving the decision variables for the workforce transfers to the left-hand side, we have the labor balance equation or constraint

$$b_1 - t_{41} + t_{12} + t_{13} = 6500$$

This form of constraint will be needed for each of the four departments. Thus, the following labor balance constraints for departments 2, 3, and 4 would be added to the model:

$$\begin{aligned} b_2 - t_{12} - t_{42} + t_{23} + t_{24} &= 6000 \\ b_3 - t_{13} - t_{23} + t_{34} \qquad\quad &= 7000 \\ b_4 - t_{24} - t_{34} + t_{41} + t_{42} &= 1400 \end{aligned}$$

Finally, Table 9.12 shows the number of hours that may be transferred from each department is limited, indicating that a transfer capacity constraint must be added for each of the four departments. The additional constraints are

$$
\begin{aligned}
t_{12} + t_{13} &\leq 400 \\
t_{13} + t_{24} &\leq 800 \\
t_{34} \quad &\leq 100 \\
t_{41} + t_{42} &\leq 200
\end{aligned}
$$

The complete linear programming model has two product decision variables (P_1 and P_2), four department workforce assignment variables (b_1, b_2, b_3, and b_4), seven transfer variables (t_{12}, t_{13}, t_{23}, t_{24}, t_{34}, t_{41}, and t_{42}), and 12 constraints. Figure 9.8 shows the optimal solution to this linear program based on Excel Solver.

FIGURE 9.8 ANSWER REPORT FOR THE MODIFIED McCORMICK MANUFACTURING COMPANY PROBLEM

Objective Cell (Max)

Name	Original Value	Final Value
Max Profit	0.000	84011.299

Variable Cells

McCormickMod

Model Name	Name	Original Value	Final Value	Integer
P1	Product 1	0.000	6824.859	Contin
P2	Product 2	0.000	1751.412	Contin
B1	Dept 1 Hours Allocated	0.000	6100.000	Contin
B2	Dept 2 Hours Allocated	0.000	5200.000	Contin
B3	Dept 3 Hours Allocated	0.000	8050.847	Contin
B4	Dept 4 Hours Allocated	0.000	1549.153	Contin
T12	From 1 To 2	0.000	0.000	Contin
T13	From 1 To 3	0.000	400.000	Contin
T23	From 2 To 3	0.000	650.847	Contin
T24	From 2 To 4	0.000	149.153	Contin
T34	From 3 To 4	0.000	0.000	Contin
T41	From 4 To 1	0.000	0.000	Contin
T42	From 4 To 2	0.000	0.000	Contin

Constraints

Constraint Number	Name	Cell Value	Status	Slack
1	Dept 1 Hours	6100.000	Binding	0.000
2	Dept 2 Hours	4559.887	Not Binding	640.113
3	Dept 3 Hours	8050.847	Binding	0.000
4	Dept 4 Hours	1549.153	Binding	0.000
5	Dept 1 Hours Allocated	6100.000	Binding	0.000
6	Dept 2 Hours Allocated	5200.000	Binding	0.000
7	Dept 3 Hours Allocated	8050.847	Binding	0.000
8	Dept 4 Hours Allocated	1549.153	Binding	0.000
9	From 1 Total	400.000	Binding	0.000
10	From 2 Total	800.000	Binding	0.000
11	From 3 Total	0.000	Not Binding	100.000
12	From 4 Total	0.000	Not Binding	200.000

Variations in the workforce assignment model could be used in situations such as allocating raw material resources to products, allocating machine time to products, and allocating salesforce time to stores or sales territories.

McCormick's profit can be increased by \$84,011 − \$73,590 = \$10,421 by taking advantage of cross-training and workforce transfers. The optimal product mix of 6825 units of product 1 and 1751 units of product 2 can be achieved if $t_{13} = 400$ hours are transferred from department 1 to department 3; $t_{23} = 651$ hours are transferred from department 2 to department 3; and $t_{24} = 149$ hours are transferred from department 2 to department 4. The resulting workforce assignments for departments 1–4 would provide 6100, 5200, 8051, and 1549 hours, respectively, after rounding.

If a manager has the flexibility to assign personnel to different departments, reduced workforce idle time, improved workforce utilization, and improved profit should result. The linear programming model in this section automatically assigns employees and labor-hours to the departments in the most profitable manner.

Blending Problems

Blending problems arise whenever a manager must decide how to blend two or more resources to produce one or more products. In these situations, the resources contain one or more essential ingredients that must be blended into final products that will contain specific percentages of each. In most of these applications, then, management must decide how much of each resource to purchase to satisfy product specifications and product demands at minimum cost.

Blending problems occur frequently in the petroleum industry (e.g., blending crude oil to produce different octane gasolines), the chemical industry (e.g., blending chemicals to produce fertilizers and weed killers), and the food industry (e.g., blending ingredients to produce soft drinks and soups). In this section we illustrate how to apply linear programming to a blending problem in the petroleum industry.

The Grand Strand Oil Company produces regular and premium gasoline for independent service stations in the southeastern United States. The Grand Strand refinery manufactures the gasoline products by blending three petroleum components. The gasolines are sold at different prices, and the petroleum components have different costs. The firm wants to determine how to mix or blend the three components into the two gasoline products and maximize profits.

Data available show that regular gasoline can be sold for \$2.90 per gallon and premium gasoline for \$3.00 per gallon. For the current production planning period, Grand Strand can obtain the three petroleum components at the cost per gallon and in the quantities shown in Table 9.13.

Product specifications for the regular and premium gasolines restrict the amounts of each component that can be used in each gasoline product. Table 9.14 lists the product specifications. Current commitments to distributors require Grand Strand to produce at least 10,000 gallons of regular gasoline.

TABLE 9.13 PETROLEUM COST AND SUPPLY FOR THE GRAND STRAND BLENDING PROBLEM

Petroleum Component	Cost/Gallon	Maximum Available
1	\$2.50	5,000 gallons
2	\$2.60	10,000 gallons
3	\$2.84	10,000 gallons

TABLE 9.14 PRODUCT SPECIFICATIONS FOR THE GRAND STRAND BLENDING PROBLEM

Product	Specifications
Regular gasoline	At most 30% component 1 At least 40% component 2 At most 20% component 3
Premium gasoline	At least 25% component 1 At most 45% component 2 At least 30% component 3

The Grand Strand blending problem is to determine how many gallons of each component should be used in the regular gasoline blend and how many should be used in the premium gasoline blend. The optimal blending solution should maximize the firm's profit, subject to the constraints on the available petroleum supplies shown in Table 9.13, the product specifications shown in Table 9.14, and the required 10,000 gallons of regular gasoline.

We define the decision variables as

$$x_{ij} = \text{gallons of component } i \text{ used in gasoline } j,$$
$$\text{where } i = 1, 2, \text{ or } 3 \text{ for components } 1, 2, \text{ or } 3,$$
$$\text{and } j = r \text{ if regular or } j = p \text{ if premium}$$

The six decision variables are

$$x_{1r} = \text{gallons of component 1 in regular gasoline}$$
$$x_{2r} = \text{gallons of component 2 in regular gasoline}$$
$$x_{3r} = \text{gallons of component 3 in regular gasoline}$$
$$x_{1p} = \text{gallons of component 1 in premium gasoline}$$
$$x_{2p} = \text{gallons of component 2 in premium gasoline}$$
$$x_{3p} = \text{gallons of component 3 in premium gasoline}$$

The total number of gallons of each type of gasoline produced is the sum of the number of gallons produced using each of the three petroleum components.

Total Gallons Produced

$$\text{Regular gasoline} = x_{1r} + x_{2r} + x_{3r}$$
$$\text{Premium gasoline} = x_{1p} + x_{2p} + x_{3p}$$

The total gallons of each petroleum component are computed in a similar fashion.

Total Petroleum Component Use

$$\text{Component 1} = x_{1r} + x_{1p}$$
$$\text{Component 2} = x_{2r} + x_{2p}$$
$$\text{Component 3} = x_{3r} + x_{3p}$$

We develop the objective function of maximizing the profit contribution by identifying the difference between the total revenue from both gasolines and the total cost of the three petroleum components. By multiplying the \$2.90 per gallon price by the total gallons of regular gasoline, the \$3.00 per gallon price by the total gallons of premium gasoline, and the component cost per gallon figures in Table 9.13 by the total gallons of each component used, we obtain the objective function:

$$\begin{aligned}\text{Max} \quad & 2.90(x_{1r} + x_{2r} + x_{3r}) + 3.00(x_{1p} + x_{2p} + x_{3p}) \\ & - 2.50(x_{1r} + x_{1p}) - 2.60(x_{2r} + x_{2p}) - 2.84(x_{3r} + x_{3p})\end{aligned}$$

When we combine terms, the objective function becomes

$$\text{Max} \quad 0.40x_{1r} + 0.30x_{2r} + 0.06x_{3r} + 0.50x_{1p} + 0.40x_{2p} + 0.16x_{3p}$$

The limitations on the availability of the three petroleum components are

$$\begin{aligned} x_{1r} + x_{1p} &\leq 5{,}000 \quad \text{Component 1} \\ x_{2r} + x_{2p} &\leq 10{,}000 \quad \text{Component 2} \\ x_{3r} + x_{3p} &\leq 10{,}000 \quad \text{Component 3} \end{aligned}$$

Six constraints are now required to meet the product specifications stated in Table 9.14. The first specification states that component 1 can account for no more than 30% of the total gallons of regular gasoline produced. That is,

$$x_{1r} \leq 0.30(x_{1r} + x_{2r} + x_{3r})$$

Rewriting this constraint with the variables on the left-hand side and a constant on the right-hand side yields

$$0.70x_{1r} - 0.30x_{2r} - 0.30x_{3r} \leq 0$$

The second product specification listed in Table 9.14 becomes

$$x_{2r} \geq 0.40(x_{1r} + x_{2r} + x_{3r})$$

and thus

$$-0.40x_{1r} + 0.60x_{2r} - 0.40x_{3r} \geq 0$$

Similarly, we write the four remaining blending specifications listed in Table 9.14 as

$$\begin{aligned} -0.20x_{1r} - 0.20x_{2r} + 0.80x_{3r} &\leq 0 \\ +0.75x_{1p} - 0.25x_{2p} - 0.25x_{3p} &\geq 0 \\ -0.45x_{1p} + 0.55x_{2p} - 0.45x_{3p} &\leq 0 \\ -0.30x_{1p} - 0.30x_{2p} + 0.70x_{3p} &\geq 0 \end{aligned}$$

The constraint for at least 10,000 gallons of regular gasoline is

$$x_{1r} + x_{2r} + x_{3r} \geq 10{,}000$$

The complete linear programming model with 6 decision variables and 10 constraints is

$$
\begin{array}{lrcl}
\text{Max} & 0.40x_{1r} + 0.30x_{2r} + 0.06x_{3r} + 0.50x_{1p} + 0.40x_{2p} + 0.16x_{3p} & & \\
\text{s.t.} & & & \\
& x_{1r} + x_{1p} & \leq & 5{,}000 \\
& x_{2r} + x_{2p} & \leq & 10{,}000 \\
& x_{3r} + x_{3p} & \leq & 10{,}000 \\
& 0.70x_{1r} - 0.30x_{2r} - 0.30x_{3r} & \leq & 0 \\
& -0.40x_{1r} + 0.60x_{2r} - 0.40x_{3r} & \geq & 0 \\
& -0.20x_{1r} - 0.20x_{2r} + 0.80x_{3r} & \leq & 0 \\
& 0.75x_{1p} - 0.25x_{2p} - 0.25x_{3p} & \geq & 0 \\
& -0.45x_{1p} + 0.55x_{2p} - 0.45x_{3p} & \leq & 0 \\
& -0.30x_{1p} - 0.30x_{2p} + 0.70x_{3p} & \geq & 0 \\
& x_{1r} + x_{2r} + x_{3r} & \geq & 10{,}000 \\
& x_{1r}, x_{2r}, x_{3r}, x_{1p}, x_{2p}, x_{3p} \geq 0 & &
\end{array}
$$

The optimal solution to the Grand Strand blending problem is shown in Figure 9.9. The optimal solution, which provides a profit of $7100, is summarized in Table 9.15. The optimal blending strategy shows that 10,000 gallons of regular gasoline should be produced. The regular gasoline will be manufactured as a blend of 8000 gallons of component 2 and 2000 gallons of component 3. The 15,000 gallons of premium gasoline will be manufactured as a blend of 5000 gallons of component 1, 2000 gallons of component 2, and 8000 gallons of component 3.

Try Problem 15 as another example of a blending model.

The interpretation of the slack and surplus variables associated with the product specification constraints (constraints 4–9) in Figure 9.9 needs some clarification. If the constraint is a ≤ constraint, the value of the slack variable can be interpreted as the gallons of component use below the maximum amount of the component use specified by the constraint. For example, the slack of 3000.000 for constraint 4 shows that component 1 use is 3000 gallons below the maximum amount of component 1 that could have been used in the production of 10,000 gallons of regular gasoline. If the product specification constraint is a ≥ constraint, a surplus variable shows the gallons of component use above the minimum amount of component use specified by the blending constraint. For example, the surplus of 4000.000 for constraint 5 shows that component 2 use is 4000 gallons above the minimum amount of component 2 that must be used in the production of 10,000 gallons of regular gasoline.

TABLE 9.15 GRAND STRAND GASOLINE BLENDING SOLUTION

	Gallons of Component (percentage)			
Gasoline	**Component 1**	**Component 2**	**Component 3**	Total
Regular	0 (0.0%)	8000 (80%)	2000 (20%)	10,000
Premium	5000 (33⅓%)	2000 (13⅓%)	8000 (53⅓%)	15,000

© Cengage Learning 2013

FIGURE 9.9 ANSWER REPORT FOR THE GRAND STRAND BLENDING PROBLEM

Objective Cell (Max)

Name	Original Value	Final Value
Max Profit	0.000	7100.000

Grand

Variable Cells

Model Variable	Name	Original Value	Final Value	Integer
X1R	Regular Component 1	0.000	0.000	Contin
X2R	Regular Component 2	0.000	8000.000	Contin
X3R	Regular Component 3	0.000	2000.000	Contin
X1P	Premium Component 1	0.000	5000.000	Contin
X2P	Premium Component 2	0.000	2000.000	Contin
X3P	Premium Component 3	0.000	8000.000	Contin

Constraints

Constraint Number	Name	Cell Value	Status	Slack
1	Total Component 1	5000.000	Binding	0.000
2	Total Component 2	10000.000	Binding	0.000
3	Total Component 3	10000.000	Binding	0.000
4	Max Comp 1 Regular	0.000	Not Binding	3000.000
5	Min Comp 2 Regular	8000.000	Not Binding	4000.000
6	Max Comp 3 Regular	2000.000	Binding	0.000
7	Min Comp 1 Premium	5000.000	Not Binding	1250.000
8	Max Comp 2 Premium	2000.000	Not Binding	4000.000
9	Min Comp 3 Premium	8000.000	Not Binding	3500.000
10	Regular Total	10000.000	Binding	0.000

NOTES AND COMMENTS

1. A convenient way to define the decision variables in a blending problem is to use a matrix in which the rows correspond to the raw materials and the columns correspond to the final products. For example, in the Grand Strand blending problem, we define the decision variables as follows: This approach has two advantages: (1) It provides a systematic way to define the decision variables for any blending problem; and (2) it provides a visual image of the decision variables in terms of how they are related to the raw materials, products, and each other.

		Final Products	
		Regular Gasoline	**Premium Gasoline**
Raw Materials	**Component 1**	x_{1r}	x_{1p}
	Component 2	x_{2r}	x_{2p}
	Component 3	x_{3r}	x_{3p}

Summary

In this chapter we presented a broad range of applications that demonstrate how to use linear programming to assist in the decision-making process. We formulated and solved problems from marketing, finance, and operations management, and interpreted the computer output.

Many of the illustrations presented in this chapter are scaled-down versions of actual situations in which linear programming has been applied. In real-world applications, the problem may not be so concisely stated, the data for the problem may not be as readily available, and the problem most likely will involve numerous decision variables and/or constraints. However, a thorough study of the applications in this chapter is a good place to begin in applying linear programming to real problems.

Problems

Note: The following problems have been designed to give you an understanding and appreciation of the broad range of problems that can be formulated as linear programs. You should be able to formulate a linear programming model for each of the problems. However, you will need access to a linear programming computer package to develop the solutions and make the requested interpretations.

1. The Westchester Chamber of Commerce periodically sponsors public service seminars and programs. Currently, promotional plans are under way for this year's program. Advertising alternatives include television, radio, and online. Audience estimates, costs, and maximum media usage limitations are as shown:

Constraint	Television	Radio	Online
Audience per advertisement	100,000	18,000	40,000
Cost per advertisement	$2000	$300	$600
Maximum media usage	10	20	10

To ensure a balanced use of advertising media, radio advertisements must not exceed 50% of the total number of advertisements authorized. In addition, television should account for at least 10% of the total number of advertisements authorized.

a. If the promotional budget is limited to $18,200, how many commercial messages should be run on each medium to maximize total audience contact? What is the allocation of the budget among the three media, and what is the total audience reached?

b. By how much would audience contact increase if an extra $100 were allocated to the promotional budget?

2. The management of Hartman Company is trying to determine the amount of each of two products to produce over the coming planning period. The following information concerns labor availability, labor utilization, and product profitability:

	Product (hours/unit)		Labor-Hours
Department	1	2	Available
A	1.00	0.35	100
B	0.30	0.20	36
C	0.20	0.50	50
Profit contribution/unit	$30.00	$15.00	

a. Develop a linear programming model of the Hartman Company problem. Solve the model to determine the optimal production quantities of products 1 and 2.

b. In computing the profit contribution per unit, management doesn't deduct labor costs because they are considered fixed for the upcoming planning period. However, suppose that overtime can be scheduled in some of the departments. Which departments would you recommend scheduling for overtime? How much would you be willing to pay per hour of overtime in each department?

c. Suppose that 10, 6, and 8 hours of overtime may be scheduled in departments A, B, and C, respectively. The cost per hour of overtime is \$18 in department A, \$22.50 in department B, and \$12 in department C. Formulate a linear programming model that can be used to determine the optimal production quantities if overtime is made available. What are the optimal production quantities, and what is the revised total contribution to profit? How much overtime do you recommend using in each department? What is the increase in the total contribution to profit if overtime is used?

3. The employee credit union at State University is planning the allocation of funds for the coming year. The credit union makes four types of loans to its members. In addition, the credit union invests in risk-free securities to stabilize income. The various revenue-producing investments together with annual rates of return are as follows:

Type of Loan/Investment	Annual Rate of Return (%)
Automobile loans	8
Furniture loans	10
Other secured loans	11
Signature loans	12
Risk-free securities	9

The credit union will have \$2 million available for investment during the coming year. State laws and credit union policies impose the following restrictions on the composition of the loans and investments:

- Risk-free securities may not exceed 30% of the total funds available for investment.
- Signature loans may not exceed 10% of the funds invested in all loans (automobile, furniture, other secured, and signature loans).
- Furniture loans plus other secured loans may not exceed the automobile loans.
- Other secured loans plus signature loans may not exceed the funds invested in risk-free securities.

How should the \$2 million be allocated to each of the loan/investment alternatives to maximize total annual return? What is the projected total annual return?

4. The Bahama Nut Company sells three different half-pound bags of peanut mixes: Party Nuts, Mixed, and Premium Mix. These generate per-bag revenue of \$1.00, \$2.10, and \$3.63, respectively. The tables below show the makeup of each mix, the available ingredients for the next week, and the cost of each ingredient.

	Ingredients			
	Peanuts	Cashews	Brazil Nuts	Hazelnuts
Party Nuts	100%			
Mixed	55%	25%	10%	10%
Premium Mix		40%	20%	40%

	Pounds Available	Cost per Pound
Peanuts	500	\$1.50
Cashews	180	\$5.35
Brazil nuts	100	\$6.25
Hazelnuts	80	\$7.50

Develop a linear programming model to help Bahama determine how many bags of each type to produce to maximize contribution to profit. How many bags of each type should be produced and what is the maximal profit? Which constraints are binding?

5. Kilgore's Deli is a small delicatessen located near a major university. Kilgore's does a large walk-in carry-out lunch business. The deli offers two luncheon chili specials, Wimpy and Dial 911. At the beginning of the day, Kilgore needs to decide how much of each special to make (he always sells out of whatever he makes). The profit on one serving of Wimpy is $.45, on one serving of Dial 911, $.58. Each serving of Wimpy requires .25 pound of beef, .25 cup of onions, and 5 ounces of Kilgore's special sauce. Each serving of Dial 911 requires .25 pound of beef, .4 cup of onions, 2 ounces of Kilgore's special sauce, and 5 ounces of hot sauce. Today, Kilgore has 20 pounds of beef, 15 cups of onions, 88 ounces of Kilgore's special sauce, and 60 ounces of hot sauce on hand.
   a. Develop a linear programming model that will tell Kilgore how many servings of Wimpy and Dial 911 to make in order to maximize his profit today.
   b. Find an optimal solution.
   c. What is the shadow price for special sauce? Interpret the shadow price.
   d. Increase the amount of special sauce available by 1 ounce and re-solve. Does the solution confirm the answer to part (c)? Give the new solution.

6. G. Kunz and Sons, Inc., manufactures two products used in the heavy equipment industry. Both products require manufacturing operations in two departments. The following are the production time (in hours) and profit contribution figures for the two products:

		Labor-Hours	
Product	**Profit per Unit**	**Dept. A**	**Dept. B**
1	$25	6	12
2	$20	8	10

For the coming production period, Kunz has available a total of 900 hours of labor that can be allocated to either of the two departments. Find the production plan and labor allocation (hours assigned in each department) that will maximize the total contribution to profit.

7. As part of the settlement for a class action lawsuit, Hoxworth Corporation must provide sufficient cash to make the following annual payments (in thousands of dollars):

Year	1	2	3	4	5	6
Payment	190	215	240	285	315	460

The annual payments must be made at the beginning of each year. The judge will approve an amount that, along with earnings on its investment, will cover the annual payments. Investment of the funds will be limited to savings (at 4% annually) and government securities, at prices and rates currently quoted in *The Wall Street Journal*.

Hoxworth wants to develop a plan for making the annual payments by investing in the following securities (par value = $1000). Funds not invested in these securities will be placed in savings.

Security	**Current Price**	**Rate (%)**	**Years to Maturity**
1	$1055	6.750	3
2	$1000	5.125	4

Assume that interest is paid annually. The plan will be submitted to the judge and, if approved, Hoxworth will be required to pay a trustee the amount that will be required to fund the plan.

a. Use linear programming to find the minimum cash settlement necessary to fund the annual payments.
b. Use the shadow price to determine how much more Hoxworth should be willing to pay now to reduce the payment at the beginning of year 6 to $400,000.
c. Use the shadow price to determine how much more Hoxworth should be willing to pay to reduce the year 1 payment to $150,000.
d. Suppose that the annual payments are to be made at the end of each year. Reformulate the model to accommodate this change. How much would Hoxworth save if this change could be negotiated?

8. The Clark County Sheriff's Department schedules police officers for 8-hour shifts. The beginning times for the shifts are 8:00 A.M., noon, 4:00 P.M., 8:00 P.M., midnight, and 4:00 A.M. An officer beginning a shift at one of these times works for the next 8 hours. During normal weekday operations, the number of officers needed varies depending on the time of day. The department staffing guidelines require the following minimum number of officers on duty:

Time of Day	Minimum Officers on Duty
8:00 A.M.–Noon	5
Noon–4:00 P.M.	6
4:00 P.M.–8:00 P.M.	10
8:00 P.M.–Midnight	7
Midnight–4:00 A.M.	4
4:00 A.M.–8:00 A.M.	6

Determine the number of police officers that should be scheduled to begin the 8-hour shifts at each of the six times (8:00 A.M., noon, 4:00 P.M., 8:00 P.M., midnight, and 4:00 A.M.) to minimize the total number of officers required. (*Hint:* Let x_1 = the number of officers beginning work at 8:00 A.M., x_2 = the number of officers beginning work at noon, and so on.)

9. Epsilon Airlines services predominantly the eastern and southeastern United States. The vast majority of Epsilon's customers make reservations through Epsilon's website, but a small percentage of customers make reservations via phones. Epsilon employs call center personnel to handle these reservations and to deal with website reservation system problems and for the rebooking of flights for customers whose plans have changed or whose travel is disrupted. Staffing the call center appropriately is a challenge for Epsilon's management team. Having too many employees on hand is a waste of money, but having too few results in very poor customer service and the potential loss of customers.

Epsilon analysts have estimated the minimum number of call center employees needed by day of the week for the upcoming vacation season (June, July, and the first two weeks of August). These estimates are as follows:

Day	Minimum Number of Employees Needed
Monday	75
Tuesday	50
Wednesday	45
Thursday	60
Friday	90
Saturday	75
Sunday	45

The call center employees work for five consecutive days and then have two consecutive days off. An employee may start work on any day of the week. Each call center employee receives the same salary. Assume that the schedule cycles and ignore start up and stopping of the schedule. Develop a model that will minimize the total number of call center employees needed to meet the minimum requirements. Find the optimal solution. Give the number of call center employees that exceed the minimum required.

10. An investment advisor at Shore Financial Services wants to develop a model that can be used to allocate investment funds among four alternatives: stocks, bonds, mutual funds, and cash. For the coming investment period, the company developed estimates of the annual rate of return and the associated risk for each alternative. Risk is measured using an index between 0 and 1, with higher risk values denoting more volatility and thus more uncertainty.

Investment	Annual Rate of Return (%)	Risk
Stocks	10	0.8
Bonds	3	0.2
Mutual funds	4	0.3
Cash	1	0.0

Because cash is held in a money market fund, the annual return is lower, but it carries essentially no risk. The objective is to determine the portion of funds allocated to each investment alternative in order to maximize the total annual return for the portfolio subject to the risk level the client is willing to tolerate.

Total risk is the sum of the risk for all investment alternatives. For instance, if 40% of a client's funds are invested in stocks, 30% in bonds, 20% in mutual funds, and 10% in cash, the total risk for the portfolio would be $0.40(0.8) + 0.30(0.2) + 0.20(0.3) + 0.10(0.0) = 0.44$. An investment advisor will meet with each client to discuss the client's investment objectives and to determine a maximum total risk value for the client. A maximum total risk value of less than 0.3 would be assigned to a conservative investor; a maximum total risk value of between 0.3 and 0.5 would be assigned to a moderate tolerance to risk; and a maximum total risk value greater than 0.5 would be assigned to a more aggressive investor.

Shore Financial Services specified additional guidelines that must be applied to all clients. The guidelines are as follows:

- No more than 75% of the total investment may be in stocks.
- The amount invested in mutual funds must be at least as much as invested in bonds.
- The amount of cash must be at least 10%, but no more than 30% of the total investment funds.

a. Suppose the maximum risk value for a particular client is 0.4. What is the optimal allocation of investment funds among stocks, bonds, mutual funds, and cash? What is the annual rate of return and the total risk for the optimal portfolio?

b. Suppose the maximum risk value for a more conservative client is 0.18. What is the optimal allocation of investment funds for this client? What is the annual rate of return and the total risk for the optimal portfolio?

c. Another more aggressive client has a maximum risk value of 0.7. What is the optimal allocation of investment funds for this client? What is the annual rate of return and the total risk for the optimal portfolio?

d. Refer to the solution for the more aggressive client in part (c). Would this client be interested in having the investment advisor increase the maximum percentage allowed in stocks or decrease the requirement that the amount of cash must be at least 10% of the funds invested? Explain.

e. What is the advantage of defining the decision variables as is done in this model rather than stating the amount to be invested and expressing the decision variables directly in dollar amounts?

11. Edwards Manufacturing Company purchases two component parts from three different suppliers. The suppliers have limited capacity, and no one supplier can meet all the company's needs. In addition, the suppliers charge different prices for the components. Component price data (in price per unit) are as follows:

	Supplier		
Component	**1**	**2**	**3**
1	$12	$13	$14
2	$10	$11	$10

Each supplier has a limited capacity in terms of the total number of components it can supply. However, as long as Edwards provides sufficient advance orders, each supplier can devote its capacity to component 1, component 2, or any combination of the two components, if the total number of units ordered is within its capacity. Supplier capacities are as follows:

Supplier	1	2	3
Capacity	600	1000	800

If the Edwards production plan for the next period includes 1000 units of component 1 and 800 units of component 2, what purchases do you recommend? That is, how many units of each component should be ordered from each supplier? What is the total purchase cost for the components?

12. The Atlantic Seafood Company (ASC) is a buyer and distributor of seafood products that are sold to restaurants and specialty seafood outlets throughout the Northeast. ASC has a frozen storage facility in New York City that serves as the primary distribution point for all products. One of the ASC products is frozen large black tiger shrimp, which are sized at 16–20 pieces per pound. Each Saturday ASC can purchase more tiger shrimp or sell the tiger shrimp at the existing New York City warehouse market price. The ASC goal is to buy tiger shrimp at a low weekly price and sell it later at a higher price. ASC currently has 20,000 pounds of tiger shrimp in storage. Space is available to store a maximum of 100,000 pounds of tiger shrimp each week. In addition, ASC developed the following estimates of tiger shrimp prices for the next four weeks:

Week	**Price/lb.**
1	$6.00
2	$6.20
3	$6.65
4	$5.55

ASC would like to determine the optimal buying/storing/selling strategy for the next four weeks. The cost to store a pound of shrimp for one week is $0.15, and to account for unforeseen changes in supply or demand, management also indicated that 25,000 pounds of tiger shrimp must be in storage at the end of week 4. Determine the optimal buying/storing/selling strategy for ASC. What is the projected four-week profit?

13. Romans Food Market, located in Saratoga, New York, carries a variety of specialty foods from around the world. Two of the store's leading products use the Romans Food Market name: Romans Regular Coffee and Romans DeCaf Coffee. These coffees are blends of Brazilian Natural and Colombian Mild coffee beans, which are purchased from a distributor located in New York City. Because Romans purchases large quantities, the coffee beans may be purchased on an as-needed basis for a price 10% higher than the market price the distributor pays for the beans. The current market price is \$0.47 per pound for Brazilian Natural and \$0.62 per pound for Colombian Mild. The compositions of each coffee blend are as follows:

	Blend	
Bean	**Regular**	**DeCaf**
Brazilian Natural	75%	40%
Colombian Mild	25%	60%

Romans sells the Regular blend for \$3.60 per pound and the DeCaf blend for \$4.40 per pound. Romans would like to place an order for the Brazilian and Colombian coffee beans that will enable the production of 1000 pounds of Romans Regular coffee and 500 pounds of Romans DeCaf coffee. The production cost is \$0.80 per pound for the Regular blend. Because of the extra steps required to produce DeCaf, the production cost for the DeCaf blend is \$1.05 per pound. Packaging costs for both products are \$0.25 per pound. Formulate a linear programming model that can be used to determine the pounds of Brazilian Natural and Colombian Mild that will maximize the total contribution to profit. What is the optimal solution, and what is the contribution to profit?

14. The production manager for the Classic Boat Corporation must determine how many units of the Classic 21 model to produce over the next four quarters. The company has a beginning inventory of 100 Classic 21 boats, and demand for the four quarters is 2000 units in quarter 1, 4000 units in quarter 2, 3000 units in quarter 3, and 1500 units in quarter 4. The firm has limited production capacity in each quarter. That is, up to 4000 units can be produced in quarter 1, 3000 units in quarter 2, 2000 units in quarter 3, and 4000 units in quarter 4. Each boat held in inventory in quarters 1 and 2 incurs an inventory holding cost of \$250 per unit; the holding cost for quarters 3 and 4 is \$300 per unit. The production costs for the first quarter are \$10,000 per unit; these costs are expected to increase by 10% each quarter because of increases in labor and material costs. Management specified that the ending inventory for quarter 4 must be at least 500 boats.
    a. Formulate a linear programming model that can be used to determine the production schedule that will minimize the total cost of meeting demand in each quarter subject to the production capacities in each quarter and also to the required ending inventory in quarter 4.
    b. Solve the linear program formulated in part (a). Then develop a table that will show for each quarter the number of units to manufacture, the ending inventory, and the costs incurred.
    c. Interpret each of the shadow prices corresponding to the constraints developed to meet demand in each quarter. Based on these shadow prices, what advice would you give the production manager?
    d. Interpret each of the shadow prices corresponding to the production capacity in each quarter. Based on each of these shadow prices, what advice would you give the production manager?

15. Bay Oil produces two types of fuels (regular and super) by mixing three ingredients. The major distinguishing feature of the two products is the octane level required.

Regular fuel must have a minimum octane level of 90 while super must have a level of at least 100. The cost per barrel, octane levels, and available amounts (in barrels) for the upcoming two-week period are shown in the following table. Likewise, the maximum demand for each end product and the revenue generated per barrel are shown.

Input	Cost/Barrel	Octane	Available (barrels)
1	\$16.50	100	110,000
2	\$14.00	87	350,000
3	\$17.50	110	300,000

	Revenue/Barrel	Max Demand (barrels)
Regular	\$18.50	350,000
Super	\$20.00	500,000

Develop and solve a linear programming model to maximize contribution to profit. What is the optimal contribution to profit?

16. The Ferguson Paper Company produces rolls of paper for use in cash registers. The rolls, which are 200 feet long, are produced in widths of $1\frac{1}{2}$, $2\frac{1}{2}$, and $3\frac{1}{2}$ inches. The production process provides 200-foot rolls in 10-inch widths only. The firm must therefore cut the rolls to the desired final product sizes. The seven cutting alternatives and the amount of waste generated by each are as follows:

Cutting Alternative	Number of Rolls			Waste (inches)
	$1\frac{1}{2}$ in.	$2\frac{1}{2}$ in.	$3\frac{1}{2}$ in.	
1	6	0	0	1
2	0	4	0	0
3	2	0	2	0
4	0	1	2	$\frac{1}{2}$
5	1	3	0	1
6	1	2	1	0
7	4	0	1	$\frac{1}{2}$

The minimum requirements for the three products are

Roll Width (inches)	$1\frac{1}{2}$	$2\frac{1}{2}$	$3\frac{1}{2}$
Units	1000	2000	4000

a. If the company wants to minimize the number of 10-inch rolls that must be manufactured, how many 10-inch rolls will be processed on each cutting alternative? How many rolls are required, and what is the total waste (inches)?
b. If the company wants to minimize the waste generated, how many 10-inch rolls will be processed on each cutting alternative? How many rolls are required, and what is the total waste (inches)?
c. What are the differences between parts (a) and (b) of this problem? In this case, which objective do you prefer? Explain. What types of situations would make the other objective more desirable?

17. Frandec Company manufactures, assembles, and rebuilds material handling equipment used in warehouses and distribution centers. One product, called a Liftmaster, is assembled from four components: a frame, a motor, two supports, and a metal strap. Frandec's production

schedule calls for 5000 Liftmasters to be made next month. Frandec purchases the motors from an outside supplier, but the frames, supports, and straps may be either manufactured by the company or purchased from an outside supplier. Manufacturing and purchase costs per unit are shown.

Component	Manufacturing Cost	Purchase Cost
Frame	$38.00	$51.00
Support	$11.50	$15.00
Strap	$ 6.50	$ 7.50

Three departments are involved in the production of these components. The time (in minutes per unit) required to process each component in each department and the available capacity (in hours) for the three departments are as follows:

	Department		
Component	Cutting	Milling	Shaping
Frame	3.5	2.2	3.1
Support	1.3	1.7	2.6
Strap	0.8	—	1.7
Capacity (hours)	350	420	680

a. Formulate and solve a linear programming model for this make-or-buy application. How many of each component should be manufactured and how many should be purchased?
b. What is the total cost of the manufacturing and purchasing plan?
c. How many hours of production time are used in each department?
d. How much should Frandec be willing to pay for an additional hour of time in the shaping department?
e. Another manufacturer has offered to sell frames to Frandec for $45 each. Could Frandec improve its position by pursuing this opportunity? Why or why not?

18. The Two-Rivers Oil Company near Pittsburgh transports gasoline to its distributors by truck. The company recently contracted to supply gasoline distributors in southern Ohio, and it has $600,000 available to spend on the necessary expansion of its fleet of gasoline tank trucks. Three models of gasoline tank trucks are available.

Truck Model	Capacity (gallons)	Purchase Cost	Monthly Operating Cost, Including Depreciation
Super Tanker	5000	$67,000	$550
Regular Line	2500	$55,000	$425
Econo-Tanker	1000	$46,000	$350

The company estimates that the monthly demand for the region will be 550,000 gallons of gasoline. Because of the size and speed differences of the trucks, the number of deliveries or round trips possible per month for each truck model will vary. Trip capacities are estimated at 15 trips per month for the Super Tanker, 20 trips per month for the Regular Line, and 25 trips per month for the Econo-Tanker. Based on maintenance and driver availability, the firm does not want to add more than 15 new vehicles to its fleet. In addition, the company has decided to purchase at least three of the new Econo-Tankers for use on short-run, low-demand routes. As a final constraint, the company does not want more than half the new models to be Super Tankers.

a. If the company wishes to satisfy the gasoline demand with a minimum monthly operating expense, how many models of each truck should be purchased?
b. If the company did not require at least three Econo-Tankers and did not limit the number of Super Tankers to at most half the new models, how many models of each truck should be purchased?

19. The Silver Star Bicycle Company will be manufacturing both men's and women's models of its Easy-Pedal bicycles during the next two months. Management wants to develop a production schedule indicating how many bicycles of each model should be produced in each month. Current demand forecasts call for 150 men's and 125 women's models to be shipped during the first month and 200 men's and 150 women's models to be shipped during the second month. Additional data are shown:

Model	Production Costs	Labor Requirements (hours)		Current Inventory
		Manufacturing	Assembly	
Men's	\$120	2.0	1.5	20
Women's	\$ 90	1.6	1.0	30

Last month the company used a total of 1000 hours of labor. The company's labor relations policy will not allow the combined total hours of labor (manufacturing plus assembly) to increase or decrease by more than 100 hours from month to month. In addition, the company charges monthly inventory at the rate of 2% of the production cost based on the inventory levels at the end of the month. The company would like to have at least 25 units of each model in inventory at the end of the two months.

a. Establish a production schedule that minimizes production and inventory costs and satisfies the labor-smoothing, demand, and inventory requirements. What inventories will be maintained, and what are the monthly labor requirements?
b. If the company changed the constraints so that monthly labor increases and decreases could not exceed 50 hours, what would happen to the production schedule? How much will the cost increase? What would you recommend?

20. Filtron Corporation produces filtration containers used in water treatment systems. Although business has been growing, the demand each month varies considerably. As a result, the company utilizes a mix of part-time and full-time employees to meet production demands. Although this approach provides Filtron with great flexibility, it resulted in increased costs and morale problems among employees. For instance, if Filtron needs to increase production from one month to the next, additional part-time employees have to be hired and trained, and costs go up. If Filtron has to decrease production, the workforce has to be reduced and Filtron incurs additional costs in terms of unemployment benefits and decreased morale. Best estimates are that increasing the number of units produced from one month to the next will increase production costs by \$1.25 per unit, and that decreasing the number of units produced will increase production costs by \$1.00 per unit. In February Filtron produced 10,000 filtration containers but only sold 7500 units; 2500 units are currently in inventory. The sales forecasts for March, April, and May are for 12,000 units, 8000 units, and 15,000 units, respectively. In addition, Filtron has the capacity to store up to 3000 filtration containers at the end of any month. Management would like to determine the number of units to be produced in March, April, and May that will minimize the total cost of the monthly production increases and decreases.

21. Star Power Company is a power company in the Midwest region of the United States. Star buys and sells energy on the spot market. Star can store power in a high-capacity battery that can store up to 60 kWh (kilowatt hours). During a particular period, Star can buy or sell electricity at the market price known as LMP (Locational Marginal Price). The maximum rate that power can be injected or withdrawn from the battery is 20 kWh per period. Star has forecasted the following LMPs for the next 10 periods:

Period	**LMP ($/kWh)**
1	$ 5
2	$27
3	$ 2
4	$25
5	$22
6	$29
7	$24
8	$20
9	$61
10	$66

The battery is full at the beginning of period 1; that is, at the start of the planning horizon, the battery contains 60 kWh of electricity.

a. Develop a linear programming model Star Power can use to determine when to buy and sell electricity in order to maximize profit over these 10 weeks. What is the maximum achievable profit?

b. Your solution to part (a) should result in a battery level of 0 at the end of period 10. Why does this make sense? Modify your model with the requirement that the battery should be full (60 kWh) at the end of period 10. How does this impact the optimal profit?

c. To further investigate the impact of requirements on the battery level at the end of period 10, solve your model from part (b) with the constraint on the ending battery level varying from 0 kWh to 60 kWh in increments of 10 kWh. Develop a graph with profit on the vertical axis and required ending battery level on the horizontal axis. Given that Star has not forecasted LMPs for periods 11, 12, and so on, what ending battery level do you recommend that Star use in its optimization model?

22. TriCity Manufacturing (TCM) makes Styrofoam cups, plates, and sandwich and meal containers. Next week's schedule calls for the production of 80,000 small sandwich containers, 80,000 large sandwich containers, and 65,000 meal containers. To make these containers, Styrofoam sheets are melted and formed into final products using three machines: M1, M2, and M3. Machine M1 can process Styrofoam sheets with a maximum width of 12 inches. The width capacity of machine M2 is 16 inches, and the width capacity of machine M3 is 20 inches. The small sandwich containers require 10-inch-wide Styrofoam sheets; thus, these containers can be produced on each of the three machines. The large sandwich containers require 12-inch-wide sheets; thus, these containers can also be produced on each of the three machines. However, the meal containers require 16-inch-wide Styrofoam sheets, so the meal containers cannot be produced on machine M1. Waste is incurred in the production of all three containers because Styrofoam is lost in the heating and forming process as well as in the final trimming of the product. The amount of waste generated varies depending upon the container produced and the machine used. The following table shows the waste in square inches for each machine and product combination. The waste material is recycled for future use.

Machine	Small Sandwich	Large Sandwich	Meal
M1	20	15	—
M2	24	28	18
M3	32	35	36

Production rates also depend upon the container produced and the machine used. The following table shows the production rates in units per minute for each machine and product combination. Machine capacities are limited for the next week. Time available is 35 hours for machine M1, 35 hours for machine M2, and 40 hours for machine M3.

Machine	Small Sandwich	Large Sandwich	Meal
M1	30	25	—
M2	45	40	30
M3	60	52	44

a. Costs associated with reprocessing the waste material have been increasing. Thus, TCM would like to minimize the amount of waste generated in meeting next week's production schedule. Formulate a linear programming model that can be used to determine the best production schedule.
b. Solve the linear program formulated in part (a) to determine the production schedule. How much waste is generated? Which machines, if any, have idle capacity?

23. EZ-Windows, Inc., manufactures replacement windows for the home remodeling business. In January, the company produced 15,000 windows and ended the month with 9000 windows in inventory. EZ-Windows' management team would like to develop a production schedule for the next three months. A smooth production schedule is obviously desirable because it maintains the current workforce and provides a similar month-to-month operation. However, given the sales forecasts, the production capacities, and the storage capabilities as shown, the management team does not think a smooth production schedule with the same production quantity each month is possible.

	February	March	April
Sales forecast	15,000	16,500	20,000
Production capacity	14,000	14,000	18,000
Storage capacity	6,000	6,000	6,000

The company's cost accounting department estimates that increasing production by one window from one month to the next will increase total costs by $1.00 for each unit increase in the production level. In addition, decreasing production by one unit from one month to the next will increase total costs by $0.65 for each unit decrease in the production level. Ignoring production and inventory carrying costs, formulate and solve a linear programming model that will minimize the cost of changing production levels while still satisfying the monthly sales forecasts.

24. Morton Financial must decide on the percentage of available funds to commit to each of two investments, referred to as A and B, over the next four periods. The following table shows the amount of new funds available for each of the four periods, as well as the cash expenditure required for each investment (negative values) or the cash income from the investment (positive values). The data shown (in thousands of dollars) reflect the amount of expenditure or income if 100% of the funds available in any period are invested in either A or B. For example, if Morton decides to invest 100% of the funds available in any period in investment A, it will incur cash expenditures of \$1000 in period 1, \$800 in period 2, \$200 in period 3, and income of \$200 in period 4. Note, however, that if Morton made the decision to invest 80% in investment A, the cash expenditures or income would be 80% of the values shown.

Period	New Investment Funds Available	Investment A	Investment B
1	\$1500	−\$1000	−\$800
2	\$ 400	−\$ 800	−\$500
3	\$ 500	−\$ 200	−\$300
4	\$ 100	−\$ 200	−\$300

The amount of funds available in any period is the sum of the new investment funds for the period, the new loan funds, the savings from the previous period, the cash income from investment A, and the cash income from investment B. The funds available in any period can be used to pay the loan and interest from the previous period, can be placed in savings, can be used to pay the cash expenditures for investment A, or can be used to pay the cash expenditures for investment B.

Assume an interest rate of 10% per period for savings and an interest rate of 18% per period on borrowed funds. Let

$$S_t = \text{the savings for period } t$$
$$L_t = \text{the new loan funds for period } t$$

Then, in any period t, the savings income from the previous period is $1.1S_{t-1}$ and the loan and interest expenditure from the previous period is $1.18L_{t-1}$.

At the end of period 4, investment A is expected to have a cash value of \$3200 (assuming a 100% investment in A), and investment B is expected to have a cash value of \$2500 (assuming a 100% investment in B). Additional income and expenses at the end of period 4 will be income from savings in period 4 less the repayment of the period 4 loan plus interest.

Suppose that the decision variables are defined as

$$x_1 = \text{the proportion of investment A undertaken}$$
$$x_2 = \text{the proportion of investment B undertaken}$$

For example, if $x_1 = 0.5$, \$500 would be invested in investment A during the first period, and all remaining cash flows and ending investment A values would be multiplied by 0.5. The same holds for investment B. The model must include constraints $x_1 \leq 1$ and $x_2 \leq 1$ to make sure that no more than 100% of the investments can be undertaken.

If no more than \$200 can be borrowed in any period, determine the proportions of investments A and B and the amount of savings and borrowing in each period that will maximize the cash value for the firm at the end of the four periods.

25. Western Family Steakhouse offers a variety of low-cost meals and quick service. Other than management, the steakhouse operates with two full-time employees who work 8 hours per day. The rest of the employees are part-time employees who are scheduled for 4-hour shifts during peak meal times. On Saturdays the steakhouse is open from 11:00 A.M. to 10:00 P.M. Management wants to develop a schedule for part-time employees that will minimize labor costs and still provide excellent customer service. The average wage rate for the part-time employees is $7.60 per hour. The total number of full-time and part-time employees needed varies with the time of day as shown.

Time	Total Number of Employees Needed
11:00 A.M.–Noon	9
Noon–1:00 P.M.	9
1:00 P.M.–2:00 P.M.	9
2:00 P.M.–3:00 P.M.	3
3:00 P.M.–4:00 P.M.	3
4:00 P.M.–5:00 P.M.	3
5:00 P.M.–6:00 P.M.	6
6:00 P.M.–7:00 P.M.	12
7:00 P.M.–8:00 P.M.	12
8:00 P.M.–9:00 P.M.	7
9:00 P.M.–10:00 P.M.	7

One full-time employee comes on duty at 11:00 A.M., works 4 hours, takes an hour off, and returns for another 4 hours. The other full-time employee comes to work at 1:00 P.M. and works the same 4-hours-on, 1-hour-off, 4-hours-on pattern.

a. Develop a minimum-cost schedule for part-time employees.
b. What is the total payroll for the part-time employees? How many part-time shifts are needed? Use the surplus variables to comment on the desirability of scheduling at least some of the part-time employees for 3-hour shifts.
c. Assume that part-time employees can be assigned either a 3-hour or a 4-hour shift. Develop a minimum-cost schedule for the part-time employees. How many part-time shifts are needed, and what is the cost savings compared to the previous schedule?

Case Problem 1 Planning an Advertising Campaign

The Flamingo Grill is an upscale restaurant located in St. Petersburg, Florida. To help plan an advertising campaign for the coming season, Flamingo's management team hired the advertising firm of Haskell & Johnson (HJ). The management team requested HJ's recommendation concerning how the advertising budget should be distributed across television, radio, and online. The budget has been set at $279,000.

In a meeting with Flamingo's management team, HJ consultants provided the following information about the industry exposure effectiveness rating per ad, their estimate of the number of potential new customers reached per ad, and the cost for each ad:

Advertising Media	Exposure Rating per Ad	New Customers per Ad	Cost per Ad
Television	90	4000	$10,000
Radio	25	2000	$ 3000
Online	10	1000	$ 1000

The exposure rating is viewed as a measure of the value of the ad to both existing customers and potential new customers. It is a function of such things as image, message recall, visual and audio appeal, and so on. As expected, the more expensive television advertisement has the highest exposure effectiveness rating along with the greatest potential for reaching new customers.

At this point, the HJ consultants pointed out that the data concerning exposure and reach were only applicable to the first few ads in each medium. For television, HJ stated that the exposure rating of 90 and the 4000 new customers reached per ad were reliable for the first 10 television ads. After 10 ads, the benefit is expected to decline. For planning purposes, HJ recommended reducing the exposure rating to 55 and the estimate of the potential new customers reached to 1500 for any television ads beyond 10. For radio ads, the preceding data are reliable up to a maximum of 15 ads. Beyond 15 ads, the exposure rating declines to 20 and the number of new customers reached declines to 1200 per ad. Similarly, for online ads, the preceding data are reliable up to a maximum of 20; the exposure rating declines to 5 and the potential number of new customers reached declines to 800 for additional ads.

Flamingo's management team accepted maximizing the total exposure rating across all media as the objective of the advertising campaign. Because of management's concern with attracting new customers, management stated that the advertising campaign must reach at least 100,000 new customers. To balance the advertising campaign and make use of all advertising media, Flamingo's management team also adopted the following guidelines:

- Use at least twice as many radio advertisements as television advertisements.
- Use no more than 20 television advertisements.
- The television budget should be at least $140,000.
- The radio advertising budget is restricted to a maximum of $99,000.
- The online advertising budget is to be at least $30,000.

HJ agreed to work with these guidelines and provide a recommendation as to how the $279,000 advertising budget should be allocated among television, radio, and online advertising.

Managerial Report

Develop a model that can be used to determine the advertising budget allocation for the Flamingo Grill. Include a discussion of the following items in your report:

1. A schedule showing the recommended number of television, radio, and online advertisements and the budget allocation for each medium. Show the total exposure and indicate the total number of potential new customers reached.
2. A discussion of how the total exposure would change if an additional $10,000 were added to the advertising budget.
3. A discussion of the ranges for the objective function coefficients. What do the ranges indicate about how sensitive the recommended solution is to HJ's exposure rating coefficients?
4. The resulting media schedule if the objective of the advertising campaign was to maximize the number of potential new customers reached instead of maximizing the total exposure rating.
5. A comparison of the two media schedules resulting from items 1 and 4, respectively. What is your recommendation for the Flamingo Grill's advertising campaign?

Case Problem 2 Schneider's Sweet Shop

Schneider's Sweet Shop specializes in homemade candies and ice cream. Schneider's produces its ice cream in-house, in batches of 50 pounds. The first stage in ice cream making is the blending of ingredients to obtain a mix, which meets prespecified requirements on the percentages of certain constituents of the mix. The desired composition is as follows:

1. Fat	16.00%
2. Serum Solids	8.00%
3. Sugar Solids	16.00%
4. Egg Solids	.35%
5. Stabilizer	.25%
6. Emulsifier	.15%
7. Water	59.25%

The mix can be composed of ingredients from the following list:

Ingredient	**Cost ($/lb.)**
1. 40% Cream	$1.19
2. 23% Cream	.70
3. Butter	2.32
4. Plastic Cream	2.30
5. Butter Oil	2.87
6. 4% Milk	.25
7. Skim Condensed Milk	.35
8. Skim Milk Powder	.65
9. Liquid Sugar	.25
10. Sugared Frozen Fresh Egg Yolk	1.75
11. Powdered Egg Yolk	4.45
12. Stabilizer	2.45
13. Emulsifier	1.68
14. Water	.00

The number of pounds of a constituent found in a pound of an ingredient is shown below. Note that a pound of stabilizer contributes only to the stabilizer requirement (1 pound), 1 pound of emulsifier contributes only to the emulsifier requirement (1 pound), and that water contributes only to the water requirement (1 pound).

Constituent	**Ingredient**													
	1	2	3	4	5	6	7	8	9	10	11	12	13	14
1	.4	.2	.8	.8	.9	.1				.5	.6			
2	.1			.1		.1	.3	1						
3									.7	.1				
4										.4	.4			
5												1		
6													1	
7	.5	.8	.2	.1	.1	.8	.7		.3					1

Young Jack Schneider has recently acquired the shop from his father. Jack's father has in the past used the following mixture: 9.73 pounds of Plastic Cream, 3.03 pounds of Skim Milk Powder, 11.37 pounds of Liquid Sugar, .44 pounds of Sugared Frozen Fresh Egg Yolk, .12 pounds of Stabilizer, .07 pounds of Emulsifier, and 25.24 pounds of water. (The scale at Schneider's is only accurate to 100ths of a pound.) Jack feels that perhaps it is possible to produce the ice cream in a more cost-effective manner. He would like to find the cheapest mix for producing a batch of ice cream which meets the requirements specified above.

Jack is also curious about the cost effect of being a little more flexible in the requirements listed above. He wants to know the cheapest mix if the composition meets the following tolerances:

1. Fat	15.00–17.00%
2. Serum Solids	7.00–9.00%
3. Sugar Solids	15.50–16.50%
4. Egg Solids	.30–.40%
5. Stabilizer	.20–.30%
6. Emulsifier	.10–20%
7. Water	58.00–59.50%

Managerial Report

Write a managerial report that compares the cost of Papa Jack's approach to (a) the cost-minimized approach using the desired composition and (b) the cost-minimized approach with the more flexible requirements. Include the following in your report:

1. The cost of 50 pounds of ice cream under each of the three approaches.
2. The amount of each ingredient used in the mix for each of the three approaches.
3. A recommendation as to which approach should be used.

Case Problem 3 Textile Mill Scheduling

The Scottsville Textile Mill[1] produces five different fabrics. Each fabric can be woven on one or more of the mill's 38 looms. The sales department's forecast of demand for the next month is shown in Table 9.16, along with data on the selling price per yard, variable cost per yard, and purchase price per yard. The mill operates 24 hours a day and is scheduled for 30 days during the coming month.

The mill has two types of looms: dobbie and regular. The dobbie looms are more versatile and can be used for all five fabrics. The regular looms can produce only three of the fabrics. The mill has a total of 38 looms: 8 are dobbie and 30 are regular. The rate of production for each fabric on each type of loom is given in Table 9.17. The time required to change over from producing one fabric to another is negligible and does not have to be considered.

The Scottsville Textile Mill satisfies all demand with either its own fabric or fabric purchased from another mill. Fabrics that cannot be woven at the Scottsville Mill because of limited loom capacity will be purchased from another mill. The purchase price of each fabric is also shown in Table 9.16.

---

[1] This case is based on the Calhoun Textile Mill Case by Jeffrey D. Camm, P. M. Dearing, and Suresh K. Tadisnia, 1987.

TABLE 9.16 MONTHLY DEMAND, SELLING PRICE, VARIABLE COST, AND PURCHASE PRICE DATA FOR SCOTTSVILLE TEXTILE MILL FABRICS

Fabric	Demand (yards)	Selling Price ($/yard)	Variable Cost ($/yard)	Purchase Price ($/yard)
1	16,500	0.99	0.66	0.80
2	22,000	0.86	0.55	0.70
3	62,000	1.10	0.49	0.60
4	7,500	1.24	0.51	0.70
5	62,000	0.70	0.50	0.70

TABLE 9.17 LOOM PRODUCTION RATES FOR THE SCOTTSVILLE TEXTILE MILL

	Loom Rate (yards/hour)	
Fabric	Dobbie	Regular
1	4.63	—
2	4.63	—
3	5.23	5.23
4	5.23	5.23
5	4.17	4.17

Note: Fabrics 1 and 2 can be manufactured only on the dobbie loom.

Managerial Report

Develop a model that can be used to schedule production for the Scottsville Textile Mill, and, at the same time, determine how many yards of each fabric must be purchased from another mill. Include a discussion and analysis of the following items in your report:

1. The final production schedule and loom assignments for each fabric.
2. The projected total contribution to profit.
3. A discussion of the value of additional loom time. (The mill is considering purchasing a ninth dobbie loom. What is your estimate of the monthly profit contribution of this additional loom?)
4. A discussion of the objective coefficients' ranges.
5. A discussion of how the objective of minimizing total costs would provide a different model than the objective of maximizing total profit contribution. (How would the interpretation of the objective coefficients' ranges differ for these two models?)

Case Problem 4 Workforce Scheduling

Davis Instruments has two manufacturing plants located in Atlanta, Georgia. Product demand varies considerably from month to month, causing Davis extreme difficulty in workforce scheduling. Recently Davis started hiring temporary workers supplied by WorkForce Unlimited, a company that specializes in providing temporary employees for firms in the greater Atlanta area. WorkForce Unlimited offered to provide temporary employees under three contract options that differ in terms of the length of employment and the cost. The three options are summarized:

Option	Length of Employment	Cost
1	One month	\$2000
2	Two months	\$4800
3	Three months	\$7500

The longer contract periods are more expensive because WorkForce Unlimited experiences greater difficulty finding temporary workers who are willing to commit to longer work assignments.

Over the next six months, Davis projects the following needs for additional employees:

Month	January	February	March	April	May	June
Employees Needed	10	23	19	26	20	14

Each month, Davis can hire as many temporary employees as needed under each of the three options. For instance, if Davis hires five employees in January under Option 2, WorkForce Unlimited will supply Davis with five temporary workers who will work two months: January and February. For these workers, Davis will have to pay 5(\$4800) = \$24,000. Because of some merger negotiations under way, Davis does not want to commit to any contractual obligations for temporary employees that extend beyond June.

Davis's quality control program requires each temporary employee to receive training at the time of hire. The training program is required even if the person worked for Davis Instruments in the past. Davis estimates that the cost of training is \$875 each time a temporary employee is hired. Thus, if a temporary employee is hired Davis will incur a training cost of \$875 in the first month of hire, but will incur no additional training cost if the employee is on a two- or three-month contract.

Managerial Report

Develop a model that can be used to determine the number of temporary employees Davis should hire each month under each contract plan in order to meet the projected needs at a minimum total cost. Include the following items in your report:

1. A schedule that shows the number of temporary employees that Davis should hire each month for each contract option.
2. A summary table that shows the number of temporary employees that Davis should hire under each contract option, the associated contract cost for each option, and the associated training cost for each option. Provide summary totals showing the total number of temporary employees hired, total contract costs, and total training costs.
3. An explanation of how reducing the cost to train each temporary employee to \$700 per month affects the hiring plan. Discuss the implications that this effect on the hiring plan has for identifying methods for reducing training costs. How much of a reduction in training costs would be required to change the hiring plan based on a training cost of \$875 per temporary employee?
4. A recommendation regarding the decision to hire additional full-time employees if Davis can hire 10 full-time employees at the beginning of January in order to satisfy part of the labor requirements over the next six months. Assume that Davis

can hire full-time employees at \$16.50 per hour, including fringe benefits, and that full-time and temporary employees both work approximately 160 hours per month. What effect would does the hiring of additional full-time employees have on total labor and training costs over the six-month period as compared to hiring only temporary employees?

Case Problem 5 Duke Energy Coal Allocation[2]

Duke Energy manufactures and distributes electricity to customers in the United States and Latin America. Duke Energy acquired Cinergy Corporation in 2005, which had generating facilities and energy customers in Indiana, Kentucky, and Ohio. For these customers Cinergy has been spending \$725 to \$750 million each year for the fuel needed to operate its coal-fired and gas-fired power plants; 92% to 95% of the fuel used is coal. In this region, Duke Energy uses 10 coal-burning generating plants: 5 located inland and 5 located on the Ohio River. Some plants have more than one generating unit. Duke Energy uses 28–29 million tons of coal per year at a cost of approximately \$2 million every day in this region.

Duke Energy purchases coal using fixed-tonnage or variable-tonnage contracts from mines in Indiana (49%), West Virginia (20%), Ohio (12%), Kentucky (11%), Illinois (5%), and Pennsylvania (3%). Duke Energy must purchase all of the coal contracted for on fixed-tonnage contracts, but on variable-tonnage contracts it can purchase varying amounts up to the limit specified in the contract. The coal is shipped from the mines to Duke Energy's generating facilities in Ohio, Kentucky, and Indiana. The cost of coal varies from \$19 to \$35 per ton, and transportation/delivery charges range from \$1.50 to \$5.00 per ton.

A model is used to determine the megawatt-hours (MWh) of electricity that each generating unit is expected to produce and to provide a measure of each generating unit's efficiency, referred to as the heat rate. The heat rate is the total British thermal units (BTUs) required to produce 1 kilowatt-hour (kWh) of electrical power.

Coal Allocation Model

Duke Energy uses a linear programming model, called the coal allocation model, to allocate coal to its generating facilities. The objective of the coal allocation model is to determine the lowest-cost method for purchasing and distributing coal to the generating units. The supply/availability of the coal is determined by the contracts with the various mines, and the demand for coal at the generating units is determined indirectly by the megawatt-hours of electricity each unit must produce.

The cost to process coal, called the add-on cost, depends upon the characteristics of the coal (moisture content, ash content, BTU content, sulfur content, and grindability) and the efficiency of the generating unit. The add-on cost plus the transportation cost are added to the purchase cost of the coal to determine the total cost to purchase and use the coal.

Current Problem

Duke Energy signed three fixed-tonnage contracts and four variable-tonnage contracts. The company would like to determine the least-cost way to allocate the coal available through

[2] The authors are indebted to Thomas Mason and David Bossee of Duke Energy Corporation, formerly Cinergy Corp., for their contribution to this case problem.

these contracts to five generating units. The relevant data for the three fixed-tonnage contracts are as follows:

Supplier	Number of Tons Contracted For	Cost ($/ton)	BTU/lb
RAG	350,000	22	13,000
Peabody Coal Sales	300,000	26	13,300
American Coal Sales	275,000	22	12,600

For example, the contract signed with RAG requires Duke Energy to purchase 350,000 tons of coal at a price of $22 per ton; each pound of this particular coal provides 13,000 BTUs.

The data for the four variable-tonnage contracts follow:

Supplier	Number of Tons Available	Cost ($/ton)	BTU/lb
Consol, Inc.	200,000	32	12,250
Cyprus Amax	175,000	35	12,000
Addington Mining	200,000	31	12,000
Waterloo	180,000	33	11,300

For example, the contract with Consol, Inc., enables Duke Energy to purchase up to 200,000 tons of coal at a cost of $32 per ton; each pound of this coal provides 12,250 BTUs.

The number of megawatt-hours of electricity that each generating unit must produce and the heat rate provided are as follows:

Generating Unit	Electricity Produced (MWh)	Heat Rate (BTU per kWh)
Miami Fort Unit 5	550,000	10,500
Miami Fort Unit 7	500,000	10,200
Beckjord Unit 1	650,000	10,100
East Bend Unit 2	750,000	10,000
Zimmer Unit 1	1,100,000	10,000

For example, Miami Fort Unit 5 must produce 550,000 megawatt-hours of electricity, and 10,500 BTUs are needed to produce each kilowatt-hour.

The transportation cost and the add-on cost in dollars per ton are shown here:

	Transportation Cost ($/ton)				
Supplier	Miami Fort Unit 5	Miami Fort Unit 7	Beckjord Unit 1	East Bend Unit 2	Zimmer Unit 1
RAG	5.00	5.00	4.75	5.00	4.75
Peabody	3.75	3.75	3.50	3.75	3.50
American	3.00	3.00	2.75	3.00	2.75
Consol	3.25	3.25	2.85	3.25	2.85
Cyprus	5.00	5.00	4.75	5.00	4.75
Addington	2.25	2.25	2.00	2.25	2.00
Waterloo	2.00	2.00	1.60	2.00	1.60

	Add-On Cost ($/ton)				
Supplier	**Miami Fort Unit 5**	**Miami Fort Unit 7**	**Beckjord Unit 1**	**East Bend Unit 2**	**Zimmer Unit 1**
RAG	10.00	10.00	10.00	5.00	6.00
Peabody	10.00	10.00	11.00	6.00	7.00
American	13.00	13.00	15.00	9.00	9.00
Consol	10.00	10.00	11.00	7.00	7.00
Cyprus	10.00	10.00	10.00	5.00	6.00
Addington	5.00	5.00	6.00	4.00	4.00
Waterloo	11.00	11.00	11.00	7.00	9.00

Managerial Report

Prepare a report that summarizes your recommendations regarding Duke Energy's coal allocation problem. Be sure to include information and analysis for the following issues:

1. Determine how much coal to purchase from each of the mining companies and how it should be allocated to the generating units. What is the cost to purchase, deliver, and process the coal?
2. Compute the average cost of coal in cents per million BTUs for each generating unit (a measure of the cost of fuel for the generating units).
3. Compute the average number of BTUs per pound of coal received at each generating unit (a measure of the energy efficiency of the coal received at each unit).
4. Suppose that Duke Energy can purchase an additional 80,000 tons of coal from American Coal Sales as an "all or nothing deal" for $30 per ton. Should Duke Energy purchase the additional 80,000 tons of coal?
5. Suppose that Duke Energy learns that the energy content of the coal from Cyprus Amax is actually 13,000 BTUs per pound. Should Duke Energy revise its procurement plan?
6. Duke Energy has learned from its trading group that Duke Energy can sell 50,000 megawatt-hours of electricity over the grid (to other electricity suppliers) at a price of $30 per megawatt-hour. Should Duke Energy sell the electricity? If so, which generating units should produce the additional electricity?

Appendix 9.1 Excel Solution of Hewlitt Corporation Financial Planning Problem

In Appendix 7.1 we showed how Excel could be used to solve the RMC linear programming problem. To illustrate the use of Excel in solving a more complex linear programming problem, we show the solution to the Hewlitt Corporation financial planning problem presented in Section 9.2.

The spreadsheet formulation and solution of the Hewlitt Corporation problem are shown in Figure 9.10. As described in Appendix 7.1, our practice is to put the data required for the problem in the top part of the worksheet and build the model in the bottom part of the worksheet. The model consists of a set of cells for the decision variables, a cell for the objective function, a set of cells for the left-hand-side functions, and a set of cells for the right-hand sides of the constraints. The cells for the decision variables are also enclosed by a boldface line. Descriptive labels are used to make the spreadsheet easy to read.

FIGURE 9.10 EXCEL SOLUTION FOR THE HEWLITT CORPORATION PROBLEM

Hewlitt

	A	B	C	D	E	F	G	H	I	J	K	L
1	**Hewlitt Corporation Cash Requirements**											
2												
3		**Cash**										
4	**Year**	**Rqmt.**				**Bond**						
5	1	430.000			1	2	3					
6	2	210.000		**Price ($1000)**	1.1500	1.0000	1.3500					
7	3	222.000		**Rate**	0.0888	0.0550	0.1175					
8	4	231.000		**Years to Maturity**	5.0000	6.0000	7.0000					
9	5	240.000										
10	6	195.000		**Annual Savings Multiple**		1.040						
11	7	225.000										
12	8	255.000										
13												
14	**Model**											
15												
16	F	B1	B2	B3	S1	S2	S3	S4	S5	S6	S7	S8
17	1728.794	144.988	187.856	228.188	636.148	501.606	349.682	182.681	0.000	0.000	0.000	0.000
18												
19					**Cash Flow**		**Net Cash**		**Cash**			
20	**Min Funds**	1728.794		**Constraint**	In	Out	**Flow**		**Rqmt.**			
21				Year 1	1728.794	1298.794	430.000	=	430.000			
22				Year 2	711.606	501.606	210.000	=	210.000			
23				Year 3	571.682	349.682	222.000	=	222.000			
24				Year 4	413.681	182.681	231.000	=	231.000			
25				Year 5	240.000	0.000	240.000	=	240.000			
26				Year 6	195.000	0.000	195.000	=	195.000			
27				Year 7	225.000	0.000	225.000	=	225.000			
28				Year 8	255.000	0.000	255.000	=	255.000			
29												

Formulation

The data and descriptive labels are contained in cells A1:G12. The cells in the bottom portion of the spreadsheet contain the key elements of the model required by the Excel Solver.

Decision Variables Cells A17:L17 are reserved for the decision variables. The optimal values (rounded to three places), are shown to be $F = 1728.794$, $B_1 = 144.988$, $B_2 = 187.856$, $B_3 = 228.188$, $S_1 = 636.148$, $S_2 = 501.606$, $S_3 = 349.682$, $S_4 = 182.681$, and $S_5 = S_6 = S_7 = S_8 = 0$.

Objective Function The formula =A17 has been placed into cell B20 to reflect the total funds required. It is simply the value of the decision variable, F. The total funds required by the optimal solution are shown to be $1,728,794.

Left-Hand Sides The left-hand sides for the eight constraints represent the annual net cash flow. They are placed into cells G21:G28.

Cell G21 = E21 − F21 (Copy to G22:G28)

For this problem, some of the left-hand-side cells reference other cells that contain formulas. These referenced cells provide Hewlitt's cash flow in and cash flow out for each of the eight years.[3] The cells and their formulas are as follows:

Cell E21 = A17
Cell E22 = SUMPRODUCT($E$7:$G$7,$B$17:$D$17)+$F$10*E17
Cell E23 = SUMPRODUCT($E$7:$G$7,$B$17:$D$17)+$F$10*F17
Cell E24 = SUMPRODUCT($E$7:$G$7,$B$17:$D$17)+$F$10*G17
Cell E25 = SUMPRODUCT($E$7:$G$7,$B$17:$D$17)+$F$10*H17
Cell E26 = (1+E7)*B17+F7*C17+G7*D17+F10*I17
Cell E27 = (1+F7)*C17+G7*D17+F10*J17
Cell E28 = (1+G7)*D17+F10*K17
Cell F21 = SUMPRODUCT(E6:G6,B17:D17)+E17
Cell F22 = F17
Cell F23 = G17
Cell F24 = H17
Cell F25 = I17
Cell F26 = J17
Cell F27 = K17
Cell F28 = L17

Right-Hand Sides The right-hand sides for the eight constraints represent the annual cash requirements. They are placed into cells I21:I28.

Cell I21 = B5 (Copy to I22:I28)

Excel Solution

We are now ready to use the information in the worksheet to determine the optimal solution to the Hewlitt Corporation problem. The following steps describe how to use Excel to obtain the optimal solution:

Step 1. Select the **Data** tab from the **Ribbon**
Step 2. Select **Solver** from the **Analysis** group
Step 3. When the **Solver Parameters** dialog box appears (see Figure 9.11):
Enter *B20* in the Set **Objective Cell** box
Select the To**: Min** option
Enter *A17:L17* in the **By Changing Variable Cells** box
Step 4. Select **Add**
When the **Add Constraint** dialog box appears:
Enter *G21:G28* in the left-hand box of the **Cell Reference** box
From the middle drop-down button, select **=**
Enter *I21:I28* in **Constraint** box
Click **OK**

---

[3] The cash flow in is the sum of the positive terms in each constraint equation in the mathematical model, and the cash flow out is the sum of the negative terms in each constraint equation.

FIGURE 9.11 EXCEL SOLVER PARAMETERS DIALOG BOX FOR THE HEWLITT CORPORATION PROBLEM

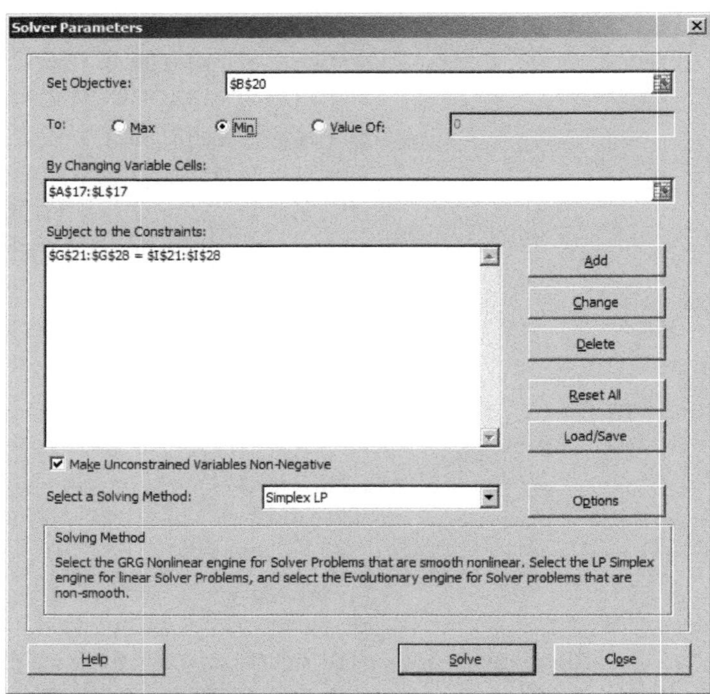

Step 5. When the **Solver Parameters** dialog box reappears (see Figure 9.11):
Click the checkbox for **Make Unconstrained Variables Non-negative**

Step 6. Select the **Select a Solving Method** drop-down button Select **Simplex LP**

Step 7. Choose **Solve**

Step 8. When the **Solver Results** dialog box appears:
Select **Keep Solver Solution**
Select **Sensitivity** in the **Reports** box
Click **OK**

The Solver Parameters dialog box is shown in Figure 9.11. The optimal solution is shown in Figure 9.10; the accompanying sensitivity report is shown in Figure 9.12.

Discussion

Recall that the Excel sensitivity report uses the term *shadow price* to describe the *change* in value of the solution per unit increase in the right-hand side of a constraint. LINGO uses the term *dual price* to describe the *improvement* in value of the solution per unit increase in the right-hand side of a constraint. For maximization problems, the shadow price and dual price are the same; for minimization problems, the shadow price and dual price have opposite signs.

FIGURE 9.12 EXCEL SOLVER SENSITIVITY REPORT FOR THE HEWLITT CORPORATION PROBLEM

Variable Cells

Cell	Name	Final Value	Reduced Cost	Objective Coefficient	Allowable Increase	Allowable Decrease
$A$17	Dollars Needed	1728.794	0.000	1.000	1E+30	1.000
$B$17	Bond 1 - Year 1	144.988	0.000	0.000	0.0670	0.013
$C$17	Bond 2 - Year 2	187.856	0.000	0.000	0.0128	0.020
$D$17	Bond 3 - Year 3	228.188	0.000	0.000	0.0229	0.750
$E$17	Savings Year 1	636.148	0.000	0.000	0.1096	0.055
$F$17	Savings Year 2	501.606	0.000	0.000	0.1433	0.057
$G$17	Savings Year 3	349.682	0.000	0.000	0.2109	0.059
$H$17	Savings Year 4	182.681	0.000	0.000	0.4136	0.061
$I$17	Savings Year 5	0.000	0.064	0.000	1E+30	0.064
$J$17	Savings Year 6	0.000	0.013	0.000	1E+30	0.013
$K$17	Savings Year 7	0.000	0.021	0.000	1E+30	0.021
$L$17	Savings Year 8	0.000	0.671	0.000	1E+30	0.671

Constraints

Cell	Name	Final Value	Shadow Price	Constraint R.H. Side	Allowable Increase	Allowable Decrease
$G$21	Year 1 Flow	430.000	1.000	430.000	1E+30	1728.794
$G$22	Year 2 Flow	210.000	0.962	210.000	1E+30	661.594
$G$23	Year 3 Flow	222.000	0.925	222.000	1E+30	521.670
$G$24	Year 4 Flow	231.000	0.889	231.000	1E+30	363.669
$G$25	Year 5 Flow	240.000	0.855	240.000	1E+30	189.988
$G$26	Year 6 Flow	195.000	0.760	195.000	2149.928	157.856
$G$27	Year 7 Flow	225.000	0.719	225.000	3027.962	198.188
$G$28	Year 8 Flow	225.000	0.671	225.000	1583.882	255.000

CHAPTER 10

Distribution and Network Models

CONTENTS

The models discussed in this chapter belong to a special class of linear programming problems called *network flow* problems. We begin by discussing models commonly encountered when dealing with problems related to supply chains, specifically transportation and transshipment problems. We then consider three other types of network problems: assignment problems, shortest-route problems, and maximal flow problems.

In each case, we present a graphical representation of the problem in the form of a *network*. We then show how the problem can be formulated and solved as a linear program. In the last section of the chapter we present a production and inventory problem that is an interesting application of the transshipment problem.

10.1 Supply Chain Models

A **supply chain** describes the set of all interconnected resources involved in producing and distributing a product. For instance, a supply chain for automobiles could include raw material producers, automotive-parts suppliers, distribution centers for storing automotive parts, assembly plants, and car dealerships. All the materials needed to produce a finished automobile must flow through the supply chain. In general, supply chains are designed to satisfy customer demand for a product at minimum cost. Those that control the supply chain must make decisions such as where to produce the product, how much should be produced, and where it should be sent. We will look at two specific types of problems common in supply chain models that can be solved using linear programing: transportation problems and transshipment problems.

Transportation Problem

The **transportation problem** arises frequently in planning for the distribution of goods and services from several supply locations to several demand locations. Typically, the quantity of goods available at each supply location (origin) is limited, and the quantity of goods needed at each of several demand locations (destinations) is known. The usual objective in a transportation problem is to minimize the cost of shipping goods from the origins to the destinations.

Let us illustrate by considering a transportation problem faced by Foster Generators. This problem involves the transportation of a product from three plants to four distribution centers. Foster Generators operates plants in Cleveland, Ohio; Bedford, Indiana; and York, Pennsylvania. Production capacities over the next three-month planning period for one particular type of generator are as follows:

Origin	Plant		Three-Month Production Capacity (units)
1	Cleveland		5,000
2	Bedford		6,000
3	York		2,500
		Total	13,500

The firm distributes its generators through four regional distribution centers located in Boston, Chicago, St. Louis, and Lexington; the three-month forecast of demand for the distribution centers is as follows:

Destination	Distribution Center	Three-Month Demand Forecast (units)
1	Boston	6,000
2	Chicago	4,000
3	St. Louis	2,000
4	Lexington	1,500
	Total	13,500

Management would like to determine how much of its production should be shipped from each plant to each distribution center. Figure 10.1 shows graphically the 12 distribution routes Foster can use. Such a graph is called a **network**; the circles are referred to as

FIGURE 10.1 THE NETWORK REPRESENTATION OF THE FOSTER GENERATORS TRANSPORTATION PROBLEM

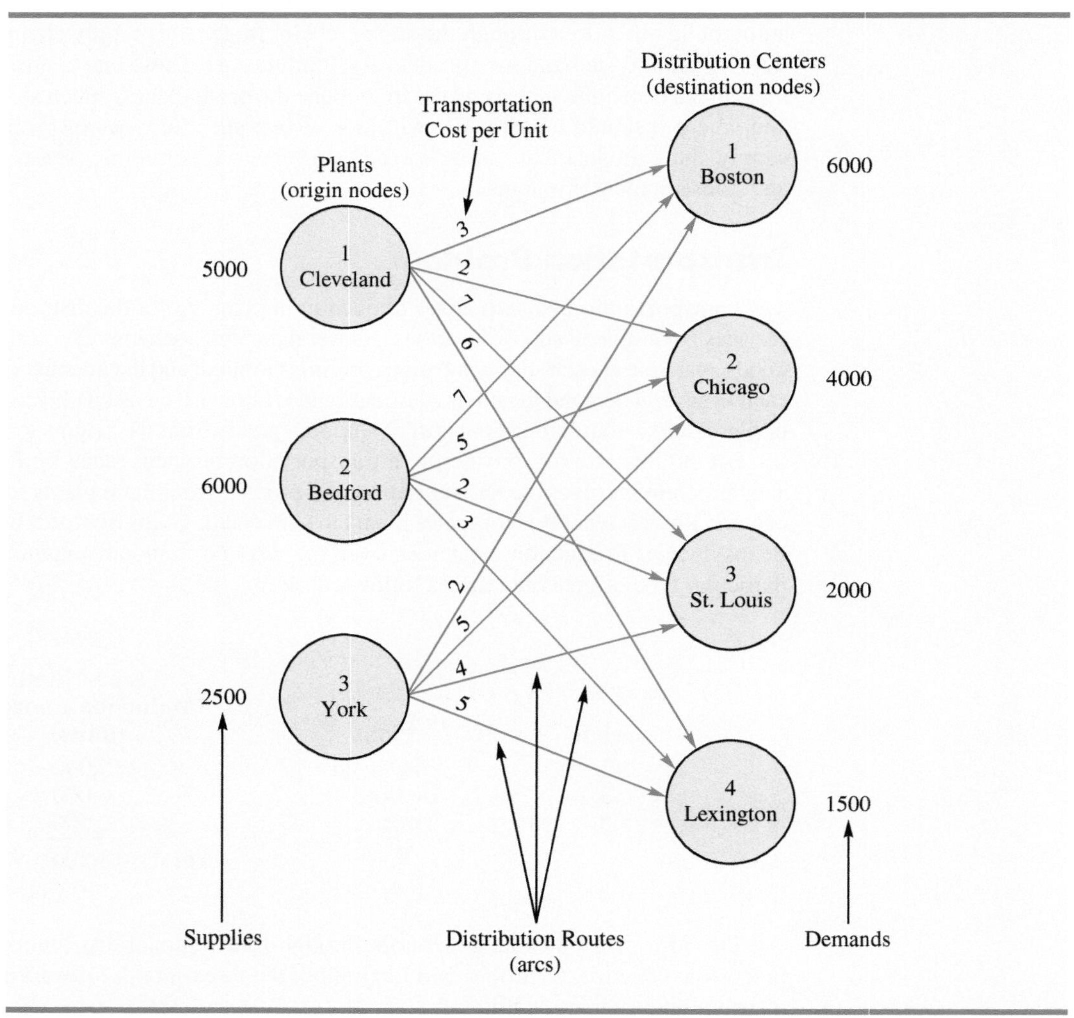

TABLE 10.1 TRANSPORTATION COST PER UNIT FOR THE FOSTER GENERATORS TRANSPORTATION PROBLEM

	Destination			
Origin	Boston	Chicago	St. Louis	Lexington
Cleveland	3	2	7	6
Bedford	7	5	2	3
York	2	5	4	5

nodes and the lines connecting the nodes as arcs. Each origin and destination is represented by a node, and each possible shipping route is represented by an arc. The amount of the supply is written next to each origin node, and the amount of the demand is written next to each destination node. The goods shipped from the origins to the destinations represent the flow in the network. Note that the direction of flow (from origin to destination) is indicated by the arrows.

Try Problem 1 for practice in developing a network model of a transportation problem.

For Foster's transportation problem, the objective is to determine the routes to be used and the quantity to be shipped via each route that will provide the minimum total transportation cost. The cost for each unit shipped on each route is given in Table 10.1 and is shown on each arc in Figure 10.1.

A linear programming model can be used to solve this transportation problem. We use double-subscripted decision variables, with x_{11} denoting the number of units shipped from origin 1 (Cleveland) to destination 1 (Boston), x_{12} denoting the number of units shipped from origin 1 (Cleveland) to destination 2 (Chicago), and so on. In general, the decision variables for a transportation problem having m origins and n destinations are written as follows:

The first subscript identifies the "from" node of the corresponding arc and the second subscript identifies the "to" node of the arc.

$$x_{ij} = \text{number of units shipped from origin } i \text{ to destination } j$$
$$\text{where } i = 1, 2, \ldots, m \text{ and } j = 1, 2, \ldots, n$$

Because the objective of the transportation problem is to minimize the total transportation cost, we can use the cost data in Table 10.1 or on the arcs in Figure 10.1 to develop the following cost expressions:

$$\begin{aligned}
&\text{Transportation costs for} \\
&\text{units shipped from Cleveland} = 3x_{11} + 2x_{12} + 7x_{13} + 6x_{14} \\
&\text{Transportation costs for} \\
&\text{units shipped from Bedford} = 7x_{21} + 5x_{22} + 2x_{23} + 3x_{24} \\
&\text{Transportation costs for} \\
&\text{units shipped from York} = 2x_{31} + 5x_{32} + 4x_{33} + 5x_{34}
\end{aligned}$$

The sum of these expressions provides the objective function showing the total transportation cost for Foster Generators.

Transportation problems need constraints because each origin has a limited supply and each destination has a demand requirement. We consider the supply constraints first. The capacity at the Cleveland plant is 5000 units. With the total number of units shipped from the Cleveland plant expressed as $x_{11} + x_{12} + x_{13} + x_{14}$, the supply constraint for the Cleveland plant is

$$x_{11} + x_{12} + x_{13} + x_{14} \leq 5000 \quad \text{Cleveland supply}$$

With three origins (plants), the Foster transportation problem has three supply constraints. Given the capacity of 6000 units at the Bedford plant and 2500 units at the York plant, the two additional supply constraints are

$$\begin{aligned} x_{21} + x_{22} + x_{23} + x_{24} &\le 6000 \quad \text{Bedford supply} \\ x_{31} + x_{32} + x_{33} + x_{34} &\le 2500 \quad \text{York supply} \end{aligned}$$

With the four distribution centers as the destinations, four demand constraints are needed to ensure that destination demands will be satisfied:

To obtain a feasible solution, the total supply must be greater than or equal to the total demand.

$$\begin{aligned} x_{11} + x_{21} + x_{31} &= 6000 \quad \text{Boston demand} \\ x_{12} + x_{22} + x_{32} &= 4000 \quad \text{Chicago demand} \\ x_{13} + x_{23} + x_{33} &= 2000 \quad \text{St. Louis demand} \\ x_{14} + x_{24} + x_{34} &= 1500 \quad \text{Lexington demand} \end{aligned}$$

Combining the objective function and constraints into one model provides a 12-variable, 7-constraint linear programming formulation of the Foster Generators transportation problem:

$$\begin{array}{ll} \text{Min} & 3x_{11} + 2x_{12} + 7x_{13} + 6x_{14} + 7x_{21} + 5x_{22} + 2x_{23} + 3x_{24} + 2x_{31} + 5x_{32} + 4x_{33} + 5x_{34} \\ \text{s.t.} & \end{array}$$

$$\begin{array}{llllllllllllll} x_{11} + & x_{12} + & x_{13} + & x_{14} & & & & & & & & & \le 5000 \\ & & & & x_{21} + & x_{22} + & x_{23} + & x_{24} & & & & & \le 6000 \\ & & & & & & & & x_{31} + & x_{32} + & x_{33} + & x_{34} & \le 2500 \\ x_{11} & & & & + x_{21} & & & & + x_{31} & & & & = 6000 \\ & x_{12} & & & & + x_{22} & & & & + x_{32} & & & = 4000 \\ & & x_{13} & & & & + x_{23} & & & & + x_{33} & & = 2000 \\ & & & x_{14} & & & & + x_{24} & & & & + x_{34} & = 1500 \end{array}$$

$$x_j \ge 0 \qquad \text{for } i = 1, 2, 3 \text{ and } j = 1, 2, 3, 4$$

Comparing the linear programming formulation to the network in Figure 10.1 leads to several observations: All the information needed for the linear programming formulation is on the network. Each node has one constraint and each arc has one variable. The sum of the variables corresponding to arcs from an origin node must be less than or equal to the origin's supply, and the sum of the variables corresponding to the arcs into a destination node must be equal to the destination's demand.

Can you now use Excel to solve a linear programming model of a transportation problem? Try Problem 2.

We solved the Foster Generators problem using Excel Solver. The optimal objective function values and optimal decision variable values are shown in Figure 10.2, which indicates that the minimum total transportation cost is $39,500. The values for the decision variables show the optimal amounts to ship over each route. For example, 3500 units should be shipped from Cleveland to Boston, and 1500 units should be shipped from Cleveland to Chicago. Other values of the decision variables indicate the remaining shipping quantities and routes. Table 10.2 shows the minimum cost transportation schedule, and Figure 10.3 summarizes the optimal solution on the network.

Problem Variations

The Foster Generators problem illustrates use of the basic transportation model. Variations of the basic transportation model may involve one or more of the following situations:

1. Total supply not equal to total demand
2. Maximization objective function
3. Route capacities or route minimums
4. Unacceptable routes

FIGURE 10.2 OPTIMAL SOLUTION FOR THE FOSTER GENERATORS TRANSPORTATION PROBLEM

Objective Cell (Min)

Name	Original Value	Final Value
Minimize Total Cost	0.000	39500.000

Variable Cells

Model Variable	Name	Original Value	Final Value	Integer
X11	Cleveland to Boston	0.000	3500.000	Contin
X12	Cleveland to Chicago	0.000	1500.000	Contin
X13	Cleveland to St. Louis	0.000	0.000	Contin
X14	Cleveland to Lexington	0.000	0.000	Contin
X21	Bedford to Boston	0.000	0.000	Contin
X22	Bedford to Chicago	0.000	2500.000	Contin
X23	Bedford to St. Louis	0.000	2000.000	Contin
X24	Bedford to Lexington	0.000	1500.000	Contin
X31	York to Boston	0.000	2500.000	Contin
X32	York to Chicago	0.000	0.000	Contin
X33	York to St. Louis	0.000	0.000	Contin
X34	York to Lexington	0.000	0.000	Contin

Foster

TABLE 10.2 OPTIMAL SOLUTION TO THE FOSTER GENERATORS TRANSPORTATION PROBLEM

Route		Units	Cost	Total
From	To	Shipped	per Unit	Cost
Cleveland	Boston	3500	$3	$10,500
Cleveland	Chicago	1500	$2	$ 3,000
Bedford	Chicago	2500	$5	$12,500
Bedford	St. Louis	2000	$2	$ 4,000
Bedford	Lexington	1500	$3	$ 4,500
York	Boston	2500	$2	$ 5,000
				$39,500

With slight modifications in the linear programming model, we can easily accommodate these situations.

Total Supply Not Equal to Total Demand Often *the total supply is not equal to the total demand.* If total supply exceeds total demand, no modification in the linear programming formulation is necessary. Excess supply will appear as slack in the linear programming solution. Slack for any particular origin can be interpreted as the unused supply or amount not shipped from the origin.

Whenever total supply is less than total demand, the model does not determine how the unsatisfied demand is handled (e.g., backorders). The manager must handle this aspect of the problem.

If total supply is less than total demand, the linear programming model of a transportation problem will not have a feasible solution. In this case, we modify the network representation by adding a **dummy origin** with a supply equal to the difference between the total demand and the total supply. With the addition of the dummy origin and an arc from the

FIGURE 10.3 NETWORK DIAGRAM FOR THE OPTIMAL SOLUTION TO THE FOSTER GENERATORS TRANSPORTATION PROBLEM

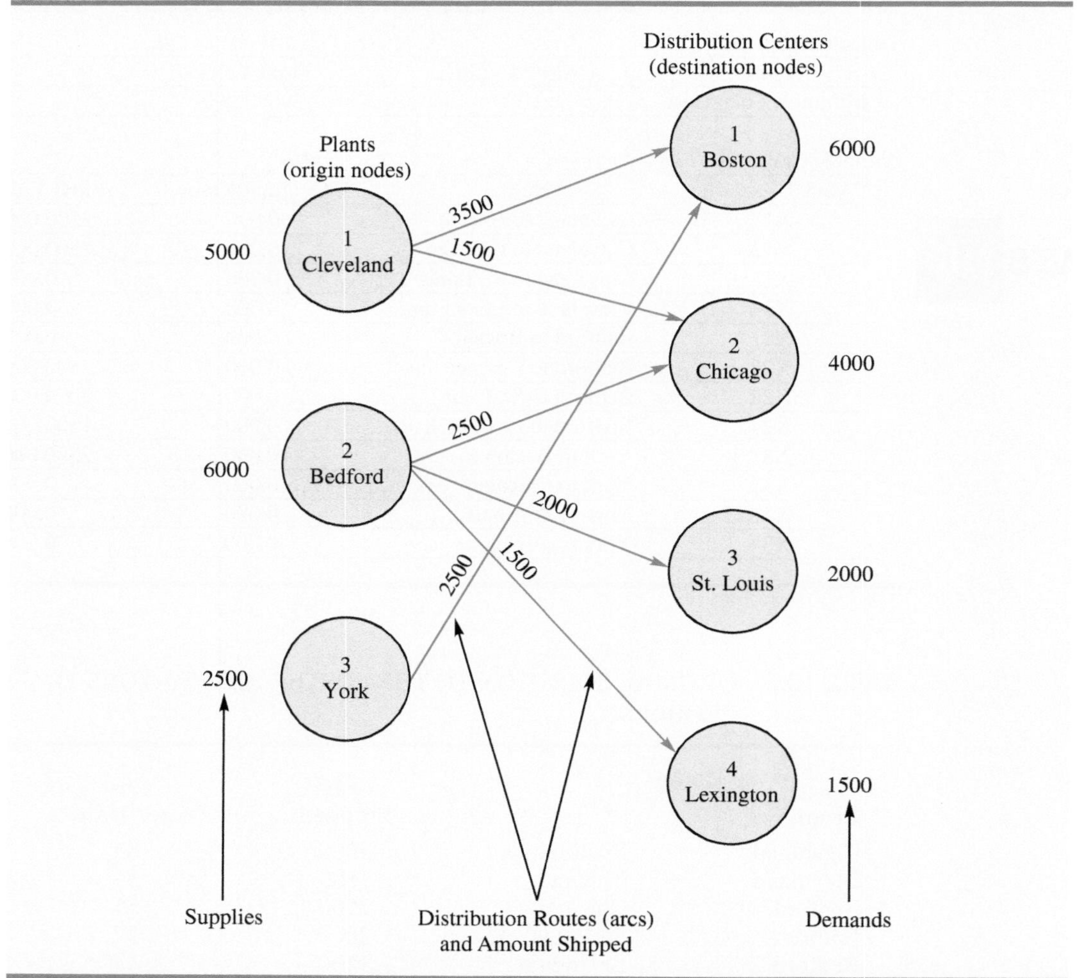

dummy origin to each destination, the linear programming model will have a feasible solution. A zero cost per unit is assigned to each arc leaving the dummy origin so that the value of the optimal solution for the revised problem will represent the shipping cost for the units actually shipped (no shipments actually will be made from the dummy origin). When the optimal solution is implemented, the destinations showing shipments being received from the dummy origin will be the destinations experiencing a shortfall or unsatisfied demand.

Try Problem 6 for practice with a case in which demand is greater than supply with a maximization objective.

Maximization Objective Function In some transportation problems, the objective is to find a solution that maximizes profit or revenue. Using the values for profit or revenue per unit as coefficients in the objective function, we simply solve a maximization rather than a minimization linear program. This change does not affect the constraints.

Route Capacities or Route Minimums The linear programming formulation of the transportation problem also can accommodate capacities or minimum quantities for one or more of the routes. For example, suppose that in the Foster Generators problem the York–Boston route (origin 3 to destination 1) had a capacity of 1000 units because of limited space availability on its normal mode of transportation. With x_{31} denoting the amount shipped from York to Boston, the route capacity constraint for the York–Boston route would be

$$x_{31} \leq 1000$$

Similarly, route minimums can be specified. For example,

$$x_{22} \geq 2000$$

would guarantee that a previously committed order for a Bedford–Chicago delivery of at least 2000 units would be maintained in the optimal solution.

Unacceptable Routes Finally, establishing a route from every origin to every destination may not be possible. To handle this situation, we simply drop the corresponding arc from the network and remove the corresponding variable from the linear programming formulation. For example, if the Cleveland–St. Louis route were unacceptable or unusable, the arc from Cleveland to St. Louis could be dropped in Figure 10.1, and x_{13} could be removed from the linear programming formulation. Solving the resulting 11-variable, 7-constraint model would provide the optimal solution while guaranteeing that the Cleveland–St. Louis route is not used.

A General Linear Programming Model

To show the general linear programming model for a transportation problem with m origins and n destinations, we use the following notation:

x_{ij} = number of units shipped from origin i to destination j
c_{ij} = cost per unit of shipping from origin i to destination j
s_i = supply or capacity in units at origin i
d_j = demand in units at destination j

The general linear programming model is as follows:

$$\begin{aligned} \text{Min} \quad & \sum_{i=1}^{m} \sum_{j=1}^{n} c_{ij} x_{ij} \\ \text{s.t.} \quad & \\ & \sum_{j=1}^{n} x_{ij} \leq s_i \qquad i = 1, 2, \ldots, m \quad \text{Supply} \\ & \sum_{i=1}^{m} x_{ij} = d_j \qquad j = 1, 2, \ldots, n \quad \text{Demand} \\ & x_{ij} \geq 0 \qquad \text{for all } i \text{ and } j \end{aligned}$$

As mentioned previously, we can add constraints of the form $x_{ij} \leq L_{ij}$ if the route from origin i to destination j has capacity L_{ij}. A transportation problem that includes constraints of this type is called a **capacitated transportation problem**. Similarly, we can add route minimum constraints of the form $x_{ij} \geq M_{ij}$ if the route from origin i to destination j must handle at least M_{ij} units.

The Q.M. in Action, Optimizing Freight Car Assignments at Union Pacific, describes how Union Pacific railroad used an optimization model to solve a transportation problem of assigning empty freight cars to customer requests.

Q.M. *in* ACTION

*OPTIMIZING FREIGHT CAR ASSIGNMENTS AT UNION PACIFIC**

Union Pacific (UP) is one of the largest railroads in North America. It owns over 100,000 freight cars, which it uses to service its customers via a network of over 30,000 miles of railroad track. In response to customer demand, UP moves empty freight cars to its customer locations, where the cars are loaded. UP then transports the loaded cars to destinations designated by the customers.

At any point in time, Union Pacific may have hundreds of customer requests for empty freight cars to transport their products. Empty freight cars are typically scattered throughout UP's rail network at previous delivery destinations. A day-to-day decision faced by UP operations managers is how to assign these empty freight cars to current freight car requests from its customers. The assignments need to be cost effective but also must meet the customers' needs in terms of service time.

UP partnered with researchers from Purdue University to develop an optimization model to assist with the empty freight car assignment problem. In order to be useful, the model had to be simple enough to be solved quickly and had to run within UP's existing information systems. A transportation model was developed, with supply being the empty freight cars at their current locations and demand being the current and forecasted requests at the customer locations. The objective function includes not just the cost of transporting the cars, but other factors such as early and late delivery penalties and customer priority. This allows the managers to trade off a variety of factors with the cost of assignments to ensure that the proper level of service is achieved. The model outputs the number of empty cars to move from each current location to the locations of customers requesting cars. The model is used on a daily basis for operations planning and is also used to study the potential impact of changes in operational policies.

*Based on A. Narisetty et al., "An Optimization Model for Empty Freight Car Assignment at Union Pacific Railroad," *Interfaces* 38, no. 2 (March/April 2008): 89–102.

Transshipment Problem

The **transshipment problem** is an extension of the transportation problem in which intermediate nodes, referred to as *transshipment nodes*, are added to account for locations such as warehouses. In this more general type of distribution problem, shipments may be made between any pair of the three general types of nodes: origin nodes, transshipment nodes, and destination nodes. For example, the transshipment problem permits shipments of goods from origins to intermediate nodes and on to destinations, from one origin to another origin, from one intermediate location to another, from one destination location to another, and directly from origins to destinations.

As was true for the transportation problem, the supply available at each origin is limited, and the demand at each destination is specified. The objective in the transshipment problem is to determine how many units should be shipped over each arc in the network so that all destination demands are satisfied with the minimum possible transportation cost.

Try Problem 11, part (a), for practice in developing a network representation of a transshipment problem.

Let us consider the transshipment problem faced by Ryan Electronics. Ryan is an electronics company with production facilities in Denver and Atlanta. Components produced at either facility may be shipped to either of the firm's regional warehouses, which are located in Kansas City and Louisville. From the regional warehouses, the firm supplies retail outlets in Detroit, Miami, Dallas, and New Orleans. The key features of the problem are shown in the network model depicted in Figure 10.4. Note that the supply at each origin and demand at each destination are shown in the left and right margins, respectively. Nodes 1 and 2 are the origin nodes; nodes 3 and 4 are the transshipment nodes; and nodes 5, 6, 7, and 8 are the destination nodes. The transportation cost per unit for each distribution route is shown in Table 10.3 and on the arcs of the network model in Figure 10.4.

FIGURE 10.4 NETWORK REPRESENTATION OF THE RYAN ELECTRONICS TRANSSHIPMENT PROBLEM

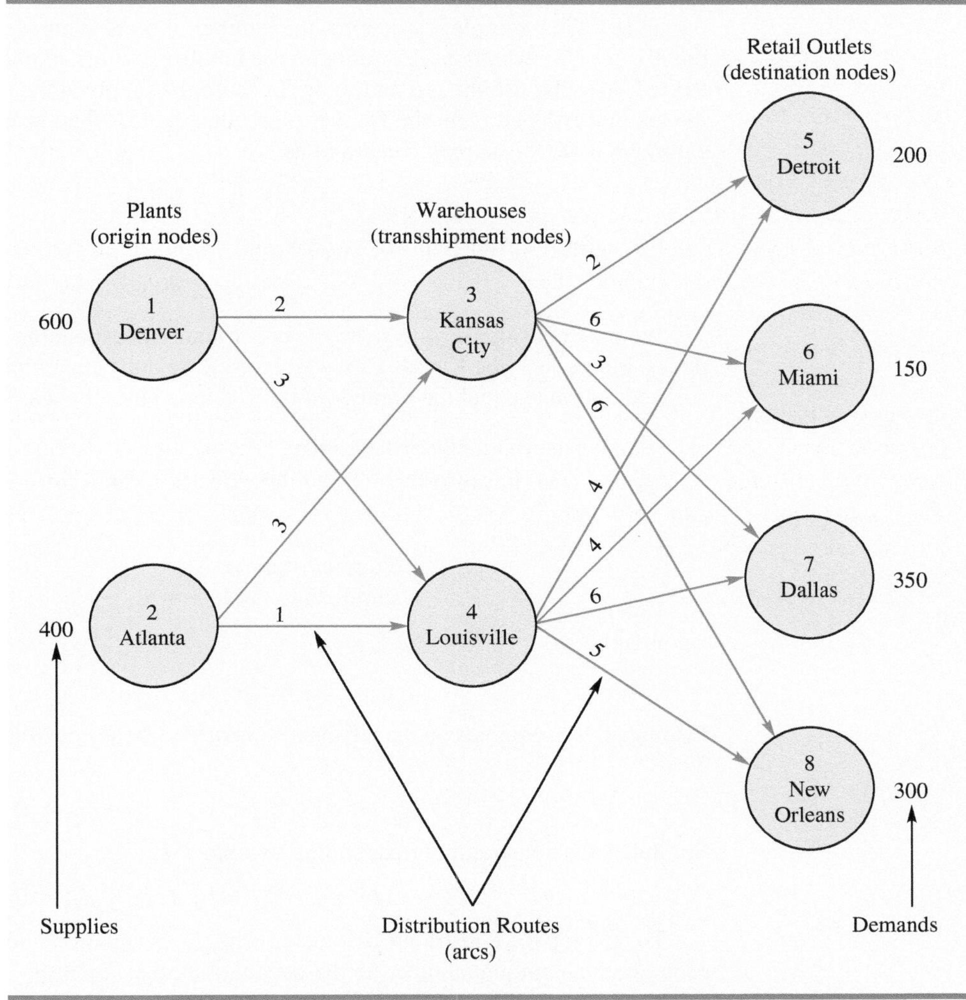

TABLE 10.3 TRANSPORTATION COST PER UNIT FOR THE RYAN ELECTRONICS TRANSSHIPMENT PROBLEM

	Warehouse	
Plant	**Kansas City**	**Louisville**
Denver	2	3
Atlanta	3	1

	Retail Outlet			
Warehouse	**Detroit**	**Miami**	**Dallas**	**New Orleans**
Kansas City	2	6	3	6
Louisville	4	4	6	5

As with the transportation problem, we can formulate a linear programming model of the transshipment problem from a network representation. Again, we need a constraint for each node and a variable for each arc. Let x_{ij} denote the number of units shipped from node i to node j. For example, x_{13} denotes the number of units shipped from the Denver plant to the Kansas City warehouse, x_{14} denotes the number of units shipped from the Denver plant to the Louisville warehouse, and so on. Because the supply at the Denver plant is 600 units, the amount shipped from the Denver plant must be less than or equal to 600. Mathematically, we write this supply constraint as

$$x_{13} + x_{14} \leq 600$$

Similarly, for the Atlanta plant we have

$$x_{23} + x_{24} \leq 400$$

We now consider how to write the constraints corresponding to the two transshipment nodes. For node 3 (the Kansas City warehouse), we must guarantee that the number of units shipped out must equal the number of units shipped into the warehouse. If

$$\text{Number of units shipped out of node 3} = x_{35} + x_{36} + x_{37} + x_{38}$$

and

$$\text{Number of units shipped into node 3} = x_{13} + x_{23}$$

we obtain

$$x_{35} + x_{36} + x_{37} + x_{38} = x_{13} + x_{23}$$

Placing all the variables on the left-hand side provides the constraint corresponding to node 3 as

$$-x_{13} - x_{23} + x_{35} + x_{36} + x_{37} + x_{38} = 0$$

Similarly, the constraint corresponding to node 4 is

$$-x_{14} - x_{24} + x_{45} + x_{46} + x_{47} + x_{48} = 0$$

To develop the constraints associated with the destination nodes, we recognize that for each node the amount shipped to the destination must equal the demand. For example, to satisfy the demand for 200 units at node 5 (the Detroit retail outlet), we write

$$x_{35} + x_{45} = 200$$

Similarly, for nodes 6, 7, and 8, we have

$$x_{36} + x_{46} = 150$$
$$x_{37} + x_{47} = 350$$
$$x_{38} + x_{48} = 300$$

Try Problem 11, parts (b) and (c), for practice in developing the linear programming model and in solving a transshipment problem on the computer.

As usual, the objective function reflects the total shipping cost over the 12 shipping routes. Combining the objective function and constraints leads to a 12-variable, 8-constraint linear programming model of the Ryan Electronics transshipment problem (see Figure 10.5). Figure 10.6 shows the optimal solution from the answer report, and Table 10.4 summarizes the optimal solution.

As mentioned at the beginning of this section, in the transshipment problem, arcs may connect any pair of nodes. All such shipping patterns are possible in a transshipment

FIGURE 10.5 LINEAR PROGRAMMING FORMULATION OF THE RYAN ELECTRONICS TRANSSHIPMENT PROBLEM

$$
\begin{array}{lll}
\text{Min} & 2x_{13} + 3x_{14} + 3x_{23} + 1x_{24} + 2x_{35} + 6x_{36} + 3x_{37} + 6x_{38} + 4x_{45} + 4x_{46} + 6x_{47} + 5x_{48} & \\
\text{s.t.} & & \\
& x_{13} + x_{14} \le 600 & \text{Origin node} \\
& x_{23} + x_{24} \le 400 & \text{constraints} \\
& -x_{13} - x_{23} + x_{35} + x_{36} + x_{37} + x_{38} = 0 & \text{Transshipment node} \\
& -x_{14} - x_{24} + x_{45} + x_{46} + x_{47} + x_{48} = 0 & \text{constraints} \\
& x_{35} + x_{45} = 200 & \\
& x_{36} + x_{46} = 150 & \text{Destination node} \\
& x_{37} + x_{47} = 350 & \text{constraints} \\
& x_{38} + x_{48} = 300 & \\
& x_{ij} \ge 0 \text{ for all } i \text{ and } j &
\end{array}
$$

FIGURE 10.6 OPTIMAL SOLUTION FOR THE RYAN ELECTRONICS TRANSSHIPMENT PROBLEM

Objective Cell (Min)

Name	Original Value	Final Value
Minimize Total Cost	0.000	5200.000

Variable Cells

Model Variable	Name	Original Value	Final Value	Integer
X13	Denver–Kansas City	0.000	550.000	Contin
X14	Denver–Louisville	0.000	50.000	Contin
X23	Atlanta–Kansas City	0.000	0.000	Contin
X24	Atlanta–Louisville	0.000	400.000	Contin
X35	Kansas City–Detroit	0.000	200.000	Contin
X36	Kansas City–Miami	0.000	0.000	Contin
X37	Kansas City–Dallas	0.000	350.000	Contin
X38	Kansas City–New Orleans	0.000	0.000	Contin
X45	Louisville–Detroit	0.000	0.000	Contin
X46	Louisville–Miami	0.000	150.000	Contin
X47	Louisville–Dallas	0.000	0.000	Contin
X48	Louisville–New Orleans	0.000	300.000	Contin

Ryan

problem. We still require only one constraint per node, but the constraint must include a variable for every arc entering or leaving the node. For origin nodes, the sum of the shipments out minus the sum of the shipments in must be less than or equal to the origin supply. For destination nodes, the sum of the shipments in minus the sum of the shipments out must equal demand. For transshipment nodes, the sum of the shipments out must equal the sum of the shipments in, as before.

For an illustration of this more general type of transshipment problem, let us modify the Ryan Electronics problem. Suppose that it is possible to ship directly from Atlanta to New Orleans at \$4 per unit and from Dallas to New Orleans at \$1 per unit. The network model corresponding to this modified Ryan Electronics problem is shown in Figure 10.7,

TABLE 10.4 OPTIMAL SOLUTION TO THE RYAN ELECTRONICS TRANSSHIPMENT PROBLEM

Route			Cost	
From	To	Units Shipped	per Unit	Total Cost
Denver	Kansas City	550	$2	$1100
Denver	Louisville	50	$3	$ 150
Atlanta	Louisville	400	$1	$ 400
Kansas City	Detroit	200	$2	$ 400
Kansas City	Dallas	350	$3	$1050
Louisville	Miami	150	$4	$ 600
Louisville	New Orleans	300	$5	$1500
				$5200

FIGURE 10.7 NETWORK REPRESENTATION OF THE MODIFIED RYAN ELECTRONICS TRANSSHIPMENT PROBLEM

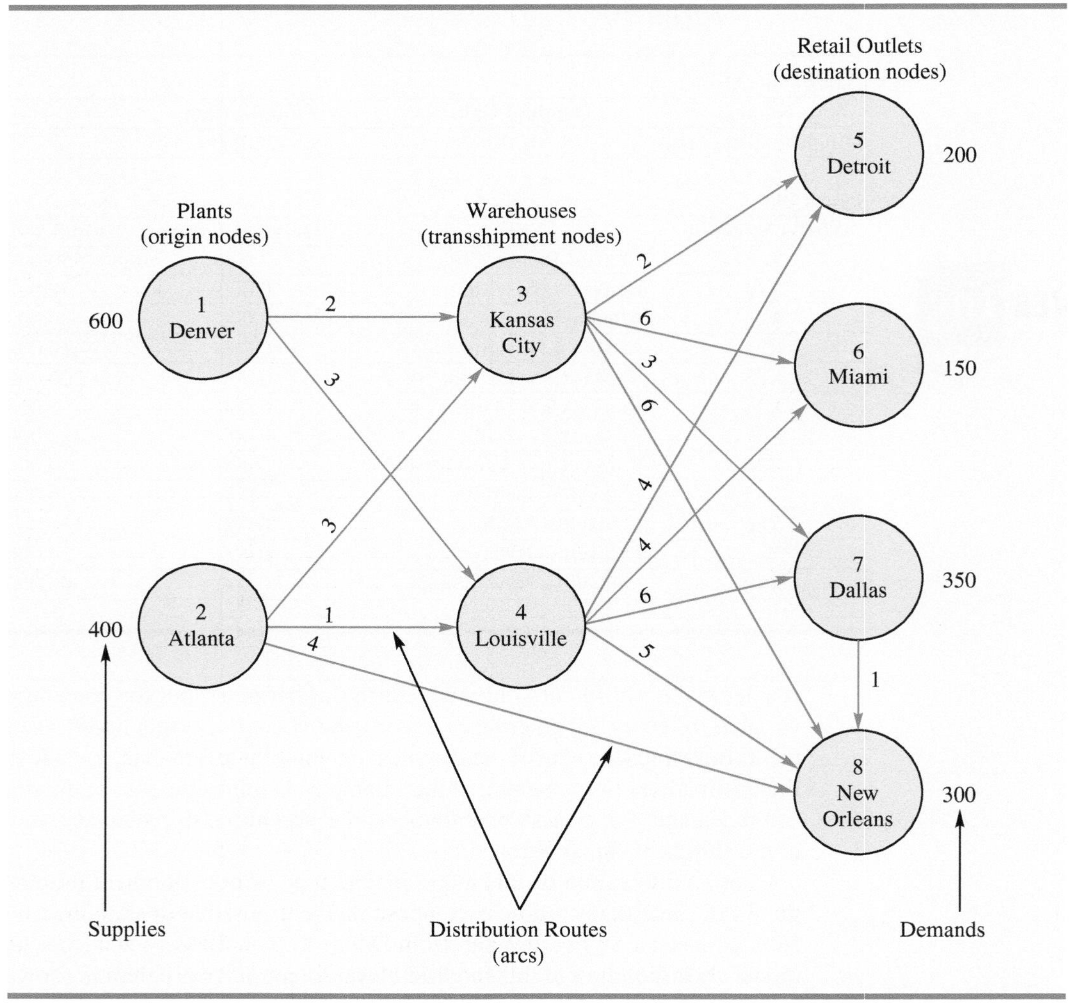

FIGURE 10.8 LINEAR PROGRAMMING FORMULATION OF THE MODIFIED RYAN ELECTRONICS TRANSSHIPMENT PROBLEM

$$\text{Min } 2x_{13} + 3x_{14} + 3x_{23} + 1x_{24} + 2x_{35} + 6x_{36} + 3x_{37} + 6x_{38} + 4x_{45} + 4x_{46} + 6x_{47} + 5x_{48} + 4x_{28} + 1x_{78}$$

s.t.

$$\begin{aligned}
x_{13} + x_{14} &\leq 600 \\
x_{23} + x_{24} + x_{28} &\leq 400 \\
-x_{13} - x_{23} + x_{35} + x_{36} + x_{37} + x_{38} &= 0 \\
-x_{14} - x_{24} + x_{45} + x_{46} + x_{47} + x_{48} &= 0 \\
x_{35} + x_{45} &= 200 \\
x_{36} + x_{46} &= 150 \\
x_{37} + x_{47} - x_{78} &= 350 \\
x_{38} + x_{48} + x_{28} + x_{78} &= 300
\end{aligned}$$

First two	Origin node constraints
Third and fourth	Transshipment node constraints
Last four	Destination node constraints

$x_{ij} \geq 0$ for all i and j

FIGURE 10.9 OPTIMAL SOLUTION FOR THE MODIFIED RYAN ELECTRONICS TRANSSHIPMENT PROBLEM

Objective Cell (Min)

Name	Original Value	Final Value
Total Cost	0.000	4600.000

Variable Cells

Model Variable	Name	Original Value	Final Value	Integer
X13	Denver–Kansas City	0.000	550.000	Contin
X14	Denver–Louisville	0.000	50.000	Contin
X23	Atlanta–Kansas City	0.000	0.000	Contin
X24	Atlanta–Louisville	0.000	100.000	Contin
X35	Kansas City–Detroit	0.000	200.000	Contin
X36	Kansas City–Miami	0.000	0.000	Contin
X37	Kansas City–Dallas	0.000	350.000	Contin
X38	Kansas City–New Orleans	0.000	0.000	Contin
X45	Louisville–Detroit	0.000	0.000	Contin
X46	Louisville–Miami	0.000	150.000	Contin
X47	Louisville–Dallas	0.000	0.000	Contin
X48	Louisville–New Orleans	0.000	0.000	Contin
X28	Atlanta–New Orleans	0.000	300.000	Contin
X78	Dallas–New Orleans	0.000	0.000	Contin

ModifiedRyan

the linear programming formulation is shown in Figure 10.8, and the optimal solution from the answer report is shown in Figure 10.9.

Try Problem 12 for practice working with transshipment problems with this more general structure.

In Figure 10.7 we added two new arcs to the network model. Thus, two new variables are necessary in the linear programming formulation. Figure 10.8 shows that the new variables x_{28} and x_{78} appear in the objective function and in the constraints corresponding to the nodes to which the new arcs are connected. Figure 10.9 shows that the value of the optimal solution has been reduced $600 by allowing these additional shipping routes. The value of $x_{28} = 300$ indicates that 300 units are being shipped directly from Atlanta to New Orleans.

The value of $x_{78} = 0$ indicates that no units are shipped from Dallas to New Orleans in this solution.[1]

Problem Variations

As with transportation problems, transshipment problems may be formulated with several variations, including

1. Total supply not equal to total demand
2. Maximization objective function
3. Route capacities or route minimums
4. Unacceptable routes

The linear programming model modifications required to accommodate these variations are identical to the modifications required for the transportation problem. When we add one or more constraints of the form $x_{ij} \leq L_{ij}$ to show that the route from node i to node j has capacity L_{ij}, we refer to the transshipment problem as a **capacitated transshipment problem**.

A General Linear Programming Model

To show the general linear programming model for the transshipment problem, we use the following notation:

$$
\begin{aligned}
x_{ij} &= \text{number of units shipped from node } i \text{ to node } j \\
c_{ij} &= \text{cost per unit of shipping from node } i \text{ to node } j \\
s_i &= \text{supply at origin node } i \\
d_j &= \text{demand at destination node } j
\end{aligned}
$$

The general linear programming model for the transshipment problem is as follows:

$$
\begin{aligned}
\text{Min} \quad & \sum_{\text{all arcs}} c_{ij}x_{ij} \\
\text{s.t.} \quad & \\
& \sum_{\text{arcs out}} x_{ij} - \sum_{\text{arcs in}} x_{ij} \leq s_i \qquad \text{Origin nodes } i \\
& \sum_{\text{arcs out}} x_{ij} - \sum_{\text{arcs in}} x_{ij} = 0 \qquad \text{Transshipment nodes} \\
& \sum_{\text{arcs in}} x_{ij} - \sum_{\text{arcs out}} x_{ij} = d_j \qquad \text{Destination nodes } j \\
& x_{ij} \geq 0 \text{ for all } i \text{ and } j
\end{aligned}
$$

The Q.M. in Action, Product Sourcing Heuristic at Procter & Gamble, describes a transshipment model used by Procter & Gamble to help make strategic decisions related to sourcing and distribution.

[1]This is an example of a linear programming with alternate optimal solutions. The solution $x_{13} = 600$, $x_{14} = 0$, $x_{23} = 0$, $x_{24} = 150$, $x_{28} = 250$, $x_{35} = 200$, $x_{36} = 0$, $x_{37} = 400$, $x_{38} = 0$, $x_{45} = 0$, $x_{46} = 150$, $x_{47} = 0$, $x_{48} = 0$, $x_{78} = 50$ is also optimal. Thus, in this solution both new routes are used: $x_{28} = 250$ units are shipped from Atlanta to New Orleans and $x_{78} = 50$ units are shipped from Dallas to New Orleans.

NOTES AND COMMENTS

1. Supply chain models used in practice usually lead to large linear programs. Problems with 100 origins and 100 destinations are not unusual. Such a problem would involve $(100 \times 100) = 10{,}000$ variables.
2. To handle a situation in which some routes may be unacceptable, we stated that you could drop the corresponding arc from the network and remove the corresponding variable from the linear programming formulation. Another approach often used is to assign an extremely large objective function cost coefficient to any unacceptable arc. If the problem has already been formulated, another option is to add a constraint to the formulation that sets the variable you want to remove equal to zero.
3. The optimal solution to a transportation model will consist of integer values for the decision variables as long as all supply and demand values are integers. The reason is the special mathematical structure of the linear programming model. Each variable appears in exactly one supply and one demand constraint, and all coefficients in the constraint equations are 1 or 0.
4. In the general linear programming formulation of the transshipment problem, the constraints for the destination nodes are often written as

$$\sum_{\text{arcs out}} x_{ij} - \sum_{\text{arcs in}} x_{ij} = -d_j$$

The advantage of writing the constraints this way is that the left-hand side of each constraint then represents the flow out of the node minus the flow in.

Q.M. *in* ACTION

*PRODUCT SOURCING HEURISTIC AT PROCTER & GAMBLE**

During a period of planning for possible changes to its supply chain, Procter & Gamble (P&G) embarked on a major strategic initiative called the North American Product Sourcing Study. P&G wanted to consolidate its product sources and optimize its distribution system design throughout North America. A decision support system used to aid in this project was called the Product Sourcing Heuristic (PSH) and was based on a transshipment model much like the ones described in this chapter.

In a preprocessing phase, the many P&G products were aggregated into groups that shared the same technology and could be made at the same plant. The PSH employing the transshipment model was then used by product strategy teams responsible for developing product sourcing options for these product groups. The various plants that could produce the product group were the source nodes, the company's regional distribution centers were the transshipment nodes, and P&G's customer zones were the destinations. Direct shipments to customer zones as well as shipments through distribution centers were employed.

The product strategy teams used the heuristic interactively to explore a variety of questions concerning product sourcing and distribution. For instance, the team might be interested in the impact of closing two of five plants and consolidating production in the three remaining plants. The product sourcing heuristic would then delete the source nodes corresponding to the two closed plants, make any capacity modifications necessary to the sources corresponding to the remaining three plants, and re-solve the transshipment problem. The product strategy team could then examine the new solution, make some more modifications, solve again, and so on.

The Product Sourcing Heuristic was viewed as a valuable decision support system by all who used it. When P&G implemented the results of the study, it realized annual savings in the $200 million range. The PSH proved so successful in North America that P&G used it in other markets around the world.

*Based on information provided by Franz Dill and Tom Chorman of Procter & Gamble.

10.2 Assignment Problem

The **assignment problem** arises in a variety of decision-making situations; typical assignment problems involve assigning jobs to machines, agents to tasks, sales personnel to sales territories, contracts to bidders, and so on. A distinguishing feature of the assignment problem is that *one* agent is assigned to *one and only one* task. Specifically, we look for the set of assignments that will optimize a stated objective, such as minimize cost, minimize time, or maximize profits.

To illustrate the assignment problem, let us consider the case of Fowle Marketing Research, which has just received requests for market research studies from three new clients. The company faces the task of assigning a project leader (agent) to each client (task). Currently, three individuals have no other commitments and are available for the project leader assignments. Fowle's management realizes, however, that the time required to complete each study will depend on the experience and ability of the project leader assigned. The three projects have approximately the same priority, and management wants to assign project leaders to minimize the total number of days required to complete all three projects. If a project leader is to be assigned to one client only, which assignments should be made?

To answer the assignment question, Fowle's management must first consider all possible project leader–client assignments and then estimate the corresponding project completion times. With three project leaders and three clients, nine assignment alternatives are possible. The alternatives and the estimated project completion times in days are summarized in Table 10.5.

Try Problem 17, part (a), for practice in developing a network model for an assignment problem.

Figure 10.10 shows the network representation of Fowle's assignment problem. The nodes correspond to the project leaders and clients, and the arcs represent the possible assignments of project leaders to clients. The supply at each origin node and the demand at each destination node are 1; the cost of assigning a project leader to a client is the time it takes that project leader to complete the client's task. Note the similarity between the network models of the assignment problem (Figure 10.10) and the transportation problem (Figure 10.1). The assignment problem is a special case of the transportation problem in which all supply and demand values equal 1, and the amount shipped over each arc is either 0 or 1.

Because the assignment problem is a special case of the transportation problem, a linear programming formulation can be developed. Again, we need a constraint for each node and a variable for each arc. As in the transportation problem, we use double-subscripted decision variables, with x_{11} denoting the assignment of project leader 1 (Terry) to client 1,

TABLE 10.5 ESTIMATED PROJECT COMPLETION TIMES (DAYS) FOR THE FOWLE MARKETING RESEARCH ASSIGNMENT PROBLEM

	Client		
Project Leader	**1**	**2**	**3**
1. Terry	10	15	9
2. Carle	9	18	5
3. McClymonds	6	14	3

FIGURE 10.10 A NETWORK MODEL OF THE FOWLE MARKETING RESEARCH ASSIGNMENT PROBLEM

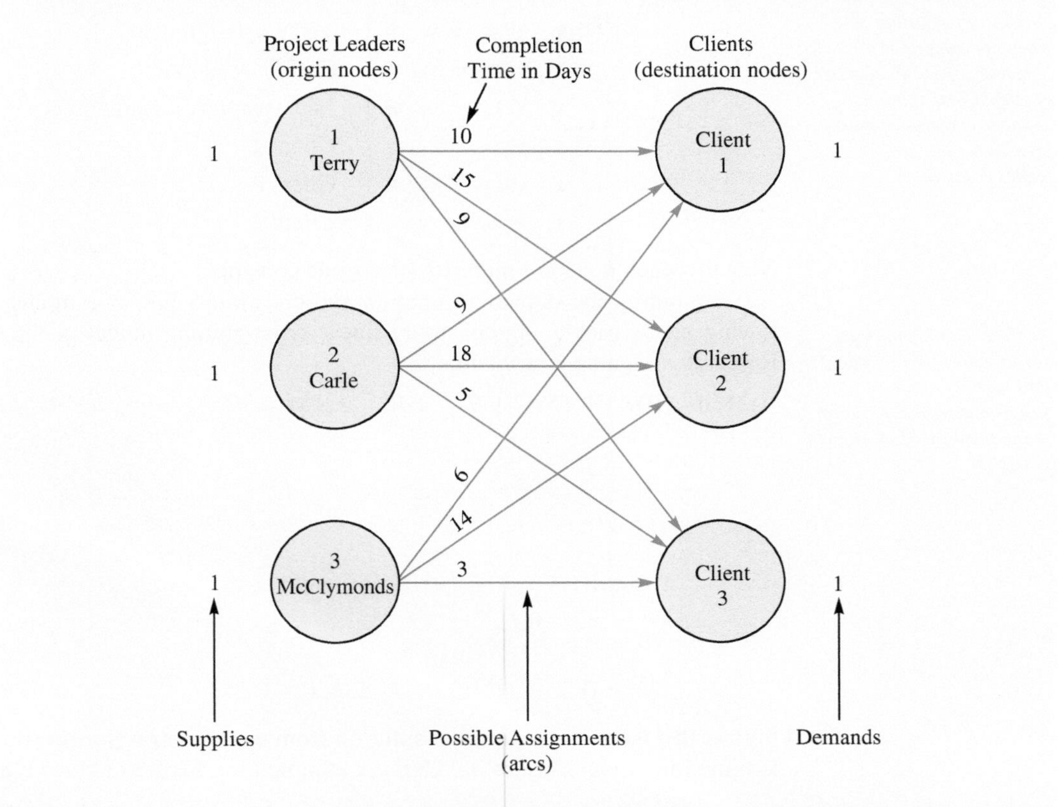

x_{12} denoting the assignment of project leader 1 (Terry) to client 2, and so on. In general, we interpret the decision variables for Fowle's assignment problem as

Due to the special structure of the assignment problem, the x_{ij} variables will either be 0 or 1 and not any value in between, e.g., 0.6. In Chapter 11, we discuss optimization problems which represent discrete choices with 0-1 (or binary) variables that must be explicitly constrained to avoid fractional values.

$$x_{ij} = \begin{cases} 1 & \text{if project leader } i \text{ is assigned to client } j \\ 0 & \text{otherwise} \end{cases}$$

$$\text{where } i = 1, 2, 3, \text{ and } j = 1, 2, 3$$

Using this notation and the completion time data in Table 10.5, we develop completion time expressions:

$$\begin{aligned} \text{Days required for Terry's assignment} &= 10x_{11} + 15x_{12} + 9x_{13} \\ \text{Days required for Carle's assignment} &= 9x_{21} + 18x_{22} + 5x_{23} \\ \text{Days required for McClymonds's assignment} &= 6x_{31} + 14x_{32} + 3x_{33} \end{aligned}$$

The sum of the completion times for the three project leaders will provide the total days required to complete the three assignments. Thus, the objective function is

$$\text{Min } 10x_{11} + 15x_{12} + 9x_{13} + 9x_{21} + 18x_{22} + 5x_{23} + 6x_{31} + 14x_{32} + 3x_{33}$$

Because the number of project leaders equals the number of clients, all the constraints could be written as equalities. But when the number of project leaders exceeds the number of clients, less-than-or-equal-to constraints must be used for the project leader constraints.

The constraints for the assignment problem reflect the conditions that each project leader can be assigned to at most one client and that each client must have one assigned project leader. These constraints are written as follows:

$$\begin{aligned} x_{11} + x_{12} + x_{13} &\leq 1 \quad \text{Terry's assignment} \\ x_{21} + x_{22} + x_{23} &\leq 1 \quad \text{Carle's assignment} \\ x_{31} + x_{32} + x_{33} &\leq 1 \quad \text{McClymonds's assignment} \\ x_{11} + x_{21} + x_{31} &= 1 \quad \text{Client 1} \\ x_{12} + x_{22} + x_{32} &= 1 \quad \text{Client 2} \\ x_{13} + x_{23} + x_{33} &= 1 \quad \text{Client 3} \end{aligned}$$

Note that each node in Figure 10.10 has one constraint.

Try Problem 17, part (b), for practice in formulating and solving a linear programming model for an assignment problem on the computer.

Combining the objective function and constraints into one model provides the following nine-variable, six-constraint linear programming model of the Fowle Marketing Research assignment problem:

$$\text{Min} \quad 10x_{11} + 15x_{12} + 9x_{13} + 9x_{21} + 18x_{22} + 5x_{23} + 6x_{31} + 14x_{32} + 3x_{33}$$

s.t.

$$\begin{array}{lllllllllll} x_{11} + & x_{12} + & x_{13} & & & & & & & & \leq 1 \\ & & & x_{21} & + x_{22} + & x_{23} & & & & & \leq 1 \\ & & & & & & x_{31} & + x_{32} + & x_{33} & & \leq 1 \\ x_{11} & & & + x_{21} & & & + x_{31} & & & & = 1 \\ & x_{12} & & & + x_{22} & & & + x_{32} & & & = 1 \\ & & x_{13} & & & + x_{23} & & & + x_{33} & & = 1 \end{array}$$

$$x_{ij} \geq 0 \quad \text{for } i = 1, 2, 3; j = 1, 2, 3$$

Figure 10.11 shows the optimal solution from the answer report for this model. Terry is assigned to client 2 ($x_{12} = 1$), Carle is assigned to client 3 ($x_{23} = 1$), and McClymonds

FIGURE 10.11 OPTIMAL SOLUTION FOR THE FOWLE MARKETING RESEARCH ASSIGNMENT PROBLEM

Objective Cell (Min)

Name	Original Value	Final Value
Minimize Completion Time	0.000	26.000

Fowle

Variable Cells

Model Variable	Name	Original Value	Final Value	Integer
X11	Terry to Client 1	0.000	0.000	Contin
X12	Terry to Client 2	0.000	1.000	Contin
X13	Terry to Client 3	0.000	0.000	Contin
X21	Carle to Client 1	0.000	0.000	Contin
X22	Carle to Client 2	0.000	0.000	Contin
X23	Carle to Client 3	0.000	1.000	Contin
X31	McClymonds to Client 1	0.000	1.000	Contin
X32	McClymonds to Client 2	0.000	0.000	Contin
X33	McClymonds to Client 3	0.000	0.000	Contin

TABLE 10.6 OPTIMAL PROJECT LEADER ASSIGNMENTS FOR THE FOWLE MARKETING RESEARCH ASSIGNMENT PROBLEM

Project Leader	Assigned Client		Days
Terry	2		15
Carle	3		5
McClymonds	1		6
		Total	26

is assigned to client 1 ($x_{31} = 1$). The total completion time required is 26 days. This solution is summarized in Table 10.6.

Problem Variations

Because the assignment problem can be viewed as a special case of the transportation problem, the problem variations that may arise in an assignment problem parallel those for the transportation problem. Specifically, we can handle

1. Total number of agents (supply) not equal to the total number of tasks (demand)
2. A maximization objective function
3. Unacceptable assignments

The situation in which the number of agents does not equal the number of tasks is analogous to total supply not equaling total demand in a transportation problem. If the number of agents exceeds the number of tasks, the extra agents simply remain unassigned in the linear programming solution. If the number of tasks exceeds the number of agents, the linear programming model will not have a feasible solution. In this situation, a simple modification is to add enough dummy agents to equalize the number of agents and the number of tasks. For instance, in the Fowle problem we might have had five clients (tasks) and only three project leaders (agents). By adding two dummy project leaders, we can create a new assignment problem with the number of project leaders equal to the number of clients. The objective function coefficients for the assignment of dummy project leaders would be zero so that the value of the optimal solution would represent the total number of days required by the assignments actually made (no assignments will actually be made to the clients receiving dummy project leaders).

If the assignment alternatives are evaluated in terms of revenue or profit rather than time or cost, the linear programming formulation can be solved as a maximization rather than a minimization problem. In addition, if one or more assignments are unacceptable, the corresponding decision variable can be removed from the linear programming formulation. This situation could happen, for example, if an agent did not have the experience necessary for one or more of the tasks.

A General Linear Programming Model

To show the general linear programming model for an assignment problem with m agents and n tasks, we use the following notation:

$$x_{ij} = \begin{cases} 1 & \text{if agent } i \text{ is assigned to task } j \\ 0 & \text{otherwise} \end{cases}$$

$$c_{ij} = \text{the cost of assigning agent } i \text{ to task } j$$

The general linear programming model is as follows:

$$\text{Min} \quad \sum_{i=1}^{m} \sum_{j=1}^{n} c_{ij} x_{ij}$$

s.t.

$$\sum_{j=1}^{n} x_{ij} \leq 1 \qquad i = 1, 2, \ldots, m \quad \text{Agents}$$

$$\sum_{i=1}^{m} x_{ij} = 1 \qquad j = 1, 2, \ldots, n \quad \text{Tasks}$$

$$x_{ij} \geq 0 \qquad \text{for all } i \text{ and } j$$

At the beginning of this section, we indicated that a distinguishing feature of the assignment problem is that *one* agent is assigned to *one and only one* task. In generalizations of the assignment problem where one agent can be assigned to two or more tasks, the linear programming formulation of the problem can be easily modified. For example, let us assume that in the Fowle Marketing Research problem Terry could be assigned up to two clients; in this case, the constraint representing Terry's assignment would be $x_{11} + x_{12} + x_{13} \leq 2$. In general, if a_i denotes the upper limit for the number of tasks to which agent i can be assigned, we write the agent constraints as

$$\sum_{j=1}^{n} x_{ij} \leq a_i \qquad i = 1, 2, \ldots, m$$

If some tasks require more than one agent, the linear programming formulation can also accommodate the situation. Use the number of agents required as the right-hand side of the appropriate task constraint.

NOTES AND COMMENTS

1. As noted, the assignment model is a special case of the transportation model. We stated in the Notes and Comments at the end of the preceding section that the optimal solution to the transportation problem will consist of integer values for the decision variables as long as the supplies and demands are integers. For the assignment problem, all supplies and demands equal 1; thus, the optimal solution must be integer valued and the integer values must be 0 or 1.
2. Combining the method for handling multiple assignments with the notion of a dummy agent provides another means of dealing with situations when the number of tasks exceeds the number of agents. That is, we add one dummy agent but provide the dummy agent with the capability to handle multiple tasks. The number of tasks the dummy agent can handle is equal to the difference between the number of tasks and the number of agents.
3. The Q.M. in Action, Assigning Consultants to Clients at Energy Education, Inc., describes how a consulting company uses an assignment problem as part of an innovative model to minimize the travel costs for their clients.

Q.M. *in* ACTION

*ASSIGNING CONSULTANTS TO CLIENTS AT ENERGY EDUCATION, INC.**

Energy Education, Inc. (EEI) is a consulting firm that provides experts to schools, universities, and other organizations to implement energy conservation programs. It is estimated that EEI has helped more than 1100 clients save in excess of $2.3 billion in energy costs over

*Based on Junfang Yu and Randy Hoff, "Optimal Routing and Assignment of Consultants for Energy Education, Inc.," *Interfaces* (March–April 2013), 142–151.

(continued)

the course of the 25 years in which EEI has provided consulting services. EEI consultants spend almost all of their time working at the client location, which results in frequent travel and high travel costs for the company. On average, a consultant for EEI spends about $1000 per week for air travel costs alone.

Because of the large expense associated with consultant travel, EEI seeks to minimize travel costs whenever possible. To help minimize consultant travel cost, EEI created models that assign consultants to clients. The objective of these models is to minimize the total number of flights required each week while meeting all client needs. These models include an assignment-type problem similar to those described in this chapter as part of a more complicated framework that also considers the optimal routing of consultants among client locations.

The models developed by EEI are solved using dedicated optimization software, and the output of the models provides a weekly assignment and travel route for each consultant. The new models resulted in a 44% reduction in flight costs for EEI over a 12-week period in comparison to the consultant assignments and travel plans used previously. The number of consultants required to meet all client demand was also reduced using the new models, leading to a direct labor cost reduction of 15%. In total, EEI realized an annual cost savings of nearly $500,000 from implementing their models for assigning consultants to clients and optimizing consultant travel.

10.3 Shortest-Route Problem

In this section we consider a problem in which the objective is to determine the **shortest route**, or *path*, between two nodes in a network. We will demonstrate the shortest-route problem by considering the situation facing the Gorman Construction Company. Gorman has several construction sites located throughout a three-county area. With multiple daily trips carrying personnel, equipment, and supplies from Gorman's office to the construction sites, the costs associated with transportation activities are substantial. The travel alternatives between Gorman's office and each construction site can be described by the road network shown in Figure 10.12. The road distances in miles between the nodes are shown above the corresponding arcs. In this application, Gorman would like to determine the route that will minimize the total travel distance between Gorman's office (located at node 1) and the construction site located at node 6.

A key to developing a model for the shortest-route problem is to understand that the problem is a special case of the transshipment problem. Specifically, the Gorman shortest-route problem can be viewed as a transshipment problem with one origin node (node 1), one destination node (node 6), and four transshipment nodes (nodes 2, 3, 4 and 5). The transshipment network for the Gorman shortest-route problem is shown in Figure 10.13. Arrows added to the arcs show the direction of flow, which is always *out* of the origin node and *into* the destination node. Note also that two directed arcs are shown between the pairs of transshipment nodes. For example, one arc going from node 2 to node 3 indicates that the shortest route may go from node 2 to node 3, and one arc going from node 3 to node 2 indicates that the shortest route may go from node 3 to node 2. The distance between two transshipment nodes is the same in either direction.

To find the shortest route between node 1 and node 6, think of node 1 as having a supply of 1 unit and node 6 as having a demand of 1 unit. Let x_{ij} denote the number of units that flow or are shipped from node i to node j. Because only 1 unit will be shipped from node 1 to node 6, the value of x_{ij} will be either 1 or 0. Thus, if $x_{ij} = 1$, the arc from node i to node j is

FIGURE 10.12 ROAD NETWORK FOR THE GORMAN COMPANY SHORTEST-ROUTE PROBLEM

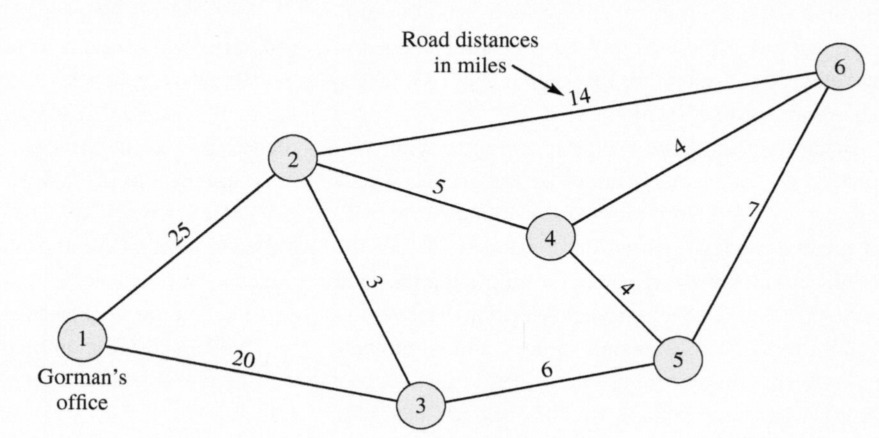

Note: (1) The length of each arc is not necessarily proportional to the travel distance it represents.
(2) All roads are two-way; thus, flow may be in either direction.

FIGURE 10.13 TRANSSHIPMENT NETWORK FOR THE GORMAN SHORTEST-ROUTE PROBLEM

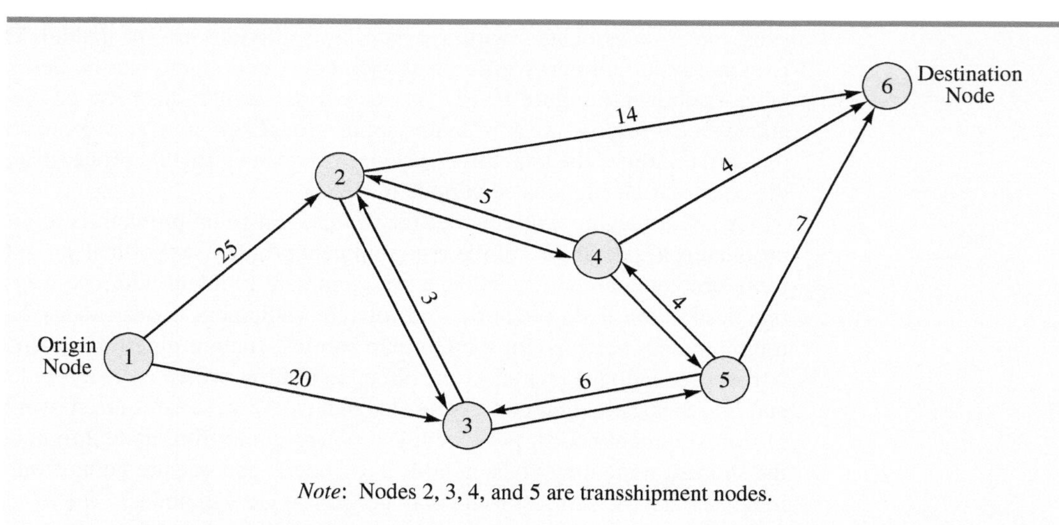

Note: Nodes 2, 3, 4, and 5 are transshipment nodes.

on the shortest route from node 1 to node 6; if $x_{ij} = 0$, the arc from node i to node j is not on the shortest route. Because we are looking for the shortest route between node 1 and node 6, the objective function for the Gorman problem is

$$\begin{aligned} \text{Min} \quad & 25x_{12} + 20x_{13} + 3x_{23} + 3x_{32} + 5x_{24} + 5x_{42} + 14x_{26} + 6x_{35} + 6x_{53} \\ & + 4x_{45} + 4x_{54} + 4x_{46} + 7x_{56} \end{aligned}$$

To develop the constraints for the model, we begin with node 1. Because the supply at node 1 is 1 unit, the flow out of node 1 must equal 1. Thus, the constraint for node 1 is written

$$x_{12} + x_{13} = 1$$

For transshipment nodes 2, 3, 4, and 5, the flow out of each node must equal the flow into each node; thus, the flow out minus the flow in must be 0. The constraints for the four transshipment nodes are as follows:

	Flow Out	**Flow In**
Node 2	$x_{23} + x_{24} + x_{26}$	$-x_{12} - x_{32} - x_{42} = 0$
Node 3	$x_{32} + x_{35}$	$-x_{13} - x_{23} - x_{53} = 0$
Node 4	$x_{42} + x_{45} + x_{46}$	$-x_{24} - x_{54} = 0$
Node 5	$x_{53} + x_{54} + x_{56}$	$-x_{35} - x_{45} = 0$

Because node 6 is the destination node with a demand of 1 unit, the flow into node 6 must equal 1. Thus, the constraint for node 6 is written as

$$x_{26} + x_{46} + x_{56} = 1$$

Including the negative constraints $x_{ij} \geq 0$ for all i and j, the linear programming model for the Gorman shortest-route problem is shown in Figure 10.14.

The optimal solution from the answer report for the Gorman shortest-route problem is shown in Figure 10.15. The objective function value of 32 indicates that the shortest route between Gorman's office located at node 1 to the construction site located at node 6 is 32 miles. With $x_{13} = 1$, $x_{32} = 1$, $x_{24} = 1$, and $x_{46} = 1$, the shortest route from node 1 to node 6

FIGURE 10.14 LINEAR PROGRAMMING FORMULATION OF THE GORMAN SHORTEST-ROUTE PROBLEM

$$\text{Min } 25x_{12} + 20x_{13} + 3x_{23} + 3x_{32} + 5x_{24} + 5x_{42} + 14x_{26} + 6x_{35} + 6x_{53} + 4x_{45} + 4x_{54} + 4x_{46} + 7x_{56}$$

s.t.

$$\begin{array}{llr}
x_{12} + x_{13} & = 1 & \text{Origin node} \\
-x_{12} + x_{23} - x_{32} + x_{24} - x_{42} + x_{26} & = 0 & \\
-x_{13} - x_{23} + x_{32} + x_{35} - x_{53} & = 0 & \text{Transshipment nodes} \\
-x_{24} + x_{42} + x_{45} - x_{54} + x_{46} & = 0 & \\
-x_{35} + x_{53} - x_{45} + x_{54} + x_{56} & = 0 & \\
x_{26} + x_{46} + x_{56} & = 1 & \text{Destination node}
\end{array}$$

$x_{ij} \geq 0$ for all i and j

FIGURE 10.15 OPTIMAL SOLUTION FOR THE GORMAN SHORTEST-ROUTE PROBLEM

Objective Cell (Min)

Name	Original Value	Final Value
Total Distance	0.000	32.000

Variable Cells

Cell	Name	Original Value	Final Value	Integer
X12	Flow from Node 1 to 2	0.000	0.000	Contin
X13	Flow from Node 1 to 3	0.000	1.000	Contin
X23	Flow from Node 2 to 3	0.000	0.000	Contin
X32	Flow from Node 3 to 2	0.000	1.000	Contin
X24	Flow from Node 2 to 4	0.000	1.000	Contin
X42	Flow from Node 4 to 2	0.000	0.000	Contin
X26	Flow from Node 2 to 6	0.000	0.000	Contin
X35	Flow from Node 3 to 5	0.000	0.000	Contin
X53	Flow from Node 5 to 3	0.000	0.000	Contin
X45	Flow from Node 4 to 5	0.000	0.000	Contin
X54	Flow from Node 5 to 4	0.000	0.000	Contin
X46	Flow from Node 4 to 6	0.000	1.000	Contin
X56	Flow from Node 5 to 6	0.000	0.000	Contin

Gorman

Try Problem 23 to practice solving a shortest-route problem.

is 1–3–2–4–6; in other words, the shortest route takes us from node 1 to node 3; then from node 3 to node 2; then from node 2 to node 4; and finally from node 4 to node 6.

A General Linear Programming Model

To show the general linear programming model for the shortest-route problem, we use the following notation:

$$x_{ij} = \begin{cases} 1 & \text{if the arc from node } i \text{ to node } j \text{ is on the shortest route} \\ 0 & \text{otherwise} \end{cases}$$

$$c_{ij} = \text{the distance, time, or cost associated with the arc from node } i \text{ to node } j$$

The general linear programming model for the shortest-route problem is as follows:

$$\text{Min} \quad \sum_{\text{all arcs}} c_{ij} x_{ij}$$

s.t.

$$\sum_{\text{arcs out}} x_{ij} = 1 \qquad \text{Origin node } i$$

$$\sum_{\text{arcs out}} x_{ij} - \sum_{\text{arcs in}} x_{ij} = 0 \qquad \text{Transshipment nodes}$$

$$\sum_{\text{arcs in}} x_{ij} = 1 \qquad \text{Destination node } j$$

NOTES AND COMMENTS

1. In the Gorman problem we assumed that all roads in the network are two-way. As a result, the road connecting nodes 2 and 3 in the road network resulted in the creation of two corresponding arcs in the transshipment network. Two decision variables, x_{23} and x_{32}, were required to show that the shortest route might go from node 2 to node 3 or from node 3 to node 2. If the road connecting nodes 2 and 3 had been a one-way road allowing flow only from node 2 to node 3, decision variable x_{32} would not have been included in the model.

10.4 Maximal Flow Problem

The objective in a **maximal flow** problem is to determine the maximum amount of flow (vehicles, messages, fluid, etc.) that can enter and exit a network system in a given period of time. In this problem, we attempt to transmit flow through all arcs of the network as efficiently as possible. The amount of flow is limited due to capacity restrictions on the various arcs of the network. For example, highway types limit vehicle flow in a transportation system, while pipe sizes limit oil flow in an oil distribution system. The maximum or upper limit on the flow in an arc is referred to as the **flow capacity** of the arc. Even though we do not specify capacities for the nodes, we do assume that the flow out of a node is equal to the flow into the node.

As an example of the maximal flow problem, consider the north–south interstate highway system passing through Cincinnati, Ohio. The north–south vehicle flow reaches a level of 15,000 vehicles per hour at peak times. Due to a summer highway maintenance program, which calls for the temporary closing of lanes and lower speed limits, a network of alternate routes through Cincinnati has been proposed by a transportation planning committee. The alternate routes include other highways as well as city streets. Because of differences in speed limits and traffic patterns, flow capacities vary depending on the particular streets and roads used. The proposed network with arc flow capacities is shown in Figure 10.16.

FIGURE 10.16 NETWORK OF HIGHWAY SYSTEM AND FLOW CAPACITIES (1000S/HOUR) FOR CINCINNATI

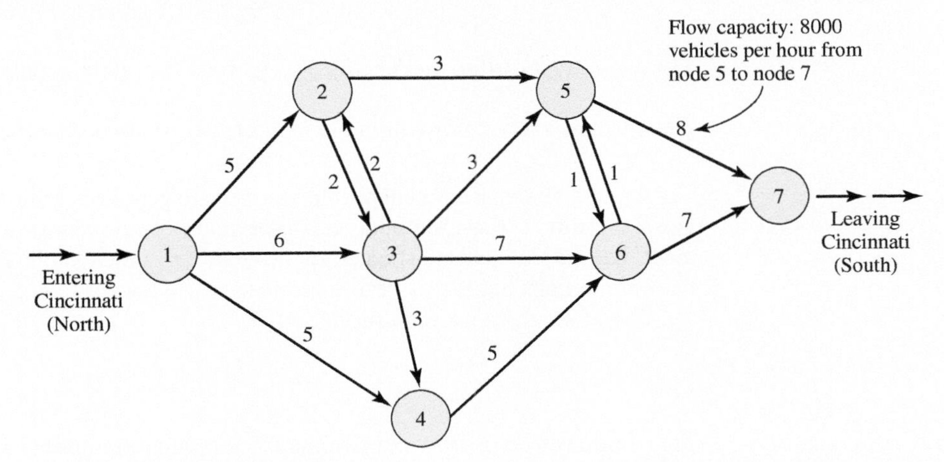

FIGURE 10.17 FLOW OVER ARC FROM NODE 7 TO NODE 1 TO REPRESENT TOTAL FLOW THROUGH THE CINCINNATI HIGHWAY SYSTEM

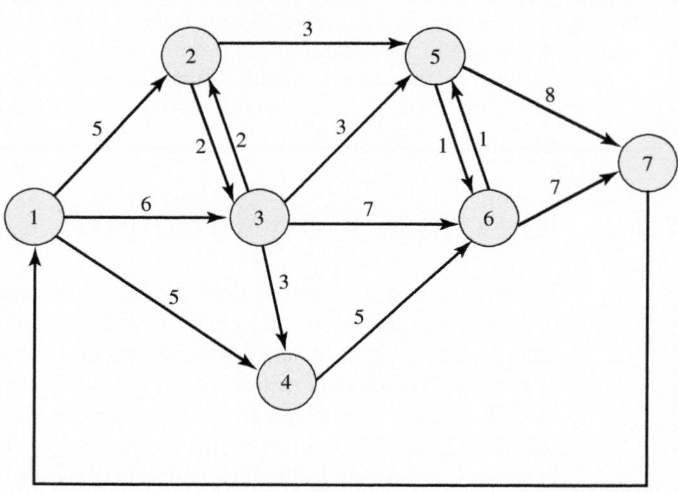

The direction of flow for each arc is indicated, and the arc capacity is shown next to each arc. Note that most of the streets are one-way. However, a two-way street can be found between nodes 2 and 3 and between nodes 5 and 6. In both cases, the capacity is the same in each direction.

We will show how to develop a capacitated transshipment model for the maximal flow problem. First, we will add an arc from node 7 back to node 1 to represent the total flow through the highway system. Figure 10.17 shows the modified network. The newly added arc shows no capacity; indeed, we will want to maximize the flow over that arc. Maximizing the flow over the arc from node 7 to node 1 is equivalent to maximizing the number of cars that can get through the north–south highway system passing through Cincinnati.

The decision variables are as follows:

$$x_{ij} = \text{amount of traffic flow from node } i \text{ to node } j$$

The objective function that maximizes the flow over the highway system is

$$\text{Max } x_{71}$$

As with all transshipment problems, each arc generates a variable and each node generates a constraint. For each node, a conservation of flow constraint represents the requirement that the flow out must equal the flow in. Or, stated another way, the flow out minus the flow in must equal zero. For node 1, the flow out is $x_{12} + x_{13} + x_{14}$, and the flow in is x_{71}. Therefore, the constraint for node 1 is

$$x_{12} + x_{13} + x_{14} - x_{71} = 0$$

The conservation of flow constraints for the other six nodes are developed in a similar fashion.

	Flow Out	Flow In	
Node 2	$x_{23} + x_{25}$	$-x_{12} - x_{32}$	$= 0$
Node 3	$x_{32} + x_{34} + x_{35} + x_{36}$	$-x_{13} - x_{23}$	$= 0$
Node 4	x_{46}	$-x_{14} - x_{34}$	$= 0$
Node 5	$x_{56} + x_{57}$	$-x_{25} - x_{35} - x_{65}$	$= 0$
Node 6	$x_{65} + x_{67}$	$-x_{36} - x_{46} - x_{56}$	$= 0$
Node 7	x_{71}	$-x_{57} - x_{67}$	$= 0$

Additional constraints are needed to enforce the capacities on the arcs. These 14 simple upper-bound constraints are given.

$$\begin{array}{llll} x_{12} \leq 5 & x_{13} \leq 6 & x_{14} \leq 5 & \\ x_{23} \leq 2 & x_{25} \leq 3 & & \\ x_{32} \leq 2 & x_{34} \leq 3 & x_{35} \leq 5 & x_{36} \leq 7 \\ x_{46} \leq 5 & & & \\ x_{56} \leq 1 & x_{57} \leq 8 & & \\ x_{65} \leq 1 & x_{67} \leq 7 & & \end{array}$$

Note that the only arc without a capacity is the one we added from node 7 to node 1.

The optimal solution from the answer report for this 15-variable, 21-constraint linear programming problem is shown in Figure 10.18. We note that the value of the optimal

FIGURE 10.18 OPTIMAL SOLUTION FOR THE CINCINNATI HIGHWAY SYSTEM MAXIMAL FLOW PROBLEM

Objective Cell (Max)

Name	Original Value	Final Value
Max Flow	0.000	14.000

Variable Cells

Cell	Name	Original Value	Final Value	Integer
X12	Flow from 1 to 2	0.000	3.000	Contin
X13	Flow from 1 to 3	0.000	6.000	Contin
X14	Flow from 1 to 4	0.000	5.000	Contin
X23	Flow from 2 to 3	0.000	0.000	Contin
X25	Flow from 2 to 5	0.000	3.000	Contin
X34	Flow from 3 to 4	0.000	0.000	Contin
X35	Flow from 3 to 5	0.000	3.000	Contin
X36	Flow from 3 to 6	0.000	3.000	Contin
X32	Flow from 3 to 2	0.000	0.000	Contin
X46	Flow from 4 to 6	0.000	5.000	Contin
X56	Flow from 5 to 6	0.000	0.000	Contin
X57	Flow from 5 to 7	0.000	7.000	Contin
X65	Flow from 6 to 5	0.000	1.000	Contin
X67	Flow from 6 to 7	0.000	7.000	Contin
X71	Flow from 7 to 1	0.000	14.000	Contin

Cincinnati

FIGURE 10.19 MAXIMAL FLOW PATTERN FOR THE CINCINNATI HIGHWAY SYSTEM NETWORK

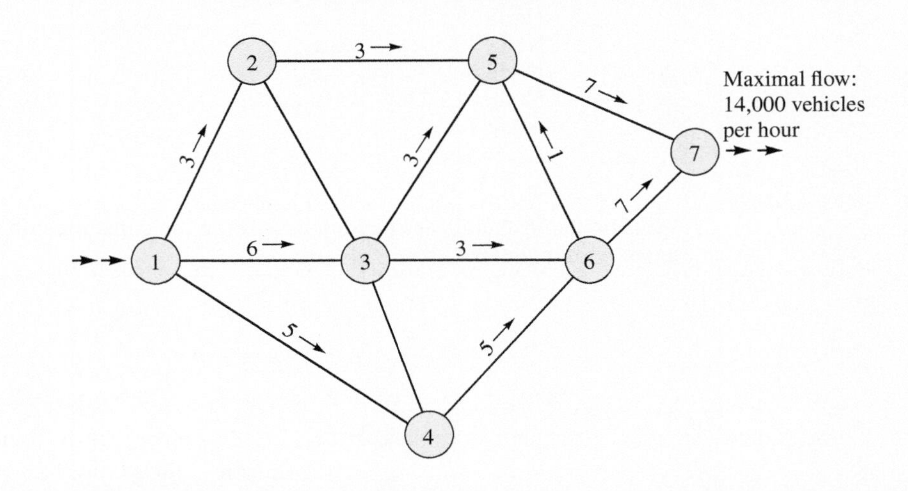

Try Problem 29 for practice in solving a maximal flow problem.

solution is 14. This result implies that the maximal flow over the highway system is 14,000 vehicles. Figure 10.19 shows how the vehicle flow is routed through the original highway network. We note, for instance, that 3000 vehicles per hour are routed between nodes 1 and 2, 6000 vehicles per hour are routed between nodes 1 and 3, 0 vehicles are routed between nodes 2 and 3, and so on.

The results of the maximal flow analysis indicate that the planned highway network system will not handle the peak flow of 15,000 vehicles per hour. The transportation planners will have to expand the highway network, increase current arc flow capacities, or be prepared for serious traffic problems. If the network is extended or modified, another maximal flow analysis will determine the extent of any improved flow. The Q.M. in Action, Finding the Shortest Paths for Containerships, describes how Danaos Corporation computes shortest path routes for their containerships to save millions of dollars in reduced fuel costs.

NOTES AND COMMENTS

1. The maximal flow problem of this section can also be solved with a slightly different formulation if the extra arc between nodes 7 and 1 is not used. The alternate approach is to maximize the flow into node 7 ($x_{57} + x_{67}$) and drop the conservation of flow constraints for nodes 1 and 7. However, the formulation used in this section is most common in practice.
2. Network models can be used to describe a variety of important problems. Unfortunately, no one network solution algorithm can be used to solve every network problem. It is important to recognize the specific type of problem being modeled in order to select the correct specialized solution algorithm.

Q.M. *in* ACTION

*FINDING THE SHORTEST PATHS FOR CONTAINERSHIPS**

Danaos Corporation is an international shipping company based in Greece that owns more than 60 containerships. Danaos' containerships travel millions of miles each year to transport millions of containers all around the world. Danaos has developed a powerful tool to improve shipping operations, known as the Operations Research in Ship Management (ORISMA) tool. Part of this tool involves the solving of shortest-path problems to determine a containership's optimal route.

Optimizing the travel route for a containership generates substantial savings through the use of less fuel and because it allows the ship to generate more revenue in less time by visiting additional ports to pick up and deliver containers. A subcomponent of ORISMA determines the shortest-path route between two given waypoints (intermediate points of a ship's complete voyage) by defining nodes in the feasible sailing space for the containership.

Danaos determined that it generated \$1.3 million in additional revenue in a single year by using ORISMA to reduce the amount of time containerships spent traveling between ports. Furthermore, it saved \$3.2 million in reduced fuel costs during the same year. Danaos estimates that further use of ORISMA will increase profitability by 7–10% annually in the future. As a nice byproduct of Danaos' reduced travel times and decreased fuel usage, carbon emissions have been cut substantially, and customers are happier to get their products with less lead time.

*Based on Takis Varelas, Sofia Archontaki, John Dimotikalis, Osman Turan, Iraklis Lazakis, and Orestis Varelas, "Optimizing Ship Routing to Maximize Fleet Revenue at Danaos," *Interfaces* (January-February 2013), 37–47.

10.5 A Production and Inventory Application

The introduction to supply chain models in Section 10.1 involved applications for the shipment of goods from several supply locations or origins to several demand sites or destinations. Although the shipment of goods is the subject of many supply chain problems, supply chain models can be developed for applications that have nothing to do with the physical shipment of goods from origins to destinations. In this section we show how to use a transshipment model to solve a production and inventory problem.

Contois Carpets is a small manufacturer of carpeting for home and office installations. Production capacity, demand, production cost per square yard, and inventory holding cost per square yard for the next four quarters are shown in Table 10.7. Note that production capacity, demand, and production costs vary by quarter, whereas the cost of carrying inventory from one quarter to the next is constant at \$0.25 per yard. Contois wants to

TABLE 10.7 PRODUCTION, DEMAND, AND COST ESTIMATES FOR CONTOIS CARPETS

Quarter	Production Capacity (square yards)	Demand (square yards)	Production Cost (\$/square yard)	Inventory Cost (\$/square yard)
1	600	400	2	0.25
2	300	500	5	0.25
3	500	400	3	0.25
4	400	400	3	0.25

determine how many yards of carpeting to manufacture each quarter to minimize the total production and inventory cost for the four-quarter period.

The network flows into and out of demand nodes are what make the model a transshipment model.

We begin by developing a network representation of the problem. First, we create four nodes corresponding to the production in each quarter and four nodes corresponding to the demand in each quarter. Each production node is connected by an outgoing arc to the demand node for the same period. The flow on the arc represents the number of square yards of carpet manufactured for the period. For each demand node, an outgoing arc represents the amount of inventory (square yards of carpet) carried over to the demand node for the next period. Figure 10.20 shows the network model. Note that nodes 1–4 represent the production for each quarter and that nodes 5–8 represent the demand for each quarter. The quarterly production capacities are shown in the left margin, and the quarterly demands are shown in the right margin.

FIGURE 10.20 NETWORK REPRESENTATION OF THE CONTOIS CARPETS PROBLEM

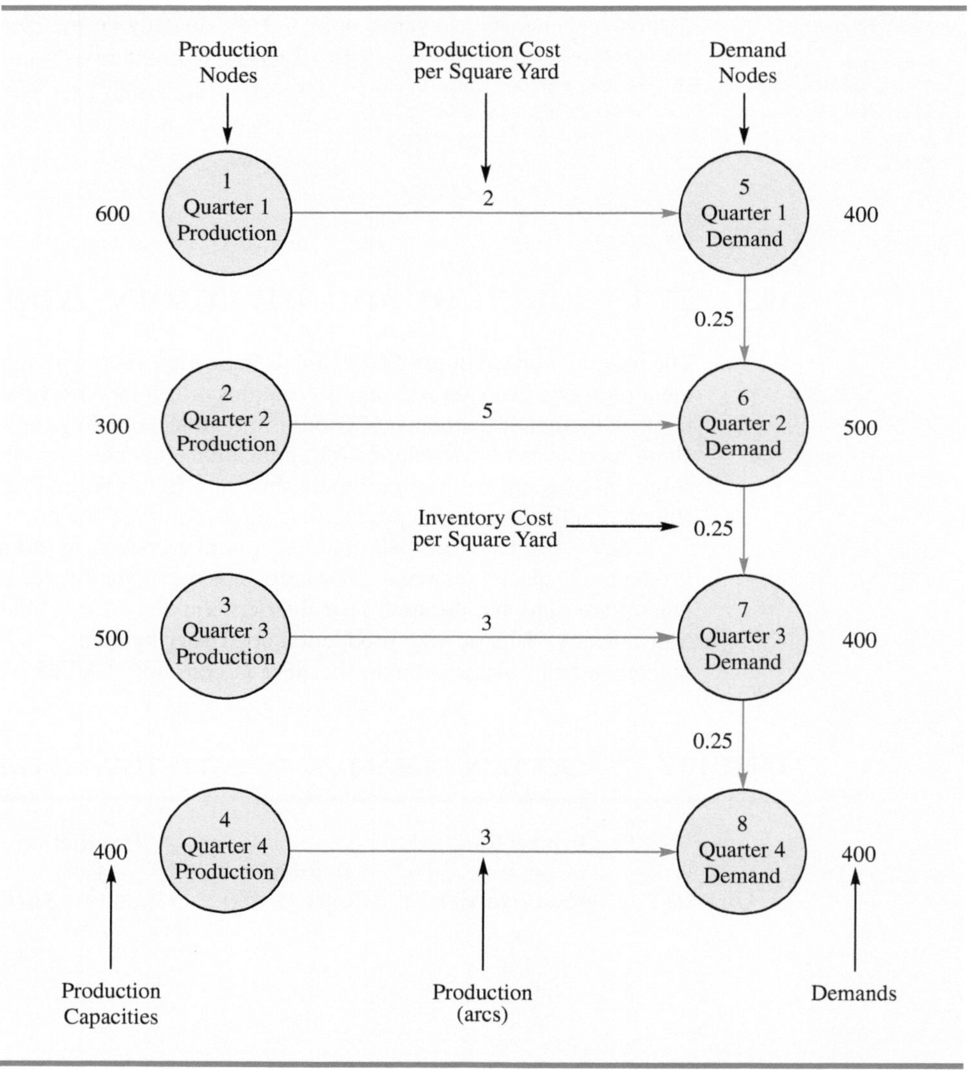

The objective is to determine a production scheduling and inventory policy that will minimize the total production and inventory cost for the four quarters. Constraints involve production capacity and demand in each quarter. As usual, a linear programming model can be developed from the network by establishing a constraint for each node and a variable for each arc.

Let x_{15} denote the number of square yards of carpet manufactured in quarter 1. The capacity of the facility is 600 square yards in quarter 1, so the production capacity constraint is

$$x_{15} \leq 300$$

Using similar decision variables, we obtain the production capacities for quarters 2–4:

$$\begin{aligned} x_{26} &\leq 300 \\ x_{37} &\leq 500 \\ x_{48} &\leq 400 \end{aligned}$$

We now consider the development of the constraints for each of the demand nodes. For node 5, one arc enters the node, which represents the number of square yards of carpet produced in quarter 1, and one arc leaves the node, which represents the number of square yards of carpet that will not be sold in quarter 1 and will be carried over for possible sale in quarter 2. In general, for each quarter the beginning inventory plus the production minus the ending inventory must equal demand. However, because quarter 1 has no beginning inventory, the constraint for node 5 is

$$x_{15} - x_{56} = 400$$

The constraints associated with the demand nodes in quarters 2, 3, and 4 are

$$\begin{aligned} x_{56} + x_{26} - x_{67} &= 500 \\ x_{67} + x_{37} - x_{78} &= 400 \\ x_{78} + x_{48} &= 400 \end{aligned}$$

Note that the constraint for node 8 (fourth-quarter demand) involves only two variables because no provision is made for holding inventory for a fifth quarter.

The objective is to minimize total production and inventory cost, so we write the objective function as

$$\text{Min} \quad 2x_{15} + 5x_{26} + 3x_{37} + 3x_{48} + 0.25x_{56} + 0.25x_{67} + 0.25x_{78}$$

The complete linear programming formulation of the Contois Carpets problem is

$$\begin{array}{lllllllll}
\text{Min} & 2x_{15} + 5x_{26} + 3x_{37} + 3x_{48} + 0.25x_{56} + 0.25x_{67} + 0.25x_{78} \\
\text{s.t.} \\
& x_{15} & & & & & & & \leq 600 \\
& & x_{26} & & & & & & \leq 300 \\
& & & x_{37} & & & & & \leq 500 \\
& & & & x_{48} & & & & \leq 400 \\
& x_{15} & & & & - x_{56} & & & = 400 \\
& & x_{26} & & & + x_{56} & - x_{67} & & = 500 \\
& & & x_{37} & & & + x_{67} & - x_{78} & = 400 \\
& & & & x_{48} & & & + x_{78} & = 400 \\
& x_{ij} \geq 0 \quad \text{for all } i \text{ and } j
\end{array}$$

FIGURE 10.21 OPTIMAL SOLUTION FOR THE CONTOIS CARPETS PROBLEM

Objective Cell (Min)

Name	Original Value	Final Value
Total Cost	0.000	5150.000

Contois

Variable Cells

Model Variable	Name	Original Value	Final Value	Integer
X15	Flow from Node 1 to 5	0.000	600.000	Contin
X26	Flow from Node 2 to 6	0.000	300.000	Contin
X37	Flow from Node 3 to 7	0.000	400.000	Contin
X48	Flow from Node 4 to 8	0.000	400.000	Contin
X56	Flow from Node 5 to 6	0.000	200.000	Contin
X67	Flow from Node 6 to 7	0.000	0.000	Contin
X78	Flow from Node 7 to 8	0.000	0.000	Contin

Figure 10.21 shows the optimal solution from the answer report for this problem. Contois Carpets should manufacture 600 square yards of carpet in quarter 1, 300 square yards in quarter 2, 400 square yards in quarter 3, and 400 square yards in quarter 4. Note also that 200 square yards will be carried over from quarter 1 to quarter 2. The total production and inventory cost is $5150.

NOTES AND COMMENTS

1. For the network models presented in this chapter, the amount leaving the starting node for an arc is always equal to the amount entering the ending node for that arc. An extension of such a network model is the case where a gain or a loss occurs as an arc is traversed. The amount entering the destination node may be greater or smaller than the amount leaving the origin node. For instance, if cash is the commodity flowing across an arc, the cash earns interest from one period to the next. Thus, the amount of cash entering the next period is greater than the amount leaving the previous period by the amount of interest earned. Networks with gains or losses are treated in more advanced texts on network flow programming.

Summary

In this chapter we introduced models related to supply chain problems—specifically, transportation and transshipment problems—as well as assignment, shortest-route, and maximal flow problems. All of these types of problems belong to the special category of linear programs called *network flow problems*. In general, the network model for these problems consists of nodes representing origins, destinations, and, if necessary, transshipment points in the network system. Arcs are used to represent the routes for shipment, travel, or flow between the various nodes.

Transportation problems and transshipment problems are commonly encountered when dealing with supply chains. The general transportation problem has *m* origins and *n* destinations. Given the supply at each origin, the demand at each destination, and unit shipping cost between each origin and each destination, the transportation model determines the optimal amounts to ship from each origin to each destination. The transshipment problem is an extension of the transportation problem involving transfer points referred to as transshipment nodes. In this more general model, we allow arcs between any pair of nodes in the network.

The assignment problem is a special case of the transportation problem in which all supply and all demand values are 1. We represent each agent as an origin node and each task as a destination node. The assignment model determines the minimum cost or maximum profit assignment of agents to tasks.

The shortest-route problem finds the shortest route or path between two nodes of a network. Distance, time, and cost are often the criteria used for this model. The shortest-route problem can be expressed as a transshipment problem with one origin and one destination. By shipping one unit from the origin to the destination, the solution will determine the shortest route through the network.

The maximal flow problem can be used to allocate flow to the arcs of the network so that flow through the network system is maximized. Arc capacities determine the maximum amount of flow for each arc. With these flow capacity constraints, the maximal flow problem is expressed as a capacitated transshipment problem.

In the last section of the chapter, we showed how a variation of the transshipment problem could be used to solve a production and inventory problem. In the chapter appendix we show how to use Excel to solve three of the distribution and network problems presented in the chapter.

Glossary

Arcs The lines connecting the nodes in a network.

Assignment problem A network flow problem that often involves the assignment of agents to tasks; it can be formulated as a linear program and is a special case of the transportation problem.

Capacitated transportation problem A variation of the basic transportation problem in which some or all of the arcs are subject to capacity restrictions.

Capacitated transshipment problem A variation of the transshipment problem in which some or all of the arcs are subject to capacity restrictions.

Dummy origin An origin added to a transportation problem to make the total supply equal to the total demand. The supply assigned to the dummy origin is the difference between the total demand and the total supply.

Flow capacity The maximum flow for an arc of the network. The flow capacity in one direction may not equal the flow capacity in the reverse direction.

Maximal flow The maximum amount of flow that can enter and exit a network system during a given period of time.

Network A graphical representation of a problem consisting of numbered circles (nodes) interconnected by a series of lines (arcs); arrowheads on the arcs show the direction of flow. Transportation, assignment, and transshipment problems are network flow problems.

Nodes The intersection or junction points of a network.

Shortest route Shortest path between two nodes in a network.

Supply chain The set of all interconnected resources involved in producing and distributing a product.

Transportation problem A network flow problem that often involves minimizing the cost of shipping goods from a set of origins to a set of destinations; it can be formulated and solved as a linear program by including a variable for each arc and a constraint for each node.

Transshipment problem An extension of the transportation problem to distribution problems involving transfer points and possible shipments between any pair of nodes.

Problems

1. A company imports goods at two ports: Philadelphia and New Orleans. Shipments of one product are made to customers in Atlanta, Dallas, Columbus, and Boston. For the next planning period, the supplies at each port, customer demands, and shipping costs per case from each port to each customer are as follows:

	Customers				Port
Port	Atlanta	Dallas	Columbus	Boston	Supply
Philadelphia	2	6	6	2	5000
New Orleans	1	2	5	7	3000
Demand	1400	3200	2000	1400	

Develop a network representation of the distribution system (transportation problem).

2. Consider the following network representation of a transportation problem:

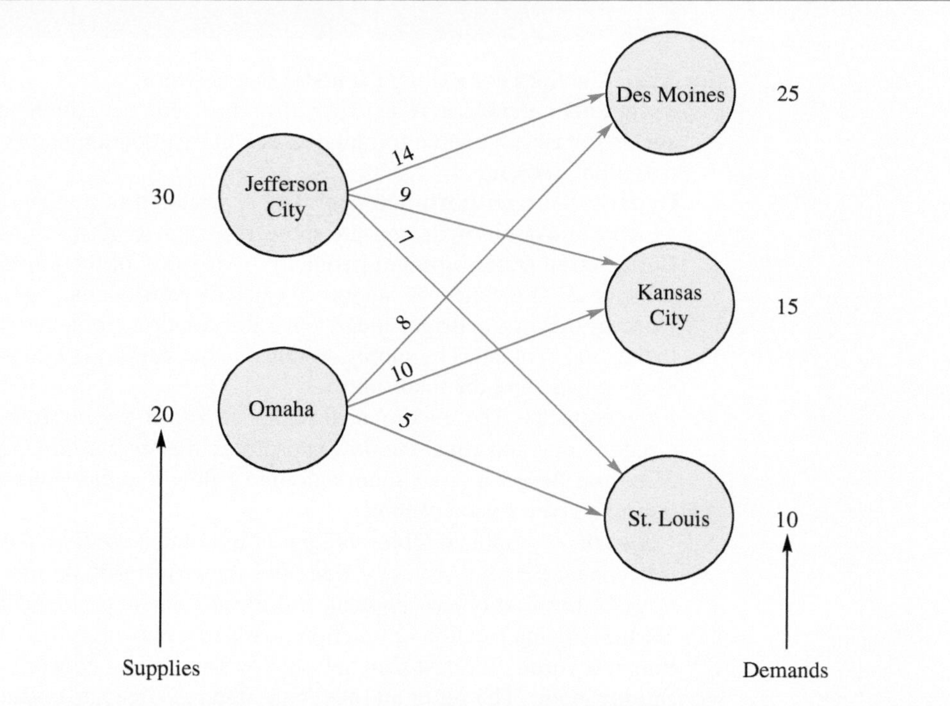

The supplies, demands, and transportation costs per unit are shown on the network.

a. Develop a linear programming model for this problem; be sure to define the variables in your model.
b. Solve the linear program to determine the optimal solution.

3. Tri-County Utilities, Inc., supplies natural gas to customers in a three-county area. The company purchases natural gas from two companies: Southern Gas and Northwest Gas. Demand forecasts for the coming winter season are as follows: Hamilton County, 400 units; Butler County, 200 units; and Clermont County, 300 units. Contracts to provide the following quantities have been written: Southern Gas, 500 units; and Northwest Gas, 400 units. Distribution costs for the counties vary, depending upon the location of the suppliers. The distribution costs per unit (in thousands of dollars) are as follows:

		To	
From	**Hamilton**	**Butler**	**Clermont**
Southern Gas	10	20	15
Northwest Gas	12	15	18

a. Develop a network representation of this problem.
b. Develop a linear programming model that can be used to determine the plan that will minimize total distribution costs.
c. Describe the distribution plan and show the total distribution cost.
d. Recent residential and industrial growth in Butler County has the potential for increasing demand by as much as 100 units. Which supplier should Tri-County contract with to supply the additional capacity?

4. GloFish, Inc. has genetically engineered a species of fish that glows in normal lighting conditions. The company believes the new fish will be a huge success as a new pet option for children and adults alike. GloFish, Inc. has developed two varieties of its glowing fish: one that glows red and one that glows blue. GloFish currently "grows" its fish at two different fish farms in the United States: one in Michigan and one in Texas. The Michigan farm can produce up to 1 million red and 1 million blue GloFish per year; the Texas farm can produce up to 600,000 GloFish, but only in the blue variety. GloFish ships its fish between the fish farms and its three retail stores using a third-party shipper. The shipment rates between origins and destinations are shown in the following table. These costs are per fish and do not depend on the color of the fish being shipped.

	Cost of Shipping GloFish		
	Retailer 1	**Retailer 2**	**Retailer 3**
Michigan	$1.00	$2.50	$0.50
Texas	$2.00	$1.50	$2.80

Estimated demands by each retailer for each color of fish are shown in the following table.

	Demand for GloFish		
	Retailer 1	**Retailer 2**	**Retailer 3**
Red	320,000	300,000	160,000
Blue	380,000	450,000	290,000

a. What is the optimal policy for the fish farms? How many red and blue fish should be produced in Michigan and shipped to each retailer? How many blue fish should be produced in Texas and shipped to each retailer?
b. What is the minimum shipping cost that can be incurred and still meet demand requirements at retailers 1, 2, and 3?
c. How much should GloFish be willing to invest to enable the Texas farm to produce both red and blue GloFish while maintaining the maximum of 600,000 total fish produced at the Texas farm?

5. Premier Consulting's two consultants, Avery and Baker, can be scheduled to work for clients up to a maximum of 160 hours each over the next four weeks. A third consultant, Campbell, has some administrative assignments already planned and is available for clients up to a maximum of 140 hours over the next four weeks. The company has four clients with projects in process. The estimated hourly requirements for each of the clients over the four-week period are as follows:

Client	Hours
A	180
B	75
C	100
D	85

Hourly rates vary for the consultant–client combination and are based on several factors, including project type and the consultant's experience. The rates (dollars per hour) for each consultant–client combination are as follows:

	Client			
Consultant	A	B	C	D
Avery	100	125	115	100
Baker	120	135	115	120
Campbell	155	150	140	130

a. Develop a network representation of the problem.
b. Formulate the problem as a linear program, with the optimal solution providing the hours each consultant should be scheduled for each client to maximize the consulting firm's billings. What is the schedule and what is the total billing?
c. New information shows that Avery doesn't have the experience to be scheduled for client B. If this consulting assignment is not permitted, what impact does it have on total billings? What is the revised schedule?

6. Klein Chemicals, Inc., produces a special oil-based material that is currently in short supply. Four of Klein's customers have already placed orders that together exceed the combined capacity of Klein's two plants. Klein's management faces the problem of deciding how many units it should supply to each customer. Because the four customers are in different industries, different prices can be charged because of the various industry pricing structures. However, slightly different production costs at the two plants and varying transportation costs between the plants and customers make a "sell to the highest bidder"

strategy unacceptable. After considering price, production costs, and transportation costs, Klein established the following profit per unit for each plant–customer alternative:

	Customer			
Plant	D_1	D_2	D_3	D_4
Clifton Springs	\$32	\$34	\$32	\$40
Danville	\$34	\$30	\$28	\$38

The plant capacities and customer orders are as follows:

Plant	Capacity (units)	Distributor Orders (units)
Clifton Springs	5000	D_1 2000
		D_2 5000
Danville	3000	D_3 3000
		D_4 2000

How many units should each plant produce for each customer to maximize profits? Which customer demands will not be met? Show your network model and linear programming formulation.

7. Aggie Power Generation supplies electrical power to residential customers for many U.S. cities. Its main power generation plants are located in Los Angeles, Tulsa, and Seattle. The following table shows Aggie Power Generation's major residential markets, the annual demand in each market (in megawatts or MW), and the cost to supply electricity to each market from each power generation plant (prices are in \$/MW).

	Distribution Costs			
City	Los Angeles	Tulsa	Seattle	Demand (MW)
Seattle	\$356.25	\$593.75	\$59.38	950.00
Portland	\$356.25	\$593.75	\$178.13	831.25
San Francisco	\$178.13	\$475.00	\$296.88	2375.00
Boise	\$356.25	\$475.00	\$296.88	593.75
Reno	\$237.50	\$475.00	\$356.25	950.00
Bozeman	\$415.63	\$415.63	\$296.88	593.75
Laramie	\$356.25	\$415.63	\$356.25	1187.50
Park City	\$356.25	\$356.25	\$475.00	712.50
Flagstaff	\$178.13	\$475.00	\$593.75	1187.50
Durango	\$356.25	\$296.88	\$593.75	1543.75

a. If there are no restrictions on the amount of power that can be supplied by any of the power plants, what is the optimal solution to this problem? Which cities should be supplied by which power plants? What is the total annual power distribution cost for this solution?
b. If at most 4000 MW of power can be supplied by any one of the power plants, what is the optimal solution? What is the annual increase in power distribution cost that results from adding these constraints to the original formulation?

8. Forbelt Corporation has a one-year contract to supply motors for all refrigerators produced by the Ice Age Corporation. Ice Age manufactures the refrigerators at four locations around the country: Boston, Dallas, Los Angeles, and St. Paul. Plans call for the following number (in thousands) of refrigerators to be produced at each location:

Boston	50
Dallas	70
Los Angeles	60
St. Paul	80

Forbelt's three plants are capable of producing the motors. The plants and production capacities (in thousands) are as follows:

Denver	100
Atlanta	100
Chicago	150

Because of varying production and transportation costs, the profit that Forbelt earns on each lot of 1000 units depends on which plant produced the lot and which destination it was shipped to. The following table gives the accounting department estimates of the profit per unit (shipments will be made in lots of 1000 units):

	Shipped To			
Produced At	**Boston**	**Dallas**	**Los Angeles**	**St. Paul**
Denver	7	11	8	13
Atlanta	20	17	12	10
Chicago	8	18	13	16

With profit maximization as a criterion, Forbelt's management wants to determine how many motors should be produced at each plant and how many motors should be shipped from each plant to each destination.

a. Develop a network representation of this problem.
b. Find the optimal solution.

9. The Ace Manufacturing Company has orders for three similar products:

Product	**Orders (units)**
A	2000
B	500
C	1200

Three machines are available for the manufacturing operations. All three machines can produce all the products at the same production rate. However, due to varying defect percentages of each product on each machine, the unit costs of the products vary depending on the machine used. Machine capacities for the next week and the unit costs are as follows:

Machine	Capacity (units)
1	1500
2	1500
3	1000

	Product		
Machine	A	B	C
1	$1.00	$1.20	$0.90
2	$1.30	$1.40	$1.20
3	$1.10	$1.00	$1.20

Use the transportation model to develop the minimum cost production schedule for the products and machines. Show the linear programming formulation.

10. Hatcher Enterprises uses a chemical called Rbase in production operations at five divisions. Only six suppliers of Rbase meet Hatcher's quality control standards. All six suppliers can produce Rbase in sufficient quantities to accommodate the needs of each division. The quantity of Rbase needed by each Hatcher division and the price per gallon charged by each supplier are as follows:

Division	Demand (1000s of gallons)
1	40
2	45
3	50
4	35
5	45

Supplier	Price per gallon ($)
1	12.60
2	14.00
3	10.20
4	14.20
5	12.00
6	13.00

The cost per gallon ($) for shipping from each supplier to each division is provided in the following table:

	Supplier					
Division	1	2	3	4	5	6
1	2.75	2.50	3.15	2.80	2.75	2.75
2	0.80	0.20	5.40	1.20	3.40	1.00
3	4.70	2.60	5.30	2.80	6.00	5.60
4	2.60	1.80	4.40	2.40	5.00	2.80
5	3.40	0.40	5.00	1.20	2.60	3.60

Hatcher believes in spreading its business among suppliers so that the company will be less affected by supplier problems (e.g., labor strikes or resource availability). Company policy requires that each division have a separate supplier.

a. For each supplier–division combination, compute the total cost of supplying the division's demand.
b. Determine the optimal assignment of suppliers to divisions.

11. The distribution system for the Herman Company consists of three plants, two warehouses, and four customers. Plant capacities and shipping costs per unit (in $) from each plant to each warehouse are as follows:

	Warehouse		
Plant	1	2	Capacity
1	4	7	450
2	8	5	600
3	5	6	380

Customer demand and shipping costs per unit (in $) from each warehouse to each customer are as follows:

	Customer			
Warehouse	1	2	3	4
1	6	4	8	4
2	3	6	7	7
Demand	300	300	300	400

a. Develop a network representation of this problem.
b. Formulate a linear programming model of the problem.
c. Solve the linear program to determine the optimal shipping plan.

12. Refer to Problem 11. Suppose that shipments between the two warehouses are permitted at $2 per unit and that direct shipments can be made from plant 3 to customer 4 at a cost of $7 per unit.
a. Develop a network representation of this problem.
b. Formulate a linear programming model of this problem.
c. Solve the linear program to determine the optimal shipping plan.

13. Sports of All Sorts produces, distributes, and sells high-quality skateboards. Its supply chain consists of three factories (located in Detroit, Los Angeles, and Austin) that produce skateboards. The Detroit and Los Angeles facilities can produce 350 skateboards per week, but the Austin plant is larger and can produce up to 700 skateboards per week. Skateboards must be shipped from the factories to one of four distribution centers, or DCs (located in Iowa, Maryland, Idaho, and Arkansas). Each distribution center can process (repackage, mark for sale, and ship) at most 500 skateboards per week.

Skateboards are then shipped from the distribution centers to retailers. Sports of All Sorts supplies three major U.S. retailers: Just Sports, Sports 'N Stuff, and The Sports Dude. The weekly demands are 200 skateboards at Just Sports, 500 skateboards at Sports 'N Stuff, and 650 skateboards at The Sports Dude. The following tables display the per-unit costs for shipping skateboards between the factories and DCs and for shipping between the DCs and the retailers.

		Shipping Costs ($ per skateboard)		
Factory/DCs	**Iowa**	**Maryland**	**Idaho**	**Arkansas**
Detroit	25.00	25.00	35.00	40.00
Los Angeles	35.00	45.00	35.00	42.50
Austin	40.00	40.00	42.50	32.50
Retailers/DCs	**Iowa**	**Maryland**	**Idaho**	**Arkansas**
Just Sports	30.00	20.00	35.00	27.50
Sports 'N Stuff	27.50	32.50	40.00	25.00
The Sports Dude	30.00	40.00	32.50	42.50

a. Draw the network representation for this problem.
b. Build a model to minimize the transportation cost of a logistics system that will deliver skateboards from the factories to the distribution centers and from the distribution centers to the retailers. What is the optimal production strategy and shipping pattern for Sports of All Sorts? What is the minimum attainable transportation cost?
c. Sports of All Sorts is considering expansion of the Iowa DC capacity to 800 units per week. The annual amortized cost of expansion is $40,000. Should the company expand the Iowa DC capacity so that it can process 800 skateboards per week? (Assume 50 operating weeks per year.)

14. The Moore & Harman Company is in the business of buying and selling grain. An important aspect of the company's business is arranging for the purchased grain to be shipped to customers. If the company can keep freight costs low, profitability will improve.

The company recently purchased three rail cars of grain at Muncie, Indiana; six rail cars at Brazil, Indiana; and five rail cars at Xenia, Ohio. Twelve carloads of grain have been sold. The locations and the amount sold at each location are as follows:

Location	Number of Rail Car Loads
Macon, GA	2
Greenwood, SC	4
Concord, SC	3
Chatham, NC	3

All shipments must be routed through either Louisville or Cincinnati. Shown are the shipping costs per bushel (in cents) from the origins to Louisville and Cincinnati and the costs per bushel to ship from Louisville and Cincinnati to the destinations.

	To		
From	**Louisville**	**Cincinnati**	
Muncie	8	6	← Cost per bushel from Muncie to Cincinnati is 6¢
Brazil	3	8	
Xenia	9	3	

	To			
From	**Macon**	**Greenwood**	**Concord**	**Chatham**
Louisville	44	34	34	32
Cincinnati	57	35	28	24

Cost per bushel from Cincinnati to Greenwood is 35¢

Determine a shipping schedule that will minimize the freight costs necessary to satisfy demand. Which (if any) rail cars of grain must be held at the origin until buyers can be found?

15. The following linear programming formulation is for a transshipment problem:

$$\text{Min} \quad 11x_{13} + 12x_{14} + 10x_{21} + 8x_{34} + 10x_{35} + 11x_{42} + 9x_{45} + 12x_{52}$$

s.t.

$$\begin{array}{rcl}
x_{13} + x_{14} - x_{21} & \leq & 5 \\
x_{21} - x_{42} - x_{52} & \leq & 3 \\
x_{13} - x_{34} - x_{35} & = & 6 \\
-x_{14} - x_{34} + x_{42} + x_{45} & \leq & 2 \\
x_{35} + x_{45} - x_{52} & = & 4
\end{array}$$

$$x_{ij} \geq 0 \quad \text{for all } i, j$$

Show the network representation of this problem.

16. A rental car company has an imbalance of cars at seven of its locations. The following network shows the locations of concern (the nodes) and the cost to move a car between locations. A positive number by a node indicates an excess supply at the node, and a negative number indicates an excess demand.

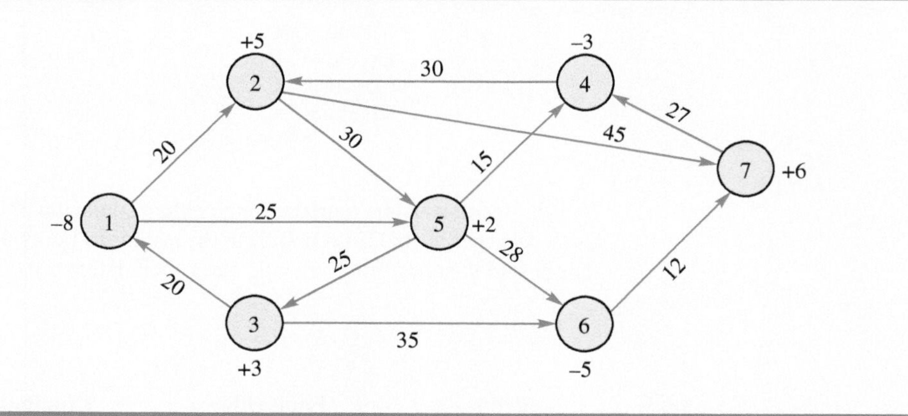

a. Develop a linear programming model of this problem.
b. Solve the model formulated in part (a) to determine how the cars should be redistributed among the locations.

17. Scott and Associates, Inc., is an accounting firm that has three new clients. Project leaders will be assigned to the three clients. Based on the different backgrounds and experiences of the leaders, the various leader–client assignments differ in terms of projected completion times. The possible assignments and the estimated completion times in days are as follows:

	Client		
Project Leader	**1**	**2**	**3**
Jackson	10	16	32
Ellis	14	22	40
Smith	22	24	34

a. Develop a network representation of this problem.
b. Formulate the problem as a linear program, and solve. What is the total time required?

18. CarpetPlus sells and installs floor covering for commercial buildings. Brad Sweeney, a CarpetPlus account executive, was just awarded the contract for five jobs. Brad must now assign a CarpetPlus installation crew to each of the five jobs. Because the commission Brad will earn depends on the profit CarpetPlus makes, Brad would like to determine an assignment that will minimize total installation costs. Currently, five installation crews are available for assignment. Each crew is identified by a color code, which aids in tracking of job progress on a large white board. The following table shows the costs (in hundreds of dollars) for each crew to complete each of the five jobs:

	Job				
Crew	**1**	**2**	**3**	**4**	**5**
Red	30	44	38	47	31
White	25	32	45	44	25
Blue	23	40	37	39	29
Green	26	38	37	45	28
Brown	26	34	44	43	28

a. Develop a network representation of the problem.
b. Formulate and solve a linear programming model to determine the minimum cost assignment.

19. A local television station plans to drop four Friday evening programs at the end of the season. Steve Botuchis, the station manager, developed a list of six potential replacement programs. Estimates of the advertising revenue ($) that can be expected for each of the new programs in the four vacated time slots are as follows. Mr. Botuchis asked you to find the assignment of programs to time slots that will maximize total advertising revenue.

	5:00–5:30 P.M.	**5:30–6:00 P.M.**	**7:00–7:30 P.M.**	**8:00–8:30 P.M.**
Home Improvement	5000	3000	6000	4000
World News	7500	8000	7000	5500
NASCAR Live	8500	5000	6500	8000
Wall Street Today	7000	6000	6500	5000
Hollywood Briefings	7000	8000	3000	6000
Ramundo & Son	6000	4000	4500	7000

20. The U.S. Cable Company uses a distribution system with five distribution centers and eight customer zones. Each customer zone is assigned a sole source supplier; each customer zone receives all of its cable products from the same distribution center. In an effort to balance demand and workload at the distribution centers, the company's vice president of logistics specified that distribution centers may not be assigned more than three customer zones. The following table shows the five distribution centers and cost of supplying each customer zone (in thousands of dollars):

	Customer Zones							
Distribution Centers	**Los Angeles**	**Chicago**	**Columbus**	**Atlanta**	**Newark**	**Kansas City**	**Denver**	**Dallas**
Plano	70	47	22	53	98	21	27	13
Nashville	75	38	19	58	90	34	40	26
Flagstaff	15	78	37	82	111	40	29	32
Springfield	60	23	8	39	82	36	32	45
Boulder	45	40	29	75	86	25	11	37

a. Determine the assignment of customer zones to distribution centers that will minimize cost.
b. Which distribution centers, if any, are not used?
c. Suppose that each distribution center is limited to a maximum of two customer zones. How does this constraint change the assignment and the cost of supplying customer zones?

21. United Express Service (UES) uses large quantities of packaging materials at its four distribution hubs. After screening potential suppliers, UES identified six vendors that can provide packaging materials that will satisfy its quality standards. UES asked each of the six vendors to submit bids to satisfy annual demand at each of its four distribution hubs over the next year. The following table lists the bids received (in thousands of dollars). UES wants to ensure that each of the distribution hubs is serviced by a different vendor. Which bids should UES accept, and which vendors should UES select to supply each distribution hub?

	Distribution Hub			
Bidder	**1**	**2**	**3**	**4**
Martin Products	190	175	125	230
Schmidt Materials	150	235	155	220
Miller Containers	210	225	135	260
D&J Burns	170	185	190	280
Larbes Furnishings	220	190	140	240
Lawler Depot	270	200	130	260

22. The analytics department head at a major midwestern university will be scheduling faculty to teach courses during the coming autumn term. Four core courses need to be covered. The four courses are at the undergraduate (UG), master of business administration (MBA), master of science (MS), and doctor of philosophy (Ph.D.) levels. Four professors will be assigned to the courses, with each professor receiving one of the courses. Student evaluations of professors are available from previous terms. Based on a rating scale of 4 (excellent), 3 (very good), 2 (average), 1 (fair), and 0 (poor), the average student evaluations for each professor are shown. Professor D does not have a Ph.D. and cannot

be assigned to teach the Ph.D. level course. If the department head makes teaching assignments based on maximizing the student evaluation ratings over all four courses, what staffing assignments should be made?

	Course			
Professor	UG	MBA	MS	Ph.D.
A	2.8	2.2	3.3	3.0
B	3.2	3.0	3.6	3.6
C	3.3	3.2	3.5	3.5
D	3.2	2.8	2.5	—

23. Find the shortest route from node 1 to node 7 in the network shown.

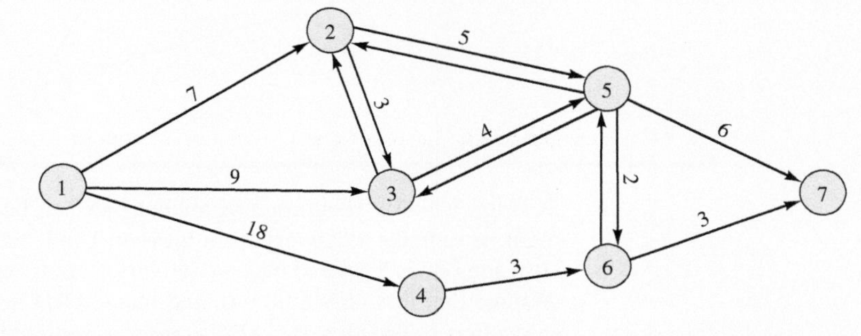

24. In the original Gorman Construction Company problem, we found the shortest distance from the office (node 1) to the construction site located at node 6. Because some of the roads are highways and others are city streets, the shortest-distance routes between the office and the construction site may not necessarily provide the quickest or shortest-time route. Shown here is the Gorman road network with travel time rather than distance. Find the shortest route from Gorman's office to the construction site at node 6 if the objective is to minimize travel time rather than distance.

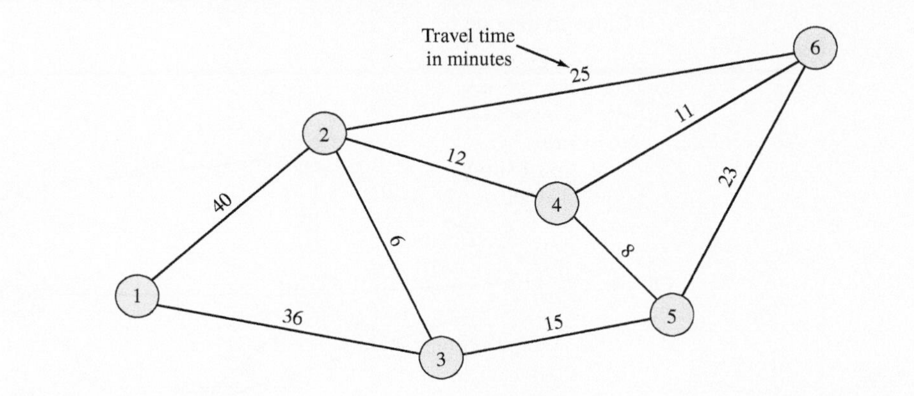

25. Cleveland Area Rapid Delivery (CARD) operates a delivery service in the Cleveland metropolitan area. Most of CARD's business involves rapid delivery of documents and

parcels between offices during the business day. CARD promotes its ability to make fast and on-time deliveries anywhere in the metropolitan area. When a customer calls with a delivery request, CARD quotes a guaranteed delivery time. The following network shows the street routes available. The numbers above each arc indicate the travel time in minutes between the two locations.

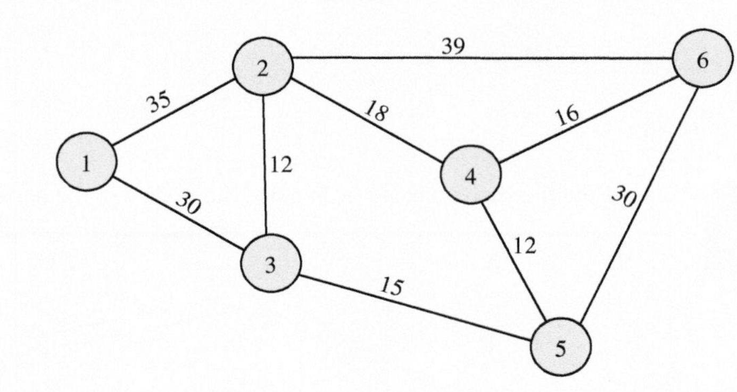

a. Develop a linear programming model that can be used to find the minimum time required to make a delivery from location 1 to location 6.
b. How long does it take to make a delivery from location 1 to location 6?
c. Assume that it is now 1:00 P.M. and that CARD just received a request for a pickup at location 1. The closest CARD courier is 8 minutes away from location 1. If CARD provides a 20% safety margin in guaranteeing a delivery time, what is the guaranteed delivery time if the package picked up at location 1 is to be delivered to location 6?

26. Morgan Trucking Company operates a special pickup and delivery service between Chicago and six other cities located in a four-state area. When Morgan receives a request for service, it dispatches a truck from Chicago to the city requesting service as soon as possible. With both fast service and minimum travel costs as objectives for Morgan, it is important that the dispatched truck take the shortest route from Chicago to the specified city. Assume that the following network (not drawn to scale) with distances given in miles represents the highway network for this problem. Find the shortest-route distances from Chicago to node 6.

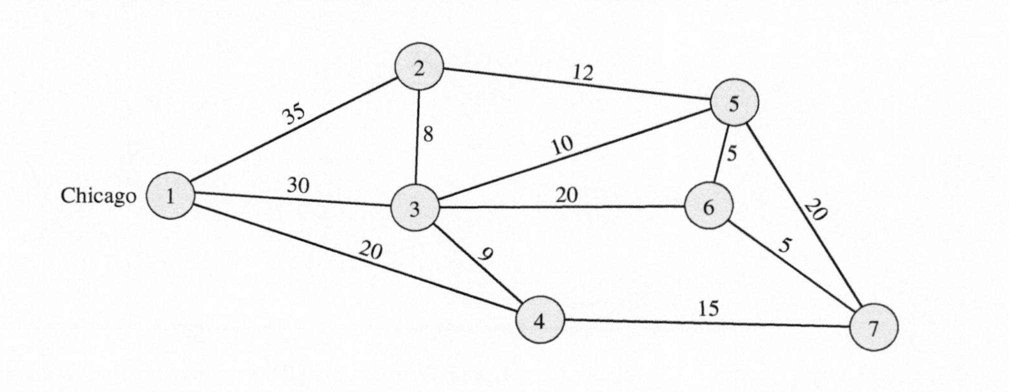

27. City Cab Company identified 10 primary pickup and drop locations for cab riders in New York City. In an effort to minimize travel time and improve customer service and the utilization of the company's fleet of cabs, management would like the cab drivers to take the shortest route between locations whenever possible. Using the following network of roads and streets, what is the route a driver beginning at location 1 should take to reach location 10? The travel times in minutes are shown on the arcs of the network. Note that there are two one-way streets and that the direction is shown by the arrows.

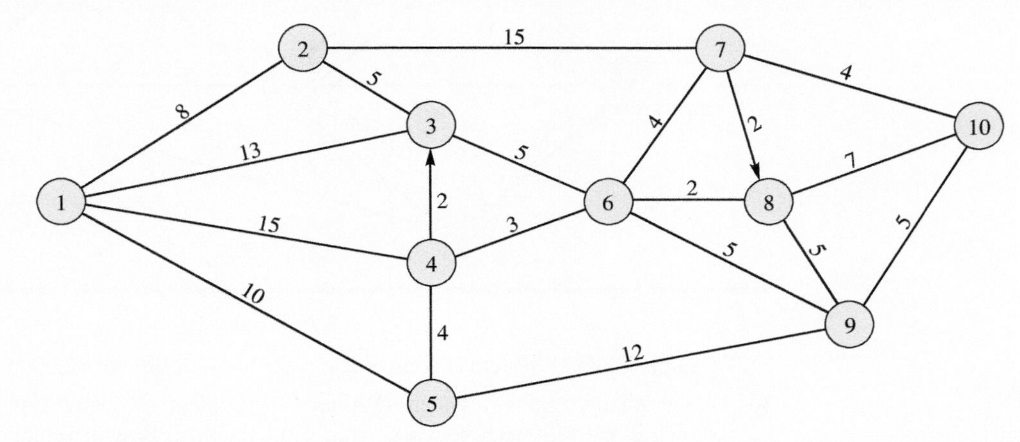

28. The five nodes in the following network represent points one year apart over a four-year period. Each node indicates a time when a decision is made to keep or replace a firm's computer equipment. If a decision is made to replace the equipment, a decision must also be made as to how long the new equipment will be used. The arc from node 0 to node 1 represents the decision to keep the current equipment one year and replace it at the end of the year. The arc from node 0 to node 2 represents the decision to keep the current equipment two years and replace it at the end of year 2. The numbers above the arcs indicate the total cost associated with the equipment replacement decisions. These costs include discounted purchase price, trade-in value, operating costs, and maintenance costs. Use a shortest-route model to determine the minimum cost equipment replacement policy for the four-year period.

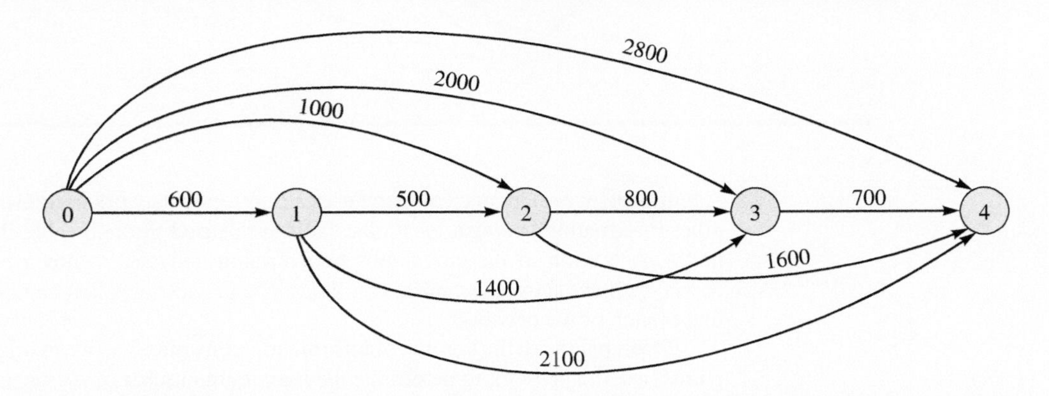

29. The north–south highway system passing through Albany, New York, can accommodate the capacities shown.

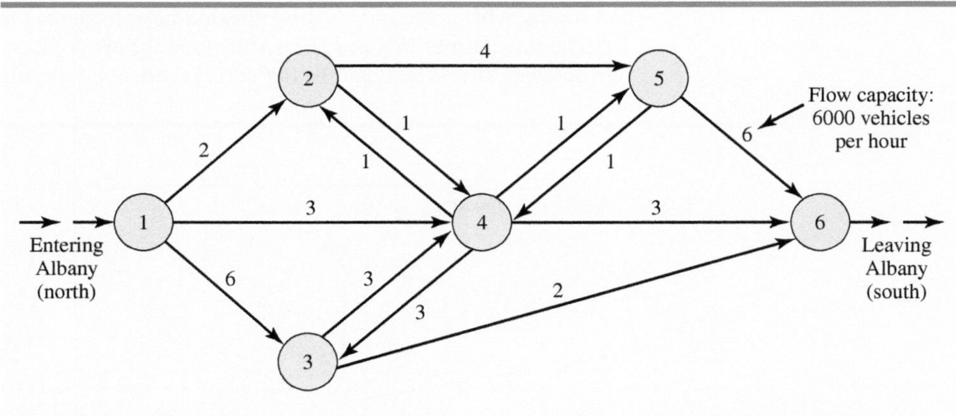

Can the highway system accommodate a north–south flow of 10,000 vehicles per hour?

30. If the Albany highway system described in Problem 29 has revised flow capacities as shown in the following network, what is the maximal flow in vehicles per hour through the system? How many vehicles per hour must travel over each road (arc) to obtain this maximal flow?

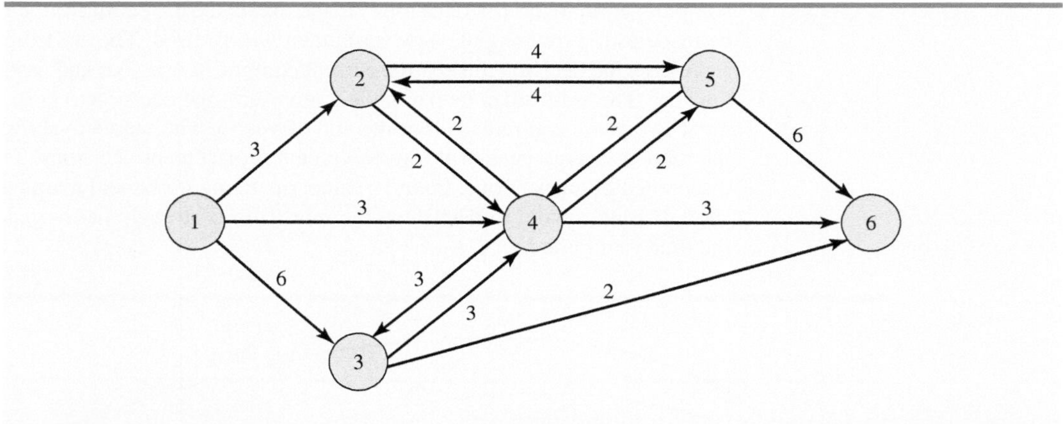

31. A long-distance telephone company uses a fiber-optic network to transmit phone calls and other information between locations. Calls are carried through cable lines and switching nodes. A portion of the company's transmission network is shown here. The numbers above each arc show the capacity in thousands of messages that can be transmitted over that branch of the network.

To keep up with the volume of information transmitted between origin and destination points, use the network to determine the maximum number of messages that may be sent from a city located at node 1 to a city located at node 7.

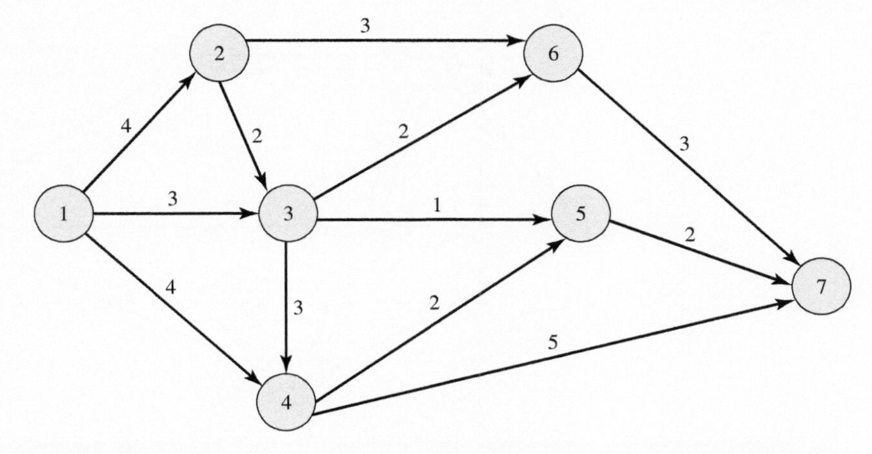

32. The High-Price Oil Company owns a pipeline network that is used to convey oil from its source to several storage locations. A portion of the network is as follows:

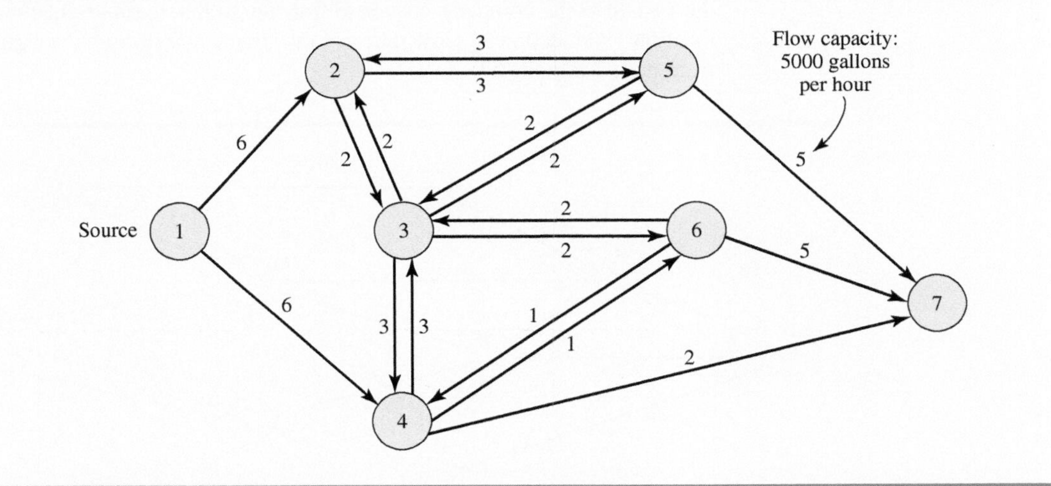

Due to the varying pipe sizes, the flow capacities vary. By selectively opening and closing sections of the pipeline network, the firm can supply any of the storage locations.

a. If the firm wants to fully utilize the system capacity to supply storage location 7, how long will it take to satisfy a location 7 demand of 100,000 gallons? What is the maximal flow for this pipeline system?

b. If a break occurs on line 2–3 and that line is closed down, what is the maximal flow for the system? How long will it take to transmit 100,000 gallons to location 7?

33. For the following highway network system, determine the maximal flow in vehicles per hour:

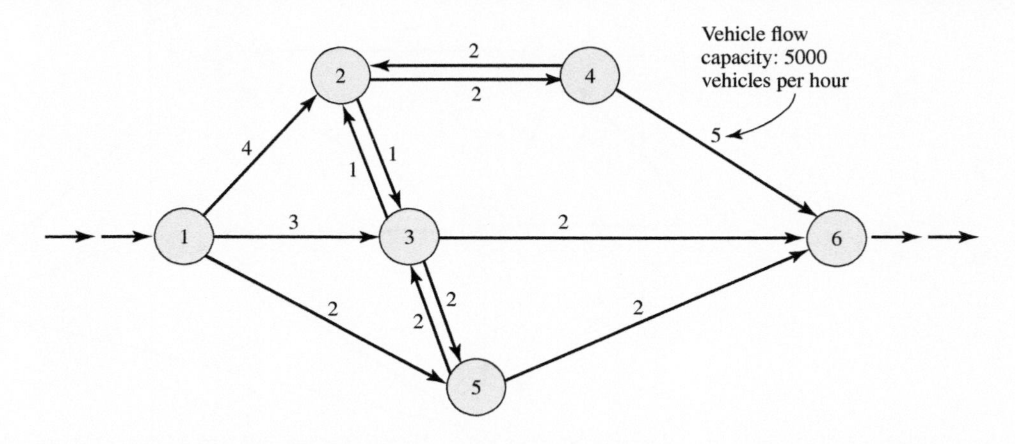

The highway commission is considering adding highway section 3–4 to permit a flow of 2000 vehicles per hour or, at an additional cost, a flow of 3000 vehicles per hour. What is your recommendation for the 3–4 arc of the network?

34. A chemical processing plant has a network of pipes that are used to transfer liquid chemical products from one part of the plant to another. The following pipe network has pipe flow capacities in gallons per minute as shown. What is the maximum flow capacity for the system if the company wishes to transfer as much liquid chemical as possible from location 1 to location 9? How much of the chemical will flow through the section of pipe from node 3 to node 5?

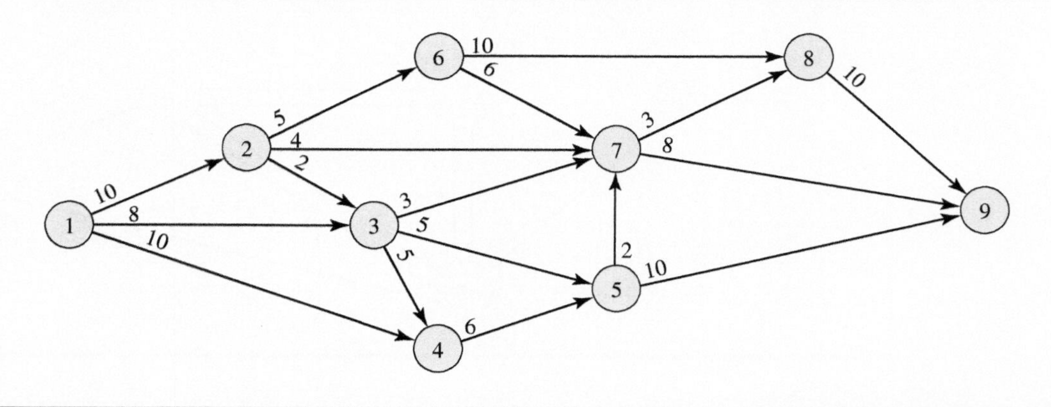

35. Refer to the Contois Carpets problem, for which the network representation is shown in Figure 10.20. Suppose that Contois has a beginning inventory of 50 yards of carpet and requires an inventory of 100 yards at the end of quarter 4.
   a. Develop a network representation of this modified problem.
   b. Develop a linear programming model and solve for the optimal solution.

36. Sanders Fishing Supply of Naples, Florida, manufactures a variety of fishing equipment that it sells throughout the United States. For the next three months, Sanders estimates demand for a particular product at 150, 250, and 300 units, respectively. Sanders can

supply this demand by producing on regular time or overtime. Because of other commitments and anticipated cost increases in month 3, the production capacities in units and the production costs per unit are as follows:

Production	Capacity (units)	Cost per Unit ($)
Month 1—Regular	275	50
Month 1—Overtime	100	80
Month 2—Regular	200	50
Month 2—Overtime	50	80
Month 3—Regular	100	60
Month 3—Overtime	50	100

Inventory may be carried from one month to the next, but the cost is \$20 per unit per month. For example, regular production from month 1 used to meet demand in month 2 would cost Sanders \$50 + \$20 = \$70 per unit. This same month 1 production used to meet demand in month 3 would cost Sanders \$50 + 2(\$20) = \$90 per unit.

a. Develop a network representation of this production scheduling problem as a transportation problem. (*Hint*: Use six origin nodes; the supply for origin node 1 is the maximum that can be produced in month 1 on regular time, and so on.)
b. Develop a linear programming model that can be used to schedule regular and overtime production for each of the three months.
c. What is the production schedule, how many units are carried in inventory each month, and what is the total cost?
d. Is there any unused production capacity? If so, where?

Case Problem 1 Solutions Plus

Solutions Plus is an industrial chemicals company that produces specialized cleaning fluids and solvents for a wide variety of applications. Solutions Plus just received an invitation to submit a bid to supply Great North American railroad with a cleaning fluid for locomotives. Great North American needs the cleaning fluid at 11 locations (railway stations); it provided the following information to Solutions Plus regarding the number of gallons of cleaning fluid required at each location (see Table 10.8).

Solutions Plus can produce the cleaning fluid at its Cincinnati plant for \$1.20 per gallon. Even though the Cincinnati location is its only plant, Solutions Plus has negotiated

TABLE 10.8 GALLONS OF CLEANING FLUID REQUIRED AT EACH LOCATION

Location	Gallons Required	Location	Gallons Required
Santa Ana	22,418	Glendale	33,689
El Paso	6,800	Jacksonville	68,486
Pendleton	80,290	Little Rock	148,586
Houston	100,447	Bridgeport	111,475
Kansas City	24,570	Sacramento	112,000
Los Angeles	64,761		

TABLE 10.9 FREIGHT COST ($ PER GALLON)

	Cincinnati	Oakland
Santa Ana	—	0.22
El Paso	0.84	0.74
Pendleton	0.83	0.49
Houston	0.45	—
Kansas City	0.36	—
Los Angeles	—	0.22
Glendale	—	0.22
Jacksonville	0.34	—
Little Rock	0.34	—
Bridgeport	0.34	—
Sacramento	—	0.15

with an industrial chemicals company located in Oakland, California, to produce and ship up to 500,000 gallons of the locomotive cleaning fluid to selected Solutions Plus customer locations. The Oakland company will charge Solutions Plus $1.65 per gallon to produce the cleaning fluid, but Solutions Plus thinks that the lower shipping costs from Oakland to some customer locations may offset the added cost to produce the product.

The president of Solutions Plus, Charlie Weaver, contacted several trucking companies to negotiate shipping rates between the two production facilities (Cincinnati and Oakland) and the locations where the railroad locomotives are cleaned. Table 10.9 shows the quotes received in terms of dollars per gallon. The "—" entries in Table 10.9 identify shipping routes that will not be considered because of the large distances involved. These quotes for shipping rates are guaranteed for one year.

To submit a bid to the railroad company, Solutions Plus must determine the price per gallon it will charge. Solutions Plus usually sells its cleaning fluids for 15% more than its cost to produce and deliver the product. For this big contract, however, Fred Roedel, the director of marketing, suggested that maybe the company should consider a smaller profit margin. In addition, to ensure that if Solutions Plus wins the bid, it will have adequate capacity to satisfy existing orders as well as accept orders for other new business, the management team decided to limit the number of gallons of the locomotive cleaning fluid produced in the Cincinnati plant to 500,000 gallons at most.

Managerial Report

You are asked to make recommendations that will help Solutions Plus prepare a bid. Your report should address, but not be limited to, the following issues:

1. If Solutions Plus wins the bid, which production facility (Cincinnati or Oakland) should supply the cleaning fluid to the locations where the railroad locomotives are cleaned? How much should be shipped from each facility to each location?
2. What is the breakeven point for Solutions Plus? That is, how low can the company go on its bid without losing money?
3. If Solutions Plus wants to use its standard 15% markup, how much should it bid?
4. Freight costs are significantly affected by the price of oil. The contract on which Solutions Plus is bidding is for two years. Discuss how fluctuation in freight costs might affect the bid Solutions Plus submits.

Case Problem 2 Supply Chain Design for the Darby Company

The Darby Company manufactures and distributes meters used to measure electric power consumption. The company started with a small production plant in El Paso and gradually built a customer base throughout Texas. A distribution center was established in Fort Worth, Texas, and later, as business expanded, a second distribution center was established in Santa Fe, New Mexico.

The El Paso plant was expanded when the company began marketing its meters in Arizona, California, Nevada, and Utah. With the growth of the West Coast business, the Darby Company opened a third distribution center in Las Vegas and just two years ago opened a second production plant in San Bernardino, California.

Manufacturing costs differ between the company's production plants. The cost of each meter produced at the El Paso plant is $10.50. The San Bernardino plant utilizes newer and more efficient equipment; as a result, manufacturing costs are $0.50 per meter less than at the El Paso plant.

Due to the company's rapid growth, not much attention had been paid to the efficiency of its supply chain, but Darby's management decided that it is time to address this issue. The cost of shipping a meter from each of the two plants to each of the three distribution centers is shown in Table 10.10.

The quarterly production capacity is 30,000 meters at the older El Paso plant and 20,000 meters at the San Bernardino plant. Note that no shipments are allowed from the San Bernardino plant to the Fort Worth distribution center.

The company serves nine customer zones from the three distribution centers. The forecast of the number of meters needed in each customer zone for the next quarter is shown in Table 10.11.

TABLE 10.10 SHIPPING COST PER UNIT FROM PRODUCTION PLANTS TO DISTRIBUTION CENTERS ($)

	Distribution Center		
Plant	**Fort Worth**	**Santa Fe**	**Las Vegas**
El Paso	3.20	2.20	4.20
San Bernardino	—	3.90	1.20

TABLE 10.11 QUARTERLY DEMAND FORECAST

Customer Zone	Demand (meters)
Dallas	6300
San Antonio	4880
Wichita	2130
Kansas City	1210
Denver	6120
Salt Lake City	4830
Phoenix	2750
Los Angeles	8580
San Diego	4460

TABLE 10.12 SHIPPING COST FROM THE DISTRIBUTION CENTERS TO THE CUSTOMER ZONES

Distribution Center	Customer Zone								
	Dallas	San Antonio	Wichita	Kansas City	Denver	Salt Lake City	Phoenix	Los Angeles	San Diego
Fort Worth	0.3	2.1	3.1	4.4	6.0	—	—	—	—
Santa Fe	5.2	5.4	4.5	6.0	2.7	4.7	3.4	3.3	2.7
Las Vegas	—	—	—	—	5.4	3.3	2.4	2.1	2.5

The cost per unit of shipping from each distribution center to each customer zone is given in Table 10.12; note that some distribution centers cannot serve certain customer zones. These are indicated by a dash, "—".

In its current supply chain, demand at the Dallas, San Antonio, Wichita, and Kansas City customer zones is satisfied by shipments from the Fort Worth distribution center. In a similar manner, the Denver, Salt Lake City, and Phoenix customer zones are served by the Santa Fe distribution center, and the Los Angeles and San Diego customer zones are served by the Las Vegas distribution center. To determine how many units to ship from each plant, the quarterly customer demand forecasts are aggregated at the distribution centers, and a transportation model is used to minimize the cost of shipping from the production plants to the distribution centers.

Managerial Report

You are asked to make recommendations for improving Darby Company's supply chain. Your report should address, but not be limited to, the following issues:

1. If the company does not change its current supply chain, what will its distribution costs be for the following quarter?
2. Suppose that the company is willing to consider dropping the distribution center limitations; that is, customers could be served by any of the distribution centers for which costs are available. Can costs be reduced? If so, by how much?
3. The company wants to explore the possibility of satisfying some of the customer demand directly from the production plants. In particular, the shipping cost is \$0.30 per unit from San Bernardino to Los Angeles and \$0.70 from San Bernardino to San Diego. The cost for direct shipments from El Paso to San Antonio is \$3.50 per unit. Can distribution costs be further reduced by considering these direct plant-to-customer shipments?
4. Over the next five years, Darby is anticipating moderate growth (5000 meters) to the north and west. Would you recommend that Darby consider plant expansion at this time?

Case Problem 3 DK Dental Care

DK Dental Care produces electric toothbrushes at facilities in Omaha, Tampa, Albuquerque, and Eugene. The finished products are shipped every four weeks to warehouses in Boise, Fort Worth, Mobile, Richmond, and Hanover. Each week Omaha produces 2000 cases of electric toothbrushes, Tampa produces 1500 cases of electric toothbrushes, Albuquerque produces 1200 cases of electric toothbrushes, and Eugene produces 2350 cases of electric toothbrushes.

The managers of DK are preparing for the next set of shipments. They have contacted the managers of their five warehouses and found that the Boise warehouse manager anticipates that she will have the capacity to store 8000 cases of electric toothbrushes, the Fort Worth warehouse manager anticipates that she will have the capacity to store 6400 cases of electric toothbrushes, the Mobile warehouse manager anticipates that he will have the capacity to store 5600 cases of electric toothbrushes, the Richmond warehouse manager anticipates that he will have the capacity to store 9200 cases of electric toothbrushes, and the Hanover warehouse manager anticipates that she will have the capacity to store 4800 cases of electric toothbrushes.

Typically, all existing inventory at the warehouses are shipped to retailers before the next shipment of toothbrushes arrives from the manufacturing facilities; however, the Hanover warehouse manager has also asked DK management to consider the large winter storm that is currently offshore in the northern Atlantic Ocean. There is a chance that this storm could develop into a major blizzard and move through Hanover at the time the shipments are due to arrive from the manufacturing facilities. If this happens, the Hanover warehouse will not be able to ship any of its current inventory to retailers and so would have no capacity for additional inventory of electric toothbrushes. Under these circumstances, the shipments to Hanover would be returned to the production facilities where they were produced and then reshipped to other warehouses, and DK would incur both the cost of shipping these electric toothbrushes to the Hanover warehouse and the cost of subsequently shipping them to alternative warehouses.

The transportation costs associated with shipping a case of electric toothbrushes from each production facility to each warehouse are provided in the following table.

	Warehouse				
Production Facility	Boise	Fort Worth	Mobile	Richmond	Hanover
Omaha	$2.15	$1.60	$2.10	$2.15	$2.20
Tampa	$2.30	$2.10	$1.25	$2.10	$2.35
Albuquerque	$1.95	$1.95	$2.25	$2.35	$2.90
Eugene	$1.85	$2.45	$2.75	$2.95	$2.75

Managerial Report

Find DK's optimal shipping plan for this month and prepare a report for the managers of DK that summarizes your findings and recommendations. Include the following:

1. Develop a "no blizzard" plan that tells DK how many cases of electric toothbrushes to ship from each production facility to each warehouse and the total cost associated with these shipments if DK were certain the potential blizzard would not prevent delivery of shipments to Hanover this month.
2. Develop an alternative "blizzard" plan that tells DK how many cases of electric toothbrushes to ship from each production facility to each warehouse and the total cost associated with these shipments if DK were certain the potential blizzard would prevent delivery of shipments to Hanover this month.
3. Suppose the National Weather Service has estimated that the probability this storm will develop into a major blizzard is 0.10, and so DK believes the probability is 0.10 that any shipment to Hanover will have to be returned to the original production facility and then shipped again to a different warehouse. Make a recommendation on whether DK should utilize the "no blizzard" plan or the "blizzard" plan and explain your recommendation.

4. For what probability of the blizzard preventing shipments to the Hanover warehouse are the expected shipping costs equal under the "no blizzard" and "blizzard" plans?

Appendix 10.1 Excel Solver Solution of Transportation, Transshipment, and Assignment Problems

In this appendix we will use an Excel worksheet and Excel Solver to solve transportation, transshipment, and assignment problems. We start with the Foster Generators transportation problem (see Section 10.1).

Transportation Problem

The first step is to enter the data for the transportation costs, the origin supplies, and the destination demands in the top portion of the worksheet. Then the linear programming model is developed in the bottom portion of the worksheet. As with all linear programs, the worksheet model has four key elements: the decision variables, the objective function, the constraint left-hand sides, and the constraint right-hand sides. For a transportation problem, the decision variables are the amounts shipped from each origin to each destination; the objective function is the total transportation cost; the left-hand sides are the number of units shipped from each origin and the number of units shipped into each destination; and the right-hand sides are the origin supplies and the destination demands.

The formulation and solution of the Foster Generators problem are shown in Figure 10.22. The data are in the top portion of the worksheet. The model appears in the bottom portion of the worksheet.

Formulation

The data and descriptive labels are contained in cells A1:F8. The transportation costs are in cells B5:E7. The origin supplies are in cells F5:F7, and the destination demands are in cells B8:E8. The key elements of the model required by the Excel Solver are the decision variables, the objective function, the constraint left-hand sides, and the constraint right-hand sides.

Decision Variables Cells B17:E19 are reserved for the decision variables. The optimal values are shown to be $x_{11} = 3500$, $x_{12} = 1500$, $x_{22} = 2500$, $x_{23} = 2000$, $x_{24} = 1500$, and $x_{41} = 2500$. All other decision variables equal zero, indicating that nothing will be shipped over the corresponding routes.

Objective Function The formula SUMPRODUCT(B5:E7,B17:E19) has been placed into cell A13 to compute the cost of the solution. The minimum cost solution is shown to have a value of $39,500.

Left-Hand Sides Cells F17:F19 contain the left-hand sides for the supply constraints, and cells B20:E20 contain the left-hand sides for the demand constraints.

Cell F17 = SUM(B17:E17) (Copy to F18:F19)
Cell B20 = SUM(B17:B19) (Copy to C20:E20)

FIGURE 10.22 EXCEL SOLVER SOLUTION OF THE FOSTER GENERATORS PROBLEM

Foster

	A	B	C	D	E	F	G	H
1	**Foster Generators**							
2								
3			**Destination**					
4	**Origin**	to Boston	to Chicago	to St. Louis	to Lexington	**Supply**		
5	Cleveland	3	2	7	6	5000		
6	Bedford	7	5	2	3	6000		
7	York	2	5	4	5	2500		
8	**Demand**	6000	4000	2000	1500			
9								
10								
11	**Model**							
12	**Minimize Total Cost**							
13	39500							
14								
15			**Destination**					
16	**Origin**	to Boston	to Chicago	to St. Louis	to Lexington	**Total**		
17	Cleveland	3500	1500	0	0	5000	<=	5000
18	Bedford	0	2500	2000	1500	6000	<=	6000
19	York	2500	0	0	0	2500	<=	2500
20	**Total**	6000	4000	2000	1500			
21		=	=	=	=			
22		6000	4000	2000	1500			
23								

Right-Hand Sides Cells H17:H19 contain the right-hand sides for the supply constraints, and cells B22:E22 contain the right-hand sides for the demand constraints.

Cell H17 = F5 (Copy to H18:H19)
Cell B22 = B8 (Copy to C22:E22)

Excel Solver Solution

The solution shown in Figure 10.22 can be obtained by selecting **Solver** from the **Analysis Group** in the **Data Ribbon**. When the **Solver Parameters** dialog box appears, enter the proper values for the constraints and the objective function, select **Simplex LP,** and click the checkbox for **Make Unconstrained Variables Non-negative.** Then click **Solve.** The information entered into the **Solver Parameters** dialog box is shown in Figure 10.23.

Transshipment Problem

The worksheet model we present for the transshipment problem can be used for all the network flow problems (transportation, transshipment, and assignment) in this chapter. We organize the worksheet into two sections: an arc section and a node section. Let us illustrate by showing the worksheet formulation and solution of the Ryan Electronics transshipment problem. Refer to Figure 10.24 as we describe the steps involved.

FIGURE 10.23 EXCEL SOLVER PARAMETERS DIALOG BOX FOR THE FOSTER GENERATORS PROBLEM

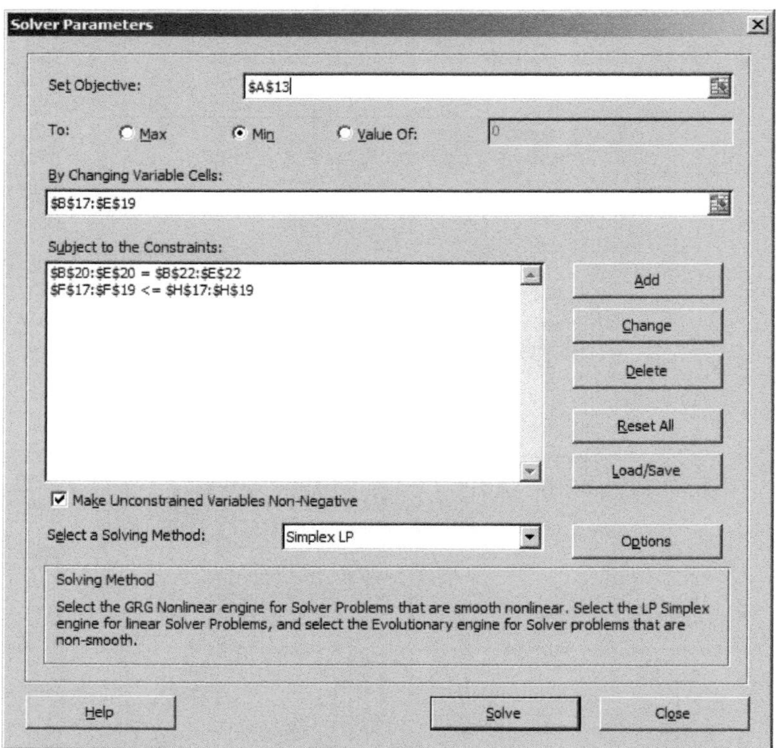

FIGURE 10.24 EXCEL SOLVER SOLUTION FOR THE RYAN ELECTRONICS PROBLEM

Ryan

	A	B	C	D	E	F	G	H	I	J	K
1	**Ryan Electronics Transshipment**										
2											
3											
4	**Arc**	**Cost**									
5	Denver - Kansas City	2	550				**Units Shipped**		**Net**		
6	Denver - Louisville	3	50			**Node**	In	Out	**Shipments**		**Supply**
7	Atlanta - Kansas City	3	0			Denver		600	600	<=	600
8	Atlanta - Louisville	1	400			Atlanta		400	400	<=	400
9	Kansas City - Detroit	2	200			Kansas City	550	550	0	=	0
10	Kansas City - Miami	6	0			Louisville	450	450	0	=	0
11	Kansas City - Dallas	3	350			Detroit	200		-200	=	-200
12	Kansas City - New Orleans	6	0			Miami	150		-150	=	-150
13	Louisville - Detroit	4	0			Dallas	350		-350	=	-350
14	Louisville - Miami	4	150			New Orleans	300		-300	=	-300
15	Louisville - Dallas	6	0								
16	Louisville - New Orleans	5	300								
17											
18				**Minimize Total Cost**			5200				
19											

Formulation

The arc section uses cells A4:C16. Each arc is identified in cells A5:A16. The arc costs are identified in cells B5:B16, and cells C5:C16 are reserved for the values of the decision variables (the amount shipped over the arcs).

The node section uses cells F5:K14. Each of the nodes is identified in cells F7:F14. The following formulas are entered into cells G7:H14 to represent the flow out and the flow in for each node:

Units shipped in: Cell G9 = C5+C7
Cell G10 = C6+C8
Cell G11 = C9+C13
Cell G12 = C10+C14
Cell G13 = C11+C15
Cell G14 = C12+C16

Units shipped out: Cell H7 = SUM(C5:C6)
Cell H8 = SUM(C7:C8)
Cell H9 = SUM(C9:C12)
Cell H10 = SUM(C13:C16)

The net shipments in cells I7:I14 are the flows out minus the flows in for each node. For supply nodes, the flow out will exceed the flow in, resulting in positive net shipments. For demand nodes, the flow out will be less than the flow in, resulting in negative net shipments. The "net" supply appears in cells K7:K14. Note that the net supply is negative for demand nodes.

Decision Variables: Cells C5:C16 are reserved for the decision variables. The optimal number of units to ship over each arc is shown.

Objective Function: The formula =SUMPRODUCT(B5:B16,C5:C16) is placed into cell G18 to show the total cost associated with the solution. As shown, the minimum total cost is $5200.

Left-Hand Sides: The left-hand sides of the constraints represent the net shipments for each node. Cells I7:I14 are reserved for these constraints.
Cell I7 = H7-G7 (Copy to I8:I14)

Right-Hand Sides: The right-hand sides of the constraints represent the supply at each node. Cells K7:K14 are reserved for these values. (Note the negative supply at the four demand nodes.)

Excel Solver Solution

The solution can be obtained by selecting **Solver** from the **Analysis Group** in the **Data Ribbon**. When the **Solver Parameters** dialog box appears, enter the proper values for the constraints and the objective function, select **Simplex LP**, and click the checkbox for **Make Unconstrained Variables Non-negative.** Then click **Solve.** The information entered into the **Solver Parameters** dialog box is shown in Figure 10.25.

FIGURE 10.25 EXCEL SOLVER PARAMETERS DIALOG BOX FOR THE RYAN ELECTRONICS PROBLEM

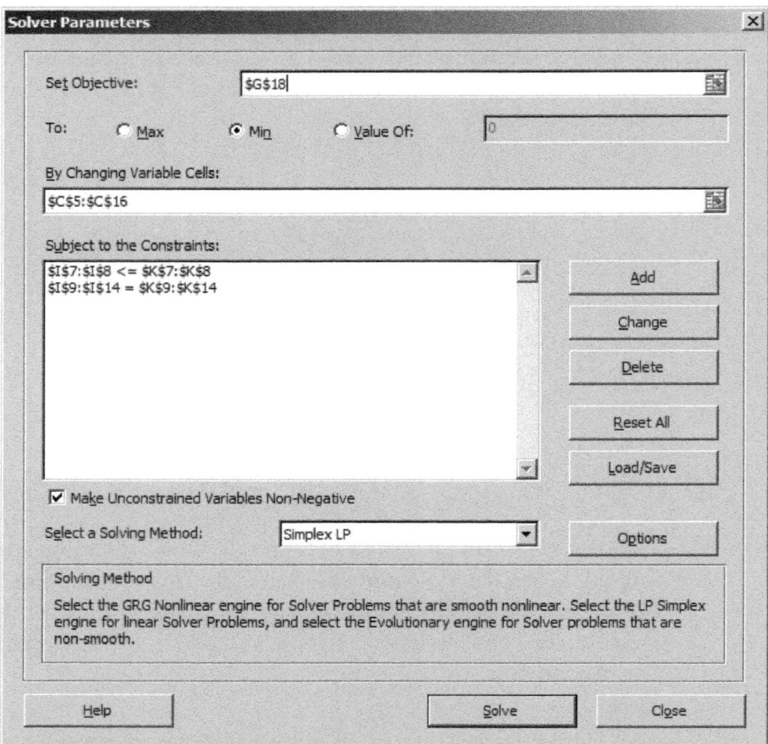

Assignment Problem

The first step is to enter the data for the assignment costs in the top portion of the worksheet. Even though the assignment model is a special case of the transportation model, it is not necessary to enter values for origin supplies and destination demands because they are always equal to 1.

The linear programming model is developed in the bottom portion of the worksheet. As with all linear programs, the model has four key elements: the decision variables, the objective function, the constraint left-hand sides, and the constraint right-hand sides. For an assignment problem the decision variables indicate whether an agent is assigned to a task (with a 1 for yes or 0 for no); the objective function is the total cost of all assignments; the constraint left-hand sides are the number of tasks that are assigned to each agent and the number of agents that are assigned to each task; and the right-hand sides are the number of tasks each agent can handle (1) and the number of agents each task requires (1). The worksheet formulation and solution for the Fowle marketing research problem are shown in Figure 10.26.

FIGURE 10.26 EXCEL SOLVER SOLUTION OF THE FOWLE MARKETING RESEARCH PROBLEM

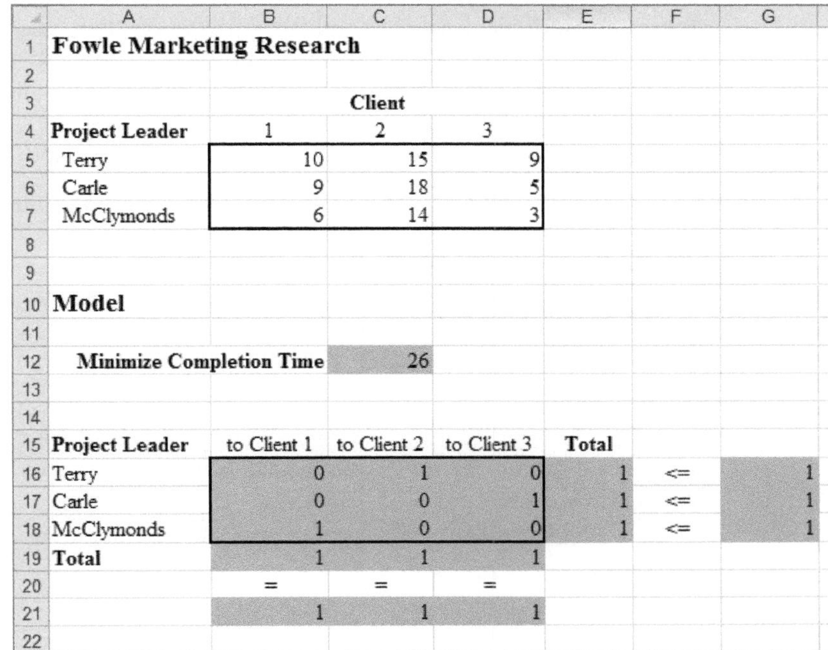

	A	B	C	D	E	F	G
1	**Fowle Marketing Research**						
2							
3			**Client**				
4	**Project Leader**	1	2	3			
5	Terry	10	15	9			
6	Carle	9	18	5			
7	McClymonds	6	14	3			
8							
9							
10	**Model**						
11							
12	**Minimize Completion Time**		26				
13							
14							
15	**Project Leader**	to Client 1	to Client 2	to Client 3	**Total**		
16	Terry	0	1	0	1	<=	1
17	Carle	0	0	1	1	<=	1
18	McClymonds	1	0	0	1	<=	1
19	**Total**	1	1	1			
20		=	=	=			
21		1	1	1			
22							

Fowle

Formulation

The data and descriptive labels are contained in cells A3:D7. Note that we have not inserted supply and demand values because they are always equal to 1 in an assignment problem. The model appears in the bottom portion of the worksheet.

Decision Variables — Cells B16:D18 are reserved for the decision variables. The optimal values are shown to be $x_{12} = 1$, $x_{23} = 1$, and $x_{31} = 1$, with all other variables $= 0$.

Objective Function — The formula =SUMPRODUCT(B5:D7,B16:D18) has been placed into cell C12 to compute the number of days required to complete all the jobs. The minimum time solution has a value of 26 days.

Left-Hand Sides — Cells E16:E18 contain the left-hand sides of the constraints for the number of clients each project leader can handle. Cells B19:D19 contain the left-hand sides of the constraints requiring that each client must be assigned a project leader.

Cell E16 = SUM(B16:D16) (Copy to E17:E18)

Cell B19 = SUM(B16:B18) (Copy to C19:D19)

Right-Hand Sides — Cells G16:G18 contain the right-hand sides for the project leader constraints, and cells B21:D21 contain the right-hand sides for the client constraints. All right-hand-side cell values are 1.

Excel Solver Solution

The solution shown in Figure 10.26 can be obtained by selecting **Solver** from the **Analysis Group** in the **Data Ribbon**. When the **Solver Parameters** dialog box appears, enter the proper values for the constraints and the objective function, select **Simplex LP,** and click the checkbox for **Make Unconstrained Variables Non-negative.** Then click **Solve.** The information entered into the **Solver Parameters** dialog box is shown in Figure 10.27.

FIGURE 10.27 EXCEL SOLVER PARAMETERS DIALOG BOX FOR THE FOWLE MARKETING RESEARCH PROBLEM

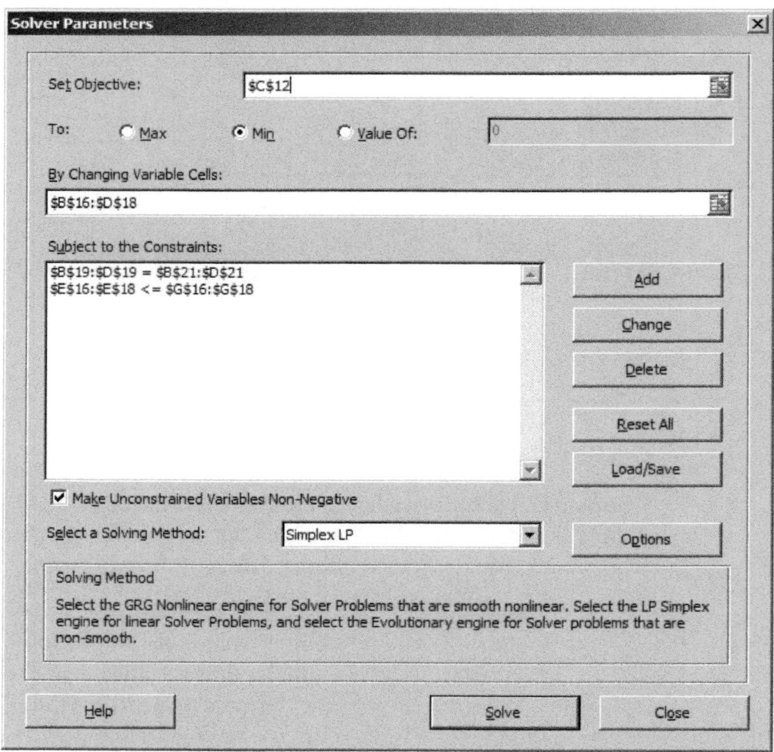

CHAPTER 11

Integer Linear Programming

CONTENTS

In this chapter we discuss a class of problems that are modeled as linear programs with the additional requirement that one or more variables must be integer. Such problems are called **integer linear programs**. If all variables must be integer, we have an all-integer linear program. If some, but not all, variables must be integer, we have a mixed-integer linear program. In many applications of integer linear programming, one or more integer variables are required to equal either 0 or 1. Such variables are called 0-1 or *binary variables*. If all variables are 0-1 variables, we have a 0-1 integer linear program.

Integer variables—especially 0-1 variables—provide substantial modeling flexibility. As a result, the number of applications that can be addressed with linear programming methodology is expanded. For instance, the Q.M. in Action, Optimizing the Transport of Oil Rig Crews, describes how Petrobras uses a model with 0-1 variables for assigning helicopters to flights for transporting crews to and from its oil rigs. Later Q.M. in Action articles describe how the Virginia Court of Appeals uses a 0-1 integer program for scheduling panels of judges to preside over appeal hearings, and how a series of three integer programming models was used to schedule volunteers for the 2003 Edmonton Folk Festival. Many other applications of integer programming are described throughout the chapter.

The objective of this chapter is to provide an applications-oriented introduction to integer linear programming. First, we discuss the different types of integer linear programming models. Then we show the formulation, graphical solution, and computer solution of an all-integer linear program. In Section 11.3 we discuss five applications of integer linear programming that make use of 0-1 variables: capital budgeting, fixed cost, supply chain design, bank location, and market share optimization problems. In Section 11.4 we provide additional illustrations of the modeling flexibility provided by 0-1 variables. Appendix 11.1 and Appendix 11.2 illustrate the use of Excel and LINGO for solving integer programs.

The cost of the added modeling flexibility provided by integer programming is that problems involving integer variables are often much more difficult to solve than linear programs. A linear programming problem with several thousand continuous variables can be solved with any of several commercial linear programming solvers. However, an all-integer linear programming problem with less than 100 variables can be extremely difficult to solve. Experienced management scientists can help identify the types of integer linear programs that are easy, or at least reasonable, to solve. Excel Solver has the capability to solve integer linear programs. Additionally, commercial computer software packages, such as LINGO, CPLEX, Xpress-MP, have extensive integer programming capability, and very robust open-source software packages for integer programming are also available.

Q.M. *in* ACTION

*OPTIMIZING THE TRANSPORT OF OIL RIG CREWS**

Petrobras, the largest corporation in Brazil, operates approximately 80 offshore oil production and exploration platforms in the oil-rich Campos Basin. One of Petrobras' biggest challenges is the planning of its logistics, including how to efficiently and safely transport nearly 1900 employees per day from its four mainland bases to the offshore platforms. Every day, planners must route and schedule the helicopters used to transport Petrobras employees from the mainland to the offshore locations and back to the mainland. This routing and scheduling

(continued)

*Based on F. Menezes et al., "Optimizing Helicopter Transport of Oil Rig Crews at Petrobras," *Interfaces* 40, no. 5 (September–October 2010): 408–416.

problem is challenging because there are over a billion possible combinations of schedules and routes.

Petrobras uses mixed integer linear optimization to solve its helicopter transport scheduling and routing problem. The objective function of the optimization model is a weighted function designed to ensure safety, minimize unmet demand, and minimize the cost of the transport of its crews. Because offshore landings are the riskiest part of the transport, the safety objective is met by minimizing the number of offshore landings required in the schedule. Numerous constraints must be met in planning these routes and schedule. These include limiting the number of departures from a platform at certain times; ensuring no time conflicts for a given helicopter and pilot; ensuring proper breaks for pilots; limiting the number of flights per day for a given helicopter and routing restrictions. The decision variables include binary variables for assigning helicopters to flights and pilots to break times, as well as variables on the number of passengers per flight.

Compared to the previously-used manual approach to this problem, the new approach using the integer optimization model transports the same number of passengers but with 18% fewer offshore landings, 8% less flight time, and a reduction in cost of 14%. The annual cost savings is estimated to be approximately $24 million.

NOTES AND COMMENTS

1. Because integer linear programs are harder to solve than linear programs, one should not try to solve a problem as an integer program if simply rounding the linear programming solution is adequate. In many linear programming problems, such as those in previous chapters, rounding has little economic consequence on the objective function, and feasibility is not an issue. But, in problems such as determining how many jet engines to manufacture, the consequences of rounding can be substantial, and integer programming methodology should be employed.
2. Some linear programming problems have a special structure, which guarantees that the variables will have integer values. The assignment, transportation, and transshipment problems of Chapter 10 have such structures. If the supply and the demand for transportation and transshipment problems are integer, the optimal linear programming solution will provide integer amounts shipped. For the assignment problem, the optimal linear programming solution will consist of 0s and 1s. So, for these specially structured problems, linear programming methodology can be used to find optimal integer solutions. Integer linear programming algorithms are not necessary.

11.1 Types of Integer Linear Programming Models

The only difference between the problems studied in this chapter and the ones studied in earlier chapters on linear programming is that one or more variables are required to be integer. If all variables are required to be integer, we have an **all-integer linear program**. The following is a two-variable, all-integer linear programming model:

$$
\begin{aligned}
\text{Max} \quad & 2x_1 + 3x_2 \\
\text{s.t.} \quad & \\
& 3x_1 + 3x_2 \leq 12 \\
& \tfrac{2}{3}x_1 + 1x_2 \leq 4 \\
& 1x_1 + 2x_2 \leq 6 \\
& x_1, x_2 \geq 0 \text{ and integer}
\end{aligned}
$$

If we drop the phrase "and integer" from the last line of this model, we have the familiar two-variable linear program. The linear program that results from dropping the integer requirements is called the **LP Relaxation** of the integer linear program.

If some, but not necessarily all, variables are required to be integer, we have a **mixed-integer linear program**. The following is a two-variable, mixed-integer linear program:

$$\begin{aligned} \text{Max} \quad & 3x_1 + 4x_2 \\ \text{s.t.} \quad & \\ & -1x_1 + 2x_2 \leq 8 \\ & 1x_1 + 2x_2 \leq 12 \\ & 2x_1 + 1x_2 \leq 16 \\ & x_1, x_2 \geq 0 \text{ and } x_2 \text{ integer} \end{aligned}$$

We obtain the LP Relaxation of this mixed-integer linear program by dropping the requirement that x_2 be integer.

In some applications, the integer variables may only take on the values 0 or 1. Then we have a **0-1 linear integer program**. As we see later in the chapter, 0-1 variables provide additional modeling capability. The Q.M. in Action, Scheduling the Virginia Court of Appeals, describes how the Virginia Court of Appeals uses a 0-1 integer program to schedule hearings for its appeals and how it constructs the panels of judges to ensure that laws governing the process are followed.

Q.M. *in* ACTION

*SCHEDULING THE VIRGINIA COURT OF APPEALS**

Every city and county in the state of Virginia has a circuit court that hears felony cases as well as claims of more than $25,000. In order to ensure fair outcomes, the Court of Appeals of the state of Virginia hears appeals of decisions handed down by the circuit courts. The Court of Appeals consists of 11 judges, who sit in panels of three judges for hearing sessions. A number of full-court sessions are also held, which by law must consist of at least 8 of the 11 judges. In order to ensure a fair and equitable judicial system for its citizens, Virginia law specifies a variety of constraints for how often, when, and where these sessions are scheduled and the makeup of each panel of judges.

The scheduling of the appeal hearings is based on forecasted case load. The construction of each panel of judges, when done by hand, is a complex and arduous task. The manual process was to use a wall-sized calendar with color-coded magnets to construct a full schedule based on extensive trial and error, often requiring 150 hours to complete. Court of Appeals staff members approached Virginia Commonwealth University about the possibility of automating the scheduling process. Working with the information technology department of the Court of Appeals, the Department of Statistics and Operations Research at Virginia Commonwealth developed a binary integer program to solve this complex problem.

Virginia law dictates that numerous restrictions must be satisfied with the schedule for the hearings. For example, no panel sessions may be scheduled during a week of a full-court session. Panels must be held in each of the state's four districts; in a given district, hearings must be at least three weeks apart. Each of the four districts must have a session in the month of September, and dates on which there are judge's conferences or retreats as well as certain holidays, must be avoided.

(continued)

*Based on J. Paul Brooks, "The Court of Appeals of Virginia Uses Integer Programming and Cloud Computing to Schedule Sessions," *Interfaces* (November/December, 2012): 544–553.

Likewise, restrictions exist on the makeup of the judges' panel for each session. Each judge must serve on a panel with every other judge at least once, and any two judges can be on at most three of the same three-judge panels. Each judge must have a panel in each district but can have at most two panels in any district that is not his/her home district. Other constraints similar to these must also be enforced.

In addition to the restrictions mentioned, each judge specifies times to be avoided if possible. The objective of the integer programing model is to minimize the number of assignments where a judge is assigned to a session that he/she requested to be avoided. The decision variables for the model are binary variables that indicate (1) if a judge is assigned to a session or not, (2) if a session is held or not, (3) if a judge serves in a given month or not, and (4) if a pair of judges works in a given session or not.

The resulting integer programming model is quite large, but with some preprocessing to eliminate obvious infeasible options, the model size was reduced from more than 80,000 variables and millions of constraints to 10,000 variables and approximately 100,000 constraints. Rather than buying software to solve the problem, the team used an optimization service available over the web to solve the problem. The solution time was about 10 hours. The team also constructed a backend solution processor in Microsoft Access to allow easy visualization of the schedule, which is important for presenting the proposed solution for approval. Through the use of the optimization model, the deputy clerk is now free to use the 150 hours that were previously spent on scheduling for more productive activities.

11.2 Graphical and Computer Solutions for an All-Integer Linear Program

Eastborne Realty has $2 million available for the purchase of new rental property. After an initial screening, Eastborne reduced the investment alternatives to townhouses and apartment buildings. Each townhouse can be purchased for $282,000, and five are available. Each apartment building can be purchased for $400,000, and the developer will construct as many buildings as Eastborne wants to purchase.

Eastborne's property manager can devote up to 140 hours per month to these new properties; each townhouse is expected to require 4 hours per month, and each apartment building is expected to require 40 hours per month. The annual cash flow, after deducting mortgage payments and operating expenses, is estimated to be $10,000 per townhouse and $15,000 per apartment building. Eastborne's owner would like to determine the number of townhouses and the number of apartment buildings to purchase to maximize annual cash flow.

We begin by defining the decision variables as follows:

$$T = \text{number of townhouse}$$
$$A = \text{number of apartment buildings}$$

The objective function for cash flow (in thousands of dollars) is

$$\text{Max } 10T + 15A$$

Three constraints must be satisfied:

$$\begin{aligned} 282T + 400A &\leq 2000 \quad && \text{Funds available (\$1000s)} \\ 4T + 40A &\leq 140 && \text{Manager's time (hours)} \\ T \qquad\quad &\leq 5 && \text{Townhouses available} \end{aligned}$$

The variables T and A must be nonnegative. In addition, the purchase of a fractional number of townhouses and/or a fractional number of apartment buildings is unacceptable. Thus, T and A must be integer. The model for the Eastborne Realty problem is the following all-integer linear program:

$$
\begin{aligned}
\text{Max} \quad & 10T + 15A \\
\text{s.t.} \quad & \\
& 282T + 400A \leq 2000 \\
& 4T + 40A \leq 140 \\
& T \leq 5 \\
& T, A \geq 0 \text{ and integer}
\end{aligned}
$$

Graphical Solution of the LP Relaxation

Suppose that we drop the integer requirements for T and A and solve the LP Relaxation of the Eastborne Realty problem. Using the graphical solution procedure, as presented in Chapter 7, the optimal linear programming solution is shown in Figure 11.1. It is $T = 2.479$ townhouses and $A = 3.252$ apartment buildings. The optimal value of the objective function is 73.574, which indicates an annual cash flow of \$73,574. Unfortunately,

FIGURE 11.1 GRAPHICAL SOLUTION TO THE LP RELAXATION OF THE EASTBORNE REALTY PROBLEM

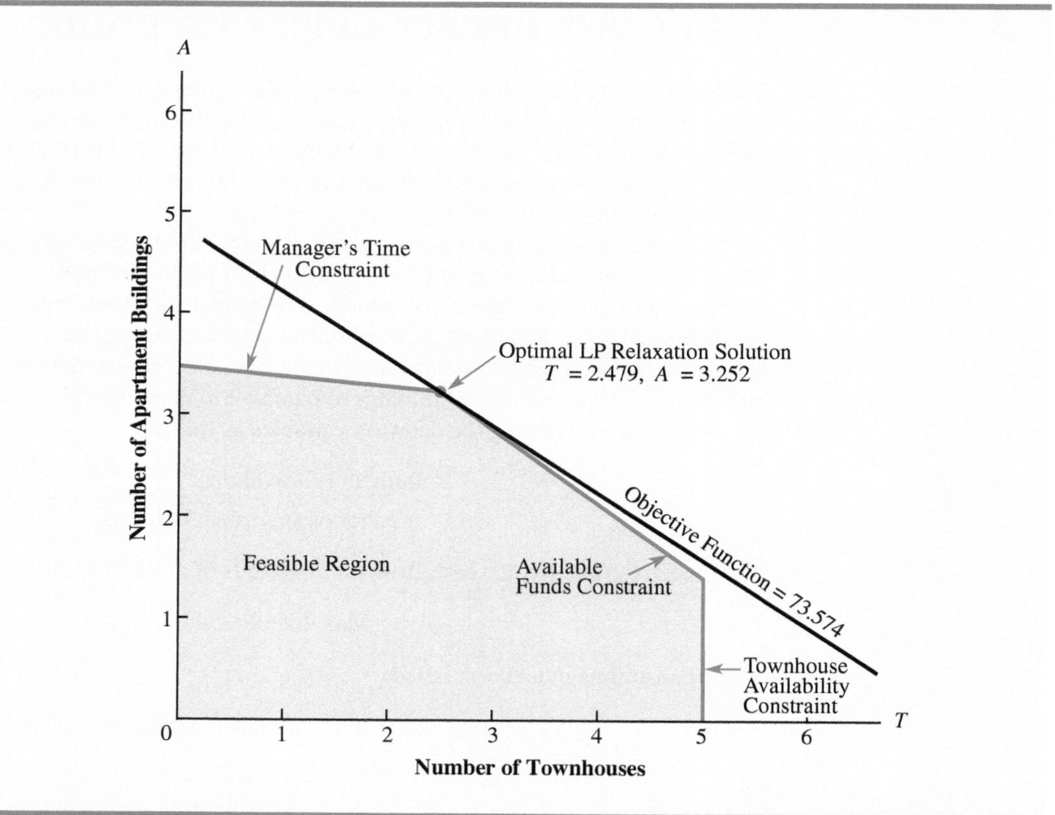

Eastborne cannot purchase fractional numbers of townhouses and apartment buildings; further analysis is necessary.

Rounding to Obtain an Integer Solution

In many cases, a noninteger solution can be rounded to obtain an acceptable integer solution. For instance, a linear programming solution to a production scheduling problem might call for the production of 15,132.4 cases of breakfast cereal. The rounded integer solution of 15,132 cases would probably have minimal impact on the value of the objective function and the feasibility of the solution. Rounding would be a sensible approach. Indeed, whenever rounding has a minimal impact on the objective function and constraints, most managers find it acceptable. A near-optimal solution is fine.

However, rounding may not always be a good strategy. When the decision variables take on small values that have a major impact on the value of the objective function or feasibility, an optimal integer solution is needed. Let us return to the Eastborne Realty problem and examine the impact of rounding. The optimal solution to the LP Relaxation for Eastborne Realty resulted in $T = 2.479$ townhouses and $A = 3.252$ apartment buildings. Because each townhouse costs \$282,000 and each apartment building costs \$400,000, rounding to an integer solution can be expected to have a significant economic impact on the problem.

If a problem has only less-than-or-equal-to constraints with positive coefficients for the variables, rounding down will always provide a feasible integer solution.

Suppose that we round the solution to the LP Relaxation to obtain the integer solution $T = 2$ and $A = 3$, with an objective function value of $10(2) + 15(3) = 65$. The annual cash flow of \$65,000 is substantially less than the annual cash flow of \$73,574 provided by the solution to the LP Relaxation. Do other rounding possibilities exist? Exploring other rounding alternatives shows that the integer solution $T = 3$ and $A = 3$ is infeasible because it requires more funds than the \$2,000,000 Eastborne has available. The rounded solution of $T = 2$ and $A = 4$ is also infeasible for the same reason. At this point, rounding has led to two townhouses and three apartment buildings with an annual cash flow of \$65,000 as the best feasible integer solution to the problem. Unfortunately, we don't know whether this solution is the best integer solution to the problem.

Rounding to an integer solution is a trial-and-error approach. Each rounded solution must be evaluated for feasibility as well as for its impact on the value of the objective function. Even in cases where a rounded solution is feasible, we do not have a guarantee that we have found the optimal integer solution. We will see shortly that the rounded solution ($T = 2$ and $A = 3$) is not optimal for Eastborne Realty.

Graphical Solution of the All-Integer Problem

Figure 11.2 shows the changes in the linear programming graphical solution procedure required to solve the Eastborne Realty integer linear programming problem. First, the graph of the feasible region is drawn exactly as in the LP Relaxation of the problem. Then, because the optimal solution must have integer values, we identify the feasible integer solutions with the dots shown in Figure 11.2. Finally, instead of moving the objective function line to the best extreme point in the feasible region, we move it in an improving direction as far as possible until reaching the dot (feasible integer point) providing the best value for the objective function. Viewing Figure 11.2, we see that the optimal integer solution occurs at $T = 4$ townhouses and $A = 2$ apartment buildings. The objective function value is $10(4) + 15(2) = 70$, providing an annual cash flow of \$70,000. This solution is significantly better than the best solution found by rounding: $T = 2$, $A = 3$ with an annual cash flow of \$65,000. Thus, we see that rounding would not have been the best strategy for Eastborne Realty.

Try Problem 2 for practice with the graphical solution of an integer program.

FIGURE 11.2 GRAPHICAL SOLUTION OF THE EASTBORNE REALTY INTEGER PROBLEM

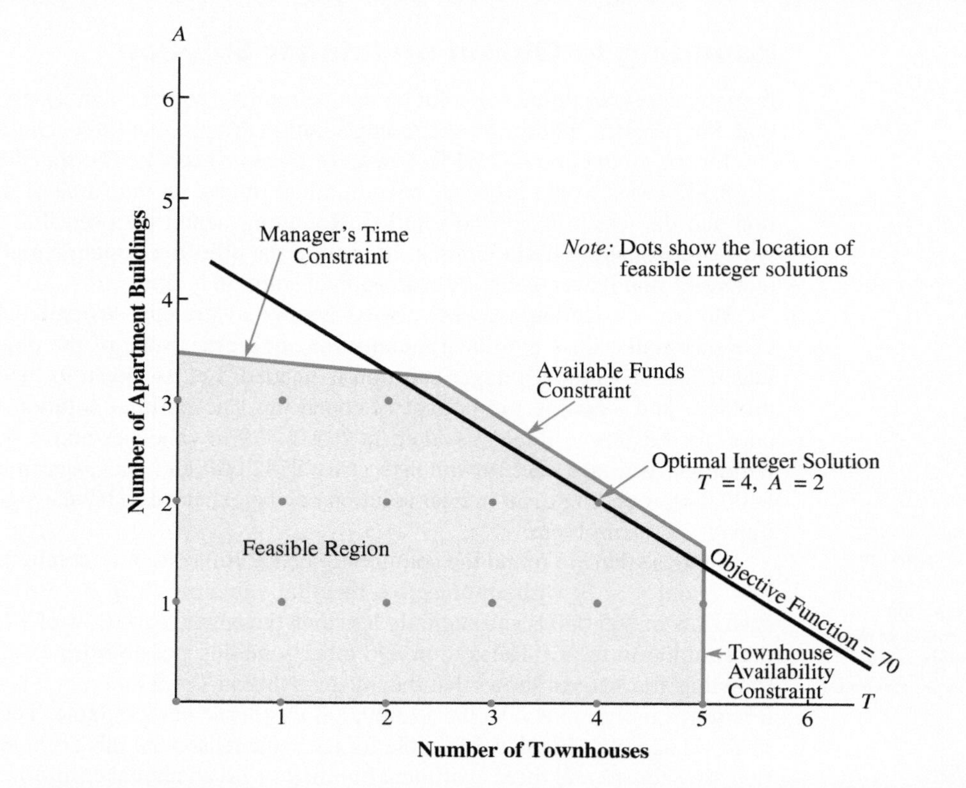

Using the LP Relaxation to Establish Bounds

An important observation can be made from the analysis of the Eastborne Realty problem. It has to do with the relationship between the value of the optimal integer solution and the value of the optimal solution to the LP Relaxation.

> For integer linear programs involving maximization, the value of the optimal solution to the LP Relaxation provides an upper bound on the value of the optimal integer solution. For integer linear programs involving minimization, the value of the optimal solution to the LP Relaxation provides a lower bound on the value of the optimal integer solution.

This observation is valid for the Eastborne Realty problem. The value of the optimal integer solution is \$70,000, and the value of the optimal solution to the LP Relaxation is \$73,574. Thus, we know from the LP Relaxation solution that the upper bound for the value of the objective function is \$73,574.

The bounding property of the LP Relaxation allows us to conclude that if, by chance, the solution to an LP Relaxation turns out to be an integer solution, it is also optimal for the integer linear program. This bounding property can also be helpful in determining whether a rounded solution is "good enough." If a rounded LP Relaxation solution is feasible and provides a value of the objective function that is "almost as good as" the value of the objective function for the LP Relaxation, we know the rounded solution is a near-optimal integer solution. In this case, we can avoid having to solve the problem as an integer linear program.

Try Problem 5 for the graphical solution of a mixed-integer program.

Computer Solution

As mentioned earlier, commercial software packages that can solve integer linear programs are widely available. Excel Solver can be used to solve all of the integer linear programs in this chapter. To use Excel Solver to solve the Eastborne Realty problem, the model worksheet is completed in the same way as for any linear program. Then variables can be defined as integer thorugh the the constraint dialog box. The step-by-step details for how to do this are given in Appnedix 11.1. Specifying both T and A as integers provides the optimal integer solution as shown in Figure 11.3. Note that in the far right column of the variables section, Excel Solver indicates that both variables have been declared integer. The solution of $T = 4$ townhouses and $A = 2$ apartment buildings has a maximum annual cash flow of $70,000. The values of the slack variables tell us that the optimal solution has $72,000 of available funds unused, 44 hours of the manager's time still available, and 1 of the available townhouses not purchased.

NOTES AND COMMENTS

1. In Appendix 11.1, we show the details of how Excel Solver can be used to solve integer linear programs such as the Eastborne Realty problem. Appendix 11.2 shows how to use LINGO to solve integer programs.

FIGURE 11.3 ANSWER REPORT FOR THE EASTBORNE REALTY PROBLEM

Objective Cell (Max)

Name	Original Value	Final Value
Max Cash Flow	0.000	70.000

Eastborne

Variable Cells

Model Variable	Name	Original Value	Final Value	Integer
T	Townhouses	0.000	4.000	Integer
A	Apt. Bldgs.	0.000	2.000	Integer

Constraints

Constraint Number	Name	Cell Value	Status	Slack
1	Funds	1928.000	Not Binding	72.000
2	Manager's Time	96.000	Not Binding	44.000
3	Townhouses	4.000	Not Binding	1.000

Applications Involving 0-1 Variables

Much of the modeling flexibility provided by integer linear programming is due to the use of 0-1 variables. In many applications, 0-1 variables provide selections or choices with the value of the variable equal to 1 if a corresponding activity is undertaken and equal to 0 if the corresponding activity is not undertaken. The capital budgeting, fixed cost, supply chain design, bank location, and product design/market share applications presented in this section make use of 0-1 variables.

Capital Budgeting

The Ice-Cold Refrigerator Company is considering investing in several projects that have varying capital requirements over the next four years. Faced with limited capital each year, management would like to select the most profitable projects. The estimated net present value for each project,[1] the capital requirements, and the available capital over the four-year period are shown in Table 11.1.

The four 0-1 decision variables are as follows:

$$P = 1 \text{ if the plant expansion project is accepted; 0 if rejected}$$
$$W = 1 \text{ if the warehouse expansion project is accepted; 0 if rejected}$$
$$M = 1 \text{ if the new machinery project is accepted; 0 if rejected}$$
$$R = 1 \text{ if the new product research project is accepted; 0 if rejected}$$

In a **capital budgeting problem**, the company's objective function is to maximize the net present value of the capital budgeting projects. This problem has four constraints: one for the funds available in each of the next four years.

A 0-1 integer linear programming model with dollars in thousands is as follows:

$$
\begin{aligned}
\text{Max} \quad & 90P + 40W + 10M + 37R \\
\text{s.t.} \quad & \\
& 15P + 10W + 10M + 15R \leq 40 \quad \text{(Year 1 capital available)} \\
& 20P + 15W + 10R \leq 50 \quad \text{(Year 2 capital available)} \\
& 20P + 20W + 10R \leq 40 \quad \text{(Year 3 capital available)} \\
& 15P + 5W + 4M + 10R \leq 35 \quad \text{(Year 4 capital available)} \\
& P, W, M, R = 0, 1
\end{aligned}
$$

[1] The estimated net present value is the net cash flow discounted back to the beginning of year 1.

TABLE 11.1 PROJECT NET PRESENT VALUE, CAPITAL REQUIREMENTS, AND AVAILABLE CAPITAL FOR THE ICE-COLD REFRIGERATOR COMPANY

	Project				
	Plant Expansion	**Warehouse Expansion**	**New Machinery**	**New Product Research**	**Total Capital Available**
Present Value	$90,000	$40,000	$10,000	$37,000	
Year 1 Cap Rqmt	$15,000	$10,000	$10,000	$15,000	$40,000
Year 2 Cap Rqmt	$20,000	$15,000		$10,000	$50,000
Year 3 Cap Rqmt	$20,000	$20,000		$10,000	$40,000
Year 4 Cap Rqmt	$15,000	$ 5,000	$ 4,000	$10,000	$35,000

FIGURE 11.4 ANSWER REPORT FOR THE ICE-COLD REFRIGERATOR COMPANY PROBLEM

Objective Cell (Max)

Name	Original Value	Final Value
Max Net Present Value	0.000	140.000

Variable Cells

Ice-Cold

Model Variable	Name	Original Value	Final Value	Integer
P	Plant Expansion	0.000	1.000	Binary
W	Warehouse Expansion	0.000	1.000	Binary
M	New Machinery	0.000	1.000	Binary
R	New Prod. Research	0.000	0.000	Binary

Constraints

Constraint Number	Name	Cell Value	Status	Slack
1	Year 1 Capital	35.000	Not Binding	5.000
2	Year 2 Capital	35.000	Not Binding	15.000
3	Year 3 Capital	40.000	Binding	0.000
4	Year 4 Capital	24.000	Not Binding	11.000

The integer programming solution is shown in Figure 11.4. The optimal solution is $P = 1$, $W = 1$, $M = 1$, $R = 0$, with a total estimated net present value of $140,000. Thus, the company should fund the plant expansion, the warehouse expansion, and the new machinery projects. The new product research project should be put on hold unless additional capital funds become available. The values of the slack variables (see Figure 11.4) show that the company will have $5,000 remaining in year 1, $15,000 remaining in year 2, and $11,000 remaining in year 4. Checking the capital requirements for the new product research project, we see that enough funds are available for this project in year 2 and year 4. However, the company would have to find additional capital funds of $10,000 in year 1 and $10,000 in year 3 to fund the new product research project.

Fixed Cost

In many applications, the cost of production has two components: a setup cost, which is a fixed cost, and a variable cost, which is directly related to the production quantity. The use of 0-1 variables makes including the setup cost possible in a model for a production application.

As an example of a **fixed cost problem**, consider the RMC problem discussed in Chapters 7 and 8. Three raw materials are used to produce three products: a fuel additive, a solvent base, and a carpet cleaning fluid. The following decision variables are used:

F = tons of fuel additive produced

S = tons of solvent base produced

C = tons of carpet cleaning fluid produced

The profit contributions are $40 per ton for the fuel additive, $30 per ton for the solvent base, and $50 per ton for the carpet cleaning fluid. Each ton of fuel additive is a blend of 0.4 tons of material 1 and 0.6 tons of material 3. Each ton of solvent base requires 0.5 tons of material 1, 0.2 tons of material 2, and 0.3 tons of material 3. Each ton of carpet cleaning fluid is a blend of 0.6 tons of material 1, 0.1 tons of material 2, and 0.3 tons of material 3. RMC has 20 tons of material 1, 5 tons of material 2, and 21 tons of material 3 and is interested in determining the optimal production quantities for the upcoming planning period.

A linear programming model of the RMC problem is shown:

$$\begin{aligned} \text{Max} \quad & 40F + 30S + 50C \\ \text{s.t.} \quad & \\ & 0.4F + 0.5S + 0.6C \leq 20 \quad \text{Material 1} \\ & 0.2S + 0.1C \leq 5 \quad \text{Material 2} \\ & 0.6F + 0.3S + 0.3C \leq 21 \quad \text{Material 3} \\ & F, S, C \geq 0 \end{aligned}$$

Using Excel Solver, we obtained an optimal solution consisting of 27.5 tons of fuel additive, 0 tons of solvent base, and 15 tons of carpet cleaning fluid, with a value of $1850, as shown in Figure 11.5.

This linear programming formulation of the RMC problem does not include a fixed cost for production setup of the products. Suppose that the following data are available concerning the setup cost and the maximum production quantity for each of the three products:

Product	**Setup Cost**	**Maximum Production**
Fuel additive	$200	50 tons
Solvent base	$ 50	25 tons
Carpet cleaning fluid	$400	40 tons

The modeling flexibility provided by 0-1 variables can now be used to incorporate the fixed setup costs into the production model. The 0-1 variables are defined as follows:

$$\begin{aligned} SF &= 1 \text{ if the fuel additive is produced; 0 if not} \\ SS &= 1 \text{ if the solvent base is produced; 0 if not} \\ SC &= 1 \text{ if the carpet cleaning fluid is produced; 0 if not} \end{aligned}$$

Using these setup variables, the total setup cost is

$$200SF + 50SS + 400SC$$

FIGURE 11.5 ANSWER REPORT FOR THE RMC PROBLEM

Objective Cell (Max)

Name	Original Value	Final Value
Max Net Profit	0.000	1850.000

Variable Cells

Model Variable	Name	Original Value	Final Value	Integer
F	Fuel Additive	0.000	27.500	Contin
S	Solvent Base	0.000	0.000	Contin
C	Cleaning Fluid	0.000	15.000	Contin

Constraints

Constraint Number	Name	Cell Value	Status	Slack
1	Material 1	20.000	Binding	0.000
2	Material 2	1.500	Not Binding	3.500
3	Material 3	21.000	Binding	0.000

We can now rewrite the objective function to include the setup cost. Thus, the net profit objective function becomes

$$\text{Max } 40F + 30S + 50C - 200SF - 50SS - 400SC$$

Next, we must write production capacity constraints so that if a setup variable equals 0, production of the corresponding product is not permitted and, if a setup variable equals 1, production is permitted up to the maximum quantity. For the fuel additive, we do so by adding the following constraint:

$$F \le 50SF$$

Note that, with this constraint present, production of the fuel additive is not permitted when $SF = 0$. When $SF = 1$, production of up to 50 tons of fuel additive is permitted. We can think of the setup variable as a switch. When it is off ($SF = 0$), production is not permitted; when it is on ($SF = 1$), production is permitted.

Similar production capacity constraints, using 0-1 variables, are added for the solvent base and carpet cleaning products:

$$S \le 25SS$$
$$C \le 40SC$$

Moving all the variables to the left-hand side of the constraints provides the following fixed cost model for the RMC problem:

$$\begin{array}{lllr}
\text{Max} & 40F + 30S + 50C - 200SF - 50SS - 400SC & & \\
\text{s.t.} & & & \\
& 0.4F + 0.5S + 0.6C & \le 20 & \text{Material 1} \\
& 0.2S + 0.1C & \le 5 & \text{Material 2} \\
& 0.6F + 0.3S + 0.3C & \le 21 & \text{Material 3} \\
& F - 50SF & \le 0 & \text{Maximum } F \\
& S - 25SS & \le 0 & \text{Maximum } S \\
& C - 40SC & \le 0 & \text{Maximum } C \\
& F, S, C \ge 0;\ SF, SS, SC = 0, 1 & &
\end{array}$$

We solved the RMC problem with setup costs using Excel Solver. As shown in Figure 11.6, the optimal solution requires 25 tons of fuel additive and 20 tons of solvent base. The value of the objective function after deducting the setup cost is \$1350. The setup cost for the fuel additive and the solvent base is \$200 + \$50 = \$250. The optimal solution includes $SC = 0$, which indicates that the more expensive \$400 setup cost for the carpet cleaning fluid should be avoided. Thus, the carpet cleaning fluid is not produced.

The key to developing a fixed-cost model is the introduction of a 0-1 variable for each fixed cost and the specification of an upper bound for the corresponding production variable. For a production quantity x, a constraint of the form $x \le My$ can then be used to allow production when the setup variable $y = 1$ and not to allow production when the setup variable $y = 0$. The value of the maximum production quantity M should be large enough to allow for all reasonable levels of production. However, research has shown that choosing values of M excessively large will slow the solution procedure.

Supply Chain Design

The Martin-Beck Company operates a plant in St. Louis with an annual capacity of 30,000 units. Product is shipped to regional distribution centers located in Boston, Atlanta, and Houston. Because of an anticipated increase in demand, Martin-Beck plans to increase capacity by

FIGURE 11.6 ANSWER REPORT FOR THE RMC PROBLEM WITH SETUP COSTS

Objective Cell (Max)

Name	Original Value	Final Value
Max Net Profit	0.000	1350.000

Variable Cells

Model Variable	Name	Original Value	Final Value	Integer
F	Fuel Additive	0.000	25.000	Contin
S	Solvent Base	0.000	20.000	Contin
C	Cleaning Fluid	0.000	0.000	Contin
SF	Setup Fuel Additive	0.000	1.000	Binary
SS	Setup Solvent Base	0.000	1.000	Binary
SC	Setup Cleaning Fluid	0.000	0.000	Binary

RMC-Setup

Constraints

Constraint Number	Name	Cell Value	Status	Slack
1	Material 1	20.000	Binding	0.000
2	Material 2	4.000	Not Binding	1.000
3	Material 3	21.000	Binding	0.000
4	Max Fuel Additive	25.000	Not Binding	25.000
5	Max Solvent Base	20.000	Not Binding	5.000
6	Max Cleaning Fluid	0.000	Binding	0.000

constructing a new plant in one or more of the following cities: Detroit, Toledo, Denver, or Kansas City. The estimated annual fixed cost and the annual capacity for the four proposed plants are as follows:

Proposed Plant	Annual Fixed Cost	Annual Capacity
Detroit	$175,000	10,000
Toledo	$300,000	20,000
Denver	$375,000	30,000
Kansas City	$500,000	40,000

The company's long-range planning group developed forecasts of the anticipated annual demand at the distribution centers as follows:

Distribution Center	Annual Demand
Boston	30,000
Atlanta	20,000
Houston	20,000

The shipping cost per unit from each plant to each distribution center is shown in Table 11.2. A network representation of the potential Martin-Beck supply chain is shown in Figure 11.7. Each potential plant location is shown; capacities and demands are shown in thousands of units. This network representation is for a transportation problem with a plant

TABLE 11.2 SHIPPING COST PER UNIT FOR THE MARTIN-BECK SUPPLY CHAIN

	Distribution Centers		
Plant Site	Boston	Atlanta	Houston
Detroit	5	2	3
Toledo	4	3	4
Denver	9	7	5
Kansas City	10	4	2
St. Louis	8	4	3

FIGURE 11.7 THE NETWORK REPRESENTATION OF THE MARTIN-BECK COMPANY SUPPLY CHAIN DESIGN PROBLEM

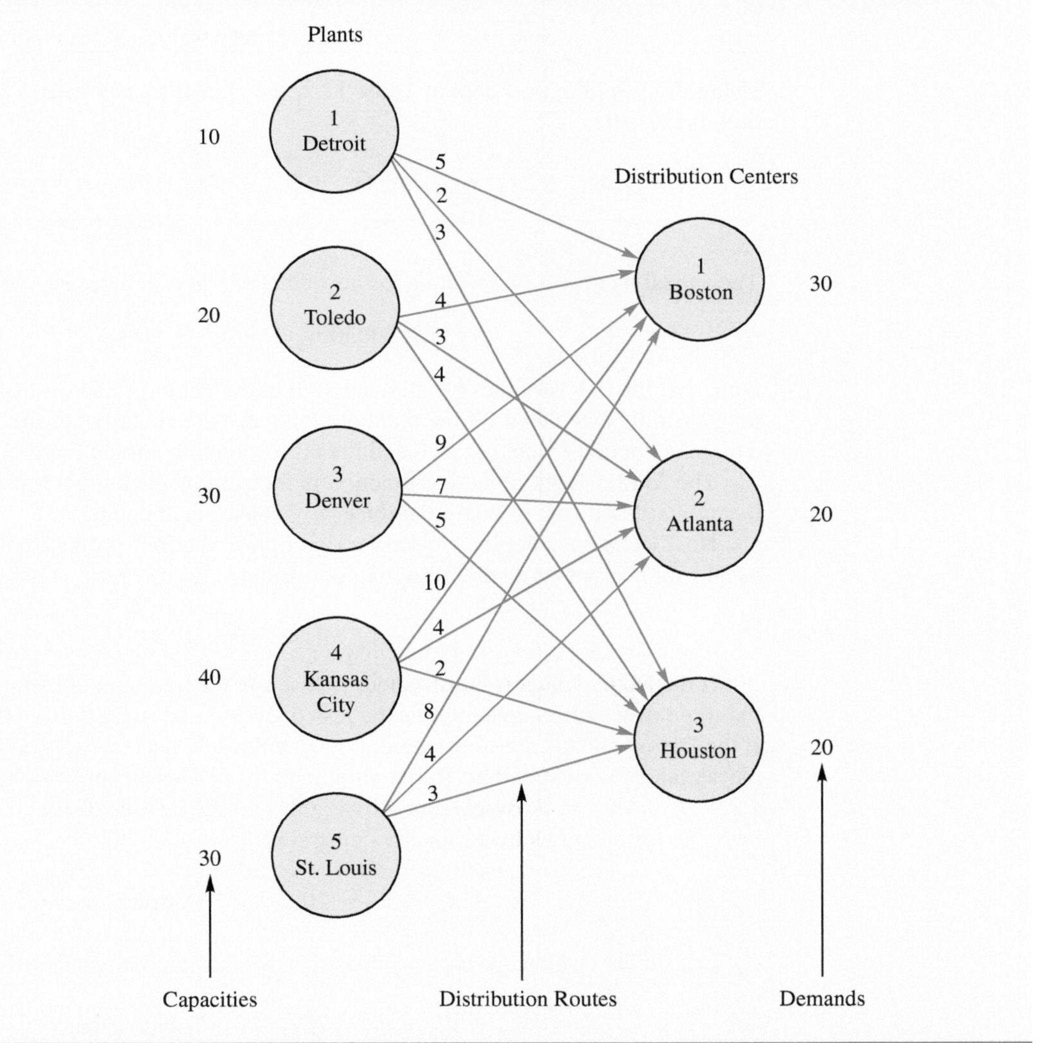

at St. Louis and at all four proposed sites. However, the decision has not yet been made as to which new plant or plants will be constructed.

Let us now show how 0-1 variables can be used in this **supply chain design problem** to develop a model for choosing the best plant locations and for determining how much to ship from each plant to each distribution center. We can use the following 0-1 variables to represent the plant construction decision:

$$y_1 = 1 \text{ if a plant is constructed in Detroit; 0 if not}$$
$$y_2 = 1 \text{ if a plant is constructed in Toledo; 0 if not}$$
$$y_3 = 1 \text{ if a plant is constructed in Denver; 0 if not}$$
$$y_4 = 1 \text{ if a plant is constructed in Kansas City; 0 if not}$$

The variables representing the amount shipped from each plant site to each distribution center are defined just as for a transportation problem.

$$x_{ij} = \text{the units shipped in thousands from plant } i \text{ to distribution center } j$$
$$i = 1, 2, 3, 4, 5 \text{ and } j = 1, 2, 3$$

Using the shipping cost data in Table 11.2, the annual transportation cost in thousands of dollars is written

$$5x_{11} + 2x_{12} + 3x_{13} + 4x_{21} + 3x_{22} + 4x_{23} + 9x_{31} + 7x_{32} + 5x_{33}$$
$$+ 10x_{41} + 4x_{42} + 2x_{43} + 8x_{51} + 4x_{52} + 3x_{53}$$

The annual fixed cost of operating the new plant or plants in thousands of dollars is written as

$$175y_1 + 300y_2 + 375y_3 + 500y_4$$

Note that the 0-1 variables are defined so that the annual fixed cost of operating the new plants is only calculated for the plant or plants that are actually constructed (i.e., $y_i = 1$). If a plant is not constructed, $y_i = 0$ and the corresponding annual fixed cost is \$0.

The Martin-Beck objective function is the sum of the annual transportation cost plus the annual fixed cost of operating the newly constructed plants.

Now let us consider the capacity constraints at the four proposed plants. Using Detroit as an example, we write the following constraint:

$$x_{11} + x_{12} + x_{13} \leq 10y_1$$

If the Detroit plant is constructed, $y_1 = 1$ and the total amount shipped from Detroit to the three distribution centers must be less than or equal to Detroit's 10,000-unit capacity. If the Detroit plant is not constructed, $y_1 = 0$ will result in a 0 capacity at Detroit. In this case, the variables corresponding to the shipments from Detroit must all equal zero: $x_{11} = 0$, $x_{12} = 0$, and $x_{13} = 0$. By placing all variables on the left-hand side of the constraints, we have the following Detroit capacity constraint:

$$x_{11} + x_{12} + x_{13} - 10y_1 \leq 0 \quad \text{Detroit capacity}$$

In a similar fashion, the capacity constraint for the proposed plant in Toledo can be written

$$x_{21} + x_{22} + x_{23} - 20y_2 \leq 0 \quad \text{Toledo capacity}$$

Similar constraints can be written for the proposed plants in Denver and Kansas City. Note that since the plant already exists in St. Louis, we do not define a 0-1 variable for this plant. Its capacity constraint can be written as follows:

$$x_{51} + x_{52} + x_{53} \leq 30 \quad \text{St. Louis capacity}$$

Three demand constraints will be needed, one for each of the three distribution centers. The demand constraint for the Boston distribution center with units in thousands is written as

$$x_{11} + x_{21} + x_{31} + x_{41} + x_{51} = 30 \quad \text{Boston demand}$$

Similar constraints appear for the Atlanta and Houston distribution centers.

The complete model for the Martin-Beck supply chain design problem is as follows:

$$\begin{aligned} \text{Min} \quad & 5x_{11} + 2x_{12} + 3x_{13} + 4x_{21} + 3x_{22} + 4x_{23} + 9x_{31} + 7x_{32} + 5x_{33} + 10x_{41} + 4x_{42} \\ & + 2x_{43} + 8x_{51} + 4x_{52} + 3x_{53} + 175y_1 + 300y_2 + 375y_3 + 500y_4 \end{aligned}$$

s.t.

$$\begin{array}{lllllll}
x_{11} + x_{12} + x_{13} & -10y_1 & & & & \leq 0 & \text{Detroit capacity} \\
x_{21} + x_{22} + x_{23} & & -20y_2 & & & \leq 0 & \text{Toledo capacity} \\
x_{31} + x_{32} + x_{33} & & & -30y_3 & & \leq 0 & \text{Denver capacity} \\
x_{41} + x_{42} + x_{43} & & & & -40y_4 & \leq 0 & \text{Kansas City capacity} \\
x_{51} + x_{52} + x_{53} & & & & & \leq 30 & \text{St. Louis capacity} \\
x_{11} + x_{21} + x_{31} + x_{41} + x_{51} & & & & & = 30 & \text{Boston demand} \\
x_{12} + x_{22} + x_{32} + x_{42} + x_{52} & & & & & = 20 & \text{Atlanta demand} \\
x_{13} + x_{23} + x_{33} + x_{43} + x_{53} & & & & & = 20 & \text{Houston demand}
\end{array}$$

$x_{ij} \geq$ for all i and j; $y_1, y_2, y_3, y_4 = 0, 1$

Using Excel Solver, we obtained the solution shown in Figure 11.8. The optimal solution calls for the construction of a plant in Kansas City ($y_4 = 1$); 20,000 units will be shipped from Kansas City to Atlanta ($x_{42} = 20$), 20,000 units will be shipped from Kansas City to Houston ($x_{43} = 20$), and 30,000 units will be shipped from St. Louis to Boston ($x_{51} = 30$). Note that the total cost of this solution including the fixed cost of \$500,000 for the plant in Kansas City is \$860,000.

This basic model can be expanded to accommodate supply chains involving direct shipments from plants to warehouses, from plants to retail outlets, and multiple products.[2] Using the special properties of 0-1 variables, the model can also be expanded to accommodate a variety of configuration constraints on the plant locations. For example, suppose in another problem site 1 was in Dallas and site 2 was in Fort Worth. A company might not want to locate plants in both Dallas and Fort Worth because the cities are so close together. To prevent this from happening, the following constraint can be added to the model:

Problem 13, which is based on the Martin-Beck supply chain design problem, provides additional practice involving 0-1 variables.

$$y_1 + y_2 \leq 1$$

This constraint allows either y_1 or y_2 to equal 1, but not both. If we had written the constraints as an equality, it would require that a plant be located in either Dallas or Fort Worth.

[2]For computational reasons, it is usually preferable to replace the m plant capacity constraints with mn shipping route capacity constraints of the form $x_{ij} \leq \text{Min}\{s_i, d_j\}\, y_i$ for $i = 1, \ldots, m$, and $j = 1, \ldots, n$. The coefficient for y_i in each of these constraints is the smaller of the origin capacity (s_i) or the destination demand (d_j). These additional constraints often cause the solution of the LP Relaxation to be integer.

FIGURE 11.8 OPTIMAL SOLUTION FOR THE MARTIN-BECK COMPANY DISTRIBUTION SYSTEM PROBLEM

Objective Cell (Max)

Name	Original Value	Final Value
Min Cost	0.000	860.000

Variable Cells

Martin-Beck

Model Variable	Name	Original Value	Final Value	Integer
X11	Detroit to Boston	0.000	0.000	Contin
X12	Detroit to Atlanta	0.000	0.000	Contin
X13	Detroit to Houston	0.000	0.000	Contin
X21	Toledo to Boston	0.000	0.000	Contin
X22	Toledo to Atlanta	0.000	0.000	Contin
X23	Toledo to Houston	0.000	0.000	Contin
X31	Denver to Boston	0.000	0.000	Contin
X32	Denver to Atlanta	0.000	0.000	Contin
X33	Denver to Houston	0.000	0.000	Contin
X41	Kansas City to Boston	0.000	0.000	Contin
X42	Kansas City to Atlanta	0.000	20.000	Contin
X43	Kansas City to Houston	0.000	20.000	Contin
X51	St. Louis to Boston	0.000	30.000	Contin
X52	St. Louis to Atlanta	0.000	0.000	Contin
X53	St. Louis to Houston	0.000	0.000	Contin
Y1	Detroit Open or Closed	0.000	0.000	Binary
Y2	Toledo Open or Closed	0.000	0.000	Binary
Y3	Denver Open or Closed	0.000	0.000	Binary
Y4	Kansas City Open or Closed	0.000	1.000	Binary

Bank Location

The long-range planning department for the Ohio Trust Company is considering expanding its operation into a 20-county region in northeastern Ohio (see Figure 11.9). Currently, Ohio Trust does not have a principal place of business in any of the 20 counties. According to the banking laws in Ohio, if a bank establishes a principal place of business (PPB) in any county, branch banks can be established in that county and in any adjacent county. However, to establish a new principal place of business, Ohio Trust must either obtain approval for a new bank from the state's superintendent of banks or purchase an existing bank.

Table 11.3 lists the 20 counties in the region and adjacent counties. For example, Ashtabula County is adjacent to Lake, Geauga, and Trumbull counties; Lake County is adjacent to Ashtabula, Cuyahoga, and Geauga counties; and so on.

As an initial step in its planning, Ohio Trust would like to determine the minimum number of PPBs necessary to do business throughout the 20-county region. A 0-1 integer programming model can be used to solve this **location problem** for Ohio Trust. We define the variables as

$$x_i = 1 \text{ if a PPB is established in county } i\text{; 0 otherwise}$$

To minimize the number of PPBs needed, we write the objective function as

$$\text{Min } x_1 + x_2 + \cdots + x_{20}$$

FIGURE 11.9 THE 20-COUNTY REGION IN NORTHEASTERN OHIO

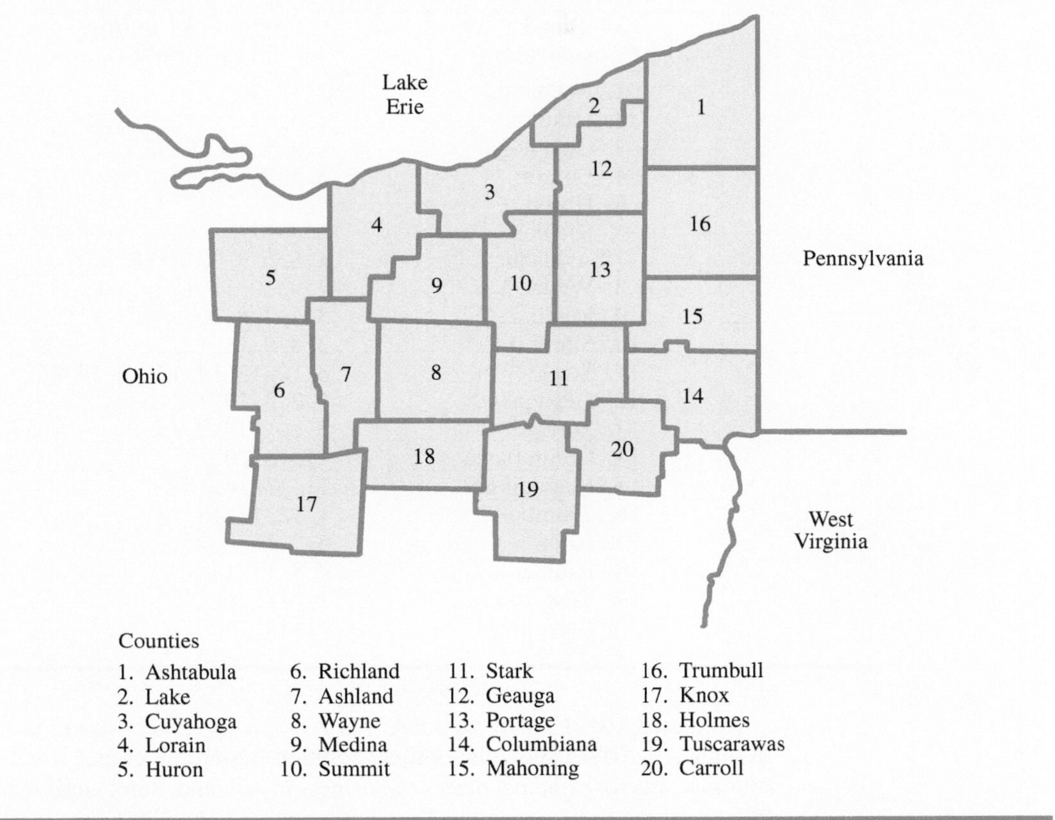

The bank may locate branches in a county if the county contains a PPB or is adjacent to another county with a PPB. Thus, the linear program will need one constraint for each county. For example, the constraint for Ashtabula County is

$$x_1 + x_2 + x_{12} + x_{16} \geq 1 \quad \text{Ashtabula}$$

Note that satisfaction of this constraint ensures that a PPB will be placed in Ashtabula County *or* in one or more of the adjacent counties. This constraint thus guarantees that Ohio Trust will be able to place branch banks in Ashtabula County.

The complete statement of the bank location problem is

$$\begin{aligned}
\text{Min} \quad & x_1 + x_2 + \cdots + x_{20} \\
\text{s.t.} \quad & \\
& x_1 + x_2 + x_{12} + x_{16} \geq 1 \quad \text{Ashtabula} \\
& x_1 + x_2 + x_3 + x_{12} \geq 1 \quad \text{Lake} \\
& \vdots \\
& x_{11} + x_{14} + x_{19} + x_{20} \geq 1 \quad \text{Carroll} \\
& x_i = 0, 1 \quad i = 1, 2, \ldots, 20
\end{aligned}$$

TABLE 11.3 COUNTIES IN THE OHIO TRUST EXPANSION REGION

Counties Under Consideration	Adjacent Counties (by Number)
1. Ashtabula	2, 12, 16
2. Lake	1, 3, 12
3. Cuyahoga	2, 4, 9, 10, 12, 13
4. Lorain	3, 5, 7, 9
5. Huron	4, 6, 7
6. Richland	5, 7, 17
7. Ashland	4, 5, 6, 8, 9, 17, 18
8. Wayne	7, 9, 10, 11, 18
9. Medina	3, 4, 7, 8, 10
10. Summit	3, 8, 9, 11, 12, 13
11. Stark	8, 10, 13, 14, 15, 18, 19, 20
12. Geauga	1, 2, 3, 10, 13, 16
13. Portage	3, 10, 11, 12, 15, 16
14. Columbiana	11, 15, 20
15. Mahoning	11, 13, 14, 16
16. Trumbull	1, 12, 13, 15
17. Knox	6, 7, 18
18. Holmes	7, 8, 11, 17, 19
19. Tuscarawas	11, 18, 20
20. Carroll	11, 14, 19

We used Excel Solver to solve this 20-variable, 20-constraint problem formulation. In Figure 11.10 we show the optimal solution. Using the output, we see that the optimal solution calls for principal places of business in Ashland, Stark, and Geauga counties. With PPBs in these three counties, Ohio Trust can place branch banks in all 20 counties (see Figure 11.11). All other decision variables have an optimal value of zero, indicating that a PPB should not be placed in these counties. Clearly the integer programming model could be enlarged to allow for expansion into a larger area or throughout the entire state.

Product Design and Market Share Optimization

Conjoint analysis is a market research technique that can be used to learn how prospective buyers of a product value the product's attributes. In this section we will show how the results of conjoint analysis can be used in an integer programming model of a **product design and market share optimization problem**. We illustrate the approach by considering a problem facing Salem Foods, a major producer of frozen foods.

Salem Foods is planning to enter the frozen pizza market. Currently, two existing brands, Antonio's and King's, have the major share of the market. In trying to develop a sausage pizza that will capture a significant share of the market, Salem determined that the four most important attributes when consumers purchase a frozen sausage pizza are crust, cheese, sauce, and sausage flavor. The crust attribute has two levels (thin and thick); the cheese attribute has two levels (mozzarella and blend); the sauce attribute has two levels (smooth and chunky); and the sausage flavor attribute has three levels (mild, medium, and hot).

In a typical conjoint analysis, a sample of consumers is asked to express their preference for specially prepared pizzas with chosen levels for the attributes. Then regression analysis is used to determine the part-worth for each of the attribute levels. In essence, the part-worth

FIGURE 11.10 OPTIMAL SOLUTION FOR THE OHIO TRUST PPB LOCATION PROBLEM

Objective Cell (Max)

Name	Original Value	Final Value
Min PPBs	0.000	3.000

Ohio-Trust

Variable Cells

Model Variable	Name	Original Value	Final Value	Integer
X1	Ashtabula	0.000	0.000	Binary
X2	Lake	0.000	0.000	Binary
X3	Cuyahoga	0.000	0.000	Binary
X4	Lorain	0.000	0.000	Binary
X5	Huron	0.000	0.000	Binary
X6	Richland	0.000	0.000	Binary
X7	Ashland	0.000	1.000	Binary
X8	Wayne	0.000	0.000	Binary
X9	Medina	0.000	0.000	Binary
X10	Summit	0.000	0.000	Binary
X11	Stark	0.000	1.000	Binary
X12	Geauga	0.000	1.000	Binary
X13	Portage	0.000	0.000	Binary
X14	Columbiana	0.000	0.000	Binary
X15	Mahoning	0.000	0.000	Binary
Y16	Trumbull	0.000	0.000	Binary
Y17	Knox	0.000	0.000	Binary
Y18	Holmes	0.000	0.000	Binary
Y19	Tuscarawas	0.000	0.000	Binary
Y20	Carroll	0.000	0.000	Binary

is the utility value that a consumer attaches to each level of each attribute. A discussion of how to use regression analysis to compute the part-worths is beyond the scope of this text, but we will show how the part-worths can be used to determine the overall value a consumer attaches to a particular pizza.

Table 11.4 shows the part-worths for each level of each attribute provided by a sample of eight potential Salem customers who are currently buying either King's or Antonio's pizza. For consumer 1, the part-worths for the crust attribute are 11 for thin crust and 2 for thick crust, indicating a preference for thin crust. For the cheese attribute, the part-worths are 6 for the mozzarella cheese and 7 for the cheese blend; thus, consumer 1 has a slight preference for the cheese blend. From the other part-worths, we see that consumer 1 shows a strong preference for the chunky sauce over the smooth sauce (17 to 3) and has a slight preference for the medium-flavored sausage. Note that consumer 2 shows a preference for the thin crust, the cheese blend, the chunky sauce, and mild-flavored sausage. The part-worths for the others consumers are interpreted in a similar manner.

The part-worths can be used to determine the overall value (utility) each consumer attaches to a particular type of pizza. For instance, consumer 1's current favorite pizza is the Antonio's brand, which has a thick crust, mozzarella cheese, chunky sauce, and medium-flavored sausage. We can determine consumer 1's utility for this particular type of pizza using the part-worths in Table 11.4. For consumer 1 the part-worths are 2 for thick crust, 6 for mozzarella cheese, 17 for chunky sauce, and 27 for medium-flavored sausage.

FIGURE 11.11 PRINCIPAL PLACE OF BUSINESS COUNTIES FOR OHIO TRUST

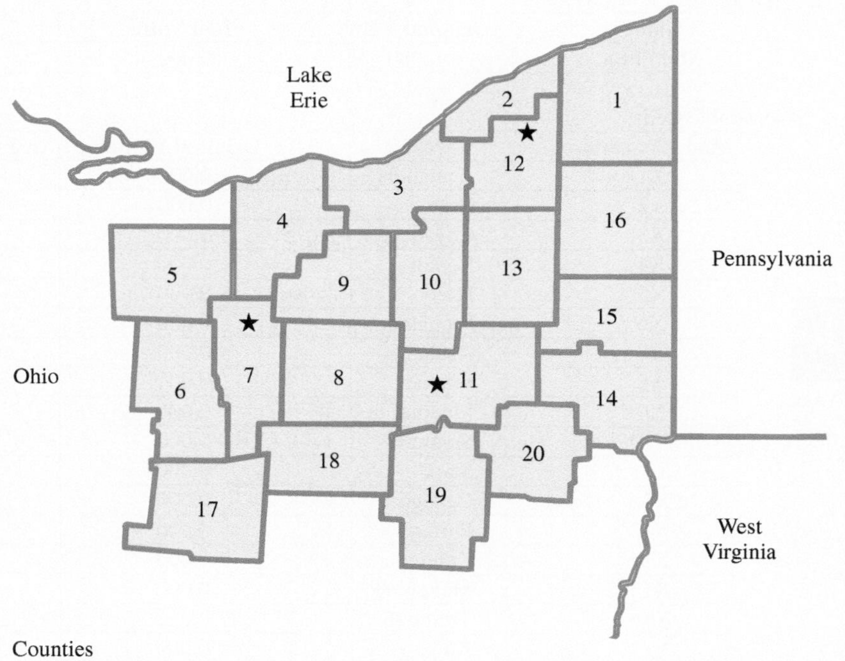

TABLE 11.4 PART-WORTHS FOR THE SALEM FOODS PROBLEM

	Crust		Cheese		Sauce		Sausage Flavor		
Consumer	Thin	Thick	Mozzarella	Blend	Smooth	Chunky	Mild	Medium	Hot
1	11	2	6	7	3	17	26	27	8
2	11	7	15	17	16	26	14	1	10
3	7	5	8	14	16	7	29	16	19
4	13	20	20	17	17	14	25	29	10
5	2	8	6	11	30	20	15	5	12
6	12	17	11	9	2	30	22	12	20
7	9	19	12	16	16	25	30	23	19
8	5	9	4	14	23	16	16	30	3

Thus, consumer 1's utility for the Antonio's brand pizza is $2 + 6 + 17 + 27 = 52$. We can compute consumer 1's utility for a King's brand pizza in a similar manner. The King's brand pizza has a thin crust, a cheese blend, smooth sauce, and mild-flavored sausage. Because the part-worths for consumer 1 are 11 for thin crust, 7 for cheese blend, 3 for smooth sauce, and 26 for mild-flavored sausage, consumer 1's utility for the King's brand pizza is 11 + 7 + 3 + 26 = 47. In general, each consumer's utility for a particular type of pizza is just the sum of the appropriate part-worths.

In order to be successful with its brand, Salem Foods realizes that it must entice consumers in the marketplace to switch from their current favorite brand of pizza to the Salem product. That is, Salem must design a pizza (choose the type of crust, cheese, sauce, and sausage flavor) that will have the highest utility for enough people to ensure sufficient sales to justify making the product. Assuming the sample of eight consumers in the current study is representative of the marketplace for frozen sausage pizza, we can formulate and solve an integer programming model that can help Salem come up with such a design. In marketing literature, the problem being solved is called the *share of choice* problem.

The decision variables are defined as follows:

$$l_{ij} = 1 \text{ if Salem chooses level } i \text{ for attribute } j\text{; 0 otherwise}$$
$$y_k = 1 \text{ if consumer } k \text{ chooses the Salem brand; 0 otherwise}$$

The objective is to choose the levels of each attribute that will maximize the number of consumers preferring the Salem brand pizza. Because the number of customers preferring the Salem brand pizza is just the sum of the y_k variables, the objective function is

$$\text{Max } y_1 + y_2 + \cdots + y_8$$

One constraint is needed for each consumer in the sample. To illustrate how the constraints are formulated, let us consider the constraint corresponding to consumer 1. For consumer 1, the utility of a particular type of pizza can be expressed as the sum of the part-worths:

$$\text{Utility for Customer 1} = 11l_{11} + 2l_{21} + 6l_{12} + 7l_{22} + 3l_{13} + 17l_{23} + 26l_{14} + 27l_{24} + 8l_{34}$$

In order for consumer 1 to prefer the Salem pizza, the utility for the Salem pizza must be greater than the utility for consumer 1's current favorite. Recall that consumer 1's current favorite brand of pizza is Antonio's, with a utility of 52. Thus, consumer 1 will only purchase the Salem brand if the levels of the attributes for the Salem brand are chosen such that

$$11l_{11} + 2l_{21} + 6l_{12} + 7l_{22} + 3l_{13} + 17l_{23} + 26l_{14} + 27l_{24} + 8l_{34} > 52$$

Given the definitions of the y_k decision variables, we want $y_1 = 1$ when the consumer prefers the Salem brand and $y_1 = 0$ when the consumer does not prefer the Salem brand. Thus, we write the constraint for consumer 1 as follows:

$$11l_{11} + 2l_{21} + 6l_{12} + 7l_{22} + 3l_{13} + 17l_{23} + 26l_{14} + 27l_{24} + 8l_{34} \geq 1 + 52y_1$$

With this constraint, y_1 cannot equal 1 unless the utility for the Salem design (the left-hand side of the constraint) exceeds the utility for consumer 1's current favorite by at least 1. Because the objective function is to maximize the sum of the y_k variables, the optimization will seek a product design that will allow as many y_k as possible to equal 1.

Placing all the decision variables on the left-hand side of the constraint enables us to rewrite constraint 1 as follows:

$$11l_{11} + 2l_{21} + 6l_{12} + 7l_{22} + 3l_{13} + 17l_{23} + 26l_{14} + 27l_{24} + 8l_{34} - 52y_1 \geq 1$$

A similar constraint is written for each consumer in the sample. The coefficients for the l_{ij} variables in the utility functions are taken from Table 11.4, and the coefficients for the y_k

Antonio's brand is the current favorite pizza for consumers 1, 4, 6, 7, and 8. King's brand is the current favorite pizza for consumers 2, 3, and 5.

variables are obtained by computing the overall utility of the consumer's current favorite brand of pizza. The following constraints correspond to the eight consumers in the study:

$$
\begin{aligned}
11l_{11} + 2l_{21} + 6l_{12} + 7l_{22} + 3l_{13} + 17l_{23} + 26l_{14} + 27l_{24} + 8l_{34} - 52y_1 &\geq 1 \\
11l_{11} + 7l_{21} + 15l_{12} + 17l_{22} + 16l_{13} + 26l_{23} + 14l_{14} + 1l_{24} + 10l_{34} - 58y_2 &\geq 1 \\
7l_{11} + 5l_{21} + 8l_{12} + 14l_{22} + 16l_{13} + 7l_{23} + 29l_{14} + 16l_{24} + 19l_{34} - 66y_3 &\geq 1 \\
13l_{11} + 20l_{21} + 20l_{12} + 17l_{22} + 17l_{13} + 14l_{23} + 25l_{14} + 29l_{24} + 10l_{34} - 83y_4 &\geq 1 \\
2l_{11} + 8l_{21} + 6l_{12} + 11l_{22} + 30l_{13} + 20l_{23} + 15l_{14} + 5l_{24} + 12l_{34} - 58y_5 &\geq 1 \\
12l_{11} + 17l_{21} + 11l_{12} + 9l_{22} + 2l_{13} + 30l_{23} + 22l_{14} + 12l_{24} + 20l_{34} - 70y_6 &\geq 1 \\
9l_{11} + 19l_{21} + 12l_{12} + 16l_{22} + 16l_{13} + 25l_{23} + 30l_{14} + 23l_{24} + 19l_{34} - 79y_7 &\geq 1 \\
5l_{11} + 9l_{21} + 4l_{12} + 14l_{22} + 23l_{13} + 16l_{23} + 16l_{14} + 30l_{24} + 3l_{34} - 59y_8 &\geq 1
\end{aligned}
$$

Four more constraints must be added, one for each attribute. These constraints are necessary to ensure that one and only one level is selected for each attribute. For attribute 1 (crust), we must add the constraint

$$l_{11} + l_{21} = 1$$

Because l_{11} and l_{21} are both 0-1 variables, this constraint requires that one of the two variables equals 1 and the other equals zero. The following three constraints ensure that one and only one level is selected for each of the other three attributes:

Salem

$$
\begin{aligned}
l_{12} + l_{22} &= 1 \\
l_{13} + l_{23} &= 1 \\
l_{14} + l_{24} + l_{34} &= 1
\end{aligned}
$$

The optimal solution to this 17-variable, 12-constraint integer linear program is $l_{11} = l_{22} = l_{23} = l_{14} = 1$ and $y_2 = y_5 = y_6 = y_7 = 1$. The value of the optimal solution is 4, indicating that if Salem makes this type of pizza, it will be preferable to the current favorite for four of the eight consumers. With $l_{11} = l_{22} = l_{23} = l_{14} = 1$, the pizza design that obtains the largest market share for Salem has a thin crust, a cheese blend, a chunky sauce, and mild-flavored sausage. Note also that with $y_2 = y_5 = y_6 = y_7 = 1$, consumers 2, 5, 6, and 7 will prefer the Salem pizza. With this information Salem may choose to market this type of pizza.

NOTES AND COMMENTS

1. Most practical applications of integer linear programming involve only 0-1 integer variables. Indeed, some mixed-integer computer codes are designed to handle only integer variables with binary values. However, if a clever mathematical trick is employed, these codes can still be used for problems involving general integer variables. The trick is called *binary expansion* and requires that an upper bound be established for each integer variable. More advanced texts on integer programming show how it can be done.
2. The Q.M. in Action, Volunteer Scheduling for the Edmonton Folk Festival, describes how a series of three integer programming models was used to schedule volunteers. Two of the models employ 0-1 variables.
3. General-purpose mixed-integer linear programming codes and some spreadsheet packages can be used for linear programming problems, all-integer problems, and problems involving some continuous and some integer variables. General-purpose codes are seldom the fastest for solving problems with special structure (such as the transportation, assignment, and transshipment problems); however, unless the problems are very large, speed is usually not a critical issue. Thus, most practitioners prefer to use one general-purpose computer package that can be used on a variety of problems rather than to maintain a variety of computer programs designed for special problems.

Q.M. *in* ACTION

*VOLUNTEER SCHEDULING FOR THE EDMONTON FOLK FESTIVAL**

The Edmonton Folk Festival is a four-day outdoor event that is run almost entirely by volunteers. In 2002, 1800 volunteers worked on 35 different crews and contributed more than 50,000 volunteer hours. With this many volunteers, coordination requires a major effort. For instance, in 2002, two volunteer coordinators used a trial-and-error procedure to develop schedules for the volunteers in the two gate crews. However, developing these schedules proved to be time consuming and frustrating; the coordinators spent as much time scheduling as they did supervising volunteers during the festival. To reduce the time spent on gate-crew scheduling, one of the coordinators asked the Centre for Excellence in Operations at the University of Alberta School of Business for help in automating the scheduling process. The Centre agreed to help.

The scheduling system developed consists of three integer programming models. Model 1 is used to determine daily shift schedules. This model determines the length of each shift (number of hours) and how many volunteers are needed for each shift to meet the peaks and valleys in demand. Model 2 is a binary integer program used to assign volunteers to shifts. The objective is to maximize volunteer preferences subject to several constraints, such as number of hours worked, balance between morning and afternoon shifts, a mix of experienced and inexperienced volunteers on each shift, no conflicting shifts, and so on. Model 3 is used to allocate volunteers between the two gates.

The coordinators of the gate crews were pleased with the results provided by the models and learned to use them effectively. Vicki Fannon, the manager of volunteers for the festival, now has plans to expand the use of the integer programming models to the scheduling of other crews in the future.

*Based on L. Gordon and E. Erkut, "Improving Volunteer Scheduling for the Edmonton Folk Festival," *Interfaces* (September/October 2004): 367–376.

11.4 Modeling Flexibility Provided by 0-1 Integer Variables

In Section 11.3 we presented four applications involving 0-1 integer variables. In this section we continue the discussion of the use of 0-1 integer variables in modeling. First, we show how 0-1 integer variables can be used to model multiple-choice and mutually exclusive constraints. Then, we show how 0-1 integer variables can be used to model situations in which k projects out of a set of n projects must be selected, as well as situations in which the acceptance of one project is conditional on the acceptance of another. We close the section with a cautionary note on the role of sensitivity analysis in integer linear programming.

Multiple-Choice and Mutually Exclusive Constraints

Recall the Ice-Cold Refrigerator capital budgeting problem introduced in Section 11.3. The decision variables were defined as

P = 1 if the plant expansion project is accepted; 0 if rejected
W = 1 if the warehouse expansion project is accepted; 0 if reject
M = 1 if the new machinery project is accepted; 0 if rejected
R = 1 if the new product research project is accepted; 0 if rejected

Suppose that, instead of one warehouse expansion project, the Ice-Cold Refrigerator Company actually has three warehouse expansion projects under consideration. One of the warehouses *must* be expanded because of increasing product demand, but new demand isn't sufficient to make expansion of more than one warehouse necessary. The following variable definitions and **multiple-choice constraint** could be incorporated into the previous 0-1 integer linear programming model to reflect this situation. Let

$W_1 = 1$ if the original warehouse expansion project is accepted; 0 if rejected
$W_2 = 1$ if the second warehouse expansion project is accepted; 0 if rejected
$W_3 = 1$ if the third warehouse expansion project is accepted; 0 if rejected

The multiple-choice constraint reflecting the requirement that exactly one of these projects must be selected is

$$W_1 + W_2 + W_3 = 1$$

If W_1, W_2, and W_3 are allowed to assume only the values 0 or 1, then one and only one of these projects will be selected from among the three choices.

If the requirement that one warehouse must be expanded did not exist, the multiple-choice constraint could be modified as follows:

$$W_1 + W_2 + W_3 \leq 1$$

This modification allows for the case of no warehouse expansion ($W_1 = W_2 = W_3 = 0$) but does not permit more than one warehouse to be expanded. This type of constraint is often called a **mutually exclusive constraint**.

k out of *n* Alternatives Constraint

An extension of the notion of a multiple-choice constraint can be used to model situations in which *k out of a set of n* projects must be selected—a ***k* out of *n* alternatives constraint**. Suppose that W_1, W_2, W_3, W_4, and W_5 represent five potential warehouse expansion projects and that two of the five projects must be accepted. The constraint that satisfies this new requirement is

$$W_1 + W_2 + W_3 + W_4 + W_5 = 2$$

If no more than two of the projects are to be selected, we would use the following less-than-or-equal-to constraint:

$$W_1 + W_2 + W_3 + W_4 + W_5 \leq 2$$

Again, each of these variables must be restricted to 0-1 values.

Conditional and Corequisite Constraints

Sometimes the acceptance of one project is conditional on the acceptance of another. For example, suppose for the Ice-Cold Refrigerator Company that the warehouse expansion project was conditional on the plant expansion project. That is, management will not consider expanding the warehouse unless the plant is expanded. With P representing plant expansion and W representing warehouse expansion, a **conditional constraint** could be introduced to enforce this requirement:

$$W \leq P$$

Both P and W must be 0 or 1; whenever P is 0, W will be forced to 0. When P is 1, W is also allowed to be 1; thus, both the plant and the warehouse can be expanded. However, we note that the preceding constraint does not force the warehouse expansion project (W) to be accepted if the plant expansion project (P) is accepted.

If the warehouse expansion project had to be accepted whenever the plant expansion project was, and vice versa, we would say that P and W represented **corequisite constraint** projects. To model such a situation, we simply write the preceding constraint as an equality:

$$W = P$$

Try Problem 7 for practice with the modeling flexibility provided by 0-1 variables.

The constraint forces P and W to take on the same value.

The Q.M. in Action, Customer Order Allocation Model at Ketron, describes how the modeling flexibility provided by 0-1 variables helped Ketron build a customer order allocation model for a sporting goods company.

Q.M. *in* ACTION

*CUSTOMER ORDER ALLOCATION MODEL AT KETRON**

Ketron Optimization provides consulting services for the design and implementation of mathematical programming applications. One such application involved the development of a mixed-integer programming model of the customer order allocation problem for a major sporting goods company. The sporting goods company markets approximately 300 products and has about 30 sources of supply (factory and warehouse locations). The problem is to determine how best to allocate customer orders to the various sources of supply such that the total manufacturing cost for the products ordered is minimized. Figure 11.12 provides a graphical representation of this problem. Note in the figure that each customer can receive shipments from only a few of the various sources of supply. For example, we see that customer 1 may be supplied by source A or B, customer 2 may be supplied only by source A, and so on.

The sporting equipment company classifies each customer order as either a "guaranteed" or "secondary" order. Guaranteed orders are single-source orders in that they must be filled by a single supplier to ensure that the complete order will be delivered to the customer at one time. This single-source requirement necessitates the use of 0-1 integer variables in the model. Approximately 80% of the company's orders are guaranteed orders. Secondary orders can be split among the various sources of supply. These orders are made by customers restocking inventory, and receiving partial shipments from different sources at different times is not a problem. The 0-1 variables are used to represent the assignment of a guaranteed order to a supplier, and continuous variables are used to represent the secondary orders.

Constraints for the problem involve raw material capacities, manufacturing capacities, and individual product capacities. A fairly typical problem has about 800 constraints, 2000 0-1 assignment variables, and 500 continuous variables associated with the secondary orders. The customer order allocation problem is solved periodically as orders are received. In a typical period, between 20 and 40 customers are to be supplied. Because most customers require several products, usually between 600 and 800 orders must be assigned to the sources of supply.

*Based on information provided by J. A. Tomlin of Ketron Optimization.

(continued)

FIGURE 11.12 GRAPHICAL REPRESENTATION OF THE CUSTOMER ORDER ALLOCATION PROBLEM

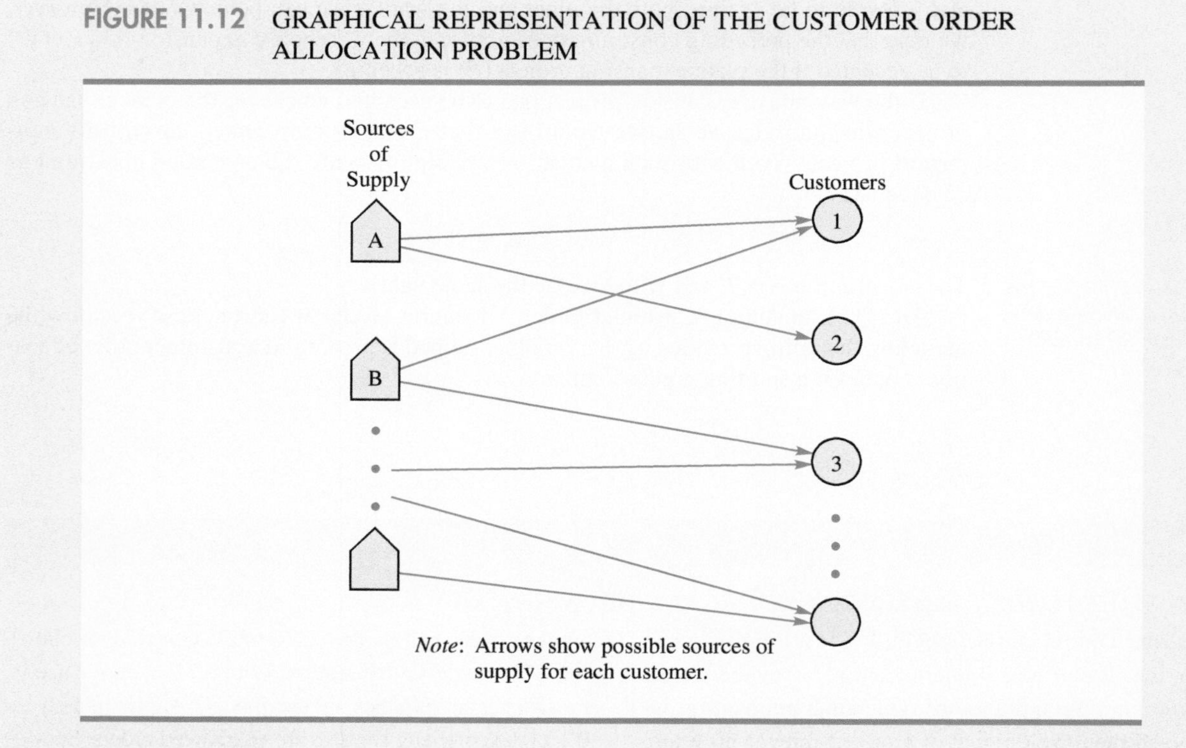

Note: Arrows show possible sources of supply for each customer.

A Cautionary Note About Sensitivity Analysis

Sensitivity analysis often is more crucial for integer linear programming problems than for linear programming problems. A small change in one of the coefficients in the constraints can cause a relatively large change in the value of the optimal solution. To understand why, consider the following integer programming model of a simple capital budgeting problem involving four projects and a budgetary constraint for a single time period:

$$\begin{aligned} \text{Max} \quad & 40x_1 + 60x_2 + 70x_3 + 160x_4 \\ \text{s.t.} \quad & \\ & 16x_1 + 35x_2 + 45x_3 + \ \ 85x_4 \leq 100 \\ & x_1, x_2, x_3, x_4 = 0, 1 \end{aligned}$$

Shadow prices cannot be used for integer programming sensitivity analysis because they are designed for linear programs. Multiple computer runs usually are necessary for sensitivity analysis of integer linear programs.

We can obtain the optimal solution to this problem by enumerating the alternatives. It is $x_1 = 1$, $x_2 = 1$, $x_3 = 1$, and $x_4 = 0$, with an objective function value of \$170. However, note that if the budget available is increased by \$1 (from \$100 to \$101), the optimal solution changes to $x_1 = 1$, $x_2 = 0$, $x_3 = 0$, and $x_4 = 1$, with an objective function value of \$200. That is, one additional dollar in the budget would lead to a \$30 increase in the return. Surely management, when faced with such a situation, would increase the budget by \$1. Because of the extreme sensitivity of the value of the optimal solution to the constraint coefficients, practitioners usually recommend re-solving the integer linear program several times with slight variations in the coefficients before attempting to choose the best solution for implementation.

Summary

In this chapter we introduced the important extension of linear programming referred to as *integer linear programming.* The only difference between the integer linear programming problems discussed in this chapter and the linear programming problems studied in previous chapters is that one or more of the variables must be integer. If all variables must be integer, we have an all-integer linear program. If some, but not necessarily all, variables must be integer, we have a mixed-integer linear program. Most integer programming applications involve 0-1 or binary variables.

Studying integer linear programming is important for two major reasons. First, integer linear programming may be helpful when fractional values for the variables are not permitted. Rounding a linear programming solution may not provide an optimal integer solution; methods for finding optimal integer solutions are needed when the economic consequences of rounding are significant. A second reason for studying integer linear programming is the increased modeling flexibility provided through the use of 0-1 variables. We showed how 0-1 variables could be used to model important managerial considerations in capital budgeting, fixed cost, supply chain design, bank location, and product design/market share applications.

The number of applications of integer linear programming continues to grow rapidly. This growth is due in part to the availability of good integer linear programming software packages. As researchers develop solution procedures capable of solving larger integer linear programs and as computer speed increases, a continuation of the growth of integer programming applications is expected.

Glossary

0-1 integer linear program An all-integer or mixed-integer linear program in which the integer variables are only permitted to assume the values 0 or 1. Also called *binary integer program.*

All-integer linear program An integer linear program in which all variables are required to be integer.

Capital budgeting problem A 0-1 integer programming problem that involves choosing which possible projects or activities provide the best investment return.

Conditional constraint A constraint involving 0-1 variables that does not allow certain variables to equal 1 unless certain other variables are equal to 1.

Corequisite constraint A constraint requiring that two 0-1 variables be equal. Thus, they are both either in or out of solution together.

Fixed cost problem A 0-1 mixed-integer programming problem in which the binary variables represent whether an activity, such as a production run, is undertaken (variable = 1) or not (variable = 0).

Integer linear program A linear program with the additional requirement that one or

***k* out of *n* alternatives constraint** An extension of the multiple-choice constraint. This constraint requires that the sum of n 0-1 variables equals k. more of the variables must be integer.

Location problem A 0-1 integer programming problem in which the objective is to select the best locations to meet a stated objective. Variations of this problem (see the bank location problem in Section 11.3) are known as covering problems.

LP Relaxation The linear program that results from dropping the integer requirements for the variables in an integer linear program.

Mixed-integer linear program An integer linear program in which some, but not necessarily all, variables are required to be integer.

Multiple-choice constraint A constraint requiring that the sum of two or more 0-1 variables equals 1. Thus, any feasible solution makes a choice of which variable to set equal to 1.

Mutually exclusive constraint A constraint requiring that the sum of two or more 0-1 variables be less than or equal to 1. Thus, if one of the variables equals 1, the others must equal 0. However, all variables could equal 0.

Product design and market share optimization problem Sometimes called the share of choice problem, it involves choosing a product design that maximizes the number of consumers preferring it.

Supply chain design problem A mixed-integer linear program in which the binary integer variables usually represent sites selected for warehouses or plants and continuous variables represent the amount shipped over arcs in the supply chain.

Problems

1. Indicate which of the following is an all-integer linear program and which is a mixed-integer linear program. Write the LP Relaxation for the problem but do not attempt to solve.

   a. Max $30x_1 + 25x_2$

   s.t.

$$
\begin{aligned}
3x_1 + 1.5x_2 &\le 400 \\
1.5x_1 + 2x_2 &\le 250 \\
1x_1 + 1x_2 &\le 150 \\
x_1, x_2 \ge 0 &\text{ and } x_2 \text{ integer}
\end{aligned}
$$

   b. Min $3x_1 + 4x_2$

   s.t.

$$
\begin{aligned}
2x_1 + 4x_2 &\ge 8 \\
2x_1 + 6x_2 &\ge 12 \\
x_1, x_2 \ge 0 &\text{ and integer}
\end{aligned}
$$

SELF test

2. Consider the following all-integer linear program:

   Max $5x_1 + 8x_2$

   s.t.

$$
\begin{aligned}
6x_1 + 5x_2 &\le 30 \\
9x_1 + 4x_2 &\le 36 \\
1x_1 + 2x_2 &\le 10 \\
x_1, x_2 \ge 0 &\text{ and integer}
\end{aligned}
$$

   a. Graph the constraints for this problem. Use dots to indicate all feasible integer solutions.
   b. Find the optimal solution to the LP Relaxation. Round down to find a feasible integer solution.
   c. Find the optimal integer solution. Is it the same as the solution obtained in part (b) by rounding down?

3. Consider the following all-integer linear program:

$$\begin{aligned} \text{Max} \quad & 1x_1 + 1x_2 \\ \text{s.t.} \quad & \\ & 4x_1 + 6x_2 \leq 22 \\ & 1x_1 + 5x_2 \leq 15 \\ & 2x_1 + 1x_2 \leq 9 \\ & x_1, x_2 \geq 0 \text{ and integer} \end{aligned}$$

   a. Graph the constraints for this problem. Use dots to indicate all feasible integer solutions.
   b. Solve the LP Relaxation of this problem.
   c. Find the optimal integer solution.

4. Consider the following all-integer linear program:

$$\begin{aligned} \text{Max} \quad & 10x_1 + 3x_2 \\ \text{s.t.} \quad & \\ & 6x_1 + 7x_2 \leq 40 \\ & 3x_1 + 1x_2 \leq 11 \\ & x_1, x_2 \geq 0 \text{ and integer} \end{aligned}$$

   a. Formulate and solve the LP Relaxation of the problem. Solve it graphically, and round down to find a feasible solution. Specify an upper bound on the value of the optimal solution.
   b. Solve the integer linear program graphically. Compare the value of this solution with the solution obtained in part (a).
   c. Suppose the objective function changes to Max $3x_1 + 6x_2$. Repeat parts (a) and (b).

5. Consider the following mixed-integer linear program:

$$\begin{aligned} \text{Max} \quad & 2x_1 + 3x_2 \\ \text{s.t.} \quad & \\ & 4x_1 + 9x_2 \leq 36 \\ & 7x_1 + 5x_2 \leq 35 \\ & x_1, x_2 \geq 0 \text{ and } x_1 \text{ integer} \end{aligned}$$

   a. Graph the constraints for this problem. Indicate on your graph all feasible mixed-integer solutions.
   b. Find the optimal solution to the LP Relaxation. Round the value of x_1 down to find a feasible mixed-integer solution. Is this solution optimal? Why or why not?
   c. Find the optimal solution for the mixed-integer linear program.

6. Consider the following mixed-integer linear program:

$$\begin{aligned} \text{Max} \quad & 1x_1 + 1x_2 \\ \text{s.t.} \quad & \\ & 7x_1 + 9x_2 \leq 63 \\ & 9x_1 + 5x_2 \leq 45 \\ & 3x_1 + 1x_2 \leq 12 \\ & x_1, x_2 \geq 0 \text{ and } x_2 \text{ integer} \end{aligned}$$

   a. Graph the constraints for this problem. Indicate on your graph all feasible mixed-integer solutions.

b. Find the optimal solution to the LP Relaxation. Round the value of x_2 down to find a feasible mixed-integer solution. Specify upper and lower bounds on the value of the optimal solution to the mixed-integer linear program.
c. Find the optimal solution to the mixed-integer linear program.

7. The following questions refer to a capital budgeting problem with six projects represented by 0-1 variables x_1, x_2, x_3, x_4, x_5, and x_6:
   a. Write a constraint modeling a situation in which two of the projects 1, 3, 5, and 6 must be undertaken.
   b. Write a constraint modeling a situation in which, if projects 3 and 5 must be undertaken, they must be undertaken simultaneously.
   c. Write a constraint modeling a situation in which project 1 or 4 must be undertaken, but not both.
   d. Write constraints modeling a situation where project 4 cannot be undertaken unless projects 1 and 3 also are undertaken.
   e. Revise the requirement in part (d) to accommodate the case in which, when projects 1 and 3 are undertaken, project 4 also must be undertaken.
8. Spencer Enterprises is attempting to choose among a series of new investment alternatives. The potential investment alternatives, the net present value of the future stream of returns, the capital requirements, and the available capital funds over the next three years are summarized as follows:

Alternative	Net Present Value ($)	Capital Requirements ($) Year 1	Year 2	Year 3
Limited warehouse expansion	4,000	3,000	1,000	4,000
Extensive warehouse expansion	6,000	2,500	3,500	3,500
Test market new product	10,500	6,000	4,000	5,000
Advertising campaign	4,000	2,000	1,500	1,800
Basic research	8,000	5,000	1,000	4,000
Purchase new equipment	3,000	1,000	500	900
Capital funds available		10,500	7,000	8,750

   a. Develop and solve an integer programming model for maximizing the net present value.
   b. Assume that only one of the warehouse expansion projects can be implemented. Modify your model of part (a).
   c. Suppose that, if test marketing of the new product is carried out, the advertising campaign also must be conducted. Modify your formulation of part (b) to reflect this new situation.
9. Hawkins Manufacturing Company produces connecting rods for 4- and 6-cylinder automobile engines using the same production line. The cost required to set up the production line to produce the 4-cylinder connecting rods is $2000, and the cost required to set up the production line for the 6-cylinder connecting rods is $3500. Manufacturing costs are $15 for each 4-cylinder connecting rod and $18 for each 6-cylinder connecting rod. Hawkins makes a decision at the end of each week as to which product will be manufactured the following week. If there is a production changeover from one week to the next, the weekend is used to reconfigure the production line. Once the line has been set up, the weekly production capacities are 6000 6-cylinder connecting rods and 8000 4-cylinder connecting rods. Let

   x_4 = the number of 4-cylinder connecting rods produced next week

   x_6 = the number of 6-cylinder connecting rods produced next week

s_4 = 1 if the production line is set up to produce the 4-cylinder connecting rods; 0 if otherwise

s_6 = 1 if the production line is set up to produce the 6-cylinder connecting rods; 0 if otherwise

a. Using the decision variables x_4 and s_4, write a constraint that limits next week's production of the 4-cylinder connecting rods to either 0 or 8000 units.
b. Using the decision variables x_6 and s_6, write a constraint that limits next week's production of the 6-cylinder connecting rods to either 0 or 6000 units.
c. Write three constraints that, taken together, limit the production of connecting rods for next week.
d. Write an objective function for minimizing the cost of production for next week.

10. Grave City is considering the relocation of several police substations to obtain better enforcement in high-crime areas. The locations under consideration together with the areas that can be covered from these locations are given in the following table:

Potential Locations for Substations	Areas Covered
A	1, 5, 7
B	1, 2, 5, 7
C	1, 3, 5
D	2, 4, 5
E	3, 4, 6
F	4, 5, 6
G	1, 5, 6, 7

a. Formulate an integer programming model that could be used to find the minimum number of locations necessary to provide coverage to all areas.
b. Solve the problem in part (a).

11. Hart Manufacturing makes three products. Each product requires manufacturing operations in three departments: A, B, and C. The labor-hour requirements, by department, are as follows:

Department	Product 1	Product 2	Product 3
A	1.50	3.00	2.00
B	2.00	1.00	2.50
C	0.25	0.25	0.25

During the next production period, the labor-hours available are 450 in department A, 350 in department B, and 50 in department C. The profit contributions per unit are $25 for product 1, $28 for product 2, and $30 for product 3.

a. Formulate a linear programming model for maximizing total profit contribution.
b. Solve the linear program formulated in part (a). How much of each product should be produced, and what is the projected total profit contribution?
c. After evaluating the solution obtained in part (b), one of the production supervisors noted that production setup costs had not been taken into account. She noted that setup costs are $400 for product 1, $550 for product 2, and $600 for product 3. If the solution developed in part (b) is to be used, what is the total profit contribution after taking into account the setup costs?

d. Management realized that the optimal product mix, taking setup costs into account, might be different from the one recommended in part (b). Formulate a mixed-integer linear program that takes setup costs into account. Management also stated that we should not consider making more than 175 units of product 1, 150 units of product 2, or 140 units of product 3.

e. Solve the mixed-integer linear program formulated in part (d). How much of each product should be produced, and what is the projected total profit contribution? Compare this profit contribution to that obtained in part (c).

12. Offhaus Manufacturing produces office supplies, but outsources the delivery of its products to third party carriers. Offhaus ships to 20 cities from its Dayton, Ohio, manufacturing facility and has asked a variety of carriers to bid on its business. Seven carriers have responded with bids. The resulting bids (in dollars per truckload) are shown in the following table. For example, the table shows that Carrier 1 bid on the business to cities 11–20. The right side of the table provides the number of truckloads scheduled for each destination in the next quarter.

Bid $/Truckload	Carrier 1	Carrier 2	Carrier 3	Carrier 4	Carrier 5	Carrier 6	Carrier 7	Destination	Demand (Truckloads)
City 1					$2188	$1666	$1790	City 1	30
City 2		$1453			$2602	$1767		City 2	10
City 3		$1534			$2283	$1857	$1870	City 3	20
City 4		$1687			$2617	$1738		City 4	40
City 5		$1523			$2239	$1771	$1855	City 5	10
City 6		$1521			$1571		$1545	City 6	10
City 7		$2100		$1922	$1938		$2050	City 7	12
City 8		$1800		$1432	$1416		$1739	City 8	25
City 9		$1134		$1233	$1181		$1150	City 9	25
City 10		$ 672		$ 610	$ 669		$ 678	City 10	33
City 11	$724		$723	$ 627	$ 657		$ 706	City 11	11
City 12	$766		$766	$ 721	$ 682		$ 733	City 12	29
City 13	$741		$745		$ 682		$ 733	City 13	12
City 14	$815	$ 800	$828		$ 745		$ 832	City 14	24
City 15	$904		$880		$ 891		$ 914	City 15	10
City 16	$958		$933		$ 891		$ 914	City 16	10
City 17	$925		$929		$ 937		$ 984	City 17	23
City 18	$892		$869	$ 822	$ 829		$ 864	City 18	25
City 19	$927		$969		$ 967		$1008	City 19	12
City 20	$963		$938		$ 955		$ 995	City 20	10
Number of Bids	10	10	10	7	20	5	18		

Because dealing with too many carriers can be a hassle, Offhaus would like to limit the number of carriers it uses to three. Also, for customer relationship reasons, Offhaus wants each city to be assigned to only one carrier (that is, there is no splitting of the demand to a given city across carriers).

a. Develop a model that will yield the three selected carriers and the city-carrier assignments so as to minimize the cost of shipping. Solve the model and report the solution.

b. Offhaus is not sure if three is the correct number of carriers to select. Run the model you developed in part (a) for allowable carriers varying from 1 up to 7. Based on results, how many carriers would you recommend and why?

13. Recall the Martin-Beck Company supply chain design problem in Section 11.3.

a. Modify the formulation shown in Section 11.3 to account for the policy restriction that a plant must be located either in Detroit or in Toledo, but not both.

b. Modify the formulation shown in Section 11.3 to account for the policy restriction that no more than two plants can be located in Denver, Kansas City, and St. Louis.

14. An automobile manufacturer has five outdated plants: one each in Michigan, Ohio, and California and two in New York. Management is considering modernizing these plants to manufacture engine blocks and transmissions for a new model car. The cost to modernize each plant and the manufacturing capacity after modernization is as follows:

Plant	Cost ($ millions)	Engine Blocks (1000s)	Transmissions (1000s)
Michigan	25	500	300
New York	35	800	400
New York	35	400	800
Ohio	40	900	600
California	20	200	300

The projected needs are for total capacities of 900,000 engine blocks and 900,000 transmissions. Management wants to determine which plants to modernize to meet projected manufacturing needs and, at the same time, minimize the total cost of modernization.

a. Develop a table that lists every possible option available to management. As part of your table, indicate the total engine block capacity and transmission capacity for each possible option, whether the option is feasible based on the projected needs, and the total modernization cost for each option.
b. Based on your analysis in part (a), what recommendation would you provide management?
c. Formulate a 0-1 integer programming model that could be used to determine the optimal solution to the modernization question facing management.
d. Solve the model formulated in part (c) to provide a recommendation for management.

OhioTrustFull

15. Consider again the Ohio Trust bank location problem discussed in Section 11.3. The file OhioTrustFull contains data for all of Ohio's 88 counties. The file contains an 88 × 88 matrix with the rows and columns each being the 88 counties. The entries in the matrix are zeros and ones and indicate if the county of the row shares a border with the county of the column (1 = yes and 0 = no).

a. Create a model to find the location of required principal places of business (PPBs) to minimize the number of PPBs needed to open all counties to branches.
b. Solve the model constructed in part (a). What is the minimum number of PPBs needed to open up the entire state to Ohio Trust branches?

16. The Northshore Bank is working to develop an efficient work schedule for full-time and part-time tellers. The schedule must provide for efficient operation of the bank, including adequate customer service, employee breaks, and so on. On Fridays the bank is open from 9:00 A.M. to 7:00 P.M. The number of tellers necessary to provide adequate customer service during each hour of operation is summarized in the following table.

Time	Number of Tellers	Time	Number of Tellers
9:00 A.M.–10:00 A.M.	6	2:00 P.M.–3:00 P.M.	6
10:00 A.M.–11:00 A.M.	4	3:00 P.M.–4:00 P.M.	4
11:00 A.M.–Noon	8	4:00 P.M.–5:00 P.M.	7
Noon–1:00 P.M.	10	5:00 P.M.–6:00 P.M.	6
1:00 P.M.–2:00 P.M.	9	6:00 P.M.–7:00 P.M.	6

Each full-time employee starts on the hour and works a 4-hour shift, followed by 1 hour for lunch and then a 3-hour shift. Part-time employees work one 4-hour shift beginning on the hour. Considering salary and fringe benefits, full-time employees cost the bank \$15 per hour (\$105 a day), and part-time employees cost the bank \$8 per hour (\$32 per day).

a. Formulate an integer programming model that can be used to develop a schedule that will satisfy customer service needs at a minimum employee cost. (*Hint:* Let x_i = number of full-time employees coming on duty at the beginning of hour i and y_i = number of part-time employees coming on duty at the beginning of hour i.)
b. Solve the LP Relaxation of your model in part (a).
c. Solve for the optimal schedule of tellers. Comment on the solution.
d. After reviewing the solution to part (c), the bank manager realized that some additional requirements must be specified. Specifically, she wants to ensure that one full-time employee is on duty at all times and that there is a staff of at least five full-time employees. Revise your model to incorporate these additional requirements and solve for the optimal solution.

OhioTrustPop

17. Consider again the Ohio Trust Inc. problem described in Problem 15. Suppose only a limted number of PPBs can be placed. Ohio Trust would like to place this limited number of PPBs in counties so that the allowable branches can reach the maximum possible population. The file OhioTrustPop contains the county adjacency matrix described in Problem 15 as well as the population of each county.
    a. Assume that only a fixed number of PPBs, denoted k. can be established. Formulate a linear binary integer program that will tell Ohio Trust Inc. where to locate the fixed number of PPBs in order to maximize the population reached. (*Hint:* Introduce variable y_i = 1 if it is possible to establish a branch in county i, and y_i = 0 otherwise; that is, if county i is covered by a PPB, then the population can be counted as covered.)
    b. Suppose that two PPBs can be established. Where should they be located to maximize the population served?
    c. Solve your model from part a for allowable number of PPBs ranging from 1 to 10. In other words, solve the model 10 times, k set to 1,2, . . . , 10. Record the population reached for each value of k. Graph the results of this analysis by plotting the population reached versus number of PPBs allowed. Based on their cost calculations, Ohio Trust considers an additional PPB to be fiscally prudent only if it increases the population reached by at least 500,000 people. Based on this graph, what is the number of PPBs you recommend to be implemented?

18. Refer to the Salem Foods share of choices problem in Section 11.3 and address the following issues. It is rumored that King's is getting out of the frozen pizza business. If so, the major competitor for Salem Foods will be the Antonio's brand pizza.
    a. Compute the overall utility for the Antonio's brand pizza for each of the consumers in Table 11.4.
    b. Assume that Salem's only competitor is the Antonio's brand pizza. Formulate and solve the share of choices problem that will maximize market share. What is the best product design, and what share of the market can be expected?

19. Burnside Marketing Research conducted a study for Barker Foods on some designs for a new dry cereal. Three attributes were found to be most influential in determining which cereal had the best taste: ratio of wheat to corn in the cereal flake, type of sweetener (sugar, honey, or artificial), and the presence or absence of flavor bits. Seven children participated in taste tests and provided the following part-worths for the attributes:

Child	Wheat/Corn Low	High	Sweetener Sugar	Honey	Artificial	Flavor Bits Present	Absent
1	15	35	30	40	25	15	9
2	30	20	40	35	35	8	11
3	40	25	20	40	10	7	14
4	35	30	25	20	30	15	18
5	25	40	40	20	35	18	14
6	20	25	20	35	30	9	16
7	30	15	25	40	40	20	11

a. Suppose the overall utility (sum of part-worths) of the current favorite cereal is 75 for each child. What is the product design that will maximize the share of choices for the seven children in the sample?
b. Assume the overall utility of the current favorite cereal for children 1–4 is 70, and the overall utility of the current favorite cereal for children 5–7 is 80. What is the product design that will maximize the share of choice for the seven children in the sample?

20. Refer to Problem 14. Suppose that management determined that its cost estimates to modernize the New York plants were too low. Specifically, suppose that the actual cost is $40 million to modernize each plant.
    a. What changes in your previous 0-1 integer linear programming model are needed to incorporate these changes in costs?
    b. For these cost changes, what recommendations would you now provide management regarding the modernization plan?
    c. Reconsider the solution obtained using the revised cost figures. Suppose that management decides that closing two plants in the same state is not acceptable. How could this policy restriction be added to your 0-1 integer programming model?
    d. Based on the cost revision and the policy restriction presented in part (c), what recommendations would you now provide management regarding the modernization plan?

21. The Bayside Art Gallery is considering installing a video camera security system to reduce its insurance premiums. A diagram of the eight display rooms that Bayside uses for exhibitions is shown in Figure 11.13; the openings between the rooms are numbered 1–13. A security firm proposed that two-way cameras be installed at some room openings. Each camera has the ability to monitor the two rooms between which the camera is located. For example, if a camera were located at opening number 4, rooms 1 and 4 would be covered; if a camera were located at opening 11, rooms 7 and 8 would be covered; and so on. Management decided not to locate a camera system at the entrance to the display rooms. The objective is to provide security coverage for all eight rooms using the minimum number of two-way cameras.
    a. Formulate a 0-1 integer linear programming model that will enable Bayside's management to determine the locations for the camera systems.
    b. Solve the model formulated in part (a) to determine how many two-way cameras to purchase and where they should be located.
    c. Suppose that management wants to provide additional security coverage for room 7. Specifically, management wants room 7 to be covered by two cameras. How would your model formulated in part (a) have to change to accommodate this policy restriction?
    d. With the policy restriction specified in part (c), determine how many two-way camera systems will need to be purchased and where they will be located.

FIGURE 11.13 DIAGRAM OF DISPLAY ROOMS FOR BAYSIDE ART GALLERY

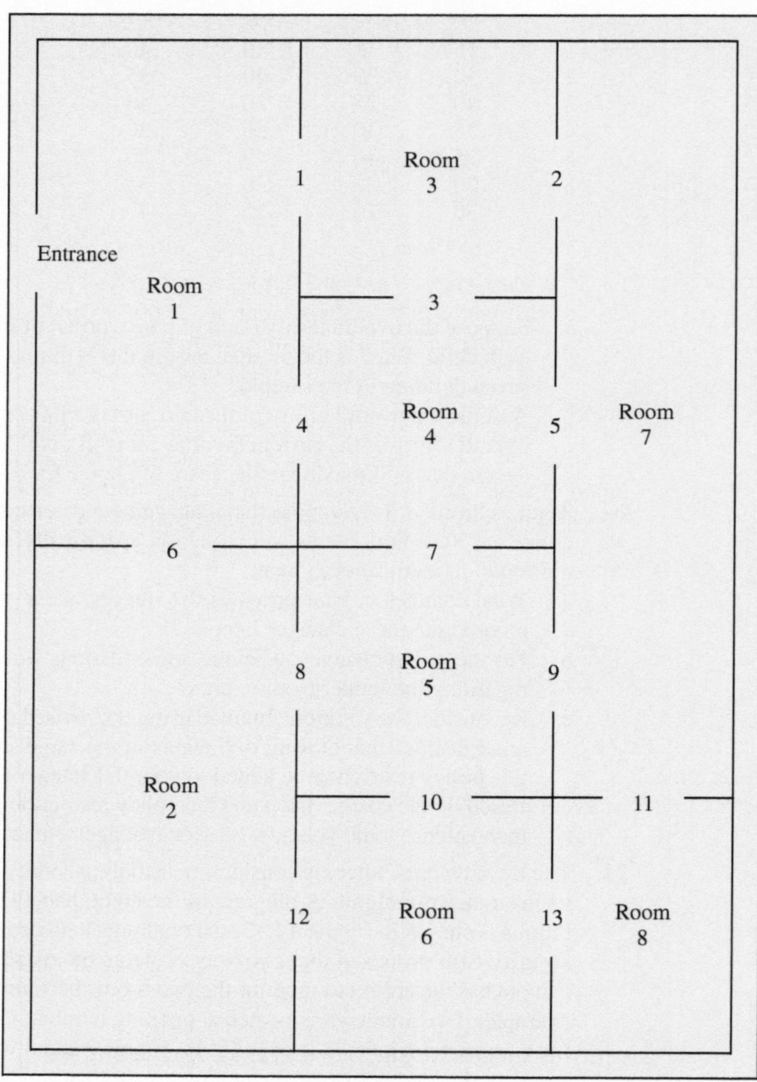

22. The Delta Group is a management consulting firm specializing in the health care industry. A team is being formed to study possible new markets, and a linear programming model has been developed for selecting team members. However, one constraint the president imposed is a team size of three, five, or seven members. The staff cannot figure out how to incorporate this requirement in the model. The current model requires that team members be selected from three departments and uses the following variable definitions:

x_1 = the number of employees selected from department 1

x_2 = the number of employees selected from department 2

x_3 = the number of employees selected from department 3

Show the staff how to write constraints that will ensure that the team will consist of three, five, or seven employees. The following integer variables should be helpful:

$$y_1 = \begin{cases} 1 & \text{if team size is 3} \\ 0 & \text{otherwise} \end{cases}$$

$$y_2 = \begin{cases} 1 & \text{if team size is 5} \\ 0 & \text{otherwise} \end{cases}$$

$$y_3 = \begin{cases} 1 & \text{if team size is 7} \\ 0 & \text{otherwise} \end{cases}$$

23. Roedel Electronics produces a variety of electrical components, including a remote control for televisions and a remote control for DVD players. Each remote control consists of three subassemblies that are manufactured by Roedel: a base, a cartridge, and a keypad. Both remote controls use the same base subassembly, but different cartridge and keypad subassemblies.

    Roedel's sales forecast indicates that 7000 TV remote controls and 5000 DVD remote controls will be needed to satisfy demand during the upcoming Christmas season. Because only 500 hours of in-house manufacturing time are available, Roedel is considering purchasing some, or all, of the subassemblies from outside suppliers. If Roedel manufactures a subassembly in-house, it incurs a fixed setup cost as well as a variable manufacturing cost. The following table shows the setup cost, the manufacturing time per subassembly, the manufacturing cost per subassembly, and the cost to purchase each of the subassemblies from an outside supplier:

Subassembly	Setup Cost ($)	Manufacturing Time per Unit (min.)	Manufacturing Cost per Unit ($)	Purchase Cost per Unit ($)
Base	1000	0.9	0.40	0.65
TV cartridge	1200	2.2	2.90	3.45
DVD cartridge	1900	3.0	3.15	3.70
TV keypad	1500	0.8	0.30	0.50
DVD keypad	1500	1.0	0.55	0.70

    a. Determine how many units of each subassembly Roedel should manufacture and how many units Roedel should purchase. What is the total manufacturing and purchase cost associated with your recommendation?
    b. Suppose Roedel is considering purchasing new machinery to produce DVD cartridges. For the new machinery, the setup cost is $3000; the manufacturing time is 2.5 minutes per cartridge, and the manufacturing cost is $2.60 per cartridge. Assuming that the new machinery is purchased, determine how many units of each subassembly Roedel should manufacture and how many units of each subassembly Roedel should purchase. What is the total manufacturing and purchase cost associated with your recommendation? Do you think the new machinery should be purchased? Explain.

24. A mathematical programming system named SilverScreener uses a 0-1 integer programming model to help theater managers decide which movies to show on a weekly basis in a multiple-screen theater. Suppose that management of Valley Cinemas would like to investigate the potential of using a similar scheduling system for their chain of multiple-screen theaters. Valley selected a small two-screen movie theater for the pilot testing and would like to develop an integer programming model to help schedule movies for the next four weeks. Six movies are available. The first week each movie is available, the last week

each movie can be shown, and the maximum number of weeks that each movie can run are shown here:

Movie	First Week Available	Last Week Available	Max. Run (weeks)
1	1	2	2
2	1	3	2
3	1	1	2
4	2	4	2
5	3	6	3
6	3	5	3

The overall viewing schedule for the theater is composed of the individual schedules for each of the six movies. For each movie a schedule must be developed that specifies the week the movie starts and the number of consecutive weeks it will run. For instance, one possible schedule for movie 2 is for it to start in week 1 and run for two weeks. Theater policy requires that once a movie is started, it must be shown in consecutive weeks. It cannot be stopped and restarted again. To represent the schedule possibilities for each movie, the following decision variables were developed:

$$x_{ijw} = \begin{cases} 1 & \text{if movie } i \text{ is scheduled to start in week } j \text{ and run for } w \text{ weeks} \\ 0 & \text{otherwise} \end{cases}$$

For example, $x_{532} = 1$ means that the schedule selected for movie 5 is to begin in week 3 and run for two weeks. For each movie, a separate variable is given for each possible schedule.

a. Three schedules are associated with movie 1. List the variables that represent these schedules.
b. Write a constraint requiring that only one schedule be selected for movie 1.
c. Write a constraint requiring that only one schedule be selected for movie 5.
d. What restricts the number of movies that can be shown in week 1? Write a constraint that restricts the number of movies selected for viewing in week 1.
e. Write a constraint that restricts the number of movies selected for viewing in week 3.

25. East Coast Trucking provides service from Boston to Miami using regional offices located in Boston, New York, Philadelphia, Baltimore, Washington, Richmond, Raleigh, Florence, Savannah, Jacksonville, and Tampa. The number of miles between each of the regional offices is provided in the following table:

	New York	Philadelphia	Baltimore	Washington	Richmond	Raleigh	Florence	Savannah	Jacksonville	Tampa	Miami
Boston	211	320	424	459	565	713	884	1056	1196	1399	1669
New York		109	213	248	354	502	673	845	985	1188	1458
Philadelphia			104	139	245	393	564	736	876	1079	1349
Baltimore				35	141	289	460	632	772	975	1245
Washington					106	254	425	597	737	940	1210
Richmond						148	319	491	631	834	1104
Raleigh							171	343	483	686	956
Florence								172	312	515	785
Savannah									140	343	613
Jacksonville										203	473
Tampa											270

The company's expansion plans involve constructing service facilities in some of the cities where a regional office is located. Each regional office must be within 400 miles of a service facility. For instance, if a service facility is constructed in Richmond, it can provide service to regional offices located in New York, Philadelphia, Baltimore, Washington, Richmond, Raleigh, and Florence. Management would like to determine the minimum number of service facilities needed and where they should be located.

a. Formulate an integer linear program that can be used to determine the minimum number of service facilities needed and their locations.
b. Solve the integer linear program formulated in part (a). How many service facilities are required and where should they be located?
c. Suppose that each service facility can only provide service to regional offices within 300 miles. How many service facilities are required and where should they be located?

26. Dave has $100,000 to invest in 10 mutual fund alternatives with the following restrictions. For diversification, no more than $25,000 can be invested in any one fund. If a fund is chosen for investment, then at least $10,000 will be invested in it. No more than two of the funds can be pure growth funds, and at least one pure bond fund must be selected. The total amount invested in pure bond funds must be at least as much as the amount invested in pure growth funds. Using the following expected returns, formulate and solve a model that will determine the investment strategy that will maximize expected annual return. What assumptions have you made in your model? How often would you expect to run your model?

Fund	Type	Expected Return
1	Growth	6.70%
2	Growth	7.65%
3	Growth	7.55%
4	Growth	7.45%
5	Growth & Income	7.50%
6	Growth & Income	6.45%
7	Growth & Income	7.05%
8	Stock & Bond	6.90%
9	Bond	5.20%
10	Bond	5.90%

Case Problem 1 Textbook Publishing

ASW Publishing, Inc., a small publisher of college textbooks, must make a decision regarding which books to publish next year. The books under consideration are listed in the following table, along with the projected three-year sales expected from each book:

Book Subject	Type of Book	Projected Sales (1000s)
Business calculus	New	20
Finite mathematics	Revision	30
General statistics	New	15
Mathematical statistics	New	10
Business statistics	Revision	25
Finance	New	18
Financial accounting	New	25
Managerial accounting	Revision	50
English literature	New	20
German	New	30

The books listed as revisions are texts that ASW already has under contract; these texts are being considered for publication as new editions. The books that are listed as new have been reviewed by the company, but contracts have not yet been signed.

Three individuals in the company can be assigned to these projects, all of whom have varying amounts of time available; John has 60 days available, and Susan and Monica both have 40 days available. The days required by each person to complete each project are shown in the following table. For instance, if the business calculus book is published, it will require 30 days of John's time and 40 days of Susan's time. An "X" indicates that the person will not be used on the project. Note that at least two staff members will be assigned to each project except the finance book.

Book Subject	John	Susan	Monica
Business calculus	30	40	X
Finite mathematics	16	24	X
General statistics	24	X	30
Mathematical statistics	20	X	24
Business statistics	10	X	16
Finance	X	X	14
Financial accounting	X	24	26
Managerial accounting	X	28	30
English literature	40	34	30
German	X	50	36

ASW will not publish more than two statistics books or more than one accounting text in a single year. In addition, management decided that one of the mathematics books (business calculus or finite math) must be published, but not both.

Managerial Report

Prepare a report for the managing editor of ASW that describes your findings and recommendations regarding the best publication strategy for next year. In carrying out your analysis, assume that the fixed costs and the sales revenues per unit are approximately equal for all books; management is interested primarily in maximizing the total unit sales volume.

The managing editor also asked that you include recommendations regarding the following possible changes:

1. If it would be advantageous to do so, Susan can be moved off another project to allow her to work 12 more days.
2. If it would be advantageous to do so, Monica can also be made available for another 10 days.
3. If one or more of the revisions could be postponed for another year, should they be? Clearly the company will risk losing market share by postponing a revision.

Include details of your analysis in an appendix to your report.

Case Problem 2 Yeager National Bank

Using aggressive mail promotion with low introductory interest rates, Yeager National Bank (YNB) built a large base of credit card customers throughout the continental United States. Currently, all customers send their regular payments to the bank's corporate office located in Charlotte, North Carolina. Daily collections from customers making their regular payments are substantial, with an average of approximately $600,000. YNB estimates that it makes about 15% on its funds and would like to ensure that customer payments are credited to the bank's account as soon as possible. For instance, if it takes five days for a customer's payment to be sent through the mail, processed, and credited to the bank's account, YNB has potentially lost five days' worth of interest income. Although the time needed for this collection process cannot be completely eliminated, reducing it can be beneficial given the large amounts of money involved.

Instead of having all its credit card customers send their payments to Charlotte, YNB is considering having customers send their payments to one or more regional collection centers, referred to in the banking industry as lockboxes. Four lockbox locations have been proposed: Phoenix, Salt Lake City, Atlanta, and Boston. To determine which lockboxes to open and where lockbox customers should send their payments, YNB divided its customer base into five geographical regions: Northwest, Southwest, Central, Northeast, and Southeast. Every customer in the same region will be instructed to send his or her payment to the same lockbox. The following table shows the average number of days it takes before a customer's payment is credited to the bank's account when the payment is sent from each of the regions to each of the potential lockboxes:

Customer Zone	Location of Lockbox				Daily Collection ($1000s)
	Phoenix	Salt Lake City	Atlanta	Boston	
Northwest	4	2	4	4	80
Southwest	2	3	4	6	90
Central	5	3	3	4	150
Northeast	5	4	3	2	180
Southeast	4	6	2	3	100

Managerial Report

Dave Wolff, the vice president for cash management, asked you to prepare a report containing your recommendations for the number of lockboxes and the best lockbox locations. Mr. Wolff is primarily concerned with minimizing lost interest income, but he wants you to also consider the effect of an annual fee charged for maintaining a lockbox at any location. Although the amount of the fee is unknown at this time, we can assume that the fees will be in the range of $20,000 to $30,000 per location. Once good potential locations have been selected, Mr. Wolff will inquire as to the annual fees.

Case Problem 3 Production Scheduling with Changeover Costs

Buckeye Manufacturing produces heads for engines used in the manufacture of trucks. The production line is highly complex, and it measures 900 feet in length. Two types of engine heads are produced on this line: the P-Head and the H-Head. The P-Head is used in heavy-duty trucks and the H-Head is used in smaller trucks. Because only one type of head can be produced at a time, the line is set up to manufacture either the P-Head or the H-Head, but not both. Changeovers are made over a weekend; costs are $500 in going from a setup for the P-Head to a setup for the H-Head, and vice versa. When set up for the P-Head, the maximum production rate is 100 units per week and when set up for the H-Head, the maximum production rate is 80 units per week.

Buckeye just shut down for the week after using the line to produce the P-Head. The manager wants to plan production and changeovers for the next eight weeks. Currently, Buckeye's inventory consists of 125 P-Heads and 143 H-Heads. Inventory carrying costs are charged at an annual rate of 19.5% of the value of inventory. The production cost for the P-Head is $225, and the production cost for the H-Head is $310. The objective in developing a production schedule is to minimize the sum of production cost, plus inventory carrying cost, plus changeover cost.

Buckeye received the following requirements schedule from its customer (an engine assembly plant) for the next nine weeks:

	Product Demand	
Week	P-Head	H-Head
1	55	38
2	55	38
3	44	30
4	0	0
5	45	48
6	45	48
7	36	58
8	35	57
9	35	58

Safety stock requirements are such that week-ending inventory must provide for at least 80% of the next week's demand.

Managerial Report

Prepare a report for Buckeye's management with a production and changeover schedule for the next eight weeks. Be sure to note how much of the total cost is due to production, how much is due to inventory, and how much is due to changeover.

Case Problem 4 Applecore Children's Clothing

Applecore Children's Clothing is a retailer that sells high-end clothes for toddlers (ages 1–3) primarily in shopping malls. Applecore also has a successful Internet-based sales division. Recently Dave Walker, vice president of the e-commerce division, has been given the directive to expand the company's Internet sales. He commissioned a major study on the effectiveness of Internet ads placed on news websites. The results were favorable: Current patrons who purchased via the Internet and saw the ads on news websites spent more, on average, than did comparable Internet customers who did not see the ads.

With this new information on Internet ads, Walker continued to investigate how new Internet customers could most effectively be reached. One of these ideas involved strategically purchasing ads on news websites prior to and during the holiday season. To determine which news sites might be the most effective for ads, Walker conducted a follow-up study. An e-mail questionnaire was administered to a sample of 1200 current Internet customers to ascertain which of 30 news sites they regularly visit. The idea is that websites with high proportions of current customer visits would be viable sources of future customers of Applecore products.

Walker would like to ascertain which news sites should be selected for ads. The problem is complicated because Walker does not want to count multiple exposures. So, if a respondent visits multiple sites with Applecore ads or visits a given site multiple times, that respondent should be counted as reached but not more than once. In other words, a customer is considered reached if he or she has visited at least one website with an Applecore ad.

Data from the customer e-mail survey have begun to trickle in. Walker wants to develop a prototype model based on the current survey results. So far, 53 surveys have been returned. To keep the prototype model manageable, Walker wants to proceed with model development using the data from the 53 returned surveys and using only the first ten news sites in the questionnaire. The costs of ads per week for the 10 websites are given in the following table, and the budget is \$10,000 per week. For each of the 53 responses received, which of the 10 websites are regularly visited is given as shown below. For a given customer–website pair, a one indicates that the customer regularly visits that website, and a zero indicates that the customer does not regularly visit that site.

Data for Applecore Customer Visits to News Websites (respondents 5–33 hidden).

Applecore

	Website									
	1	**2**	**3**	**4**	**5**	**6**	**7**	**8**	**9**	**10**
Cost/Wk (\$000)	\$5.0	\$8.0	\$3.5	\$5.5	\$7.0	\$4.5	\$6.0	\$5.0	\$3.0	\$2.2
	Website									
Customer	1	2	3	4	5	6	7	8	9	10
1	0	0	0	0	0	0	0	0	0	1
2	1	0	0	1	0	0	0	0	0	0
3	1	0	0	0	0	0	0	0	0	0
4	0	0	0	0	1	1	0	0	0	0
34	0	0	0	1	1	0	0	0	0	0
35	1	0	0	0	1	1	0	0	0	0
36	1	0	1	0	0	0	0	0	0	0
37	0	0	1	0	1	0	0	1	0	0
38	0	0	1	0	0	0	0	0	0	0
39	0	1	0	0	0	0	1	0	0	0
40	0	1	0	0	0	0	1	0	0	0
41	0	0	0	0	0	0	1	0	0	0
42	0	0	0	1	1	1	0	0	0	0
43	0	0	0	0	0	0	0	0	0	0
44	0	0	0	0	1	0	0	0	0	1
45	1	1	0	0	0	0	0	0	0	0
46	0	0	0	0	0	0	1	0	0	0
47	1	0	0	0	1	0	0	0	0	1
48	0	0	1	0	0	0	0	0	0	0
49	1	0	1	1	0	0	0	0	0	0
50	0	0	0	0	0	0	0	0	0	0
51	0	1	0	0	0	1	0	0	0	0
52	0	0	0	0	0	0	0	0	0	0
53	0	1	0	0	1	0	0	1	1	1

Managerial Report

1. Develop a model that will allow Applecore to maximize the number of customers reached for a budget of \$10,000 for one week of promotion.
2. Solve the model. What is the maximum number of customers reached for the \$10,000 budget?

3. Perform a sensitivity analysis on the budget for values from \$5,000 to \$35,000 in increments of \$5,000. Construct a graph of percentage reach versus budget. Is the additional increase in percentage reach monotonically decreasing as the budget allocation increases? Why or why not? What is your recommended budget? Explain.

Appendix 11.1 Excel Solver Solution of Integer Linear Programs

Worksheet formulation and solution for integer linear programs is similar to that for linear programming problems. Actually the worksheet formulation is exactly the same, but some additional information must be provided when setting up the Solver Parameters and Integer Options dialog boxes. First, constraints must be added in the Solver Parameters dialog box to identify the integer variables. In addition, the value for Tolerance in the Integer Options dialog box may need to be adjusted to obtain a solution.

Let us demonstrate the Excel solution of an integer linear program by showing how Excel Solver can be used to solve the Eastborne Realty problem. The worksheet with the optimal solution is shown in Figure 11.14. We will describe the key elements of the worksheet and how to obtain the solution, and then interpret the solution.

Formulation

The data and descriptive labels appear in cells A1:G7 of the worksheet in Figure 11.14. The cells in the lower portion of the worksheet contain the information required by Excel Solver (decision variables, objective function, constraint left-hand sides, and constraint right-hand sides).

Decision Variables Cells B17:C17 are reserved for the decision variables. The optimal solution is to purchase four townhouses and two apartment buildings.

FIGURE 11.14 EXCEL SOLVER SOLUTION FOR THE EASTBORNE REALTY PROBLEM

	A	B	C	D	E	F	G	H	I
1	Eastborne Realty Problem								
2									
3		Townhouse	Apt. Bldg.						
4	Price($1000s)	282	400			Funds Avl.($1000s)	2000		
5	Mgr. Time	4	40			Mgr. Time Avl.	140		
6						Townhouses Avl.	5		
7	Ann. Cash Flow ($1000s)	10	15						
8									
9									
10	Model								
11									
12									
13	Max Cash Flow	70							
14					Constraints	LHS		RHS	
15		Number of			Funds	1928	<=	2000	
16		Townhouses	Apt. Bldgs.		Time	96	<=	140	
17	Purchase Plan	4	2		Townhouses	4	<=	5	
18									
19									
20									
21									

Objective Function	The formula *=SUMPRODUCT(B7:C7,B17:C17)* has been placed into cell B13 to reflect the annual cash flow associated with the solution. The optimal solution provides an annual cash flow of $70,000.
Left-Hand Sides	The left-hand sides for the three constraints are placed into cells F15:F17. Cell F15 *=SUMPRODUCT(B4:C4, $B$17:$C$17)* (Copy to cell F16) Cell F17 *=B17*
Right-Hand Sides	The right-hand sides for the three constraints are placed into cells H15:H17. Cell H15 *=G4* (Copy to cells H16:H17)

Excel Solver Solution

0-1 variables are identified with the "bin" designation in the Solver Parameters dialog box.

Begin the solution procedure by selecting the **Data** tab from the Ribbon and then select **Solver** in the **Analysis** group. Enter the proper values into the **Solver Parameters** dialog box as shown in Figure 11.15. The first constraint shown is $B$17:$C$17 = integer. This

FIGURE 11.15 EXCEL SOLVER PARAMETERS DIALOG BOX FOR THE EASTBORNE REALTY PROBLEM

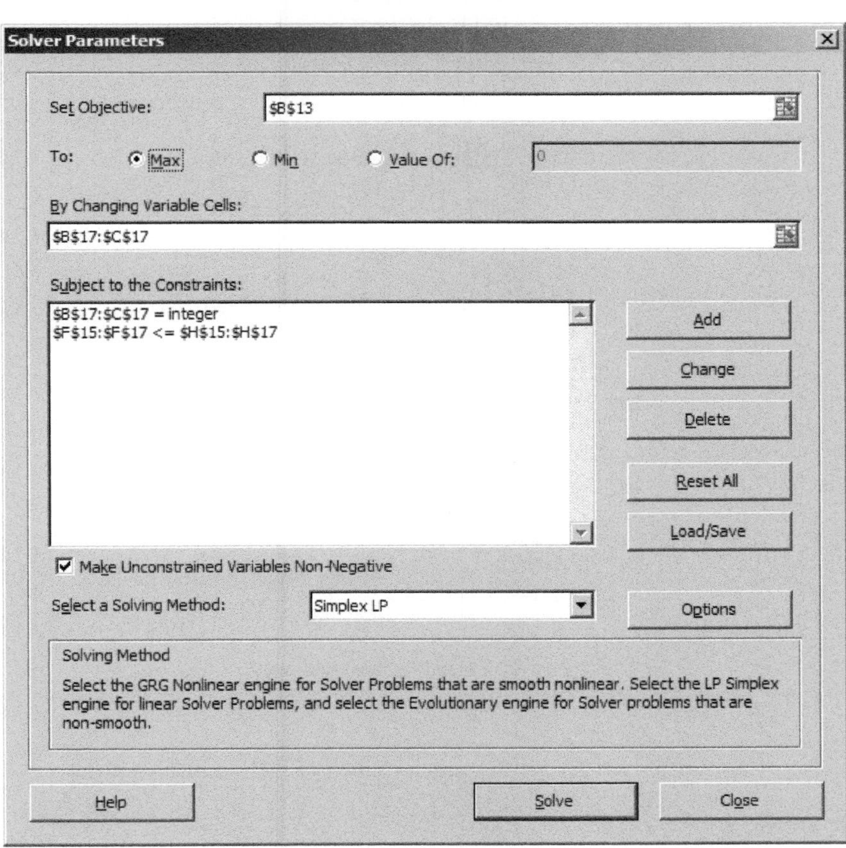

constraint tells Solver that the decision variables in cell B17 and cell C17 must be integer. The integer requirement is created by using the **Add-Constraint** procedure. $B$17:$C$17 is entered as the **Cell Reference** and **int** rather than ≤, =, or ≥ is selected as the form of the constraint. When **int** is selected, the term "integer" automatically appears as the right-hand side of the constraint. Figure 11.15 shows the additional information required to complete the **Solver Parameters** dialog box.

Check the **Make Unconstrained Variables Non-Negative** option and select **Simplex LP** as the **Solving Method**. Next the **Options** button must be selected. Figure 11.16 shows the completed **Solver Options** dialog box for the Eastborne Realty problem. To ensure we find the optimal integer solution, under the **All Methods** tab, we must set the **Integer Optimality** (%): to zero as shown in Figure 11.16.

Clicking **OK** in the **Solver Options** dialog box and selecting **Solve** in the **Solver Parameters** dialog box will instruct Excel Solver to compute the optimal integer solution. The worksheet in Figure 11.14 shows that the optimal solution is to purchase four townhouses and two apartment buildings. The annual cash flow is $70,000.

FIGURE 11.16 EXCEL SOLVER OPTIONS DIALOG BOX FOR THE EASTBORNE REALTY PROBLEM

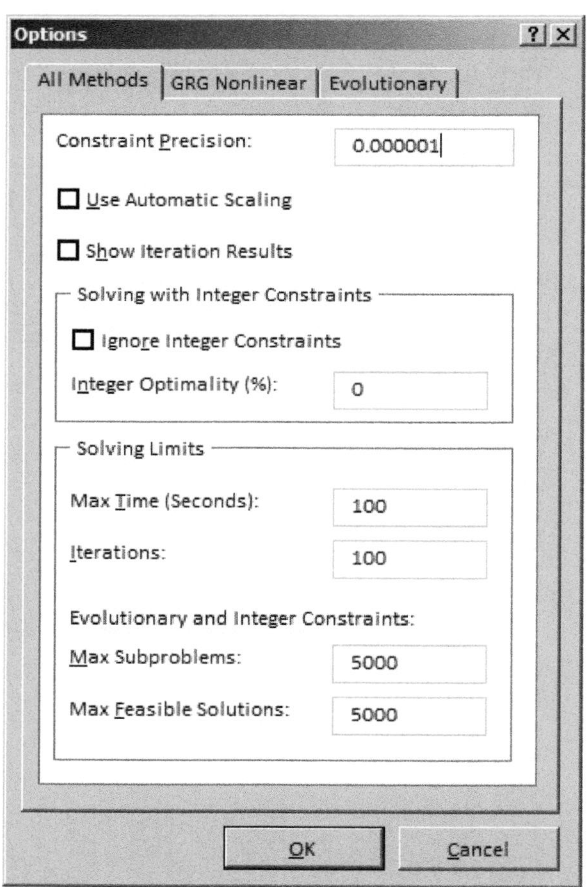

If binary variables are present in an integer linear programming problem, you must select the designation **bin** instead of int when setting up the constraints in the **Solver Parameters** dialog box.

The time required to obtain an optimal solution can be highly variable for integer linear programs. If an optimal solution cannot be found within a reasonable amount of time, the **Integer Optimality (%)**: can be reset to 5%, or some higher value, so that the search procedure may stop when a near-optimal solution (within the tolerance of being optimal) has been found. This can shorten the solution time, since if the **Integer Optimality (%)**: is set to 5%, Solver can stop when it knows it is within 5% of optimal rather then having to complete the search. In general, unless you are experiencing excessive run times, we recommend you set the **Integer Optimaility (%)**: to zero.

Appendix 11.2 LINGO Solution of Integer Linear Programs

LINGO may be used to solve linear integer programs. An integer linear model is entered into LINGO exactly as described in Appendix 7.2, but with additional statements for declaring variables as either general integer or binary. For example, to declare a variable x integer, you need to include the following statement:

```
@GIN(x) ;
```

Note the use of the semicolon to end the statement. GIN stands for general integer. Likewise to declare a variable y a binary variable, the following statement is required:

```
@BIN(y) ;
```

BIN stands for binary.

To illustrate the use of integer variables, we will use LINGO statements to model the Eastborne Realty problem discussed in this chapter. First we enter the following:

```
MODEL:
TITLE   EASTBORNE REALTY;
```

This statement gives the LINGO model the title Eastborne Realty. Next we enter the following two lines to document the definition of our decision variables (recall that ! denotes a comment, and each comment ends with a semicolon).

```
! T = NUMBER OF TOWNHOUSES PURCHASED;
! A = NUMBER OF APARTMENT BUILDINGS PURCHASED;
```

Next we enter the objective function and constraints, each with a descriptive comment.

```
! MAXIMIZE THE CASH FLOW;
MAX = 10*T + 15*A;

! FUNDS AVAILABLE ($1000);
282*T + 400*A <= 2000;
```

```
! TIME AVAILABLILITY;
4*T + 40*A <= 140;

! TOWNHOUSES AVAILABLE;
T <= 5;
```

Finally, we must declare the variables T and A as general integer variables. Again, to document the model we begin with a descriptive comment and then declare each variable as a general integer variable:

```
! DECLARE THE VARIABLES TO BE GENERAL INTEGER VARIABLES;
@GIN(T);
@GIN(A);
```

The complete LINGO model is available on the website that accompanies this book.

CHAPTER 16

Simulation

CONTENTS

Q.M. *in* ACTION

*REDUCING PATIENT INFECTIONS IN THE ICU**

Approximately 2 million patients acquire an infection after being admitted to the hospital in the United States each year. More than 100,000 of these patients die as a result of their hospital-acquired infections. This problem is expected to worsen as pathogens continue to develop greater resistance to antibiotics.

Two methods of decreasing the rate of hospital-acquired infections are (1) patient isolation and (2) greater adherence to hand-washing hygiene. If infected patients can be identified quickly, they can be quarantined to prevent greater outbreaks. Furthermore, proper hand washing can greatly reduce the number of pathogens present on the skin and thereby also lead to fewer infections. Yet previous studies have found that less than half of all health workers completely and correctly follow hand-hygiene protocols.

A group of researchers used data from the intensive-care unit (ICU) at Cook County Hospital in Chicago to create a simulation model of the movements of patients, health care workers, hospital visitors, and actual pathogens that lead to infections. The researchers were able to simulate both the creation of a new isolation ward in the ICU and model better hand-hygiene habits. The simulation estimated rates of infection and impacts on hospital costs in each scenario.

The simulation showed that both patient isolation and better hand-hygiene can greatly reduce infection rates. Improving hand-hygiene is considerably cheaper than building and maintaining additional quarantine facilities, but the researchers point out that even the best simulations do not consider psychological responses of health care workers. The simulation cannot detect why hand-hygiene compliance is currently low, so improving adherence in practice could be challenging.

*From R. Hagtvedt, P. Griffin, P. Keskinocak, and R. Roberts, "A Simulation Model to Compare Strategies for the Reduction of Health-Care-Associated Infections," *Interfaces* 39, no. 3 (May–June): 2009.

Uncertainty pervades decision making in business, government, and our personal lives. This chapter introduces the use of **simulation** to evaluate the impact of uncertainty on a decision. Simulation models have been successfully used in a variety of disciplines. Financial applications include investment planning, project selection, and option pricing. Marketing applications include new product development and the timing of market entry for a product. Management applications include project management, inventory ordering (especially important for seasonal products), capacity planning, and revenue management (prominent in the airline, hotel, and car rental industries). In each of these applications, there are uncertain quantities that complicate the decision process.

As we will demonstrate, a spreadsheet simulation analysis requires a model foundation of logical formulas that correctly express the relationships between **parameters** and decisions to generate outputs of interest. A simulation model replaces the use of single values for parameters with a range of possible values. For example, a simple spreadsheet model may compute a clothing retailer's profit, given values for the number of ski jackets ordered from the manufacturer and the number of ski jackets demanded by customers. A simulation analysis extends this model by replacing the single value used for ski jacket demand with a **probability distribution** of possible values of ski jacket demand. A probability distribution of ski jacket demand represents not only the range of possible values but also the relative likelihood of various levels of demand.

To evaluate a decision with a simulation model, an analyst identifies parameters that are not known with a high degree of certainty and treats these parameters as random, or uncertain, variables. The values for the **random variables** or **uncertain variables** are randomly generated from the specified probability distributions. The simulation model uses the randomly generated values of the random variables and the relationships between parameters and decisions to compute the corresponding values of an output. Specifically, a simulation experiment produces a *distribution* of output values that correspond to the randomly generated values of the uncertain input variables. This probability distribution of the output values describes the range of possible outcomes as well as the relative likelihood of each outcome. After reviewing the simulation results, the analyst is often able to make decision recommendations for the controllable inputs that not only address the *average* output but also the *variability* of the output.

16.1 What-If Analysis

When making a decision in the presence of uncertainty, decision makers should not only be interested in the average, or expected, outcome, but they should also be interested in information regarding the range of possible outcomes. In particular, decision makers are interested risk analysis (i.e., quantifying the likelihood and magnitude of an undesirable outcome). In this section, we show how to perform a basic risk analysis by considering a small set of what-if scenarios.

Sanotronics

Sanotronics is a startup company that manufactures medical devices for use in hospital clinics. Inspired by experiences with family members who have battled cancer, Sanotronics's founders have developed a prototype for a new device that limits health care workers' exposure to chemotherapy treatments while they are preparing, administering, and disposing of these hazardous medications. This new device features an innovative design and has the potential to capture a substantial share of the market.

Santronics would like an analysis of the first-year profit potential of the device. Because of Sanotronics's tight cash flow situation, management is particularly concerned about the potential for a loss. Sanotronics has identified the key parameters in determining first-year profit: selling price per unit (p), first-year administrative and advertising costs (c_a), direct labor cost per unit (c_l), parts cost per unit (c_p), and first-year demand (d). After conducting market research and a financial analysis, Sanotronics estimates with a high level of certainty that the device's selling price will be $249 per unit, and the first-year administrative and advertising costs will total $1,000,000.

Sanotronics is not certain about the values for the cost of direct labor, the cost of parts, and the first-year demand. At this stage of the planning process, Sanotronics's base estimates of these inputs are $45 per unit for the direct labor cost, $90 per unit for the parts cost, and 15,000 units for the first-year demand.

Base-Case Scenario

Sanotronics' first-year profit is computed by

$$\text{Profit} = (p - c_l - c_p) \times d - c_a \qquad \textbf{(16.1)}$$

Recall that Sanotronics is certain of a selling price of $249 per unit, and administrative and advertising costs total $1,000,000. Substituting these values into equation (16.1) yields

$$\text{Profit} = (249 - c_l - c_p) \times d - 1{,}000{,}000 \qquad \textbf{(16.2)}$$

Sanotronics's base-case estimates of the direct labor cost per unit, the parts cost per unit, and first-year demand are \$45, \$90, and 15,000 units, respectively. These values constitute the **base-case scenario** for Sanotronics. Substituting these values into equation (16.2) yields the following profit projection:

$$\text{Profit} = (249 - 45 - 90)(15{,}000) - 1{,}000{,}000 = 710{,}000$$

Thus, the base-case scenario leads to an anticipated profit of \$710,000.

While the base-case scenario looks appealing, Sanotronics is aware that the values of direct labor cost per unit, parts cost per unit, and first-year demand are uncertain, so the base-case scenario may not occur. To help Sanotronics gauge the impact of the uncertainty, a **what-if analysis** involves considering alternative values for the random variables (direct labor cost, parts cost, and first-year demand) and computing the resulting value for the output (profit).

Sanotronics is interested in what happens if the estimates of the direct labor cost per unit, parts cost per unit, and first-year demand do not turn out to be as expected under the base-case scenario. For instance, suppose that Sanotronics believes that direct labor costs could range from \$43 to \$47 per unit, the parts cost could range from \$80 to \$100 per unit, and the first-year demand could range from 0 to 30,000 units. Using these ranges, what-if analysis can be used to evaluate a **worst-case scenario** and a **best-case scenario**.

Worst-Case Scenario

The worst-case value for the direct labor cost is \$47 (the highest value), the worst-case value for the parts cost is \$100 (the highest value), and the worst-case value for demand is 0 units (the lowest value). Substituting these values into equation (16.2) leads to the following profit projection:

$$\text{Profit} = (249 - 47 - 100)(0) - 1{,}000{,}000 = -1{,}000{,}000$$

So, the worst-case scenario leads to a projected *loss* of \$1,000,000.

Best-Case Scenario

The best-case value for the direct labor cost is \$43 (the lowest value), the best-case value for the parts cost is \$80 (the lowest value), and the best-case value for demand is 30,000 units (the highest value). Substituting these values into equation (16.2) leads to the following profit projection:

$$\text{Profit} = (249 - 43 - 80)(30{,}000) - 1{,}000{,}000 = 2{,}780{,}000$$

So the best-case scenario leads to a projected profit of \$2,780,000.

At this point the what-if analysis provides the conclusion that profits may range from a loss of \$1,000,000 to a profit of \$2,780,000 with a base-case profit of \$710,000. Although the base-case profit of \$710,000 is possible, the what-if analysis indicates that either a substantial loss or a substantial profit is also possible. Sanotronics can repeat this what-if analysis for other scenarios. However, simple what-if analyses do not indicate the likelihood of the various profit or loss values. In particular, we do not know anything about the probability of a loss. To conduct a more thorough evaluation of risk by obtaining insight on the potential magnitude and probability of undesirable outcomes, we now turn to developing a spreadsheet simulation model.

Simulation of Sanotronics Problem

In this section, we show how to construct a simulation model and conduct a risk analysis using native Excel functionality. The first step in constructing a spreadsheet simulation model is to express the relationship between the inputs and the outputs with appropriate formula logic. Figure 16.1 provides the formula and value view for the Sanotronics spreadsheet. Data on selling price per unit, administrative and advertising cost, direct labor cost per unit, parts cost per unit, and demand are in cells B4 to B8. The profit calculation, corresponding to equation (16.1), is expressed in cell B11 using appropriate cell references and formula logic. For the values shown in Figure 16.1, the spreadsheet model computes profit for the base-case scenario. By changing one or more values for the input parameters, the spreadsheet model can be used to conduct a manual what-if analysis (e.g., the best-case and worst-case scenarios).

In the chapter appendix we demonstrate how the Excel add-in Analytic Solver Platform facilitates the construction of simulation models.

Use of Probability Distributions to Represent Random Variables

Sanotronics

Using the what-if approach to risk analysis, we manually select values for the random variables (direct labor cost per unit, parts cost per unit, and first-year demand) and then compute the resulting profit. Instead of manually selecting the values for the random variables, a simulation model randomly generates values for the random variables so that the values used reflect what we might observe in practice. A probability distribution describes the possible values of a random variable and the relative likelihood of the random variable realizing these values. The analyst can use historical data and knowledge of the random variable (such as the range, mean, mode, standard deviation) to specify the probability distribution for a random variable. As described below, Sanotronics examined the random variables to identify probability distributions for the direct labor cost per unit, the parts cost per unit, and first-year demand.

FIGURE 16.1 EXCEL WORKSHEET FOR SANOTRONICS

	A	B
1	Sanotronics	
2		
3	Parameters	
4	Selling Price per Unit	249
5	Administrative & Advertising Cost	1000000
6	Direct Labor Cost per Unit	45
7	Parts Cost per Unit	90
8	Demand	15000
9		
10	Model	
11	Profit	=((B4-B6-B7)*B8)-B5
12		

	A	B
1	Sanotronics	
2		
3	Parameters	
4	Selling Price per Unit	$249.00
5	Administrative & Advertising Cost	$1,000,000
6	Direct Labor Cost per Unit	$45.00
7	Parts Cost per Unit	$90.00
8	Demand	15,000
9		
10	Model	
11	Profit	$710,000.00

Direct Labor Cost Based on recent wage rates and estimated processing requirements of the device, Sanotronics believes that the direct labor cost will range from \$43 to \$47 per unit and is described by the discrete probability distribution shown in Figure 16.2. Thus, we see that there is 0.1 probability that the direct labor cost will be \$43 per unit, a 0.2 probability that the direct labor cost will be \$44 per unit, and so on. The highest probability of 0.4 is associated with a direct labor cost of \$45 per unit. Because we have assumed that the direct labor cost per unit is best described by a **discrete probability distribution**, this means that the direct labor cost per unit can *only* take on a value of \$43, \$44, \$45, \$46, or \$47.

Parts Cost Sanotronics is relatively unsure of the value of the parts cost because it depends on many factors, including the general economy, the overall demand for parts, and the pricing policy of Sanotronics's parts suppliers. Sanotronics is confident that the parts cost will be between \$80 and \$100 per unit but is unsure if any particular values between \$80 and \$100 are more likely than others. Therefore, Sanotronics decides to describe the uncertainty in parts cost with a uniform probability distribution, as shown in Figure 16.3. Costs per unit between \$80 and \$100 are equally likely. A uniform probability distribution is an example of a **continuous probability distribution**; this means that the parts cost can take on *any* value between \$80 and \$100 with equal likelihood.

FIGURE 16.2 PROBABILITY DISTRIBUTION FOR DIRECT LABOR COST PER UNIT

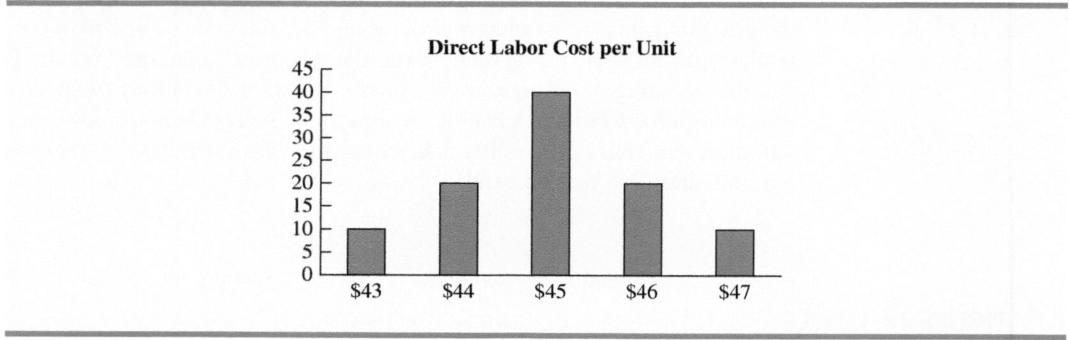

FIGURE 16.3 UNIFORM PROBABILITY DISTRIBUTION FOR PARTS COST PER UNIT

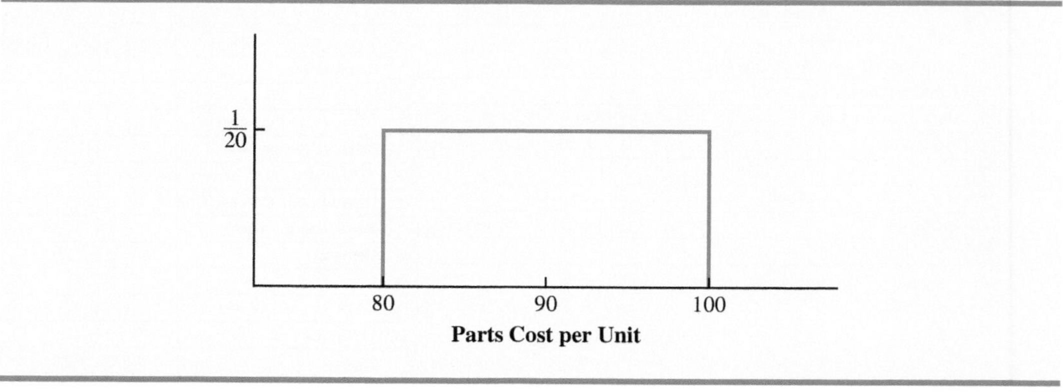

FIGURE 16.4 NORMAL PROBABILITY DISTRIBUTION FOR FIRST-YEAR DEMAND

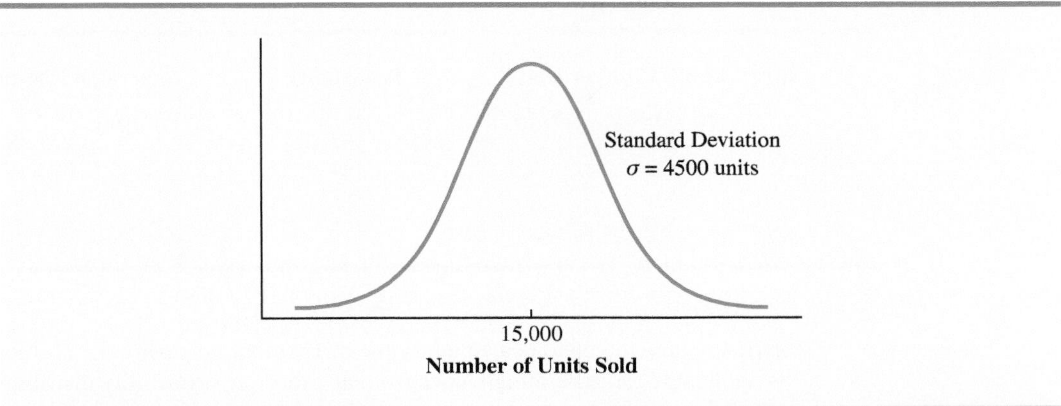

One advantage of simulation is that the analyst can adjust the probability distributions of the random variables to determine the impact of the assumptions about the "shape" of the uncertainty on the results (and ultimately the sensitivity of the decision to the distribution assumptions about the random variables).

First-Year Demand Based on sales of comparable medical devices, Sanotronics believes that first-year demand is described by the normal probability distribution shown in Figure 16.4. The mean or expected value of first-year demand is 15,000 units. The standard deviation of 4500 units describes the variability in the first-year demand. The normal probability distribution is a continuous probability distribution in which any value is possible, but values far larger or smaller than the mean are increasingly unlikely.

Generating Values for Random Variables with Excel

To simulate the Sanotronics problem, we must generate values for the three random variables and compute the resulting profit. A set of values for the random variables is called a trial. We then generate another trial, compute a second value for profit, and so on. We continue this process until we are satisfied that sufficient trials have been conducted to describe the probability distribution for profit. Put simply, simulation is the process of generating values of random variables and computing the corresponding output measures.

In the Sanotronics model, representative values must be generated for the random variables corresponding to the direct labor cost per unit, the parts cost per unit, and the first-year demand. To illustrate how to generate these values, we need to introduce the concept of computer-generated random numbers.

Computer-generated random numbers[1] are randomly selected numbers from 0 up to, but not including, 1; this interval is denoted [0, 1). All values of the computer-generated random numbers are equally likely and so are uniformly distributed over the interval from 0 to 1. Computer-generated random numbers can be obtained using built-in functions available in computer simulation packages and spreadsheets. For example, placing the formula =RAND() in a cell of an Excel worksheet will result in a random number between 0 and 1 being placed into that cell.

Let us show how random numbers can be used to generate values corresponding to the probability distributions for the random variables in the Sanotronics example. We begin by

[1]Computer-generated random numbers are formally called pseudorandom numbers because they are generated through the use of mathematical formulas and are therefore not technically random. The difference between random numbers and pseudorandom numbers is primarily philosophical, and we use the term random numbers regardless of whether they are generated by a computer.

TABLE 16.1 RANDOM NUMBER INTERVALS FOR GENERATING VALUE OF DIRECT LABOR COST PER UNIT

Direct Labor Cost per Unit	Probability	Interval of Random Numbers
\$43	0.1	[0.0, 0.1)
\$44	0.2	[0.1, 0.3)
\$45	0.4	[0.3, 0.7)
\$46	0.2	[0.7, 0.9)
\$47	0.1	[0.9, 1.0)

showing how to generate a value for the direct labor cost per unit. The approach described is applicable for generating values from any discrete probability distribution.

Table 16.1 illustrates the process of partitioning the interval from 0 to 1 into subintervals so that the probability of generating a random number in a subinterval is equal to the probability of the corresponding direct labor cost. The interval of random numbers from 0 up to but not including 0.1, [0, 0.1), is associated with a direct labor cost of \$43, the interval of random numbers from 0.1 up to but not including 0.3, [0.1, 0.3), is associated with a direct labor cost of \$44, and so on. With this assignment of random number intervals to the possible values of the direct labor cost, the probability of generating a random number in any interval is equal to the probability of obtaining the corresponding value for the direct labor cost. Thus, to select a value for the direct labor cost, we generate a random number between 0 and 1 using the RAND function in Excel. If the random number is at least 0.0 but less than 0.1, we set the direct labor cost equal to \$43. If the random number is at least 0.1 but less than 0.3, we set the direct labor cost equal to \$44, and so on.

Each trial of the simulation requires a value for the direct labor cost. Suppose that on the first trial the random number is 0.9109. From Table 16.1, because 0.9109 is in the interval [0.9, 1.0), the corresponding simulated value for the direct labor cost is \$47 per unit. Suppose that on the second trial the random number is 0.2841. From Table 16.1, the simulated value for the direct labor cost is \$44 per unit.

Each trial in the simulation also requires a value of the parts cost and first-year demand. Let us now turn to the issue of generating values for the parts cost. The probability distribution for the parts cost per unit is the uniform distribution shown in Figure 16.3. Because this random variable has a different probability distribution than direct labor cost, we use random numbers in a slightly different way to generate simulated values for parts cost. To generate a value for a random variable characterized by a continuous uniform distribution, the following Excel formula is used:

$$\begin{aligned}\text{Value of uniform random variable} &= \text{lower bound} + \\ &(\text{upper bound} - \text{lower bound}) \times \text{RAND()}\end{aligned} \tag{16.3}$$

For Sanotronics, parts cost per unit is a uniformly distributed random variable with a lower bound of \$80 and an upper bound of \$100. Applying equation (16.3) leads to the following formula for generating the parts cost:

$$\text{Parts cost} = 80 + 20 \times \text{RAND()} \tag{16.4}$$

FIGURE 16.5 GENERATION OF VALUE FOR PARTS COST PER UNIT CORRESPONDING TO RANDOM NUMBER 0.4576

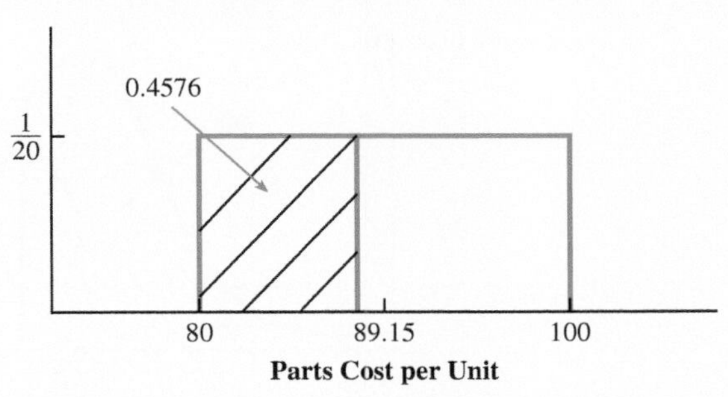

By closely examining equation (16.4), we can understand how it uses random numbers to generate uniformly distributed values for parts cost. The first term of equation (16.4) is 80, since Sanotronics is assuming that the parts cost will never drop below \$80 per unit. Since RAND is between 0 and 1, the second term, 20 × RAND(), corresponds to how much more than the lower bound the simulated value of parts cost is. Since RAND is equally likely to be any value between 0 and 1, the simulated value for the parts cost is equally likely to be between the lower bound (80 + 0 = 80) and the upper bound (80 + 20 = 100). For example, suppose that a random number of 0.4576 is obtained. As illustrated by Figure 16.5, the value for the parts cost is

$$\text{Parts cost} = 80 + 20 \times 0.4576 = 80 + 9.15 = 89.15 \text{ per unit}$$

Suppose that a random number of 0.5842 is generated on the next trial. The value for the parts cost is

$$\text{Parts cost} = 80 + 20 \times 0.5842 = 80 + 11.68 = 91.68 \text{ per unit}$$

With appropriate choices of the lower bound and the upper bound, equation (16.3) can be used to generate values for any uniform probability distribution.

Lastly, we need a procedure for generating the first-year demand from computer-generated random numbers. Because first-year demand is normally distributed with a mean of 15,000 units and a standard deviation of 4500 units (see Figure 16.4), we need a procedure for generating random values from this normal probability distribution.

Once again we will use random numbers between 0 and 1 to simulate values for first-year demand. To generate a value for a random variable characterized by a normal distribution with a specified mean and standard deviation, the following Excel formula is used:

$$\text{Value of normal random variable} = \text{NORM.INV(RAND(), mean, standard deviation)} \quad (16.5)$$

Versions of Excel prior to Excel 2010 do not recognize the function NORM.INV; in these earlier versions of Excel, one can use the function NORMINV. The results will be identical.

For Sanotronics, first-year demand is a normally distributed random variable with a mean of 15,000 and a standard deviation of 4500. Applying equation (16.5) leads to the following formula for generating the first-year demand:

$$\text{Demand} = \text{NORM.INV(RAND(),15000,4500)} \quad (16.6)$$

FIGURE 16.6 GENERATION OF VALUE FOR FIRST-YEAR DEMAND CORRESPONDING TO RANDOM NUMBER 0.6026

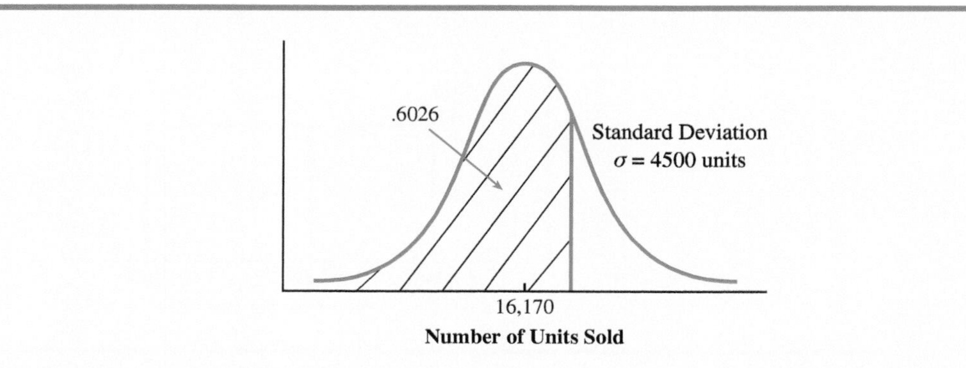

With appropriate specification of the mean and standard deviation, equation (16.5) can be used to generate values for any normal probability distribution.

Suppose that the random number of 0.6026 is produced by the RAND function; applying equation (16.6) then results in Demand =NORM.INV(0.6026, 15000, 4500) = 16,170 units. To understand how equation (16.6) uses random numbers to generate normally distributed values for first-year demand, we note that the Excel expression =NORM.INV(0.6026, 15000, 4500) provides the value for a normal distribution with a mean of 15,000 and a standard deviation of 4500, such that 60.26% of the area under the normal curve is to the left of this value (see Figure 16.6). Now suppose that the random number produced by the RAND function is 0.3551; applying equation (16.6) then results in Demand =NORM.INV(0.3551, 15000, 4500) = 13,328 units. Because half of this normal distribution lies below the mean of 15,000 and half lies above, RAND values less than 0.5 result in values of first-year demand below the average of 15,000 units and RAND value above 0.5 correspond to values of first-year demand above the average of 15,000 units.

For further description of the VLOOKUP function, refer to Appendix A.

Now that we know how to randomly generate values for the random variables (direct labor cost, parts cost, first-year demand) from their respective probability distributions, we modify the spreadsheet by adding this information. The static values in Figure 16.1 for these parameters in cells B6, B7, and B8 are replaced with cell formulas that will randomly generate values whenever the spreadsheet is recalculated (as shown in Figure 16.7). Corresponding to Table 16.1, cell B6 uses a random number generated by the RAND function and looks up the corresponding cost per unit by applying the VLOOKUP function to the table of intervals contained in cells A15:C19 (which corresponds to Table 16.1). Cell B7 executes equation (16.4) using references to the lower bound and upper bound of the uniform distribution of the parts cost in cells F14 and F15, respectively.[2] Cell B8 executes equation (16.6) using references to the mean and standard deviation of the normal distribution of the first-year demand in cells F18 and F19, respectively.[3]

---

[2]Technically, random variables modeled with continuous probability distributions should be appropriately rounded to avoid modeling error (e.g., the simulated values of parts cost per unit should be rounded to the nearest penny). To simplify exposition, we do not worry about the small amount of error that occurs in this case. To model these random variables more accurately, the formula in cell B7 should be =ROUND(F12+(F13-F12)*RAND(),2).

[3]In addition to being a continuous distribution that technically requires rounding when applied to discrete phenomena (like units of medical device demand), the normal distribution also allows negative values. The probability of a negative value is quite small in the case of first-year demand, and we simply ignore the small amount of modeling error for the sake of simplicity. To model first-year demand more accurately, the formula in cell B8 should be =MAX(ROUND(NORM.INV(RAND(),F16,F17),0),0).

FIGURE 16.7 FORMULA WORKSHEET FOR SANOTRONICS

	A	B	C	D	E	F
1	**Sanotronics**					
2						
3	**Parameters**					
4	**Selling Price per Unit**	249				
5	**Administrative & Advertising Cost**	1000000				
6	**Direct Labor Cost per Unit**	=VLOOKUP(RAND(),A15:C19,3,TRUE)				
7	**Parts Cost per Unit**	=F14+(F15-F14)*RAND()				
8	**Demand**	=NORM.INV(RAND(),F18,F19)				
9						
10	**Model**					
11	**Profit**	=((B4-B6-B7)*B8)-B5				
12						
13	**Direct Labor Cost**				**Parts Cost (Uniform Distribution)**	
14	Lower End of Interval	Upper End of Interval	Cost per Unit	Probability	Lower Bound	80
15	0	=D15+A15	43	0.1	Upper Bound	100
16	=B15	=D16+A16	44	0.2		
17	=B16	=D17+A17	45	0.4	**Demand (Normal Distribution)**	
18	=B17	=D18+A18	46	0.2	Mean	15000
19	=B18	1	47	0.1	Standard Deviation	4500
20						

Executing Simulation Trials with Excel

For a detailed description of Excel's Data Table functionality, see Appendix A.

Each trial in the simulation involves randomly generating values for the random variables (direct labor cost, parts cost, and first-year demand) and computing profit. To facilitate the execution of multiple simulation trials, we use Excel's Data Table functionality in an unorthodox, but effective, manner. To set up the spreadsheet for the execution of 1000 simulation trials, we structure a table as shown in cells A21 through E1021 in Figure 16.8. As Figure 16.8 shows, A22:A1021 numbers the 1000 simulation trials (rows 25 through 1019 are hidden). To populate the data table in cells A23 through E1021, we execute the following steps:

Sanotronics

These steps iteratively select the simulation trial number from the range A22 through A1021 and substitute it into the blank cell selected in Step 4 (D1). This substitution has no bearing on the spreadsheet, but it forces Excel to recalculate the spreadsheet each time, thereby generating new random numbers with the RAND functions in cells B6, B7, and B8.

Step 1. Select cell range A22:E1021
Step 2. Click the **DATA** tab in the Ribbon
Step 3. Click **What-If Analysis** in the **Data Tools** group and select **Data Table**
Step 4. When the **Data Table** dialog box appears, enter any blank cell in the spreadsheet (e.g., D1) into the **Column input cell:** box
Step 6. Click **OK**

Figure 16.8 shows the results of our simulation. After executing the simulation with the data table, each row in this table corresponds to a distinct simulation trial consisting of different values of the random variables. In trial 1 (row 22 in the spreadsheet), we see that the direct labor cost is $45 per unit, the parts cost is $86.29 per unit, and first-year demand is 19,976 units, resulting in profit of $1,351,439. In trial 2 (row 23 in the spreadsheet), we observe random variables of $45 for the direct labor cost, $81.02 for the parts cost, and 14,910 for first-year demand. These values provide a simulated profit of $833,700 on the second simulation trial.

FIGURE 16.8 SETTING UP SANOTRONICS SPREADSHEET FOR MULTIPLE SIMULATION TRIALS

	A	B	C	D	E	F
1	**Sanotronics**					
2						
3	**Parameters**					
4	Selling Price per Unit	249				
5	Administrative & Advertising Cost	1000000				
6	Direct Labor Cost per Unit	-VLOOKUP(RAND(), A15:C19,3,TRUE)				
7	Parts Cost per Unit	-F14+(F15-F14)*RAND()				
8	Demand	-NORM.INV(RAND(),F18,F19)				
9						
10	**Model**					
11	Profit	-((B4-B6-B7)*B8)-B5				
12						
13	Direct Labor Cost				Parts Cost (Uniform Distribution)	
14	Lower End of Interval	Upper End of Interval	Cost per Unit	Probability	Lower Bound	80
15	0	-D15+A15	43	0.1	Upper Bound	100
16	-B15	-D16+A16	44	0.2		
17	-B16	-D17+A17	45	0.4	Demand (Normal Distribution)	
18	-B17	-D18+A18	46	0.2	Mean	15000
19	-B18	1	47	0.1	Standard Deviation	4500
20						
21	Simulation Trial	Direct Labor Cost per Unit	Parts Cost per Unit	Demand	Profit	
22	1	-B6	-B7	-B8	-B11	
23	2					
24	3					
1019	998					
1020	999					
1021	1000					

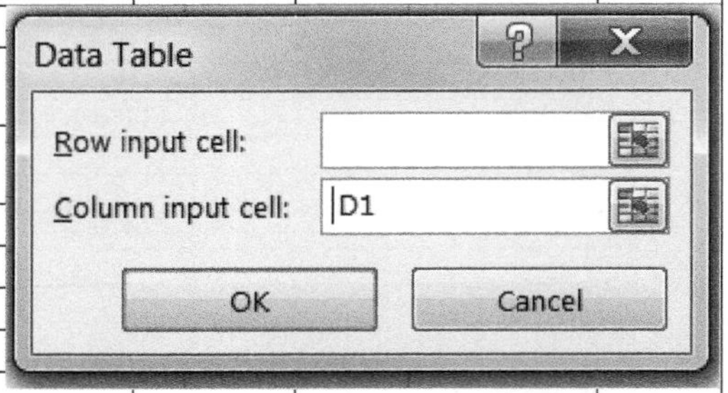

Data Table

Row input cell:

Column input cell: D1

OK Cancel

Measuring and Analyzing Simulation Output

Pressing the F9 key recalculates the spreadsheet, thereby generating a new set of simulation trials.

The analysis of the output observed over the set of simulation trials is a critical part of the simulation process. For the collection of simulation trials, it is helpful to compute descriptive statistics such as sample average, sample standard deviation, minimum, maximum, and sample proportion. To compute these statistics for the Sanotronics example, we use the following Excel functions:

Excel versions prior to Excel 2010 do not recognize the STDEV.S function; in these versions of Excel one can use the function STDEV. The results will be identical.

Cell H22 =AVERAGE(E22:E1021)

Cell H23 =STDEV.S(E22:E1021)

Cell H24 =MIN(E22:E1021

Cell H25 =MAX(E22:E1021)

Cell H26 =COUNTIF(E22:E1021,"<0") / COUNT(E22:E1021)

Simulation studies enable an objective estimate of the probability of a loss, which is an important aspect of risk analysis.

Cell H26 computes the ratio of the number of trials whose profit is less than zero over the total number of trials. By changing the value of the second argument in the COUNTIF function, the probability that the profit is less than any specified value can be computed in cell H26.

As shown in Figure 16.9, we observe a mean profit of \$717,663, standard deviation of \$521,536, extremes ranging between −\$996,547 and \$2,253,674, and a 0.078 estimated probability of a loss.

To visualize the distribution of profit on which these descriptive statistics are based, we create a histogram using the FREQUENCY function and a column chart. We note that the

FIGURE 16.9 OUTPUT FROM SANOTRONICS SIMULATION

	A	B	C	D	E	F	G	H	I	J	K	L	M
1	**Sanotronics**												
2													
3	**Parameters**												
4	**Selling Price per Unit**	$249											
5	**Administrative & Advertising Cost**	$1,000,000											
6	**Direct Labor Cost per Unit**	$45											
7	**Parts Cost per Unit**	$86.29											
8	**Demand**	19,976											
9													
10	**Model**												
11	**Profit**	$1,351,439											
12													
13	**Direct Labor Cost**				**Parts Cost (Uniform Distribution)**								
14	Lower End of Interval	Upper End of Interval	Cost per Unit	Probability	Lower Bound	$80							
15	0.0	0.1	$43	0.1	Upper Bound	$100							
16	0.1	0.3	$44	0.2									
17	0.3	0.7	$45	0.4	**Demand (Normal Distribution)**								
18	0.7	0.9	$46	0.2	Mean	15,000							
19	0.9	1.0	$47	0.1	Standard Deviation	4,500							
20													
21	**Simulation Trial**	**Direct Labor Cost per Unit**	**Parts Cost per Unit**	**Demand**	**Profit**		**Profit Summary Statistics**						
22	1	$45	$86.29	19,976	$1,351,439		**Mean**	$717,663		**Bin**	**Frequency**		
23	2	$45	$81.02	14,910	$833,700		**Standard Deviation**	$521,536		–$1,500,000	0		
24	3	$46	$98.15	18,570	$947,064		**Minimum Profit**	–$996,547		–$1,250,000	0		
25	4	$45	$92.29	12,561	$403,085		**Maximum Profit**	$2,253,674		–$1,000,000	0		
26	5	$47	$88.82	6,844	–$225,345		**P(Profit < $0)**	0.078		–$750,000	3		
27	6	$45	$95.98	15,337	$656,778					–$500,000	4		
28	7	$44	$88.23	18,723	$1,186,276					–$250,000	22		
29	8	$47	$96.20	17,589	$861,005					$0	49		
30	9	$44	$85.97	19,967	$1,376,760					$250,000	113		
31	10	$45	$89.62	14,056	$607,650					$500,000	151		
32	11	$45	$85.96	11,204	$322,448					$750,000	188		
33	12	$45	$92.06	11,150	$248,172					$1,000,000	193		
34	13	$47	$85.34	11,880	$385,901					$1,250,000	122		
35	14	$44	$80.05	24,733	$2,090,469					$1,500,000	79		
36	15	$46	$92.47	10,933	$208,447					$1,750,000	47		
37	16	$45	$81.61	17,453	$1,136,087					$2,000,000	20		
38	17	$45	$84.16	13,205	$582,483					$2,250,000	7		
39	18	$45	$93.07	15,809	$753,735					$2,500,000	2		
40	19	$47	$85.33	9,422	$99,247					$2,750,000	0		
41	20	$43	$83.58	13,599	$664,800					$3,000,000	0		
42	21	$47	$92.23	17,168	$884,578					>$3,000,000	0		
1021	1,000	$45	$92.87	22,467	$1,496,677								
1022													

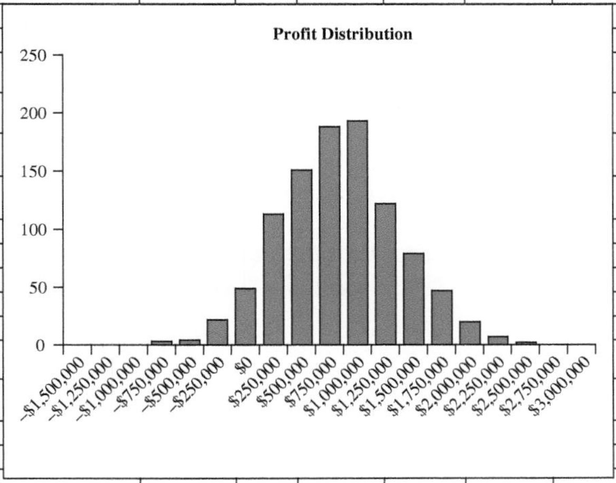

Profit Distribution

250
200
150
100
50
0
–$1,500,000 –$1,250,000 –$1,000,000 –$750,000 –$500,000 –$250,000 $0 $250,000 $500,000 $750,000 $1,000,000 $1,250,000 $1,500,000 $1,750,000 $2,000,000 $2,250,000 $2,500,000 $2,750,000 $3,000,000

distribution of profit values is fairly symmetric, with a large number of values in the range of \$250,000 to \$1,250,000. The probability of a large loss or a large gain is small. Only 7 trials out of 1000 resulted in a loss of more than \$500,000, and only 9 trials resulted in a profit greater than \$2,000,000. The bin with the largest number of values has profit ranging between \$750,000 and \$1,000,000.

For a detailed description of the FREQUENCY function, see Appendix A.

In comparing the simulation approach to the manual what-if approach, we observe that much more information is obtained by using simulation. Recall from the what-if analysis in Section 16.1, we learned that the base-case scenario projected a profit of \$710,000, the worst-case scenario projected a loss of \$1,000,000, and the best-case scenario projected a profit of \$2,591,000. From the 1000 trials of the simulation run, we see that the worst- and best-case scenarios, although possible, are unlikely. Indeed, the advantage of simulation for risk analysis is the information it provides on the likely values of the output. We now know the probability of a loss, how the profit values are distributed over their range, and what profit values are most likely.

The simulation results help Sanotronics's management better understand the profit/loss potential of the new medical device. The 0.078 probability of a loss may be acceptable to management. On the other hand, Sanotronics might want to conduct further market research before deciding whether to introduce the product. In any case, the simulation results should be helpful in reaching an appropriate decision.

NOTES AND COMMENTS

1. In general, the value k of a random variable X corresponding to a computer-generated random number r between 0 and 1 is the smallest value k such that $P(X \leq k) \geq r$.
2. In the preceding section, we showed how to generate values for random variables from a custom discrete distribution, a uniform distribution, and an normal distribution. Generating values for a normally distributed random variable required the use of NORM.INV and the RAND functions. In Appendix 16.1, we describe several additional types of random variables and how to generate them with Excel functions. Using a different probablity distribution for a random variable simply changes the relative likelihood of the random variable realizing certain values. The choice of probability distribution to use for a random variable should be based on historical data and knowledge of the analyst.

16.3 Inventory Simulation

In this section, we describe how simulation can be used to establish an inventory policy for a product that has an uncertain demand. In our example, we consider the Butler Internet Company, which distributes a wireless router. Each router costs Butler \$75 and sells for \$125. Thus Butler realizes a gross profit of \$125 − \$75 = \$50 for each router sold. Monthly demand for the router is described by a normal probability distribution with a mean of 100 units and a standard deviation of 20 units.

Butler receives monthly deliveries from its supplier and replenishes its inventory to a level of Q at the beginning of each month. This beginning inventory level is referred to as the replenishment level. If monthly demand is less than the replenishment level, an inventory holding cost of \$15 is charged for each unit that is not sold. However, if monthly demand is greater than the replenishment level, a stock-out occurs and a shortage cost is incurred. Because Butler assigns a loss-of-goodwill cost of \$30 for each customer turned away, a shortage cost of \$30 is charged for each unit of demand that cannot be satisfied.

Management would like to use a simulation model to determine the average monthly net profit resulting from using particular replenishment levels. Management would also like information on the percentage of total demand that will be satisfied. This percentage is referred to as the *service level.*

The controllable input to the Butler simulation model is the replenishment level, Q. The monthly demand, D, is a random variable. The two output measures are the average monthly net profit and the service level. Computation of the service level requires that we keep track of the number of routers sold each month and the total demand for routers for each month. The service level will be computed at the end of the simulation run as the ratio of total units sold to total demand.

When demand is less than or equal to the replenishment level ($D \leq Q$), D units are sold, and an inventory holding cost of \$15 is incurred for each of the $Q - D$ units that remain in inventory. Net profit for this case is computed as follows:

Case 1: $D \leq Q$

$$\begin{aligned}\text{Gross profit} &= \$50D \\ \text{Holding cost} &= \$15(Q - D) \\ \text{Net profit} &= \text{Gross profit} - \text{Holding cost} = \$50D - \$15(Q - D)\end{aligned}$$

When demand is greater than the replenishment level ($D > Q$), Q routers are sold, and a shortage cost of \$30 is imposed for each of the $D - Q$ units of demand not satisfied. Net profit for this case is computed as follows:

Case 2: $D > Q$

$$\begin{aligned}\text{Gross profit} &= \$50Q \\ \text{Holding cost} &= \$30(D - Q) \\ \text{Net profit} &= \text{Gross profit} - \text{Holding cost} = \$50Q - \$30(D - Q)\end{aligned}$$

Figure 16.10 shows a flowchart that defines the sequence of logical and mathematical operations required to simulate the Butler inventory system. Each trial in the simulation represents one month of operation. The simulation is run for 1000 months using a given replenishment level, Q. Then, the average profit and service level output measures are computed. Let us describe the steps involved in the simulation by illustrating the results for the first two months of a simulation run using a replenishment level of $Q = 100$.

The first block of the flowchart in Figure 16.10 sets the values of the model parameters: gross profit = \$50 per unit, holding cost = \$15 per unit, and shortage cost = \$30 per unit. The next block shows that a replenishment level of Q is selected; in our illustration, $Q = 100$. A value for monthly demand is then generated from a normal distribution with a mean of 100 units and a standard deviation of 20 units; this can be done in Excel with the command =NORM.INV(RAND(), 100, 20). Suppose that a value of $D = 79$ is generated on the first trial. This value of demand is then compared with the replenishment level, Q. With the replenishment level set at $Q = 100$, demand is less than the replenishment level, and the left branch of the flowchart is followed. Sales are set equal to demand (79), and gross profit, holding cost, and net profit are computed as follows:

$$\begin{aligned}\text{Gross profit} &= 50D = 50(79) = 3950 \\ \text{Holding cost} &= 15(Q - D) = 15(100 - 79) = 315 \\ \text{Net profit} &= \text{Gross profit} - \text{Holding cost} = 3950 - 315 = 3635\end{aligned}$$

FIGURE 16.10 FLOWCHART FOR THE BUTLER INVENTORY SIMULATION

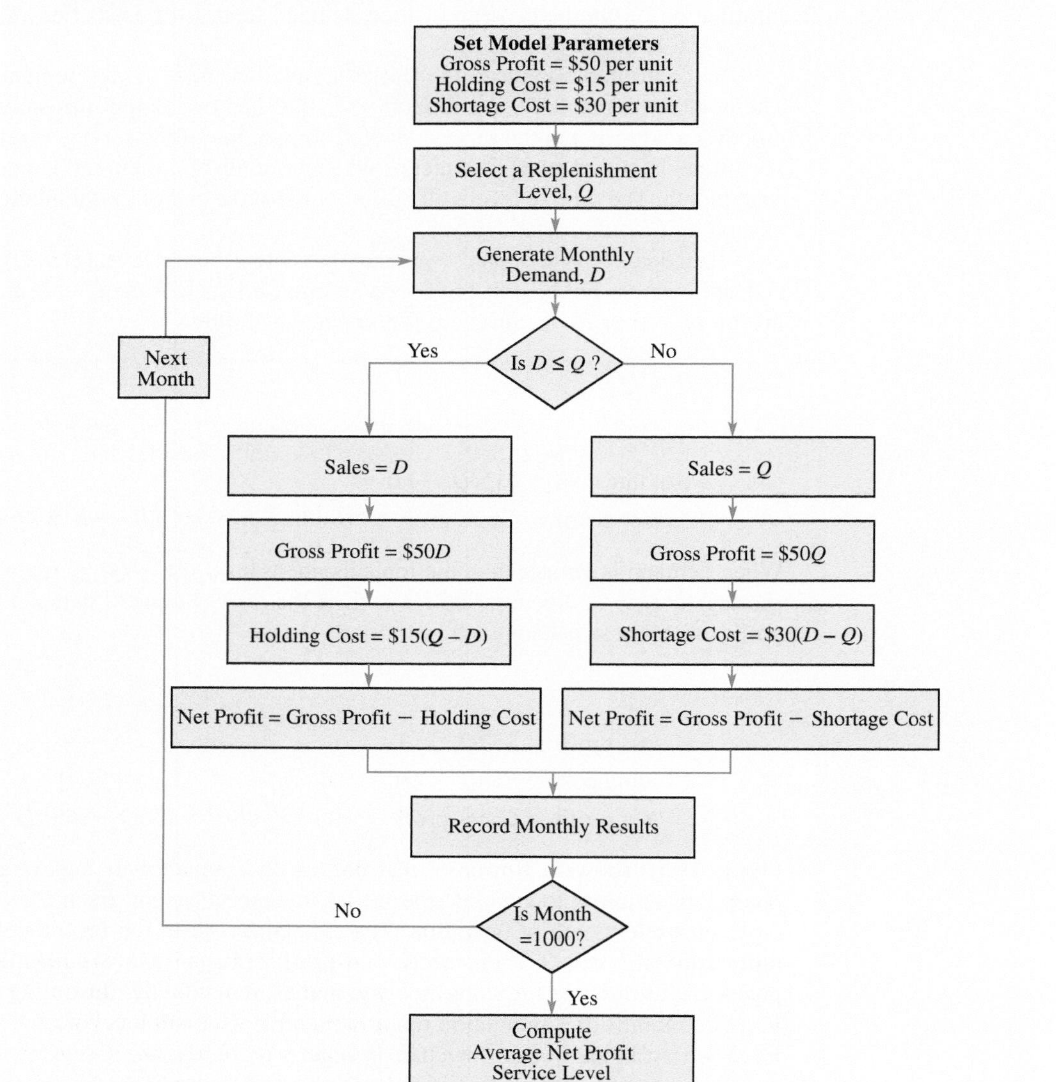

The values of demand, sales, gross profit, holding cost, and net profit are recorded for the first month. The first row of Table 16.2 summarizes the information for this first trial.

For the second month, suppose that a value of 111 is generated for monthly demand. Because demand is greater than the replenishment level, the right branch of the flowchart is followed. Sales are set equal to the replenishment level (100), and gross profit, shortage cost, and net profit are computed as follows:

$$\begin{aligned}\text{Gross profit} &= 50Q = 50(100) = 5000\\ \text{Shortage cost} &= 30(D - Q) = 30(111 - 100) = 330\\ \text{Net profit} &= \text{Gross profit} - \text{Shortage cost} = 5000 - 330 = 4670\end{aligned}$$

TABLE 16.2 BUTLER INVENTORY SIMULATION RESULTS FOR FIVE TRIALS WITH $Q = 100$

Month	Demand	Sales	Gross Profit ($)	Holding Cost ($)	Shortage Cost ($)	Net Profit ($)
1	79	79	3,950	315	0	3,635
2	111	100	5,000	0	330	4,670
3	93	93	4,650	105	0	4,545
4	100	100	5,000	0	0	5,000
5	118	100	5,000	0	540	4,460
Totals	501	472	23,600	420	870	22,310
Average	100	94	$4,720	$84	$174	$4,462

The values of demand, sales, gross profit, holding cost, shortage cost, and net profit are recorded for the second month. The second row of Table 16.2 summarizes the information generated in the second trial.

Table 16.2 shows results for five trials (months) of the simulation. The totals show an accumulated total net profit of $22,310, which is an average monthly net profit of $22,310/5 = $4,462. Total unit sales are 472, and total demand is 501. Thus, the service level is 472/501 = 0.942, indicating Butler has been able to satisfy 94.2% of demand during the five-month period.

Simulation of the Butler Inventory Problem

Butler

Using Excel, we simulate the Butler inventory operation for 1000 months. The worksheet used to carry out the simulation is shown in Figure 16.11. Note that the simulation results for months 22 through 999 have been hidden so that the results can be displayed in a reasonably sized figure. If desired, the rows for these months can be shown and the simulation results displayed for all 1000 months. Let us describe the details of the Excel worksheet that provided the Butler inventory simulation.

The gross profit per unit, holding cost per unit, and shortage cost per unit data are entered directly into cells B4, B5, and B6. The mean and standard deviation of the normal probability distribution for demand are entered into cells E6 and E7. The replenishment level (a controllable input) is entered into cell B10. At this point, we are ready to insert Excel formulas that will be executed for each simulation month or trial.

To generate values for demand, the cell formula in cell B7 is =NORM.INV(RAND(),E6,E7). Next, compute the sales, which is equal to demand (cell B7) if demand is less than or equal to the replenishment level, or is equal to the replenishment level (cell B10) if demand is greater than the replenishment level.

Cell B11 Compute sales =MIN(B7,B10)

Cell B12 Calculate gross profit =B11*B4

Cell B13 Calculate the holding cost if demand is less than or equal to the replenishment level

=IF(B10>B7,(B10-B7)*B5,0)

Cell B14 Calculate the shortage cost if demand is greater than the replenishment level

=IF(B7>B10,(B7-B10)*B6,0)

Cell B15 Calculate net profit =B12-B13-B14

FIGURE 16.11 OUTPUT FROM BUTLER INVENTORY SIMULATION

Butler			
Parameters			
Gross Profit per Unit	$50		
Holding Cost per Unit	$15	**Demand (Normal Distribution)**	
Shortage Cost per Unit	$30	Mean	100
Demand	106	Standard Deviation	20
Model			
Replenishment Level (Q)	100		
Sales	100		
Gross Profit	$5,000		
Holding Cost	$0		
Shortage Cost	$191		
Net Profit	$4,809.39		

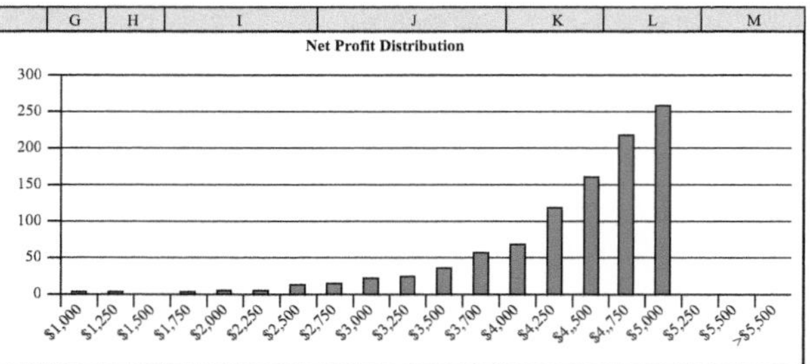

Net Profit Distribution

Simulation Trial	Demand	Sales	Gross Profit	Holding Cost	Shortage Cost	Profit
1	106	100	$5,000	$0	$191	$4,809
2	90	90	$4,477	$157	$0	$4,320
3	109	100	$5,000	$0	$265	$4,735
4	106	100	$5,000	$0	$168	$4,832
5	107	100	$5,000	$0	$225	$4,775
6	121	100	$5,000	$0	$627	$4,373
7	94	94	$4,696	$91	$0	$4,605
8	80	80	$3,999	$300	$0	$3,699
9	76	76	$3,806	$358	$0	$3,447
10	77	77	$3,830	$351	$0	$3,479
11	104	100	$5,000	$0	$120	$4,880
12	58	58	$2,896	$631	$0	$2,264
13	81	81	$4,060	$282	$0	$3,778
14	142	100	$5,000	$0	$1,254	$3,746
15	101	100	$5,000	$0	$18	$4,982
16	108	100	$5,000	$0	$247	$4,753
17	121	100	$5,000	$0	$623	$4,377
18	74	74	$3,715	$386	$0	$3,329
19	115	100	$5,000	$0	$449	$4,551
20	59	59	$2,938	$619	$0	$2,320
21	103	100	$5,000	$0	$103	$4,897
1,000	102	100	$5,000	$0	$57	$4,943

Net Profit Summary Statistics	
Mean	$4,276
Standard Deviation	$661
Minimum	$883
Maximum	$4,997
Service Level	0.924

Bin	Frequency
$1,000	1
$1,250	1
$1,500	0
$1,750	3
$2,000	5
$2,250	4
$2,500	12
$2,750	14
$3,000	21
$3,250	24
$3,500	36
$3,750	57
$4,000	68
$4,250	117
$4,500	160
$4,750	218
$5,000	259
$5,250	0
$5,500	0
>$5,500	0

The table of simulation trials in cells A18:G1017 and the summary statistics are generated using the steps described in Section 16.2. The summary statistics in Figure 16.11 show what can be anticipated over 1000 months if Butler operates its inventory system using a replenishment level of 100. The average net profit is $4276 per month and the service level is 92.4%. A closer look at the distribution of net profit shows that the maximum net profit never exceeds $5000 (indeed the maximum monthly net profit of $5000 occurs when monthly demand is 100 routers and matches the replenishment level). The most likely monthly net profit levels are between $4750 and $5000, but net profits below $1000 are also possible.

By varying the values of controllable inputs, simulation models can be used to identify good operating policies and decisions. For Butler, the simulation model can be used to test the impact of different replenishment levels on the monthly net profit. Table 16.3 summarizes the results of varying the replenishment levels of 110, 120, 130, and 140 units by showing the average monthly net profit, standard deviation of monthly net profit, and the service level for the respective replenishment levels. From Table 16.3, we observe that average monthly net profit increases as the replenishment level increases from 100 to 120, but then decreases as the replenishment level is further increased to 130 and beyond. The standard deviation of monthly net profit increases as the replenishment level increases, suggesting that the monthly profit is more variable as Butler stocks more inventory. This occurs because as Butler increases its replenishment level, it can achieve more sales during months with high demand, but also is exposed to increased holding costs during months with low demand. The service level increases as the replenishment level increases because with more inventory on-hand, Butler is more likely to be able to satisfy demand.

TABLE 16.3 BUTLER INVENTORY SIMULATION RESULTS FOR 1000 TRIALS

Replenishment Level	Average Net Profit ($)	Standard Deviation Profit ($)	Service Level (%)
100	4276	661	92.4
110	4498	853	96.2
120	4573	1078	98.1
130	4462	1201	99.4
140	4327	1247	99.9

Simulation allows the user to consider different operating policies and changes to model parameters and then observe the impact of the changes on output measures such as profit or service level.

On the basis of these results, Butler selected a replenishment level of $Q = 120$, which achieves the highest monthly net profit of $4573 with an acceptable service level of 98.1%. Experimental simulation studies, such as this one for Butler's inventory policy, can help identify good operating policies and decisions. Butler's management used simulation to choose a replenishment level of 120 for the wireless router. With the simulation model in place, management can also explore the sensitivity of this decision to some of the model parameters. For instance, we assigned a shortage cost of $30 for any customer demand not met. With this shortage cost, the replenishment level was $Q = 120$ and the service level was 98.6%. If management felt a more appropriate shortage cost was $10 per unit, running the simulation again using $10 as the shortage cost would be a simple matter.

Earlier we mentioned that simulation is not an optimization technique. Even though we used simulation to choose a replenishment level, it does not guarantee that this choice is optimal. All possible replenishment levels were not tested. Perhaps a manager would like to consider additional simulation runs with replenishment levels of $Q = 115$ and $Q = 125$ to search for a superior inventory policy. We also have no guarantee that the replenishment level with the highest profit would be the same for another set of 300 randomly generated demand values. However, with a large number of simulation trials, we should find a near-optimal solution.

16.4 Waiting Line Simulation

The simulation models discussed thus far have been based on independent trials (i.e., trials in which the results for one trial do not affect what happens in subsequent trials). In this sense, the system being modeled does not change or evolve over time. Simulation models such as these are referred to as **static simulation models**. In this section, we develop a simulation model of a waiting line system where the state of the system, including the number of customers in the waiting line and whether the service facility is busy or idle, changes or evolves over time. To incorporate time into the simulation model, we use a simulation clock to record the time that each customer arrives for service as well as the time that each customer completes service. Simulation models that must take into account how the system changes or evolves over time are referred to as **dynamic simulation models**. In a situation in which the simulation experiment is managed as a discrete sequence of events (e.g., arrivals and departures of customers) over time, the simulation models is also referred to as a **discrete-event simulation**.

One common application of discrete-event simulation is the analysis of waiting lines. In a waiting line simulation, the random variables are the interarrival times of the customers and the service times of the servers, which together determine the waiting time and completion time of the customers. In Chapter 15 we presented formulas that could be used to compute the steady-state operating characteristics of a waiting line, including the average waiting time, the average number of units in the waiting line, the probability of waiting, and so on. In most cases, the waiting line formulas were based on specific assumptions about the probability distribution for arrivals, the probability distribution for service times, the queue discipline, and so on. Simulation, as an alternative for studying waiting lines, is more flexible. In applications where the assumptions required by the waiting line formulas are not reasonable, simulation may be the only feasible approach to studying the waiting line system. In this section, we discuss the simulation of the waiting line at the quality inspection department for Black Sheep Scarves.

Black Sheep Scarves

Black Sheep Scarves will open several new production facilities during the coming year. Each new production facility is designed to have one quality inspector who checks the knitting of the wool scarves before they are shipped to retailers. The arrival of hand-knit wool scarves to the quality inspection department is variable over the 24-hour work day. A concern is that during busy periods, the shipment of scarves to retailers may be delayed as they wait to be inspected. This concern prompted Black Sheep Scarves to undertake a study of the flow of scarves into the quality inspection department as a waiting line. Black Sheep Scarves's vice president wants to determine whether one quality inspector per facility will be sufficient. Black Sheep Scarves established service guidelines stating that the average delay waiting for quality inspection should be no more than one minute. Let us show how a simulation model can be used to study the quality inspection for a particular production facility. Note that each scarf can be viewed as a customer in this example, since scarves are the flow unit passing through the system.

Customer (Scarf) Arrival Times

A uniform probability distribution of interarrival times is used here to illustrate the simulation computations. Actually, any interarrival time probability distribution can be assumed, and the fundamental logic of the waiting line simulation model will not change.

One random variable in the Black Sheep Scarves simulation model is the arrival times of scarves to the quality inspection department. In waiting line simulations, arrival times are determined by randomly generating the time between successive arrivals, referred to as the *interarrival time*. For the quality inspection department being studied, the scarf interarrival times are assumed to be uniformly distributed between 0 and 5 minutes, as shown in Figure 16.12. As shown by equation (16.3) in Section 16.2, values from a uniform probability distribution with a lower bound of 0 and upper bound of 5 can be generated using the Excel function =RAND()*5.

Assume that the simulation run begins at time = 0. A random number of 0.2804 generates an interarrival time of 5(0.2804) = 1.4 minutes for scarf 1. Thus, scarf 1 arrives

FIGURE 16.12 UNIFORM PROBABILITY DISTRIBUTION OF INTERARRIVAL TIMES FOR THE BLACK SHEEP SCARVES PROBLEM

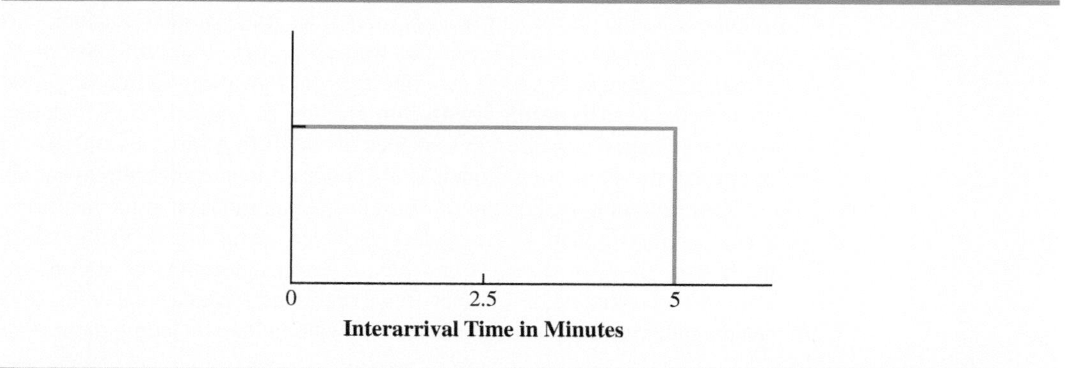

FIGURE 16.13 NORMAL PROBABILITY DISTRIBUTION OF SERVICE TIMES FOR THE BLACK SHEEP SCARVES PROBLEM

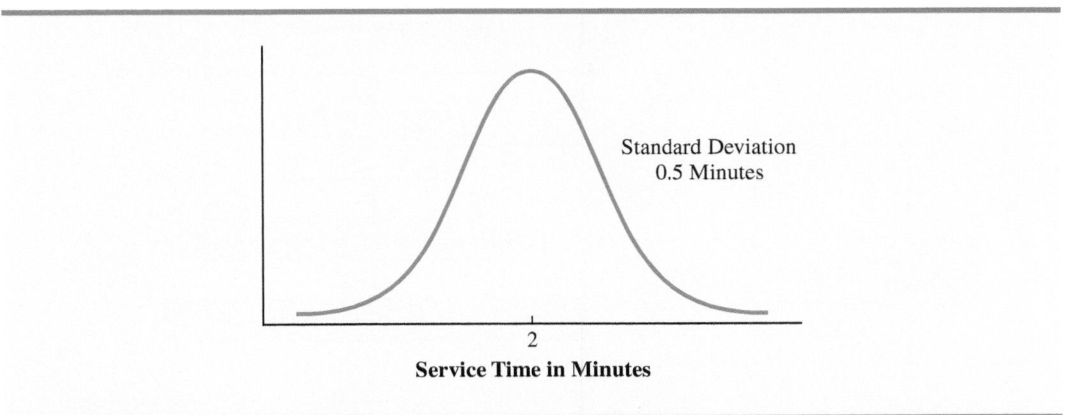

1.4 minutes after the simulation run begins. A second random number of 0.2598 generates an interarrival time of 5(0.2598) = 1.3 minutes, indicating that scarf 2 arrives 1.3 minutes after scarf 1. Thus, scarf 2 arrives 1.4 + 1.3 = 2.7 minutes after the simulation begins. Continuing, a third random number of 0.9802 indicates that scarf 3 arrives 4.9 minutes after scarf 2, which is 7.6 minutes after the simulation begins.

Customer (Scarf) Service (Inspection) Times

Another random variable in the Black Sheep Scarves simulation model is service time, which is the time it takes a quality inspector to check a scarf. Past data from similar quality inspection departments indicate that a normal probability distribution with a mean of 2 minutes and a standard deviation of 0.5 minutes, as shown in Figure 16.13, can be used to describe service (inspection) times. As shown by equation (16.5) in Section 16.2, values from a normal probability distribution with mean 2 and standard deviation 0.5 can be generated using the Excel function =NORMINV(RAND(),2,0.5). For example, the random number of 0.7257 generates a scarf service time of 2.3 minutes.

Simulation Model

The random variables for the Black Sheep Scarves simulation model are the interarrival time and the service time. The controllable input is the number of quality inspectors. The output will consist of various operating characteristics such as the probability of waiting, the average waiting time, the maximum waiting time, and so on. Figure 16.14 shows a flowchart that defines the sequence of logical and mathematical operations required to simulate the Black Sheep Scarves system. The flowchart uses the following notation:

IAT = Interarrival time generated

Arrival time (i) = Time at which scarf i arrives

Start time (i) = Time at which scarf i starts service

Wait time (i) = Waiting time for scarf i

ST = Service time generated

Completion time (i) = Time at which scarf i completes service

System time (i) = System time for scarf i (completion time − arrival time)

FIGURE 16.14 FLOWCHART OF THE BLACK SHEEP SCARVES SIMULATION

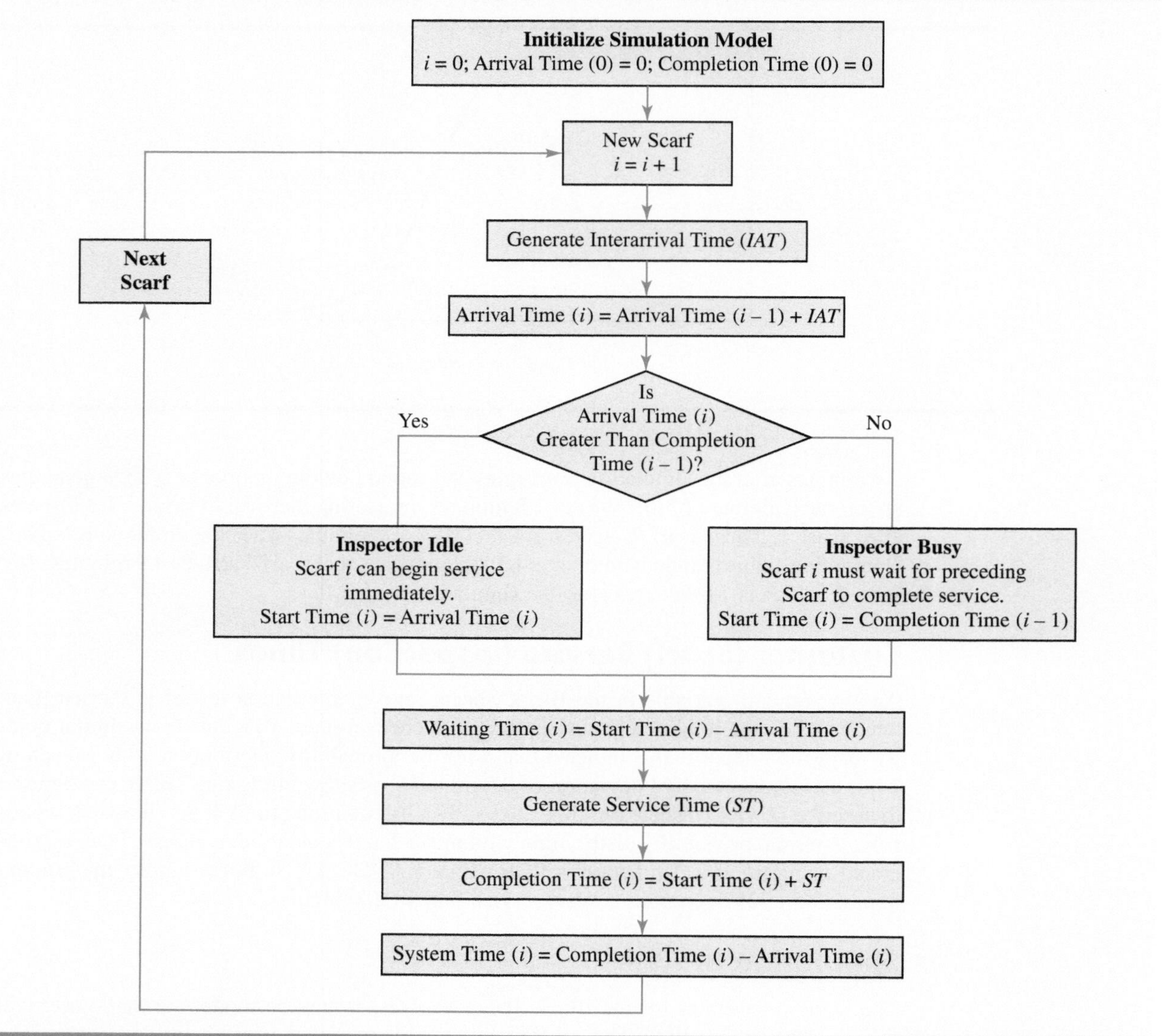

The decision rule for deciding whether the server (the quality inspector in the Black Sheep Scarves example) is idle or busy is the most difficult aspect of the logic in a waiting line simulation model.

Referring to Figure 16.14, we see that the simulation is initialized in the first block of the flowchart. A new scarf is then created. An interarrival time is generated to determine the time that has passed since the preceding scarf arrived.[4] The arrival time for the new scarf is then computed by adding the interarrival time to the arrival time of the preceding scarf.

The arrival time for the new scarf must be compared to the completion time of the preceding scarf to determine whether the quality inspector is idle or busy. If the arrival time of the new scarf is greater than the completion time of the preceding scarf, the preceding scarf will have finished service (been inspected) prior to the arrival of the new scarf. In this

[4]For the first scarf, the interarrival time determines how much time since the beginning of the simulation (t = 0) that the first scarf arrives.

case, the quality inspector will be idle, and the new scarf can begin service immediately. In such cases the service start time for the new scarf is equal to the arrival time of the new scarf. However, if the arrival time for the new scarf is not greater than the completion time of the preceding scarf, the new scarf arrived before the preceding scarf finished service. In this case, the quality inspector is busy, and inspection of the new scarf cannot begin until the quality inspector completes the inspection of the preceding scarf. The service start time for the new scarf is equal to the completion time of the preceding scarf.

Note that the time the new scarf has to wait to use the quality inspector is the difference between the scarf's service start time and the scarf's arrival time. At this point, the scarf is ready to use the quality inspector, and the simulation run continues with the generation of the scarf's service time. The time at which the scarf begins service plus the service time generated determine the scarf's completion time, which then becomes the earliest start time for inspection of the next scarf that arrives. Finally, the total time the scarf spends in the system is the difference between the scarf's service completion time and the scarf's arrival time. At this point, the computations are complete for the current scarf, and the simulation continues with the next scarf. The simulation is continued until a specified number of scarves have been served by the quality inspector.

Simulation results for a set of 10 scarves are shown in Table 16.4. We discuss the computations for the first three scarves to illustrate the logic of the simulation model and to show how the information in Table 16.4 was developed.

Scarf 1

- An interarrival time of $IAT = 1.4$ minutes is generated.
- Because the simulation run begins at time 0, the arrival time for scarf 1 is $0 + 1.4 = 1.4$ minutes.
- Scarf 1 may begin service immediately with a start time of 1.4 minutes.
- The waiting time for scarf 1 is the start time minus the arrival time: $1.4 - 1.4 = 0$ minutes.
- A service time of $ST = 2.3$ minutes is generated for scarf 1.
- The completion time for scarf 1 is the start time plus the service time: $1.4 + 2.3 = 3.7$ minutes.
- The time in the system for scarf 1 is the completion time minus the arrival time: $3.7 - 1.4 = 2.3$ minutes.

TABLE 16.4 SIMULATION RESULTS FOR 10 SCARVES

Scarf	Interarrival Time	Arrival Time	Service Start Time	Waiting Time	Service Time	Completion Time	Time in System
1	1.4	1.4	1.4	0.0	2.3	3.7	2.3
2	1.3	2.7	3.7	1.0	1.5	5.2	2.5
3	4.9	7.6	7.6	0.0	2.2	9.8	2.2
4	3.5	11.1	11.1	0.0	2.5	13.6	2.5
5	0.7	11.8	13.6	1.8	1.8	15.4	3.6
6	2.8	14.6	15.4	0.8	2.4	17.8	3.2
7	2.1	16.7	17.8	1.1	2.1	19.9	3.2
8	0.6	17.3	19.9	2.6	1.8	21.7	4.4
9	2.5	19.8	21.7	1.9	2.0	23.7	3.9
10	1.9	21.7	23.7	2.0	2.3	26.0	4.3
Totals	21.7			11.2	20.9		32.1
Averages	2.17			1.12	2.09		3.21

Scarf 2

- An interarrival time of $IAT = 1.3$ minutes is generated.
- Because the arrival time of scarf 1 is 1.4, the arrival time for scarf 2 is $1.4 + 1.3 = 2.7$ minutes.
- Because the completion time of scarf 1 is 3.7 minutes, the arrival time of scarf 2 is not greater than the completion time of scarf 1; thus, the quality inspector is busy when scarf 2 arrives.
- Scarf 2 must wait for scarf 1 to complete service before beginning service. Scarf 1 completes service at 3.7 minutes, which becomes the start time for scarf 2.
- The waiting time for scarf 2 is the start time minus the arrival time: $3.7 - 2.7 = 1$ minute.
- A service time of $ST = 1.5$ minutes is generated for scarf 2.
- The completion time for scarf 2 is the start time plus the service time: $3.7 + 1.5 = 5.2$ minutes.
- The time in the system for scarf 2 is the completion time minus the arrival time: $5.2 - 2.7 = 2.5$ minutes.

Scarf 3

- An interarrival time of $IAT = 4.9$ minutes is generated.
- Because the arrival time of scarf 2 was 2.7 minutes, the arrival time for scarf 3 is $2.7 + 4.9 = 7.6$ minutes.
- The completion time of scarf 2 is 5.2 minutes, so the arrival time for scarf 3 is greater than the completion time of scarf 2. Thus, the quality inspector is idle when scarf 3 arrives.
- Scarf 3 begins service immediately with a start time of 7.6 minutes.
- The waiting time for scarf 3 is the start time minus the arrival time: $7.6 - 7.6 = 0$ minutes.
- A service time of $ST = 2.2$ minutes is generated for scarf 3.
- The completion time for scarf 3 is the start time plus the service time: $7.6 + 2.2 = 9.8$ minutes.
- The time in the system for scarf 3 is the completion time minus the arrival time: $9.8 - 7.6 = 2.2$ minutes.

Using the totals in Table 16.4, we can compute an average waiting time for the 10 scarves of $11.2/10 = 1.12$ minutes, and an average time in the system of $32.1/10 = 3.21$ minutes. Table 16.4 shows that 7 of the 10 scarves had to wait. The total time for the 10-scarf simulation is given by the completion time of the 10th scarf: 26.0 minutes. However, at this point, we realize that a simulation for 10 scarves is much too short a period to draw any firm conclusions about the operation of the waiting line.

Simulation of Black Sheep Scarves

Using an Excel worksheet, we simulated the operation of the waiting line for the Black Sheep Scarves's quality inspection of 1000 scarves. The worksheet used to carry out the simulation is shown in Figure 16.15. Note that the simulation results for scarves 3 through 998 have been hidden so that the results can be shown in a reasonably sized figure. If desired, the rows for these scarves can be shown and the simulation results displayed for all 1000 scarves.

Before discussing the summary statistics, let us point out that many simulation studies of dynamic systems focus on the operation of the system during its long-run or steady-state operation. To ensure that the effects of start-up conditions are not included in the steady-state

FIGURE 16.15 OUTPUT FOR BLACK SHEEP SCARVES WITH ONE QUALITY INSPECTOR

	A	B	C	D	E	F	G	H
1	**Black sheep Scarves with One Quality Inspector**							
2								
3	**Parameters**							
4	**Interarrival Times (Uniform Distribution)**							
5	Smallest Value	0.0						
6	Largest Value	5.0						
7								
8	**Service Times (Normal Distribution)**							
9	Mean	2.0						
10	Standard Dev	0.5						
11								
12	**Model**							
13	Customer	Interarrival Time	Arrival Time	Service Start Time	Waiting Time	Service Time	Completion Time	Time in System
14	1	2.6	2.6	2.6	0.0	1.8	4.4	1.8
15	2	0.6	3.1	4.4	1.3	1.7	6.1	3.0
16	3	4.1	7.3	7.3	0.0	0.9	8.2	0.9
1012	999	2.9	2565.7	2565.9	0.3	1.9	2567.8	2.1
1013	1000	4.5	2570.1	2570.1	0.0	1.9	2572.0	1.9
1014								
1015	**Summary Statistic**			**Wait Time Range**	**Bin**	**Frequency**		
1016	Number Waiting	531		0–1	1	521.0		
1017	Number of Customers	900		1–2	2	164.0		
1018	Probability of Waiting	0.5900		2–3	3	89.0		
1019	Average Waiting Time	1.21		3–4	4	65.0		
1020	Maximum Waiting Time	8.6		4–5	5	29.0		
1021	Utilization of Quality Inspector	0.7829		5–6	6	15.0		
1022	Number Waiting > 1 Min	379		6–7	7	12.0		
1023	Probability Waiting > 1 Min	0.4211		7–8	8	3.0		
1024				8–9	9	2.0		
1025				9–10	10	0.0		

BlackSheep1 Inspector

calculations, a dynamic simulation model is usually run for a specified period without collecting any data about the operation of the system. The length of the start-up period can vary depending on the application but can be determined by experimenting with the simulation model. Because the Black Sheep Scarves production facility operates 24 hours per day, we will avoid the transient effects by treating the results for the first 100 scarves as the startup period. Thus, the summary statistics shown in Figure 16.15 are for the 900 scarves arriving during the steady-state period.

The summary statistics show that 531 of the 900 scarves had to wait. This result provides a 531/900 = 0.59 probability that a scarf will have to wait for service. In other words, approximately 59% of the scarves will have to wait some amount of time because the quality inspector is in use when they arrive. The average waiting time is 1.21 minutes per scarf, with at least one scarf waiting the maximum time of 8.6 minutes. The utilization rate of 0.7829 indicates that the quality inspector is in use approximately 78% of the time. Finally, 379 of the 900 scarves had to wait more than 1 minute (approximately 42% of all scarves). From the wait time distribution, we observe 17 scarves (about 2% of all scarves) had a wait time greater than 6 minutes. Note that if we had used all 1000 simulated arrivals, these estimates could have been substantially different because the scarves that arrived early in the simulation had to wait less often and for less time.

The simulation supports the conclusion that the production facility will have a busy quality inspection department. With an average scarf wait time of 1.21 minutes, the system does not satisfy Black Sheep's service guideline of an average scarf wait time of less than one minute. This production facility is a good candidate for a second quality inspector or a more efficient inspection process.

Simulation with Two Quality Inspectors

In this section, we extend the logic of the Black Sheep simulation model to account for two quality inspectors. For the second quality inspector we also assume that the service time is normally distributed with a mean of 2 minutes and a standard deviation of 0.5 minutes. Table 16.5 shows the simulation results for the first 10 scarves. In comparing the two quality inspector system results in Table 16.5 with the single quality inspector simulation results shown in Table 16.4, we see that two additional columns are needed. These two columns show when each quality inspector becomes available for scarf service. We assume that, when a new scarf arrives, the scarf will be served by the quality inspector who is available first. When the simulation begins, the first scarf is arbitrarily assigned to quality inspector 1.

Table 16.5 shows that scarf 7 is the first scarf that has to wait to use a quality inspector. We describe how scarves 6, 7, and 8 are processed to show how the logic of the simulation run for two quality inspectors differs from that with a single quality inspector.

Scarf 6

- An interarrival time of 1.3 minutes is generated, and scarf 6 arrives 9.1 + 1.3 = 10.4 minutes into the simulation.
- From the scarf 5 row, we see that quality inspector 1 frees up at 5.8 minutes, and quality inspector 2 will free up at 11.3 minutes into the simulation. Because quality inspector 1 is free, scarf 6 does not wait and begins service on quality inspector 1 at the arrival time of 10.4 minutes.
- A service time of 1.6 minutes is generated for scarf 6. So scarf 6 has a completion time of 10.4 + 1.6 = 12.0 minutes.
- The time quality inspector 1 will next become available is set at 12.0 minutes; the time available for quality inspector 2 remains 11.3 minutes.

TABLE 16.5 SIMULATION RESULTS FOR 10 SCARVES FOR A TWO-QUALITY INSPECTOR SYSTEM

Scarf	Interarrival Time	Arrival Time	Service Start Time	Waiting Time	Service Time	Completion Time	Time in System	Time Available QI 1	Time Available QI 2
1	1.7	1.7	1.7	0.0	2.1	3.8	2.1	3.8	0.0
2	0.7	2.4	2.4	0.0	2.0	4.4	2.0	3.8	4.4
3	2.0	4.4	4.4	0.0	1.4	5.8	1.4	5.8	4.4
4	0.1	4.5	4.5	0.0	0.9	5.4	0.9	5.8	5.4
5	4.6	9.1	9.1	0.0	2.2	11.3	2.2	5.8	11.3
6	1.3	10.4	10.4	0.0	1.6	12.0	1.6	12.0	11.3
7	0.6	11.0	11.3	0.3	1.7	13.0	2.0	12.0	13.0
8	0.3	11.3	12.0	0.7	2.2	14.2	2.9	14.2	13.0
9	3.4	14.7	14.7	0.0	2.9	17.6	2.9	14.2	17.6
10	0.1	14.8	14.8	0.0	2.8	17.6	2.8	17.6	17.6
Totals	14.8			1.0	19.8		20.8		
Averages	1.48			0.1	1.98		2.08		

Scarf 7

- An interarrival time of 0.6 minute is generated, and scarf 7 arrives 10.4 + 0.6 = 11.0 minutes into the simulation.
- From the previous row, we see that quality inspector 1 will not be available until 12.0 minutes, and quality inspector 2 will not be available until 11.3 minutes. So scarf 7 must wait to use a quality inspector. Because quality inspector 2 will free up first, scarf 7 begins service on that machine at a start time of 11.3 minutes. With an arrival time of 11.0 and a service start time of 11.3, scarf 7 experiences a waiting time of 11.3 − 11.0 = 0.3 minute.
- A service time of 1.7 minutes is generated, leading to a completion time of 11.3 + 1.7 = 13.0 minutes.
- The time available for quality inspector 2 is updated to 13.0 minutes, and the time available for quality inspector 1 remains at 12.0 minutes.

Scarf 8

- An interarrival time of 0.3 minute is generated, and scarf 8 arrives 11.0 + 0.3 = 11.3 minutes into the simulation.
- From the previous row, we see that quality inspector 1 will be the first available. Thus, scarf 8 starts service on quality inspector 1 at 12.0 minutes, resulting in a waiting time of 12.0 − 11.3 = 0.7 minute.
- A service time of 2.2 minutes is generated, resulting in a completion time of 12.0 + 2.2 = 14.2 minutes and a system time of 0.7 + 2.2 = 2.9 minutes.
- The time available for quality inspector 1 is updated to 14.2 minutes, and the time available for quality inspector 2 remains at 13.0 minutes.

From the totals in Table 16.5, we see that the average waiting time for these 10 scarves is only 1.0/10 = 0.1 minute. Of course, a much longer simulation will be necessary before any reliable conclusions can be drawn.

Simulation Results with Two Quality Inspectors

The Excel worksheet that we used to conduct a simulation for 1000 scarves using two quality inspectors is shown in Figure 16.16. Results for the first 100 scarves were discarded to account for the startup period. With two quality inspectors, the number of scarves that had to wait was reduced from 531 to 87. This reduction results in a 87/900 = 0.0967 probability that a scarf will have to wait for service when two quality inspectors are used. The two-quality inspector system also reduced the average waiting time to 0.07 minute (4.2 seconds) per scarf. The maximum waiting time was reduced from 8.6 to 2.8 minutes, and the quality inspectors were in use 39.61% of the time. Finally, only 24 of the 900 scarves had to wait more than 1 minute for a quality inspector to become available. Thus, only 2.67% of scarves had to wait more than 1 minute. The simulation results demonstrate the performance benefits of adding a second quality inspector, and in combination with cost information of this second quality inspector, Black Sheep Scarves can evaluate the decision to expand to two quality inspectors.

BlackSheep2 Inspectors

The simulation models that we developed can now be used to study the quality inspection at other production facilities. In each case, assumptions must be made about the appropriate interarrival time and service time probability distributions. However, once appropriate assumptions have been made, the same simulation models can be used to determine the operating characteristics of the quality inspector waiting line system.

FIGURE 16.16 OUTPUT FOR BLACK SHEEP SCARVES WITH TWO QUALITY INSPECTORS

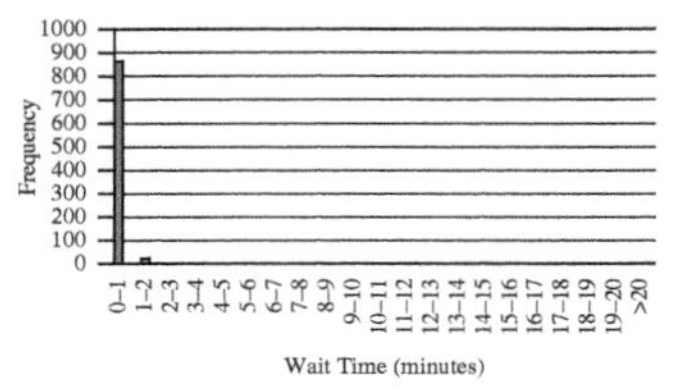

	A	B	C	D	E	F	G	H	I	J
1	**Black Sheep Scarves with Two Quality Inspectors**			Frequency: 1000, 900, 800, 700, 600, 500, 400, 300, 200, 100, 0; Wait Time (minutes): 0–1, 1–2, 2–3, 3–4, 4–5, 5–6, 6–7, 7–8, 8–9, 9–10, 10–11, 11–12, 12–13, 13–14, 14–15, 15–16, 16–17, 17–18, 18–19, 19–20, >20						
2										
3	**Parameters**									
4	**Interarrival Times (Uniform Distribution**									
5	Smallest value	0.0								
6	Largest Value	5.0								
7										
8	**Service Times (Normal Diribution)**									
9	Mean	2.0								
10	Standerd Dev	0.5								
11										
12	**Model**									
13	Customer	Interarrival Time	Arrival Time	Service Start Time	Waiting Time	Service Time	Completion Time	Time in System	Inspector 1 Available	Inspector 2 Available
14	1	4.4	4.4	4.4	0.0	1.6	6.0	1.6	6.0	0.0
15	2	0.8	5.2	5.2	0.0	2.0	7.2	2.0	6.0	7.2
16	3	2.1	7.3	7.3	0.0	1.8	9.1	1.8	9.1	7.2
1012	999	2.6	2507.0	2507.0	0.0	2.3	2509.3	2.3	2507.3	2509.3
1013	1000	3.0	2510.0	2510.0	0.0	3.0	2513.0	3.0	2513.0	2509.3
1014										
1015	**Summary Statistics**			**Wait Time Range**	**Bin**	**Frequency**				
1016	Number Waiting	87		0–1	1	876.0				
1017	Number of Customers	900		1–2	2	18.0				
1018	Probability of Waiting	0.0967		2–3	3	6.0				
1019	Average Waiting Time	0.07		3–4	4	0.0				
1020	Maximum Waiting Time	2.8		4–5	5	0.0				
1021	Utilization of Quality Inspectors	0.3961		5–6	6	0.0				
1022	Number Waiting > 1 Min	24		6–7	7	0.0				
1023	Probability of Waiting > 1 Min	0.0267		7–8	8	0.0				
1024				8–9	9	0.0				
1025				9–10	10	0.0				
1026				10–11	11	0.0				
1027				11–12	12	0.0				

NOTES AND COMMENTS

1. The Black Sheep Scarves waiting line model was based on uniformly distributed interarrival times and normally distributed service times. One advantage of simulation is its flexibility in accommodating a variety of different probability distributions. For instance, if we believe an exponential distribution is more appropriate for interarrival times, this waiting line simulation could easily be repeated by simply changing the way the interarrival times are generated.
2. At the beginning of this section, we defined discrete-event simulation as involving a dynamic system that evolves over time. The simulation computations focus on the sequence of events as they occur at discrete points in time. In the Black Sheep Scarves waiting line example, scarf arrivals and the scarf service completions were the discrete events. Referring to the arrival times and completion times in the following table, we see that the first five discrete events for this waiting line simulation were as follows:

Event	**Time**
Scarf 1 arrives	1.4
Scarf 2 arrives	2.7
Scarf 1 finished	3.7
Scarf 2 finished	5.2
Scarf 3 arrives	7.6

3. We did not keep track of the number of scarves in the quality inspection waiting line as we carried out the quality inspection simulation computations on a scarf-by-scarf basis. However, we can determine the average number of scarves in the waiting line from other information in the simulation output. The following relationship is valid for any waiting line system:

$$\text{Average number in waiting line} = \frac{\text{Total waiting time}}{\text{Total time of simulation}}$$

For the system with one quality inspector, suppose the 100th scarf completed service at 247.8 minutes into the simulation. Thus, the total time of the simulation for the next 900 scarves was 2572.0 − 247.8 = 2324.2 minutes. The average waiting time was 1.21 minutes. During the simulation, the 900 scarves had a total waiting time of 900(1.21) = 1089 minutes. Therefore, the average number of scarves in the waiting line is

$$\text{Average number in waiting line} = 1089/2324.2 = 0.47 \text{ scarf}$$

4. While it is possible to conduct small discrete-event simulations with native Excel functionality or with a Monte Carlo simulation package such as Analytic Solver Platform, discrete-event simulation modeling is best conducted with special-purpose software such as Arena®, ProModel®, and GPSS®. These packages have built-in simulation clocks, simplified methods for generating random variables, and procedures for collecting and summarizing the simulation output.

16.5 Simulation Considerations

Verification and Validation

An important step in any simulation study is confirmation that the simulation model accurately describes the real system. Inaccurate simulation models cannot be expected to provide worthwhile information. Thus, before using simulation results to draw conclusions about a real system, one must take steps to verify and validate the simulation model.

Verification is the process of determining that the computer procedure performing the simulation calculations is logically correct. Verification is largely a debugging task to ensure that there are no errors in the computer procedure that implements the simulation. In some cases, an analyst may compare computer results for a limited number of events with independent hand calculations. In other cases, tests may be performed to verify that the random variables are being generated correctly and that the output from the simulation model appears to be reasonable. The verification step is not complete until the user develops a high degree of confidence that the computer procedure is error free.

Validation is the process of ensuring that the simulation model provides an accurate representation of a real system. Validation requires an agreement among analysts and managers that the logic and the assumptions used in the design of the simulation model accurately reflect how the real system operates. The first phase of the validation process is done prior to, or in conjunction with, the development of the computer procedure for the simulation process. Validation continues after the computer program has been developed, with the analyst reviewing the simulation output to see whether the simulation results closely approximate the performance of the real system. If possible, the output of the simulation model is compared to the output of the existing real system to make sure that the simulation output closely approximates the performance of the real system. If this form of validation is not possible, an analyst can experiment with the simulation model, and one or more individuals experienced with the operation of the real system can review the simulation output to determine whether it is a reasonable approximation of what would be obtained with the real system under similar conditions.

Verification and validation are not tasks to be taken lightly. They are key steps in any simulation study and are necessary to ensure that decisions and conclusions based on the simulation results are appropriate for the real system.

Advantages and Disadvantages of Using Simulation

The primary advantages of simulation are that it is easy to understand and that the methodology can be used to model and learn about the behavior of complex systems that would be difficult, if not impossible, to deal with analytically. Simulation models are flexible; they can be used to describe systems without requiring the assumptions that are often required by mathematical models. In general, the larger the number of random variables a system has, the more likely that a simulation model will provide the most suitable approach for studying the system. Another advantage of simulation is that a simulation model provides a convenient experimental laboratory for the real system. Changing assumptions or operating policies in the simulation model and rerunning it can provide results that help us understand how such changes will affect the operation of the real system. Experimenting directly with a real system is often expensive or not feasible. Simulation models often warn against poor decision strategies by projecting disastrous outcomes such as system failures, large financial losses, and so on.

Simulation is not without disadvantages. For complex systems, the process of developing, verifying, and validating a simulation model can be time-consuming and expensive (however, the process of developing the model generally leads to a better understanding of the system, which is an important benefit). As with all mathematical models, the analyst must be mindful of the assumptions of the model in order to understand its limitations. In addition, each simulation run provides only a sample of how the real system will operate. As such, the summary of the simulation data provides only estimates or approximations about the real system. Nonetheless, the danger of obtaining poor solutions is greatly mitigated if the analyst exercises good judgment in developing the simulation model, follows proper verification and validation steps, and if the simulation process is run long enough under a wide variety of conditions so that the analyst has sufficient data to predict how the real system will operate.

Summary

Simulation is a method for learning about a real system by experimenting with a model that represents the system. Some of the reasons simulation is frequently used are

1. It can be used for a wide variety of practical problems.
2. The simulation approach is relatively easy to explain and understand. As a result, management confidence is increased, and acceptance of the results is more easily obtained.
3. Spreadsheet packages now provide another alternative for model implementation, and third-party vendors have developed add-ins that expand the capabilities of the spreadsheet packages.
4. Computer software developers have produced simulation packages that make it easier to develop and implement simulation models for more complex problems.

In this chapter, we first analyzed uncertainty by considering the base-case, best-case, and worst-case scenarios. Then, we showed how native Excel functions can be used to execute a simulation to evaluate risk involving the development of a new product, the Sanotronics device. Next we used the Butler Inventory problem to demonstrate another example of simulation modeling. Finally, we illustrated how to use Excel to create a discrete-event simulation for the Black Sheep problem. These examples represent a wide range of problems that can be addressed with simulation modeling.

Our approach throughout this chapter was to develop simulation models that contained both controllable inputs and random variables. Procedures were developed for randomly generating values for the random variables, the sequence of logical and mathematical operations that describe the steps of the simulation process were modeled, and simulation results were obtained by running the simulation for a suitable number of trials. Simulation results were obtained and conclusions were drawn about the operation of the real system.

Summary of Steps for Conducting a Simulation Analysis

1. **Construct a spreadsheet model that computes output measures for given values of inputs.** The foundation of a good simulation model is logic that correctly relates input values to outputs. Audit the spreadsheet to assure that the cell formulas correctly evaluate the outputs over the entire range of possible input values.
2. **Identify inputs that are uncertain and specify probability distributions for these cells** (rather than just static numbers). Note that not all inputs may have a large enough degree of uncertainty to require modeling with a probability distribution. Other inputs may actually be decision variables, which are values that the decision-maker can control and so are not random quantities to model with probability distributions.
3. **Select one or more outputs to record over the simulation trials.** Typical information recorded for an output include a histogram of output values and summary statistics such as the mean, standard deviation, maximum, minimum, percentile values, etc.
4. **Execute the simulation for a specified number of trials**. For most small- to moderate-sized simulation problems, we recommend the use of 10,000 trials. The amount of sampling error can be monitored by observing the degree by which simulation output measures fluctuate across multiple simulation runs.
5. **Analyze the outputs and interpret the implications on the decision-making process.** In addition to estimates of the mean output, simulation allows us to construct a distribution of possible output values.

Recall that for dynamic simulation models (discussed in Section 16.3), outputs are recorded for simulation trials occurring after an initial start-up period.

Glossary

Base-case scenario Determining output assuming the most likely values for the random variables of a model.
Best-case scenario Determining the output assuming the best values that can be expected for the random variables of a model.
Continuous probability distribution A probability distribution where the possible values for a random variable can take any value between two specified values. The specified values can include negative and positive infinity.
Controllable input Input to a simulation model that is selected by the decision maker.
Discrete-event simulation model A simulation model that describes how a system evolves over time by managing a discrete sequence of events (i.e., customer arrival or departure, over time).
Discrete probability distribution A probability distribution where the possible values for a random variable can take on only specified discrete values.
Dynamic simulation model A simulation model used in situations where the state of the system affects how the system changes or evolves over time.
Parameters Numerical values that appear in the mathematical relationships of a model.
Probability distribution A description of the range and relative likelihood of possible values of an uncertain variable.

Random variable or uncertain variable Input to a simulation model whose value is uncertain and described by a probability distribution.
Risk analysis The process of evaluating a decision in the face of uncertainty by quantifying the likelihood and magnitude of an undesirable outcome.
Simulation A method that uses repeated random sampling of values to represent uncertainty in a model representing a real system and computes the values of model outputs.
Static simulation model A simulation model in which each trial used in situations where the state of the system at one point in time does not affect the state of the system at future points in time. Each trial of the simulation is independent.
Validation The process of determining that a simulation model provides an accurate representation of a real system.
Verification The process of determining that a computer program implements a simulation model as it is intended.
What-if analysis A trial-and-error approach to learning about the range of possible outputs for a model. Trial values are chosen for the model inputs (these are the what-ifs) and the value of the output(s) is computed.
Worst-case scenario Determining the output assuming the worst values that can be expected for the random variables of a model.

Problems

1. The management of Brinkley Corporation is interested in using simulation to estimate the profit per unit for a new product. The selling price for the product will be $45 per unit. Probability distributions for the purchase cost, the labor cost, and the transportation cost are estimated as follows:

Procurement Cost ($)	Probability	Labor Cost ($)	Probability	Transportation Cost ($)	Probability
10	0.25	20	0.10	3	0.75
11	0.45	22	0.25	5	0.25
12	0.30	24	0.35		
		25	0.30		

   a. Compute profit per unit for the base-case, worst-case, and best-case scenarios.
   b. Construct a simulation model to estimate the mean profit per unit.
   c. Why is the simulation approach to risk analysis preferable to generating a variety of what-if scenarios?
   d. Management believes the project may not be sustainable if the profit per unit is less than $5. Use simulation to estimate the probability the profit per unit will be less than $5.

2. The management of Madeira Computing is considering the introduction of a wearable electronic device with the functionality of a laptop computer and phone. The fixed cost to launch this new product is $300,000. The variable cost for the product is expected to be between $160 and $240, with a most likely value of $200 per unit. The product will sell for $300 per unit. Demand estimates for the produce vary widely, ranging from 0 to 20,000 units, with an average of 4000 units.
   a. Compute profit for the base-case, worst-case, and best-case scenarios.
   b. Assume the variable cost is a uniform random variable between $16 and $24 and the product demand is an exponential random variable with a mean of 4000 units. Construct a simulation model to estimate the mean profit and the probability that the project will result in a loss.

3. Grear Tire Company has produced a new tire with an estimated mean lifetime mileage of 36,500 miles. Management also believes that the standard deviation is 5000 miles and that tire mileage is normally distributed. To promote the new tire, Grear has offered to refund a portion of the purchase price if the tire fails to reach 30,000 miles before the tire needs to be replaced. Specifically, for tires with a lifetime below 30,000 miles, Grear will refund a customer $1 per 100 miles short of 30,000.
   a. For each tire sold, what is the expected cost of the promotion?
   b. What is the probability that Grear will refund more than $50 for a tire?
   c. What mileage should Grear set the promotion claim if it wants the expected cost to be $2?

4. Construct a spreadsheet simulation in which each trial consists of rolling of four dice. That is, there are four random variables each with an outcome of 1, 2, 3, 4, 5, or 6. For each trial, record the value of the first dice, the sum of the first two dice, the sum of the first three dice, and the sum of the first four dice. Using the FREQUENCY command, create a frequency distribution for each of these four computations on a separate plot. What phenomenon do you observe?

5. To generate leads for new business, Gustin Investment Services offers free financial planning seminars at major hotels in Southwest Florida. Gustin conducts seminars for groups of 25 individuals. Each seminar costs Gustin $3500, and the average first-year commission for each new account opened is $5000. Gustin estimates that for each individual attending the seminar, there is a 0.01 probability that he/she will open a new account.
   a. Determine the equation for computing Gustin's profit per seminar, given values of the relevant parameters.
   b. What type of random variable is the number of new accounts opened? Hint: Review Appendix 16.1 for descriptions of various types of probability distributions.
   c. Construct a spreadsheet simulation model to analyze the profitability of Gustin's seminars. Would you recommend that Gustin continue running the seminars?
   d. How large of an audience does Gustin need before a seminar's expected profit is greater than zero?

6. The Statewide Auto Insurance Company developed the following probability distribution for automobile collision claims paid during the past year.
   a. Set up a table of intervals of random numbers that can be used with a VLOOKUP to generate automobile collision claim payments.
   b. Construct a simulation model to estimate the mean and standard deviation of claims payments. How accurate are these estimates? Compare them to the analytical calculation of the mean, $\mu = x_1 \times P(x = x_1) + x_2 \times P(x = x_2) + \cdots x_n \times P(x = x_n)$, and standard deviation, $\sqrt{\sigma = (x_1 - \mu)^2 \times P(x = x_1) + (x_2 - \mu)^2 \times P(x = x_2) + \cdots (x_n - \mu)^2 \times P(x = x_n)(x_n - \mu)^2 \times P(x = x_n)}$. How can we improve the accuracy of the simulation estimates?

Payment($)	**Probability**
0	0.83
500	0.06
1,000	0.05
2,000	0.02
5,000	0.02
8,000	0.01
10,000	0.01

7. Baseball's World Series is a maximum of seven games, with the winner being the first team to win four games. Assume that the Atlanta Braves and the Minnesota Twins are playing in the World Series and that the first two games are to be played in Atlanta, the

next three games at the Twins' ballpark, and the last two games, if necessary, back in Atlanta. Taking into account the projected starting pitchers for each game and the home field advantage, the probabilities of Atlanta winning each game are as follows:

Game	1	2	3	4	5	6	7
Probability of Win	0.60	0.55	0.48	0.45	0.48	0.55	0.50

a. Set up a spreadsheet simulation model for which whether Atlanta wins or loses each game is a random variable.
b. What is the probability that the Atlanta Braves win the World Series?
c. What is the average number of games played regardless of winner?

8. The current price of a share of a particular stock listed on the New York Stock Exchange is $39. The following probability distribution shows how the price per share is expected to change over a three-month period:

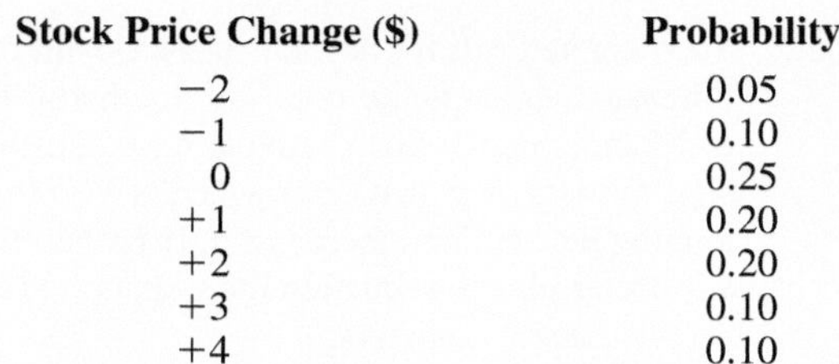

Stock Price Change ($)	Probability
−2	0.05
−1	0.10
0	0.25
+1	0.20
+2	0.20
+3	0.10
+4	0.10

a. Construct a spreadsheet simulation model that computes the value of the stock price in 3 months, 6 months, 9 months, and 12 months under the assumption that the change in stock price over any 3-month period is independent of the change in stock price over any other 3-month period.
b. With the current price of $39 per share, simulate the price per share for the next four 3-month periods. What is the average stock price per share in 12 months? What is the standard deviation of the stock price in 12 months?
c. Based on the model assumptions, what are the lowest and highest possible prices for this stock in 12 months? Based on your knowledge of the stock market, how valid do you think these prices are? Propose an alternative to modeling how stock prices evolve over 3-month periods.

9. The Iowa Energy of the National Basketball Association Developmental League (NBA-DL) are scheduled to play against the Maine Red Claws in an upcoming game. Because a player in the NBA-DL is still developing his skills, the number of points he scores in a game can vary dramatically. Assume that each player's point production can be represented as an integer uniform variable with the ranges provided in the table below.
a. Develop a spreadsheet model that simulates the points scored by each team.
b. What is the average and standard deviation of points scored by the Iowa Energy? What is the shape of the distribution of points scored by the Iowa Energy?
c. What are the average and standard deviation of points scored by the Maine Red Claws? What is the shape of the distribution of points scored by the Maine Red Claws?
d. Let Point Differential = Iowa Energy points − Maine Red Claw points. What is the average point differential between the Iowa Energy and Maine Red Claws? What is the standard deviation in the point differential? What is the shape of the point differential distribution?
e. What is the probability of that the Iowa Energy scores more points than the Maine Red Claws?

f. The coach of the Iowa Energy feels that they are the underdog and is considering a “riskier” game strategy. The effect of the riskier game strategy is that the range of each Energy player’s point production increases symmetrically so that the new range is [0, original upper bound + original lower bound]. For example, Energy player 1’s range with the risky strategy is [0, 25]. How does the new strategy affect the average and standard deviation of the Energy point total? How is the probability of the Iowa Energy scoring more points that the Maine Red Claws affected?

Player	Iowa Energy	Maine Red Claws
1	[5, 20]	[7, 12]
2	[7, 20]	[15, 20]
3	[5, 10]	[10, 20]
4	[10, 40]	[15, 30]
5	[6, 20]	[5, 10]
6	[3, 10]	[1, 20]
7	[2, 5]	[1, 4]
8	[2, 4]	[2, 4]

10. A project has four activities (A, B, C, and D) that must be performed sequentially. The probability distributions for the time required to complete each of the activities are as follows:

Activity	Activity Time (weeks)	Probability
A	5	0.25
	6	0.35
	7	0.25
	8	0.15
B	3	0.20
	5	0.55
	7	0.25
C	10	0.10
	12	0.25
	14	0.40
	16	0.20
	18	0.05
D	8	0.60
	10	0.40

a. Construct a spreadsheet simulation model to estimate the average length of the project and the standard deviation of the project length.

b. What is the estimated probability that the project will be completed in 35 weeks or less?

11. In preparing for the upcoming holiday season, Fresh Toy Company (FTC) designed a new doll called The Dougie that teaches children how to dance. The fixed cost to produce the doll is $100,000. The variable cost, which includes material, labor, and shipping costs, is $34 per doll. During the holiday selling season, FTC will sell the dolls for $42 each. If FTC overproduces the dolls, the excess dolls will be sold in January through a distributor who has agreed to pay FTC $10 per doll. Demand for new toys during the holiday selling season is extremely uncertain. Forecasts are for expected sales of 60,000 dolls with a

standard deviation of 15,000. The normal probability distribution is assumed to be a good description of the demand. FTC has tentatively decided to produce 60,000 units (the same as average demand), but it wants to conduct an analysis regarding this production quantity before finalizing the decision.

a. Create a what-if spreadsheet model using a formula that relate the values of production quantity, demand, sales, revenue from sales, amount of surplus, revenue from sales of surplus, total cost, and net profit. What is the profit corresponding to average demand (60,000 units)?
b. Modeling demand as a normal random variable with a mean of 60,000 and a standard deviation of 15,000, simulate the sales of the Dougie doll using a production quantity of 60,000 units. What is the estimate of the average profit associated with the production quantity of 60,000 dolls? How does this compare to the profit corresponding to the average demand (as computed in part (a))?
c. Before making a final decision on the production quantity, management wants an analysis of a more aggressive 70,000-unit production quantity and a more conservative 50,000-unit production quantity. Run your simulation with these two production quantities. What is the mean profit associated with each?
d. In addition to mean profit, what other factors should FTC consider in determining a production quantity? Compare the three production quantities (50,000, 60,000, and 70,000) using all these factors. What trade-offs occur? What is your recommendation?

12. South Central Airlines (SCA) operates a commuter flight between Atlanta and Charlotte. The regional jet holds 50 passengers, and currently SCA only books up to 50 reservations. Past data show that SCA always sells all 50 reservations, but on average, two passengers do not show up for the flight. As a result, with 50 reservations the flight is often being flown with empty seats. To capture additional profit, SCA is considering an overbooking strategy in which they would accept 52 reservations even though the airplane holds only 50 passengers. SCA believes that it will be able to always book all 52 reservations. The probability distribution for the number of passengers showing up when 52 reservations are accepted is estimated as follows:

Passengers Showing Up	Probability
48	0.05
49	0.25
50	0.50
51	0.15
52	0.05

SCA receives a marginal profit of $100 for each passenger who books a reservation (regardless whether they show up or not). The airline will also incur a cost for any passenger denied seating on the flight. This cost covers added expenses of rescheduling the passenger as well as loss of goodwill, estimated to be $150 per passenger. Develop a spreadsheet simulation model for this overbooking system and simulate the number of passengers that show up for a flight.

a. What is the average net profit for each flight with the overbooking strategy?
b. What is the probability that the net profit with the overbooking strategy will be less than the net profit without overbooking (50*$100 = $5000)?
c. Explain how your simulation model could be used to evaluate other overbooking levels such as 51, 53, and 54 and for recommending a best overbooking strategy.

13. The wedding date for a couple is quickly approaching, and the wedding planner must provide the caterer an estimate of how many people will attend the reception so that the appropriate quantity of food is prepared for the buffet. The following table contains

information on the number of RSVP guests for the 145 invitations. Unfortunately, the number of guests does not always correspond to the number of RSVPed guests.

Based on her experience, the wedding planner knows it is extremely rare for guests to attend a wedding if they notified that they will not be attending. Therefore, the wedding planner will assume that no one from these 50 invitations will attend. The wedding planner estimates that the each of the 25 guests planning to come solo has a 75% chance of attending alone, a 20% chance of not attending, and a 5% chance of bringing a companion. For each of the 60 RSVPs who plan to bring a companion, there is a 90% chance that she or he will attend with a companion, a 5% chance of attending solo, and a 5% chance of not attending at all. For the 10 people who have not responded, the wedding planner assumes that there is an 80% chance that each will not attend, a 15% chance each will attend alone, and a 5% chance each will attend with a companion.

RSVPed Guests	Number of Invitations
0	50
1	25
2	60
No response	10

a. Assist the wedding planner by constructing a spreadsheet simulation model to determine the expected number of guests who will attend the reception.
b. To be accommodating hosts, the couple has instructed the wedding planner to use the Monte Carlo simulation model to determine X, the minimum number of guests for which the caterer should prepare the meal, so that there is at least a 90% chance that the actual attendance is less than or equal to X. What is the best estimate for the value of X?

14. A building contractor is preparing a bid on a new construction project. Two other contractors will be submitting bids for the same project. Based on past bidding practices and the requirements of the project, the bid from Contractor A can be described with a uniform distribution between $600,000 and $800,000, while the bid from Contractor B can be described with a normal distribution with a mean of $700,000 and standard deviation of $50,000.
   a. If the building contractor submits a bid of $750,000, what is the probability that the building contractor will obtain the bid?
   b. The building contractor is also considering bids of $765,000 and $775,000. If the building contract would like to bid such that the probability of winning the bid is about 0.80, what bid would you recommend? Repeat the simulation with bids of $765,000 and $775,000 to justify your recommendation.

15. Strassel Investors buys real estate, develops it, and resells it for a profit. A new property is available, and Bud Strassel, the president and owner of Strassel Investors, believes if he purchases and develops this property it can then be sold for $160,000. The current property owner has asked for bids and stated that the property will be sold for the highest bid in excess of $100,000. Two competitors will be submitting bids for the property. Strassel does not know what the competitors will bid, but he assumes for planning purposes that the amount bid by each competitor will be uniformly distributed between $100,000 and $150,000.
   a. Develop a worksheet that can be used to simulate the bids made by the two competitors. Strassel is considering a bid of $130,000 for the property. Using a simulation of 1000 trials, what is the estimate of the probability Strassel will be able to obtain the property using a bid of $130,000?

You will need to use native Excel functionality to solve Problems 13, 14, and 15 because the Educational version of ASP has a limit of 100 random variables.

b. How much does Strassel need to bid to be assured of obtaining the property? What is the profit associated with this bid?
c. Use the simulation model to compute the profit for each trial of the simulation run. With maximization of profit as Strassel's objective, use simulation to evaluate Strassel's bid alternatives of $130,000, $140,000, or $150,000. What is the recommended bid, and what is the expected profit?

BurgerDome

16. The Burger Dome is a fast-food restaurant that is currently appraising its customer service. In its current operation, an employee takes a customer's order, tabulates the cost, receives payment from the customer, and then fills the order. Once the customer's order is filled, the employee takes the order of the next customer waiting for service. Assume that time between each customer's arrival is an exponential random variable with a mean of 1.35 minutes. Assume also that the time for the employee to complete the customer's service is an exponential random variable with mean of 1 minute. Use the BurgerDome.xlsx template to complete a simulation model for the waiting line at Burger Dome for a 14-hour work day. Using the summary statistics gathered at the bottom of the spreadsheet model, answer the following questions.
    a. What is the average wait time experienced by a customer?
    b. What is the longest wait time experienced by a customer?
    c. What is the probability that a customer waits more than 2 minutes?
    d. Create a histogram depicting the wait time distribution.
    e. By pressing the F9 key to generate a new set of simulation trials, one can observe the variability in the summary statistics from simulation to simulation. Typically, this variability can be reduced by increasing the number of trials. Why is this approach not appropriate for this problem?
17. One advantage of simulation is that a simulation model can be altered easily to reflect a change in the assumptions. Refer back to the Burger Dome analysis in Problem 16. Assume that the service time is more accurately described by a normal distribution with a mean of 1 minute and a standard deviation of 0.2 minutes. This distribution has less variability than the exponential distribution originally used. What is the impact of this change on the output measures?

BurgerDome TwoServers

18. Refer back to the Burger Dome analysis in Problem 16. Burger Dome wants to consider the effect of hiring a second employee to serve customers (in parallel with the first employee). Use the BurgerDomeTwoServers.xlsx template to complete a simulation model that accounts for the second employee. Hint: The time that a customer begins service will depend on the availability of employees. What is the impact of this change on the output measures?
19. Telephone calls come into an 24-hour airline call center (handling calls worldwide) randomly at the mean rate of 15 calls per hour. The time between calls follows an exponential distribution with a mean of 4 minutes. When the two reservation agents are busy, a telephone message tells the caller that the call is important and to please wait on the line until the next reservation agent becomes available. The service time for each reservation agent is normally distributed with a mean of 4 minutes and a standard deviation of 1 minute. Use a two-server waiting line simulation model to evaluate this waiting line system. Simulate the operation of the call center for 800 customers. Discard the first 100 customers, and collect data over the next 700 customers.
    a. Compute the mean interarrival time and the mean service time. If your simulation model is operating correctly, both of these should have means of approximately 4 minutes.
    b. What is the mean customer waiting time for this system?
    c. Use the =COUNTIF function to determine the number of customers who have to wait for a reservation agent. What percentage of the customers have to wait?

20. Blackjack, or 21, is a popular casino game that begins with each player and the dealer being dealt two cards. The value of each hand is determined by the point total of the cards in the hand. Face cards and 10s count 10 points, aces can be counted as either 1 or 11 points, and all other cards count at their face value. For instance, the value of a hand consisting of a jack and an 8 is 18; the value of a hand consisting of an ace and a two is either 3 or 13, depending on whether player counts the ace as 1 or 11 points. The goal is to obtain a hand with a value as close as possible to 21 without exceeding 21. After the initial deal, each player and the dealer may draw additional cards (called "taking a hit") in order to improve her or his hand. If a player or the dealer takes a hit and the value of the hand exceeds 21, that person "goes broke" and loses. The dealer's advantage is that each player must decide whether to take a hit before the dealer decides whether to take a hit. If a player takes a hit and goes over 21, the player loses even if the dealer later takes a hit and goes over 21. For this reason, players will often decide not to take a hit when the value of their hand is 12 or greater.

    The dealer's hand is dealt with one card up (face showing) and one card down (face hidden). The player then decides whether to take a hit based on knowledge of the dealer's up card.

    a. A gambling professional determined that when the dealer's up card is a 6, the following probabilities describe the ending value of the dealer's hand:

Value of Hand	17	18	19	20	21	Broke
Probability	0.1654	0.1063	0.1063	0.1017	0.0972	0.4231

    Set up intervals of random numbers that can be used to simulate the ending value of the dealer's hand when the dealer has a 6 as the up card.

    b. Suppose you are playing blackjack and your hand has a value of 16 for the two cards initially dealt. If you decide to take a hit, the following cards will improve your hand: ace, 2, 3, 4, and 5. Any card with a point count greater than 5 will result in you going broke. Assume that if you have a hand with a value of 16 and decide to take a hit, the following probabilities describe the ending value of your hand:

Value of Hand	17	18	19	20	21	Broke
Probability	0.0769	0.0769	0.0769	0.0769	0.0769	0.6155

    c. Set up intervals of random numbers that can be used to simulate the ending value of your hand after taking a hit with a value of 16.

    d. Use the results of parts (a) and (b) to simulate the result of 20 blackjack hands when the dealer has a 6 up and the player chooses to take a hit with a hand that has a value of 16. What is the probability of the dealer winning, a push (a tie), and the player winning, respectively?

    e. If the player has a hand with a value of 16 and doesn't take a hit, the only way the player can win is if the dealer goes broke. How many of the hands in part (b) result in the player winning without taking a hit? On the basis of this result and the results in part (d), would you recommend the player take a hit if the player has a hand with a value of 16 and the dealer has a 6 up?

Case Problem 1 Four Corners

What will your portfolio be worth in 10 years? In 20 years? When can you stop working? The Human Resources Department at Four Corners Corporation was asked to develop a financial planning model that would help employees address these questions. Tom Gifford was asked to lead this effort and decided to begin by developing a financial plan for himself. Tom is 40 years old, has a degree in business, and earns an annual salary of $85,000. Through contributions to his company's retirement program and the receipt of a small inheritance, Tom has accumulated a portfolio valued at $50,000. Tom plans to work 20 more years and hopes to accumulate a portfolio valued at $1,000,000. Can he do it?

Tom began with a few assumptions about his future salary, his new investment contributions, and his portfolio growth rate. He assumed a 5% annual salary growth rate and plans to make new investment contributions at 6% of his salary. After some research on historical stock market performance, Tom decided that a 10% annual portfolio growth rate was reasonable. Using these assumptions, Tom developed the Excel worksheet shown in the figure below. The worksheet provides a financial projection for the next five years. In computing the portfolio earnings for a given year, Tom assumed that his new investment contribution would occur evenly throughout the year, and thus half of the new investment could be included in the computation of the portfolio earnings for the year. From the figure below, we see that at age 45, Tom is projected to have a portfolio valued at $116,321.

Tom's plan was to use this worksheet as a template to develop financial plans for the company's employees. The data in the spreadsheet would be tailored for each employee, and rows would be added to the worksheet to reflect the employee's planning horizon. After adding another 15 rows to the worksheet, Tom found that he could expect to have a portfolio of $772,722 after 20 years. Tom then took his results to show his boss, Kate Krystkowiak.

Although Kate was pleased with Tom's progress, she voiced several criticisms. One of the criticisms was the assumption of a constant annual salary growth rate. She noted that most employees experience some variation in the annual salary growth rate from year to year. In addition, she pointed out that the constant annual portfolio growth rate was unrealistic and that the actual growth rate would vary considerably from year to year. She further suggested that a simulation model for the portfolio projection might allow Tom to account for the random variability in the salary growth rate and the portfolio growth rate.

After some research, Tom and Kate decided to assume that the annual salary growth rate would vary from 0% to 5% and that a uniform probability distribution would provide a realistic approximation. Four Corners's accountants suggested that the annual portfolio growth rate could be approximated by a normal probability distribution with a mean of 10% and a standard deviation of 5%. With this information, Tom set off to redesign his spreadsheet so that it could be used by the company's employees for financial planning.

FourCorners

	A	B	C	D	E	F	G
1	**Four Corners**						
2							
3	Age	40					
4	Current Salary	$85,000					
5	Current Portfolio	$50,000					
6	Annual Investment Rate	6%					
7	Salary Growth Rate	5%					
8	Portfolio Growth Rate	10%					
9							
10	Year	Beginning Balance	Salary	New Investment	Earnings	Ending Balance	Age
11	1	$50,000	$85,000	$5,100	$5,255	$60,355	41
12	2	$60,355	$89,250	$5,355	$6,303	$72,013	42
13	3	$72,013	$93,713	$5,623	$7,482	$85,118	43
14	4	$85,118	$98,398	$5,904	$8,807	$99,829	44
15	5	$99,829	$103,318	$6,199	$10,293	$116,321	45
16							

Play the role of Tom Gifford and develop a simulation model for financial planning. Write a report for Tom's boss and, at a minimum, include the following:

1. Without considering the random variability, extend the current worksheet to 20 years. Confirm that by using the constant annual salary growth rate and the constant annual portfolio growth rate, Tom can expect to have a 20-year portfolio of $772,722. What would Tom's annual investment rate have to increase to in order for his portfolio to reach a 20-year, $1,000,000 goal? Hint: Use Goal Seek.
2. Redesign the spreadsheet model to incorporate the random variability of the annual salary growth rate and the annual portfolio growth rate into a simulation model. Assume that Tom is willing to use the annual investment rate that predicted a 20-year, $1,000,000 portfolio in part 1. Show how to simulate Tom's 20-year financial plan. Use results from the simulation model to comment on the uncertainty associated with Tom reaching the 20-year, $1,000,000 goal.
3. What recommendations do you have for employees with a current profile similar to Tom's after seeing the impact of the uncertainty in the annual salary growth rate and the annual portfolio growth rate?
4. Assume that Tom is willing to consider working 25 more years instead of 20 years. What is your assessment of this strategy if Tom's goal is to have a portfolio worth $1,000,000?
5. Discuss how the financial planning model developed for Tom Gifford can be used as a template to develop a financial plan for any of the company's employees.

For a review of Goal Seek, refer to Appendix A.

Case Problem 2 Harbor Dunes Golf Course

Harbor Dunes Golf Course was recently honored as one of the top public golf courses in South Carolina. The course, situated on land that was once a rice plantation, offers some of the best views of saltwater marshes available in the Carolinas. Harbor Dunes targets the upper end of the golf market, and in the peak spring golfing season it charges green fees of $160 per person and golf cart fees of $20 per person.

Harbor Dunes accepts reservations for tee times for groups of four players (foursomes) every nine minutes between 7:30 A.M. and 1:21 P.M. Two foursomes start at the same time: one on the front nine and one on the back nine of the course, with a new pair of foursomes teeing off every nine minutes. With the last tee time of the day set at 1:21 P.M. to ensure all players can complete 18 holes before dusk, Harbor Dunes can sell a maximum of 20 afternoon tee times.

Last year, Harbor Dunes was able to sell every morning tee time available for every day of the spring golf season. The same result is anticipated for the coming year. Afternoon tee times, however, are generally more difficult to sell. An analysis of the sales data for last year enabled Harbor Dunes to develop the probability distribution of sales for the afternoon tee times as shown in Table 16.6. For the season, Harbor Dunes averaged selling approximately 14 of the 20 available afternoon tee times. The average income from afternoon green fees and cart fees has been $10,240. However, the average of six unused tee times per day resulted in lost revenue.

In an effort to increase the sale of afternoon tee times, Harbor Dunes is considering an idea popular at other golf courses. These courses offer foursomes that play in the morning the option to play another round of golf in the afternoon by paying a reduced fee for the afternoon round. Harbor Dunes is considering two replay options: (1) a green fee of $25 per player plus a cart fee of $20 per player; (2) a green fee of $50 per player plus a

TABLE 16.6 PROBABILITY DISTRIBUTION OF SALES FOR THE AFTERNOON TEE TIMES

Number of Tee Times Sold	Probability
8	0.01
9	0.04
10	0.06
11	0.08
12	0.10
13	0.11
14	0.12
15	0.15
16	0.10
17	0.09
18	0.07
19	0.05
20	0.02

cart fee of $20 per player. For option 1, each foursome will generate additional revenues of $180; for option 2, each foursome will generate additional revenues of $280. The decision as to which option is best depends upon the number of groups that are induced to play a second round by each replay offer. Working with a consultant who has expertise in statistics and the golf industry, Harbor Dunes developed probability distributions for the number of foursomes requesting a replay for each of the two options. These probability distributions are shown in Table 16.7.

In offering these replay options, Harbor Dunes's first priority will be to sell full-price afternoon advance reservations. If the demand for replay tee times exceeds the number of afternoon tee times available, Harbor Dunes will post a notice that the course is full. In this case, any excess replay requests will not be accepted.

TABLE 16.7 PROBABILITY DISTRIBUTIONS FOR THE NUMBER OF GROUPS REQUESTING A REPLAY

Option 1: $25 per Person + Cart Fee		Option 2: $50 per Person + Cart Fee	
Number of Foursomes Requesting a Replay	Probability	Number of Foursomes Requesting a Replay	Probability
0	0.01	0	0.06
1	0.03	1	0.09
2	0.05	2	0.12
3	0.05	3	0.17
4	0.11	4	0.20
5	0.15	5	0.13
6	0.17	6	0.11
7	0.15	7	0.07
8	0.13	8	0.05
9	0.09		
10	0.06		

Managerial Report

Develop simulation models for both replay options using Analytic Solver Platform. Run each simulation for 10,000 trials. Prepare a report that will help management of Harbor Dunes Golf Course decide which replay option to implement for the upcoming spring golf season. In preparing your report, be sure to include the following:

1. Statistical summaries of the revenue expected under each replay option
2. Your recommendation as to the best replay option
3. Assuming a 90-day spring golf season, an estimate of the added revenue using your recommendation
4. Any other recommendations you have that might improve the income for Harbor Dunes

Case Problem 3 County Beverage Drive-Thru

County Beverage Drive-Thru, Inc., operates a chain of beverage supply stores in northern Illinois. Each store has a single service lane; cars enter at one end of the store and exit at the other end. Customers pick up soft drinks, beer, snacks, and party supplies without getting out of their cars. When a new customer arrives at the store, the customer waits until the preceding customer's order is complete and then drives into the store for service.

Typically, three employees operate each store during peak periods; two clerks take and fill orders, and a third clerk serves as cashier and store supervisor. County Beverage is considering a revised store design in which computerized order-taking and payment are integrated with specialized warehousing equipment. Management hopes that the new design will permit operating each store with one clerk. To determine whether the new design is beneficial, management decided to build a new store using the revised design.

County Beverage's new store will be located near a major shopping center. Based on experience at other locations, management believes that during the peak late afternoon and evening hours, the time between arrivals will follow an exponential probability distribution with a mean of six minutes. These peak hours are the most critical time period for the company; most of their profit is generated during these peak hours.

An extensive study of times required to fill orders with a single clerk led to the following probability distribution of service times:

Service Time (minutes)	Probability
2	0.24
3	0.20
4	0.15
5	0.14
6	0.12
7	0.08
8	0.05
9	0.02
Total	1.00

In case customer waiting times prove to be too long with just a single clerk, County Beverage's management is considering two design alternatives: (1) adding a second clerk to assist the first clerk with bagging, taking orders, and related tasks (still serving one car at a time as a single-server system), or (2) enlarging the drive-through area so that two cars can be served at once (operating as a two-server system). With the two-server option, service times are expected to be the same for each server. With the second clerk teaming with the first clerk in the single server design, service times will be reduced and would be given by the probability distribution in the following table.

Service Time (minutes)	Probability
1	0.20
2	0.35
3	0.30
4	0.10
5	0.05
Total	1.00

County Beverage's management would like you to develop a spreadsheet simulation model of the new system and use it to compare the operation of the system using the following three designs:

Design	
A	Single-server system operated by one clerk
B	Single-server system operated by two clerks
C	Two-server system operated by two clerks

Management is especially concerned with how long customers have to wait for service. As a guideline, management requires the average waiting time to be less than 1.5 minutes.

Managerial Report

Prepare a report that discusses the general development of the spreadsheet simulation model, and make any recommendations that you have regarding the best store design and staffing plan for County Beverage. One additional consideration is that the design allowing for a two-server system will cost an additional $10,000 to build.

1. Construct a separate simulation model to evaluate the performance of each design alternative.
2. Execute the simulation for 360 minutes (representing the peak hours of 4 P.M. to 10 P.M). You may assume that the system begins empty at 4 P.M You may want to make more than one run with each alternative. Record relevant summary statistics over the simulation runs and use this information to support your final recommendation.

Appendix 16.1 Probability Distributions for Random Variables

Selecting the appropriate probability distribution to characterize a random variable in a simulation model can be a critical modeling decision. In this appendix, we review several of the distributions from which one can easily generate values with native Excel functionality. For each distribution, the parameters are the values required to completely specify the distribution. The range provides the minimum and maximum values that can be taken by a random variable that follows the given distribution. We also provide a short description of the overall shape and/or common uses of the distribution.

Continuous Probability Distributions

Random variables which can be many possible values (even if these values are discrete) are often modeled with a continuous probability distribution.

Normal Distribution

Parameters: mean (μ), stdev (σ)
Range: $-\infty$ to $+\infty$
Excel command: NORM.INV(RAND(), μ, σ)
Description: The normal distribution is a bell-shaped, symmetric distribution centered at its mean μ. The normal distribution is often a good way to characterize a quantity that is the sum of many independent random variables.
Example: In human resource management, employee performance is often well-represented by a normal distribution. Typically the performance of 68 percent of employees is within one standard deviation of the average performance and the performance of 95 percent of the employees is within two standard deviations. Employees with exceptionally low or high performance are rare.

Beta Distribution

Parameters: shape1 (α), shape2 (β), min (A), max (B)
Range: A to B
Excel command: BETA.INV(RAND(), α, β, A, B)
Description: The beta distribution has a very flexible shape (manipulated by adjusting α and β) over the range between values A and B. The beta distribution is useful in modeling an uncertain quantity that has a known minimum and maximum value.
Example: Setting $A = 0$ and $B = 1$, the beta distribution can be used to describe the likelihood of values for the true proportion of drivers in an age group who would favor one model of car over another.

Exponential Distribution

Parameters: mean (μ)
Range: 0 to $+\infty$
Excel command: LN(RAND())*($-\mu$)
Description: The exponential distribution is characterized by a mean value that is equal to its standard deviation and a long right tail stretching from a mode value of 0.
Example: The time between events, such as customer arrivals or customer defaults on bill payment, are commonly modeled with an exponential distribution. An exponential random variable possesses the "memoryless" property: the probability that there will be 25 or more minutes between customer arrivals if 10 minutes have passed since the last customer arrival is the same as the probability that there will be more than 15 minutes until the next arrival if a customer just arrived. That is, the probability of a customer arrival occurring in the next X minutes does not depend on how long it's been since the last arrival.

As the exponential distribution with mean μ is equivalent to the gamma distribution with parameters alpha = 1 and beta = ($1/\mu$), an exponential random variable can also be generated by GAMMA.INV(RAND(), 1, $1/\mu$).

Uniform Distribution

Parameters: min (a), max (b)
Range: a to b
Excel command: RAND()*($b - a$) + a
Description: The uniform distribution is appropriate when a random variable is equally likely to be any value between a and b. In the case where little is known about a phenomenon besides its minimum and maximum possible values, the uniform distribution can be a safe choice to model an uncertain quantity.
Example: A service technician making a house call may quote a four-hour time window in which he will arrive. If the technician is equally likely to arrive any time during this time window, then the arrival time of the technician in this time window may be described with a uniform distribution.

Discrete Probability Distributions

Random variables which can be only a relatively small number of discrete values are often best modeled with a discrete distribution. The appropriate choice of discrete distribution relies on the specific situation. For discrete distributions, we provide the parameters required to specify the distribution, the possible values taken by a random variable that follows the distribution, and a short description of the distribution and an example of a possible application.

As the Bernoulli distribution with probability of success p is equivalent to the binomial distribution with a single trial and probability of success p, a Bernoulli random variable can also be generated by BINOM.INV(1, p, RAND()).

Bernoulli Distribution

Parameters: prob (p)
Possible values: 0 (event doesn't occur) or 1 (event occurs)
Excel command: IF(RAND() $< p$, 1, 0)
Description: A Bernoulli random variable corresponds to whether or not an event successfully occurs given a probability p of successfully occurring.
Example: Whether or not a particular stock increases in value over a defined length of time is a Bernoulli random variable.

Binomial Distribution

Parameters: trials (n), prob (p)
Possible values: 0, 1, 2, . . . , n
Excel command: BINOM.INV(n, p, RAND())
Description: A binomial random variable corresponds to the number of times an event successfully occurs in n trials, and the probability of a success at each trial is p and independent of whether a success occurs on other trials. Note that for $n = 1$, the binomial is equivalent to the Bernoulli distribution.
Example: In a portfolio of 20 similar stocks, each of which has the same probability of increasing in value of $p = 0.6$, the total number of stocks that increase in value can be described by a binomial distribution with parameters $n = 20$ and $p = 0.6$.

Integer Uniform Distribution

Parameters: lower (l), upper (u)
Possible values: $l, l + 1, l + 2, \ldots, u - 2, u - 1, u$
Excel command: RANDBETWEEN(l, u)
Description: An integer uniform random variable assumes that the integer values between l and u are equally likely.

Example: The number of philanthropy volunteers from a class of 10 students may be an integer uniform variable with values 0, 1, 2, . . . , 10.

Discrete Uniform Distribution

Parameters: set of values $\{v_1, v_2, v_3, \ldots, v_k\}$
Possible values: $v_1, v_2, v_3, \ldots, v_k$
Excel command: CHOOSE(RANDBETWEEN(1, k), $v_1, v_2, \ldots, v_k$)
Description: A discrete uniform random variable is equally likely to be any of the specified set of values $\{v_1, v_2, v_3, \ldots, v_k\}$.
Example: Consider six envelopes containing \$1, \$5, \$10, \$20, \$50, \$100. If the game show reward that a contestant receives is randomly selected from one of these six, then the reward is a discrete uniform random variable with values {1, 5, 10, 20, 50, 100}.

Custom Discrete Distribution

Parameters: set of values $\{v_1, v_2, v_3, \ldots, v_k\}$ and corresponding weights $\{w_1, w_2, w_3, \ldots, w_k\}$ where $\sum_{j=1}^{k} w_j = 1$
Possible values: $v_1, v_2, v_3, \ldots, v_k$
Excel command: Use VLOOKUP with table of values and likelihoods (see direct labor cost in Figure 16.7).
Description: A custom discrete distribution can be used to create a tailored distribution to model a discrete, uncertain quantity. The value of a custom discrete random variable is equal to the value v_i with probability w_i.
Example: Analysis of daily sales for the past 50 days at a car dealership shows that on 2 days no cars were sold, on 5 days one car was sold, on 9 days two cars were sold, on 24 days three cars were sold, on 7 days four cars were sold, and on 3 days five cars were sold. We can estimate the probability distribution of daily sales using the relative frequencies. An estimate of the probability that no cars are sold on a given day is 2/50 = 0.04, an estimate of the probability the one car is sold is 5/50 = 0.10, and so on. Daily sales may then be described by a custom discrete distribution with values of {0, 1, 2, 3, 4, 5} with respective weights of {0.04, 0.10, 0.18, 0.48, 0.14, 0.06}.

Appendix 16.2 Simulation with Analytic Solver Platform

ButlerASP

In Section 16.3 we constructed a spreadsheet simulation model to analyze the inventory policy for the Butler Internet Company. This simulation model was constructed using only native Excel functionality. The use of specialized simulation packages facilitates the construction and analysis of simulation models. In this appendix, we demonstrate how the Analytic Solver Platform (ASP) can be used to execute the Butler simulation model. We will run the simulation for 10,000 trials here.

Formulating a Model in Analytic Solver Platform

The first steps for building an Excel simulation model are very similar whether using native Excel functionality or ASP. As in Section 16.3, we begin by entering the problem data and cell formulas into the top portion of the worksheet. For the Butler model, we must enter the following parameters: gross profit per unit, holding cost per unit, shortage cost per unit, as well as the mean and standard deviation of the normally distributed demand. The controllable input (replenishment level) is entered and cell formula are entered to compute sales, gross profit, holding cost, shortage cost, and net profit.

Instead of constructing a table of simulation trials and manually collecting summary statistics, ASP provides functionality to ease the process of executing simulation trials and analyzing the output. Recall that monthly demand is a random variable in the Butler problem. ASP refers to random variables as uncertain variables. ASP allows you to characterize each cell containing an uncertain variable with a distribution that describes its possible values and the corresponding likelihood of these values.

Generating Values for Butler's Uncertain Demand

We are now ready to define the probability distribution for the demand for Butler's routers.

Step 1. Select cell B7
Step 2. Click the **ANALYTIC SOLVER PLATFORM** tab in the Ribbon
Step 3. Click **Distributions** in the **Simulation Model** group
Select **Common** and click **Normal**
Step 4. When the **$B$7** dialog box appears, in the **Parameters** area enter *E6* in the box to the right of **mean** and *E7* in the box to the right of **stdev** (see Figure 16.17)
Step 5. Click **Save**

Figure 16.18 summarizes the construction of the model at this stage. Observe that ASP has placed the formula =PsiNormal(100,20) in cell B7, and pressing the F9 key causes the spreadsheet to generate a new value for demand from a normal distribution with mean of 100 units and standard deviation of 20 units.

FIGURE 16.17 NORMAL DISTRIBUTION FOR ROUTER DEMAND

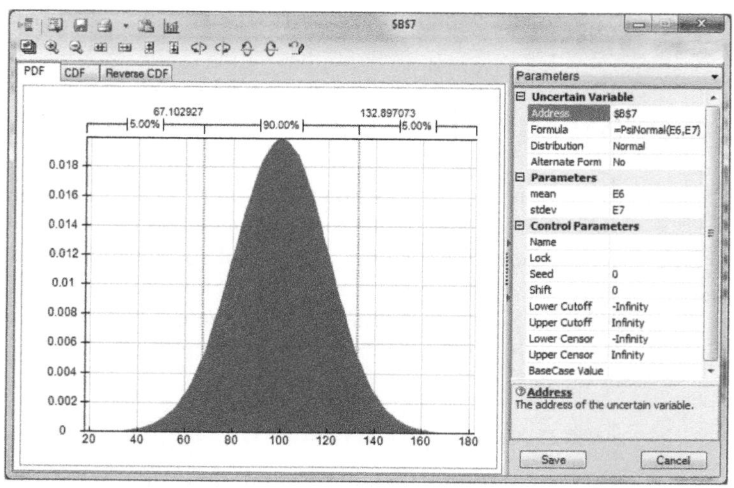

FIGURE 16.18 FORMULA VIEW OF BUTLER SIMULATION MODEL

	A	B	C	D	E
1	**Butler**				
2					
3	**Parameters**				
4	Gross Profit per Unit	50			
5	Holding Cost per Unit	15		**Demand (Normal Distribution)**	
6	Shortage Cost per Unit	30		Mean	100
7	Demand	=PsiNormal(100,20)		Standard Deviation	20
8					
9	**Model**				
10	Replenishment Level (Q)	140			
11	Sales	=MIN(B7,B10)			
12	Gross Profit	=B11*B4			
13	Holding Cost	=IF(B10>B7,(B10-B7)*B5,0)			
14	Shortage Cost	=IF(B7>B10,(B7-B10)*B6,0)			
15	Net Profit	=B12-B13-B14			

Tracking Output for Butler

After defining the distribution for demand, we are ready to track the simulation output. The following steps show this process for cell B16, which is the cell calculating Butler's monthly net profit:

Step 1. Select cell B16
Step 2. Click the **ANALYTIC SOLVER PLATFORM** tab in the Ribbon
Step 3. Click **Distributions** in the **Simulation Model** group
Select **Output**, and click **In Cell**

This procedure appends the formula in cell B15 with "+PsiOutput()" which triggers ASP to record the cell's value for each of the simulation trials. By collecting the value of net profit resulting from each simulation trial, ASP can then create a distribution of net profit.

Increasing the number of trials per simulation reduces the error in estimating the output. Unless the simulation model is extremely complex, it is recommended to use 10,000 trials (the maximum allowed in the educational version of ASP).

Setting Simulation Options

For the Butler simulation, we only need to specify the number of trials.

Step 1. Click the **ANALYTIC SOLVER PLATFORM** tab in the Ribbon
Step 2. Click the **Options** icon in the **Options** group
Step 3. Click the **Simulation** tab. In the **General** area, enter *10000* in the **Trials per Simulation:** box (see Figure 16.19)
Step 4. Click **OK**

FIGURE 16.19 SIMULATION OPTIONS MENU

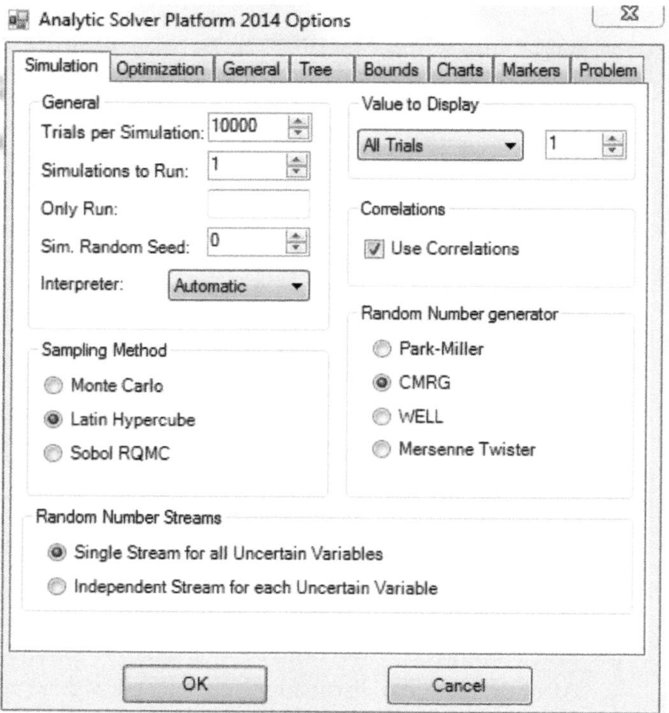

Running the Simulation

For each of the 10,000 simulation trials, ASP automatically repeats three tasks:

1. A value is generated for demand according to the defined probability distributions.
2. A new simulated net profit is computed based on the new value of demand.
3. The new simulated net profit is recorded.

When the interactive simulation in ASP is activated, the spreadsheet will automatically rerun the simulation whenever the spreadsheet is changed or the F9 key is pressed.

The following steps describe how to execute the set of 10,000 simulation trials and to analyze simulation output.

Step 1. Click the **ANALYTIC SOLVER PLATFORM** tab in the Ribbon
Step 2. Click the arrow under **Simulate** from the **Solve Action** group
From the drop-down menu that appears, select **Interactive**

When the run of 10,000 trials is complete, ASP displays the $B$15 dialog box, which shows a frequency distribution of the simulated net profit values obtained during the simulation run (see Figure 16.20). The chart for $B$15 in Figure 16.20 displays the distribution of Butler's monthly net profit over the 10,000 simulation trials (months). We see that the mean net profit in this simulation is $4,383.81. The worst result obtained in these 10,000 trials is a loss of $1,134.60, and the best result is a profit of $6,999.96. These values are similar to the results obtained in Section 16.3. The differences result from the different random numbers used in the two simulations. If you perform another simulation, your results will differ slightly.

Note that the minimum and maximum values of net profit will tend to be more extreme as the number of simulation trials increases.

FIGURE 16.20 BUTLER SIMULATION OUTPUT

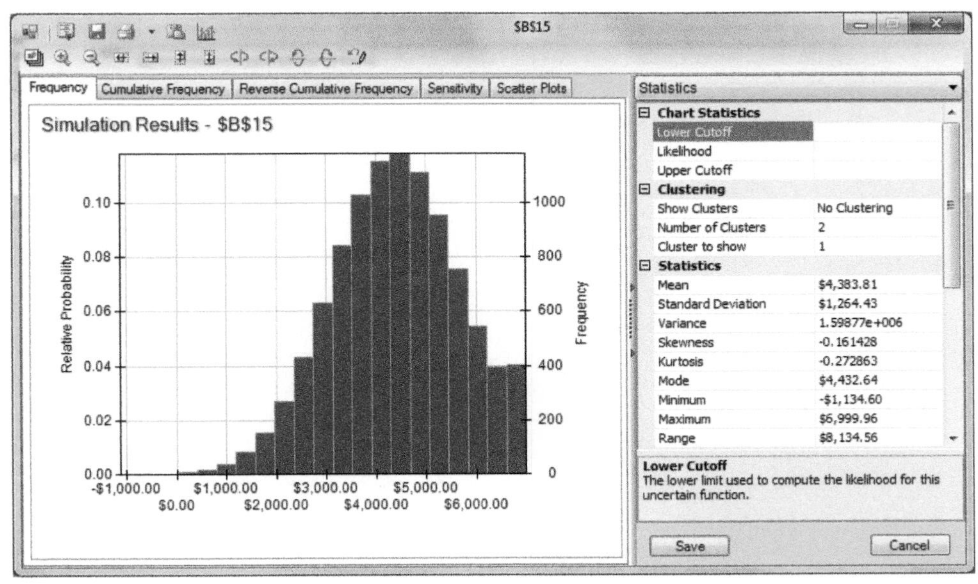

APPENDIXES

Appendix A Building Spreadsheet Models

The purpose of this appendix is twofold. First, we provide an overview of Excel and discuss the basic operations needed to work with Excel workbooks and worksheets. Second, we provide an introduction to building mathematical models using Excel, including a discussion of how to find and use particular Excel functions, how to design and build good spreadsheet models, and how to ensure that these models are free of errors.

Overview of Microsoft Excel

A workbook is a file containing one or more worksheets.

When using Excel for modeling, the data and the model are displayed in workbooks, each of which contains a series of worksheets. Figure A.1 shows the layout of a blank workbook created each time Excel is opened. The workbook is named Book1 and contains a worksheet named Sheet1. Note that cell A1 is initially selected.

The wide bar located across the top of the workbook is referred to as the Ribbon. Tabs, located at the top of the Ribbon, provide quick access to groups of related commands. There are eight tabs: Home, Insert, Page Layout, Formulas, Data, Review, View, and Add-Ins. Each tab contains several groups of related commands. Note that the HOME tab is selected when Excel is opened. The seven groups associated with the HOME tab are displayed in Figure A.2. Under the HOME tab there are seven groups of related commands: Clipboard, Font, Alignment, Number, Styles, Cells, and Editing. Commands are arranged within each group. For example, to change selected text to boldface, click the HOME tab and click the Bold button **B** in the Font group.

FIGURE A.1 BLANK WORKBOOK CREATED WHEN EXCEL IS STARTED

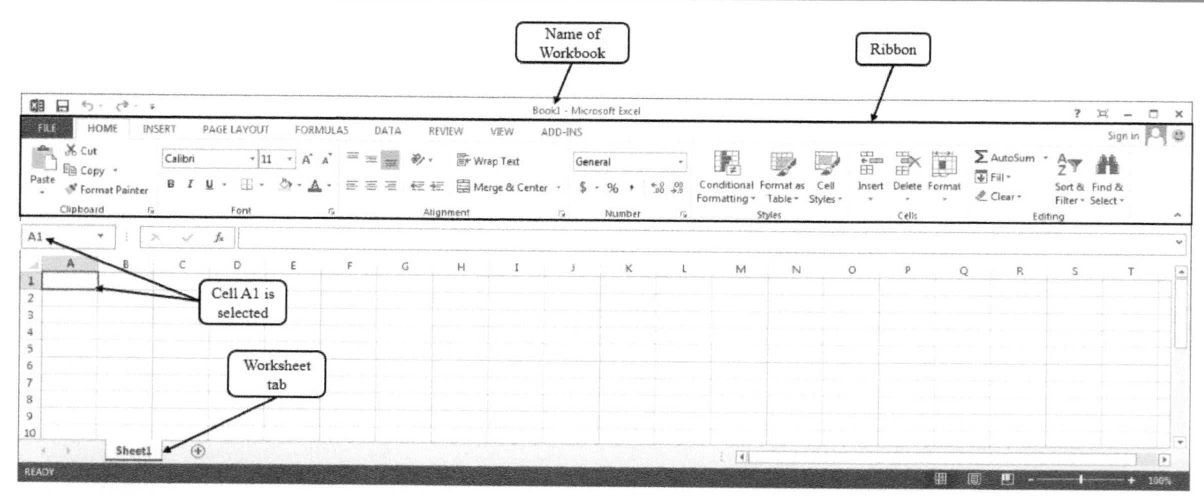

FIGURE A.2 PORTION OF THE HOME TAB

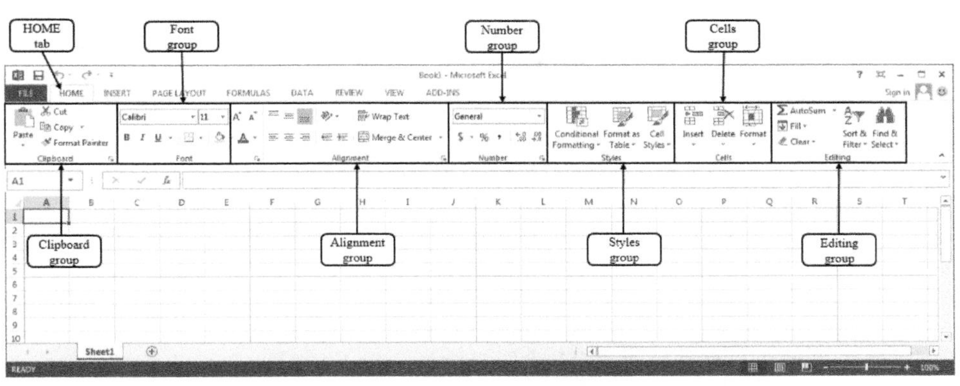

FIGURE A.3 EXCEL FILE TAB, QUICK ACCESS TOOLBAR, AND FORMULA BAR

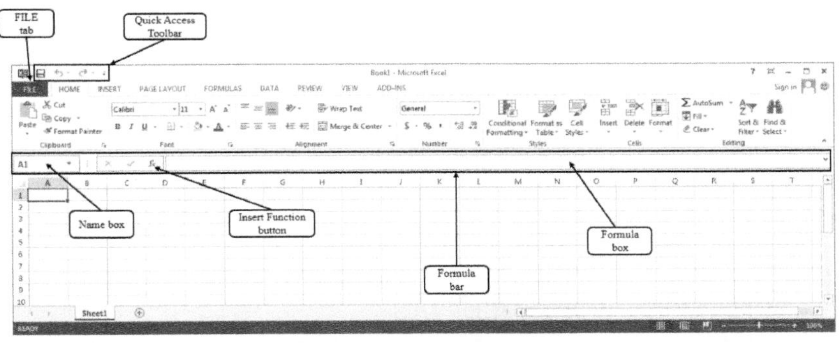

Figure A.3 illustrates the location of the FILE tab, the Quick Access Toolbar, and the Formula Bar. When you click the FILE tab, Excel provides a list of workbook options such as opening, saving, and printing (worksheets). The Quick Access Toolbar allows you to quickly access these workbook options. For instance, the Quick Access Toolbar shown in Figure A.3 includes a Save button that can be used to save files without having to first click the FILE tab. To add or remove features on the Quick Access Toolbar click the Customize Quick Access Toolbar button on the Quick Access Toolbar.

The Formula Bar contains a Name box, the Insert Function button *fx*, and a Formula box. In Figure A.3, "A1" appears in the Name box because cell A1 is selected. You can select any other cell in the worksheet by using the mouse to move the cursor to another cell and clicking or by typing the new cell location in the name box and pressing the enter key. The Formula box is used to display the formula in the currently selected cell.

For instance, if you had entered =A1+A2 into cell A3, whenever you select cell A3, the formula =A1+A2 will be shown in the Formula box. This feature makes it very easy to see and edit a formula in a particular cell. The Insert Function button allows you to quickly access all of the functions available in Excel. Later, we show how to find and use a particular function.

Basic Workbook Operations

Figure A.4 illustrates the worksheet options that can be performed after right clicking on a worksheet tab. For instance, to change the name of the current worksheet from "Sheet1" to "NowlinModel," right click the worksheet tab named "Sheet1" and select the Rename option. The current worksheet name (Sheet1) will be highlighted. Then, simply type the new name (NowlinModel) and press the Enter key to rename the worksheet.

Suppose that you wanted to create a copy of "Sheet 1." After right clicking the tab named "Sheet1," select the Move or Copy option. When the Move or Copy dialog box appears, select Create a Copy and click OK. The name of the copied worksheet will appear as "Sheet1 (2)." You can then rename it, if desired.

To add a worksheet to the workbook, right click any worksheet tab and select the Insert option; when the Insert dialog box appears, select Worksheet and click OK. An additional blank worksheet titled Sheet2 will appear in the workbook. You can also insert a new worksheet by clicking the Insert Worksheet tab button ⊕ that appears to the right of the last worksheet tab displayed. Worksheets can be deleted by right clicking the worksheet tab and choosing Delete. After clicking Delete, a window will appear warning you that any data appearing in the worksheet will be lost. Click Delete to confirm that you do want to delete the worksheet. Worksheets can also be moved to other workbooks or a different position in the current workbook by using the Move or Copy option.

FIGURE A.4 WORKSHEET OPTIONS OBTAINED AFTER RIGHT CLICKING ON A WORKSHEET TAB

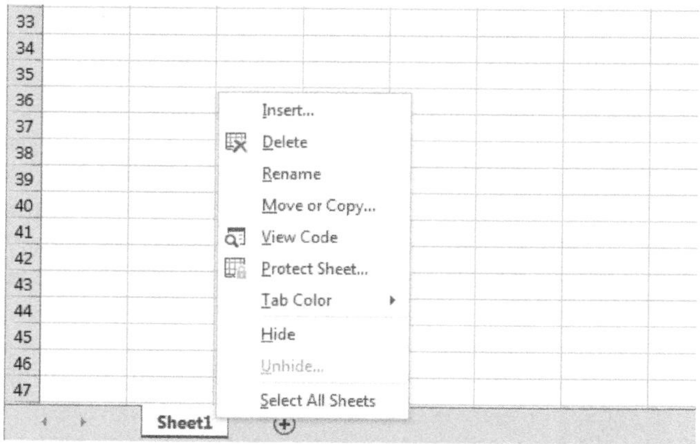

Creating, Saving, and Opening Files

As an illustration of manually entering, saving, and opening a file, we will use the Nowlin Plastics production example from Chapter 1. The objective is to compute the breakeven point for a product that has a fixed cost of $3000, a variable cost per unit of $2, and a selling price per unit of $5. We begin by creating a worksheet containing the problem data.

If you have just opened Excel, a blank workbook containing Sheet1 will be displayed. The Nowlin data can now be entered manually by simply typing the fixed cost of $3000, the variable cost of $2, and the selling price of $5 into one of the worksheets. If Excel is currently running and no blank workbook is displayed, you can create a new blank workbook using the following steps:

Step 1. Click the **FILE** tab
Step 2. Click **New** in the list of options
Step 3. Click **Blank Workbook**

A new workbook will appear.

We will place the data for the Nowlin example in the top portion of Sheet1 of the new workbook. First, we enter the label "Nowlin Plastics" into cell A1. To identify each of the three data values we enter the label "Fixed Cost" into cell A3, the label "Variable Cost Per Unit" into cell A5, and the label "Selling Price Per Unit" into cell A7. Next, we enter the actual cost and price data into the corresponding cells in column B: the value of $3000 in cell B3; the value of $2 in cell B5; and the value of $5 into cell B7. Finally, we will change the name of the worksheet from "Sheet1" to "NowlinModel" using the procedure described previously. Figure A.5 shows a portion of the worksheet we have just developed.

Before we begin the development of the model portion of the worksheet, we recommend that you first save the current file; this will prevent you from having to reenter the

FIGURE A.5 NOWLIN PLASTICS DATA

	A	B
1	**Nowlin Plastics**	
2		
3	**Fixed Cost**	$3,000
4		
5	**Variable Cost Per Unit**	$2
6		
7	**Selling Price Per Unit**	$5
8		
9		
10		
11		
12		
13		
14		
15		
16		
17		
18		

data in case something happens that causes Excel to close. To save the workbook using the filename "Nowlin," we perform the following steps:

Step 3 is only necessary for Excel 2013. In previous versions of Excel you may skip to Step 4.

Step 1. Click the **FILE** tab on the Ribbon
Step 2. Click **Save** in the list of options
Step 3. Select **Computer** under **Save As** and click **Browse**
Step 4. When the **Save As** dialog box appears:
Select the location where you want to save the file
Enter the file name *Nowlin* in the **File name** box
Click **Save**

Excel's Save command is designed to save the file as an Excel workbook. As you work with and build models in Excel, you should follow the practice of periodically saving the file so you will not lose any work. Simply follow the procedure described above, using the Save command.

*Keyboard shortcut: To save the file, press **CTRL S**.*

Sometimes you may want to create a copy of an existing file. For instance, suppose you change one or more of the data values and would like to save the modified file using the filename "NowlinMod." The following steps show how to save the modified workbook using filename "NowlinMod."

Step 1. Click the **FILE** tab in the Ribbon
Step 2. Click **Save As** in the list of options
Step 3. Select **Computer** under **Save As** and click **Browse**
Step 4. When the **Save As** dialog box appears:
Select the location where you want to save the file
Type the file name *NowlinMod* in the **File name** box
Click **Save**

Once the NowlinMod workbook has been saved, you can continue to work with the file to perform whatever type of analysis is appropriate. When you are finished working with the file, simply click the close window button × located at the top right-hand corner of the Ribbon.

You can easily access a saved file at another point in time. For example, the following steps show how to open the previously saved Nowlin workbook.

Step 3 is only necessary in Excel 2013. The filename Nowlin *may also appear under the **Recent Workbooks** list in Excel to allow you to open it directly without navigating to where you saved the file.*

Step 1. Click the **FILE** tab in the Ribbon
Step 2. Click **Open** in the list of options
Step 3. Select **Computer** under **Open** and click **Browse**
Step 4. When the **Open** dialog box appears:
Find the location where you previously saved the *Nowlin* file
Click on the filename **Nowlin** so that it appears in the **File name** box
Click **Open**

The procedures we showed for saving or opening a workbook begin by clicking on the FILE tab to access the Save and Open commands. Once you have used Excel for a while, you will probably find it more convenient to add these commands to the Quick Access Toolbar.

Cells, References, and Formulas in Excel

Assume that the Nowlin workbook is open again and that we would like to develop a model that can be used to compute the profit or loss associated with a given production volume. We will use the bottom portion of the worksheet shown in Figure A.5 to develop the model. The model will contain formulas that *refer to the location of the data cells* in the upper section of the worksheet. By putting the location of the data cells in the formula, we will build a model that can be easily updated with new data. This will be discussed in more detail later in this appendix in the section Principles for Building Good Spreadsheet Models.

We enter the label "Model" into cell A10 to provide a visual reminder that the bottom portion of this worksheet will contain the model. Next, we enter the labels "Production Volume" into cell A12, "Total Cost" into cell A14, "Total Revenue" into cell A16, and "Total Profit (Loss)" into cell A18. Cell B12 is used to contain a value for the production volume. We will now enter formulas into cells B14, B16, and B18 that use the production volume in cell B12 to compute the values for total cost, total revenue, and total profit or loss.

*To display all formulas in the cells of a worksheet, hold down the **CTRL** key and then press the ` key.*

Total cost is the sum of the fixed cost (cell B3) and the total variable cost. The total variable cost is the product of the variable cost per unit (cell B5) and production volume (cell B12). Thus, the formula for total variable cost is B5*B12 and to compute the value of total cost, we enter the formula =B3+B5*B12 into cell B14. Next, assuming we are able to sell all that we produce, total revenue is the product of the selling price per unit (cell B7) and the number of units produced (cell B12), which we enter in cell B16 as the formula =B7*B12. Finally, the total profit or loss is the difference between the total revenue (cell B16) and the total cost (cell B14). Thus, in cell B18 we enter the formula =B16-B14. Figure A.6 shows a portion of the formula worksheet just described.

We can now compute the total profit or loss for a particular production volume by entering a value for the production volume into cell B12. Figure A.7 shows the results after entering a value of 800 into cell B12. We see that a production volume of 800 units results in a total cost of $4600, a total revenue of $4000, and a loss of $600.

FIGURE A.6 NOWLIN PLASTICS DATA AND MODEL

	A	B
1	**Nowlin Plastics**	
2		
3	**Fixed Cost**	3000
4		
5	**Variable Cost Per Unit**	2
6		
7	**Selling Price Per Unit**	5
8		
9		
10	**Model**	
11		
12	**Production Volume**	
13		
14	**Total Cost**	=B3+B5*B12
15		
16	**Total Revenue**	=B7*B12
17		
18	**Total Profit (Loss)**	=B16-B14

FIGURE A.7 NOWLIN PLASTICS RESULTS

	A	B
1	**Nowlin Plastics**	
2		
3	**Fixed Cost**	$3,000
4		
5	**Variable Cost Per Unit**	$2
6		
7	**Selling Price Per Unit**	$5
8		
9		
10	**Model**	
11		
12	**Production Volume**	800
13		
14	**Total Cost**	$4,600
15		
16	**Total Revenue**	$4,000
17		
18	**Total Profit (Loss)**	−$600

What-If Analysis

Excel offers a number of tools to facilitate what-if analysis. In this section we introduce two such tools, Data Tables and Goal Seek. Both of these tools are designed to rid the user of the tedious manual trial-and-error approach to analysis. Let us see how these two tools can help us analyze Nowlin's breakeven decision as discussed in Section 1.4.

Data Tables

An Excel **Data Table** quantifies the impact of changing the value of a specific input on an output of interest. Excel can generate either a **one-way data table**, which summarizes a single input's impact on the output, or a **two-way data table**, which summarizes two inputs' impact on the output.

Let us consider how profit changes as the quantity of Vipers produced changes. A one-way data table changing the production volume and reporting total profit (or loss) would be very useful. We will use the previously developed Nowlin spreadsheet for this analysis.

The first step in creating a one-way data table is to construct a sorted list of the values you would like to consider for the input. Let us investigate the production volume over a range from 0 to 1600 in increments of 100 units. Figure A.8 shows we have entered these data in cells D5 through D21, with a column label in D4. This column of data is the set of values that Excel will use as inputs for production volume. Since the output of interest is profit (or loss) (located in cell B18), we have entered the formula =B18 in cell E4. In general, set the cell to the right of the label to the cell location of the output

FIGURE A.8 THE INPUT FOR CONSTRUCTING A ONE-WAY DATA TABLE FOR NOWLIN PLASTICS

	A	B	C	D	E	F	G	H
1	**Nowlin Plastics**							
2								
3	**Fixed Cost**	$3,000						
4				Production Volume	-$600			
5	**Variable Cost Per Unit**	$2		0				
6				100				
7	**Selling Price Per Unit**	$5		200				
8				300				
9				400				
10	**Model**			500				
11				600				
12	**Production Volume**	800		700				
13				800				
14	**Total Cost**	$4,600		900				
15				1000				
16	**Total Revenue**	$4,000		1100				
17				1200				
18	**Total Profit (Loss)**	-$600		1300				
19				1400				
20				1500				
21				1600				

Data Table
Row input cell:
Column input cell: $B$12
OK Cancel

variable of interest. Once the basic structure is in place, we invoke the Data Table tool using the following steps:

*Entering B12 in the **Column input cell**: box indicates that the column of data corresponds to different values of the input located in cell B12.*

Step 1. Select cells D4:E21
Step 2. Click the **DATA** tab in the Ribbon
Step 3. Click **What-If Analysis** in the **Data Tools** group, and select **Data Table**
Step 4. When the **Data Table** dialog box appears, enter *B12* in the **Column input cell:** box
Click **OK**

As shown in Figure A.9, the table will be populated with profit (or loss) for each production volume in the table. For example, when production volume = 1200, profit = $600 and when production = 500, profit = −$1,500. We see that for a production volume of 1000 units, profit = 0. Hence, 1000 units is the breakeven volume. If Nowlin produces more than 1000 units, it will earn a profit; if Nowlin produces fewer than 1000 units, it will suffer a loss.

Suppose Nowlin would like to better understand how the breakeven production volume changes as selling price changes. A two-way data table with rows corresponding to production quantity and columns corresponding to various selling prices would be helpful.

In Figure A.10, we have entered various quantities in cells D5 through D21, as in the one-way table. These correspond to cell B12 in our model. In cells E4 through L4, we have entered selling prices from $3 to $10 in increments of $1. These correspond to B7, the selling price per unit. In cell D4, above the column input values and to the left of the row input values, we have entered the formula =B18, the location of the output of interest, in

FIGURE A.9 RESULTS OF ONE-WAY DATA TABLE FOR NOWLIN PLASTICS

	A	B	C	D	E	F
1	**Nowlin Plastics**					
2						
3	**Fixed Cost**	$3,000				
4				Production Volume	-$600	
5	**Variable Cost Per Unit**	$2		0	-$3,000	
6				100	-$2,700	
7	**Selling Price Per Unit**	$5		200	-$2,400	
8				300	-$2,100	
9				400	-$1,800	
10	**Model**			500	-$1,500	
11				600	-$1,200	
12	**Production Volume**	800		700	-$900	
13				800	-$600	
14	**Total Cost**	$4,600		900	-$300	
15				1000	$0	
16	**Total Revenue**	$4,000		1100	$300	
17				1200	$600	
18	**Total Profit (Loss)**	-$600		1300	$900	
19				1400	$1,200	
20				1500	$1,500	
21				1600	$1,800	

FIGURE A.10 THE INPUT FOR CONSTRUCTING A TWO-WAY DATA TABLE FOR NOWLIN PLASTICS

	A	B	C	D	E	F	G	H	I	J	K	L	M
1	**Nowlin Plastics**												
2													
3	**Fixed Cost**	$3,000											
4				-$600	$3	$4	$5	$6	$7	$8	$9	$10	
5	**Variable Cost Per Unit**	$2		0									
6				100									
7	**Selling Price Per Unit**	$5		200									
8				300									
9				400									
10	**Model**			500									
11				600									
12	**Production Volume**	800		700									
13				800									
14	**Total Cost**	$4,600		900									
15				1000									
16	**Total Revenue**	$4,000		1100									
17				1200									
18	**Total Profit (Loss)**	-$600		1300									
19				1400									
20				1500									
21				1600									
22													

Data Table

Row input cell: $B$7

Column input cell: $B$12

OK Cancel

this case, profit (or loss). Once the table inputs have been entered into the spreadsheet, we perform the following steps to construct the two-way Data Table.

Step 1. Select cells D4:L21
Step 2. Click the **DATA** tab in the Ribbon
Step 3. Click **What-If Analysis** in the **Data Tools** group, and select **Data Table**
Step 4. When the **Data Table** dialog box appears:
Enter *B7* in the **Row input cell:** box
Enter *B12* in the **Column input cell:** box
Click **OK**

Figure A.10 shows the selected cells and the **Data Table** dialog box. The results are shown in Figure A.11.

From this two-way data table, we can make a number of observations about the breakeven production volume for various selling prices. For example, consider a selling price of $3; since losses are smaller at higher production volumes and there is a loss at 1600 units, we know that the breakeven production volume exceeds 1600 units. Likewise, we know the breakeven point for a selling price of $4 is 1500 units ($0 profit there). Similarly, we know the exact breakeven points for selling prices of $5, $7, and $8 are 1000, 600, and 500, respectively. Because of the change in sign from negative to positive (indicating a change from loss to profit), we see that the breakeven production volume for a selling price of $6 is between 700 and 800 units. For a selling price of $9, the breakeven is between 400 and 500 units, and for a selling price of $10 it is between 300 and 400 units. Next we show how to use Excel's Goal Seek tool to find the exact breakeven production volume for these selling prices.

FIGURE A.11 RESULTS OF TWO-WAY DATA TABLE FOR NOWLIN PLASTICS

	A	B	C	D	E	F	G	H	I	J	K	L	M
1	**Nowlin Plastics**												
2													
3	**Fixed Cost**	$3,000											
4				-$600	$3	$4	$5	$6	$7	$8	$9	$10	
5	**Variable Cost Per Unit**	$2		0	-$3,000	-$3,000	-$3,000	-$3,000	-$3,000	-$3,000	-$3,000	-$3,000	
6				100	-$2,900	-$2,800	-$2,700	-$2,600	-$2,500	-$2,400	-$2,300	-$2,200	
7	**Selling Price Per Unit**	$5		200	-$2,800	-$2,600	-$2,400	-$2,200	-$2,000	-$1,800	-$1,600	-$1,400	
8				300	-$2,700	-$2,400	-$2,100	-$1,800	-$1,500	-$1,200	-$900	-$600	
9				400	-$2,600	-$2,200	-$1,800	-$1,400	-$1,000	-$600	-$200	$200	
10	**Model**			500	-$2,500	-$2,000	-$1,500	-$1,000	-$500	$0	$500	$1,000	
11				600	-$2,400	-$1,800	-$1,200	-$600	$0	$600	$1,200	$1,800	
12	**Production Volume**	800		700	-$2,300	-$1,600	-$900	-$200	$500	$1,200	$1,900	$2,600	
13				800	-$2,200	-$1,400	-$600	$200	$1,000	$1,800	$2,600	$3,400	
14	**Total Cost**	$4,600		900	-$2,100	-$1,200	-$300	$600	$1,500	$2,400	$3,300	$4,200	
15				1000	-$2,000	-$1,000	$0	$1,000	$2,000	$3,000	$4,000	$5,000	
16	**Total Revenue**	$4,000		1100	-$1,900	-$800	$300	$1,400	$2,500	$3,600	$4,700	$5,800	
17				1200	-$1,800	-$600	$600	$1,800	$3,000	$4,200	$5,400	$6,600	
18	**Total Profit (Loss)**	-$600		1300	-$1,700	-$400	$900	$2,200	$3,500	$4,800	$6,100	$7,400	
19				1400	-$1,600	-$200	$1,200	$2,600	$4,000	$5,400	$6,800	$8,200	
20				1500	-$1,500	$0	$1,500	$3,000	$4,500	$6,000	$7,500	$9,000	
21				1600	-$1,400	$200	$1,800	$3,400	$5,000	$6,600	$8,200	$9,800	
22													

Goal Seek

Excel's Goal Seek tool allows the user to determine the value of an input cell that will cause the value of a related output cell to equal some specified value (the *goal*). In the case of Nowlin Plastics, suppose we want to know the exact breakeven production volume for a selling price of $6. We know from the two-way data table in Figure A.11 that the breakeven volume for a selling price of $6 is between 700 and 800 units (that is where the profit goes from negative to positive). Somewhere in this range of 700 to 800 units, the profit equals zero, and the production quantity where this occurs is the breakeven point. After setting cell B7 to $6, the following steps show how to use Goal Seek to find the breakeven point for this selling price.

Step 1. Click the **DATA** tab in the Ribbon
Step 2. Click **What-If Analysis** in the **Data Tools** group, and select **Goal Seek**
Step 3. When the **Goal Seek** dialog box appears (Figure A.12):
Enter *B18* in the **Set cell:** box
Enter *0* in the **To value**: box
Enter *B12* in the **By changing cell:** box
Click **OK**
Step 4. When the **Goal Seek Status** dialog box appears, click **OK**

The completed Goal Seek dialog box is shown in Figure A.12.

The results from Goal Seek are shown in Figure A.13. We see that the breakeven point for a selling price of $6 is 750 units.

FIGURE A.12 GOAL SEEK DIALOG BOX FOR NOWLIN PLASTICS

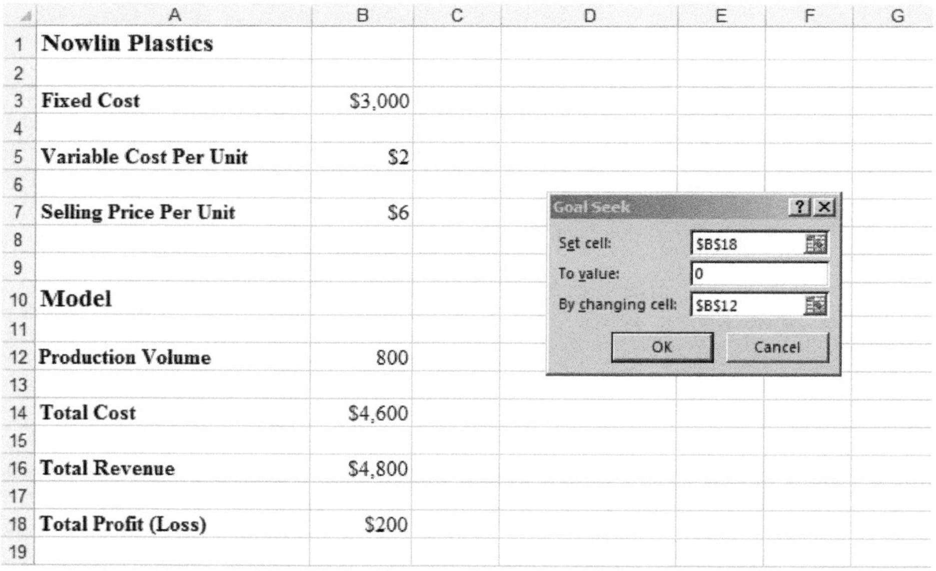

	A	B	C	D	E	F	G
1	**Nowlin Plastics**						
2							
3	**Fixed Cost**	$3,000					
4							
5	**Variable Cost Per Unit**	$2					
6							
7	**Selling Price Per Unit**	$6					
8							
9							
10	**Model**						
11							
12	**Production Volume**	800					
13							
14	**Total Cost**	$4,600					
15							
16	**Total Revenue**	$4,800					
17							
18	**Total Profit (Loss)**	$200					
19							

Goal Seek
Set cell: $B$18
To value: 0
By changing cell: $B$12
OK Cancel

FIGURE A.13 RESULTS FROM GOAL SEEK FOR NOWLIN PLASTICS

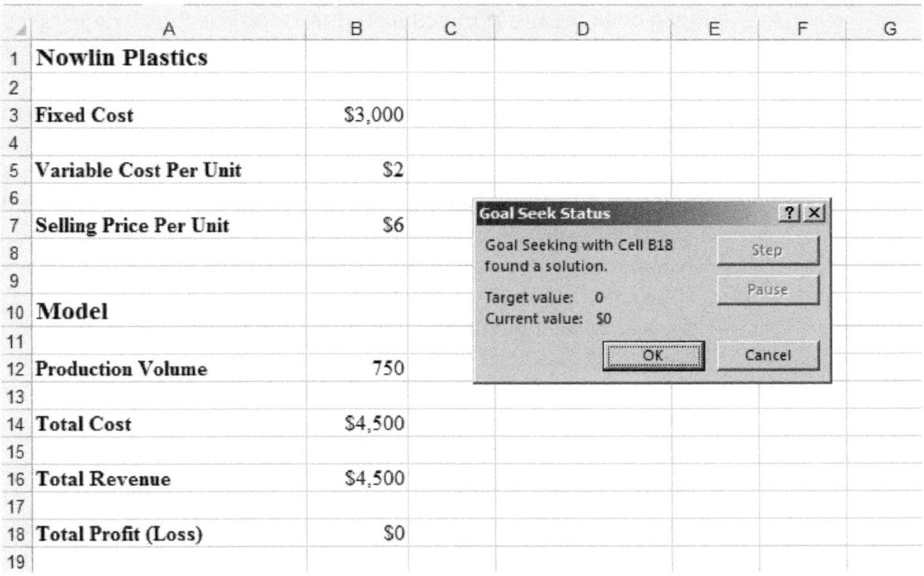

	A	B	C	D	E	F	G
1	**Nowlin Plastics**						
2							
3	**Fixed Cost**	$3,000					
4							
5	**Variable Cost Per Unit**	$2					
6							
7	**Selling Price Per Unit**	$6					
8							
9							
10	**Model**						
11							
12	**Production Volume**	750					
13							
14	**Total Cost**	$4,500					
15							
16	**Total Revenue**	$4,500					
17							
18	**Total Profit (Loss)**	$0					
19							

Goal Seek Status

Goal Seeking with Cell B18 found a solution.

Target value: 0

Current value: $0

Step | Pause | OK | Cancel

NOTES AND COMMENTS

1. We emphasize the location of the reference to the desired output in a one-way versus a two-way Data Table. For a one-way table, the reference to the output cell location is placed in the cell above and to the right of the column of input data so that it is in the cell just to the right of the label of the column of input data. For a two-way table, the reference to the output cell location is placed above the column of input data and to the left of the row input data.
2. Notice that in Figures A.9 and A.11, the tables are formatted as currency. This must be done manually after the table is constructed using the options in the **Number** group under the **HOME** tab in the Ribbon. It also a good idea to label the rows and the columns of the table.
3. For very complex functions, Goal Seek might not converge to a stable solution. Trying several different initial values (the actual value in the cell referenced in the **By changing cell:** box) when invoking Goal Seek may help.

Using Excel Functions

Excel provides a wealth of built-in formulas or functions for developing mathematical models. If we know which function is needed and how to use it, we can simply enter the function into the appropriate worksheet cell. However, if we are not sure which functions are available to accomplish a task or are not sure how to use a particular function, Excel can provide assistance.

Finding the Right Excel Function

To identify the functions available in Excel, click the FORMULAS tab on the Ribbon and then click the Insert Function button in the Function Library group. Alternatively, click the Insert Function button *fx* on the formula bar. Either approach provides the Insert Function dialog box shown in Figure A.14.

The Search for a function box at the top of the Insert Function dialog box enables us to type a brief description for what we want to do. After doing so and clicking Go, Excel will search for and display, in the Select a function box, the functions that may accomplish our task. In many situations, however, we may want to browse through an entire category of functions to see what is available. For this task, the Or select a category box is helpful. It contains a dropdown list of several categories of functions provided by Excel. Figure A.14 shows that we selected the Math & Trig category. As a result, Excel's Math & Trig functions appear in alphabetical order in the Select a function box. We see the ABS function listed first, followed by the ACOS function, and so on.

Colon Notation

Although many functions, such as the ABS function, have a single argument, some Excel functions depend on arrays. Colon notation provides an efficient way to convey arrays and matrices of cells to functions. The colon notation may be described as follows: B3:B5 means cell B1 "through" cell B5, namely the array of values stored in the locations

FIGURE A.14 INSERT FUNCTION DIALOG BOX

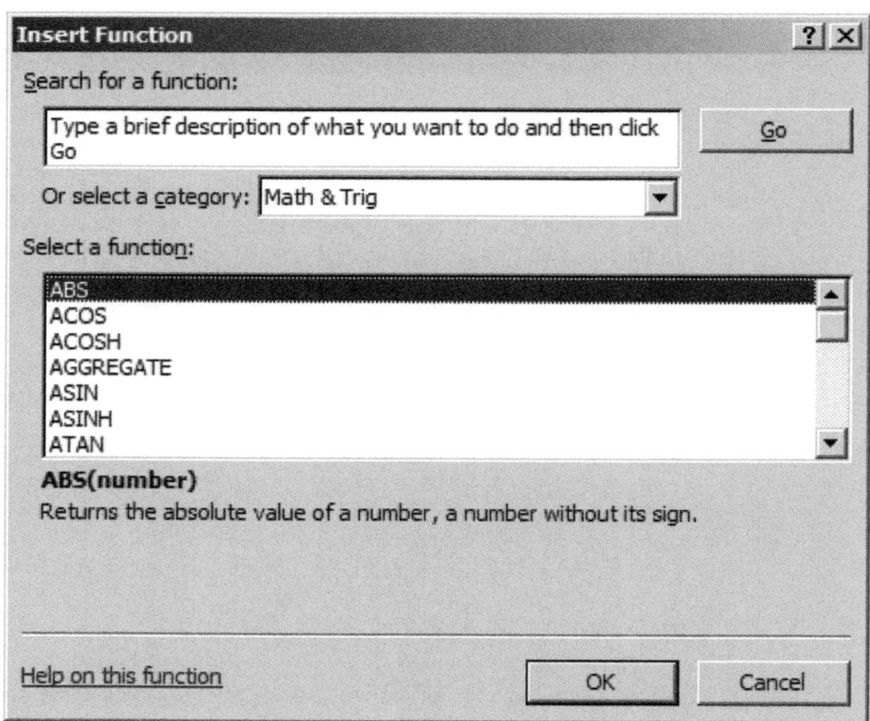

(B1,B2,B3,B4,B5). Consider, for example, the following function =SUM(B1:B5). The sum function adds up the elements contained in the function's argument. Hence, =SUM(B1:B5) evaluates the following formula:

=B1+B2+B3+B4+B5

Inserting a Function into a Worksheet Cell

Through the use of an example, we will now show how to use the Insert Function and Function Arguments dialog boxes to select a function, develop its arguments, and insert the function into a worksheet cell. We also illustrate the use of the SUMPRODUCT function, and how to use colon notation in the argument of a function.

The SUMPRODUCT function, as shown in Figure A.15, is used in many of the Solver examples in this textbook. Note that SUMPRODUCT is now highlighted, and that immediately below the Select a function box we see SUMPRODUCT(array1,array2,array3, . . .), which indicates that the SUMPRODUCT function contains the array arguments array1, array2, array3, ... In addition, we see that the description of the SUMPRODUCT function is "Returns the sum of the products of corresponding ranges or arrays." For example, the function =SUMPRODUCT(A1:A3, B1:B3) evaluates the formula A1*B1 + A2*B2 + A3*B3. As shown in the following example, this function can be very useful in calculations of cost, profit, and other such functions involving multiple arrays of numbers.

FIGURE A.15 DESCRIPTION OF THE SUMPRODUCT FUNCTION IN THE INSERT FUNCTION DIALOG BOX

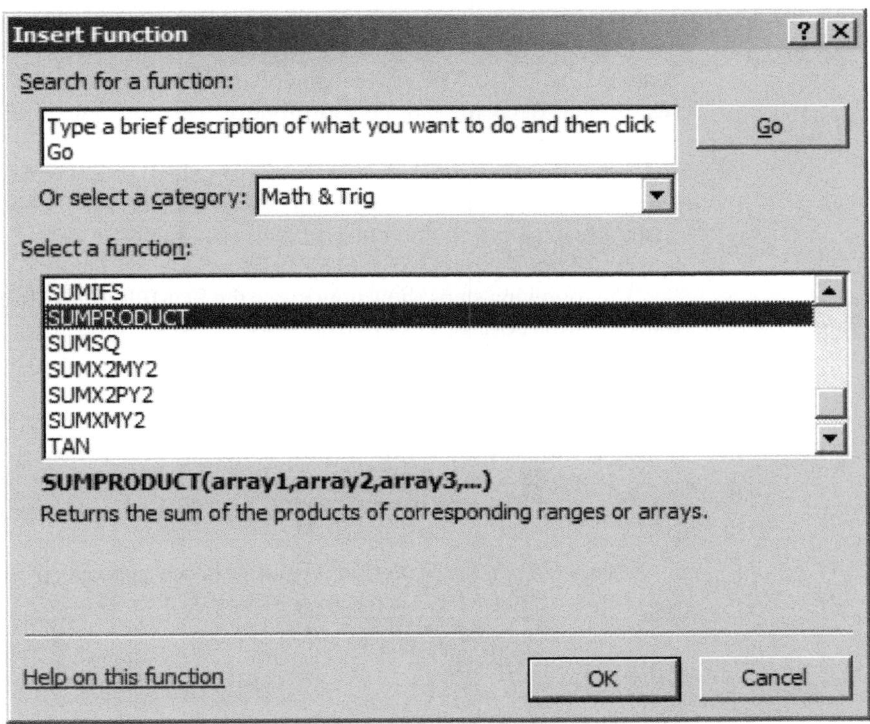

FIGURE A.16 EXCEL WORKSHEET USED TO CALCULATE TOTAL SHIPPING COSTS FOR THE FOSTER GENERATORS TRANSPORTATION PROBLEM

FosterGenerators

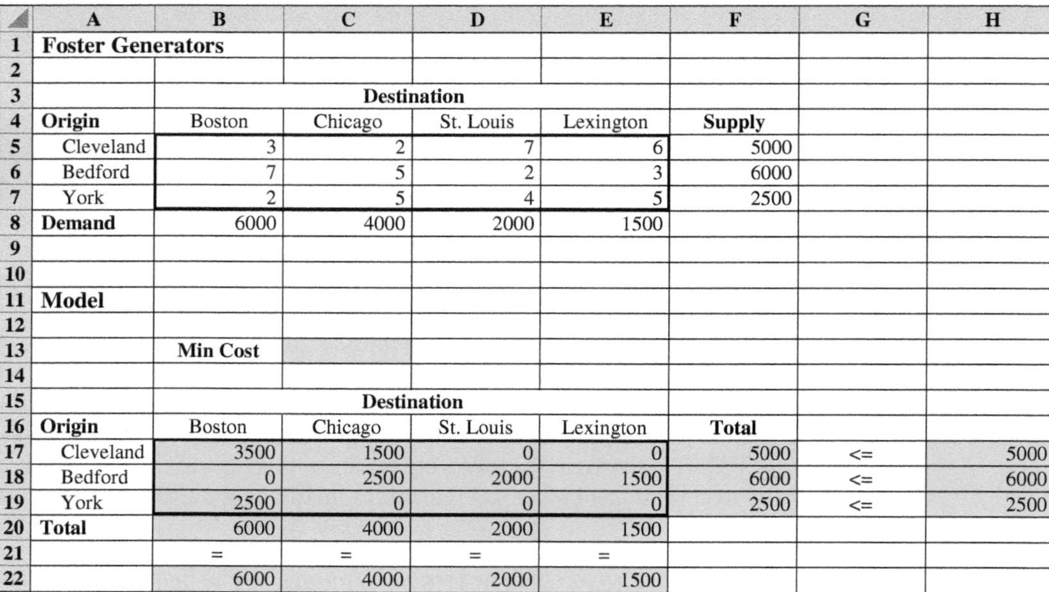

	A	B	C	D	E	F	G	H
1	**Foster Generators**							
2								
3			**Destination**					
4	**Origin**	Boston	Chicago	St. Louis	Lexington	**Supply**		
5	Cleveland	3	2	7	6	5000		
6	Bedford	7	5	2	3	6000		
7	York	2	5	4	5	2500		
8	**Demand**	6000	4000	2000	1500			
9								
10								
11	**Model**							
12								
13		**Min Cost**						
14								
15			**Destination**					
16	**Origin**	Boston	Chicago	St. Louis	Lexington	**Total**		
17	Cleveland	3500	1500	0	0	5000	<=	5000
18	Bedford	0	2500	2000	1500	6000	<=	6000
19	York	2500	0	0	0	2500	<=	2500
20	**Total**	6000	4000	2000	1500			
21		=	=	=	=			
22		6000	4000	2000	1500			

Figure A.16 displays an Excel worksheet for the Foster Generators Problem that appears in Chapter 10. This problem involves the transportation of a product from three plants (Cleveland, Bedford, and York) to four distribution centers (Boston, Chicago, St. Louis, and Lexington). The costs for each unit shipped from each plant to each distribution center are shown in cells B5:E7, and the values in cells B17:E19 are the number of units shipped from each plant to each distribution center. Cell B13 will contain the total transportation cost corresponding to the transportation cost values in cells B5:E7 and the values of the number of units shipped in cells B17:E19.

The following steps show how to use the SUMPRODUCT function to compute the total transportation cost for Foster Generators.

Step 1. Select **cell C13**
Step 2. Click *fx* on the formula bar
Step 3. When the **Insert Function** dialog box appears:
Select **Math & Trig** in the **Or select a category** box
Select **SUMPRODUCT** in the **Select a function** box (as shown in Figure A.15)
Click **OK**
Step 4. When the **Function Arguments** box appears (see Figure A.17):
Enter *B5:E7* in the **Array1** box
Enter *B17:E19* in the **Array2** box
Click **OK**

The worksheet then appears as shown in Figure A.18. The value of the total transportation cost in cell C13 is 39500, or $39,500.

FIGURE A.17 COMPLETED FUNCTION ARGUMENTS DIALOG BOX FOR THE SUMPRODUCT FUNCTION

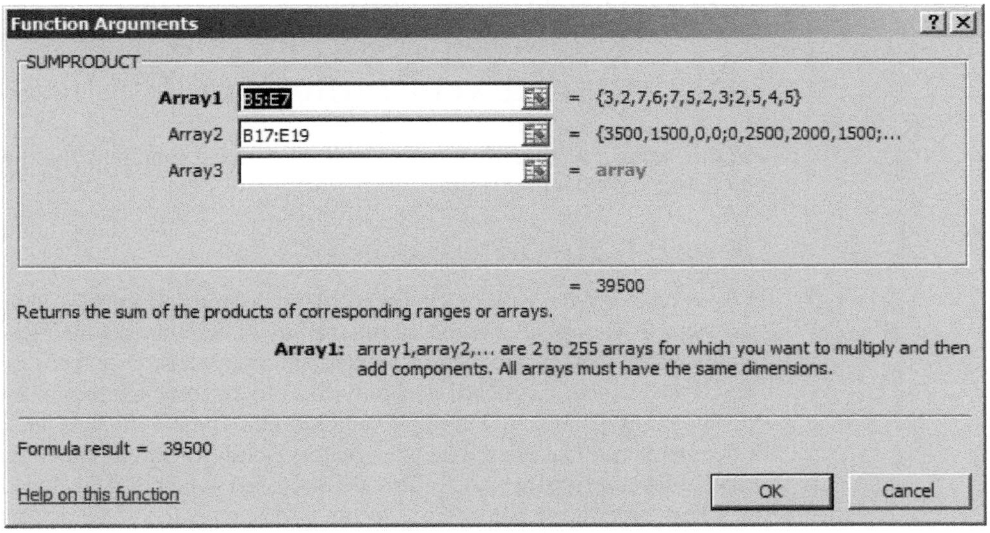

Function Arguments

SUMPRODUCT

Array1 B5:E7 = {3,2,7,6;7,5,2,3;2,5,4,5}

Array2 B17:E19 = {3500,1500,0,0;0,2500,2000,1500;...

Array3 = array

= 39500

Returns the sum of the products of corresponding ranges or arrays.

Array1: array1,array2,... are 2 to 255 arrays for which you want to multiply and then add components. All arrays must have the same dimensions.

Formula result = 39500

Help on this function

OK Cancel

FIGURE A.18 EXCEL WORKSHEET SHOWING THE USE OF EXCEL'S SUMPRODUCT FUNCTION TO CALCULATE TOTAL SHIPPING COSTS

	A	B	C	D	E	F	G	H
1	**Foster Generators**							
2								
3				**Destination**				
4	**Origin**	Boston	Chicago	St. Louis	Lexington	**Supply**		
5	Cleveland	3	2	7	6	5000		
6	Bedford	7	5	2	3	6000		
7	York	2	5	4	5	2500		
8	**Demand**	6000	4000	2000	1500			
9								
10								
11	**Model**							
12								
13		**Min Cost**	39500					
14								
15				**Destination**				
16	**Origin**	Boston	Chicago	St. Louis	Lexington	**Total**		
17	Cleveland	3500	1500	0	0	5000	<=	5000
18	Bedford	0	2500	2000	1500	6000	<=	6000
19	York	2500	0	0	0	2500	<=	2500
20	**Total**	6000	4000	2000	1500			
21		=	=	=	=			
22		6000	4000	2000	1500			

We illustrated the use of Excel's capability to provide assistance in using the SUMPRODUCT function. The procedure is similar for all Excel functions. This capability is especially helpful if you do not know which function to use or forget the proper name and/or syntax for a function.

Additional Excel Functions for Modeling

In this section we introduce some additional Excel functions that have proven useful in modeling decision problems.

IF and COUNTIF Functions

Let us consider the case of Gambrell Manufacturing. Gambrell Manufacturing produces car stereos. Stereos are composed of a variety of components that the company must carry in inventory to keep production running smoothly. However, because inventory can be a costly investment, Gambrell generally likes to keep the amount of inventory of the components it uses in manufacturing to a minimum. To help monitor and control its inventory of components, Gambrell uses an inventory policy known as an "order up to" policy. This type of inventory policy and others are discussed in detail in Chapter 14.

The "order up to policy" is as follows. Whenever the inventory on hand drops below a certain level, enough units are ordered to return the inventory to that predetermined level. If the current number of units in inventory, denoted by H, drops below M units, we order enough to get the inventory level back up to M units. M is called the Order Up to Point. Stated mathematically, if Q is the amount we order, then

$$Q = M - H$$

An inventory model for Gambrell Manufacturing appears in Figure A.19. In this worksheet, labeled "OrderQuantity" in the upper half of the worksheet, the component ID number, inventory on hand (H), order up to point (M), and cost per unit are given for each of four components. Also given in this sheet is the fixed cost per order. The fixed cost is interpreted as follows: Each time a component is ordered, it costs Gambrell \$120 to process the order. The fixed cost of \$120 is incurred regardless of how many units are ordered.

The model portion of the worksheet calculates the order quantity for each component. For example, for component 570, $M = 100$ and $H = 5$, so $Q = M - H = 100 - 5 = 95$. For component 741, $M = 70$ and $H = 70$ and no units are ordered because the on-hand inventory of 70 units is equal to the up to order point of 70. The calculations are similar for the other two components.

Depending on the number of units ordered, Gambrell receives a discount on the cost per unit. If 50 or more units are ordered, there is a quantity discount of 10% on every unit purchased. For example, for component 741, the cost per unit is \$4.50 and 95 units are ordered. Because 95 exceeds the 50-unit requirement, there is a 10% discount and the cost per unit is reduced to \$4.50 − 0.1(\$4.50) = \$4.50 − \$0.45 = \$4.05. Not including the fixed cost, the cost of goods purchased is then \$4.05(95) = \$384.75.

The Excel functions used to perform these calculations are shown in Figure A.20. The IF function is used to calculate the purchase cost of goods for each component in row 15. The general form of the IF function is

=IF(*condition, result if condition is true, result if condition is false*)

For example, in cell B15 we have =IF(B14>=50,0.9*B7,B7)*B14. This statement says if the order quantity (cell B14) is greater than or equal to 50, then the cost per unit is 0.9*B7 (there

FIGURE A.19 THE GAMBRELL MANUFACTURING COMPONENT ORDERING MODEL

	A	B	C	D	E	F
4	Component ID	570	578	741	755	
5	Inventory On-Hand	5	30	70	17	
6	Order Up to Point	100	55	70	45	
7	Cost per unit	$4.50	$12.50	$3.26	$4.15	
8						
9	Fixed Cost per Order	$120				
10						
11	**Model**					
12						
13	Component ID	570	578	741	755	
14	Order Quantity	95	25	0	28	
15	Cost of Goods	$384.75	$312.50	$0.00	$116.20	
16						
17	Total Number of Orders	3				
18						
19	Total Fixed costs	$360.00				
20	Total Cost of Goods	$813.45				
21	Total Cost	$1,173.45				
22						

FIGURE A.20 FORMULAS AND FUNCTIONS FOR GAMBRELL MANUFACTURING

	A	B	C	D	E
1					
2	**Gambrell Manufacturing**				
3					
4	Component ID	570	578	741	755
5	Inventory On-Hand	5	30	70	17
6	Order Up to Point	100	55	70	45
7	Cost per unit	4.5	12.5	3.26	4.15
8					
9	Fixed Cost per Order	120			
10					
11	**Model**				
12					
13	Component ID	=B4	=C4	=D4	=E4
14	Order Quantity	=B6-B5	=C6-C5	=D6-D5	=E6-E5
15	Cost of Goods	=IF(B14>=50,0.9*B7,B7)*B14	=IF(C14>=50, 0.9*C7,C7)*C14	=IF(D14>=50, 0.9*D7,D7)*D14	=IF(E14>=50, 0.9*E7,E7)*E14
16					
17	Total Number of Orders	=COUNTIF(B14:E14,">0")			
18					
19	Total Fixed Costs	=B17*B9			
20	Total Cost of Goods	=SUM(B15:E15)			
21	Total Cost	=SUM(B19:B20)			
22					

is a 10% discount); otherwise, there is no discount and the cost per unit is the amount given in cell B7. The purchase cost of goods for the other components are computed in a like manner.

The total cost in cell B21 is the sum of the purchase cost of goods ordered in row 15 and the fixed ordering costs. Because we place three orders (one each for components 570, 578, and 755), the fixed cost of the orders is 3*120 = $360.

The COUNTIF function in cell B17 is used to count how many times we order. In particular, it counts the number of components having a positive order quantity. The general form of the COUNTIF function is

=COUNTIF(*range, condition*)

The *range* is the range to search for the *condition*. The condition is the test to be counted when satisfied. *Note that quotes are required for the condition with the COUNTIF function.* In the Gambrell model in Figure A.20, cell B17 counts the number of cells that are greater than zero in the range of cells B14:E14. In the model, because only cells B14, C14, and E14 are greater than zero, the COUNTIF function in cell B17 returns 3.

As we have seen, IF and COUNTIF are powerful functions that allow us to make calculations based on a condition holding (or not). There are other such conditional functions available in Excel. In the problems at the end of this appendix, we ask you to investigate one such function, the SUMIF function. Another conditional function that is extremely useful in modeling is the VLOOKUP function. We discuss the VLOOKUP function with an example in the next section.

VLOOKUP Function

Next, consider the workbook named *OM455* shown in Figure A.21. The worksheet named Grades is shown. This worksheet calculates the course grades for the course OM 455. There are 11 students in the course. Each student has a midterm exam score and a final exam score,

FIGURE A.21 OM455 GRADE SPREADSHEET

OM455

	A	B	C	D	E	F
1	**OM455**					
2	**Section 001**					
3	**Course Grading Scale Based on Course Average:**					
4		**Lower**	**Upper**	**Course**		
5		**Limit**	**Limit**	**Grade**		
6		0	59	F		
7		60	69	D		
8		70	79	C		
9		80	89	B		
10		90	100	A		
11						
12		Midterm	Final	Course	Course	
13	Lastname	Score	Score	Average	Grade	
14	Benson	70	56	63.0	D	
15	Chin	95	91	93.0	A	
16	Choi	82	80	81.0	B	
17	Cruz	45	78	61.5	D	
18	Doe	68	45	56.5	F	
19	Honda	91	98	94.5	A	
20	Hume	87	74	80.5	B	
21	Jones	60	80	70.0	C	
22	Miranda	80	93	86.5	B	
23	Murigami	97	98	97.5	A	
24	Ruebush	90	91	90.5	A	
25						

and these are averaged in column D to get the course average. The scale given in the upper portion of the worksheet is used to determine the course grade for each student. Consider, for example, the performance of student Choi in row 16. This student earned an 82 on the midterm, an 80 on the final, and a course average of 81. From the grading scale, this equates to a course grade of B.

The course average is simply the average of the midterm and final scores, but how do we get Excel to look in the grading scale table and automatically assign the correct course letter grade to each student? The VLOOKUP function allows us to do just that. The formulas and functions used in *OM455* are shown in Figure A.22.

The VLOOKUP function allows the user to pull a subset of data from a larger table of data based on some criterion. The general form of the VLOOKUP function is

=VLOOKUP(arg1,arg2,arg3,arg4)

where arg1 is the value to search for in the first column of the table, arg2 is the table location, arg3 is the column location in the table to be returned, and arg4 is TRUE if looking for the first partial match of arg1 and FALSE for looking for an exact match of arg1. We will explain the difference between a partial and exact match in a moment. VLOOKUP assumes that the first column of the table is sorted in ascending order.

The VLOOKUP function for student Choi in cell E16 is as follows:

=VLOOKUP(D16,B6:D10,3,TRUE)

FIGURE A.22 THE FORMULAS AND FUNCTIONS USED IN OM 455

	A	B	C	D	E
1	**OM 455**				
2	**Section 001**				
3	**Course Grading Scale Based on Course Average:**				
4		**Lower**	**Upper**	**Course**	
5		**Limit**	**Limit**	**Grade**	
6		0	59	F	
7		60	69	D	
8		70	79	C	
9		80	89	B	
10		90	100	A	
11					
12		Midterm	Final	Course	Course
13	Lastname	Score	Score	Average	Grade
14	Benson	70	56	=AVERAGE(B14:C14)	=VLOOKUP(D14,B6:D10,3,TRUE)
15	Chin	95	91	=AVERAGE(B15:C15)	=VLOOKUP(D15,B6:D10,3,TRUE)
16	Choi	82	80	=AVERAGE(B16:C16)	=VLOOKUP(D16,B6:D10,3,TRUE)
17	Cruz	45	78	=AVERAGE(B17:C17)	=VLOOKUP(D17,B6:D10,3,TRUE)
18	Doe	68	45	=AVERAGE(B18:C18)	=VLOOKUP(D18,B6:D10,3,TRUE)
19	Honda	91	98	=AVERAGE(B19:C19)	=VLOOKUP(D19,B6:D10,3,TRUE)
20	Hume	87	74	=AVERAGE(B20:C20)	=VLOOKUP(D20,B6:D10,3,TRUE)
21	Jones	60	80	=AVERAGE(B21:C21)	=VLOOKUP(D21,B6:D10,3,TRUE)
22	Miranda	80	93	=AVERAGE(B22:C22)	=VLOOKUP(D22,B6:D10,3,TRUE)
23	Murigami	97	98	=AVERAGE(B23:C23)	=VLOOKUP(D23,B6:D10,3,TRUE)
24	Ruebush	90	91	=AVERAGE(B24:C24)	=VLOOKUP(D24,B6:D10,3,TRUE)
25					

This function uses the course average from cell D16 and searches the first column of the table defined by B6:D10. In the first column of the table (column B), Excel searches from the top until it finds a number strictly greater than the value of D16 (81). It then backs up one row (to row 9). That is, it finds the last value in the first column less than or equal to 81. Because there is a 3 in the third argument of the VLOOKUP function, it takes the element in row 9 in the third column of the table, which is the letter "B." In summary, the VLOOKUP takes the first argument and searches the first column of the table for the last row that is less than or equal to the first argument. It then selects from that row the element in the column number of the third argument.

Note: If the last element of the VLOOKUP function is "False," the only change is that Excel searches for an exact match of the first argument in the first column of the data. VLOOKUP is very useful when you seek subsets of a table based on a condition.

Principles for Building Good Spreadsheet Models

We have covered some of the fundamentals of building spreadsheet models. There are some generally accepted guiding principles for how to build a spreadsheet so that it is more easily used by others and so that the risk of error is mitigated. In this section we discuss some of those principles.

Separate the Data from the Model

One of the first principles of good modeling is to separate the data from the model. This enables the user to update the model parameters without fear of mistakenly typing over a formula or function. For this reason, it is good practice to have a data section at the top of the spreadsheet. A separate model section should contain all calculations and in general should not be updated by a user. For a what-if model or an optimization model, there might also be a separate section for decision cells (values that are not data or calculations, but are the outputs we seek from the model).

The Nowlin model in Figure A.6 is a good example. The data section is in the upper part of the spreadsheet followed by the model section that contains the calculations. The Gambrell model in Figure A.19 does not totally employ the principle of data/model separation. A better model would have the 50-unit hurdle and the 90% cost (10% discount) as data in the upper section. Then the formulas in row 15 would simply refer to the cells in the upper section. This would allow the user to easily change the discount, for example, without having to change all four formulas in row 15.

Document the Model

A good spreadsheet model is well documented. Clear labels and proper formatting and alignment make the spreadsheet easier to navigate and understand. For example, if the values in a worksheet are cost, currency formatting should be used. No cells should be unlabeled. A new user should be able to easily understand the model and its calculations. Figure A.23 shows a better-documented version of the Foster Generators model previously discussed (Figure A.16). The tables are more explicitly labeled, and shading focuses the user on the objective and the decision cells (amount to ship). The per-unit shipping cost data and total (Min) cost have been properly formatted as currency.

FIGURE A.23 A BETTER-DOCUMENTED FOSTER GENERATORS MODEL

FosterRev

	A	B	C	D	E	F	G	H
1	**Foster Generators**							
2								
3	Origin to Destination—Cost per unit to ship							
4			**Destination**					
5	**Origin**	Boston	Chicago	St. Louis	Lexington	**Units Available**		
6	Cleveland	$3.00	$2.00	$7.00	$6.00	5000		
7	Bedford	$7.00	$5.00	$2.00	$3.00	6000		
8	York	$2.00	$5.00	$4.00	$5.00	2500		
9	**Units Demanded**	6000	4000	2000	1500			
10								
11								
12	**Model**							
13								
14		**Min Cost**	$39,500.00					
15								
16	Origin to Destination—Units Shipped							
17			**Destination**					
18	**Origin**	Boston	Chicago	St. Louis	Lexington	**Units Shipped**		
19	Cleveland	3500	1500	0	0	5000	<=	5000
20	Bedford	0	2500	2000	1500	6000	<=	6000
21	York	2500	0	0	0	2500	<=	2500
22	**Units Received**	6000	4000	2000	1500			
23		=	=	=	=			
24		6000	4000	2000	1500			

Use Simple Formulas and Cell Names

Clear formulas can eliminate unnecessary calculations, reduce errors, and make it easier to maintain your spreadsheet. Long and complex calculations should be divided into several cells. This makes the formula easier to understand and easier to edit. Avoid using numbers in a formula. Instead, put the number in a cell in the data section of your worksheet and refer to the cell location of the data in the formula. Building the formula in this manner avoids having to edit the formula for a simple data change.

Using cell names can make a formula much easier to understand. To assign a name to a cell, use the following steps:

Step 1. Select the cell or range of cells you would like to name
Step 2. Select the **FORMULAS** tab from the Ribbon
Step 3. Choose **Define Name** from the Defined Names section
Step 4. The **New Name** dialog box will appear, as shown in Figure A.24
Enter the name you would like to use in the top portion of the dialog box and Click **OK**

Following this procedure and naming all cells in the *Nowlin Plastics* spreadsheet model leads to the model shown in Figure A.25. Compare this to Figure A.6 to easily understand the formulas in the model.

A name is also easily applied to range as follows. First, highlight the range of interest. Then click on the Name Box in the Formula Bar (refer back to Figure A.3) and type in the desired range name.

FIGURE A.24 THE DEFINE NAME DIALOG BOX

NowlinPlastics

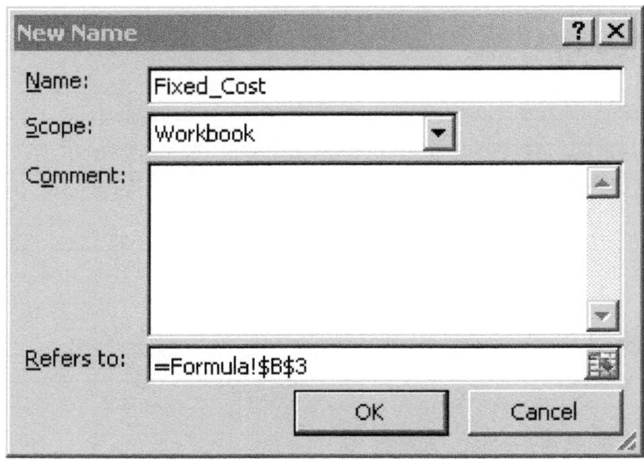

FIGURE A.25 THE NOWLIN PLASTIC MODEL FORMULAS WITH NAMED CELLS

	A	B
1	**Nowlin Plastics**	
2		
3	**Fixed Cost**	3000
4		
5	**Variable Cost Per Unit**	2
6		
7	**Selling Price Per Unit**	5
8		
9		
10	**Model**	
11		
12	**Production Volume**	800
13		
14	**Total Cost**	=Fixed_Cost+Variable_Cost*Production_Volume
15		
16	**Total Revenue**	=Selling_Price*Production_Volume
17		
18	**Total Profit (Loss)**	=Total_Revenue-Total_Cost

Use of Relative and Absolute Cell References

There are a number of ways to copy a formula from one cell to another in an Excel worksheet. One way to copy the a formula from one cell to another is presented here:

Step 1. Select the cell you would like to copy
Step 2. Right click on the mouse
Step 3. Click **Copy**

Step 4. Select the cell where you would like to put the copy
Step 5. Right click on the mouse
Step 6. Click **Paste**

When copying in Excel, one can use a relative or an absolute address. When copied, a relative address adjusts with the move of the copy, whereas an absolute address stays in its original form. Relative addresses are of the form C7. Absolute addresses have $ in front of the column and row, for example, $C$7. How you use relative and absolute addresses can have an impact on the amount of effort it takes to build a model and the opportunity for error in constructing the model.

Let us reconsider the OM455 grading spreadsheet previously discussed in this appendix and shown in Figure A.22. Recall that we used the VLOOKUP function to retrieve the appropriate letter grade for each student. The following formula is in cell E14:

=VLOOKUP(D14,B6:D10,3,TRUE)

Note that this formula contains only relative addresses. If we copy this to cell E15, we get the following result:

=VLOOKUP(D15,B7:D11,3,TRUE)

Although the first argument has correctly changed to D15 (we want to calculate the letter grade for the student in row 15), the table in the function has also shifted to B7:D11. What we desired was for this table location to remain the same. A better approach would have been to use the following formula in cell E14:

=VLOOKUP(D14,$B$6:$D$10,3,TRUE)

Copying this formula to cell E15 results in the following formula:

=VLOOKUP(D15,$B$6:$D$10,3,TRUE)

This correctly changes the first argument to D15 and keeps the data table intact. Using absolute referencing is extremely useful if you have a function that has a reference that should not change when applied to another cell and you are copying the formula to other locations. In the case of the OM455 workbook, instead of typing the VLOOKUP for each student, we can use absolute referencing on the table and then copy from row 14 to rows 15 through 24.

In this section we have discussed guidelines for good spreadsheet model building. In the next section we discuss EXCEL tools available for checking and debugging spreadsheet models.

Auditing Excel Models

EXCEL contains a variety of tools to assist you in the development and debugging of spreadsheet models. These tools are found in the Formula Auditing group of the FORMULAS tab as shown in Figure A.26. Let us review each of the tools available in this group.

Trace Precedents and Dependents

The Trace Precedents button, Trace Precedents, creates arrows pointing to the selected cell from cells that are part of the formula in that cell. The Trace Dependents button, Trace Dependents, on the other hand, shows arrows pointing from the selected cell to

FIGURE A.26 THE FORMULA AUDITING GROUP OF THE FORMULAS TAB

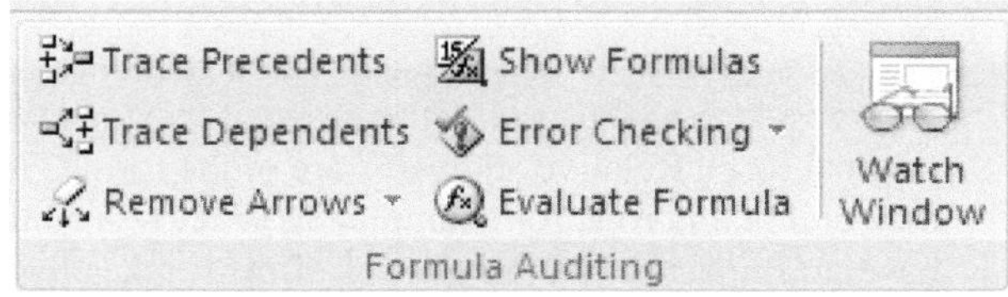

cells that depend on the selected cell. Both of these tools are excellent for quickly ascertaining how parts of a model are linked.

An example of Trace Precedents is shown in Figure A.27. Here we have opened the *Foster Rev* worksheet, selected cell C14, and clicked the Trace Precedents button in the Formula Auditing Group. Recall that the cost in cell C14 is calculated as the SUMPRODUCT of the per-unit shipping cost and units shipped. In Figure A.27, to show this relationship, arrows are drawn to these respective areas of the spreadsheet to cell C14. These arrows may be removed by clicking on the Remove Arrows button in the Auditing Tools Group.

An example of Trace Dependents is shown in Figure A.28. We have selected cell E20, the units shipped from Bedford to Lexington, and clicked on the Trace Dependents button

FIGURE A.27 TRACE PRECEDENTS FOR CELL C14 (COST) IN THE FOSTER GENERATORS REV MODEL

C14 fx =SUMPRODUCT(B6:E8,B19:E21)

	A	B	C	D	E	F	G	H
1	**Foster Generators**							
2								
3	Origin to Destination—Cost per unit to ship							
4			**Destination**					
5	**Origin**	Boston	Chicago	St. Louis	Lexington	**Units Available**		
6	Cleveland	$3.00	$2.00	$7.00	$6.00	5000		
7	Bedford	$7.00	$5.00	$2.00	$3.00	6000		
8	York	$2.00	$5.00	$4.00	$5.00	2500		
9	**Units Demanded**	6000	4000	2000	1500			
10								
11								
12	**Model**							
13								
14		**Min Cost**	$39,500.00					
15								
16	Origin to Destination—Units Shipped							
17			**Destination**					
18	**Origin**	Boston	Chicago	St. Louis	Lexington	**Units Shipped**		
19	Cleveland	3500	1500	0	0	5000	<=	5000
20	Bedford	0	2500	2000	1500	6000	<=	6000
21	York	2500	0	0	0	2500	<=	2500
22	**Units Received**	6000	4000	2000	1500			
23		=	=	=	=			
24		6000	4000	2000	1500			

FosterRev

FIGURE A.28 TRACE DEPENDENTS FOR CELL C14 (COST) IN THE FOSTER GENERATORS REV MODEL

E20 fx 1500

	A	B	C	D	E	F	G	H
12	**Model**							
13								
14		**Min Cost**	$39,500.00					
15								
16	Origin to Destination—Units Shipped							
17			**Destination**					
18	**Origin**	Boston	Chicago	St. Louis	Lexington	**Units Shipped**		
19	Cleveland	3500	1500	0	0	5000	<=	5000
20	Bedford	0	2500	2000	1500	6000	<=	6000
21	York	2500	0	0	0	2500	<=	2500
22	**Units Received**	6000	4000	2000	1500			
23		=	=	=	=			
24		6000	4000	2000	1500			

in the Formula Auditing Group. As shown in Figure A.28, units shipped from Bedford to Lexington impacts the cost function in cell C14, the total units shipped from Bedford given in cell F20, and the total units shipped to Lexington in cell E22. These arrows may be removed by clicking on the Remove Arrows button in the Auditing Tools Group.

Trace Precedents and Trace Dependents can highlight errors in copying and formula construction by showing that incorrect sections of the worksheet are referenced.

Show Formulas

The Show Formulas button, Show Formulas, does exactly that. To see the formulas in a worksheet, simply click on any cell in the worksheet and then click on Show Formulas. You will see the formulas that exist in that worksheet. To go back to hiding the formulas, click again on the Show Formulas button. Figure A.6 gives an example of the show formulas view. This allows you to inspect each formula in detail in its cell location.

Evaluate Formulas

The Evaluate Formula button, Evaluate Formula, allows you to investigate the calculations of particular cell in great detail. To invoke this tool, we simply select a cell containing a formula and click on the Evaluate Formula button in the Formula Auditing Group. As an example, we select cell B15 of the Gambrell Manufacturing model (see Figures A.19 and A.20). Recall we are calculating cost of goods based upon whether or not there is a quantity discount. Clicking on the Evaluate button allows you to evaluate this formula explicitly. The Evaluate Formula dialog box appears in Figure A.29. Figure A.30 shows the result of one click of the Evaluate button. Cell B14 has changed to its value of 95. Further clicks would evaluate in order, from left to right, the remaining components of the formula. We ask the reader to further explore this tool in an exercise at the end of this appendix.

The Evaluate Formula tool provides an excellent means of identifying the exact location of an error in a formula.

FIGURE A.29 THE EVALUATE FORMULA DIALOG BOX FOR CELL B15 OF THE GAMBRELL MANUFACTURING MODEL

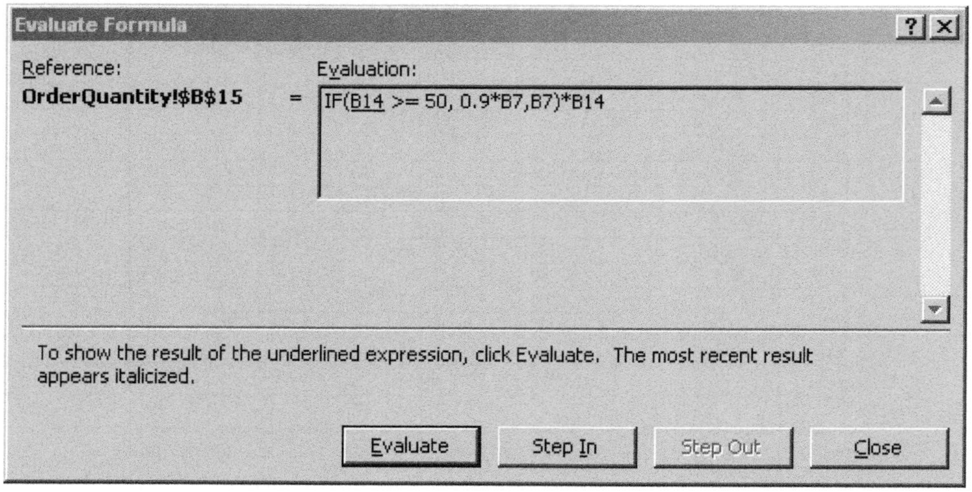

FIGURE A.30 THE EVALUATE FORMULA AFTER ONE CLICK OF THE EVALUATE BUTTON FOR CELL B15 OF THE GAMBRELL MANUFACTURING MODEL

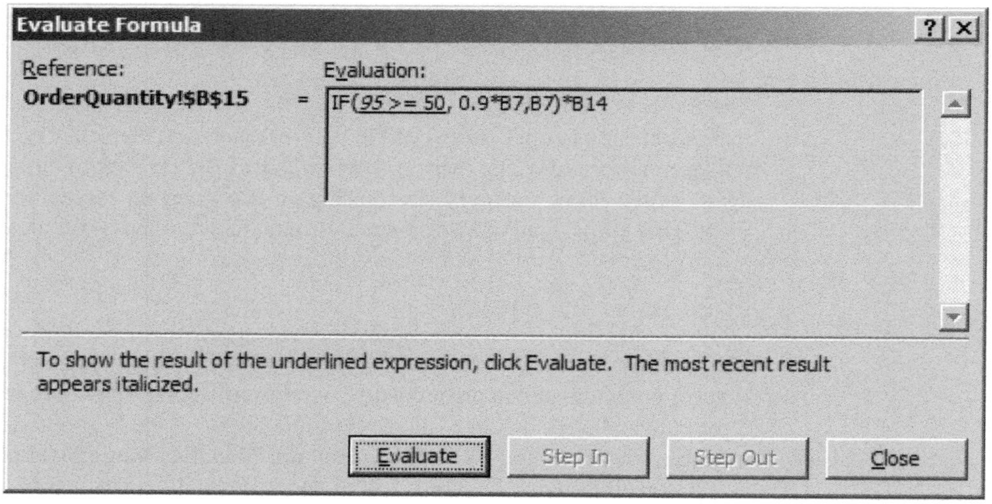

Error Checking

The Error Checking button, Error Checking, provides an automatic means of checking for mathematical errors within formulas of a worksheet. Clicking on the Error Checking button causes Excel to check every formula in the sheet for calculation errors. If an error is found, the Error Checking dialog box appears. An example for a hypothetical division by

FIGURE A.31 THE ERROR CHECKING DIALOG BOX FOR A DIVISION BY ZERO ERROR

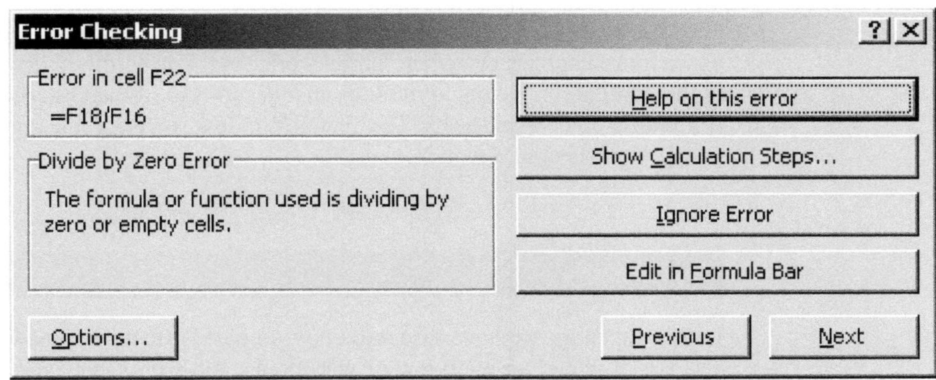

zero error is shown in Figure A.31. From this box, the formula can be edited or the calculation steps can be observed (as in the previous section on Evaluate Formulas).

Watch Window

The Watch Window, located in the Formula Auditing Group, allows the user to observe the values of cells included in the Watch Window box list. This is useful for large models when not all the model is observable on the screen or when multiple worksheets are used. The user can monitor how the listed cells change with a change in the model without searching through the worksheet or changing from one worksheet to another.

A Watch Window for the Gambrell Manufacturing model is shown in Figure A.32. The following steps were used from the OrderQuantity worksheet to add cell B15 of the OrderQuantity worksheet to the watch list:

Step 1. Select the **FORMULAS** tab
Step 2. Select **Watch Window** from the Formula Auditing Group
The Watch Window will appear
Step 3. Select **Add Watch**
Step 4. Click on the cell you would like to add to the watch list (in this case B15)

FIGURE A.32 THE WATCH WINDOW FOR THE GAMBRELL MANUFACTURING MODEL

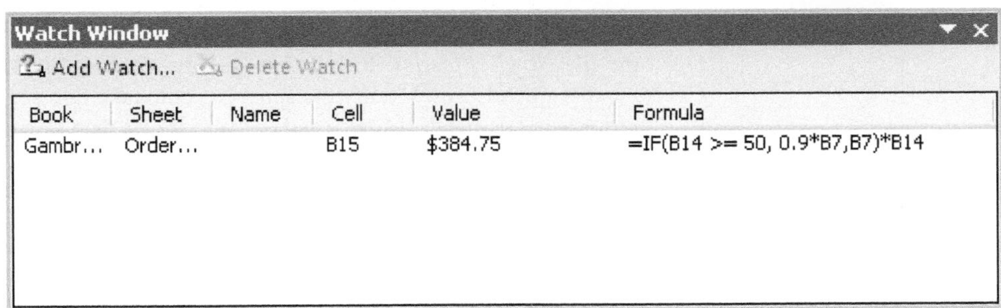

As shown in Figure A.32, the list gives the workbook name, worksheet name, cell name (if used), cell location, cell value, and cell formula. To delete a cell from the watch list, select the entry from the list and then click on the Delete Watch button in the upper part of the Watch Window.

The Watch Window, as shown in Figure A.32, allows us to monitor the value of B15 as we make changes elsewhere in the worksheet. Furthermore, if we had other worksheets in this workbook, we could monitor changes to B15 of the OrderQuantity worksheet even from these other worksheets. The Watch Window is observable regardless of where we are in any worksheet of a workbook.

Summary

In this appendix we have discussed how to build effective spreadsheet models using Excel. We provided an overview of workbooks and worksheets and details on useful Excel functions. We also discussed a set of principles for good modeling and tools for auditing spreadsheet models.

Problems

NowlinPlastics

1. Open the file *NowlinPlastics*. Recall that we have modeled total profit for the product CD-50 in this spreadsheet. Suppose we have a second product called a CD-100, with the following characteristics:

$$\text{Fixed Cost} = \$2500$$
$$\text{Variable Cost per Unit} = \$1.67$$
$$\text{Selling Price per Unit} = \$4.40$$

Extend the model so that the profit is calculated for each product and then totaled to give an overall profit generated for the two products. Use a CD-100 production volume of 1200. Save this file as *NowlinPlastics2*. *Hint:* Place the data for CD-100 in column C and copy the formulas in rows 14, 16, and 18 to column C.

2. Assume that in an empty Excel worksheet in cell A1 you enter the formula =B1*$F$3. You now copy this formula into cell E6. What is the modified formula that appears in E6?

FosterRev

3. Open the file *FosterRev*. Select cells B6:E8 and name these cells Shipping_Cost. Select cells B19:E21 and name these cells Units_Shipped. Use these names in the SUMPRODUCT function in cell C14 to compute cost and verify that you obtain the same cost ($39,500).

4. Open the file *NowlinPlastics*. Recall that we have modeled total profit for the product CD-50 in this spreadsheet. Modify the spreadsheet to take into account production capacity and forecasted demand. If forecasted demand is less than or equal to capacity, Nowlin will produce only the forecasted demand; otherwise, they will produce the full capacity. For this example, use forecasted demand of 1200 and capacity of 1500. *Hint:* Enter demand and capacity into the data section of the model. Then use an IF statement to calculate production volume.

CoxElectric

5. Cox Electric, which makes electronic components, has estimated the following for a new design of one of its products:

$$\text{Fixed cost} = \$10{,}000$$
$$\text{Material cost per unit} = \$0.15$$
$$\text{Labor cost per unit} = \$0.10$$
$$\text{Revenue per unit} = \$0.65$$

These data are given in the file *CoxElectric*. Note that fixed cost is incurred regardless of the amount produced. Per-unit material and labor cost together make up the variable cost per unit.

Assuming Cox Electric sells all that it produces, profit is calculated by subtracting the fixed cost and total variable cost from total revenue.

a. Build a spreadsheet model that will calculate profit for Cox Electric using the principles of good spreadsheet design.
b. If Cox Electric produces 12,000 units of the new product, what is the resulting profit?

6. Use the Cox Electric spreadsheet model constructed for Problem 5 to answer the following:
a. Construct a one-way data table with production volume as the column input and profit as the output. Breakeven occurs when profit goes from a negative to a positive value; that is, breakeven is when total revenue = total cost, yielding a profit of zero. Vary production volume from 0 to 100,000 in increments of 10,000. In which interval of production volume does breakeven occur?
b. Use Goal Seek to find the exact breakeven point. Assign **Set cell:** equal to the location of profit, **To value:** = 0, and **By changing cell:** equal to the location of the production volume in your model.

7. Eastman Publishing Company is considering publishing an electronic textbook on spreadsheet applications for business. The fixed cost of manuscript preparation, textbook design, and website construction is estimated to be $160,000. Variable processing costs are estimated to be $6 per book. The publisher plans to sell access to the book for $46 each.
a. Build a spreadsheet model to calculate the profit/loss for a given demand. What profit can be anticipated with a demand of 3500 copies?
b. Use a data table to vary demand from 1000 to 6000 increments of 200 to assess the sensitivity of profit to demand.
c. Use Goal Seek to determine the access price per copy that the publisher must charge to break even with a demand of 3500 copies.

OM455

8. Open the workbook *OM455*. Save the file under a new name, *OM455COUNTIF*. Suppose we wish to automatically count the number of each letter grade.
a. Begin by putting the letters A, B, C, D, and F in cells C29:C33. Use the COUNTIF function in cells D29:D33 to count the number of each letter grade. *Hint:* Create the necessary COUNTIF function in cell D29. Use absolute referencing on the range ($E14:$E$24) and then copy the function to cells D30:D33 to count the number of each of the other letter grades.
b. We are considering a different grading scale as follows:

Lower	Upper	Grade
0	69	F
70	76	D
77	84	C
85	92	B
93	100	A

For the current list of students, use the COUNTIF function to determine the number of A, B, C, D, and F letter grades earned under this new system.

OM455

9. Open the workbook *OM455*. Save the file under a new name, *OM455Revised*. Suppose we wish to use a more refined grading system, as shown below:

Lower	Upper	Grade
0	59	F
60	69	D
70	72	C−
73	76	C−
77	79	C+
80	82	B−
83	86	B
87	89	B+
90	92	A−
93	100	A

Update the file to use this more refined grading system. How many of each letter grade are awarded under the new system? *Hint:* Build a new grading table and use VLOOKUP and an absolute reference to the table. Then use COUNTIF to count the number of each letter grade.

10. Richardson Ski Racing (RSR) sells equipment needed for downhill ski racing. One of RSR's products is fencing used on downhill courses. The fence product comes in 150-foot rolls and sells for $215 per roll. However, RSR offers quantity discounts. The following table shows the price per roll depending on order size:

RSR

Quantity Ordered		
From	To	Price per Roll
1	50	$215
51	100	$195
101	200	$175
201	and up	$155

The file RSR contains 172 orders that have arrived for the coming six weeks.

a. Use the VLOOKUP function with the preceding pricing table to determine the total revenue from these orders.

b. Use the COUNTIF function to determine the number of orders in each price bin.

NewtonData

11. Newton Manufacturing produces scientific calculators. The models are N350, N450, and the N900. Newton has planned its distribution of these products around eight customer zones: Brazil, China, France, Malaysia, U.S. Northeast, U.S. Southeast, U.S. Midwest, and U.S. West. Data for the current quarter (volume to be shipped in thousands of units) for each product and each customer zone are given in the file *NewtonData*.

Newton would like to know the total number of units going to each customer zone and also the total units of each product shipped. There are several ways to get this information from the data set. One way is to use the SUMIF function.

The SUMIF function extends the SUM function by allowing the user to add the values of cells meeting a logical condition. This general form of the function is

=SUMIF(*test range, condition, range to be summed*)

The *test range* is an area to search to test the *condition,* and the *range to be summed* is the position of the data to be summed. So, for example, using the *NewtonData* file, we would use the following function to get the total units sent to Malaysia:

=SUMIF(A3:A26,A3,C3:C26)

Here, A3 is Malaysia, A3:A26 is the range of customer zones, and C3:C26 are the volumes for each product for these customer zones. The SUMIF looks for matches of Malaysia in column A and, if a match is found, adds the volume to the total. Use the SUMIF function to get each total volume by zone and each total volume by product.

Williamson

12. Consider the transportation model given in the Excel file *Williamson.* It is a model that is very similar to the Foster Generators model. Williamson produces a single product and has plants in Atlanta, Lexington, Chicago, and Salt Lake City and warehouses in Portland, St. Paul, Las Vegas, Tuscon, and Cleveland. Each plant has a capacity and each warehouse has a demand. Williamson would like to find a low-cost shipping plan. Mr. Williamson has reviewed the results and notices right away that the total cost is way out of line. Use the Formula Auditing Tools under the FORMULAS tab in Excel to find any errors in this model. Correct the errors. *Hint:* There are two errors in this model. Be sure to check every formula.

Appendix B Binomial Probabilities

Entries in the following table give the probability of x successes in n trials of a binomial experiment, where p is the probability of a success on one trial. For example, with $n = 6$ trials and $p = 0.40$, the probability of $x = 2$ successes is 0.3110.

		p									
n	x	**0.05**	**0.10**	**0.15**	**0.20**	**0.25**	**0.30**	**0.35**	**0.40**	**0.45**	**0.50**
1	0	0.9500	0.9000	0.8500	0.8000	0.7500	0.7000	0.6500	0.6000	0.5500	0.5000
	1	0.0500	0.1000	0.1500	0.2000	0.2500	0.3000	0.3500	0.4000	0.4500	0.5000
2	0	0.9025	0.8100	0.7225	0.6400	0.5625	0.4900	0.4225	0.3600	0.3025	0.2500
	1	0.0950	0.1800	0.2550	0.3200	0.3750	0.4200	0.4550	0.4800	0.4950	0.5000
	2	0.0025	0.0100	0.0225	0.0400	0.0625	0.0900	0.1225	0.1600	0.2025	0.2500
3	0	0.8574	0.7290	0.6141	0.5120	0.4219	0.3430	0.2746	0.2160	0.1664	0.1250
	1	0.1354	0.2430	0.3251	0.3840	0.4219	0.4410	0.4436	0.4320	0.4084	0.3750
	2	0.0071	0.0270	0.0574	0.0960	0.1406	0.1890	0.2389	0.2880	0.3341	0.3750
	3	0.0001	0.0010	0.0034	0.0080	0.0156	0.0270	0.0429	0.0640	0.0911	0.1250
4	0	0.8145	0.6561	0.5220	0.4096	0.3164	0.2401	0.1785	0.1296	0.0915	0.0625
	1	0.1715	0.2916	0.3685	0.4096	0.4219	0.4116	0.3845	0.3456	0.2995	0.2500
	2	0.0135	0.0486	0.0975	0.1536	0.2109	0.2646	0.3105	0.3456	0.3675	0.3750
	3	0.0005	0.0036	0.0115	0.0256	0.0469	0.0756	0.1115	0.1536	0.2005	0.2500
	4	0.0000	0.0001	0.0005	0.0016	0.0039	0.0081	0.0150	0.0256	0.0410	0.0625
5	0	0.7738	0.5905	0.4437	0.3277	0.2373	0.1681	0.1160	0.0778	0.0503	0.0312
	1	0.2036	0.3280	0.3915	0.4096	0.3955	0.3602	0.3124	0.2592	0.2059	0.1562
	2	0.0214	0.0729	0.1382	0.2048	0.2637	0.3087	0.3364	0.3456	0.3369	0.3125
	3	0.0011	0.0081	0.0244	0.0512	0.0879	0.1323	0.1811	0.2304	0.2757	0.3125
	4	0.0000	0.0004	0.0022	0.0064	0.0146	0.0284	0.0488	0.0768	0.1128	0.1562
	5	0.0000	0.0000	0.0001	0.0003	0.0010	0.0024	0.0053	0.0102	0.0185	0.0312
6	0	0.7351	0.5314	0.3771	0.2621	0.1780	0.1176	0.0754	0.0467	0.0277	0.0156
	1	0.2321	0.3543	0.3993	0.3932	0.3560	0.3025	0.2437	0.1866	0.1359	0.0938
	2	0.0305	0.0984	0.1762	0.2458	0.2966	0.3241	0.3280	0.3110	0.2780	0.2344
	3	0.0021	0.0146	0.0415	0.0819	0.1318	0.1852	0.2355	0.2765	0.3032	0.3125
	4	0.0001	0.0012	0.0055	0.0154	0.0330	0.0595	0.0951	0.1382	0.1861	0.2344
	5	0.0000	0.0001	0.0004	0.0015	0.0044	0.0102	0.0205	0.0369	0.0609	0.0938
	6	0.0000	0.0000	0.0000	0.0001	0.0002	0.0007	0.0018	0.0041	0.0083	0.0156
7	0	0.6983	0.4783	0.3206	0.2097	0.1335	0.0824	0.0490	0.0280	0.0152	0.0078
	1	0.2573	0.3720	0.3960	0.3670	0.3115	0.2471	0.1848	0.1306	0.0872	0.0547
	2	0.0406	0.1240	0.2097	0.2753	0.3115	0.3177	0.2985	0.2613	0.2140	0.1641
	3	0.0036	0.0230	0.0617	0.1147	0.1730	0.2269	0.2679	0.2903	0.2918	0.2734
	4	0.0002	0.0026	0.0109	0.0287	0.0577	0.0972	0.1442	0.1935	0.2388	0.2734
	5	0.0000	0.0002	0.0012	0.0043	0.0115	0.0250	0.0466	0.0774	0.1172	0.1641
	6	0.0000	0.0000	0.0001	0.0004	0.0013	0.0036	0.0084	0.0172	0.0320	0.0547
	7	0.0000	0.0000	0.0000	0.0000	0.0001	0.0002	0.0006	0.0016	0.0037	0.0078

Binomial Probabilities (*Continued*)

		p									
n	*x*	**0.05**	**0.10**	**0.15**	**0.20**	**0.25**	**0.30**	**0.35**	**0.40**	**0.45**	**0.50**
8	0	0.6634	0.4305	0.2725	0.1678	0.1001	0.0576	0.0319	0.0168	0.0084	0.0039
	1	0.2793	0.3826	0.3847	0.3355	0.2670	0.1977	0.1373	0.0896	0.0548	0.0312
	2	0.0515	0.1488	0.2376	0.2936	0.3115	0.2965	0.2587	0.2090	0.1569	0.1094
	3	0.0054	0.0331	0.0839	0.1468	0.2076	0.2541	0.2786	0.2787	0.2568	0.2188
	4	0.0004	0.0046	0.0185	0.0459	0.0865	0.1361	0.1875	0.2322	0.2627	0.2734
	5	0.0000	0.0004	0.0026	0.0092	0.0231	0.0467	0.0808	0.1239	0.1719	0.2188
	6	0.0000	0.0000	0.0002	0.0011	0.0038	0.0100	0.0217	0.0413	0.0703	0.1094
	7	0.0000	0.0000	0.0000	0.0001	0.0004	0.0012	0.0033	0.0079	0.0164	0.0312
	8	0.0000	0.0000	0.0000	0.0000	0.0000	0.0001	0.0002	0.0007	0.0017	0.0039
9	0	0.6302	0.3874	0.2316	0.1342	0.0751	0.0404	0.0207	0.0101	0.0046	0.0020
	1	0.2985	0.3874	0.3679	0.3020	0.2253	0.1556	0.1004	0.0605	0.0339	0.0176
	2	0.0629	0.1722	0.2597	0.3020	0.3003	0.2668	0.2162	0.1612	0.1110	0.0703
	3	0.0077	0.0446	0.1069	0.1762	0.2336	0.2668	0.2716	0.2508	0.2119	0.1641
	4	0.0006	0.0074	0.0283	0.0661	0.1168	0.1715	0.2194	0.2508	0.2600	0.2461
	5	0.0000	0.0008	0.0050	0.0165	0.0389	0.0735	0.1181	0.1672	0.2128	0.2461
	6	0.0000	0.0001	0.0006	0.0028	0.0087	0.0210	0.0424	0.0743	0.1160	0.1641
	7	0.0000	0.0000	0.0000	0.0003	0.0012	0.0039	0.0098	0.0212	0.0407	0.0703
	8	0.0000	0.0000	0.0000	0.0000	0.0001	0.0004	0.0013	0.0035	0.0083	0.0176
	9	0.0000	0.0000	0.0000	0.0000	0.0000	0.0000	0.0001	0.0003	0.0008	0.0020
10	0	0.5987	0.3487	0.1969	0.1074	0.0563	0.0282	0.0135	0.0060	0.0025	0.0010
	1	0.3151	0.3874	0.3474	0.2684	0.1877	0.1211	0.0725	0.0403	0.0207	0.0098
	2	0.0746	0.1937	0.2759	0.3020	0.2816	0.2335	0.1757	0.1209	0.0763	0.0439
	3	0.0105	0.0574	0.1298	0.2013	0.2503	0.2668	0.2522	0.2150	0.1665	0.1172
	4	0.0010	0.0112	0.0401	0.0881	0.1460	0.2001	0.2377	0.2508	0.2384	0.2051
	5	0.0001	0.0015	0.0085	0.0264	0.0584	0.1029	0.1536	0.2007	0.2340	0.2461
	6	0.0000	0.0001	0.0012	0.0055	0.0162	0.0368	0.0689	0.1115	0.1596	0.2051
	7	0.0000	0.0000	0.0001	0.0008	0.0031	0.0090	0.0212	0.0425	0.0746	0.1172
	8	0.0000	0.0000	0.0000	0.0001	0.0004	0.0014	0.0043	0.0106	0.0229	0.0439
	9	0.0000	0.0000	0.0000	0.0000	0.0000	0.0001	0.0005	0.0016	0.0042	0.0098
	10	0.0000	0.0000	0.0000	0.0000	0.0000	0.0000	0.0000	0.0001	0.0003	0.0010
12	0	0.5404	0.2824	0.1422	0.0687	0.0317	0.0138	0.0057	0.0022	0.0008	0.0002
	1	0.3413	0.3766	0.3012	0.2062	0.1267	0.0712	0.0368	0.0174	0.0075	0.0029
	2	0.0988	0.2301	0.2924	0.2835	0.2323	0.1678	0.1088	0.0639	0.0339	0.0161
	3	0.0173	0.0853	0.1720	0.2362	0.2581	0.2397	0.1954	0.1419	0.0923	0.0537
	4	0.0021	0.0213	0.0683	0.1329	0.1936	0.2311	0.2367	0.2128	0.1700	0.1208
	5	0.0002	0.0038	0.0193	0.0532	0.1032	0.1585	0.2039	0.2270	0.2225	0.1934
	6	0.0000	0.0005	0.0040	0.0155	0.0401	0.0792	0.1281	0.1766	0.2124	0.2256
	7	0.0000	0.0000	0.0006	0.0033	0.0115	0.0291	0.0591	0.1009	0.1489	0.1934
	8	0.0000	0.0000	0.0001	0.0005	0.0024	0.0078	0.0199	0.0420	0.0762	0.1208
	9	0.0000	0.0000	0.0000	0.0001	0.0004	0.0015	0.0048	0.0125	0.0277	0.0537
	10	0.0000	0.0000	0.0000	0.0000	0.0000	0.0002	0.0008	0.0025	0.0068	0.0161
	11	0.0000	0.0000	0.0000	0.0000	0.0000	0.0000	0.0001	0.0003	0.0010	0.0029
	12	0.0000	0.0000	0.0000	0.0000	0.0000	0.0000	0.0000	0.0000	0.0001	0.0002
15	0	0.4633	0.2059	0.0874	0.0352	0.0134	0.0047	0.0016	0.0005	0.0001	0.0000
	1	0.3658	0.3432	0.2312	0.1319	0.0668	0.0305	0.0126	0.0047	0.0016	0.0005
	2	0.1348	0.2669	0.2856	0.2309	0.1559	0.0916	0.0476	0.0219	0.0090	0.0032

Binomial Probabilities (*Continued*)

		p									
n	*x*	**0.05**	**0.10**	**0.15**	**0.20**	**0.25**	**0.30**	**0.35**	**0.40**	**0.45**	**0.50**
	3	0.0307	0.1285	0.2184	0.2501	0.2252	0.1700	0.1110	0.0634	0.0318	0.0139
	4	0.0049	0.0428	0.1156	0.1876	0.2252	0.2186	0.1792	0.1268	0.0780	0.0417
	5	0.0006	0.0105	0.0449	0.1032	0.1651	0.2061	0.2123	0.1859	0.1404	0.0916
	6	0.0000	0.0019	0.0132	0.0430	0.0917	0.1472	0.1906	0.2066	0.1914	0.1527
	7	0.0000	0.0003	0.0030	0.0138	0.0393	0.0811	0.1319	0.1771	0.2013	0.1964
	8	0.0000	0.0000	0.0005	0.0035	0.0131	0.0348	0.0710	0.1181	0.1647	0.1964
	9	0.0000	0.0000	0.0001	0.0007	0.0034	0.0116	0.0298	0.0612	0.1048	0.1527
	10	0.0000	0.0000	0.0000	0.0001	0.0007	0.0030	0.0096	0.0245	0.0515	0.0916
	11	0.0000	0.0000	0.0000	0.0000	0.0001	0.0006	0.0024	0.0074	0.0191	0.0417
	12	0.0000	0.0000	0.0000	0.0000	0.0000	0.0001	0.0004	0.0016	0.0052	0.0139
	13	0.0000	0.0000	0.0000	0.0000	0.0000	0.0000	0.0001	0.0003	0.0010	0.0032
	14	0.0000	0.0000	0.0000	0.0000	0.0000	0.0000	0.0000	0.0000	0.0001	0.0005
	15	0.0000	0.0000	0.0000	0.0000	0.0000	0.0000	0.0000	0.0000	0.0000	0.0000
18	0	0.3972	0.1501	0.0536	0.0180	0.0056	0.0016	0.0004	0.0001	0.0000	0.0000
	1	0.3763	0.3002	0.1704	0.0811	0.0338	0.0126	0.0042	0.0012	0.0003	0.0001
	2	0.1683	0.2835	0.2556	0.1723	0.0958	0.0458	0.0190	0.0069	0.0022	0.0006
	3	0.0473	0.1680	0.2406	0.2297	0.1704	0.1046	0.0547	0.0246	0.0095	0.0031
	4	0.0093	0.0700	0.1592	0.2153	0.2130	0.1681	0.1104	0.0614	0.0291	0.0117
	5	0.0014	0.0218	0.0787	0.1507	0.1988	0.2017	0.1664	0.1146	0.0666	0.0327
	6	0.0002	0.0052	0.0301	0.0816	0.1436	0.1873	0.1941	0.1655	0.1181	0.0708
	7	0.0000	0.0010	0.0091	0.0350	0.0820	0.1376	0.1792	0.1892	0.1657	0.1214
	8	0.0000	0.0002	0.0022	0.0120	0.0376	0.0811	0.1327	0.1734	0.1864	0.1669
	9	0.0000	0.0000	0.0004	0.0033	0.0139	0.0386	0.0794	0.1284	0.1694	0.1855
	10	0.0000	0.0000	0.0001	0.0008	0.0042	0.0149	0.0385	0.0771	0.1248	0.1669
	11	0.0000	0.0000	0.0000	0.0001	0.0010	0.0046	0.0151	0.0374	0.0742	0.1214
	12	0.0000	0.0000	0.0000	0.0000	0.0002	0.0012	0.0047	0.0145	0.0354	0.0708
	13	0.0000	0.0000	0.0000	0.0000	0.0000	0.0002	0.0012	0.0045	0.0134	0.0327
	14	0.0000	0.0000	0.0000	0.0000	0.0000	0.0000	0.0002	0.0011	0.0039	0.0117
	15	0.0000	0.0000	0.0000	0.0000	0.0000	0.0000	0.0000	0.0002	0.0009	0.0031
	16	0.0000	0.0000	0.0000	0.0000	0.0000	0.0000	0.0000	0.0000	0.0001	0.0006
	17	0.0000	0.0000	0.0000	0.0000	0.0000	0.0000	0.0000	0.0000	0.0000	0.0001
	18	0.0000	0.0000	0.0000	0.0000	0.0000	0.0000	0.0000	0.0000	0.0000	0.0000
20	0	0.3585	0.1216	0.0388	0.0115	0.0032	0.0008	0.0002	0.0000	0.0000	0.0000
	1	0.3774	0.2702	0.1368	0.0576	0.0211	0.0068	0.0020	0.0005	0.0001	0.0000
	2	0.1887	0.2852	0.2293	0.1369	0.0669	0.0278	0.0100	0.0031	0.0008	0.0002
	3	0.0596	0.1901	0.2428	0.2054	0.1339	0.0716	0.0323	0.0123	0.0040	0.0011
	4	0.0133	0.0898	0.1821	0.2182	0.1897	0.1304	0.0738	0.0350	0.0139	0.0046
	5	0.0022	0.0319	0.1028	0.1746	0.2023	0.1789	0.1272	0.0746	0.0365	0.0148
	6	0.0003	0.0089	0.0454	0.1091	0.1686	0.1916	0.1712	0.1244	0.0746	0.0370
	7	0.0000	0.0020	0.0160	0.0545	0.1124	0.1643	0.1844	0.1659	0.1221	0.0739
	8	0.0000	0.0004	0.0046	0.0222	0.0609	0.1144	0.1614	0.1797	0.1623	0.1201
	9	0.0000	0.0001	0.0011	0.0074	0.0271	0.0654	0.1158	0.1597	0.1771	0.1602
	10	0.0000	0.0000	0.0002	0.0020	0.0099	0.0308	0.0686	0.1171	0.1593	0.1762
	11	0.0000	0.0000	0.0000	0.0005	0.0030	0.0120	0.0336	0.0710	0.1185	0.1602
	12	0.0000	0.0000	0.0000	0.0001	0.0008	0.0039	0.0136	0.0355	0.0727	0.1201
	13	0.0000	0.0000	0.0000	0.0000	0.0002	0.0010	0.0045	0.0146	0.0366	0.0739
	14	0.0000	0.0000	0.0000	0.0000	0.0000	0.0002	0.0012	0.0049	0.0150	0.0370

Binomial Probabilities (*Continued*)

		p									
n	*x*	**0.05**	**0.10**	**0.15**	**0.20**	**0.25**	**0.30**	**0.35**	**0.40**	**0.45**	**0.50**
	15	0.0000	0.0000	0.0000	0.0000	0.0000	0.0000	0.0003	0.0013	0.0049	0.0148
	16	0.0000	0.0000	0.0000	0.0000	0.0000	0.0000	0.0000	0.0003	0.0013	0.0046
	17	0.0000	0.0000	0.0000	0.0000	0.0000	0.0000	0.0000	0.0000	0.0002	0.0011
	18	0.0000	0.0000	0.0000	0.0000	0.0000	0.0000	0.0000	0.0000	0.0000	0.0002
	19	0.0000	0.0000	0.0000	0.0000	0.0000	0.0000	0.0000	0.0000	0.0000	0.0000
	20	0.0000	0.0000	0.0000	0.0000	0.0000	0.0000	0.0000	0.0000	0.0000	0.0000

Binomial Probabilities (*Continued*)

n	x	0.55	0.60	0.65	0.70	0.75	0.80	0.85	0.90	0.95
						p				
2	0	0.2025	0.1600	0.1225	0.0900	0.0625	0.0400	0.0225	0.0100	0.0025
	1	0.4950	0.4800	0.4550	0.4200	0.3750	0.3200	0.2550	0.1800	0.0950
	2	0.3025	0.3600	0.4225	0.4900	0.5625	0.6400	0.7225	0.8100	0.9025
3	0	0.0911	0.0640	0.0429	0.0270	0.0156	0.0080	0.0034	0.0010	0.0001
	1	0.3341	0.2880	0.2389	0.1890	0.1406	0.0960	0.0574	0.0270	0.0071
	2	0.4084	0.4320	0.4436	0.4410	0.4219	0.3840	0.3251	0.2430	0.1354
	3	0.1664	0.2160	0.2746	0.3430	0.4219	0.5120	0.6141	0.7290	0.8574
4	0	0.0410	0.0256	0.0150	0.0081	0.0039	0.0016	0.0005	0.0001	0.0000
	1	0.2005	0.1536	0.1115	0.0756	0.0469	0.0256	0.0115	0.0036	0.0005
	2	0.3675	0.3456	0.3105	0.2646	0.2109	0.1536	0.0975	0.0486	0.0135
	3	0.2995	0.3456	0.3845	0.4116	0.4219	0.4096	0.3685	0.2916	0.1715
	4	0.0915	0.1296	0.1785	0.2401	0.3164	0.4096	0.5220	0.6561	0.8145
5	0	0.0185	0.0102	0.0053	0.0024	0.0010	0.0003	0.0001	0.0000	0.0000
	1	0.1128	0.0768	0.0488	0.0284	0.0146	0.0064	0.0022	0.0005	0.0000
	2	0.2757	0.2304	0.1811	0.1323	0.0879	0.0512	0.0244	0.0081	0.0011
	3	0.3369	0.3456	0.3364	0.3087	0.2637	0.2048	0.1382	0.0729	0.0214
	4	0.2059	0.2592	0.3124	0.3601	0.3955	0.4096	0.3915	0.3281	0.2036
	5	0.0503	0.0778	0.1160	0.1681	0.2373	0.3277	0.4437	0.5905	0.7738
6	0	0.0083	0.0041	0.0018	0.0007	0.0002	0.0001	0.0000	0.0000	0.0000
	1	0.0609	0.0369	0.0205	0.0102	0.0044	0.0015	0.0004	0.0001	0.0000
	2	0.1861	0.1382	0.0951	0.0595	0.0330	0.0154	0.0055	0.0012	0.0001
	3	0.3032	0.2765	0.2355	0.1852	0.1318	0.0819	0.0415	0.0146	0.0021
	4	0.2780	0.3110	0.3280	0.3241	0.2966	0.2458	0.1762	0.0984	0.0305
	5	0.1359	0.1866	0.2437	0.3025	0.3560	0.3932	0.3993	0.3543	0.2321
	6	0.0277	0.0467	0.0754	0.1176	0.1780	0.2621	0.3771	0.5314	0.7351
7	0	0.0037	0.0016	0.0006	0.0002	0.0001	0.0000	0.0000	0.0000	0.0000
	1	0.0320	0.0172	0.0084	0.0036	0.0013	0.0004	0.0001	0.0000	0.0000
	2	0.1172	0.0774	0.0466	0.0250	0.0115	0.0043	0.0012	0.0002	0.0000
	3	0.2388	0.1935	0.1442	0.0972	0.0577	0.0287	0.0109	0.0026	0.0002
	4	0.2918	0.2903	0.2679	0.2269	0.1730	0.1147	0.0617	0.0230	0.0036
	5	0.2140	0.2613	0.2985	0.3177	0.3115	0.2753	0.2097	0.1240	0.0406
	6	0.0872	0.1306	0.1848	0.2471	0.3115	0.3670	0.3960	0.3720	0.2573
	7	0.0152	0.0280	0.0490	0.0824	0.1335	0.2097	0.3206	0.4783	0.6983
8	0	0.0017	0.0007	0.0002	0.0001	0.0000	0.0000	0.0000	0.0000	0.0000
	1	0.0164	0.0079	0.0033	0.0012	0.0004	0.0001	0.0000	0.0000	0.0000
	2	0.0703	0.0413	0.0217	0.0100	0.0038	0.0011	0.0002	0.0000	0.0000
	3	0.1719	0.1239	0.0808	0.0467	0.0231	0.0092	0.0026	0.0004	0.0000
	4	0.2627	0.2322	0.1875	0.1361	0.0865	0.0459	0.0185	0.0046	0.0004
	5	0.2568	0.2787	0.2786	0.2541	0.2076	0.1468	0.0839	0.0331	0.0054
	6	0.1569	0.2090	0.2587	0.2965	0.3115	0.2936	0.2376	0.1488	0.0515
	7	0.0548	0.0896	0.1373	0.1977	0.2670	0.3355	0.3847	0.3826	0.2793
	8	0.0084	0.0168	0.0319	0.0576	0.1001	0.1678	0.2725	0.4305	0.6634

Binomial Probabilities (*Continued*)

n	x	0.55	0.60	0.65	0.70	0.75	0.80	0.85	0.90	0.95
9	0	0.0008	0.0003	0.0001	0.0000	0.0000	0.0000	0.0000	0.0000	0.0000
	1	0.0083	0.0035	0.0013	0.0004	0.0001	0.0000	0.0000	0.0000	0.0000
	2	0.0407	0.0212	0.0098	0.0039	0.0012	0.0003	0.0000	0.0000	0.0000
	3	0.1160	0.0743	0.0424	0.0210	0.0087	0.0028	0.0006	0.0001	0.0000
	4	0.2128	0.1672	0.1181	0.0735	0.0389	0.0165	0.0050	0.0008	0.0000
	5	0.2600	0.2508	0.2194	0.1715	0.1168	0.0661	0.0283	0.0074	0.0006
	6	0.2119	0.2508	0.2716	0.2668	0.2336	0.1762	0.1069	0.0446	0.0077
	7	0.1110	0.1612	0.2162	0.2668	0.3003	0.3020	0.2597	0.1722	0.0629
	8	0.0339	0.0605	0.1004	0.1556	0.2253	0.3020	0.3679	0.3874	0.2985
	9	0.0046	0.0101	0.0207	0.0404	0.0751	0.1342	0.2316	0.3874	0.6302
10	0	0.0003	0.0001	0.0000	0.0000	0.0000	0.0000	0.0000	0.0000	0.0000
	1	0.0042	0.0016	0.0005	0.0001	0.0000	0.0000	0.0000	0.0000	0.0000
	2	0.0229	0.0106	0.0043	0.0014	0.0004	0.0001	0.0000	0.0000	0.0000
	3	0.0746	0.0425	0.0212	0.0090	0.0031	0.0008	0.0001	0.0000	0.0000
	4	0.1596	0.1115	0.0689	0.0368	0.0162	0.0055	0.0012	0.0001	0.0000
	5	0.2340	0.2007	0.1536	0.1029	0.0584	0.0264	0.0085	0.0015	0.0001
	6	0.2384	0.2508	0.2377	0.2001	0.1460	0.0881	0.0401	0.0112	0.0010
	7	0.1665	0.2150	0.2522	0.2668	0.2503	0.2013	0.1298	0.0574	0.0105
	8	0.0763	0.1209	0.1757	0.2335	0.2816	0.3020	0.2759	0.1937	0.0746
	9	0.0207	0.0403	0.0725	0.1211	0.1877	0.2684	0.3474	0.3874	0.3151
	10	0.0025	0.0060	0.0135	0.0282	0.0563	0.1074	0.1969	0.3487	0.5987
12	0	0.0001	0.0000	0.0000	0.0000	0.0000	0.0000	0.0000	0.0000	0.0000
	1	0.0010	0.0003	0.0001	0.0000	0.0000	0.0000	0.0000	0.0000	0.0000
	2	0.0068	0.0025	0.0008	0.0002	0.0000	0.0000	0.0000	0.0000	0.0000
	3	0.0277	0.0125	0.0048	0.0015	0.0004	0.0001	0.0000	0.0000	0.0000
	4	0.0762	0.0420	0.0199	0.0078	0.0024	0.0005	0.0001	0.0000	0.0000
	5	0.1489	0.1009	0.0591	0.0291	0.0115	0.0033	0.0006	0.0000	0.0000
	6	0.2124	0.1766	0.1281	0.0792	0.0401	0.0155	0.0040	0.0005	0.0000
	7	0.2225	0.2270	0.2039	0.1585	0.1032	0.0532	0.0193	0.0038	0.0002
	8	0.1700	0.2128	0.2367	0.2311	0.1936	0.1329	0.0683	0.0213	0.0021
	9	0.0923	0.1419	0.1954	0.2397	0.2581	0.2362	0.1720	0.0852	0.0173
	10	0.0339	0.0639	0.1088	0.1678	0.2323	0.2835	0.2924	0.2301	0.0988
	11	0.0075	0.0174	0.0368	0.0712	0.1267	0.2062	0.3012	0.3766	0.3413
	12	0.0008	0.0022	0.0057	0.0138	0.0317	0.0687	0.1422	0.2824	0.5404
15	0	0.0000	0.0000	0.0000	0.0000	0.0000	0.0000	0.0000	0.0000	0.0000
	1	0.0001	0.0000	0.0000	0.0000	0.0000	0.0000	0.0000	0.0000	0.0000
	2	0.0010	0.0003	0.0001	0.0000	0.0000	0.0000	0.0000	0.0000	0.0000
	3	0.0052	0.0016	0.0004	0.0001	0.0000	0.0000	0.0000	0.0000	0.0000
	4	0.0191	0.0074	0.0024	0.0006	0.0001	0.0000	0.0000	0.0000	0.0000
	5	0.0515	0.0245	0.0096	0.0030	0.0007	0.0001	0.0000	0.0000	0.0000
	6	0.1048	0.0612	0.0298	0.0116	0.0034	0.0007	0.0001	0.0000	0.0000
	7	0.1647	0.1181	0.0710	0.0348	0.0131	0.0035	0.0005	0.0000	0.0000
	8	0.2013	0.1771	0.1319	0.0811	0.0393	0.0138	0.0030	0.0003	0.0000
	9	0.1914	0.2066	0.1906	0.1472	0.0917	0.0430	0.0132	0.0019	0.0000
	10	0.1404	0.1859	0.2123	0.2061	0.1651	0.1032	0.0449	0.0105	0.0006
	11	0.0780	0.1268	0.1792	0.2186	0.2252	0.1876	0.1156	0.0428	0.0049

Binomial Probabilities (*Continued*)

		p								
n	*x*	**0.55**	**0.60**	**0.65**	**0.70**	**0.75**	**0.80**	**0.85**	**0.90**	**0.95**
	12	0.0318	0.0634	0.1110	0.1700	0.2252	0.2501	0.2184	0.1285	0.0307
	13	0.0090	0.0219	0.0476	0.0916	0.1559	0.2309	0.2856	0.2669	0.1348
	14	0.0016	0.0047	0.0126	0.0305	0.0668	0.1319	0.2312	0.3432	0.3658
	15	0.0001	0.0005	0.0016	0.0047	0.0134	0.0352	0.0874	0.2059	0.4633
18	0	0.0000	0.0000	0.0000	0.0000	0.0000	0.0000	0.0000	0.0000	0.0000
	1	0.0000	0.0000	0.0000	0.0000	0.0000	0.0000	0.0000	0.0000	0.0000
	2	0.0001	0.0000	0.0000	0.0000	0.0000	0.0000	0.0000	0.0000	0.0000
	3	0.0009	0.0002	0.0000	0.0000	0.0000	0.0000	0.0000	0.0000	0.0000
	4	0.0039	0.0011	0.0002	0.0000	0.0000	0.0000	0.0000	0.0000	0.0000
	5	0.0134	0.0045	0.0012	0.0002	0.0000	0.0000	0.0000	0.0000	0.0000
	6	0.0354	0.0145	0.0047	0.0012	0.0002	0.0000	0.0000	0.0000	0.0000
	7	0.0742	0.0374	0.0151	0.0046	0.0010	0.0001	0.0000	0.0000	0.0000
	8	0.1248	0.0771	0.0385	0.0149	0.0042	0.0008	0.0001	0.0000	0.0000
	9	0.1694	0.1284	0.0794	0.0386	0.0139	0.0033	0.0004	0.0000	0.0000
	10	0.1864	0.1734	0.1327	0.0811	0.0376	0.0120	0.0022	0.0002	0.0000
	11	0.1657	0.1892	0.1792	0.1376	0.0820	0.0350	0.0091	0.0010	0.0000
	12	0.1181	0.1655	0.1941	0.1873	0.1436	0.0816	0.0301	0.0052	0.0002
	13	0.0666	0.1146	0.1664	0.2017	0.1988	0.1507	0.0787	0.0218	0.0014
	14	0.0291	0.0614	0.1104	0.1681	0.2130	0.2153	0.1592	0.0700	0.0093
	15	0.0095	0.0246	0.0547	0.1046	0.1704	0.2297	0.2406	0.1680	0.0473
	16	0.0022	0.0069	0.0190	0.0458	0.0958	0.1723	0.2556	0.2835	0.1683
	17	0.0003	0.0012	0.0042	0.0126	0.0338	0.0811	0.1704	0.3002	0.3763
	18	0.0000	0.0001	0.0004	0.0016	0.0056	0.0180	0.0536	0.1501	0.3972
20	0	0.0000	0.0000	0.0000	0.0000	0.0000	0.0000	0.0000	0.0000	0.0000
	1	0.0000	0.0000	0.0000	0.0000	0.0000	0.0000	0.0000	0.0000	0.0000
	2	0.0000	0.0000	0.0000	0.0000	0.0000	0.0000	0.0000	0.0000	0.0000
	3	0.0002	0.0000	0.0000	0.0000	0.0000	0.0000	0.0000	0.0000	0.0000
	4	0.0013	0.0003	0.0000	0.0000	0.0000	0.0000	0.0000	0.0000	0.0000
	5	0.0049	0.0013	0.0003	0.0000	0.0000	0.0000	0.0000	0.0000	0.0000
	6	0.0150	0.0049	0.0012	0.0002	0.0000	0.0000	0.0000	0.0000	0.0000
	7	0.0366	0.0146	0.0045	0.0010	0.0002	0.0000	0.0000	0.0000	0.0000
	8	0.0727	0.0355	0.0136	0.0039	0.0008	0.0001	0.0000	0.0000	0.0000
	9	0.1185	0.0710	0.0336	0.0120	0.0030	0.0005	0.0000	0.0000	0.0000
	10	0.1593	0.1171	0.0686	0.0308	0.0099	0.0020	0.0002	0.0000	0.0000
	11	0.1771	0.1597	0.1158	0.0654	0.0271	0.0074	0.0011	0.0001	0.0000
	12	0.1623	0.1797	0.1614	0.1144	0.0609	0.0222	0.0046	0.0004	0.0000
	13	0.1221	0.1659	0.1844	0.1643	0.1124	0.0545	0.0160	0.0020	0.0000
	14	0.0746	0.1244	0.1712	0.1916	0.1686	0.1091	0.0454	0.0089	0.0003
	15	0.0365	0.0746	0.1272	0.1789	0.2023	0.1746	0.1028	0.0319	0.0022
	16	0.0139	0.0350	0.0738	0.1304	0.1897	0.2182	0.1821	0.0898	0.0133
	17	0.0040	0.0123	0.0323	0.0716	0.1339	0.2054	0.2428	0.1901	0.0596
	18	0.0008	0.0031	0.0100	0.0278	0.0669	0.1369	0.2293	0.2852	0.1887
	19	0.0001	0.0005	0.0020	0.0068	0.0211	0.0576	0.1368	0.2702	0.3774
	20	0.0000	0.0000	0.0002	0.0008	0.0032	0.0115	0.0388	0.1216	0.3585

Appendix C Poisson Probabilities

Entries in the following table give the probability of x occurrences for a Poisson process with a mean λ. For example, when $\lambda = 2.5$, the probability of $x = 4$ occurrences is 0.1336.

	λ									
x	**0.1**	**0.2**	**0.3**	**0.4**	**0.5**	**0.6**	**0.7**	**0.8**	**0.9**	**1.0**
0	0.9048	0.8187	0.7408	0.6703	0.6065	0.5488	0.4966	0.4493	0.4066	0.3679
1	0.0905	0.1637	0.2222	0.2681	0.3033	0.3293	0.3476	0.3595	0.3659	0.3679
2	0.0045	0.0164	0.0333	0.0536	0.0758	0.0988	0.1217	0.1438	0.1647	0.1839
3	0.0002	0.0011	0.0033	0.0072	0.0126	0.0198	0.0284	0.0383	0.0494	0.0613
4	0.0000	0.0001	0.0002	0.0007	0.0016	0.0030	0.0050	0.0077	0.0111	0.0153
5	0.0000	0.0000	0.0000	0.0001	0.0002	0.0004	0.0007	0.0012	0.0020	0.0031
6	0.0000	0.0000	0.0000	0.0000	0.0000	0.0000	0.0001	0.0002	0.0003	0.0005
7	0.0000	0.0000	0.0000	0.0000	0.0000	0.0000	0.0000	0.0000	0.0000	0.0001

	λ									
x	**1.1**	**1.2**	**1.3**	**1.4**	**1.5**	**1.6**	**1.7**	**1.8**	**1.9**	**2.0**
0	0.3329	0.3012	0.2725	0.2466	0.2231	0.2019	0.1827	0.1653	0.1496	0.1353
1	0.3662	0.3614	0.3543	0.3452	0.3347	0.3230	0.3106	0.2975	0.2842	0.2707
2	0.2014	0.2169	0.2303	0.2417	0.2510	0.2584	0.2640	0.2678	0.2700	0.2707
3	0.0738	0.0867	0.0998	0.1128	0.1255	0.1378	0.1496	0.1607	0.1710	0.1804
4	0.0203	0.0260	0.0324	0.0395	0.0471	0.0551	0.0636	0.0723	0.0812	0.0902
5	0.0045	0.0062	0.0084	0.0111	0.0141	0.0176	0.0216	0.0260	0.0309	0.0361
6	0.0008	0.0012	0.0018	0.0026	0.0035	0.0047	0.0061	0.0078	0.0098	0.0120
7	0.0001	0.0002	0.0003	0.0005	0.0008	0.0011	0.0015	0.0020	0.0027	0.0034
8	0.0000	0.0000	0.0001	0.0001	0.0001	0.0002	0.0003	0.0005	0.0006	0.0009
9	0.0000	0.0000	0.0000	0.0000	0.0000	0.0000	0.0001	0.0001	0.0001	0.0002

	λ									
x	**2.1**	**2.2**	**2.3**	**2.4**	**2.5**	**2.6**	**2.7**	**2.8**	**2.9**	**3.0**
0	0.1225	0.1108	0.1003	0.0907	0.0821	0.0743	0.0672	0.0608	0.0550	0.0498
1	0.2572	0.2438	0.2306	0.2177	0.2052	0.1931	0.1815	0.1703	0.1596	0.1494
2	0.2700	0.2681	0.2652	0.2613	0.2565	0.2510	0.2450	0.2384	0.2314	0.2240
3	0.1890	0.1966	0.2033	0.2090	0.2138	0.2176	0.2205	0.2225	0.2237	0.2240
4	0.0992	0.1082	0.1169	0.1254	0.1336	0.1414	0.1488	0.1557	0.1622	0.1680
5	0.0417	0.0476	0.0538	0.0602	0.0668	0.0735	0.0804	0.0872	0.0940	0.1008
6	0.0146	0.0174	0.0206	0.0241	0.0278	0.0319	0.0362	0.0407	0.0455	0.0540
7	0.0044	0.0055	0.0068	0.0083	0.0099	0.0118	0.0139	0.0163	0.0188	0.0216

Poisson Probabilities (*Continued*)

x	2.1	2.2	2.3	2.4	2.5	2.6	2.7	2.8	2.9	3.0
8	0.0011	0.0015	0.0019	0.0025	0.0031	0.0038	0.0047	0.0057	0.0068	0.0081
9	0.0003	0.0004	0.0005	0.0007	0.0009	0.0011	0.0014	0.0018	0.0022	0.0027
10	0.0001	0.0001	0.0001	0.0002	0.0002	0.0003	0.0004	0.0005	0.0006	0.0008
11	0.0000	0.0000	0.0000	0.0000	0.0000	0.0001	0.0001	0.0001	0.0002	0.0002
12	0.0000	0.0000	0.0000	0.0000	0.0000	0.0000	0.0000	0.0000	0.0000	0.0001

x	3.1	3.2	3.3	3.4	3.5	3.6	3.7	3.8	3.9	4.0
0	0.0450	0.0408	0.0369	0.0344	0.0302	0.0273	0.0247	0.0224	0.0202	0.0183
1	0.1397	0.1304	0.1217	0.1135	0.1057	0.0984	0.0915	0.0850	0.0789	0.0733
2	0.2165	0.2087	0.2008	0.1929	0.1850	0.1771	0.1692	0.1615	0.1539	0.1465
3	0.2237	0.2226	0.2209	0.2186	0.2158	0.2125	0.2087	0.2046	0.2001	0.1954
4	0.1734	0.1781	0.1823	0.1858	0.1888	0.1912	0.1931	0.1944	0.1951	0.1954
5	0.1075	0.1140	0.1203	0.1264	0.1322	0.1377	0.1429	0.1477	0.1522	0.1563
6	0.0555	0.0608	0.0662	0.0716	0.0771	0.0826	0.0881	0.0936	0.0989	0.1042
7	0.0246	0.0278	0.0312	0.0348	0.0385	0.0425	0.0466	0.0508	0.0551	0.0595
8	0.0095	0.0111	0.0129	0.0148	0.0169	0.0191	0.0215	0.0241	0.0269	0.0298
9	0.0033	0.0040	0.0047	0.0056	0.0066	0.0076	0.0089	0.0102	0.0116	0.0132
10	0.0010	0.0013	0.0016	0.0019	0.0023	0.0028	0.0033	0.0039	0.0045	0.0053
11	0.0003	0.0004	0.0005	0.0006	0.0007	0.0009	0.0011	0.0013	0.0016	0.0019
12	0.0001	0.0001	0.0001	0.0002	0.0002	0.0003	0.0003	0.0004	0.0005	0.0006
13	0.0000	0.0000	0.0000	0.0000	0.0001	0.0001	0.0001	0.0001	0.0002	0.0002
14	0.0000	0.0000	0.0000	0.0000	0.0000	0.0000	0.0000	0.0000	0.0000	0.0001

x	4.1	4.2	4.3	4.4	4.5	4.6	4.7	4.8	4.9	5.0
0	0.0166	0.0150	0.0136	0.0123	0.0111	0.0101	0.0091	0.0082	0.0074	0.0067
1	0.0679	0.0630	0.0583	0.0540	0.0500	0.0462	0.0427	0.0395	0.0365	0.0337
2	0.1393	0.1323	0.1254	0.1188	0.1125	0.1063	0.1005	0.0948	0.0894	0.0842
3	0.1904	0.1852	0.1798	0.1743	0.1687	0.1631	0.1574	0.1517	0.1460	0.1404
4	0.1951	0.1944	0.1933	0.1917	0.1898	0.1875	0.1849	0.1820	0.1789	0.1755
5	0.1600	0.1633	0.1662	0.1687	0.1708	0.1725	0.1738	0.1747	0.1753	0.1755
6	0.1093	0.1143	0.1191	0.1237	0.1281	0.1323	0.1362	0.1398	0.1432	0.1462
7	0.0640	0.0686	0.0732	0.0778	0.0824	0.0869	0.0914	0.0959	0.1002	0.1044
8	0.0328	0.0360	0.0393	0.0428	0.0463	0.0500	0.0537	0.0575	0.0614	0.0653
9	0.0150	0.0168	0.0188	0.0209	0.0232	0.0255	0.0280	0.0307	0.0334	0.0363
10	0.0061	0.0071	0.0081	0.0092	0.0104	0.0118	0.0132	0.0147	0.0164	0.0181
11	0.0023	0.0027	0.0032	0.0037	0.0043	0.0049	0.0056	0.0064	0.0073	0.0082
12	0.0008	0.0009	0.0011	0.0014	0.0016	0.0019	0.0022	0.0026	0.0030	0.0034
13	0.0002	0.0003	0.0004	0.0005	0.0006	0.0007	0.0008	0.0009	0.0011	0.0013
14	0.0001	0.0001	0.0001	0.0001	0.0002	0.0002	0.0003	0.0003	0.0004	0.0005
15	0.0000	0.0000	0.0000	0.0000	0.0001	0.0001	0.0001	0.0001	0.0001	0.0002

Poisson Probabilities (*Continued*)

	λ									
x	**5.1**	**5.2**	**5.3**	**5.4**	**5.5**	**5.6**	**5.7**	**5.8**	**5.9**	**6.0**
0	0.0061	0.0055	0.0050	0.0045	0.0041	0.0037	0.0033	0.0030	0.0027	0.0025
1	0.0311	0.0287	0.0265	0.0244	0.0225	0.0207	0.0191	0.0176	0.0162	0.0149
2	0.0793	0.0746	0.0701	0.0659	0.0618	0.0580	0.0544	0.0509	0.0477	0.0446
3	0.1348	0.1293	0.1239	0.1185	0.1133	0.1082	0.1033	0.0985	0.0938	0.0892
4	0.1719	0.1681	0.1641	0.1600	0.1558	0.1515	0.1472	0.1428	0.1383	0.1339
5	0.1753	0.1748	0.1740	0.1728	0.1714	0.1697	0.1678	0.1656	0.1632	0.1606
6	0.1490	0.1515	0.1537	0.1555	0.1571	0.1587	0.1594	0.1601	0.1605	0.1606
7	0.1086	0.1125	0.1163	0.1200	0.1234	0.1267	0.1298	0.1326	0.1353	0.1377
8	0.0692	0.0731	0.0771	0.0810	0.0849	0.0887	0.0925	0.0962	0.0998	0.1033
9	0.0392	0.0423	0.0454	0.0486	0.0519	0.0552	0.0586	0.0620	0.0654	0.0688
10	0.0200	0.0220	0.0241	0.0262	0.0285	0.0309	0.0334	0.0359	0.0386	0.0413
11	0.0093	0.0104	0.0116	0.0129	0.0143	0.0157	0.0173	0.0190	0.0207	0.0225
12	0.0039	0.0045	0.0051	0.0058	0.0065	0.0073	0.0082	0.0092	0.0102	0.0113
13	0.0015	0.0018	0.0021	0.0024	0.0028	0.0032	0.0036	0.0041	0.0046	0.0052
14	0.0006	0.0007	0.0008	0.0009	0.0011	0.0013	0.0015	0.0017	0.0019	0.0022
15	0.0002	0.0002	0.0003	0.0003	0.0004	0.0005	0.0006	0.0007	0.0008	0.0009
16	0.0001	0.0001	0.0001	0.0001	0.0001	0.0002	0.0002	0.0002	0.0003	0.0003
17	0.0000	0.0000	0.0000	0.0000	0.0000	0.0001	0.0001	0.0001	0.0001	0.0001

	λ									
x	**6.1**	**6.2**	**6.3**	**6.4**	**6.5**	**6.6**	**6.7**	**6.8**	**6.9**	**7.0**
0	0.0022	0.0020	0.0018	0.0017	0.0015	0.0014	0.0012	0.0011	0.0010	0.0009
1	0.0137	0.0126	0.0116	0.0106	0.0098	0.0090	0.0082	0.0076	0.0070	0.0064
2	0.0417	0.0390	0.0364	0.0340	0.0318	0.0296	0.0276	0.0258	0.0240	0.0223
3	0.0848	0.0806	0.0765	0.0726	0.0688	0.0652	0.0617	0.0584	0.0552	0.0521
4	0.1294	0.1249	0.1205	0.1162	0.1118	0.1076	0.1034	0.0992	0.0952	0.0912
5	0.1579	0.1549	0.1519	0.1487	0.1454	0.1420	0.1385	0.1349	0.1314	0.1277
6	0.1605	0.1601	0.1595	0.1586	0.1575	0.1562	0.1546	0.1529	0.1511	0.1490
7	0.1399	0.1418	0.1435	0.1450	0.1462	0.1472	0.1480	0.1486	0.1489	0.1490
8	0.1066	0.1099	0.1130	0.1160	0.1188	0.1215	0.1240	0.1263	0.1284	0.1304
9	0.0723	0.0757	0.0791	0.0825	0.0858	0.0891	0.0923	0.0954	0.0985	0.1014
10	0.0441	0.0469	0.0498	0.0528	0.0558	0.0588	0.0618	0.0649	0.0679	0.0710
11	0.0245	0.0265	0.0285	0.0307	0.0330	0.0353	0.0377	0.0401	0.0426	0.0452
12	0.0124	0.0137	0.0150	0.0164	0.0179	0.0194	0.0210	0.0227	0.0245	0.0264
13	0.0058	0.0065	0.0073	0.0081	0.0089	0.0098	0.0108	0.0119	0.0130	0.0142
14	0.0025	0.0029	0.0033	0.0037	0.0041	0.0046	0.0052	0.0058	0.0064	0.0071
15	0.0010	0.0012	0.0014	0.0016	0.0018	0.0020	0.0023	0.0025	0.0029	0.0033
16	0.0004	0.0005	0.0005	0.0006	0.0007	0.0008	0.0010	0.0011	0.0013	0.0014
17	0.0001	0.0002	0.0002	0.0002	0.0003	0.0003	0.0004	0.0004	0.0005	0.0006
18	0.0000	0.0001	0.0001	0.0001	0.0001	0.0001	0.0001	0.0002	0.0002	0.0002
19	0.0000	0.0000	0.0000	0.0000	0.0000	0.0000	0.0000	0.0001	0.0001	0.0001

Poisson Probabilities (*Continued*)

	λ									
x	**7.1**	**7.2**	**7.3**	**7.4**	**7.5**	**7.6**	**7.7**	**7.8**	**7.9**	**8.0**
0	0.0008	0.0007	0.0007	0.0006	0.0006	0.0005	0.0005	0.0004	0.0004	0.0003
1	0.0059	0.0054	0.0049	0.0045	0.0041	0.0038	0.0035	0.0032	0.0029	0.0027
2	0.0208	0.0194	0.0180	0.0167	0.0156	0.0145	0.0134	0.0125	0.0116	0.0107
3	0.0492	0.0464	0.0438	0.0413	0.0389	0.0366	0.0345	0.0324	0.0305	0.0286
4	0.0874	0.0836	0.0799	0.0764	0.0729	0.0696	0.0663	0.0632	0.0602	0.0573
5	0.1241	0.1204	0.1167	0.1130	0.1094	0.1057	0.1021	0.0986	0.0951	0.0916
6	0.1468	0.1445	0.1420	0.1394	0.1367	0.1339	0.1311	0.1282	0.1252	0.1221
7	0.1489	0.1486	0.1481	0.1474	0.1465	0.1454	0.1442	0.1428	0.1413	0.1396
8	0.1321	0.1337	0.1351	0.1363	0.1373	0.1382	0.1388	0.1392	0.1395	0.1396
9	0.1042	0.1070	0.1096	0.1121	0.1144	0.1167	0.1187	0.1207	0.1224	0.1241
10	0.0740	0.0770	0.0800	0.0829	0.0858	0.0887	0.0914	0.0941	0.0967	0.0993
11	0.0478	0.0504	0.0531	0.0558	0.0585	0.0613	0.0640	0.0667	0.0695	0.0722
12	0.0283	0.0303	0.0323	0.0344	0.0366	0.0388	0.0411	0.0434	0.0457	0.0481
13	0.0154	0.0168	0.0181	0.0196	0.0211	0.0227	0.0243	0.0260	0.0278	0.0296
14	0.0078	0.0086	0.0095	0.0104	0.0113	0.0123	0.0134	0.0145	0.0157	0.0169
15	0.0037	0.0041	0.0046	0.0051	0.0057	0.0062	0.0069	0.0075	0.0083	0.0090
16	0.0016	0.0019	0.0021	0.0024	0.0026	0.0030	0.0033	0.0037	0.0041	0.0045
17	0.0007	0.0008	0.0009	0.0010	0.0012	0.0013	0.0015	0.0017	0.0019	0.0021
18	0.0003	0.0003	0.0004	0.0004	0.0005	0.0006	0.0006	0.0007	0.0008	0.0009
19	0.0001	0.0001	0.0001	0.0002	0.0002	0.0002	0.0003	0.0003	0.0003	0.0004
20	0.0000	0.0000	0.0001	0.0001	0.0001	0.0001	0.0001	0.0001	0.0001	0.0002
21	0.0000	0.0000	0.0000	0.0000	0.0000	0.0000	0.0000	0.0000	0.0001	0.0001

	λ									
x	**8.1**	**8.2**	**8.3**	**8.4**	**8.5**	**8.6**	**8.7**	**8.8**	**8.9**	**9.0**
0	0.0003	0.0003	0.0002	0.0002	0.0002	0.0002	0.0002	0.0002	0.0001	0.0001
1	0.0025	0.0023	0.0021	0.0019	0.0017	0.0016	0.0014	0.0013	0.0012	0.0011
2	0.0100	0.0092	0.0086	0.0079	0.0074	0.0068	0.0063	0.0058	0.0054	0.0050
3	0.0269	0.0252	0.0237	0.0222	0.0208	0.0195	0.0183	0.0171	0.0160	0.0150
4	0.0544	0.0517	0.0491	0.0466	0.0443	0.0420	0.0398	0.0377	0.0357	0.0337
5	0.0882	0.0849	0.0816	0.0784	0.0752	0.0722	0.0692	0.0663	0.0635	0.0607
6	0.1191	0.1160	0.1128	0.1097	0.1066	0.1034	0.1003	0.0972	0.0941	0.0911
7	0.1378	0.1358	0.1338	0.1317	0.1294	0.1271	0.1247	0.1222	0.1197	0.1171
8	0.1395	0.1392	0.1388	0.1382	0.1375	0.1366	0.1356	0.1344	0.1332	0.1318
9	0.1256	0.1269	0.1280	0.1290	0.1299	0.1306	0.1311	0.1315	0.1317	0.1318
10	0.1017	0.1040	0.1063	0.1084	0.1104	0.1123	0.1140	0.1157	0.1172	0.1186
11	0.0749	0.0776	0.0802	0.0828	0.0853	0.0878	0.0902	0.0925	0.0948	0.0970
12	0.0505	0.0530	0.0555	0.0579	0.0604	0.0629	0.0654	0.0679	0.0703	0.0728
13	0.0315	0.0334	0.0354	0.0374	0.0395	0.0416	0.0438	0.0459	0.0481	0.0504
14	0.0182	0.0196	0.0210	0.0225	0.0240	0.0256	0.0272	0.0289	0.0306	0.0324

Poisson Probabilities (*Continued*)

	λ									
x	**8.1**	**8.2**	**8.3**	**8.4**	**8.5**	**8.6**	**8.7**	**8.8**	**8.9**	**9.0**
15	0.0098	0.0107	0.0116	0.0126	0.0136	0.0147	0.0158	0.0169	0.0182	0.1094
16	0.0050	0.0055	0.0060	0.0066	0.0072	0.0079	0.0086	0.0093	0.0101	0.0109
17	0.0024	0.0026	0.0029	0.0033	0.0036	0.0040	0.0044	0.0048	0.0053	0.0058
18	0.0011	0.0012	0.0014	0.0015	0.0017	0.0019	0.0021	0.0024	0.0026	0.0029
19	0.0005	0.0005	0.0006	0.0007	0.0008	0.0009	0.0010	0.0011	0.0012	0.0014
20	0.0002	0.0002	0.0002	0.0003	0.0003	0.0004	0.0004	0.0005	0.0005	0.0006
21	0.0001	0.0001	0.0001	0.0001	0.0001	0.0002	0.0002	0.0002	0.0002	0.0003
22	0.0000	0.0000	0.0000	0.0000	0.0001	0.0001	0.0001	0.0001	0.0001	0.0001

	λ									
x	**9.1**	**9.2**	**9.3**	**9.4**	**9.5**	**9.6**	**9.7**	**9.8**	**9.9**	**10**
0	0.0001	0.0001	0.0001	0.0001	0.0001	0.0001	0.0001	0.0001	0.0001	0.0000
1	0.0010	0.0009	0.0009	0.0008	0.0007	0.0007	0.0006	0.0005	0.0005	0.0005
2	0.0046	0.0043	0.0040	0.0037	0.0034	0.0031	0.0029	0.0027	0.0025	0.0023
3	0.0140	0.0131	0.0123	0.0115	0.0107	0.0100	0.0093	0.0087	0.0081	0.0076
4	0.0319	0.0302	0.0285	0.0269	0.0254	0.0240	0.0226	0.0213	0.0201	0.0189
5	0.0581	0.0555	0.0530	0.0506	0.0483	0.0460	0.0439	0.0418	0.0398	0.0378
6	0.0881	0.0851	0.0822	0.0793	0.0764	0.0736	0.0709	0.0682	0.0656	0.0631
7	0.1145	0.1118	0.1091	0.1064	0.1037	0.1010	0.0982	0.0955	0.0928	0.0901
8	0.1302	0.1286	0.1269	0.1251	0.1232	0.1212	0.1191	0.1170	0.1148	0.1126
9	0.1317	0.1315	0.1311	0.1306	0.1300	0.1293	0.1284	0.1274	0.1263	0.1251
10	0.1198	0.1210	0.1219	0.1228	0.1235	0.1241	0.1245	0.1249	0.1250	0.1251
11	0.0991	0.1012	0.1031	0.1049	0.1067	0.1083	0.1098	0.1112	0.1125	0.1137
12	0.0752	0.0776	0.0799	0.0822	0.0844	0.0866	0.0888	0.0908	0.0928	0.0948
13	0.0526	0.0549	0.0572	0.0594	0.0617	0.0640	0.0662	0.0685	0.0707	0.0729
14	0.0342	0.0361	0.0380	0.0399	0.0419	0.0439	0.0459	0.0479	0.0500	0.0521
15	0.0208	0.0221	0.0235	0.0250	0.0265	0.0281	0.0297	0.0313	0.0330	0.0347
16	0.0118	0.0127	0.0137	0.0147	0.0157	0.0168	0.0180	0.0192	0.0204	0.0217
17	0.0063	0.0069	0.0075	0.0081	0.0088	0.0095	0.0103	0.0111	0.0119	0.0128
18	0.0032	0.0035	0.0039	0.0042	0.0046	0.0051	0.0055	0.0060	0.0065	0.0071
19	0.0015	0.0017	0.0019	0.0021	0.0023	0.0026	0.0028	0.0031	0.0034	0.0027
20	0.0007	0.0008	0.0009	0.0010	0.0011	0.0012	0.0014	0.0015	0.0017	0.0019
21	0.0003	0.0003	0.0004	0.0004	0.0005	0.0006	0.0006	0.0007	0.0008	0.0009
22	0.0001	0.0001	0.0002	0.0002	0.0002	0.0002	0.0003	0.0003	0.0004	0.0004
23	0.0000	0.0001	0.0001	0.0001	0.0001	0.0001	0.0001	0.0001	0.0002	0.0002
24	0.0000	0.0000	0.0000	0.0000	0.0000	0.0000	0.0000	0.0001	0.0001	0.0001

Poisson Probabilities (*Continued*)

	λ									
x	**11**	**12**	**13**	**14**	**15**	**16**	**17**	**18**	**19**	**20**
0	0.0000	0.0000	0.0000	0.0000	0.0000	0.0000	0.0000	0.0000	0.0000	0.0000
1	0.0002	0.0001	0.0000	0.0000	0.0000	0.0000	0.0000	0.0000	0.0000	0.0000
2	0.0010	0.0004	0.0002	0.0001	0.0000	0.0000	0.0000	0.0000	0.0000	0.0000
3	0.0037	0.0018	0.0008	0.0004	0.0002	0.0001	0.0000	0.0000	0.0000	0.0000
4	0.0102	0.0053	0.0027	0.0013	0.0006	0.0003	0.0001	0.0001	0.0000	0.0000
5	0.0224	0.0127	0.0070	0.0037	0.0019	0.0010	0.0005	0.0002	0.0001	0.0001
6	0.0411	0.0255	0.0152	0.0087	0.0048	0.0026	0.0014	0.0007	0.0004	0.0002
7	0.0646	0.0437	0.0281	0.0174	0.0104	0.0060	0.0034	0.0018	0.0010	0.0005
8	0.0888	0.0655	0.0457	0.0304	0.0194	0.0120	0.0072	0.0042	0.0024	0.0013
9	0.1085	0.0874	0.0661	0.0473	0.0324	0.0213	0.0135	0.0083	0.0050	0.0029
10	0.1194	0.1048	0.0859	0.0663	0.0486	0.0341	0.0230	0.0150	0.0095	0.0058
11	0.1194	0.1144	0.1015	0.0844	0.0663	0.0496	0.0355	0.0245	0.0164	0.0106
12	0.1094	0.1144	0.1099	0.0984	0.0829	0.0661	0.0504	0.0368	0.0259	0.0176
13	0.0926	0.1056	0.1099	0.1060	0.0956	0.0814	0.0658	0.0509	0.0378	0.0271
14	0.0728	0.0905	0.1021	0.1060	0.1024	0.0930	0.0800	0.0655	0.0514	0.0387
15	0.0534	0.0724	0.0885	0.0989	0.1024	0.0992	0.0906	0.0786	0.0650	0.0516
16	0.0367	0.0543	0.0719	0.0866	0.0960	0.0992	0.0963	0.0884	0.0772	0.0646
17	0.0237	0.0383	0.0550	0.0713	0.0847	0.0934	0.0963	0.0936	0.0863	0.0760
18	0.0145	0.0256	0.0397	0.0554	0.0706	0.0830	0.0909	0.0936	0.0911	0.0844
19	0.0084	0.0161	0.0272	0.0409	0.0557	0.0699	0.0814	0.0887	0.0911	0.0888
20	0.0046	0.0097	0.0177	0.0286	0.0418	0.0559	0.0692	0.0798	0.0866	0.0888
21	0.0024	0.0055	0.0109	0.0191	0.0299	0.0426	0.0560	0.0684	0.0783	0.0846
22	0.0012	0.0030	0.0065	0.0121	0.0204	0.0310	0.0433	0.0560	0.0676	0.0769
23	0.0006	0.0016	0.0037	0.0074	0.0133	0.0216	0.0320	0.0438	0.0559	0.0669
24	0.0003	0.0008	0.0020	0.0043	0.0083	0.0144	0.0226	0.0328	0.0442	0.0557
25	0.0001	0.0004	0.0010	0.0024	0.0050	0.0092	0.0154	0.0237	0.0336	0.0446
26	0.0000	0.0002	0.0005	0.0013	0.0029	0.0057	0.0101	0.0164	0.0246	0.0343
27	0.0000	0.0001	0.0002	0.0007	0.0016	0.0034	0.0063	0.0109	0.0173	0.0254
28	0.0000	0.0000	0.0001	0.0003	0.0009	0.0019	0.0038	0.0070	0.0117	0.0181
29	0.0000	0.0000	0.0001	0.0002	0.0004	0.0011	0.0023	0.0044	0.0077	0.0125
30	0.0000	0.0000	0.0000	0.0001	0.0002	0.0006	0.0013	0.0026	0.0049	0.0083
31	0.0000	0.0000	0.0000	0.0000	0.0001	0.0003	0.0007	0.0015	0.0030	0.0054
32	0.0000	0.0000	0.0000	0.0000	0.0001	0.0001	0.0004	0.0009	0.0018	0.0034
33	0.0000	0.0000	0.0000	0.0000	0.0000	0.0001	0.0002	0.0005	0.0010	0.0020
34	0.0000	0.0000	0.0000	0.0000	0.0000	0.0000	0.0001	0.0002	0.0006	0.0012
35	0.0000	0.0000	0.0000	0.0000	0.0000	0.0000	0.0000	0.0001	0.0003	0.0007
36	0.0000	0.0000	0.0000	0.0000	0.0000	0.0000	0.0000	0.0001	0.0002	0.0004
37	0.0000	0.0000	0.0000	0.0000	0.0000	0.0000	0.0000	0.0000	0.0001	0.0002
38	0.0000	0.0000	0.0000	0.0000	0.0000	0.0000	0.0000	0.0000	0.0000	0.0001
39	0.0000	0.0000	0.0000	0.0000	0.0000	0.0000	0.0000	0.0000	0.0000	0.0001

Appendix D Areas for the Standard Normal Distribution

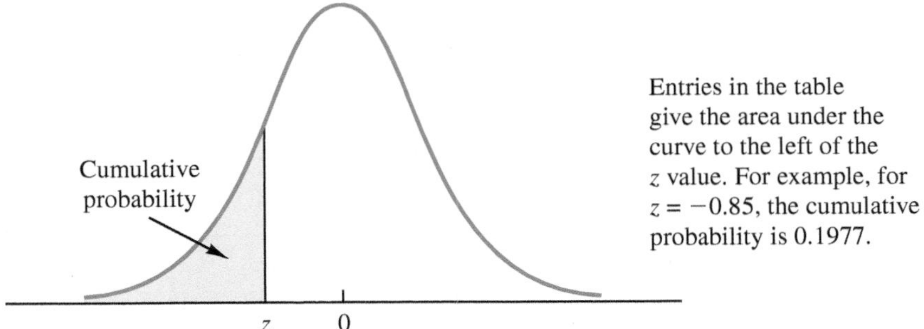

z	**0.00**	**0.01**	**0.02**	**0.03**	**0.04**	**0.05**	**0.06**	**0.07**	**0.08**	**0.09**
−3.0	0.0013	0.0013	0.0013	0.0012	0.0012	0.0011	0.0011	0.0011	0.0010	0.0010
−2.9	0.0019	0.0018	0.0018	0.0017	0.0016	0.0016	0.0015	0.0015	0.0014	0.0014
−2.8	0.0026	0.0025	0.0024	0.0023	0.0023	0.0022	0.0021	0.0021	0.0020	0.0019
−2.7	0.0035	0.0034	0.0033	0.0032	0.0031	0.0030	0.0029	0.0028	0.0027	0.0026
−2.6	0.0047	0.0045	0.0044	0.0043	0.0041	0.0040	0.0039	0.0038	0.0037	0.0036
−2.5	0.0062	0.0060	0.0059	0.0057	0.0055	0.0054	0.0052	0.0051	0.0049	0.0048
−2.4	0.0082	0.0080	0.0078	0.0075	0.0073	0.0071	0.0069	0.0068	0.0066	0.0064
−2.3	0.0107	0.0104	0.0102	0.0099	0.0096	0.0094	0.0091	0.0089	0.0087	0.0084
−2.2	0.0139	0.0136	0.0132	0.0129	0.0125	0.0122	0.0119	0.0116	0.0113	0.0110
−2.1	0.0179	0.0174	0.0170	0.0166	0.0162	0.0158	0.0154	0.0150	0.0146	0.0143
−2.0	0.0228	0.0222	0.0217	0.0212	0.0207	0.0202	0.0197	0.0192	0.0188	0.0183
−1.9	0.0287	0.0281	0.0274	0.0268	0.0262	0.0256	0.0250	0.0244	0.0239	0.0233
−1.8	0.0359	0.0351	0.0344	0.0336	0.0329	0.0322	0.0314	0.0307	0.0301	0.0294
−1.7	0.0446	0.0436	0.0427	0.0418	0.0409	0.0401	0.0392	0.0384	0.0375	0.0367
−1.6	0.0548	0.0537	0.0526	0.0516	0.0505	0.0495	0.0485	0.0475	0.0465	0.0455
−1.5	0.0668	0.0655	0.0643	0.0630	0.0618	0.0606	0.0594	0.0582	0.0571	0.0559
−1.4	0.0808	0.0793	0.0778	0.0764	0.0749	0.0735	0.0721	0.0708	0.0694	0.0681
−1.3	0.0968	0.0951	0.0934	0.0918	0.0901	0.0885	0.0869	0.0853	0.0838	0.0823
−1.2	0.1151	0.1131	0.1112	0.1093	0.1075	0.1056	0.1038	0.1020	0.1003	0.0985
−1.1	0.1357	0.1335	0.1314	0.1292	0.1271	0.1251	0.1230	0.1210	0.1190	0.1170
−1.0	0.1587	0.1562	0.1539	0.1515	0.1492	0.1469	0.1446	0.1423	0.1401	0.1379
−0.9	0.1841	0.1814	0.1788	0.1762	0.1736	0.1711	0.1685	0.1660	0.1635	0.1611
−0.8	0.2119	0.2090	0.2061	0.2033	0.2005	0.1977	0.1949	0.1922	0.1894	0.1867
−0.7	0.2420	0.2389	0.2358	0.2327	0.2296	0.2266	0.2236	0.2206	0.2177	0.2148
−0.6	0.2743	0.2709	0.2676	0.2643	0.2611	0.2578	0.2546	0.2514	0.2483	0.2451
−0.5	0.3085	0.3050	0.3015	0.2981	0.2946	0.2912	0.2877	0.2843	0.2810	0.2776
−0.4	0.3446	0.3409	0.3372	0.3336	0.3300	0.3264	0.3228	0.3192	0.3156	0.3121
−0.3	0.3821	0.3783	0.3745	0.3707	0.3669	0.3632	0.3594	0.3557	0.3520	0.3483
−0.2	0.4207	0.4168	0.4129	0.4090	0.4052	0.4013	0.3974	0.3936	0.3897	0.3859
−0.1	0.4602	0.4562	0.4522	0.4483	0.4443	0.4404	0.4364	0.4325	0.4286	0.4247
−0.0	0.5000	0.4960	0.4920	0.4880	0.4840	0.4801	0.4761	0.4721	0.4681	0.4641

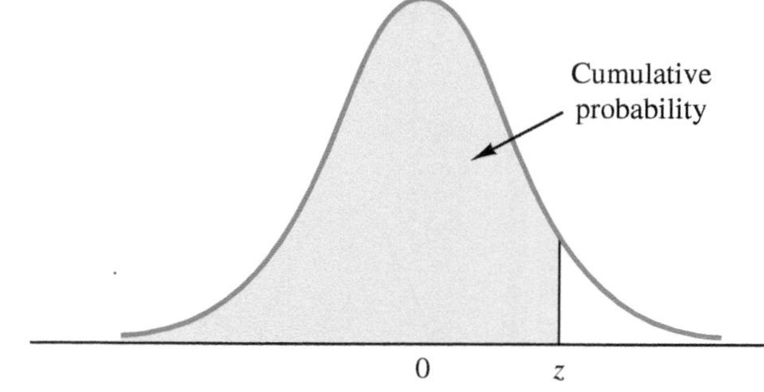

Entries in the table give the area under the curve to the left of the z value. For example, for $z = 1.25$, the cumulative probability is 0.8944.

z	**0.00**	**0.01**	**0.02**	**0.03**	**0.04**	**0.05**	**0.06**	**0.07**	**0.08**	**0.09**
0.0	0.5000	0.5040	0.5080	0.5120	0.5160	0.5199	0.5239	0.5279	0.5319	0.5359
0.1	0.5398	0.5438	0.5478	0.5517	0.5557	0.5596	0.5636	0.5675	0.5714	0.5753
0.2	0.5793	0.5832	0.5871	0.5910	0.5948	0.5987	0.6026	0.6064	0.6103	0.6141
0.3	0.6179	0.6217	0.6255	0.6293	0.6331	0.6368	0.6406	0.6443	0.6480	0.6517
0.4	0.6554	0.6591	0.6628	0.6664	0.6700	0.6736	0.6772	0.6808	0.6844	0.6879
0.5	0.6915	0.6950	0.6985	0.7019	0.7054	0.7088	0.7123	0.7157	0.7190	0.7224
0.6	0.7257	0.7291	0.7324	0.7357	0.7389	0.7422	0.7454	0.7486	0.7517	0.7549
0.7	0.7580	0.7611	0.7642	0.7673	0.7704	0.7734	0.7764	0.7794	0.7823	0.7852
0.8	0.7881	0.7910	0.7939	0.7967	0.7995	0.8023	0.8051	0.8078	0.8106	0.8133
0.9	0.8159	0.8186	0.8212	0.8238	0.8264	0.8289	0.8315	0.8340	0.8365	0.8389
1.0	0.8413	0.8438	0.8461	0.8485	0.8508	0.8531	0.8554	0.8577	0.8599	0.8621
1.1	0.8643	0.8665	0.8686	0.8708	0.8729	0.8749	0.8770	0.8790	0.8810	0.8830
1.2	0.8849	0.8869	0.8888	0.8907	0.8925	0.8944	0.8962	0.8980	0.8997	0.9015
1.3	0.9032	0.9049	0.9066	0.9082	0.9099	0.9115	0.9131	0.9147	0.9162	0.9177
1.4	0.9192	0.9207	0.9222	0.9236	0.9251	0.9265	0.9279	0.9292	0.9306	0.9319
1.5	0.9332	0.9345	0.9357	0.9370	0.9382	0.9394	0.9406	0.9418	0.9429	0.9441
1.6	0.9452	0.9463	0.9474	0.9484	0.9495	0.9505	0.9515	0.9525	0.9535	0.9545
1.7	0.9554	0.9564	0.9573	0.9582	0.9591	0.9599	0.9608	0.9616	0.9625	0.9633
1.8	0.9641	0.9649	0.9656	0.9664	0.9671	0.9678	0.9686	0.9693	0.9699	0.9706
1.9	0.9713	0.9719	0.9726	0.9732	0.9738	0.9744	0.9750	0.9756	0.9761	0.9767
2.0	0.9772	0.9778	0.9783	0.9788	0.9793	0.9798	0.9803	0.9808	0.9812	0.9817
2.1	0.9821	0.9826	0.9830	0.9834	0.9838	0.9842	0.9846	0.9850	0.9854	0.9857
2.2	0.9861	0.9864	0.9868	0.9871	0.9875	0.9878	0.9881	0.9884	0.9887	0.9890
2.3	0.9893	0.9896	0.9898	0.9901	0.9904	0.9906	0.9909	0.9911	0.9913	0.9916
2.4	0.9918	0.9920	0.9922	0.9925	0.9927	0.9929	0.9931	0.9932	0.9934	0.9936
2.5	0.9938	0.9940	0.9941	0.9943	0.9945	0.9946	0.9948	0.9949	0.9951	0.9952
2.6	0.9953	0.9955	0.9956	0.9957	0.9959	0.9960	0.9961	0.9962	0.9963	0.9964
2.7	0.9965	0.9966	0.9967	0.9968	0.9969	0.9970	0.9971	0.9972	0.9973	0.9974
2.8	0.9974	0.9975	0.9976	0.9977	0.9977	0.9978	0.9979	0.9979	0.9980	0.9981
2.9	0.9981	0.9982	0.9982	0.9983	0.9984	0.9984	0.9985	0.9985	0.9986	0.9986
3.0	0.9987	0.9987	0.9987	0.9988	0.9988	0.9989	0.9989	0.9989	0.9990	0.9990

Appendix E Values of $e^{-\lambda}$

λ	$e^{-\lambda}$	λ	$e^{-\lambda}$	λ	$e^{-\lambda}$
0.05	0.9512	2.05	0.1287	4.05	0.0174
0.10	0.9048	2.10	0.1225	4.10	0.0166
0.15	0.8607	2.15	0.1165	4.15	0.0158
0.20	0.8187	2.20	0.1108	4.20	0.0150
0.25	0.7788	2.25	0.1054	4.25	0.0143
0.30	0.7408	2.30	0.1003	4.30	0.0136
0.35	0.7047	2.35	0.0954	4.35	0.0129
0.40	0.6703	2.40	0.0907	4.40	0.0123
0.45	0.6376	2.45	0.0863	4.45	0.0117
0.50	0.6065	2.50	0.0821	4.50	0.0111
0.55	0.5769	2.55	0.0781	4.55	0.0106
0.60	0.5488	2.60	0.0743	4.60	0.0101
0.65	0.5220	2.65	0.0707	4.65	0.0096
0.70	0.4966	2.70	0.0672	4.70	0.0091
0.75	0.4724	2.75	0.0639	4.75	0.0087
0.80	0.4493	2.80	0.0608	4.80	0.0082
0.85	0.4274	2.85	0.0578	4.85	0.0078
0.90	0.4066	2.90	0.0550	4.90	0.0074
0.95	0.3867	2.95	0.0523	4.95	0.0071
1.00	0.3679	3.00	0.0498	5.00	0.0067
1.05	0.3499	3.05	0.0474	5.05	0.0064
1.10	0.3329	3.10	0.0450	5.10	0.0061
1.15	0.3166	3.15	0.0429	5.15	0.0058
1.20	0.3012	3.20	0.0408	5.20	0.0055
1.25	0.2865	3.25	0.0388	5.25	0.0052
1.30	0.2725	3.30	0.0369	5.30	0.0050
1.35	0.2592	3.35	0.0351	5.35	0.0047
1.40	0.2466	3.40	0.0334	5.40	0.0045
1.45	0.2346	3.45	0.0317	5.45	0.0043
1.50	0.2231	3.50	0.0302	5.50	0.0041
1.55	0.2122	3.55	0.0287	5.55	0.0039
1.60	0.2019	3.60	0.0273	5.60	0.0037
1.65	0.1920	3.65	0.0260	5.65	0.0035
1.70	0.1827	3.70	0.0247	5.70	0.0033
1.75	0.1738	3.75	0.0235	5.75	0.0032
1.80	0.1653	3.80	0.0224	5.80	0.0030
1.85	0.1572	3.85	0.0213	5.85	0.0029
1.90	0.1496	3.90	0.0202	5.90	0.0027
1.95	0.1423	3.95	0.0193	5.95	0.0026
2.00	0.1353	4.00	0.0183	6.00	0.0025
				7.00	0.0009
				8.00	0.000335
				9.00	0.000123
				10.00	0.000045

Appendix F References and Bibliography

Chapter 1 Introduction

Churchman, C. W., R. L. Ackoff, and E. L. Arnoff. *Introduction to Operations Research.* Wiley, 1957.

Horner, P. "The Sabre Story." *OR/MS Today* (June 2000).

Leon, L., Z. Przasnyski, and K. C. Seal. "Spreadsheets and OR/MS Models: An End-User Perspective." *Interfaces* (March/April 1996).

Powell, S. G. "Innovative Approaches to Management Science." *OR/MS Today* (October 1996).

Savage, S. "Weighing the Pros and Cons of Decision Technology and Spreadsheets." *OR/MS Today* (February 1997).

Winston, W. L. "The Teachers' Forum: Management Science with Spreadsheets for MBAs at Indiana University." *Interfaces* (March/April 1996).

Chapters 2 and 3 Probability

Anderson, D. R., D. J. Sweeney, and T. A. Williams. *Statistics for Business and Economics,* 10th ed. South-Western, 2008.

Hogg, R. V., and E. A. Tanis. *Probability and Statistical Inference,* 6th ed. Prentice Hall, 2001.

Ross, S. M. *Introduction to Probability Models,* 7th ed. Academic Press, 1993.

Wackerly, D. D., W. Mendenhall, and R. L. Scheaffer. *Mathematical Statistics with Applications,* 6th ed. Duxbury Press, 2002.

Chapters 4 and 5 Decision Analysis and Game Theory

Clemen, R. T., and T. Reilly. *Making Hard Decisions with Decision Tools.* Duxbury Press, 2001.

Davis, M. D. *Game Theory: A Nontechnical Introduction.* Dover, 1997.

Goodwin, P., and G. Wright. *Decision Analysis for Management Judgment,* 2nd ed. Wiley, 1999.

McMillian, J. *Games, Strategies, and Managers.* Oxford University Press, 1992.

Myerson, R. B. *Game Theory: Analysis of Conflict.* Harvard University Press, 1997.

Osborne, M. J. *An Introduction to Game Theory.* Oxford University Press, 2004.

Pratt, J. W., H. Raiffa, and R. Schlaiter. *Introduction to Statistical Decision Theory.* MIT Press, 1995.

Raiffa, H. *Decision Analysis.* McGraw-Hill, 1997.

Schlaiter, R. *Analysis of Decisions Under Uncertainty.* Krieger, 1978.

Chapter 6 Forecasting

Bowerman, B. L., and R. T. O'Connell. *Forecasting and Time Series: An Applied Approach,* 3rd ed. Duxbury Press, 1993.

Box, G. E. P., G. M. Jenkins, and G. C. Reinsel. *Time Series Analysis: Forecasting and Control,* 3rd ed. Prentice Hall, 1994.

Hanke, J. E., and A. G. Reitsch. *Business Forecasting,* 6th ed. Prentice Hall, 1998.

Makridakis, S. G., S. C. Wheelwright, and R. J. Hyndman. *Forecasting: Methods and Applications,* 3rd ed. Wiley, 1997.

Wilson, J. H., and B. Keating. *Business Forecasting,* 3rd ed. Irwin, 1998.

Chapters 7 to 11 Linear Programming, Distribution and Network Models, Integer Programming Problems

Ahuja, R. K., T. L. Magnanti, and J. B. Orlin. *Network Flows, Theory, Algorithms, and Applications.* Prentice-Hall 1993.

Bazarra, M. S., J. J. Jarvis, and H. D. Sherali. *Linear Programming and Network Flows,* 2nd ed. Wiley, 1990.

Dantzig, G. B. *Linear Programming and Extensions.* Princeton University Press, 1963.

Greenberg, H. J. "How to Analyze the Results of Linear Programs—Part 1: Preliminaries." *Interfaces* 23, no. 4 (July/August 1993): 56–67.

Greenberg, H. J. "How to Analyze the Results of Linear Programs—Part 2: Price Interpretation." *Interfaces* 23, no. 5 (September/October 1993): 97–114.

Greenberg, H. J. "How to Analyze the Results of Linear Programs—Part 3: Infeasibility Diagnosis." *Interfaces* 23, no. 6 (November/December 1993): 120–139.

Lillien, G., and A. Rangaswamy. *Marketing Engineering: Computer-Assisted Marketing Analysis and Planning.* Addison-Wesley, 1998.

Nemhauser, G. L., and L. A. Wolsey. *Integer and Combinatorial Optimization.* Wiley, 1988.

Schrage, L. *Optimization Modeling with LINGO,* 4th ed. LINDO Systems Inc., 2000.

Winston, W. L., and S. C. Albright. *Practical Management Science,* 2nd ed. Duxbury Press, 2001.

Chapter 12 Advanced Optimization Applications

Bazarra, M. S., H. D. Sherali, and C. M. Shetty. *Nonlinear Programming Theory and Applications*. Wiley, 1993.

Benninga, S. *Financial Modeling*. The MIT Press, 2000.

Luenberger, D. *Linear and Nonlinear Programming*, 2nd ed. Addison-Wesley Publishing Company, 1984.

Rardin, R. L. *Optimization in Operations Research*. Prentice-Hall, 1998.

Chapter 13 Project Scheduling: PERT/CPM

Moder, J. J., C. R. Phillips, and E. W. Davis. *Project Management with CPM, PERT and Precedence Diagramming*, 3rd ed. Blitz, 1995.

Wiest, J., and F. Levy. *Management Guide to PERT-CPM*, 2nd ed. Prentice Hall, 1977.

Chapter 14 Inventory Models

Fogarty, D. W., J. H. Blackstone, and T. R. Hoffman. *Production and Inventory Management*, 2nd ed. South-Western, 1990.

Hillier, F., and G. J. Lieberman. *Introduction to Operations Research*, 7th ed. McGraw-Hill, 2000.

Narasimhan, S. L., D. W. McLeavey, and P. B. Lington. *Production Planning and Inventory Control*, 2nd ed. Prentice Hall, 1995.

Orlicky, J., and G. W. Plossi. *Orlicky's Material Requirements Planning*. McGraw-Hill, 1994.

Vollmann, T. E., W. L. Berry, and D. C. Whybark. *Manufacturing Planning and Control Systems*, 4th ed. McGraw-Hill, 1997.

Zipkin, P. H. *Foundations of Inventory Management*. McGraw-Hill/Irwin, 2000.

Chapter 15 Waiting Line Models

Bunday, B. D. *An Introduction to Queueing Theory*. Wiley, 1996.

Gross, D., and C. M. Harris. *Fundamentals of Queueing Theory*, 3rd ed. Wiley, 1997.

Hall, R. W. *Queueing Methods: For Service and Manufacturing*. Prentice Hall, 1991.

Hillier, F., and G. J. Lieberman. *Introduction to Operations Research*, 7th ed. McGraw-Hill, 2000.

Kao, E. P. C. *An Introduction to Stochastic Processes*. Duxbury Press, 1996.

Chapter 16 Simulation

Banks, J., J. S. Carson, and B. L. Nelson. *Discrete-Event System Simulation*, 2nd ed. Prentice Hall, 1995.

Fishwick, P. A. *Simulation Model Design and Execution: Building Digital Worlds*. Prentice Hall, 1995.

Harrell, C. R., and K. Tumau. *Simulation Made Easy: A Manager's Guide*. Institute of Industrial Engineers, 1996.

Kelton, W. D., R. P. Sadowski, and D. T. Sturrock. *Simulation with Arena*, 4th ed. McGraw-Hill, 2007.

Law, A. M., and W. D. Kelton. *Simulation Modeling and Analysis*, 3rd ed. McGraw-Hill, 1999.

Pidd, M. *Computer Simulation in Management Science*, 4th ed. Wiley, 1998.

Savage, S. *The Flaw of Averages: Why We Underestimate Risk in the Face of Uncertainty*. Wiley, 2012.

Thesen, A., and L. E. Travis. *Simulation for Decision Making*. Wadsworth, 1992.

Chapter 17 Markov Processes

Bharucha-Reid, A. T. *Elements of the Theory of Markov Processes and Their Applications*. Dover, 1997.

Filar, J. A., and K. Vrieze. *Competitive Markov Decision Processes*. Springer-Verlag, 1996.

Norris, J. *Markov Chains*. Cambridge, 1997.

Appendix G Self-Test Solutions and Answers to Even-Numbered Problems

Chapter 1

2. Define the problem; identify the alternatives; determine the criteria; evaluate the alternatives; choose an alternative.

4. A quantitative approach should be considered because the problem is large, complex, important, new, and repetitive.

6. Quicker to formulate, easier to solve, and/or more easily understood

8. a. Max $10x + 5y$

s.t.

$$5x + 2y \leq 40$$
$$x \geq 0, y \geq 0$$

b. Controllable inputs: x and y
Uncontrollable inputs: profit (10, 5), labor-hours (5, 2), and labor-hour availability (40)

c. See Figure G1.8c.

d. $x = 0, y = 20$; Profit = \$100 (solution by trial and error)

e. Deterministic

10. a. Total units received $= x + y$

b. Total cost $= 0.20x + 0.25y$

c. $x + y = 5000$

d. $x \leq 4000$ Kansas City
$y \leq 3000$ Minneapolis

e. Min $0.20x + 0.25y$

s.t.

$$x + y = 5000$$
$$x \leq 4000$$
$$y \leq 3000$$
$$x, y \geq 0$$

FIGURE G1.8c

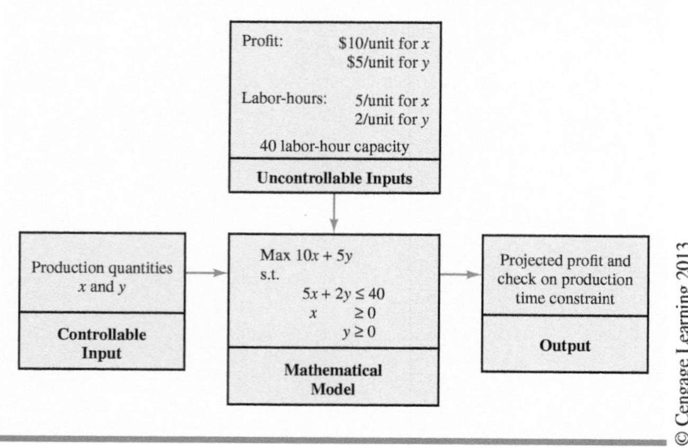

© Cengage Learning 2013

12. a. If x represents the number of pairs of shoes produced, a mathematical model for the total cost of producing x pairs of shoes is $TC = 2000 + 60x$. The two components of total cost in this model are fixed cost (\$2,000) and variable cost ($60x$).

b. If P represents the total profit, the total revenue (TR) is $80x$ and a mathematical model for the total profit realized from an order for x pairs of shoes is $P = TR - TC = 80x - (2000 + 60x) = 20x - 2000$.

c. The breakeven point is the number of shoes produced (x) at the point of no profit ($P = 0$).
Thus the breakeven point is the value of x when $P = 20x - 2000 = 0$. This occurs when $20x = 2000$ or $x = 100$ (i.e., the breakeven point is 100 pairs of shoes).

14. a. If x represents the number of copies of the book that are sold, total revenue (TR) $= 46x$ and total cost (TC) $= 160{,}000 + 6x$, so Profit $= TR - TC = 46x - (160{,}000 + 6x) = 40x - 160{,}000$. The breakeven point is the number of books produced (x) at the point of no profit ($P = 0$). Thus the breakeven point is the value of x when $P = 40x - 160{,}000 = 0$. This occurs when $40x = 160{,}00$ or $x = 4000$ (i.e., the breakeven point is 4000 copies of the book).

b. At a demand of 3800 copies, the publisher can expect a profit of $40(3800) - 160{,}000 = 152{,}000 - 160{,}000 = -8000$ (i.e., a loss of \$8,000).

c. Here we know demand ($d = 3800$) and want to determine the price p at which we will breakeven (the point at which profit is 0). The minimum price per copy that the publisher must charge to break even is Profit $= p(3800) - (160{,}000 + 6(3800)) = 3800p - 182{,}800$. This occurs where $3800p = 182{,}800$ or $p = 48.10526316$ or a price of approximately \$48.

d. If the publisher believes demand will remain at 4000 copies if the price per copy is increased to \$50.95, then the publisher could anticipate a profit of $TR - TC = 50.95(4000) - (160{,}000 + 6(4000)) = 203{,}800 - 184{,}000 = 19{,}800$ or a profit of \$19,800. This is a return of $p/TC = 10.8\%$ on the total cost of \$184,000, and the publisher should proceed if this return is sufficient.

16. a. The annual return per share of Oil Alaska is \$6.00 and the annual return per share of Southwest Petroleum is \$4.00, so the objective function that maximizes the total annual return is Max $6x + 4y$.

b. The price per share of Oil Alaska is \$50.00 and the price per share of Southwest Petroleum is \$30.00, so (1) the mathematical expression for the constraint that limits total investment funds to \$800,000 is $50x + 30y \leq 800000$,
(2) the mathematical expression for the constraint that limits investment in Oil Alaska to \$500,000 is $50x \leq 500000$, and
(3) the mathematical expression for the constraint that limits investment in Southwest Petroleum to \$450,000 is $30x \leq 450000$.

Chapter 2

1. a. Record the number of persons waiting at the X-ray department at 9:00 A.M.

b. The experimental outcomes (sample points) are the number of people waiting: 0, 1, 2, 3, and 4. (*Note:* Although it is theoretically possible for more than four people to be waiting, we use what has actually been observed to define the experimental outcomes.)

c.

Number Waiting	Probability
0	0.10
1	0.25
2	0.30
3	0.20
4	0.15
Total	1.00

d. The relative frequency method

2. a. Choose a person at random, and have him/her taste the four blends of coffee and state a preference.

b. Assign a probability of $^1/_4$ to each blend, using the classical method of equally likely outcomes.

c.

Blend	Probability
1	0.20
2	0.30
3	0.35
4	0.15
Total	1.00

The relative frequency method was used.

4. a. 31,675,935/132,275,830 = 0.239.

b. 122,742,594/132,275,830 = 0.928.

c. (12,893,802 + 2,288,550 + 265,612)/132,275,830 = 15,447,964/132,275,830 = 0.117.

d. 0.01(26,463,973) = 264,639.73 (or 264,640).

e. 0.0173(\$13,045,221,000.00) = \$225,699,891.81.

6. a. $P(A) = P(150 - 199) + P(200 \text{ and over})$
$= \frac{26}{100} + \frac{5}{100}$
$= 0.31$

b. $P(B) = P(\text{less than } 50) + P(50 - 99) + P(100 - 149)$
$= 0.13 + 0.22 + 0.34$
$= 0.69$

7. a. $P(A) = 0.40$, $P(B) = 0.40$, $P(C) = 0.60$

b. $P(A < B) = P(E_1, E_2, E_3, E_4) = 0.80$.
Yes, $P(A < B) = P(A) + P(B)$

c. $A^c = \{E_3, E_4, E_5\}$; $C^c = \{E_1, E_4\}$; $P(A^c) = 0.60$; $P(C^c) = 0.40$

d. $A < B^c = \{E_1, E_2, E_5\}$; $P(A < B^c) = 0.60$

e. $P(B < C) = P(E_2, E_3, E_4, E_5) = 0.80$

8. a. Let $P(A)$ be the probability a hospital had a daily inpatient volume of at least 200 and $P(B)$ be the probability a hospital had a nurse to patient ratio of at least 3.0. From the list of 30 hospitals, 16 had a daily inpatient volume of at least 200, so by the relative frequency approach the probability one of these hospitals had a daily inpatient volume of at least 200 is $P(A) = 16/30 = 0.533$, Similarly, since 10 (one-third) of the hospitals had a nurse-to-patient ratio of at least 3.0, the probability of a hospital having a nurse-to-patient ratio of at least 3.0 is $P(B) = 10/30 = 0.333$. Finally, since seven of the hospitals had both a daily inpatient volume of at least 200 and a nurse-to-patient ratio of at least 3.0, the probability of a hospital having both a daily inpatient volume of at least 200 and a nurse-to-patient ratio of at least 3.0 is $P(A \cap B) = 7/30 = 0.233$.

b. The probability that a hospital had a daily inpatient volume of at least 200 or a nurse-to-patient ratio of at least 3.0 or both is $P(A \cup B) = P(A) + P(B) - P(A \cap B) = 16/30 + 10/30 - 7/30 = (16 + 10 - 7)/30 = 19/30 = 0.633$.

c. The probability that a hospital had neither a daily inpatient volume of at least 200 nor a nurse-to-patient ratio of at least 3.0 is $1 - P(A \cup B) = 1 - 19/30 = 11/30 = 0.367$.

10. $P(\text{Defective and Minor}) = 4/25$
$P(\text{Defective and Major}) = 2/25$
$P(\text{Defective}) = (4/25) + (2/25) = 6/25$
$P(\text{Major Defect} \mid \text{Defective}) = P(\text{Defective and Major})/P(\text{Defective}) = (2/25)/(6/25) = 2/6 = 1/3$.

12. a. $P(A \mid B) = \frac{P(A \cap B)}{P(B)} = \frac{0.40}{0.60} = 0.6667$

b. $P(B \mid A) = \frac{P(A \cap B)}{P(A)} = \frac{0.40}{0.50} = 0.80$

c. No, because $P(A \mid B) \neq P(A)$

13. a.

	Reason for Applying			
	Quality	Cost/ Convenience	Other	Total
Full Time	0.218	0.204	0.039	0.461
Part Time	0.208	0.307	0.024	0.539
Total	0.426	0.511	0.063	1.000

b. A student will most likely cite cost or convenience as the first reason: probability = 0.511; school quality is the first reason cited by the second largest number of students: probability = 0.426.
c. $P(\text{Quality} \mid \text{Full Time}) = 0.218/0.461 = 0.473$
d. $P(\text{Quality} \mid \text{Part Time}) = 0.208/0.539 = 0.386$
e. $P(B) = 0.426$ and $P(B \mid A) = 0.473$
Because $P(B) \neq P(B \mid A)$, the events are dependent.

14.

	\$0–\$499	\$500–\$999	≥\$1000	
<2 yrs	120	240	90	450
≥2 yrs	75	275	200	550
	195	515	290	1000
<2 yrs	0.12	0.24	0.09	0.45
≥2 yrs	0.075	0.275	0.2	0.55
	0.195	0.515	0.29	1.00

a. $P(< 2 \text{ yrs}) = 0.45$
b. $P(\geq \$1000) = 0.29$
c. $P(2 \text{ accounts have} \geq \$1000) = (0.29)(0.29) = 0.0841$
d. $P(\$500 - \$999 \mid \geq 2 \text{ yrs}) = P(\$500 - \$999 \text{ and } \geq 2 \text{ yrs})/P(\geq 2\text{yrs}) = 0.275/0.55 = 0.5$
e. $P(< 2 \text{ yrs and} \geq \$1000) = 0.09$
f. $P(\geq 2 \text{ yrs} \mid \$500 - \$999) = 0.275/0.515 = 0.5340$

16. a. 0.19
b. 0.71
c. 0.29

18. a. 0.25, 0.40, 0.10
b. 0.25
c. Independent; program does not help

20. a. $P(B \cap A_1) = P(A_1)P(B \mid A_1) = (0.20)(0.50) = 0.10$
$P(B \cap A_2) = P(A_2)P(B \mid A_2) = (0.50)(0.40) = 0.20$
$P(B \cap A_3) = P(A_3)P(B \mid A_3) = (0.30)(0.30) = 0.09$

b. $P(A_2 \mid B) = \dfrac{0.20}{0.10 + 0.20 + 0.09} = 0.51$

c.

Events	$P(A_i)$	$P(B \mid A_i)$	$P(A_i \cap B)$	$P(A_i \mid B)$
A_1	0.20	0.50	0.10	0.26
A_2	0.50	0.40	0.20	0.51
A_3	0.30	0.30	0.09	0.23
	1.00		0.39	1.00

22. a. 0.40
b. 0.67

24. Let S = speeding is reported
S^C = speeding is not reported
F = Accident results in fatality for vehicle occupant
We have $P(S) = 0.129$, so $P(S^C) = 0.871$. Also $P(F \mid S) = 0.196$ and $P(F \mid S^C) = 0.05$. Using the tabular form of Bayes' theorem provides:

Events	Prior Probabilities	Conditional Probabilities	Joint Probabilities	Posterior Probabilities
S	0.129	0.196	0.0384	0.939
S^C	0.871	0.050	0.0025	0.061
	1.000		0.0409	1.000

25. a. $P(\text{defective part}) = 0.0065$ (see below)

Events	$P(A_i)$	$P(D \mid A_i)$	$P(A_i \cap D)$	$P(A_i \cap D)$
Supplier A	0.60	0.0025	0.0015	0.23
Supplier B	0.30	0.0100	0.0030	0.46
Supplier C	0.10	0.020	0.0020	0.31
	1.00		$P(D) = 0.0065$	1.00

b. Supplier B (prob. = 0.46) is the most likely source.

26. a. $P(D_1 \mid S_1) = 0.2195$, $P(D_2 \mid S_1) = 0.7805$
b. $P(D_1 \mid S_2) = 0.5000$, $P(D_2 \mid S_2) = 0.5000$
c. $P(D_1 \mid S_3) = 0.8824$, $P(D_2 \mid S_3) = 0.1176$
d. 0.1582 and 0.8418

28. a. $P(A_1) = .095$
$P(A_2) = .905$
$P(W \mid A_1) = .60$
$P(W \mid A_2) = .49$
b. $P(A_1 \mid W) = .1139$
c. $P(A_1 \mid M) = .0761$
d. $P(W) = .50045$
$P(M) = .49965$

30. a.

	Male Applicants	Female Applicants
Accept	70	40
Deny	90	80

After combining these two crosstabulations into a single crosstabulation with Accept and Deny as the row labels and Male and Female as the column labels, we see that the rate of acceptance for males across the university is $70/(70 + 90) = 0.4375$ or approximately 44%, while the rate of acceptance for females across the university is $40/(40 + 80) = 0.33$ or 33%.

b. If we focus solely on the overall data, we would conclude that the university's admission process is biased in favor of male applicant. However, this occurs because most females apply to the College of Business (which has a far lower rate of acceptance that the College of Engineering). When we look at each college's acceptance rate by gender, we see that the acceptance rate of males and females are equal in the College of Engineering (75%) and the acceptance rate of males and females are equal in the College of Business (33%). The data do not support the accusation that the university favors male applicants in its admissions process.

Chapter 3

1. a. Values: 0, 1, 2, . . . , 20 discrete
b. Values: 0, 1, 2, . . . discrete
c. Values: 0, 1, 2, . . . , 50 discrete
d. Values: $0 \le x \le 8$ continuous
e. Values: $x \ge 0$ continuous

2. a. 0.05; probability of a $200,000 profit
b. 0.70
c. 0.40

3. a.

x	$f(x)$
1	3/20 = 0.15
2	5/20 = 0.25
3	8/20 = 0.40
4	4/20 = 0.20
	Total 1.00

b.

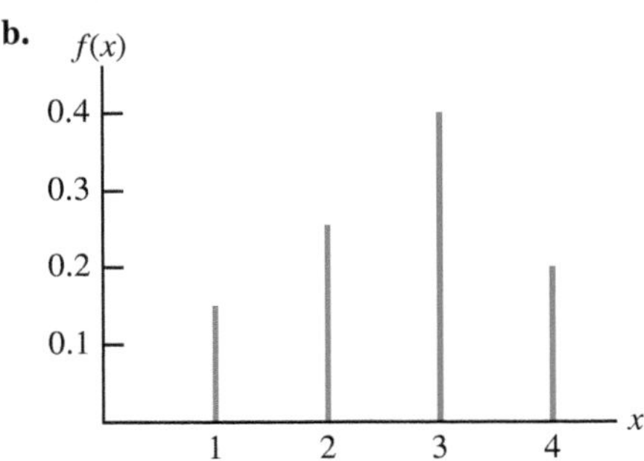

c. $f(x) \ge 0$ for $x = 1, 2, 3, 4$
$\Sigma f(x) = 1$

4. a. $E(x) = \mu = 6.00$
b. $\text{Var}(x) = \sigma^2 = 4.50$
c. $\sigma = \sqrt{4.50} = 2.12$

6. a.

x	$f(x)$
1	0.97176
2	0.026675
3	0.00140
4	0.00014
5	0.00002

If we let $x = 5$ represent quintuplets or more, the probability distribution of the number children born per pregnancy in 1996 is provided in the first two columns of the preceding table.

b. $E[x] = 1.030$ and $\text{Var}[x] = \sigma^2 = 0.03305$.

c.

y	$f(y)$
1	0.965964
2	0.0333143
3	0.0014868
4	0.0000863
5	0.0000163

If we let $y = 5$ represent quintuplets or more, the probability distribution of the number children born per pregnancy in 2006 is provided in the first two columns of the preceding table.

d. $E[y] = 1.030$ and $\text{Var}[y] = \sigma^2 = 0.0390$.

e. The number of children born per pregnancy is greater in 2006 than in 1996, and the variation in the number of children born per pregnancy is also greater in 2006 than in 1996. However, these data provide no information on which we could base a determination of causes of this upward trend.

8. a. Medium 145; large 140; prefer medium
b. Medium 2725; large 12,400; prefer medium

9. a. $f(1) = \binom{2}{1}(0.4)^1(0.6)^1 = \frac{2!}{1!1!}(0.4)(0.6) = 0.48$

b. $f(0) = \binom{2}{0}(0.4)^0(0.6)^2 = \frac{2!}{0!2!}(1)(0.36) = 0.36$

c. $f(2) = \binom{2}{2}(0.4)^2(0.6)^0 = \frac{2!}{2!0!}(0.16)(1) = 0.16$

d. $P(x \ge 1) = f(1) + f(2) = 0.48 + 0.16 = 0.64$

e. $E(x) = np = 2(0.4) = 0.8$
$\text{Var}(x) = np(1 - p) = 2(0.4)(0.6) = 0.48$
$\sigma = \sqrt{0.48} = 0.6928$

10. a. $f(0) = 0.3487$
b. $f(2) = 0.1937$
c. 0.9298

d. 0.6513
e. 1
f. $\sigma_2 = 0.9000$, $\sigma = 0.9487$

12. a. Probability of a defective part being produced must be 0.03 for each trial; trials must be independent.
b. Two outcomes result in exactly one defect.
c. $P(\text{no defects}) = (0.97)(0.97) = 0.9409$
$P(1 \text{ defect}) = 2(0.03)(0.97) = 0.0582$
$P(2 \text{ defects}) = (0.03)(0.03) = 0.0009$

14. a. $f(x) = \dfrac{2^x e^{-2}}{x!}$
b. $\mu = 6$ for 3 time periods
c. $f(x) = \dfrac{6^x e^{-6}}{x!}$
d. $f(2) = \dfrac{2^2 e^{-2}}{2!} = \dfrac{4(0.1353)}{2} = 0.2706$
e. $f(6) = \dfrac{6^6 e^{-6}}{6!} = 0.1606$
f. $f(5) = \dfrac{4^5 e^{-4}}{5!} = 0.1563$

16. a. 0.0009
b. 0.9927
c. 0.0302
d. 0.8271

18. a. $f(x)$

3
2
1
0.5 1.0 1.5 x

b. $P(x = 1.25) = 0$; the probability of any single point is zero because the area under the curve above any single point is zero.
c. $P(1.0 \le x \le 1.25) = 2(0.25) = 0.50$
d. $P(1.2 < x < 1.5) = 2(0.30) = 0.60$

20. a.

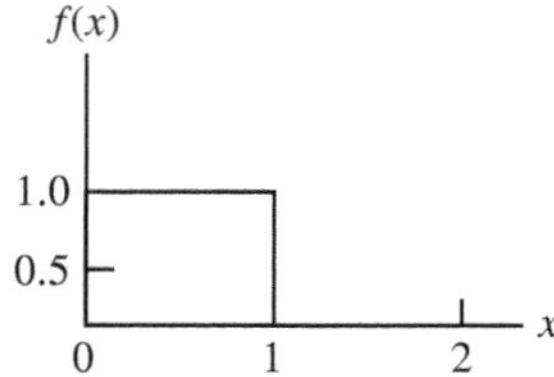

b. 0.50
c. 0.30
d. 0.40

21. a. $P(0 \le z \le 0.83) = 0.7967 - 0.5000 = 0.2967$
b. $P(-1.57 \le z \le 0) = 0.5000 - 0.0582 = 0.4418$
c. $P(z > 0.44) = 1.0000 - 0.6700 = 0.2300$
d. $P(z \ge -0.23) = 1.0000 - 0.4090 = 0.5910$
e. $P(z < 1.20) = 0.8849$
f. $P(z < -0.71) = 0.2389$

22. a. 1.96
b. 1.96
c. 0.61
d. 1.12
e. 0.44
f. 0.44

23. a. Area = 0.2119 $z = -0.80$
b. Area outside the interval 0.0970 must be split between the two tails.
Cumulative probability = 0.5(0.0970) + 0.9030 = 0.9515 $z = 1.66$
c. Area outside the interval 0.7948 must be split between the two tails.
Cumulative probability = 0.5(0.7948) + 0.2052 = 0.6026 $z = 0.26$
d. Area = 0.9948 $z = 2.56$
e. Area = 1.0000 − 0.6915 = 0.3085 $z = -0.50$

24. a. 0.3830
b. 0.1056
c. 0.0062
d. 0.1603

26. a. 0.7745
b. 36.32 days
c. 19%

28. $\mu = 19.23$

29. a. $P(x \le x_0) = 1 - e^{-x_0/3}$
b. $P(x \le 2) = 1 - e^{-2/3} = 1 - 0.5134 = 0.4866$
c. $P(x \ge 3) = 1 - P(x \le 3) = 1 - (1 - e^{-3/3}) = e^{-1} = 0.3679$
d. $P(x \le 5) = 1 - e^{-5/3} = 1 - 0.1889 = 0.8111$
e. $P(2 \le x \le 5) = P(x \le 5) - P(x \le 2) = 0.8111 - 0.4866 = 0.3245$

30. a. 0.5809
b. 0.2713
c. 0.1478

31. a.

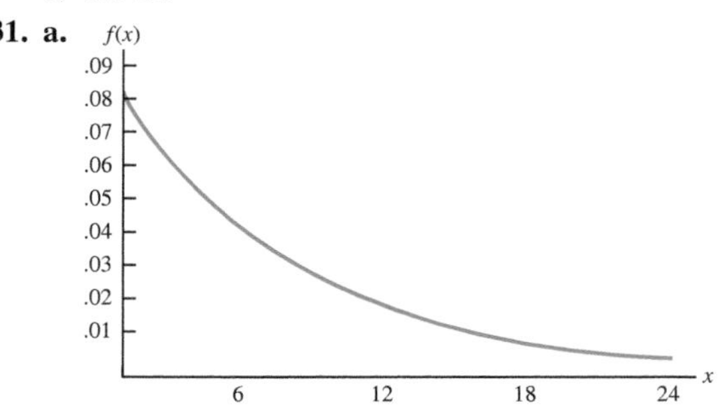

b. $P(x \le 12) = 1 - e^{-12/12} = 0.6321$
c. $P(x \le 6) = 1 - e^{-6/12} = 0.3935$
d. $P(x \ge 30) = 1 - P(x < 30) = 1 - (1 - e^{-30/12}) = 0.0821$

32. a. 50 hours
b. 0.3935
c. 0.1353

34. a. 0.5130
b. 0.1655
c. 0.3679

Chapter 4

1. a.

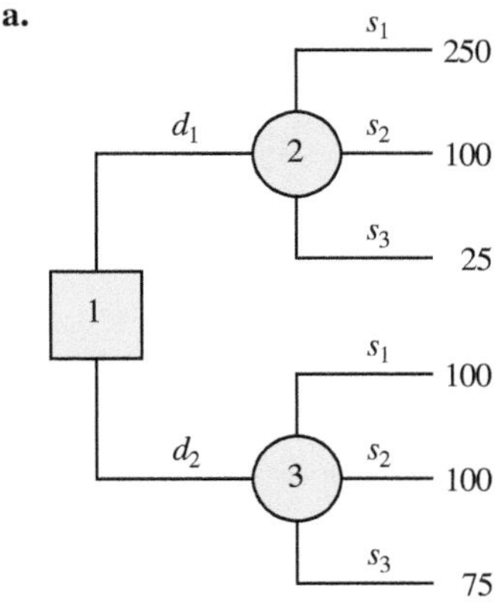

b.

Decision	Maximum Profit	Minimum Profit
d_1	250	25
d_2	100	75

Optimistic approach: Select d_1
Conservative approach: Select d_2
Regret or opportunity loss table:

Decision	s_1	s_2	s_3
d_1	0	0	50
d_2	150	0	0

Maximum regret: select d_1

2. a. Optimistic: d_1
Conservative: d_3
Minimax regret: d_3
b. The choice of which approach to use is up to the decision maker.
c. Optimistic: d_1
Conservative: d_2 or d_3
Minimax regret: d_2

3. a. Decision: Choose the best plant size from the two alternatives—a small plant and a large plant.
Chance event: Market demand for the new product line with three possible outcomes (states of nature): low, medium, and high

b. Influence Diagram:

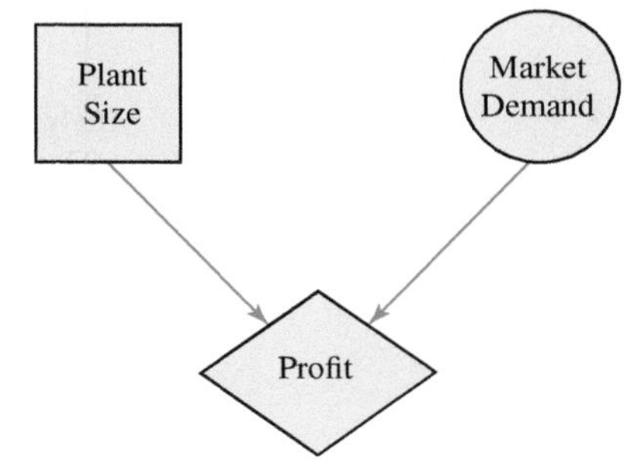

c.

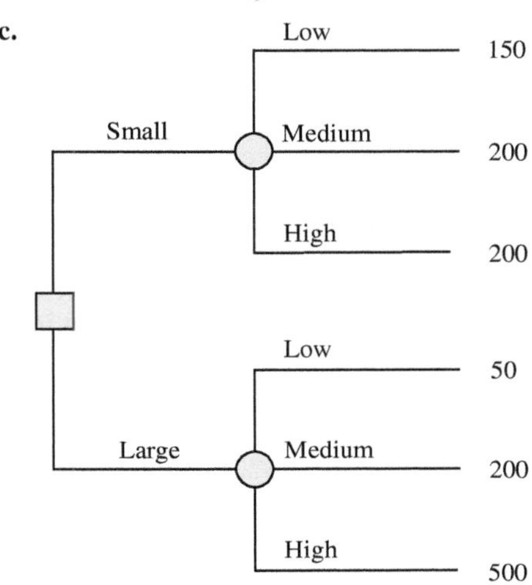

d.

Decision	Maximum Profit	Minimum Profit	Maximum Regret
Small	200	150	300
Large	500	50	100

Optimistic Approach: Large plant
Conservative Approach: Small plant
Minimax Regret: Large plant

4. a. The decision faced by Amy is to select the best lease option from three alternatives (Hepburn Honda, Midtown Motors, and Hopkins Automotive). The chance event is the number of miles Amy will drive.
b. The payoff table for Amy's problem is:

	Actual Miles Driven Annually		
Dealer	**12,000**	**15,000**	**18,000**
Hepburn Honda	\$10,764	\$12,114	\$13,464
Midtown Motors	\$11,160	\$11,160	\$12,960
Hopkins Automotive	\$11,700	\$11,700	\$11,700

c. The minimum and maximum payoffs for each of Amy's three alternatives are:

Dealer	Minimum Cost	Maximum Cost
Hepburn Honda	\$10,764	\$13,464
Midtown Motors	\$11,160	\$12,960
Hopkins Automotive	\$11,700	\$11,700

Thus:
The optimistic approach results in selection of the Hepburn Automotive lease option.
The conservative approach results in selection of the Hopkins Automotive lease option.
The minimax regret approach results in selection of the Hopkins Automotive lease option (which has the smallest regret of the three alternatives: \$936).

d. The expected value approach results in selection of the Midtown Motors lease option (which has the minimum expected value of the three alternatives—\$11,340).

e. The risk profile for the decision to lease from Midtown Motors is as follows:

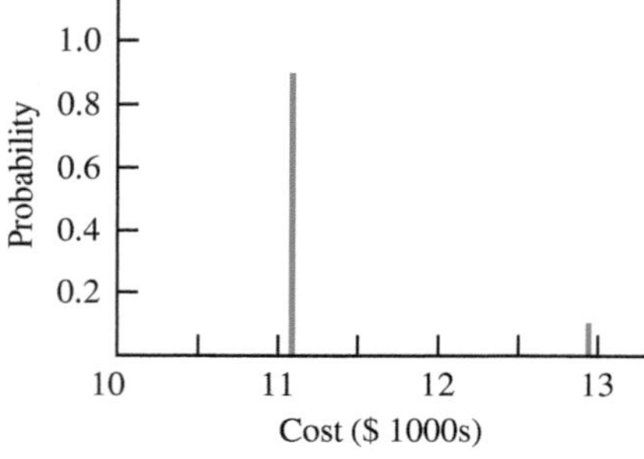

f. The expected value approach results in selection of either the Midtown Motors lease option or the Hopkins Automotive lease option (both of which have the minimum expected value of the three alternatives—\$11,700).

6. a. Pharmaceuticals; 3.4%
b. Financial; 4.6%

7. a. EV(own staff) = 0.2(650) + 0.5(650) + 0.3(600) = 635
EV(outside vendor) = 0.2(900) + 0.5(600) + 0.3(300) = 570
EV(combination) = 0.2(800) + 0.5(650) + 0.3(500) = 635
Optimal decision: Hire an outside vendor with an expected cost of \$570,000

b.

	Cost	Probability
Own staff	300	0.3
Outside vendor	600	0.5
Combination	900	0.2
		1.0

8. a. $EV(d_1) = p(10) + (1 - p)(1) = 9p + 1$
$EV(d_2) = p(4) + (1 - p)(3) = 1p + 3$

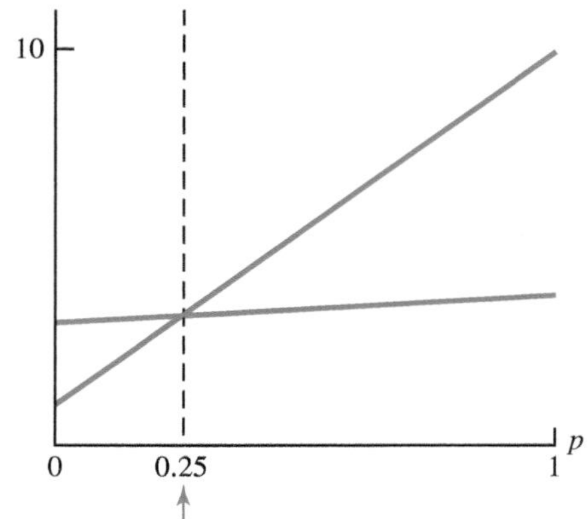

$9p + 1 = 1p + 3$ and hence $p = 0.25$
d_2 is optimal for $p \geq 0.25$, d_1 is optimal for $p \geq 0.25$

b. d_2

c. As long as the payoff for $s_1 \geq 2$, then d_2 is optimal.

10. a.

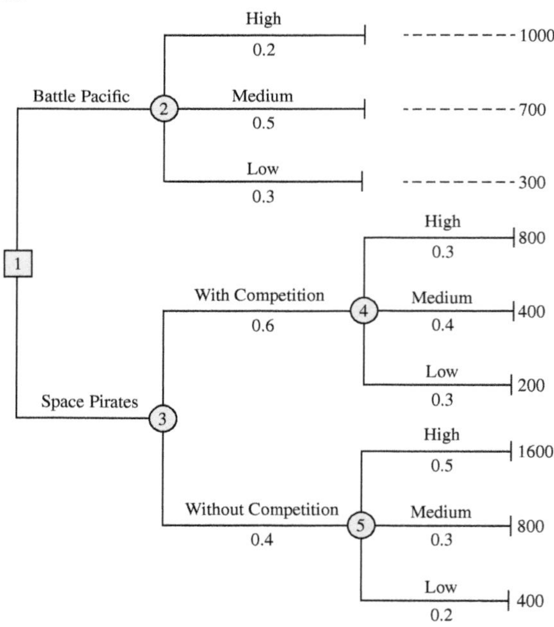

b. Space Pirates

c.
\$200 0.18
\$400 0.32
\$800 0.30
\$1600 0.20

d. $P(\text{Competition}) > 0.7273$

12. a. Decision: Whether to lengthen the runway
Chance event: The location decisions of Air Express and DRI
Consequence: Annual revenue
b. \$255,000
c. \$270,000
d. No
e. Lengthen the runway.

14. a. If s_1, then d_1; if s_2, then d_1 or d_2; if s_3, then d_2
b. EVwPI = 0.65(250) + 0.15(100) + 0.20(75) = 192.5
c. From the solution to Problem 5, we know that EV(d_1) = 182.5 and EV(d_2) = 95; thus, recommended decision is d_1; hence, EvwoPI = 182.5.
d. EVPI = EVwPI − EVwoPI = 192.5 − 182.5 = 10

16. a.

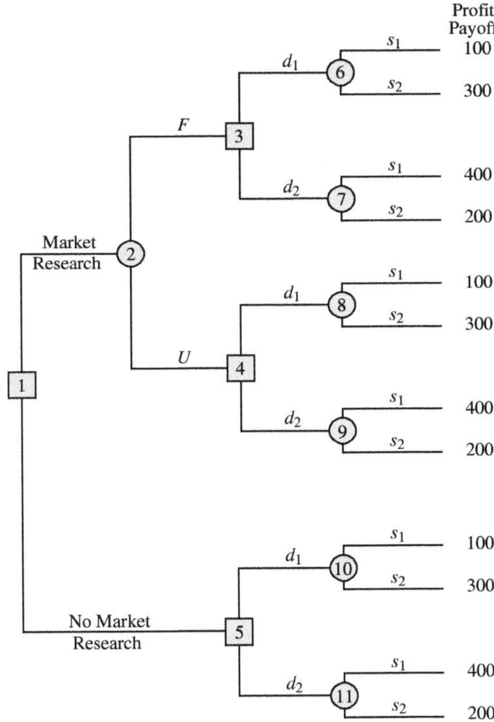

b. EV (node 6) = 0.57(100) + 0.43(300) = 186
EV (node 7) = 0.57(400) + 0.43(200) = 314
EV (node 8) = 0.18(100) + 0.82(300) = 264
EV (node 9) = 0.18(400) + 0.82(200) = 236
EV (node 10) = 0.40(100) + 0.60(300) = 220
EV (node 11) = 0.40(400) + 0.60(200) = 280
EV (node 3) = Max(186,314) = 314d_2
EV (node 4) = Max(264,236) = 264d_1
EV (node 5) = Max(220,280) = 280d_2
EV (node 2) = 0.56(314) + 0.44(264) = 292
EV (node 1) = Max(292,280) = 292
∴ Market Research
If favorable, decision d_2
If unfavorable, decision d_1

18. a. Outcome 1: 2650
Outcome 2: 650
b. Bid on the contract; do not do the market research; build the complex
c. Cost would have to decrease by at least \$130,000.
d.

Payoff (in millions)	Probability
−\$200	0.20
800	0.32
2800	0.48
	1.00

20. a.

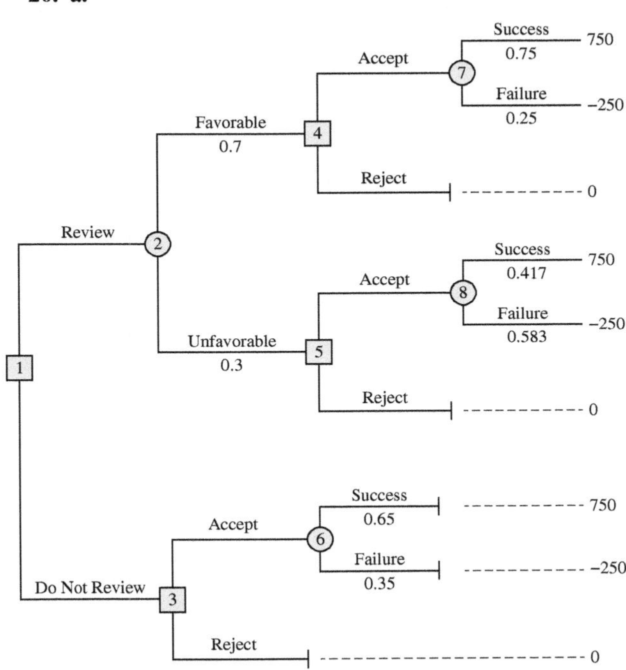

b. Always Accept
c. Do not review; EVSI = \$0
d. EVPI = \$87,500; a better procedure for assessing market potential for the textbook may be worthwhile

22. a. Order two lots; \$60,000
b. If E, order two lots
If V, order one lot
EV = \$60,500
c. EVPI = \$14,000
EVSI = \$500
Efficiency = 3.6%
Yes, use consultant.

23.

State of Nature	$P(s_j)$	$P(I \mid s_j)$	$P(I \cap s_j)$	$P(s_j \mid I)$
s_1	0.2	0.10	0.020	0.1905
s_2	0.5	0.05	0.025	0.2381
s_3	0.3	0.20	0.060	0.5714
	1.0		$P(I) = 0.105$	1.0000

24. a. $P(C) = 0.695$, $P(O) = 0.215$, $P(R) = 0.090$
$P(s_1 \mid C) = 0.98$, $P(s_2 \mid C) = 0.02$
$P(s_1 \mid O) = 0.79$, $P(s_2 \mid O) = 0.21$
$P(s_1 \mid R) = 0.00$, $P(s_2 \mid R) = 1.00$

b.

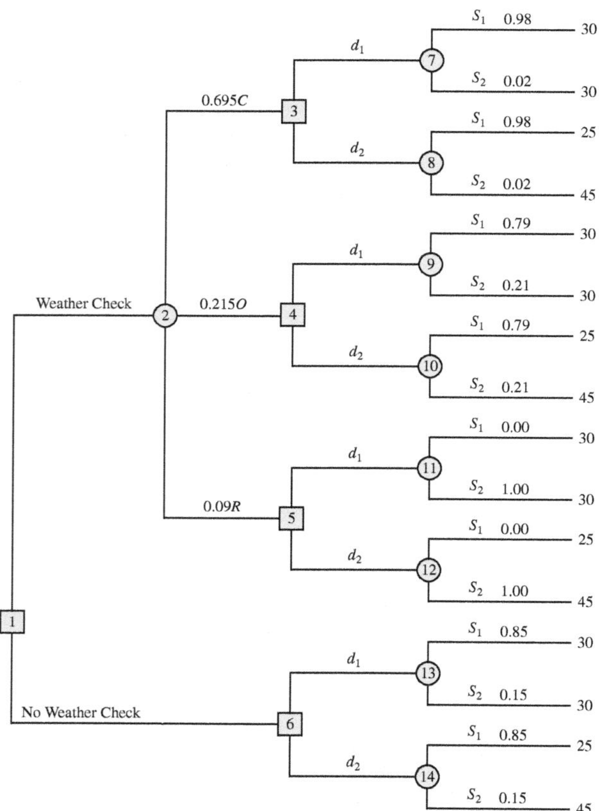

c. Check the weather. If C, Expressway
If O, Expressway
If R, Queen City
26.6 minutes

Chapter 5

1. a. $EV(d_1) = 0.40(100) + 0.30(25) + 0.30(0) = 47.5$
$EV(d_2) = 0.40(75) + 0.30(50) + 0.30(25) = 52.5$
$EV(d_3) = 0.40(50) + 0.30(50) + 0.30(50) = 50.0$
The optimal solution is d_2.

b. Using utilities

Decision Maker A	Decision Maker B
$EU(d_1) = 4.9$	$EU(d_1) = 4.45$ Best
$EU(d_2) = 5.9$	$EU(d_2) = 3.75$
$EU(d_1) = 6.0$ Best	$EU(d_1) = 3.00$

c. Difference in attitude toward risk; decision maker A tends to avoid risk, whereas decision maker B tends to take a risk for the opportunity of a large payoff.

2. a. d_2; $EV(d_2) = \$5000$
b. p = probability of a \$0 cost
$1 - p$ = probability of a \$200,000 cost
c. d_1; $EV(d_1) = 9.9$
d. Expected utility approach; it avoids risk of large loss.

4. a. Route B; EV = 58.5
b. p = probability of a 45-minute travel time
$1 - p$ = probability of a 90-minute travel time
c. Route A; EV = 7.6; risk avoider

5. a.

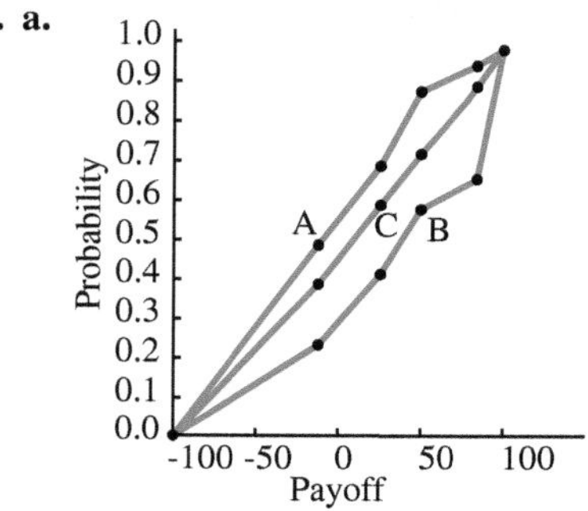

b. A—risk avoider
B—risk taker
C—risk neutral

c. Risk avoider A, at \$20 payoff $p = 0.70$
EV(Lottery) $= 0.70(100) + 0.30(-100) = \$40$
Therefore, will pay $40 - 20 = \$20$
Risk taker B, at \$20 payoff $p = 0.45$
EV(Lottery) $= 0.45(100) + 0.55(-100) = -\$10$
Therefore, will pay $20 - (-10) = \$30$

6. A: d_1; B: d_2; C: d_2

8. a.

	Win	Lose
Bet	350	−10
Do not bet	0	0

b. d_2
c. Risk takers
d. Between 0 and 0.26

10. a. EV(Comedy) $= 0.30(30\%) + 0.60(25\%) + 0.10(20\%) = 26.0\%$
and
EV(Reality Show) $= 0.30(40\%) + 0.40(20\%) + 0.30(15\%) = 24.5\%$

Using the expected value approach, the manager should choose the Comedy.

b. p = probability of a 40% percentage of viewing audience

$1 - p$ = probability of a 15% percentage of viewing audience

c. Arbitrarily using a utility of 10 for the best payoff and a utility of 0 for the worst payoff, the utility table is as follows:

Percentage of Viewing Audience	Indifference Value of p	Utility Value
40%	Does not apply	10
30%	0.40	4
25%	0.30	3
20%	0.10	1
15%	Does not apply	0

and so the expected payoffs in terms of utilities are as follows:

EV(Comedy) = 0.30(4) + 0.60(3) + 0.10(1) = 3.1

and

EV(Reality Show) = 0.30(10) + 0.40(1) + 0.30(0) = 3.4

Using the expected utility approach, the manager should choose the Reality Show.

Although the Comedy has the higher expected payoff in terms of percentage of viewing audience, the Reality Show has the higher expected utility. This suggests the manager is a risk taker.

11.

		Player B			
		b_1	b_2	b_3	Minimum
Player A	a_1	8	5	7	(5)
	a_2	2	4	10	2
	Maximum	8	(5)	10	

The maximum of the row minimums is 5 and the minimum of the column maximums is 5. The game has a pure strategy. Player A should take strategy a_1 and Player B should take strategy b_2. The value of the game is 5.

12. a. The payoff table is as follows:

		Blue Army		
		Attack	Defend	Minimum
Red Army	Attack	30	50	30
	Defend	40	0	0
	Maximum	40	50	

The maximum of the row minimums is 30 and the minimum of the column maximums is 40. Because these values are not equal, a mixed strategy is optimal. Therefore, we must determine the best probability, p, for which the Red Army should choose the Attack strategy. Assume the Red Army chooses Attack with probability p and Defend with probability $1 - p$. If the Blue Army chooses Attack, the expected payoff is $30p + 40(1 - p)$. If the Blue Army chooses Defend, the expected payoff is $50p + 0(1 - p)$.

Setting these equations equal to each other and solving for p, we get $p = 2/3$.

Red Army should choose to Attack with probability 2/3 and Defend with probability 1/3.

b. Assume the Blue Army chooses Attack with probability q and Defend with probability $1 - q$. If the Red Army chooses Attack, the expected payoff for the Blue Army is $30q + 50(1 - q)$. If the Red Army chooses Defend, the expected payoff for the Blue Army is $40q + 0(1 - q)$. Setting these equations equal to each other and solving for q, we get $q = 0.833$. Therefore, the Blue Army should choose to Attack with probability 0.833 and Defend with probability $1 - 0.833 = 0.167$.

14. a. Strategy a_3 dominated by a_2

Strategy b_1 dominated by b_2

		Player B	
		b_2	b_3
Player A	a_1	−1	2
	a_2	4	−3

b. Let p = probability of a_1 and $(1 - p)$ = probability of a_2

If b_1, EV $= -1p + 4(1 - p)$

If b_2, EV $= 2p - 3(1 - p)$

$$-1p + 4(1 - p) = 2p - 3(1 - p)$$
$$-1p + 4 - 4p = 2p - 3 + 3p$$
$$10p = 7$$
$$p = 0.70$$

$p(a_1) = p = 0.70$

$p(a_2) = 1 - 0.70 = 0.30$

Let q = probability of b_2 and $(1 - q)$ = probability of b_3

If a_1, EV $= -1q + 2(1 - q)$

If a_2, EV $= 4q - 3(1 - q)$

$$-1q + 2(1 - q) = 4q - 3(1 - q)$$
$$-1q + 2 - 2q = 4q - 3 + 3q$$
$$10q = 5$$
$$q = 0.50$$

$P(b_2) = q = 0.50$

$P(b_3) = 1 - 0.50 = 0.50$

c. $-1p + 4(1 - p) = -(0.70) + 4(0.30) = +0.50$

16. A: $P(a_3) = 0.80$, $P(a_4) = 0.20$

B: $P(b_1) = 0.40$, $P(b_2) = 0.60$

Value = 2.8

Chapter 6

1. The following table shows the calculations for parts (a), (b), and (c).

Week	Time Series Value	Forecast	Forecast Error	Absolute Value of Forecast Error	Squared Forecast Error	Percentage Error	Absolute Value of Percentage Error
1	18						
2	13	18	−5	5	25	−38.46	38.46
3	16	13	3	3	9	18.75	18.75
4	11	16	−5	5	25	−45.45	45.45
5	17	11	6	6	36	35.29	35.29
6	14	17	−3	3	9	−21.43	21.43
			Totals	22	104	−51.30	159.38

a. MAE = 22/5 = 4.4
b. MSE = 104/5 = 20.8
c. MAPE = 159.38/5 = 31.88
d. The forecast for week 7 is $F_7 = Y_7 = 14$.

2. The following table shows the calculations for parts (a), (b), and (c).

Week	Time Series Value	Forecast	Forecast Error	Absolute Value of Forecast Error	Squared Forecast Error	Percentage Error	Absolute Value of Percentage Error
1	18						
2	13	18.00	−5.00	5.00	25.00	−38.46	38.46
3	16	15.50	0.50	0.50	0.25	3.13	3.13
4	11	15.67	−4.67	4.67	21.81	−42.45	42.45
5	17	14.50	2.50	2.50	6.25	14.71	14.71
6	14	15.00	−1.00	1.00	1.00	−7.14	7.14
			Totals	13.67	54.31	−70.21	105.86

a. MAE = 13.67/5 = 2.73
b. MSE = 54.31/5 = 10.86
c. MAPE = 105.89/5 = 21.18
d. The forecast for week 7 is $F_7 = (Y_1 + Y_2 + Y_3 + Y_4 + Y_5 + Y_6)/6 = (18 + 13 + 16 + 11 + 17 + 14)/6 = 14.83$.

3. The following table shows the measures of forecast error for both methods.

	Exercise 1	Exercise 2
MAE	4.40	2.73
MSE	20.80	10.86
MAPE	31.88	21.18

For each measure of forecast accuracy, the average of all the historical data provided more accurate forecasts than simply using the most recent value.

4. a.

Month	Time Series Value	Forecast	Forecast Error	Squared Forecast Error
1	24			
2	13	24	−11	121
3	20	13	7	49
4	12	20	−8	64
5	19	12	7	49
6	23	19	4	16
7	15	23	−8	64
			Total	363

MSE = 363/6 = 60.5

The forecast for month 8 is $F_8 = Y_8 = 15$.

b.

Week	Time Series Value	Forecast	Forecast Error	Squared Forecast Error
1	24			
2	13	24.00	−11.00	121.00
3	20	18.50	1.50	2.25
4	12	19.00	−7.00	49.00
5	19	17.25	1.75	3.06
6	23	17.60	5.40	29.16
7	15	18.50	−3.50	12.25
			Total	216.72

MSE = 216.72/6 = 36.12

Forecast for month 8 is $F_8 = (Y_1 + Y_2 + Y_3 + Y_4 + Y_5 + Y_6 + Y_7)/7 = (24 + 13 + 20 + 12 + 19 + 23 + 15)/7 = 18$.

c. The average of all the previous values is better because MSE is smaller.

5. a.

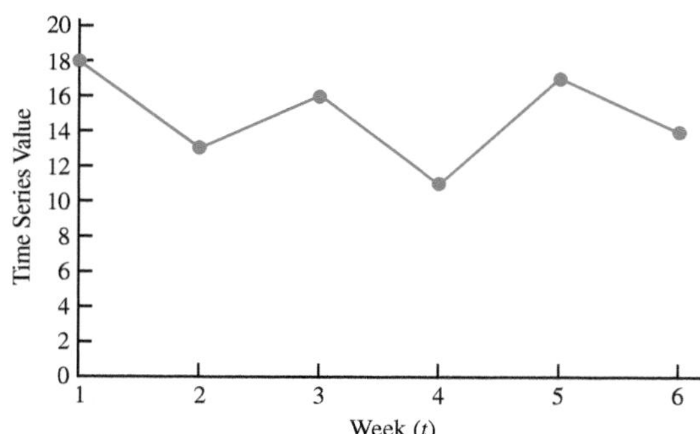

The data appear to follow a horizontal pattern.

b. Three-week moving average

Week	Time Series Value	Forecast	Forecast Error	Squared Forecast Error
1	18			
2	13			
3	16			
4	11	15.67	−4.67	21.78
5	17	13.33	3.67	13.44
6	14	14.67	−0.67	0.44
			Total	35.67

MSE = 35.67/3 = 11.89.

The forecast for week 7 is $F_7 = (Y_4 + Y_5 + Y_6)/3 = (11 + 17 + 14)/3 = 14$.

c. Smoothing constant $\alpha = 0.2$

Week	Time Series Value	Forecast	Forecast Error	Squared Forecast Error
1	18			
2	13	18.00	−5.00	25.00
3	16	17.00	−1.00	1.00
4	11	16.80	−5.80	33.64
5	17	15.64	1.36	1.85
6	14	15.91	−1.91	3.66
			Total	65.15

MSE = 65.15/5 = 13.03

The forecast for week 7 is $F_7 = \alpha Y_6 + (1 - \alpha)F_6 = 0.2(14) + (1 - 0.2)15.91 = 15.53$.

d. The three-week moving average provides a better forecast since it has a smaller MSE.

e. Several values of α will yield an MSE smaller than the MSE associated with $\alpha = 0.2$. The value of α that yields the minimum MSE is $\alpha = 0.367694922$, which yields an MSE of 12.060999.

$\alpha = 0.367694922$

Week	Time Series Value	Forecast	Forecast Error	Squared Forecast Error
1	18			
2	13	18	−5.00	25.00
3	16	16.16	−0.16	0.03
4	11	16.10	−5.10	26.03
5	17	14.23	2.77	7.69
6	14	15.25	−1.25	1.55
			Total	60.30

MSE = 60.30/5 = 12.060999

6. a.

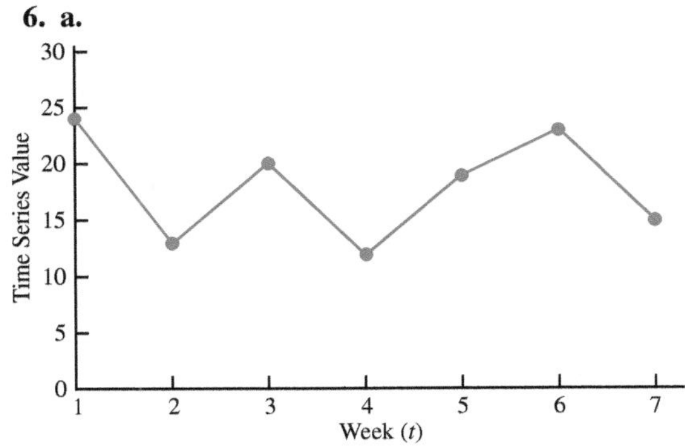

The data appear to follow a horizontal pattern.

b. Three-week moving average

Week	Time Series Value	Forecast	Forecast Error	Squared Forecast Error
1	24			
2	13			
3	20			
4	12	19.00	−7.00	49.00
5	19	15.00	4.00	16.00
6	23	17.00	6.00	36.00
7	15	18.00	−3.00	9.00
			Total	110.00

MSE = 110/4 = 27.5.

The forecast for week 8 is $F_8 = (Y_5 + Y_6 + Y_7)/3 = (19 + 23 + 15)/3 = 19$.

c. Smoothing constant $\alpha = 0.2$

Week	Time Series Value	Forecast	Forecast Error	Squared Forecast Error
1	24			
2	13	24.00	−11.00	121.00
3	20	21.80	−1.80	3.24
4	12	21.44	−9.44	89.11
5	19	19.55	−0.55	0.30
6	23	19.44	3.56	12.66
7	15	20.15	−5.15	26.56
			Total	252.87

MSE = 252.87/6 = 42.15

The forecast for week 8 is $F_8 = \alpha Y_7 + (1 - \alpha)F_7 = 0.2(15) + (1 - 0.2)20.15 = 19.12$.

d. The three-week moving average provides a better forecast since it has a smaller MSE.

e. Several values of α will yield an MSE smaller than the MSE associated with $\alpha = 0.2$. The value of α that yields the minimum MSE is $\alpha = 0.351404848$, which yields an MSE of 39.61428577.

$\alpha = 0.351404848$

Week	Time Series Value	Forecast	Forecast Error	Squared Forecast Error
1	24			
2	13	24.00	−11.00	121.00
3	20	20.13	−0.13	0.02
4	12	20.09	−8.09	65.40
5	19	17.25	1.75	3.08
6	23	17.86	5.14	26.40
7	15	19.67	−4.67	21.79
			Total	237.69

MSE = 237.69/6 = 39.61428577

8. a.

Week	Time Series Value	Weighted Moving Average Forecast	Forecast Error	Squared Forecast Error
1	17			
2	21			
3	19			
4	23	19.33	3.67	13.47
5	18	21.33	−3.33	11.09
6	16	19.83	−3.83	14.67
7	20	17.83	2.17	4.71
8	18	18.33	−0.33	0.11
9	22	18.33	3.67	13.47
10	20	20.33	−0.33	0.11
11	15	20.33	−5.33	28.41
12	22	17.83	4.17	17.39
			Total	103.43

b. MSE = 103.43/9 = 11.49
Prefer the unweighted moving average here; it has a smaller MSE.

c. You could always find a weighted moving average at least as good as the unweighted moving average. Actually, the unweighted moving average is a special case of the weighted average for which the weights are equal.

9. a. Exponential smoothing forecasts using $\alpha = .1$:

Week	Time Series Value	Forecast
1	17	17.00
2	21	17.00
3	19	17.40
4	23	17.56
5	18	18.10
6	16	18.09
7	20	17.88
8	18	18.10
9	22	18.09
10	20	18.48
11	15	18.63
12	22	18.27

For a smoothing constant of $\alpha = .2$:

Week	Time Series Value	Forecast	Forecast Error	Squared Forecast Error
1	17	17.00		
2	21	17.00	4.00	16.00
3	19	17.40	1.60	2.56
4	23	17.56	5.44	29.59
5	18	18.10	−0.10	0.01
6	16	18.09	−2.09	4.38
7	20	17.88	2.12	4.48
8	18	18.10	−0.10	0.01
9	22	18.09	3.91	15.32
10	20	18.48	1.52	2.32
11	15	18.63	−3.63	13.18
12	22	18.27	3.73	13.94
			Total	101.78

MSE = 101.78/11 = 9.253

For a smoothing constant of $\alpha = .2$:

Week	Time Series Value	Forecast	Forecast Error	Squared Forecast Error
1	17	17.00		
2	21	17.00	4.00	16.00
3	19	17.80	1.20	1.44
4	23	18.04	4.96	24.60
5	18	19.03	−1.03	1.07
6	16	18.83	−2.83	7.98
7	20	18.26	1.74	3.03
8	18	18.61	−0.61	0.37
9	22	18.49	3.51	12.34
10	20	19.19	0.81	0.66
11	15	19.35	−4.35	18.94
12	22	18.48	3.52	12.38
			Total	98.80

MSE = 98.80/11 = 8.982

Applying the MSE measure of forecast accuracy, a smoothing constant of $\alpha = .2$ produces a smaller MSE and so is preferred.

b. For a smoothing constant of $\alpha = .1$:

Week	Time Series Value	Forecast	Forecast Error	Absolute Forecast Error
1	17	17.00		
2	21	17.00	4.00	4.00
3	19	17.40	1.60	1.60
4	23	17.56	5.44	5.44
5	18	18.10	−0.10	0.10
6	16	18.09	−2.09	2.09
7	20	17.88	2.12	2.12
8	18	18.10	−0.10	0.10

Week	Time Series Value	Forecast	Forecast Error	Absolute Forecast Error
9	22	18.09	3.91	3.91
10	20	18.48	1.52	1.52
11	15	18.63	−3.63	3.63
12	22	18.27	3.73	3.73
			Total	28.25

MAE = 28.25/11 = 2.568

For a smoothing constant of $\alpha = .2$:

Week	Time Series Value	Forecast	Forecast Error	Absolute Forecast Error
1	17	17.00		
2	21	17.00	4.00	4.00
3	19	17.80	1.20	1.20
4	23	18.04	4.96	4.96
5	18	19.03	−1.03	1.03
6	16	18.83	−2.83	2.83
7	20	18.26	1.74	1.74
8	18	18.61	−0.61	0.61
9	22	18.49	3.51	3.51
10	20	19.19	0.81	0.81
11	15	19.35	−4.35	4.35
12	22	18.48	3.52	3.52
			Total	28.56

MAE = 28.56/11 = 2.596

Applying the MAE measure of forecast accuracy, a smoothing constant of $\alpha = .1$ produces a slightly smaller MAE and so is preferred.

c. For a smoothing constant of $\alpha = .1$:

Week	Time Series Value	Forecast	Forecast Error	100*(Forecast Error/Time Series Value)	Absolute Value of 100*(Forecast Error/Time Series Value)
1	17	17.00			
2	21	17.00	4.00	19.05	19.05
3	19	17.40	1.60	8.42	8.42
4	23	17.56	5.44	23.65	23.65
5	18	18.10	−0.10	−0.58	0.58
6	16	18.09	−2.09	−13.09	13.09
7	20	17.88	2.12	10.58	10.58
8	18	18.10	−0.10	−0.53	0.53
9	22	18.09	3.91	17.79	17.79
10	20	18.48	1.52	7.61	7.61
11	15	18.63	−3.63	−24.20	24.20
12	22	18.27	3.73	16.97	16.97
				Total	142.46

MAPE = 142.46/11 = 12.95

For a smoothing constant of $\alpha = .2$:

Week	Time Series Value	Forecast	Forecast Error	100*(Forecast Error/ Time Series Value)	Absolute Value of 100*(Forecast Error/ Time Series Value)
1	17	17.00			
2	21	17.00	4.00	19.05	19.05
3	19	17.80	1.20	6.32	6.32
4	23	18.04	4.96	21.57	21.57
5	18	19.03	−1.03	−5.73	5.73
6	16	18.83	−2.83	−17.66	17.66
7	20	18.26	1.74	8.70	8.70
8	18	18.61	−0.61	−3.38	3.38
9	22	18.49	3.51	15.97	15.97
10	20	19.19	0.81	4.05	4.05
11	15	19.35	−4.35	−29.01	29.01
12	22	18.48	3.52	15.99	15.99
				Total	147.43

MAPE = 147.43/11 = 13.40

Applying the MAPE measure of forecast accuracy, a smoothing constant of $\alpha = .1$ produces a smaller MAPE and so is preferred.

10. a. $F_{13} = 0.2Y_{12} + 0.16Y_{11} + 0.64(0.2Y_{10} + 0.8F_{10}) = 0.2Y_{12} + 0.16Y_{11} + 0.128Y_{10} + 0.512F_{10}$

$F_{13} = 0.2Y_{12} + 0.16Y_{11} + 0.128Y_{10} + 0.512(0.2Y_9 + 0.8F_9) = 0.2Y_{12} + 0.16Y_{11} + 0.128Y_{10} + 0.1024Y_9 + 0.4096F_9$

$F_{13} = 0.2Y_{12} + 0.16Y_{11} + 0.128Y_{10} + 0.1024Y_9 + 0.4096(0.2Y_8 + 0.8F_8) = 0.2Y_{12} + 0.16Y_{11} + 0.128Y_{10} + 0.1024Y_9 + 0.08192Y_8 + 0.32768F_8$

b. The more recent data receive the greater weight or importance in determining the forecast. The moving averages method weights the last n data values equally in determining the forecast.

12. a.

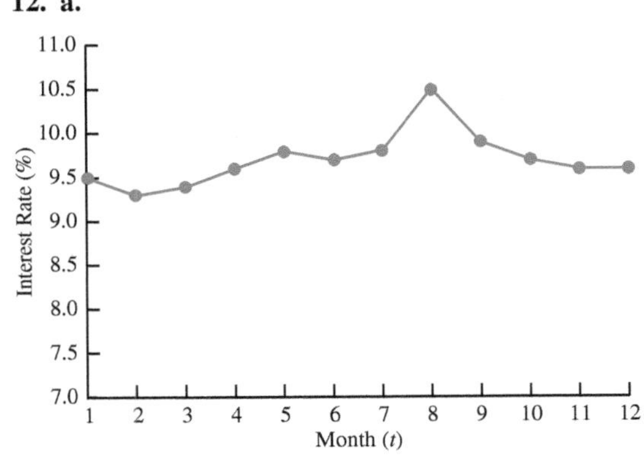

The data appear to follow a horizontal pattern.

b.

Month	Time Series Value	3-Month Moving Average Forecast	$(\text{Error})^2$	4-Month Moving Average Forecast	$(\text{Error})^2$
1	9.5				
2	9.3				
3	9.4				
4	9.6	9.40	0.04		
5	9.8	9.43	0.14	9.45	0.12
6	9.7	9.60	0.01	9.53	0.03
7	9.8	9.70	0.01	9.63	0.03
8	10.5	9.77	0.53	9.73	0.59
9	9.9	10.00	0.01	9.95	0.00
10	9.7	10.07	0.14	9.98	0.08
11	9.6	10.03	0.18	9.97	0.14
12	9.6	9.73	0.02	9.92	0.10
			1.08		1.09

MSE(3-Month) = 1.08/9 = 0.12

MSE(4-Month) = 1.09/8 = 0.14

The MSE for the 3-month moving average is smaller, so use the 3-month moving average.

c. The forecast for month 13 is $F_{13} = (Y_{10} + Y_{11} + Y_{12})/3 = (9.7 + 9.6 + 9.6)/3 = 9.63$.

13. a.

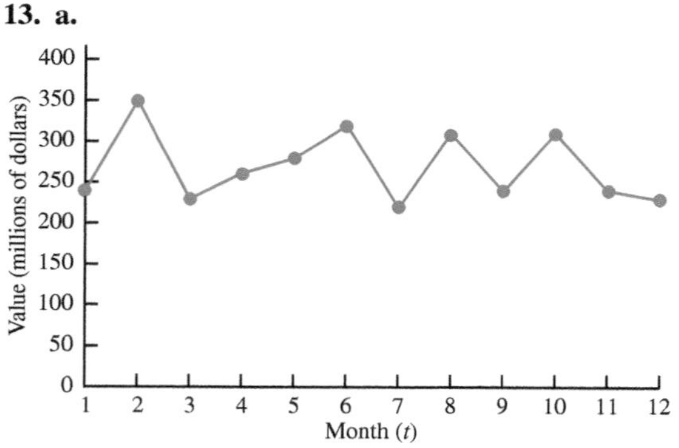

The data appear to follow a horizontal pattern.

b.

$\alpha = 0.2$

Month	Time Series Value	3-Month Moving Average Forecast	$(\text{Error})^2$	Average Forecast	$(\text{Error})^2$
1	240				
2	350		240.00	12100.00	
3	230		262.00	1024.00	
4	260	273.33	177.69	255.60	19.36
5	280	280.00	0.00	256.48	553.19
6	320	256.67	4010.69	261.18	3459.79
7	220	286.67	4444.89	272.95	2803.70
8	310	273.33	1344.69	262.36	2269.57
9	240	283.33	1877.49	271.89	1016.97
10	310	256.67	2844.09	265.51	1979.36
11	240	286.67	2178.09	274.41	1184.05
12	230	263.33	1110.89	267.53	1408.50
			17,988.52		27,818.49

MSE(3-Month) = 17,988.52/9 = 1998.72

MSE(α = 0.2) = 27,818.49/11 = 2528.95

Based on the above MSE values, the 3-month moving average appears better. However, exponential smoothing was penalized by including month 2, which was difficult for any method to forecast. Using only the errors for months 4 to 12, the MSE for exponential smoothing is as follows:

MSE(α = 0.2) = 14,694.49/9 = 1632.72

Thus, exponential smoothing was better considering months 4 to 12.

c. Using exponential smoothing,

$F_{13} = \alpha Y_{12} + (1 - \alpha)F_{12} = 0.20(230) + 0.80(267.53) = 260.$

14. a.

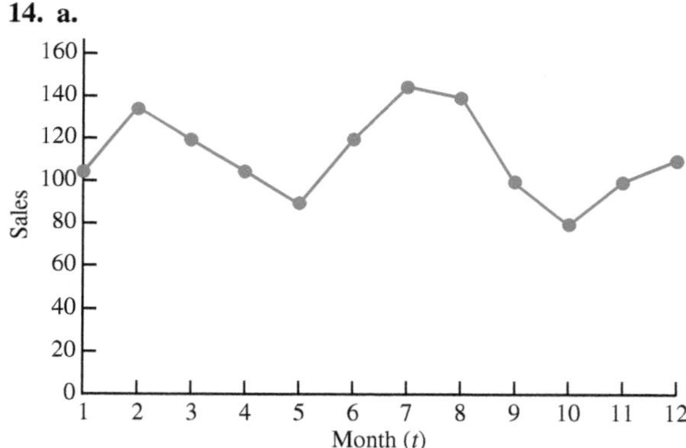

The data appear to follow a horizontal pattern.

b. Smoothing constant $\alpha = 0.3$.

Month t	Time Series Value Y_t	Forecast F_t	Forecast Error $Y_t - F_t$	Squared Error $(Y_t - F_t)^2$
1	105			
2	135	105.00	30.00	900.00
3	120	114.00	6.00	36.00
4	105	115.80	−10.80	116.64

Month t	Time Series Value Y_t	Forecast F_t	Forecast Error $Y_t - F_t$	Squared Error $(Y_t - F_t)^2$
5	90	112.56	−22.56	508.95
6	120	105.79	14.21	201.92
7	145	110.05	34.95	1221.50
8	140	120.54	19.46	378.69
9	100	126.38	−26.38	695.90
10	80	118.46	−38.46	1479.17
11	100	106.92	−6.92	47.89
12	110	104.85	5.15	26.52
			Total	5613.18

MSE = 5613.18/11 = 510.29

The forecast for month 13 is $F_{13} = \alpha Y_{12} + (1 - \alpha)F_{12} = 0.3(110) + 0.7(104.85) = 106.4$.

c. The value of α that yields the smallest possible MSE is $\alpha = 0.032564518$, which yields an MSE of 459.6929489.

$\alpha = 0.032564518$

Month	Time Series Value	Forecast	Forecast Error	Squared Error
1	105			
2	135	105	30.00	900.00
3	120	105.98	14.02	196.65
4	105	106.43	−1.43	2.06
5	90	106.39	−16.39	268.53
6	120	105.85	14.15	200.13
7	145	106.31	38.69	1496.61
8	140	107.57	32.43	1051.46
9	100	108.63	−8.63	74.47
10	80	108.35	−28.35	803.65
11	100	107.43	−7.43	55.14
12	110	107.18	2.82	7.93
			Total	5056.62

MSE = 5056.62/11 = 459.6929489

16. a.

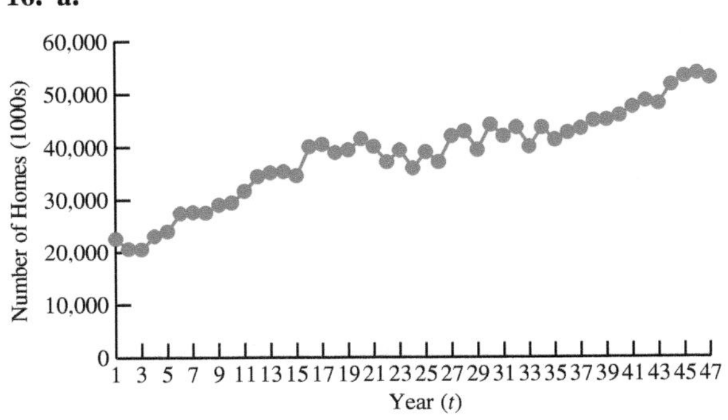

b. This time series plot indicates a possible linear trend in the data, so forecasting methods discussed in this chapter are appropriate to develop forecasts for this time series.

c. The following values are needed to compute the slope and intercept:

$\Sigma t = 1128 \quad \Sigma t^2 = 35720 \quad \Sigma Y_t = 1808715 \quad \Sigma tY_t = 48566536$

Computation of slope:

$$b_1 = \frac{\sum tY_t - \left(\sum t \sum Y_t\right)/n}{\sum t^2 - \left(\sum t\right)^2/n} = \frac{48566536 - (1128)(1808715)/47}{35720 - (1128)^2/47}$$

$= 596.3663$

Computation of intercept:

$b_0 = \bar{Y} - b_1\bar{t} = (38483.30/47) - (596.366)(1128/47) = 24170.506$

Equation for linear trend: $\hat{y}_t = 24170.506 + 596.366t$

The annual increase in households viewing the Super Bowl is approximately 596,366.

17. a.

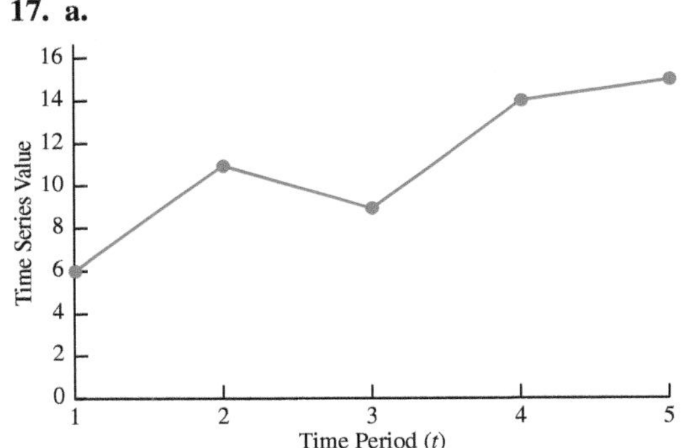

The time series plot shows a linear trend.

b. The regression estimates for the slope and y-intercept are as follows:

$$b_1 = \frac{\sum_{t=1}^{n} tY_t - \sum_{t=1}^{n} t \sum_{t=1}^{n} Y_t / n}{\sum_{t=1}^{n} t^2 - \left(\sum_{t=1}^{n} t\right)^2 / n} = \frac{186 - (15)(55)/5}{55 - (15)^2/5} = 2.10$$

$$b_0 = \bar{Y} - b_1\bar{t} = \frac{55}{5} - 2.10\left(\frac{15}{3}\right) = 4.70$$

which results in the following forecasts, errors, and MSE:

Year	Sales	Forecast	Forecast Error	Squared Forecast Error
1	6.00	6.80	−0.80	0.64
2	11.00	8.90	2.10	4.41
3	9.00	11.00	−2.00	4.00
4	14.00	13.10	0.90	0.81
5	15.00	15.20	−0.20	0.04
6		17.30	Total	9.9

MSE = 9.9/5 = 1.982.475

c. $F_6 = b_0 + b_1 t = 4.7 + 2.1(6) = 17.3$

18. a.

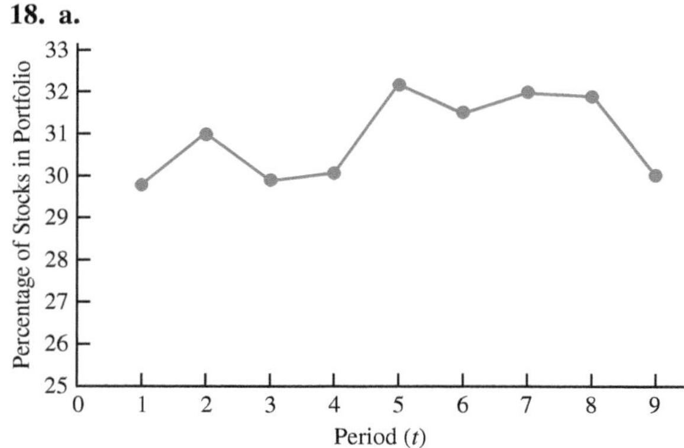

b. The value of the MSE will vary depending on the ultimate value of α that you select. The value of α that yields the smallest possible MSE is $\alpha = 0.467307293$, which yields an MSE of 1.222838367.

$\alpha = 0.467307293$

Period	Stock%	Forecast	Forecast Error	Squared Forecast Error
1st-2007	29.8			
2nd-2007	31.0	29.80	1.20	1.44
3rd-2007	29.9	30.36	−0.46	0.21
4th-2007	30.1	30.15	−0.05	0.00
1st-2008	32.2	30.12	2.08	4.31
2nd-2008	31.5	31.09	0.41	0.16
3rd-2008	32.0	31.28	0.72	0.51
4th-2008	31.9	31.62	0.28	0.08
1st-2009	30.0	31.75	−1.75	3.06
2nd-2009		30.93	Total	9.78

MSE = 1.222838367

c. The forecast for the next period will vary depending on the ultimate value of α that you selected in part (b). Using an exponential smoothing model with $\alpha = 0.467307293$, the forecast is 30.93.

20. a.

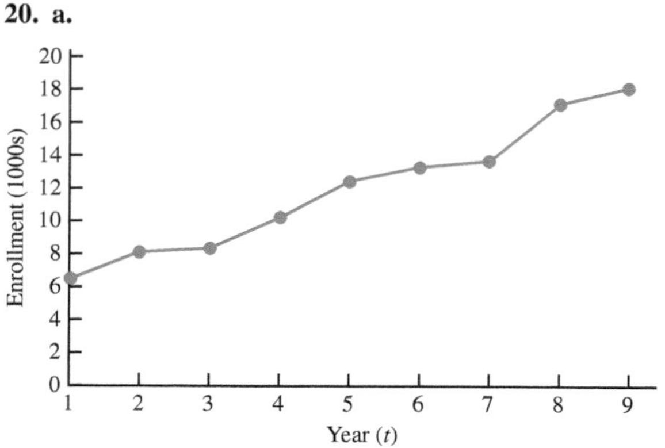

The time series plot shows a linear trend.

b. The regression estimates for the slope and y-intercept are as follows:

$$b_1 = \frac{\sum_{t=1}^{n} tY_t - \sum_{t=1}^{n} t \sum_{t=1}^{n} Y_t \Big/ n}{\sum_{t=1}^{n} t^2 - \left(\sum_{t=1}^{n} t\right)^2 \Big/ n} = \frac{627.4 - (45)(108)/9}{285 - (45)^2/9} = 4.7167$$

$$b_0 = \bar{Y} - b_1\bar{t} = \frac{108}{9} - 4.7167\left(\frac{45}{9}\right) = 1.4567$$

which results in the following forecasts, errors, and MSE:

Period	Year	Enroll-ment	Forecast	Forecast Error	Squared Forecast Error
1	2001	6.50	6.17	0.33	0.11
2	2002	8.10	7.63	0.47	0.22
3	2003	8.40	9.09	−0.69	0.47
4	2004	10.20	10.54	−0.34	0.12
5	2005	12.50	12.00	0.50	0.25
6	2006	13.30	13.46	−0.16	0.02
7	2007	13.70	14.91	−1.21	1.47
8	2008	17.20	16.37	0.83	0.69
9	2009	18.10	17.83	0.27	0.07
10	2010		19.28	**Total**	3.427

MSE = 0.3808

c. $F_{10} = b_0 + b_1 t = 4.7167 + 1.4567(10) = 19.28$

22. a.

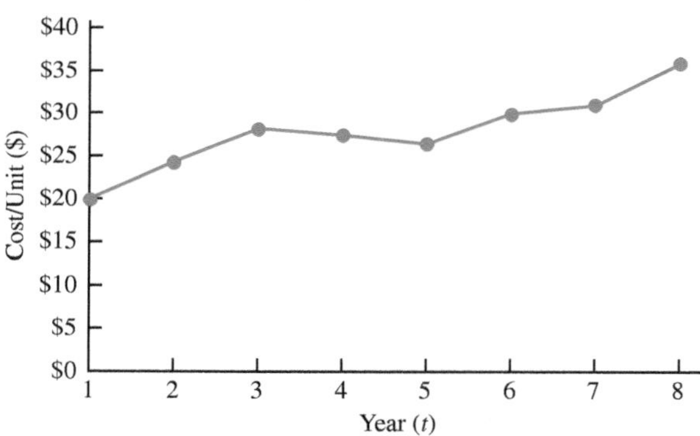

The time series plot shows an upward linear trend.

b. The regression estimates for the slope and y-intercept are as follows:

$$b_1 = \frac{\sum_{t=1}^{n} tY_t - \sum_{t=1}^{n} t \sum_{t=1}^{n} Y_t \Big/ n}{\sum_{t=1}^{n} t^2 - \left(\sum_{t=1}^{n} t\right)^2 \Big/ n} = \frac{1081.6 - (36)(223.8)/8}{204 - (36)^2/8} = 1.7738$$

$$b_0 = \bar{Y} - b_1\bar{t} = \frac{223.8}{8} - 1.774\left(\frac{36}{8}\right) = 19.9928$$

which results in the following forecasts, errors, and MSE:

Year	Cost/ Unit($)	Forecast	Forecast Error	Squared Forecast Error
1	20.00	21.77	−1.77	3.12
2	24.50	23.54	0.96	0.92
3	28.20	25.31	2.89	8.33
4	27.50	27.09	0.41	0.17
5	26.60	28.86	−2.26	5.12
6	30.00	30.64	−0.64	0.40
7	31.00	32.41	−1.41	1.99
8	36.00	34.18	1.82	3.30
9		35.96	**Total**	23.34619

MSE = 2.9183

c. The average cost/unit has been increasing by approximately $1.77 per year.

d. $F_9 = b_0 + b_1 t = 19.9928 + 1.7738(9) = 35.96$

24. a.

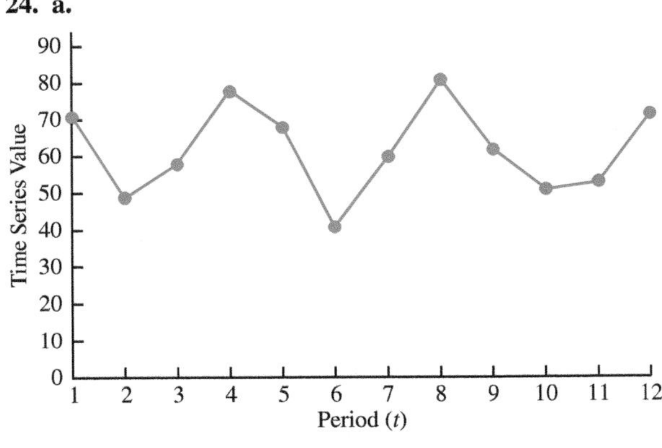

The time series plot shows a horizontal pattern. But there is a seasonal pattern in the data. For instance, in each year the lowest value occurs in quarter 2 and the highest value occurs in quarter 4.

b. After putting the data into the following format:

Year	Quarter	Dummy Variables Quarter 1	Quarter 2	Quarter 3	Y_t
1	1	1	0	0	71
1	2	0	1	0	48
1	3	0	0	1	58
1	4	0	0	0	78
2	1	1	0	0	68
2	2	0	1	0	41
2	3	0	0	1	60
2	4	0	0	0	81
3	1	1	0	0	62
3	2	0	1	0	51
3	3	0	0	1	53
3	4	0	0	0	72

we can use the LINEST function to find the regression model:

Value = 77.00 − 10.00 Qtr1 − 30.33 Qtr2 − 20.00 Qtr3

c. The quarterly forecasts for next year are as follows:

Quarter 1 forecast = 77.0 − 10.0(1) − 30.33(0) − 20.0(0) = 67.00

Quarter 2 forecast = 77.0 − 10.0(0) − 30.33(1) − 20.0(0) = 46.67

Quarter 3 forecast = 77.0 − 10.0(0) − 30.33(0) − 20.0(1) = 57.00

Quarter 4 forecast = 77.0 − 10.0(0) − 30.33(0) − 20.0(0) = 77.00

26. a.

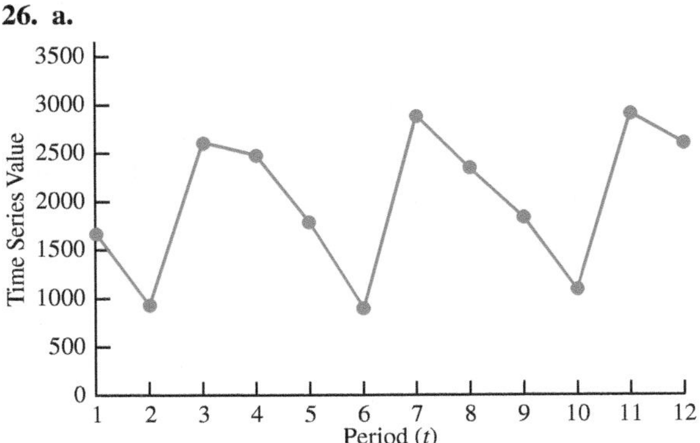

There appears to be a seasonal pattern in the data and perhaps a moderate upward linear trend.

b. After putting the data into the following format:

Year	Quarter	Dummy Variables Quarter 1	Quarter 2	Quarter 3	Y_t
1	1	1	0	0	1690
1	2	0	1	0	940
1	3	0	0	1	2625
1	4	0	0	0	2500
2	1	1	0	0	1800
2	2	0	1	0	900
2	3	0	0	1	2900
2	4	0	0	0	2360
3	1	1	0	0	1850
3	2	0	1	0	1100
3	3	0	0	1	2930
3	4	0	0	0	2615

we can use the LINEST function to find the regression model:

Value = 2491.67 − 711.67 Qtr1 − 1511.67 Qtr2 + 326.67 Qtr3

c. The quarterly forecasts for next year are as follows:

Quarter 1 forecast = 2491.67 − 711.67(1) − 1511.67(0) + 326.67(0) = 1780.00

Quarter 2 forecast = 2491.67 − 711.67(0) − 1511.67(1) + 326.67(0) = 980.00
Quarter 3 forecast = 2491.67 − 711.67(0) − 1511.67(0) + 326.67(1) = 2818.33
Quarter 4 forecast = 2491.67 − 711.67(0) − 1511.67(0) + 326.67(0) = 2491.67

d. After putting the data into the following format:

		Dummy Variables				
Year	Quarter	Quarter 1	Quarter 2	Quarter 3	t	Y_t
1	1	1	0	0	1	1690
1	2	0	1	0	2	940
1	3	0	0	1	3	2625
1	4	0	0	0	4	2500
2	1	1	0	0	5	1800
2	2	0	1	0	6	900
2	3	0	0	1	7	2900
2	4	0	0	0	8	2360
3	1	1	0	0	9	1850
3	2	0	1	0	10	1100
3	3	0	0	1	11	2930
3	4	0	0	0	12	2615

we can use the LINEST function to find the regression model:

Value = 2306.67 − 642.29 Qtr1 − 1465.42 Qtr2 + 349.79 Qtr3 + 23.13t

The quarterly forecasts for next year are as follows:

Quarter 1 forecast = 2306.67 − 642.29(1) − 1465.42(0) + 349.79(0) + 23.13(13) = 1965.00
Quarter 2 forecast = 2306.67 − 642.29(0) − 1465.42(1) + 349.79(0) + 23.13(14) = 1165.00
Quarter 3 forecast = 2306.67 − 642.29(0) − 1465.42(0) + 349.79(1) + 23.13(15) = 2011.33
Quarter 4 forecast = 2306.67 − 642.29(0) − 1465.42(0) + 349.79(0) + 23.13(16) = 2676.67

28. a.

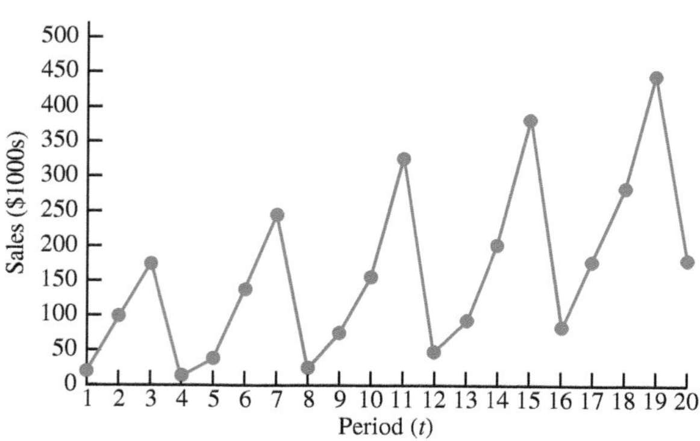

The time series plot shows both a linear trend and seasonal effects.

b. After putting the data into the following format:

		Dummy Variables			
Year	Quarter	Quarter 1	Quarter 2	Quarter 3	Y_t
1	1	1	0	0	20
1	2	0	1	0	100
1	3	0	0	1	175
1	4	0	0	0	13
2	1	1	0	0	37
2	2	0	1	0	136
2	3	0	0	1	245
2	4	0	0	0	26
3	1	1	0	0	75
3	2	0	1	0	155
3	3	0	0	1	326
3	4	0	0	0	48
4	1	1	0	0	92
4	2	0	1	0	202
4	3	0	0	1	384
4	4	0	0	0	82
5	1	1	0	0	176
5	2	0	1	0	282
5	3	0	0	1	445
5	4	0	0	0	181

we can use the LINEST function to find the regression model:

Revenue = 70.0 + 10.0 Qtr1 + 105 Qtr2 + 245 Qtr3

Quarter 1 forecast = 70.0 + 10.0(1) + 105(0) + 245(0) = 80
Quarter 2 forecast = 70.0 + 10.0(0) + 105(1) + 245(0) = 175
Quarter 3 forecast = 70.0 + 10.0(0) + 105(0) + 245(1) = 315
Quarter 4 forecast = 70.0 + 10.0(0) + 105(0) + 245(0) = 70

c. After putting the data into the following format:

		Dummy Variables				
Year	Quarter	Quarter 1	Quarter 2	Quarter 3	t	Y_t
1	1	1	0	0	1	20
1	2	0	1	0	2	100
1	3	0	0	1	3	175
1	4	0	0	0	4	13
2	1	1	0	0	5	37
2	2	0	1	0	6	136
2	3	0	0	1	7	245
2	4	0	0	0	8	26
3	1	1	0	0	9	75
3	2	0	1	0	10	155
3	3	0	0	1	11	326
3	4	0	0	0	12	48
4	1	1	0	0	13	92
4	2	0	1	0	14	202
4	3	0	0	1	15	384
4	4	0	0	0	16	82
5	1	1	0	0	17	176
5	2	0	1	0	18	282
5	3	0	0	1	19	445
5	4	0	0	0	20	181

we can use the LINEST function to find the regression model:

$$\text{Revenue} = -70.10 + 45.03\ \text{Qtr1} + 128.35\ \text{Qtr2} + 256.68\ \text{Qtr3} + 11.68t$$

$$\text{Quarter 1 forecast} = -70.10 + 45.03(1) + 128.35(0) + 256.68(0) + 11.68(21) = 221$$

$$\text{Quarter 2 forecast} = -70.10 + 45.03(0) + 128.35(1) + 256.68(0) + 11.68(22) = 315$$

$$\text{Quarter 3 forecast} = -70.10 + 45.03(0) + 128.35(0) + 256.68(1) + 11.68(23) = 456$$

$$\text{Quarter 4 forecast} = -70.10 + 45.03(0) + 128.35(0) + 256.68(0) + 11.68(24) = 211$$

Chapter 7

1. Parts (a), (b), and (e) are acceptable linear programming relationships.
   Part (c) is not acceptable because of $-2x_2^2$.
   Part (d) is not acceptable because of $3\sqrt{x_1}$.
   Part (f) is not acceptable because of $1x_1x_2$.
   Parts (c), (d), and (f) could not be found in a linear programming model because they contain nonlinear terms.

2. a.

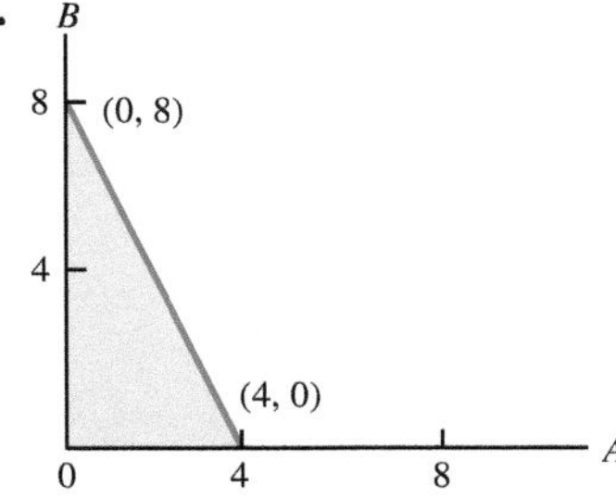

b.

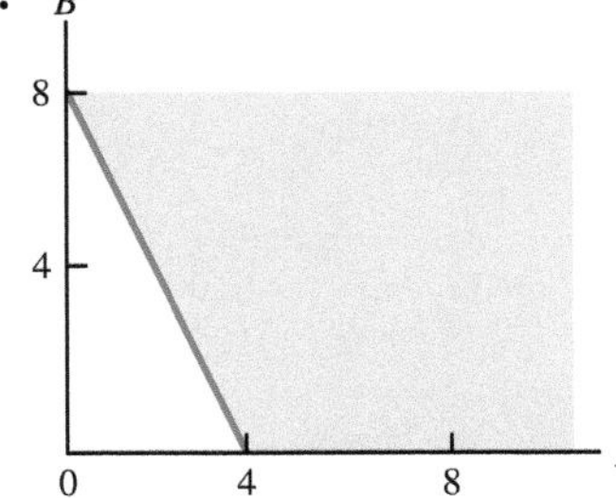

c.

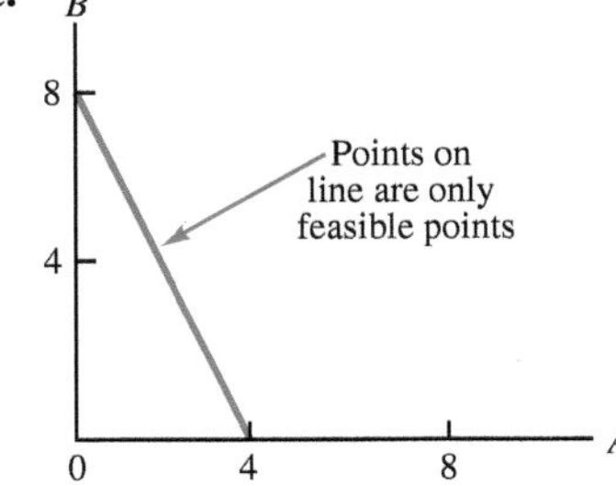

4. a.

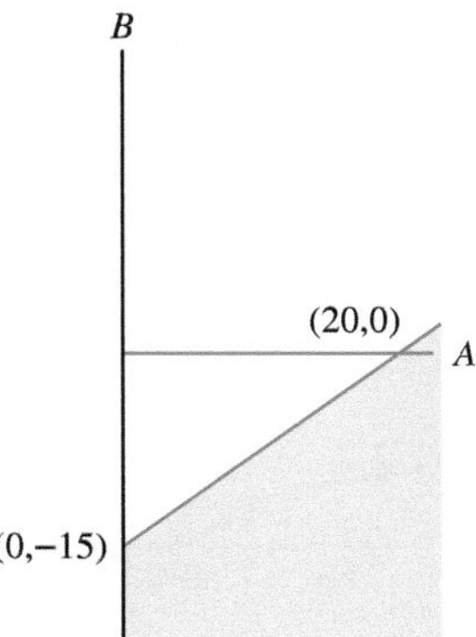

b.

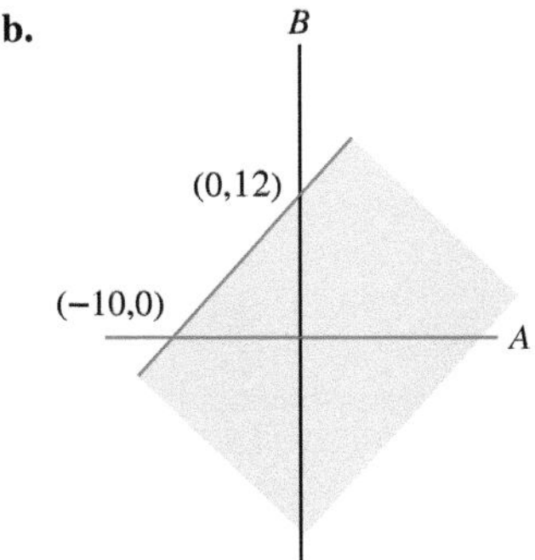

c.

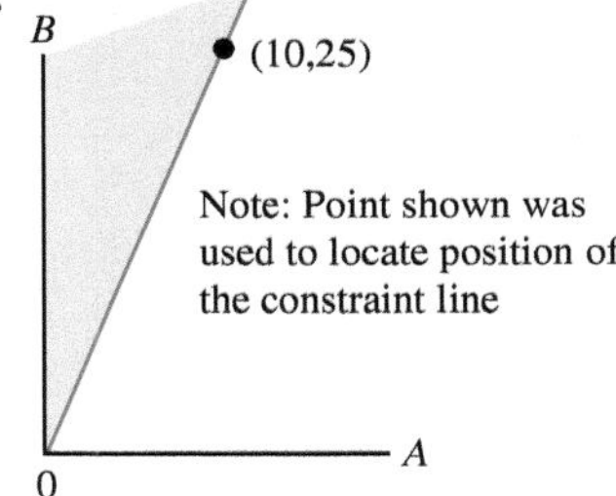

6. $7A + 10B = 420$
   $6A + 4B = 420$
   $4A + 7B = 420$

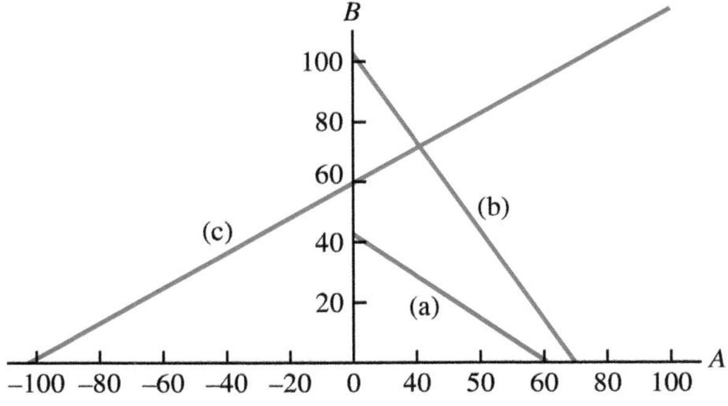

7.

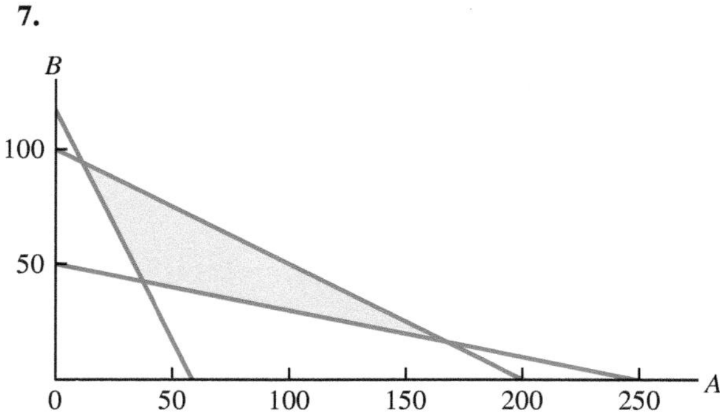

10.

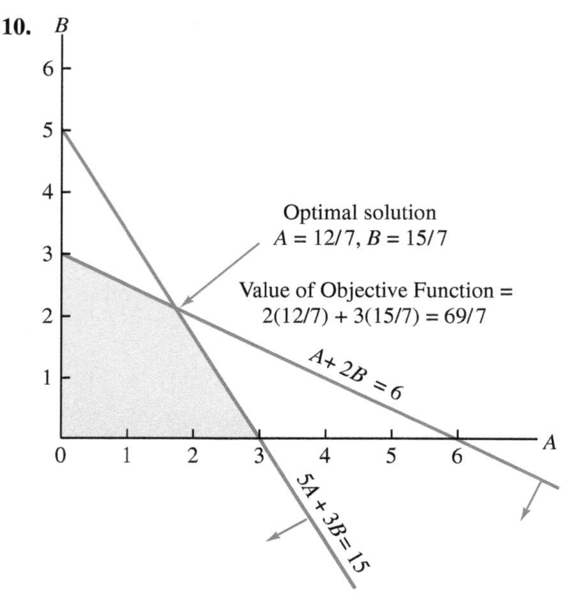

	$A + 2B = 6$	(1)
	$5A + 3B = 15$	(2)
Equation (1) times 5:	$5A + 10B = 30$	(3)
Equation (2) minus equation (3):	$-7B = -15$	
	$B = 15/7$	
From equation (1):	$A = 6 - 2(15/7)$	
	$= 6 - 30/7 = 12/7$	

12. a. $A = 3, B = 1.5$; Value of optimal solution = 13.5

b. $A = 0, B = 3$; Value of optimal solution = 18

c. Four: (0, 0), (4, 0), (3, 1.5), and (0.3)

13. a.

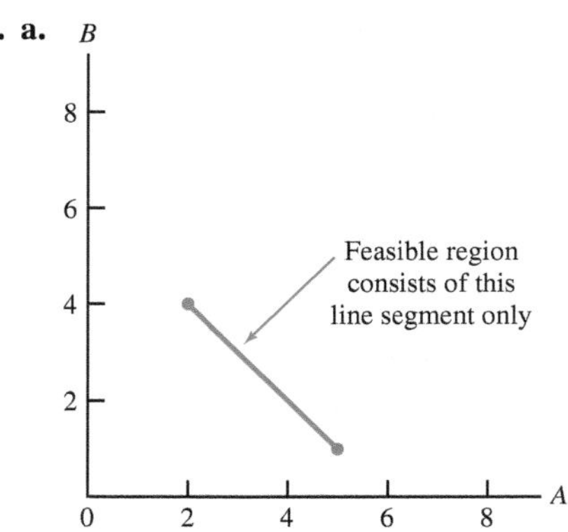

b. The extreme points are (5, 1) and (2, 4).

c.

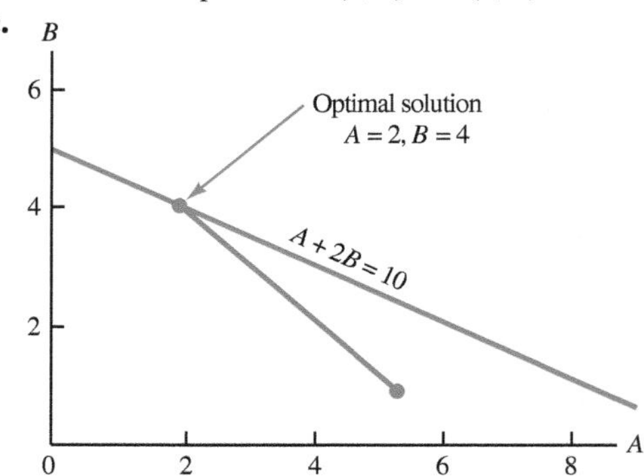

14. a. 540 standard bags, 252 deluxe bags
b. 7668
c. 630, 480, 708, 117
d. 0, 120, 0, 18

16. a. $3S + 9D$
b. (0,540)
c. 90, 150, 348, 0

17. Max $5A + 2B + 0s_1 + 0s_2 + 0s_3$

s.t.

$$\begin{aligned} 1A - 2B + 1s_1 \quad\quad\quad &= 420 \\ 2A + 3B - \quad + 1s_2 \quad &= 610 \\ 6A - 1B + \quad\quad + 1s_3 &= 125 \\ A, B, s_1, s_2, s_3 &\geq 0 \end{aligned}$$

18. b. $A = 18/7, B = 15/7$
c. $0, 0, 4/7$

20. b. $A = 3.43, B = 3.43$
c. 2.86, 0, 1.43, 0

22. b.

Extreme Point	Coordinates	Profit ($)
1	(0, 0)	0
2	(1700, 0)	8500
3	(1400, 600)	9400
4	(800, 1200)	8800
5	(0, 1680)	6720

Extreme point 3 generates the highest profit.

c. $A = 1400, C = 600$

d. Cutting and dyeing constraint and the packaging constraint

e. $A = 800, C = 1200$; profit = \$9200

24. a. Let R = number of units of regular model
C = number of units of catcher's model

$$\begin{aligned}
\text{Max} \quad & 5R + 8C \\
& 1R + C + {}^3\!/_2 C \leq 900 \quad \text{Cutting and sewing} \\
& {}^1\!/_2 R + {}^1\!/_3 C \leq 300 \quad \text{Finishing} \\
& {}^1\!/_8 R + {}^1\!/_4 C \leq 100 \quad \text{Packaging and shipping} \\
& R, C \geq 0
\end{aligned}$$

b.

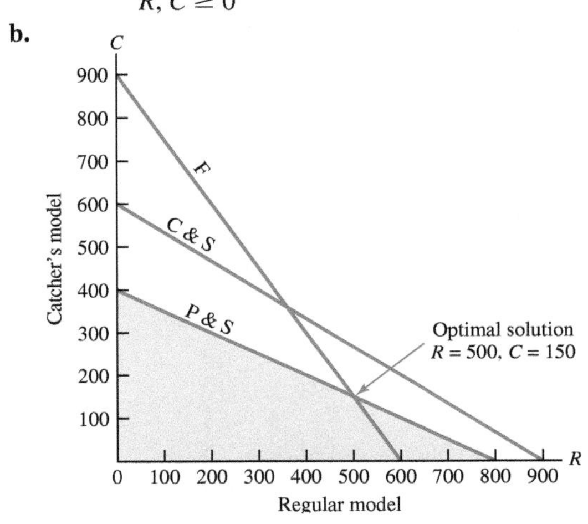

c. $5(500) + 8(150) = \$3700$

d.

C & S	$1(500) + {}^3\!/_2(150) = 725$
F	${}^1\!/_2(500) + {}^1\!/_3(150) = 300$
P & S	${}^1\!/_8(500) + {}^1\!/_4(150) = 100$

e.

Department	Capacity	Usage	Slack
Cutting and sewing	900	725	175 hours
Finishing	300	300	0 hours
Packaging and shipping	100	100	0 hours

26. a. Max $50N + 80R$

s.t.

$$\begin{aligned}
N + R &= 1000 \\
N &\geq 250 \\
R &\geq 250 \\
N - 2R &\geq 0 \\
N, R &\geq 0
\end{aligned}$$

b. $N = 666.67, R = 333.33$; Audience exposure = 60,000

28. a. Max $1W + 1.25M$

s.t.

$$\begin{aligned}
5W + 7M &\leq 4480 \\
3W + 1M &\leq 2080 \\
2W + 2M &\leq 1600 \\
W, M &\geq 0
\end{aligned}$$

b. $W = 560, M = 240$; Profit = 860

30. a. Max $15E + 18C$

s.t.

$$\begin{aligned}
40E + 25C &\leq 50{,}000 \\
40E &\geq 15{,}000 \\
25C &\geq 10{,}000 \\
25C &\leq 25{,}000 \\
E, C &\geq 0
\end{aligned}$$

c. (375, 400); (1000, 400); (625, 1000); (375, 1000)

d. $E = 625, C = 1000$
Total return = \$27,375

31.

B
6
4
2
Feasible region
2 4 6 8
A
Optimal solution
$A = 3, B = 1$
$3A + 4B = 13$

Objective function value = 13

32.

Extreme Points	Objective Function Value	Surplus Demand	Stock Total Production	Processing Time
(250, 100)	800	125	—	—
(125, 225)	925	—	—	125
(125, 350)	1300	—	125	—

34. a.

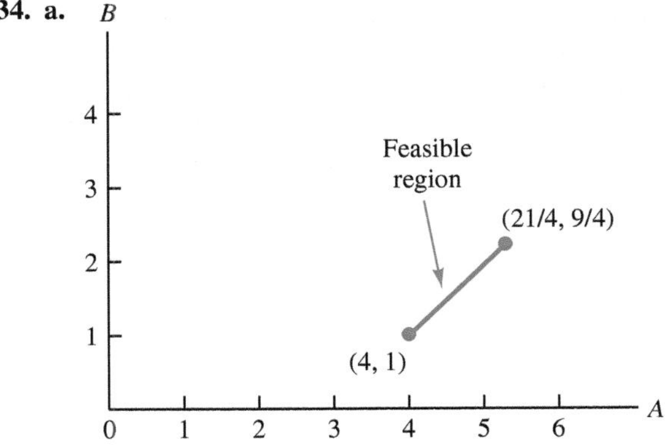

b. There are two extreme points:

$(A = 4, B = 1)$ and $(A = 21/4, B = 9/4)$

c. The optimal solution [see part (a)] is $A = 4, B = 1$.

35. a. Min $6A + 4B + 0s_1 + 0s_2 + 0s_3$

s.t.

$$\begin{aligned} 2A + 1B - s_1 \qquad &= 12 \\ 1A + 1B \qquad - s_2 \qquad &= 10 \\ 1B \qquad\qquad + s_3 &= 4 \\ A, B, s_1, s_2, s_3 \geq 0 \end{aligned}$$

b. The optimal solution is $A = 6, B = 4$

c. $s_1 = 4, s_2 = 0, s_3 = 0$

36. a. Min $10{,}000T + 8000P$

s.t.

$$\begin{aligned} T \qquad &\geq 8 \\ P &\geq 10 \\ T + \quad P &\geq 25 \\ 3T + \quad 2P &\leq 84 \end{aligned}$$

c. (15, 10); (21.33, 10); (8, 30); (8, 17)

d. $T = 8, P = 17$

Total cost = $216,000

38. a. Min $7.50S + 9.00P$

s.t.

$$\begin{aligned} 0.10S + 0.30P &\geq 6 \\ 0.06S + 0.12P &\leq 3 \\ S + \quad P &= 30 \\ S, P &\geq 0 \end{aligned}$$

c. The optimal solution is $S = 15, P = 15$.

d. No

e. Yes

40. $P_1 = 30, P_2 = 25$, Cost = $55

42.

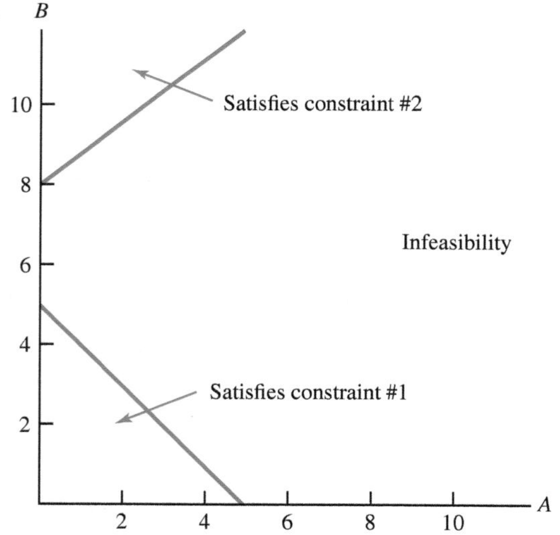

43.

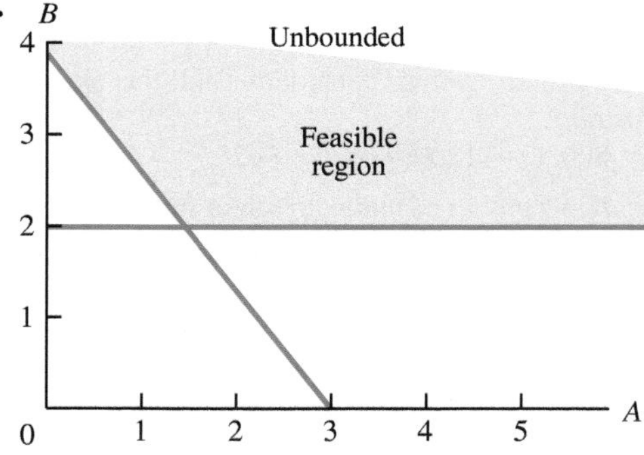

44. a. $A = 30/16, B = 30/16$; Value of optimal solution = $^{60}/_{16}$

b. $A = 0, B = 3$; Value of optimal solution = 6

46. a. 180, 20

b. Alternative optimal solutions

c. 120, 80

48. No feasible solution

50. $M = 65.45, R = 261.82$; Profit = $45,818

52. $S = 384, O = 80$

54. a. Max $160M_1 + 345M_2$

s.t.

$$\begin{aligned} M_1 \qquad &\leq 15 \\ M_2 &\leq 10 \\ M_1 \qquad &\geq 5 \\ M_2 &\geq 5 \\ 40M_1 + \quad 50M_2 &\leq 1000 \\ M_1, M_2 &\geq 0 \end{aligned}$$

b. $M_1 = 12.5, M_2 = 10$

Chapter 8

1. a.

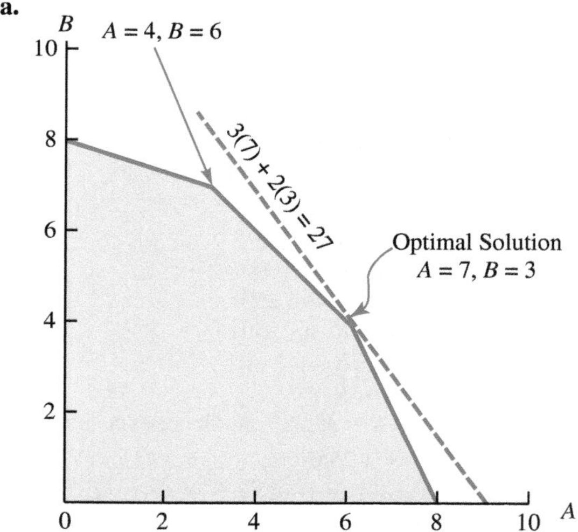

b. The same extreme point, $A = 7$ and $B = 3$, remains optimal; Value of the objective function becomes $5(7) + 2(3) = 41$.

c. A new extreme point, $A = 4$ and $B = 6$, becomes optimal; Value of the objective function becomes $3(4) + 4(6) = 36$.

d. The objective coefficient range for variable A is 2 to 6; the optimal solution, $A = 7$ and $B = 3$, does not change. The objective coefficient range for variable B is 1 to 3; resolve the problem to find the new optimal solution.

2. a. The feasible region becomes larger with the new optimal solution of $A = 6.5$ and $B = 4.5$.

b. Value of the optimal solution to the revised problem is $3(6.5) + 2(4.5) = 28.5$; the one-unit increase in the right-hand side of constraint 1 increases the value of the optimal solution by $28.5 - 27 = 1.5$; therefore, the shadow price for constraint 1 is 1.5.

c. The right-hand-side range for constraint 1 is 8 to 11.2; as long as the right-hand side stays within this range, the shadow price of 1.5 is applicable.

d. The value of the optimal solution will increase by 0.5 for every unit increase in the right-hand side of constraint 2 as long as the right-hand side is between 18 and 30.

4. a. $X = 2.5$, $Y = 2.5$

b. -2

c. 5 to 11

d. The value of the optimal solution will increase by 3 for every unit increase in the right-hand side of constraint 2 as long as the right-hand side is between 9 and 18.

5. a. Regular glove = 500; Catcher's mitt = 150;
Value = 3700

b. The finishing, packaging, and shipping constraints are binding; there is no slack.

c. Cutting and sewing = 0
Finishing = 3
Packaging and shipping = 28
Additional finishing time is worth \$3 per unit, and additional packaging and shipping time is worth \$28 per unit.

d. In the packaging and shipping department, each additional hour is worth \$28.

6. a. The optimal value for the Regular Glove variable is 5, the Allowable Decrease is 1, and the Allowable Increase is 7. The optimal value for the Catcher's Mitt variable is 8, the Allowable Decrease is 4.667, and the Allowable Increase is 2. Therefore, we can express the Objective Coefficient Ranges as follows:

Variable	Objective Coefficient Range
Regular Glove	$5 - 1 = 4$ to $5 + 7 = 12$
Catcher's Mitt	$8 - 4.667 = 3.333$ to $8 + 2 = 10$

b. As long as the profit contribution for the regular glove is between \$4.00 and \$12.00, the current solution is optimal; as long as the profit contribution for the catcher's mitt stays between \$3.33 and \$10.00, the current solution is optimal; the optimal solution is not sensitive to small changes in the profit contributions for the gloves.

c. The shadow prices for the resources are applicable over the following ranges:

Constraint	Right-Hand-Side Range
Cutting and sewing	$900 - 175 = 725$ to No Upper Limit
Finishing	$300 - 166.667 = 133.333$ to $300 + 100 = 400$
Packaging	$100 - 25 = 75$ to $100 + 35 = 135$

d. The shadow price of packaging and shipping constraint is 28, so the amount of increase $= (28)(20) = \$560$.

8. a. More than \$7.00

b. More than \$3.50

c. None

10. a. $S = 4000$
$M = 10{,}000$
Total risk $= 8(4000) + 3(10{,}000) = 62{,}000$

b.

Variable	Objective Coefficient Range
S	$8.000 - 4.250 = 3.750$ to No Upper Limit
M	No Upper Limit to $3.000 + 3.400 = 6.400$

c. $5(4000) + 4(10{,}000) = \$60{,}000$

d. $60{,}000/1{,}200{,}000 = 0.05$ or 5%

e. 0.057 risk units

f. $0.057(100) = 5.7\%$

12. a. $E = 80$, $S = 120$, $D = 0$
Profit $= 63(80) + 95(120) + 135(0) = \$16{,}440$

b. Fan motors and cooling coils

c. The manufacturing time constraint has slack; $2400 - 2080 = 320$ hours are available.

d. This represents an increase in the objective function coefficient for D of $\$150 - \$135 = \$15$. Because this is less than the allowable increase of \$24 for the objective function coefficient for D, there is no change in the optimal solution.

13. a. The range of optimality for each objective function coefficient is as follows:

E $63.000 - 15.5000 = 47.500$ to $63.000 + 12.000 = 75$
S $95.000 - 8.000 = 87.000$ to $95.000 + 31.000 = 126$
D No lower limit to $135.000 + 24.000 = 159.000$

b. Because more than one objective function coefficient value is changing at the same time here, we must resolve the problem to answer this question. Re-solving the problem with the new profit values shows that the optimal solution will not change. However, the change in total profit will be 69(80) + 93(120) + 135(0) = \$16,680.

c. The range of feasibility for the right-hand side values for each constraint is as follows:

Fan motors constraint	200.000 − 40.000 = 160.000 to 200.000 + 80.000 = 280.000
Cooling coils constraint	320.000 − 120.000 = 200.000 to 320.000 + 80.000 = 400.000
Manufacturing time constraint	2400.000 − 320.000 = 2080.000 to No Upper Limit

d. Yes, 100 is greater than the allowable increase for the fan motors constraint (80.000).

The shadow price will change.

14. a. The optimal solution is to manufacture 100 cases of model A and 60 cases of model B and purchase 90 cases of model B.

Total Cost = 10(100) + 6(60) + 14(0) + 9(90) = \$2170

b. Demand for A, demand for B, assembly time

c.

Constraint	Shadow Price
1	12.25
2	9.0
3	0
4	−0.375

If demand for model A increases by 1 unit, total cost will increase by \$12.25.
If demand for model B increases by 1 unit, total cost will increase by \$9.00.
If an additional minute of assembly time is available, total cost will decrease by \$.375.

d. Assembly time constraint

16. a. 100 suits, 150 sport coats
Profit = \$40,900
40 hours of cutting overtime

b. Optimal solution will not change.

c. Consider ordering additional material.
\$34.50 is the maximum price.

d. Profit will improve by \$875.

18. a. The linear programming model is as follows:

$$\begin{aligned}
\text{Min}\quad & 30AN + 50AO + 25BN + 40BO \\
& AN + AO \geq 50{,}000 \\
& BN + BO \geq 70{,}000 \\
& AN + BN \leq 80{,}000 \\
& AO + BO \leq 60{,}000 \\
& AN, AO, BN, BO \geq 0
\end{aligned}$$

b. Optimal solution

	New Line	Old Line
Model A	50,000	0
Model B	30,000	40,000

Total cost: \$3,850,000

c. The first three constraints are binding.

d. The shadow price for the new production line capacity constraint is −15. Because the shadow price is negative, increasing the right-hand side of constraint 3 will cause the objective function to decrease. Thus, every 1-unit increase in the right hand side of this constraint will actually reduce the total production cost by \$15. In other words, an increase in capacity for the new production line is desirable.

e. Because constraint 4 is not a binding constraint, any increase in the production line capacity of the old production line will have no effect on the optimal solution; thus, increasing the capacity of the old production line results in no benefit.

f. The reduced cost for model A made on the old production line is 5; thus, the cost would have to decrease by at least \$5 before any units of model A would be produced on the old production line.

g. The right-hand-side range for constraint 2 shows an allowable decrease of 40,000. Thus, if the minimum production requirement is reduced 10,000 units to 60,000, the shadow price of 40 is applicable. Thus, total cost would decrease by 10,000(40) = \$400,000.

20. a.

$$\begin{aligned}
\text{Max}\quad & 0.07H + 0.12P + 0.09A \\
& H + P + A = 1{,}000{,}000 \\
& 0.6H - 0.4P - 0.4A \geq 0 \\
& P - 0.6A \leq 0 \\
& H, P, A \geq 0
\end{aligned}$$

b. H = \$400,000, P = \$225,000, A = \$375,000
Total annual return = \$88,750
Annual percentage return = 8.875%

c. No change

d. Increase of \$890

e. Increase of \$312.50, or 0.031%

22. a.

$$\begin{aligned}
\text{Min}\quad & 30L + 25D + 18S \\
& L + D + S = 100 \\
& 0.6L - 0.4D \geq 0 \\
& -0.15L - 0.15D + 0.85S \geq 0 \\
& -0.25L - 0.25D + S \leq 0 \\
& L \leq 50 \\
& L, D, S \geq 0
\end{aligned}$$

b. $L = 48$, $D = 72$, $S = 30$
Total cost = \$3780

c. No change
d. No change

24. a. Solution: $A = 333.3$, $B = 0$, $C = 833.3$, $D = 2500$

Risk: 14,666.7

Return: 18,000 (or 9%)

b.

Variable	Objective Coefficient Range
A	9.5 to 11
B	3.33 to No Upper Limit
C	3.2 to 4.4
D	No Lower Limit to 3.33

Individual changes in the risk measure coefficients within these ranges will not cause a change in the optimal investment decisions.

c. The shadow price associated with the rate of return constraint is 0.833. If the firm requires a 10% rate of return, this will increase the right-hand side of this constraint to 0.1*200,000 = 20,000, which is an increase of 2000 units. Because this increase is within the right-hand-side range, this means that we would expect the objective function to increase by 2000*0.833 = 1666 units. In other words, the increased rate of return would result in an increase in risk of 1660 units.

26. a. Let M_1 = units of component 1 manufactured
M_2 = units of component 2 manufactured
M_3 = units of component 3 manufactured
P_1 = units of component 1 purchased
P_2 = units of component 2 purchased
P_3 = units of component 3 purchased

$$\begin{array}{llr}
\text{Min} & 4.50M_1 + 5.00M_2 + 2.75M_3 + 6.50P_1 + 8.80P_2 + 7.00P_3 & \\
& 2M_1 + 3M_2 + 4M_3 \leq 21{,}600 & \text{Production} \\
& 1M_1 + 1.5M_2 + 3M_3 \leq 15{,}000 & \text{Assembly} \\
& 1.5M_1 + 2M_2 + 5M_3 \leq 18{,}000 & \text{Testing/Packaging} \\
& 1M_1 + 1P_1 = 6{,}000 & \text{Component 1} \\
& 1M_2 + 1P_2 = 4{,}000 & \text{Component 2} \\
& 1M_3 + 1P_3 = 3{,}500 & \text{Component 3} \\
& M_1, M_2, M_3, P_1, P_2, P_3 \geq 0 &
\end{array}$$

b.

Source	Component 1	Component 2	Component 3
Manufacture	2000	4000	1400
Purchase	4000		2100

Total Cost $73,550

c. Production: $54.36 per hour
Testing & Packaging: $7.50 per hour

d. Shadow prices = $7.969; it would cost Benson $7.969 to add a unit of component 2.

28. a. Let G = amount invested in growth stock fund
S = amount invested in income stock fund
M = amount invested in money market fund

$$\begin{array}{ll}
\text{Max} & 0.20G + 0.10S + 0.06M \\
\text{s.t.} & \\
& 0.10G + 0.05S + 0.01M \leq (0.05)(300{,}000) \\
& G \geq (0.10)(300{,}000) \\
& S \geq (0.10)(300{,}000) \\
& M \geq (0.20)(300{,}000) \\
& G + S + M \leq 300{,}000 \\
& G, S, M \geq 0
\end{array}$$

b. $G = 120{,}000$; $S = 30{,}000$; $M = 150{,}000$
c. 0.15 to 0.60; No Lower Limit to 0.122; 0.02 to 0.20
d. 4668
e. $G = 48{,}000$; $S = 192{,}000$; $M = 60{,}000$
f. The client's risk index and the amount of funds available

30. a. $L = 3$, $N = 7$, $W = 5$, $S = 5$
b. Each additional minute of broadcast time increases cost by $100.
c. If local coverage is increased by 1 minute, total cost will increase by $100.
d. If the time devoted to local and national news is increased by 1 minute, total cost will increase by $100.
e. Increasing the sports by 1 minute will have no effect because the shadow price is 0.

32. a. Let P_1 = number of PT-100 battery packs produced at the Philippines plant
P_2 = number of PT-200 battery packs produced at the Philippines plant
P_3 = number of PT-300 battery packs produced at the Philippines plant
M_1 = number of PT-100 battery packs produced at the Mexico plant
M_2 = number of PT-200 battery packs produced at the Mexico plant
M_3 = number of PT-300 battery packs produced at the Mexico plant

$$\begin{array}{ll}
\text{Min} & 1.13P_1 + 1.16P_2 + 1.52P_3 + 1.08M_1 + 1.16M_2 + 1.25M_3 \\
& P_1 + M_1 = 200{,}000 \\
& P_2 + M_2 = 100{,}000 \\
& P_3 + M_3 = 150{,}000 \\
& P_1 + P_2 \leq 175{,}000 \\
& M_1 + M_2 \leq 160{,}000 \\
& P_3 \leq 75{,}000 \\
& M_3 \leq 100{,}000 \\
& P_1, P_2, P_3, M_1, M_2, M_3 \geq 0
\end{array}$$

b. The optimal solution is as follows:

	Philippines	Mexico
PT-100	40,000	160,000
PT-200	100,000	0
PT-300	50,000	100,000

Total production and transportation cost is $535,000.

c. The range of optimality for the objective function coefficient for P_1 shows a lower limit of \$1.08; thus, the production and/or shipping cost would have to decrease by at least 5 cents per unit.

d. The range of optimality for the objective function coefficient for M_1 shows a lower limit of \$1.11; thus, the production and/or shipping cost would have to decrease by at least 5 cents per unit.

Chapter 9

1. a. Let T = number of television spot advertisements
R = number of radio advertisements
N = number of online advertisements

Max $100{,}000T + 18{,}000R + 40{,}000N$
s.t.

$$
\begin{aligned}
2{,}000T + 300R + 600N &\leq 18{,}200 && \text{Budget} \\
T &\leq 10 && \text{Max TV} \\
R &\leq 20 && \text{Max Radio} \\
N &\leq 10 && \text{Max Online} \\
-0.5T + 0.5R - 0.5N &\leq 0 && \text{Max 50\% Radio} \\
0.9T - 0.1R - 0.1N &\geq 0 && \text{Min 10\% TV} \\
T, R, N, &\geq 0
\end{aligned}
$$

	Budget \$
Solution: $T = 4$	\$ 8000
$R = 14$	4200
$N = 10$	6000
	\$18,200

Audience = 1,052,000

b. The shadow price for the budget constraint is 51.30. Thus, a \$100 increase in budget should provide an increase in audience coverage of approximately 5130. The right-hand-side range for the budget constraint will show this interpretation is correct.

2. a. Let x_1 = units of product 1 produced
x_2 = units of product 2 produced

Max $30x_1 + 15x_2$
s.t.

$$
\begin{aligned}
x_1 + 0.35x_2 &\leq 100 && \text{Dept. A} \\
0.30x_1 + 0.20x_2 &\leq 36 && \text{Dept. B} \\
0.20x_1 + 0.50x_2 &\leq 50 && \text{Dept. C} \\
x_1, x_2 &\leq 0
\end{aligned}
$$

Solution: $x_1 = 77.89$, $x_2 = 63.16$; Profit = \$3284.21

b. The shadow price for Department A is \$15.79; for Department B it is \$47.37; and for Department C it is \$0.00. Therefore, we would attempt to schedule overtime in Departments A and B. Assuming the current labor available is a sunk cost, we should be willing to pay up to \$15.79 per hour in Department A and up to \$47.37 in Department B.

c. Let x_A = hours of overtime in Department A
x_B = hours of overtime in Department B
x_C = hours of overtime in Department C

Max $30x_1 + 15x_2 - 18x_A - 22.5x_B - 12x_C$
s.t.

$$
\begin{aligned}
x_1 + 0.35x_2 - x_A &\leq 100 \\
0.30x_1 + 0.20x_2 - x_B &\leq 36 \\
0.20x_1 + 0.50x_2 - x_C &\leq 50 \\
x_A &\leq 10 \\
x_B &\leq 6 \\
x_C &\leq 8 \\
x_1, x_2, x_A, x_B, x_C &\leq 0
\end{aligned}
$$

$x_1 = 87.21$
$x_2 = 65.12$
Profit = \$3341.34

	Overtime
Department A	10 hours
Department B	3.186 hours
Department C	0 hours

Increase in profit from overtime = \$3341.34 − 3284.21 = \$57.13

4. Let X_1 = the number of pounds of Party Nuts to produce
X_2 = the number of pounds of Mixed Nuts to produce
X_3 = the number of pounds of Premium Nuts to produce

Max $2(1.00)X_1 + 2(2.10)X_2 + 2(3.63)X_3 - 1.5(X_1 + 0.55X_2) - 5.35(0.25X_2 + 0.40X_3) - 6.25(0.1X_2 + 0.2X_3)$
s.t.

$$
\begin{aligned}
X_1 + 0.55X_2 &\leq 500 && \text{(Peanuts)} \\
0.25X_2 + 0.40X_2 &\leq 180 && \text{(Cashews)} \\
0.1X_2 + 0.2X_2 &\leq 100 && \text{(Brazil Nuts)} \\
0.1X_2 + 0.4X_2 &\leq 80 && \text{(Hazelnuts)} \\
X_1, X_2, X_2 &\geq 0
\end{aligned}
$$

The optimal solution is as follows:
$133\frac{1}{3}$ pounds of Party Nuts (or $266\frac{2}{3}$ bags)
$666\frac{2}{3}$ pounds of Mixed Nuts (or $1333\frac{1}{3}$ bags)
$33\frac{1}{3}$ pounds of Premium Nuts (or $66\frac{2}{3}$ bags)
Profit of \$537.33
The binding constraints are Peanuts, Cashews, and Hazelnuts.
Brazil Nuts are not binding (only $73\frac{1}{3}$ pounds are used, resulting in slack of $26\frac{2}{3}$ pounds).

6. Let x_1 = units of product 1
x_2 = units of product 2
b_1 = labor-hours Department A
b_2 = labor-hours Department B

Max $25x_1 + 20x_2 + 0b_1 + 0b_2$
s.t.

$$
\begin{aligned}
6x_1 + 8x_2 - 1b_1 &= 0 \\
12x_1 + 10x_2 - 1b_2 &= 0 \\
1b_1 + 1b_2 &\leq 900 \\
x_1, x_2, b_1, b_2 &\geq 0
\end{aligned}
$$

Solution: $x_1 = 50$, $x_2 = 0$, $b_1 = 300$, $b_2 = 600$; Profit: \$1250

8. Let x_1 = the number of officers scheduled to begin at 8:00 A.M.
x_2 = the number of officers scheduled to begin at noon
x_3 = the number of officers scheduled to begin at 4:00 P.M.
x_4 = the number of officers scheduled to begin at 8:00 P.M.
x_5 = the number of officers scheduled to begin at midnight
x_6 = the number of officers scheduled to begin at 4:00 A.M.

The objective function to minimize the number of officers required is as follows:

Min $x_1 + x_2 + x_3 + x_4 + x_5 + x_6$

The constraints require the total number of officers on duty each of the six 4-hour periods to be at least equal to the minimum officer requirements. The constraints for the six 4-hour periods are as follows:

Time of Day	
8:00 A.M.–Noon	$x_1 + x_6 \geq 5$
Noon-4:00 P.M.	$x_1 + x_2 \geq 6$
4:00 P.M.–8:00 P.M.	$x_2 + x_3 \geq 10$
8:00 P.M.–Midnight	$x_3 + x_4 \geq 7$
Midnight–4:00 A.M.	$x_4 + x_5 \geq 4$
4:00 A.M.–8:00 A.M.	$x_5 + x_6 \geq 6$

$x_1, x_2, x_3, x_4, x_5, x_6 \geq 0$

Schedule 19 officers as follows:

x_1 = 3 begin at 8:00 A.M.
x_2 = 3 begin at noon
x_3 = 7 begin at 4:00 P.M.
x_4 = 0 begin at 8:00 P.M.
x_5 = 4 begin at midnight
x_6 = 2 begin at 4:00 A.M.

9. Let X_i = the number of call center employees who start work on day i.

($i = 1$ = Monday, $i = 2$ = Tuesday...)

Min $X_1 + X_2 + X_3 + X_4 + X_5 + X_6 + X_7$

s.t.

$X_1 + X_4 + X_5 + X_6 + X_7 \geq 75$
$X_1 + X_2 + X_5 + X_6 + X_7 \geq 50$
$X_1 + X_2 + X_3 + X_6 + X_7 \geq 45$
$X_1 + X_2 + X_3 + X_4 + X_7 \geq 60$
$X_1 + X_2 + X_3 + X_4 + X_5 \geq 90$
$X_2 + X_3 + X_4 + X_5 + X_6 \geq 75$
$X_3 + X_4 + X_5 + X_6 + X_7 \geq 45$
$X_1, X_2, X_3, X_4, X_5, X_6, X_7 \geq 0$

Solution: $X_1 = 20$, $X_2 = 20$, $X_3 = 0$, $X_4 = 45$, $X_5 = 5$, $X_6 = 5$, $X_7 = 0$

Total Number of Employees = 95

Excess employees: Thursday = 25, Sunday = 10, all others = 0

Note: There are alternative optima to this problem (number of employees may differ from above, but will have objective function value = 95).

10. a. Let S = the proportion of funds invested in stocks
B = the proportion of funds invested in bonds
M = the proportion of funds invested in mutual funds
C = the proportion of funds invested in cash

The linear program and optimal solution are as follows:

Max $0.1S + 0.03B + 0.04M + 0.01C$

s.t.

(1) $1S + 1B + 1M + 1C = 1$
(2) $0.8S + 0.2B + 0.3M < 0.4$
(3) $1S < (0.75$
(4) $-1B + 1M > 0$
(5) $1C > 0.1$
(6) $1C < 0.3$

The optimal allocation among the four investment alternatives:

Stocks	40.9%
Bonds	14.5%
Mutual Funds	14.5%
Cash	30.0%

The annual return associated with the optimal portfolio is 5.4%.

Total risk = 0.409(0.8) + 0.145(0.2) + 0.145(0.3) + 0.300(0.0) = 0.4

b. Changing the right-hand-side value for constraint 2 to 0.18 and re-solving, we obtain the following optimal solution:

Stocks	0.0%
Bonds	36.0%
Mutual Funds	36.0%
Cash	28.0%

The annual return associated with the optimal portfolio is 2.52%.

Total risk = 0.0(0.8) + 0.36(0.2) + 0.36(0.3) + 0.28(0.0) = 0.18

c. Changing the right-hand-side value for constraint 2 to 0.7 and re-solving, we obtain the following optimal allocation among the four investment alternatives:

Stocks	75.0%
Bonds	0.0%
Mutual Funds	15.0%
Cash	10.0%

The annual return associated with the optimal portfolio is 8.2%.

Total risk = 0.75(0.8) + 0.0(0.2) + 0.15(0.3) + 0.10(0.0) = 0.65

d. Note that a maximum risk of 0.7 was specified for this aggressive investor, but that the risk index for the portfolio is only 0.65. Thus, this investor is willing to take more risk than the solution shown above provides. There are only two ways the investor can become even more aggressive: by increasing the proportion invested in stocks to more than 75% or reducing the cash requirement of at least 10% so that additional cash could be put into stocks. For the data given here, the investor should ask the investment advisor to relax either or both of these constraints.

e. Defining the decision variables as proportions means the investment advisor can use the linear programming model for any investor, regardless of the amount of the investment. All the investor advisor must do is to establish the maximum total risk for the investor and resolve the problem using the new value for maximum total risk.

12. Let B_i = pounds of shrimp bought in week i, $i = 1, 2, 3, 4$
S_i = pounds of shrimp sold in week i, $i = 1, 2, 3, 4$
I_i = pounds of shrimp held in storage (inventory) in week i

Total purchase cost $= 6.00B_1 + 6.20B_2 + 6.65B_3 + 5.55B_4$
Total sales revenue $= 6.00S_1 + 6.20S_2 + 6.65S_3 + 5.55S_4$
Total storage cost $= 0.15I_1 + 0.15I_2 + 0.15I_3 + 0.15I_4$
Total profit contribution = (Total sales revenue) − (Total purchase cost) − (Total storage cost)
Objective: Maximize total profit contribution subject to balance equations for each week, storage capacity for each week, and ending inventory requirement for week 4.

Max $6.00S_1 + 6.20S_2 + 6.65S_3 + 5.55S_4 - 6.00B_1 - 6.20B_2 - 6.65B_3 - 5.55B_4 - 0.15I_1 - 0.15I_2 - 0.15I_3 - 0.15I_4$

s.t.

$20{,}000 + B_1 - S_1 = I_1$	Balance equation—week 1
$I_1 + B_2 - S_2 = I_2$	Balance equation—week 2
$I_2 + B_3 - S_3 = I_3$	Balance equation—week 3
$I_3 + B_4 - S_4 = I_4$	Balance equation—week 4
$I_1 \le 100{,}000$	Storage capacity—week 1
$I_2 \le 100{,}000$	Storage capacity—week 2
$I_3 \le 100{,}000$	Storage capacity—week 3
$I_4 \le 100{,}000$	Storage capacity—week 4
$I_4 \le 25{,}000$	Required inventory—week 4
all variables ≥ 0	

Note that the first four constraints can be written as follows:

$$I_1 - B_1 + S_1 = 20{,}000$$
$$I_1 - I_2 + B_2 - S_2 = 0$$
$$I_2 - I_3 + B_3 - S_3 = 0$$
$$I_3 - I_4 + B_4 - S_4 = 0$$

The optimal solution follows:

Week (i)	B_i	S_i	I_i
1	80,000	0	100,000
2	0	0	100,000
3	0	100,000	0
4	25,000	0	25,000

Total profit contribution = \$12,500
Note, however, that ASC started week 1 with 20,000 pounds of shrimp and ended week 4 with 25,000 pounds of shrimp. During the 4-week period, ASC has taken profits to reinvest and build inventory by 5000 pounds in anticipation of future higher prices. The amount of profit reinvested in inventory is (\$5.55 + \$0.15)(5000) = \$28,500. Thus, total profit for the 4-week period including reinvested profit is \$12,500 + \$28,500 = \$41,000.

14. a. Let x_i = number of Classic 21 boats produced in Quarter i; $i = 1, 2, 3, 4$
s_i = ending inventory of Classic 21 boats in Quarter i; $i = 1, 2, 3, 4$

Min $10{,}000x_1 + 11{,}000x_2 + 12{,}100x_3 + 13{,}310x_4 + 250s_1 + 250s_2 + 300s_3 + 300s_4$

s.t.

$x_1 - s_1 = 1900$	Quarter 1 demand
$s_1 + x_2 - s_2 = 4000$	Quarter 2 demand
$s_2 + x_3 - s_3 = 3000$	Quarter 3 demand
$s_3 + x_4 - s_4 = 1500$	Quarter 4 demand
$s_4 \ge 500$	Ending Inventory
$x_1 \le 4000$	Quarter 1 capacity
$x_2 \le 3000$	Quarter 2 capacity
$x_3 \le 2000$	Quarter 3 capacity
$x_4 \le 4000$	Quarter 4 capacity

b.

Quarter	Production	Ending Inventory	Cost (\$)
1	4000	2100	40,525,000
2	3000	1100	33,275,000
3	2000	100	24,230,000
4	1900	500	25,439,000
			\$123,469,000

c. The shadow prices tell us how much it would cost if demand were to increase by one additional unit. For example, in Quarter 2 the shadow price is \$12,760; thus, demand for one more boat in Quarter 2 will increase costs by \$12,760.

d. The shadow price of 0 for Quarter 4 tells us we have excess capacity in Quarter 4. The negative shadow prices in Quarters 1–3 tell us how much increasing the production capacity will decrease costs. For example, the shadow price of −\$2510 for Quarter 1 tells us that if capacity were increased by 1 unit for this quarter, costs would go down \$2510.

15. Let R_i = the number of barrels of input i to use to produce Regular, $i = 1, 2, 3$

S_i = the number of barrels of input i to use to produce Super, $i = 1, 2, 3$

Max $\{18.5\,(R_1 + R_2 + R_3) + 20(R_1 + R_2 + R_3) - 16.5(R_1 + S_1) - 14(R_2 + S_2) - 17.5(R_3 + S_3)\}$

s.t.

$R_1 + S_1 \leq 110000$ Input 1 Capacity
$R_2 + S_2 \leq 350000$ Input 2 Capacity
$R_3 + S_3 \leq 300000$ Input 3 Capacity

$R_1 + R_2 + R_3 \leq 350000$ Max Demand for Regular
$S_1 + S_2 + S_3 \leq 500000$ Max Demand for Super

$100R_1 + 87R_2 + 110R_3 \geq 90\,(R_1 + R_2 + R_3)$ Required Octane Level, Regular

$100S_1 + 87S_2 + 110S_3 \geq 100\,(S_1 + S_2 + S_3)$ Required Octane Level, Super

$R_1, R_2, R_3, S_1, S_2, S_3 \geq 0$

Maximum Profit = \$2,845,000 by making 260,000 barrels of Regular and 500,000 barrels of Super. All available inputs are used (binding). The limit on maximum amount of Super we can sell is binding, as is the Octane Requirement for Super.

16. Let x_i = number of 10-inch rolls of paper processed by cutting alternative i; $i = 1, 2, \ldots, 7$

Min $x_1 + x_2 + x_3 + x_4 + x_5 + x_6 + x_7$

s.t.

$6x_1 + 2x_3 + x_5 + x_6 + 4x_7 \geq 1000$ $1^1/_2$" production
$4x_2 + x_4 + 3x_5 + 2x_6 \geq 2000$ $2^1/_2$" production
$2x_3 + 2x_4 + x_6 + x_7 \geq 4000$ $3^1/_2$" production
$x_1, x_2, x_3, x_4, x_5, x_6, x_7 \geq 0$

$x_1 = 0$
$x_2 = 125$
$x_3 = 500$
$x_4 = 1500$
$x_5 = 0$
$x_6 = 0$
$x_7 = 0$

Total Rolls = 125 + 500 + 1500 = 2125 Rolls

Production:
$1^1/_2$" 1000
$2^1/_2$" 2000
$3^1/_2$" 4000

Waste: Cut alternative 4 ($^1/_2$" per roll)

Therefore, waste = $^1/_2$(1500) = 750 inches

b. Only the objective function needs to be changed. An objective function minimizing waste production and the new optimal solution are given.

Min $x_1 + 0x_2 + 0x_3 + 0.5x_4 + x_5 + 0x_6 + 0.5x_7$

$x_1 = 0$
$x_2 = 500$
$x_3 = 2000$
$x_4 = 0$
$x_5 = 0$
$x_6 = 0$
$x_7 = 0$

Total Rolls = 2500 Rolls

Production:
$1^1/_2$" 4000
$2^1/_2$" 2000
$3^1/_2$" 4000

Waste is 0; however, we have overproduced the $1^1/_2$" size by 3000 units. Perhaps these can be inventoried for future use.

c. Minimizing waste may cause you to overproduce. In this case, we used 375 more rolls to generate a 3000 surplus of the $1^1/_2$" product. Alternative b might be preferred on the basis that the 3000 surplus could be held in inventory for later demand. However, in some trim problems, excess production cannot be used and must be scrapped. If this were the case, the 3000 unit $1^1/_2$" size would result in 4500 inches of waste, and thus alternative 1 would be the preferred solution.

18. a. Let x_1 = number of Super Tankers purchased

x_2 = number of Regular Line Tankers purchased

x_3 = number of Econo-Tankers purchased

Min $550x_1 + 425x_2 + 350x_3$

s.t.

$6700x_1 + 55000x_2 + 4600x_3 \leq 600{,}000$ Budget
$15(5000)x_1 + 20(2500)x_2 + 25(1000)x_3 \geq 550{,}000$

or

$75000x_1 + 50000x_2 + 25000x_3 \geq 550{,}000$ Meet Demand
$x_1 + x_2 + x_3 \leq 15$ Max. Total Vehicles
$x_3 \geq 3$ Min. Econo-Tankers

$x_1 \leq {}^1/_2\,(x_1 + x_2 + x_3)$

or

$^1/_2x_1 - {}^1/_2x_2 - {}^1/_2x_3 \leq 0$ No more than 50% Super Tankers
$x_1, x_2, x_3 \geq 0$

Solution: 5 Super Tankers, 2 Regular Tankers, 3 Econo-Tankers

Total Cost: \$583,000

Monthly Operating Cost: \$4650

b. The last two constraints in the preceding formulation must be deleted and the problem re-solved.

The optimal solution calls for $7^1/_3$ Super Tankers at an annual operating cost of \$4033. However, because a partial Super Tanker can't be purchased, we must round up to find a feasible solution of 8 Super Tankers with a monthly operating cost of \$4400.

Actually, this is an integer programming problem, because partial tankers can't be purchased. We were fortunate in part (a) that the optimal solution turned out integer.

The true optimal integer solution to part (b) is $x_1 = 6$ and $x_2 = 2$, with a monthly operating cost of \$4150. This is 6 Super Tankers and 2 Regular Line Tankers.

19. a. Let x_{11} = amount of men's model in month 1
x_{21} = amount of women's model in month 1
x_{12} = amount of men's model in month 2
x_{22} = amount of women's model in month 2
s_{11} = inventory of men's model at end of month 1
s_{21} = inventory of women's model at end of month 1
s_{12} = inventory of men's model at end of month 2
s_{22} = inventory of women's model at end of month 2

The model formulation for part (a) is given.

Min $120x_{11} + 90x_{21} + 120x_{12} + 90x_{22} + 2.4s_{11} + 1.8s_{21} + 2.4s_{12} + 1.8s_{22}$

s.t.

$20 + x_{11} - s_{11} = 150$

or

$x_{11} - s_{11} = 130$	Satisfy Demand	(1)

$30 + x_{21} - s_{21} = 125$

or

$x_{21} - s_{21} = 95$	Satisfy Demand	(2)
$s_{11} + x_{12} - s_{12} = 200$	Satisfy Demand	(3)
$s_{21} + x_{22} - s_{22} = 150$	Satisfy Demand	(4)
$s_{12} \geq 25$	Ending Inventory	(5)
$s_{22} \geq 25$	Ending Inventory	(6)

Labor-hours: Men's $= 2.0 + 1.5 = 3.5$
Women's $= 1.6 + 1.0 = 2.6$

$3.5x_{11} + 2.6x_{21} \geq 900$	Labor Smoothing for	(7)
$3.5x_{11} + 2.6x_{21} \leq 1100$	Month 1	(8)
$3.5x_{11} + 2.6x_{21} - 3.5x_{12} - 2.6x_{22} \leq 100$	Labor Smoothing for	(9)
$3.5x_{11} + 2.6x_{21} + 3.5x_{12} + 2.6x_{22} \leq 100$	Month 2	(10)

$x_{11}, x_{12}, x_{21}, x_{22}, s_{11}, s_{12}, s_{21}, s_{22} \geq 0$

The optimal solution is to produce 193 of the men's model in month 1, 162 of the men's model in month 2, 95 units of the women's model in month 1, and 175 of the women's model in month 2. Total Cost = \$67,156.

Inventory Schedule

Month 1	63 Men's	0 Women's
Month 2	25 Men's	25 Women's

Labor Levels

Previous month	1000.00 hours
Month 1	922.25 hours
Month 2	1022.25 hours

b. To accommodate this new policy, the right-hand sides of constraints 7–10 must be changed to 950, 1050, 50, and 50, respectively. The revised optimal solution is given.

$x_{11} = 201$
$x_{21} = 95$
$x_{12} = 154$
$x_{22} = 175$ Total Cost = \$67,175

We produce more men's models in the first month and carry a larger men's model inventory; the added cost, however, is only \$19. This seems to be a small expense to have less drastic labor force fluctuations. The new labor levels are 1000, 950, and 994.5 hours each month. Because the added cost is only \$19, management might want to experiment with the labor force smoothing restrictions to enforce even less fluctuations. You may want to experiment yourself to see what happens.

20. Let x_m = number of units produced in month m
I_m = increase in the total production level in month m
D_m = decrease in the total production level in month m
s_m = inventory level at the end of month m

where

$m = 1$ refers to March
$m = 2$ refers to April
$m = 3$ refers to May

Min $1.25\,I_1 + 1.25\,I_2 + 1.25\,I_3 + 1.00\,D_1 + 1.00\,D_2 + 1.00\,D_3$

s.t.

Change in production level in March:

$$x_1 - 10{,}000 = I_1 - D_1$$

or

$$x_1 - I_1 + D_1 = 10{,}000$$

Change in production level in April:

$$x_2 - x_1 = I_2 - D_2$$

or

$$x_2 - x_1 - I_2 + D_2 = 0$$

Change in production level in May:

$$x_3 - x_2 = I_3 - D_3$$

or

$$x_3 - x_2 - I_3 + D_3 = 0$$

Demand in March:

$$2500 + x_1 - s_1 = 12{,}000$$

or

$$x_1 - s_1 = 9500$$

Demand in April:

$$s_1 + x_2 - s_2 = 8000$$

Demand in May:

$$s_2 + x_3 = 15{,}000$$

Inventory capacity in March:

$$s_1 \leq 3000$$

Inventory capacity in April:

$$s_2 \leq 3000$$

Optimal Solution:

Total cost of monthly production increases and decreases = \$2500

$x_1 = 10{,}250$	$I_1 = 250$	$D_1 = 0$
$x_2 = 10{,}250$	$I_2 = 0$	$D_2 = 0$
$x_3 = 12{,}000$	$I_3 = 1750$	$D_3 = 0$
$s_1 = 750$		
$s_2 = 3000$		

22. Let SM_1 = No. of small on machine M_1
SM_2 = No. of small on machine M_2

SM_3 = No. of small on machine M_3
LM_1 = No. of large on machine M_1
LM_2 = No. of large on machine M_2
LM_3 = No. of large on machine M_3
MM_2 = No. of meal on machine M_2
MM_3 = No. of meal on machine M_3

The formulation and solution follows. Note that constraints 1–3 guarantee that next week's schedule will be met and constraints 4–6 enforce machine capacities.

```
MIN
20SM1+24SM2+32SM3+15LM1+28LM2+35LM3+18MM2+36MM3

   S.T.

      1)   1SM1+1SM2+1SM3≤80000
      2)   +1LM1+1LM2+1LM3≥80000
      3)   +1MM2+1MM3≥65000
      4)   0.03333SM1+0.04LM1≤2100
      5)   +0.02222SM2+0.025LM2+0.03333MM2≤2100
      6)   +0.01667SM3+0.01923LM3+0.02273MM3≤2400

  Optimal Solution

  Objective Function Value =        5515886.58866

     Variable             Value
  ------------       ------------        SM1   0.00000
      SM2                 0.00000
      SM3             80000.00000
      LM1             52500.00000
      LM2                 0.00000
      LM3             27500.00000
      MM2             63006.30063
      MM3              1993.69937


     Constraint            Slack/Surplus
   ------------          --------------
        1                     0.00000
        2                     0.00000
        3                     0.00000
        4                     0.00000
        5                     0.00000
        6                   492.25821
```

Note that 5,515,887 square inches of waste are generated. Machine 3 has 492 minutes of idle capacity.

24. Let x_1 = proportion of investment A undertaken
x_2 = proportion of investment B undertaken
s_1 = funds placed in savings for period 1
s_2 = funds placed in savings for period 2
s_3 = funds placed in savings for period 3
s_4 = funds placed in savings for period 4
L_1 = funds received from loan in period 1
L_2 = funds received from loan in period 2
L_3 = funds received from loan in period 3
L_4 = funds received from loan in period 4

Objective Function:
In order to maximize the cash value at the end of the four periods, we must consider the value of investment A, the value of investment B, savings income from period 4, and loan expenses for period 4.

$$\text{Max} \quad 3200x_1 + 2500x_2 + 1.1s_4 - 1.18L_4$$

Constraints require the *use* of funds to equal the *source* of funds for each period.

Period 1:

$$1000x_1 + 800x_2 + s_1 = 1500 + L_1$$

or

$$1000x_1 + 800x_2 + s_1 - L_1 = 1500$$

Period 2:

$$800x_1 + 500x_2 + s_2 + 1.18L_1 = 400 + 1.1s_1 + L_2$$

or

$$800x_1 + 500x_2 - 1.1s_1 + s_2 + 1.18L_1 - L_2 = 400$$

Period 3:

$$200x_1 + 300x_2 + s_3 + 1.18L_2 = 500 + 1.1s_2 + L_3$$

or

$$200x_1 + 300x_2 - 1.1s_2 + s_3 + 1.18L_2 - L_3 = 500$$

Period 4:

$$s_4 + 1.18L_3 = 100 + 200x_1 + 300x_2 + 1.1s_3 + L_4$$

or

$$-200x_1 - 300x_2 - 1.1s_3 + s_4 + 1.18L_3 - L_4 = 100$$

Limits on Loan Funds Available:

$L_1 \leq 200$
$L_2 \leq 200$
$L_3 \leq 200$
$L_4 \leq 200$

Proportion of Investment Undertaken:

$x_1 \leq 1$
$x_2 \leq 1$

Optimal Solution: \$4340.40

Investment A	$x_1 = 0.458$	or	45.8%
Investment B	$x_2 = 1.0$	or	100.0%

Savings/Loan Schedule:

	Period 1	Period 2	Period 3	Period 4
Savings	242.11	—	—	341.04
Loan	—	200.00	127.58	—

Chapter 10

1. The network model is shown:

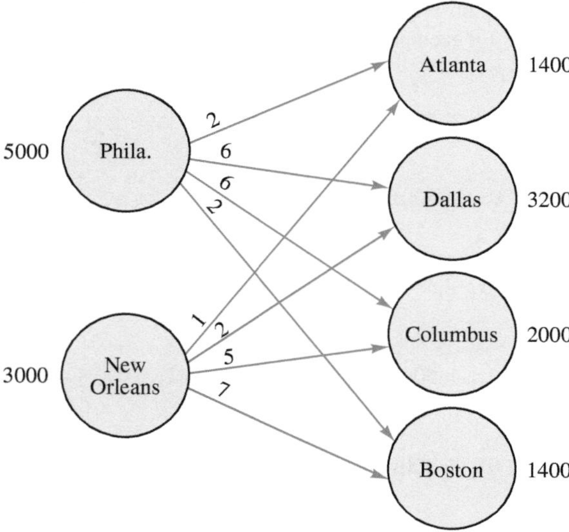

2. a. Let x_{11} = amount shipped from Jefferson City to Des Moines
x_{12} = amount shipped from Jefferson City to Kansas City
.
.
.

$$\text{Min } 14x_{11} + 9x_{12} + 7x_{13} + 8x_{21} + 10x_{22} + 5x_{23}$$

s.t.

$$\begin{aligned}
x_{11} + x_{12} + x_{13} \qquad\qquad\qquad & \le 30 \\
x_{21} + x_{22} + x_{23} & \le 20 \\
x_{11} \qquad + x_{21} \qquad\qquad & = 25 \\
x_{12} \qquad + x_{22} \qquad & = 15 \\
x_{13} \qquad + x_{23} & = 10 \\
x_{11}, x_{12}, x_{13}, x_{21}, x_{22}, x_{23} & \ge 0
\end{aligned}$$

b. Optimal Solution:

	Amount	Cost
Jefferson City–Des Moines	5	70
Jefferson City–Kansas City	15	135
Jefferson City–St. Louis	10	70
Omaha–Des Moines	20	160
	Total	435

4. The optimization model can be written as
x_{ij} = Red GloFish shipped from i to j $i = M$ for Michigan, T for Texas; $j = 1, 2, 3$.
y_{ij} = Blue GloFish shipped from i to j, $i = M$ for Michigan, T for Texas; $j = 1, 2, 3$.

$$\text{Min} x_{M1} + 2.50x_{M2} + 0.50x_{M3} + y_{M1} + 2.50y_{M2} + 0.50y_{M3} + 2.00y_{T1} + 1.50y_{T2} + 2.80y_{T3}$$

subject to

$$\begin{aligned}
x_{M1} + x_{M2} + x_{M3} &\le 1{,}000{,}000 \\
y_{M1} + y_{M2} + y_{M3} &\le 1{,}000{,}000 \\
y_{T1} + y_{T2} + y_{T3} &\le 600{,}000 \\
x_{M1} &\ge 320{,}000 \\
x_{M2} &\ge 300{,}000 \\
x_{M3} &\ge 160{,}000 \\
y_{M1} + y_{T1} &\ge 380{,}000 \\
y_{M2} + y_{T2} &\ge 450{,}000 \\
y_{M3} + y_{T3} &\ge 290{,}000
\end{aligned}$$

$xij \ge 0$

a. Solving this linear program using Solver, we find that we should produce 780,000 red GloFish in Michigan, 670,000 blue GloFish in Michigan, and 450,000 blue GloFish in Texas.

Using the notation in the model, the number of GloFish shipped from each farm to each retailer can be expressed as follows:
$x_{M1} = 320{,}000$
$x_{M2} = 300{,}000$
$x_{M3} = 160{,}000$
$y_{M1} = 380{,}000$
$y_{M2} = 0$
$y_{M3} = 290{,}000$
$y_{T1} = 0$
$y_{T2} = 450{,}000$
$y_{T3} = 0$

b. From Solver, the minimum transportation cost is \$2.35 million.

c. We have to add variables x_{T1}, x_{T2}, and x_{T3} for Red GloFish shipped between Texas and Retailers 1, 2 and 3. The revised objective function is
Minimize $x_{M1} + 2.50x_{M2} + 0.50x_{M3} + y_{M1} + 2.50y_{M2} + 0.50y_{M3} + 2.00y_{T1} + 1.50y_{T2} + 2.80y_{T3} + x_{T1} + 2.50x_{T2} + 0.50x_{T3}$
We replace the third constraint above with
$x_{T1} + x_{T2} + x_{T3} + y_{T1} + y_{T2} + y_{T3} \le 600{,}000$

And we change the constraints

$$\begin{aligned}
x_{M1} &\ge 320{,}000 \\
x_{M2} &\ge 300{,}000 \\
x_{M3} &\ge 160{,}000
\end{aligned}$$

to

$$\begin{aligned}
x_{M1} + x_{T1} &\ge 320{,}000 \\
x_{M2} + x_{T2} &\ge 300{,}000 \\
x_{M3} + x_{T3} &\ge 160{,}000
\end{aligned}$$

Using this new objective function and constraint the optimal solution is \$2.2 million, so the savings are \$150,000.

6. The network model, the linear programming formulation, and the optimal solution are shown. Note that the third constraint corresponds to the dummy origin. The variables x_{31}, x_{32}, x_{33}, and x_{34} are the amounts shipped out of the dummy origin; they do not appear in the objective function because they are given a coefficient of zero.

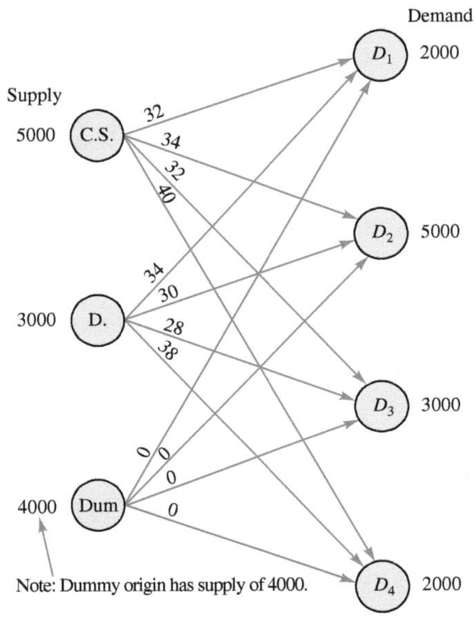

$$
\begin{array}{llllllllll}
\text{Max} & 32x_{11} + 34x_{12} + 32x_{13} + 40x_{14} + 34x_{21} + 30x_{22} + 28x_{23} + 38x_{24} \\
\text{s.t.} \\
& x_{11} + x_{12} + x_{13} + x_{14} & & & \leq 5000 \\
& & x_{21} + x_{22} + x_{23} + x_{24} & & \leq 3000 \\
& & & x_{31} + x_{32} + x_{33} + x_{34} & \leq 4000 & \text{Dummy} \\
& x_{11} & + x_{21} & + x_{31} & = 2000 \\
& x_{12} & + x_{22} & + x_{32} & = 5000 \\
& x_{13} & + x_{23} & + x_{33} & = 3000 \\
& x_{14} & + x_{24} & + x_{34} & = 2000 \\
& x_{ij} \geq 0 \quad \text{for all } i, j
\end{array}
$$

Optimal Solution	Units	Cost
Clifton Springs–D_2	4000	\$136,000
Clifton Springs–D_4	1000	40,000
Danville–D_1	2000	68,000
Danville–D_4	1000	38,000
	Total Cost	\$282,000

Customer 2 demand has a shortfall of 1000.

Customer 3 demand of 3000 is not satisfied.

8. a.

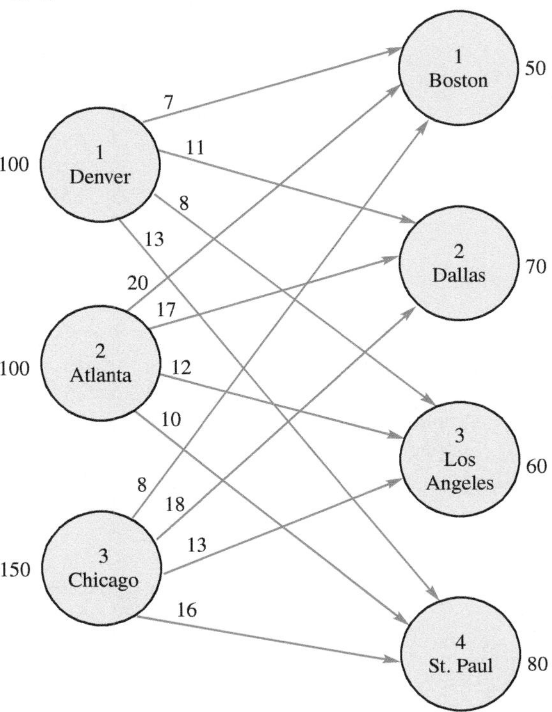

b. There are alternative optimal solutions.

Solution 1		**Solution 2**	
Denver to St. Paul:	10	Denver to St. Paul:	10
Atlanta to Boston:	50	Atlanta to Boston:	50
Atlanta to Dallas:	50	Atlanta to Los Angeles:	50
Chicago to Dallas:	20	Chicago to Dallas:	70
Chicago to Los Angeles:	60	Chicago to Los Angeles:	10
Chicago to St. Paul:	70	Chicago to St. Paul:	70
Total Profit: \$4240			

If solution 1 is used, Forbelt should produce 10 motors at Denver, 100 motors at Atlanta, and 150 motors at Chicago. There will be idle capacity for 90 motors at Denver.

If solution 2 is used, Forbelt should adopt the same production schedule but a modified shipping schedule.

10. a. The total cost is the sum of the purchase cost and the transportation cost. We show the calculation for Division 1–Supplier 1 and present the result for the other Division-Supplier combinations.

Division 1–Supplier 1

Purchase cost (40,000 × \$12.60)	\$504,000
Transportation Cost (40,000 × \$2.75)	110,000
Total Cost:	\$614,000

Cost Matrix ($1000s)

	Supplier					
Division	**1**	**2**	**3**	**4**	**5**	**6**
1	614	660	534	680	590	630
2	603	639	702	693	693	630
3	865	830	775	850	900	930
4	532	553	511	581	595	553
5	720	648	684	693	657	747

b. Optimal Solution:

Supplier 1–Division 2	$ 603
Supplier 2–Division 5	648
Supplier 3–Division 3	775
Supplier 5–Division 1	590
Supplier 6–Division 4	553
Total	$3169

11. a. Network Model

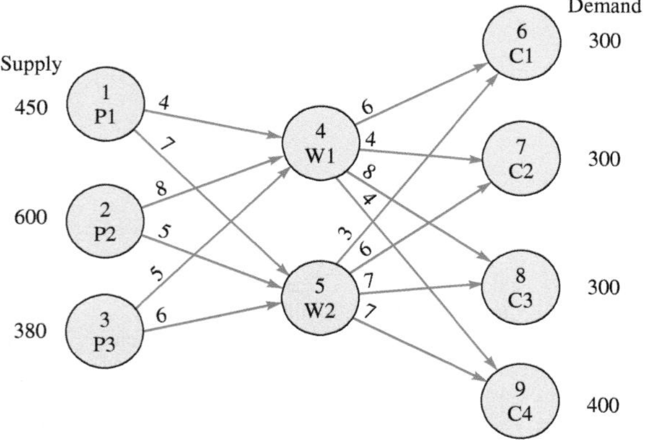

b. & c. The linear programming formulation and solution are shown below:

```
LINEAR PROGRAMMING PROBLEM

MIN 4X14 + 7X15 + 8X24 + 5X25 + 5X34 +
6X35 + 6X46 + 4X47 + 8X48 + 4X49 + 3X56
+ 6X57 + 7X58 + 7X59

S.T.

(1) X14 + X15 < 450
(2) X24 + X25 < 600
(3) X34 + X35 < 380
(4) X46 + X47 + X48 + X49 - X14 - X24
    - X34 = 0
(5) X56 + X57 + X58 + X59 - X15 - X25
    - X35 = 0
(6) X46 + X56 = 300
(7) X47 + X57 = 300
(8) X48 + X58 = 300
(9) X49 + X59 = 400
```

```
OPTIMAL SOLUTION

Objective Function Value =      11850.000

  Variable           Value        Reduced Costs
-----------       ----------      -------------
    X14             450.000           0.000
    X15               0.000           3.000
    X24               0.000           3.000
    X25             600.000           0.000
    X34             250.000           0.000
    X35               0.000           1.000
    X46               0.000           3.000
    X47             300.000           0.000
    X48               0.000           1.000
    X49             400.000           0.000
    X56             300.000           0.000
    X57               0.000           2.000
    X58             300.000           0.000
    X59               0.000           3.000
```

There is an excess capacity of 130 units at plant 3.

12. a. Three arcs must be added to the network model in Problem 11a. The new network is shown:

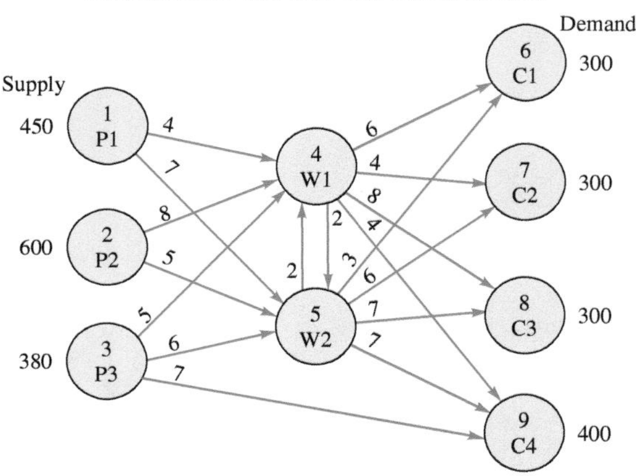

b. & c. The linear programming formulation and optimal solution are shown below:

```
LINEAR PROGRAMMING PROBLEM

MIN 4X14 + 7X15 + 8X24 + 5X25 + 5X34 +
6X35 + 6X46 + 4X47 + 8X48 + 4X49 + 3X56 +
6X57 + 7X58 + 7X59 + 7X39 + 2X45 + 2X54

S.T.

(1) X14 + X15 < 450
(2) X24 + X25 < 600
(3) X34 + X35 + X39 < 380
(4) X45 + X46 + X47 + X48 + X49 - X14 -
    X24 - X34 - X54 = 0
(5) X54 + X56 + X57 + X58 + X59 - X15 -
    X25 - X35 - X45 = 0
(6) X46 + X56 = 300
(7) X47 + X57 = 300
(8) X48 + X58 = 300
(9) X39 + X49 + X59 = 400
```

```
OPTIMAL SOLUTION

Objective Function Value =  11220.000

   Variable           Value        Reduced Costs
 -----------       ----------      -------------
     X14            320.000            0.000
     X15              0.000            2.000
     X24              0.000            4.000
     X25            600.000            0.000
     X34              0.000            2.000
     X35              0.000            2.000
     X46              0.000            2.000
     X47            300.000            0.000
     X48              0.000            0.000
     X49             20.000            0.000
     X56            300.000            0.000
     X57              0.000            3.000
     X58            300.000            0.000
     X59              0.000            4.000
     X39            380.000            0.000
     X45              0.000            1.000
     X54              0.000            3.000
```

The value of the solution here is \$630 less than the value of the solution for Problem 23. The new shipping route from plant 3 to customer 4 has helped (x_{39} = 380). There is now excess capacity of 130 units at plant 1.

14.

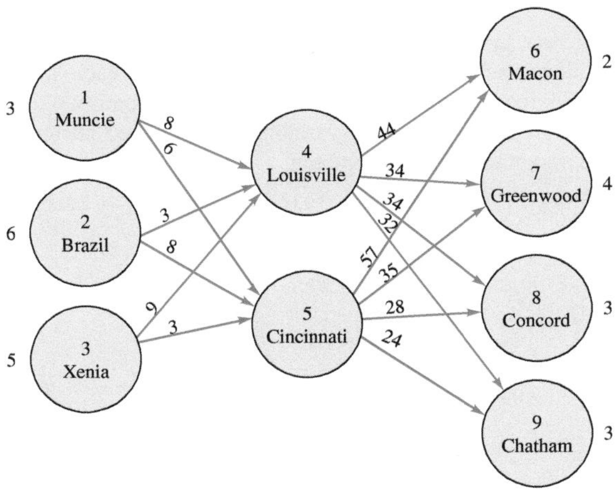

A linear programming model is

Min $8x_{14}+6x_{15}+3x_{24}+8x_{25}+9x_{34}+3x_{35}+44x_{46}+34x_{47}+34x_{48}+32x_{49}+57x_{56}+35x_{57}+28x_{58}+24x_{59}$

s.t.

$$
\begin{aligned}
x_{14} + x_{15} &\le 3\\
x_{24} + x_{25} &\le 6\\
x_{34} + x_{35} &\le 5\\
-x_{14} - x_{24} - x_{34} + x_{46} + x_{47} + x_{48} + x_{49} &= 0\\
- x_{15} - x_{25} - x_{35} + x_{56} + x_{57} + x_{58} + x_{59} &= 0\\
x_{46} + x_{56} &= 2\\
x_{47} + x_{57} &= 4\\
x_{48} + x_{58} &= 3\\
x_{49} + x_{59} &= 3
\end{aligned}
$$

$x_{ij} \ge 0$ for all i, j

Optimal Solution	Units Shipped	Cost
Muncie–Cincinnati	1	6
Cincinnati–Concord	3	84
Brazil–Louisville	6	18
Louisville–Macon	2	88
Louisville–Greenwood	4	136
Xenia–Cincinnati	5	15
Cincinnati–Chatham	3	72
		419

Two rail cars must be held at Muncie until a buyer is found.

16. a.

Min $20x_{12} + 25x_{15} + 30x_{25} + 45x_{27} + 20x_{31} + 35x_{36} + 30x_{42} + 25x_{53} + 15x_{54} + 28x_{56} + 12x_{67} + 27x_{74}$

s.t.

$$
\begin{aligned}
x_{31} - x_{12} - x_{15} &= 8\\
x_{25} + x_{27} - x_{12} - x_{42} &= 5\\
x_{31} + x_{36} - x_{53} &= 3\\
x_{54} + x_{74} - x_{42} &= 3\\
x_{53} + x_{54} + x_{56} - x_{15} - x_{25} &= 2\\
x_{36} + x_{56} - x_{67} &= 5\\
x_{74} - x_{27} - x_{67} &= 6
\end{aligned}
$$

$x_{ij} \ge 0$ for all i, j

b.

$x_{12} = 0$	$x_{53} = 5$
$x_{15} = 0$	$x_{54} = 0$
$x_{25} = 8$	$x_{56} = 5$
$x_{27} = 0$	$x_{67} = 0$
$x_{31} = 8$	$x_{74} = 6$
$x_{36} = 0$	$x_{56} = 5$
$x_{42} = 3$	

Total cost of redistributing cars = \$917

17. a.

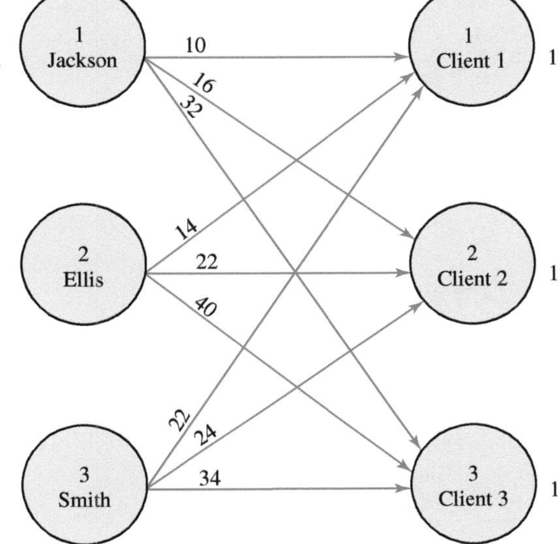

b.

Min $10x_{11} + 16x_{12} + 32x_{13} + 14x_{21} + 22x_{22} + 40x_{23} + 22x_{31} + 24x_{32} + 34x_{33}$

s.t.

$$
\begin{aligned}
x_{11} + x_{12} + x_{13} &\le 1 \\
x_{21} + x_{22} + x_{23} &\le 1 \\
x_{31} + x_{32} + x_{33} &\le 1 \\
x_{11} + x_{21} + x_{31} &= 1 \\
x_{12} + x_{22} + x_{32} &= 1 \\
x_{13} + x_{23} + x_{33} &= 1
\end{aligned}
$$

$x_{ij} \ge 0$ for all i, j

Solution: $x_{12} = 1, x_{21} = 1, x_{33} = 1$

Total completion time = 64

18. a.

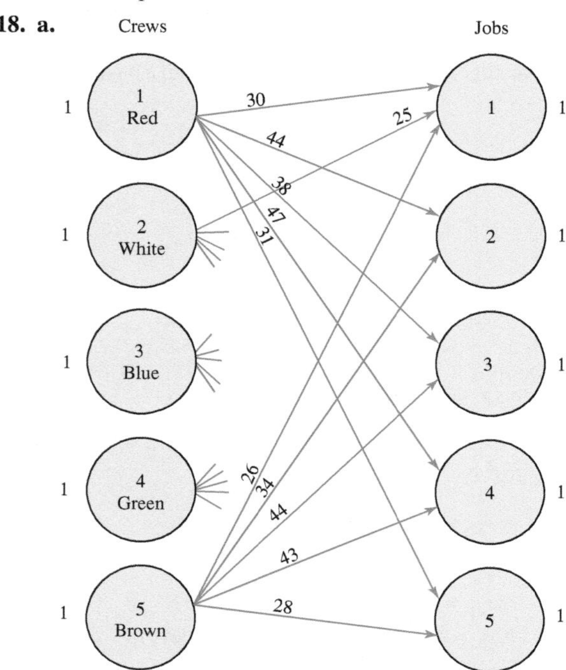

b.

Min $30x_{11} + 44x_{12} + 38x_{13} + 47x_{14} + 31x_{15} + 25x_{21} + \cdots + 28x_{55}$

s.t.

$$
\begin{aligned}
x_{11} + x_{12} + x_{13} + x_{14} + x_{15} &\le 1 \\
x_{21} + x_{22} + x_{23} + x_{24} + x_{25} &\le 1 \\
x_{31} + x_{32} + x_{33} + x_{34} + x_{35} &\le 1 \\
x_{41} + x_{42} + x_{43} + x_{44} + x_{45} &\le 1 \\
x_{51} + x_{52} + x_{53} + x_{54} + x_{55} &\le 1 \\
x_{11} + x_{21} + x_{31} + x_{41} + x_{51} &= 1 \\
x_{12} + x_{22} + x_{32} + x_{42} + x_{52} &= 1 \\
x_{13} + x_{23} + x_{33} + x_{43} + x_{53} &= 1 \\
x_{14} + x_{24} + x_{34} + x_{44} + x_{54} &= 1 \\
x_{15} + x_{25} + x_{35} + x_{45} + x_{55} &= 1
\end{aligned}
$$

$x_{ij} \ge 0,\ i = 1, 2, \ldots, 5;\ j = 1, 2, \ldots, 5$

Optimal Solution:

Green to Job 1	\$ 26
Brown to Job 2	34
Red to Job 3	38
Blue to Job 4	39
White to Job 5	25
	\$162

Because the data are in hundreds of dollars, the total installation cost for the five contracts is \$16,200.

20. a. This is the variation of the assignment problem in which multiple assignments are possible. Each distribution center may be assigned up to three customer zones.

The linear programming model of this problem has 40 variables (one for each combination of distribution center and customer zone). It has 13 constraints. There are 5 supply (≤ 3) constraints and 8 demand ($=1$) constraints.

The optimal solution is as follows:

	Assignments	Cost (\$1000s)
Plano	Kansas City, Dallas	34
Flagstaff	Los Angeles	15
Springfield	Chicago, Columbus, Atlanta	70
Boulder	Newark, Denver	97
	Total Cost	\$216

b. The Nashville distribution center is not used.

c. All the distribution centers are used. Columbus is switched from Springfield to Nashville. Total cost increases by \$11,000 to \$227,000.

22. A linear programming formulation of this problem can be developed as follows. Let the first letter of each variable name represent the professor and the second two the course. Note that a *DPH* variable is not created because the assignment is unacceptable.

Max $2.8AUG + 2.2AMB + 3.3AMS + 3.0APH + 3.2BUG + \cdots + 2.5DMS$

s.t.

$$
\begin{aligned}
AUG + AMB + AMS + APH &\le 1 \\
BUG + BMB + BMS + BPH &\le 1 \\
CUG + CMB + CMS + CPH &\le 1 \\
DUG + DMB + DMS &\le 1 \\
AUG + BUG + CUG + DUG &= 1 \\
AMB + BMB + CMB + DMB &= 1 \\
AMS + BMS + CMS + DMS &= 1 \\
APH + BPH + CPH &= 1
\end{aligned}
$$

All Variables ≥ 0

Optimal Solution	Rating
A to MS course	3.3
B to Ph.D. course	3.6
C to MBA course	3.2
D to Undergraduate course	3.2
Max Total Rating	13.3

23. Origin—Node 1
Transshipment—Nodes 2–5
Destination—Node 7

The linear program will have 14 variables for the arcs and 7 constraints for the nodes.

Let

$$x_{ij} = \begin{cases} 1 & \text{if the arc from node } i \text{ to node } j \text{ is on the shortest route} \\ 0 & \text{otherwise} \end{cases}$$

$$\begin{aligned} \text{Min } & 7x_{12} + 9x_{13} + 18x_{14} + 3x_{23} + 5x_{25} + 3x_{32} + 4x_{35} \\ & + 3x_{46} + 5x_{52} + 4x_{53} + 2x_{56} + 6x_{57} + 2x_{65} + 3x_{67} \end{aligned}$$

s.t.

	Flow Out	Flow In	
Node 1	$x_{12} + x_{13} + x_{14}$		$= 1$
Node 2	$x_{23} + x_{25}$	$-x_{12} - x_{32} - x_{52}$	$= 0$
Node 3	$x_{32} + x_{35}$	$-x_{13} - x_{23} - x_{53}$	$= 0$
Node 4	x_{46}	$-x_{14}$	$= 0$
Node 5	$x_{52} + x_{53} + x_{56} + x_{57}$	$-x_{25} - x_{35} - x_{65}$	$= 0$
Node 6	$x_{65} + x_{67}$	$-x_{46} - x_{56}$	$= 0$
Node 7		$+x_{57} + x_{67}$	$= 1$

$x_{ij} \geq 0$ for all i and j

Optimal Solution: $x_{12} = 1$, $x_{25} = 1$, $x_{56} = 1$, and $x_{67} = 1$
Shortest Route: 1–2–5–6–7
Length = 17

24. The linear program has 13 variables for the arcs and 6 constraints for the nodes. Use the same 6 constraints for the Gorman shortest route problem, as shown in the text. The objective function changes to travel time as follows:

$$\begin{aligned} \text{Min } & 40x_{12} + 36x_{13} + 6x_{23} + 6x_{32} + 12x_{24} + 12x_{42} + 25x_{26} \\ & + 15x_{35} + 15x_{53} + 8x_{45} + 8x_{54} + 11x_{46} + 23x_{56} \end{aligned}$$

Optimal Solution: $x_{12} = 1$, $x_{24} = 1$, and $x_{46} = 1$
Shortest Route: 1–2–4–6
Total Time = 63 minutes

26. Origin—Node 1
Transshipment—Nodes 2–5 and node 7
Destination—Node 6

The linear program will have 18 variables for the arcs and 7 constraints for the nodes.

Let

$$x_{ij} = \begin{cases} 1 & \text{if the arc from node } i \text{ to node } j \text{ is on the shortest route} \\ 0 & \text{otherwise} \end{cases}$$

$$\begin{aligned} \text{Min } & 35x_{12} + 30x_{13} + 20x_{14} + 8x_{23} + 12x_{25} + 8x_{32} + 9x_{34} + 10x_{35} \\ & + 20x_{36} + 9x_{43} + 15x_{47} + 12x_{52} + 10x_{53} + 5x_{56} + 20x_{57} + 15x_{74} \\ & + 20x_{75} + 5x_{76} \end{aligned}$$

s.t.

	Flow Out	Flow In	
Node 1	$x_{12} + x_{13} + x_{14}$		$= 1$
Node 2	$x_{23} + x_{25}$	$-x_{12} - x_{32} - x_{52}$	$= 0$
Node 3	$x_{32} + x_{34} + x_{35} + x_{36}$	$-x_{13} - x_{23} - x_{43} - x_{53}$	$= 0$
Node 4	$x_{43} + x_{47}$	$-x_{14} - x_{34} - x_{74}$	$= 0$
Node 5	$x_{52} + x_{53} + x_{56} + x_{57}$	$-x_{25} - x_{35} - x_{75}$	$= 0$
Node 6		$+x_{36} + x_{56} + x_{76}$	$= 1$
Node 7	$x_{74} + x_{75} + x_{76}$	$-x_{47} - x_{57}$	$= 0$

$x_{ij} \geq 0$ for all i and j

Optimal Solution: $x_{14} = 1$, $x_{47} = 1$, and $x_{76} = 1$
Shortest Route: 1–4–7–6
Total Distance = 40 miles

28. Origin—Node 0
Transshipment—Nodes 1 to 3
Destination—Node 4

The linear program will have 10 variables for the arcs and 5 constraints for the nodes.

Let

$$x_{ij} = \begin{cases} 1 & \text{if the arc from node } i \text{ to node } j \text{ is on the minimum cost route} \\ 0 & \text{otherwise} \end{cases}$$

$$\begin{aligned} \text{Min } & 600x_{01} + 1000x_{02} + 2000x_{03} + 2800x_{04} + 500x_{12} + \\ & 1400x_{13} + 2100x_{14} + 800x_{23} + 1600x_{24} + 700x_{34} \end{aligned}$$

s.t.

	Flow Out	Flow In	
Node 0	$x_{01} + x_{02} + x_{03} + x_{04}$		$= 1$
Node 1	$x_{12} + x_{13} + x_{14}$	$-x_{01}$	$= 0$
Node 2	$x_{23} + x_{24}$	$-x_{02} - x_{12}$	$= 0$
Node 3	x_{34}	$-x_{03} - x_{13} - x_{23}$	$= 0$
Node 4		$-x_{04} - x_{14} - x_{24} - x_{34}$	$= 1$

$x_{ij} \geq 0$ for all i and j

Optimal Solution: $x_{02} = 1$, $x_{23} = 1$, and $x_{34} = 1$
Shortest Route: 0–2–3–4
Total Cost = $2500

29. The capacitated transshipment problem to solve is given:

Max x_{61}

s.t.

$$\begin{aligned} x_{12} + x_{13} + x_{14} - x_{61} &= 0 \\ x_{24} + x_{25} - x_{12} - x_{42} &= 0 \\ x_{34} + x_{36} - x_{13} - x_{43} &= 0 \\ x_{42} + x_{43} + x_{45} + x_{46} - x_{14} - x_{24} - x_{34} - x_{54} &= 0 \\ x_{54} + x_{56} - x_{25} - x_{45} &= 0 \\ x_{61} - x_{36} + x_{46} - x_{56} &= 0 \end{aligned}$$

$x_{12} \leq 2 \quad x_{13} \leq 6 \quad x_{14} \leq 3$
$x_{24} \leq 1 \quad x_{25} \leq 4$
$x_{34} \leq 3 \quad x_{36} \leq 2$
$x_{42} \leq 1 \quad x_{43} \leq 3 \quad x_{45} \leq 1 \quad x_{46} \leq 3$
$x_{54} \leq 1 \quad x_{56} \leq 6$
$x_{ij} \geq 0$ for all i, j

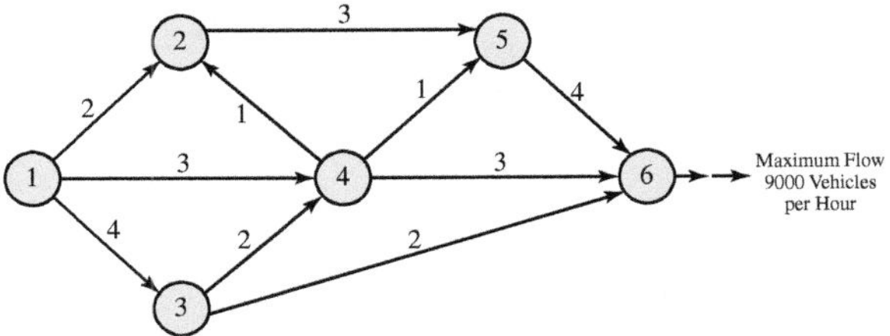

The system cannot accommodate a flow of 10,000 vehicles per hour.

30.

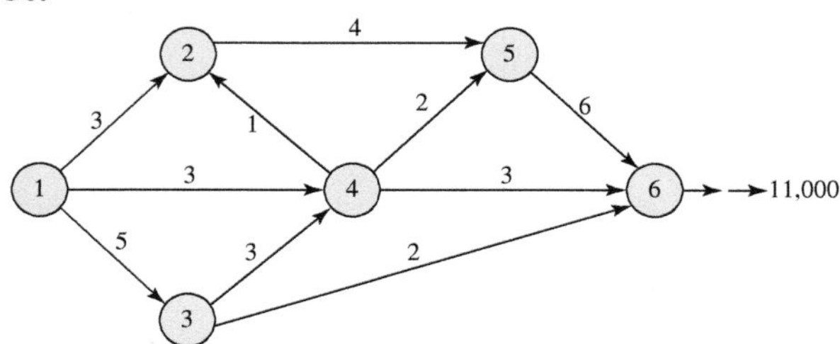

32. a. 10,000 gallons per hour or 10 hours
b. Flow reduced to 9000 gallons per hour; 11.1 hours.

34. Maximal Flow = 23 gallons/minute. Five gallons will flow from node 3 to node 5.

36. a. Let R_1, R_2, R_3 represent regular time production in months 1, 2, 3
O_1, O_2, O_3 represent overtime production in months 1, 2, 3
D_1, D_2, D_3 represent demand in months 1, 2, 3

Using these nine nodes, a network model is shown:

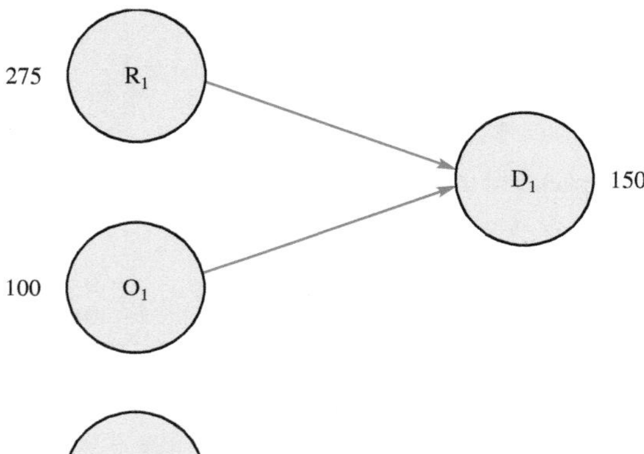

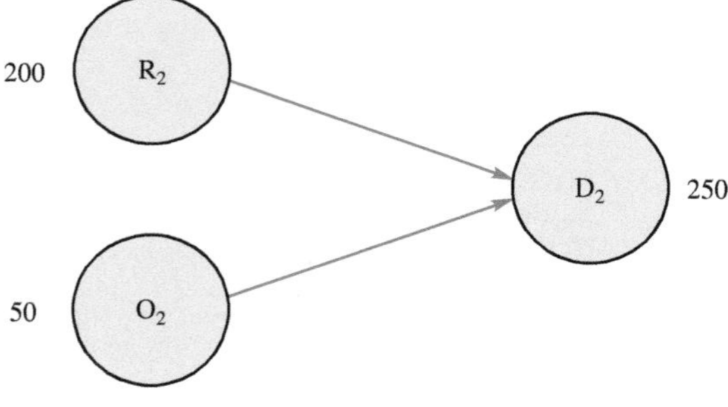

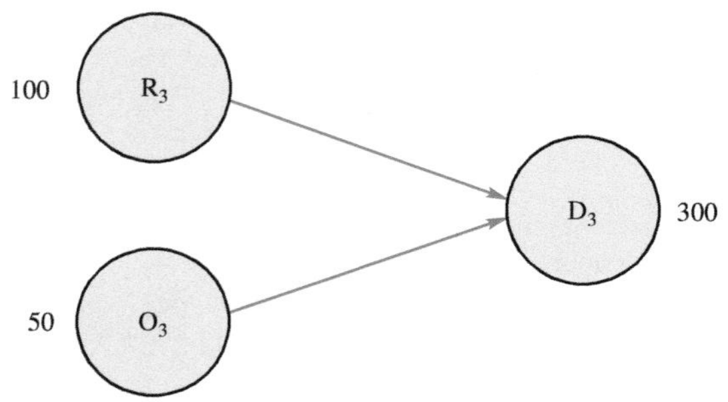

b. Use the following notation to define the variables: The first two characters designate the "from node" and the second two characters designate the "to node" of the arc. For instance, R_1D_1 is amount of regular time production available to satisfy demand in month 1; O_1D_1 is amount of overtime production in month 1 available to satisfy demand in month 1; D_1D_2 is the amount of inventory carried over from month 1 to month 2; and so on.

$$\text{Min } 50R_1D_1 + 80O_1D_1 + 20D_1D_2 + 50R_2D_2 + 80O_2D_2 + 20D_2D_3 + 60R_3D_3 + 100O_3D_3$$

S.T.

(1) $R_1D_1 \le 275$
(2) $O_1D_1 \le 100$
(3) $R_2D_2 \le 200$
(4) $O_2D_2 \le 50$
(5) $R_3D_3 \le 100$
(6) $O_3D_3 \le 50$
(7) $R_1D_1 + O_1D_1 - D_1D_2 = 150$
(8) $R_2D_2 + O_2D_2 + D_1D_2 - D_2D_3 = 250$
(9) $R_3D_3 + O_3D_3 + D_2D_3 = 300$

c. Optimal Solution:

Variable	Value
R_1D_1	275.000
O_1D_1	25.000
D_1D_2	150.000
R_2D_2	200.000
O_2D_2	50.000
D_2D_3	150.000
R_3D_3	100.000
O_3D_3	50.000

Value = $46,750
Note: Slack variable for constraint 2 = 75

d. The values of the slack variables for constraints 1 through 6 represent unused capacity. The only nonzero slack variable is for constraint 2; its value is 75. Thus, there are 75 units of unused overtime capacity in month 1.

Chapter 11

2. a.

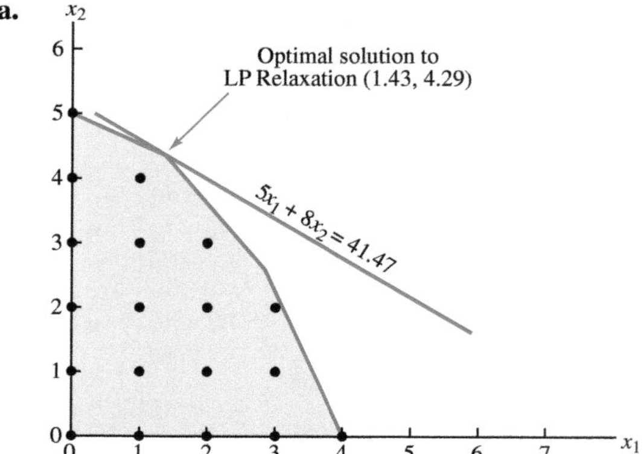

b. The optimal solution to the LP Relaxation is given by $x_1 = 1.43$, $x_2 = 4.29$ with an objective function value of 41.47. Rounding down gives the feasible integer solution $x_1 = 1$, $x_2 = 4$; its value is 37.

c.

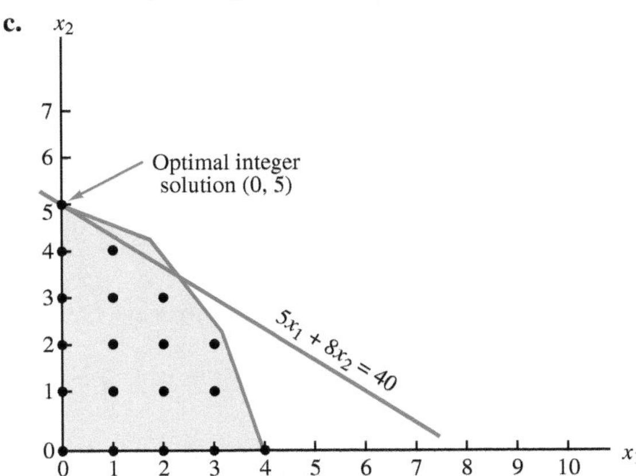

The optimal solution is given by $x_1 = 0$, $x_2 = 5$; its value is 40. It is not the same solution as found by rounding down; it provides a 3-unit increase in the value of the objective function.

4. a. $x_1 = 3.67$, $x_2 = 0$; Value $= 36.7$
Rounded: $x_1 = 3$, $x_2 = 0$; Value $= 30$
Lower bound $= 30$; Upper bound $= 36.7$

b. $x_1 = 3$, $x_2 = 2$; Value $= 36$

c. Alternative optimal solutions: $-x_1 = 0$, $x_2 = 5$
$x_1 = 2$, $x_2 = 4$

5. a. The feasible mixed-integer solutions are indicated by the boldface vertical lines in the graph.

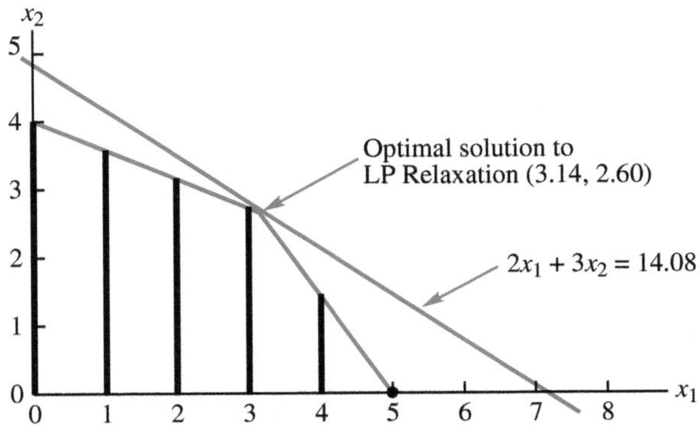

b. The optimal solution to the LP Relaxation is given by $x_1 = 3.14$, $x_2 = 2.60$; its value is 14.08.

Rounding down the value of x_1 to find a feasible mixed-integer solution yields $x_1 = 3$, $x_2 = 2.60$ with a value of 13.8; this solution is clearly not optimal; with $x_1 = 3$, x_2 can be made larger without violating the constraints.

c. The optimal solution to the MILP is given by $x_1 = 3$, $x_2 = 2.67$; its value is 14, as shown in the following figure:

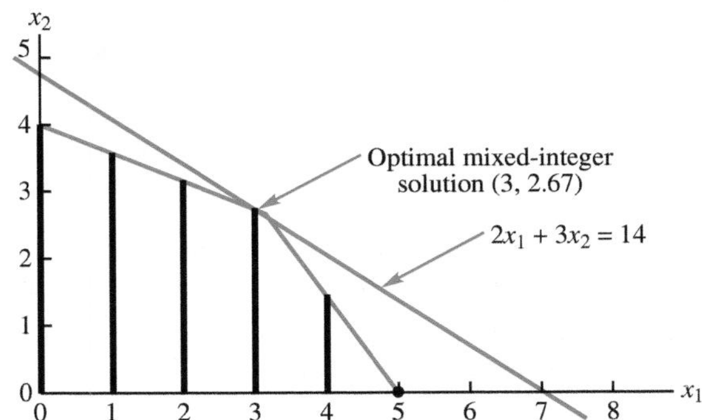

6. b. $x_1 = 1.96$, $x_2 = 5.48$; Value $= 7.44$
Rounded: $x_1 = 1.96$, $x_2 = 5$; Value $= 6.96$
Lower bound $= 6.96$; Upper bound $= 7.44$

c. $x_1 = 1.29$, $x_2 = 6$; Value $= 7.29$

7. a. $x_1 + x_3 + x_5 + x_6 = 2$

b. $x_3 - x_5 = 0$

c. $x_1 + x_4 = 1$

d. $x_4 \le x_1$
$x_4 \le x_3$

e. $x_4 \le x_1$
$x_4 \le x_3$
$x_4 \le x_1 + x_3 - 1$

8. a. $x_3 = 1$, $x_4 = 1$, $x_6 = 1$; Value $= 17{,}500$

b. Add $x_1 + x_2 \le 1$.

c. Add $x_3 - x_4 = 0$.

10. b. Choose locations B and E.

12. a. We use the following data:

b_{ij} = the bid for city i from carrier j,
$i = 1, 2, \ldots 20$ $\quad j = 1, 2, \ldots 7$
dem_i = the demand in truckload for city i
$i = 1, 2, \ldots 20$
c_{ij} = the cost of assigning city i to carrier j
$i = 1, 2, \ldots 20$ $\quad j = 1, 2, \ldots 7$

Note: $c_{ij} = (dem_i)(b_{ij})$ used in the objective function.

Let $y[j] = 1$ if carrier j is selected, 0 if not $j = 1, 2, \ldots 7$

$x[i, j] = 1$ if city i is assigned to carrier j, 0 if not
$i = 1, 2, \ldots 20$ $\quad j = 1, 2, \ldots 7$

Minimize the cost of city-carrier assignments (note: for brevity, zeros are not shown).

Minimize

65640*x[1, 5] + 49980*x[1, 6] + 53700*x[1, 7] + 14530*x[2, 2] + 26020*x[2, 5] + 17670*x[2, 6] + 30680*x[3, 2] + 45660*x[3, 5] + 37140*x[3, 6] + 37400*x[3, 7] + 67480*x[4, 2] + 104680*x[4, 5] + 69520*x[4, 6] + 15230*x[5, 2] + 22390*x[5, 5] + 17710*x[5, 6] +

18550*x[5, 7] + 15210*x[6, 2] + 15710*x[6, 5] + 15450*x[6, 7] + 25200*x[7, 2] + 23064*x[7, 4] + 23256*x[7, 5] + 24600*x[7, 7] + 45000*x[8, 2] + 35800*x[8, 4] + 35400*x[8, 5] + 43475*x[8, 7] + 28350*x[9, 2] + 30825*x[9, 4] + 29525*x[9, 5] + 28750*x[9, 7] + 22176*x[10, 2] + 20130*x[10, 4] + 22077*x[10, 5] + 22374*x[10, 7] + 7964*x[11, 1] + 7953*x[11, 3] + 6897*x[11, 4] + 7227*x[11, 5] + 7766*x[11, 7] + 22214*x[12, 1] + 22214*x[12, 3] + 20909*x[12, 4] + 19778*x[12, 5] + 21257*x[12, 7] + 8892*x[13, 1] + 8940*x[13, 3] + 8184*x[13, 5] + 8796*x[13, 7] + 19560*x[14, 1] + 19200*x[14, 2] + 19872*x[14, 3] + 17880*x[14, 5] + 19968*x[14, 7] + 9040*x[15, 1] + 8800*x[15, 3] + 8910*x[15, 5] + 9140*x[15, 7] + 9580*x[16, 1] + 9330*x[16, 3] + 8910*x[16, 5] + 9140*x[16, 7] + 21275*x[17, 1] + 21367*x[17, 3] + 21551*x[17, 5] + 22632*x[17, 7] + 22300*x[18, 1] + 21725*x[18, 3] + 20550*x[18, 4] + 20725*x[18, 5] + 21600*x[18, 7] + 11124*x[19, 1] + 11628*x[19, 3] + 11604*x[19, 5] + 12096*x[19, 7] + 9630*x[20, 1] + 9380*x[20, 3] + 9550*x[20, 5] + 9950*x[20, 7]

subject to

Every city is assigned to exactly one carrier:

x[1, 1] + x[1, 2] + x[1, 3] + x[1, 4] + x[1, 5] + x[1, 6] + x[1, 7] = 1
x[2, 1] + x[2, 2] + x[2, 3] + x[2, 4] + x[2, 5] + x[2, 6] + x[2, 7] = 1
x[3, 1] + x[3, 2] + x[3, 3] + x[3, 4] + x[3, 5] + x[3, 6] + x[3, 7] = 1
x[4, 1] + x[4, 2] + x[4, 3] + x[4, 4] + x[4, 5] + x[4, 6] + x[4, 7] = 1
x[5, 1] + x[5, 2] + x[5, 3] + x[5, 4] + x[5, 5] + x[5, 6] + x[5, 7] = 1
x[6, 1] + x[6, 2] + x[6, 3] + x[6, 4] + x[6, 5] + x[6, 6] + x[6, 7] = 1
x[7, 1] + x[7, 2] + x[7, 3] + x[7, 4] + x[7, 5] + x[7, 6] + x[7, 7] = 1
x[8, 1] + x[8, 2] + x[8, 3] + x[8, 4] + x[8, 5] + x[8, 6] + x[8, 7] = 1
x[9, 1] + x[9, 2] + x[9, 3] + x[9, 4] + x[9, 5] + x[9, 6] + x[9, 7] = 1
x[10, 1] + x[10, 2] + x[10, 3] + x[10, 4] + x[10, 5] + x[10, 6] + x[10, 7] = 1
x[11, 1] + x[11, 2] + x[11, 3] + x[11, 4] + x[11, 5] + x[11, 6] + x[11, 7] = 1
x[12, 1] + x[12, 2] + x[12, 3] + x[12, 4] + x[12, 5] + x[12, 6] + x[12, 7] = 1
x[13, 1] + x[13, 2] + x[13, 3] + x[13, 4] + x[13, 5] + x[13, 6] + x[13, 7] = 1
x[14, 1] + x[14, 2] + x[14, 3] + x[14, 4] + x[14, 5] + x[14, 6] + x[14, 7] = 1
x[15, 1] + x[15, 2] + x[15, 3] + x[15, 4] + x[15, 5] + x[15, 6] + x[15, 7] = 1
x[16, 1] + x[16, 2] + x[16, 3] + x[16, 4] + x[16, 5] + x[16, 6] + x[16, 7] = 1
x[17, 1] + x[17, 2] + x[17, 3] + x[17, 4] + x[17, 5] + x[17, 6] + x[17, 7] = 1
x[18, 1] + x[18, 2] + x[18, 3] + x[18, 4] + x[18, 5] + x[18, 6] + x[18, 7] = 1
x[19, 1] + x[19, 2] + x[19, 3] + x[19, 4] + x[19, 5] + x[19, 6] + x[19, 7] = 1
x[20, 1] + x[20, 2] + x[20, 3] + x[20, 4] + x[20, 5] + x[20, 6] + x[20, 7] = 1

If a carrier is selected, it can be assigned only the number of bids made:

Note:

The idea here is that if carrier *j* is not chosen, then no cities can be assigned to that carrier. Hence if y[j] = 0, the sum must be less than or equal to zero and hence all the associated *x*'s must be zero. If y[j] = 1, then the constraint becomes redundant. It could also be modeled as x[i,j] <= y[j], but this would generate more constraints:

x[1, 1] + x[2, 1] + x[3, 1] + x[4, 1] + x[5, 1] + x[6, 1] + x[7, 1] + x[8, 1] + x[9, 1] + x[10, 1] + x[11, 1] + x[12, 1] + x[13, 1] + x[14, 1] + x[15, 1] + x[16, 1] + x[17, 1] + x[18, 1] + x[19, 1] + x[20, 1] <= 10*y[1]

x[1, 2] + x[2, 2] + x[3, 2] + x[4, 2] + x[5, 2] + x[6, 2] + x[7, 2] + x[8, 2] + x[9, 2] + x[10, 2] + x[11, 2] + x[12, 2] + x[13, 2] + x[14, 2] + x[15, 2] + x[16, 2] + x[17, 2] + x[18, 2] + x[19, 2] + x[20, 2] <= 10*y[2]

x[1, 3] + x[2, 3] + x[3, 3] + x[4, 3] + x[5, 3] + x[6, 3] + x[7, 3] + x[8, 3] + x[9, 3] + x[10, 3] + x[11, 3] + x[12, 3] + x[13, 3] + x[14, 3] + x[15, 3] + x[16, 3] + x[17, 3] + x[18, 3] + x[19, 3] + x[20, 3] <= 10*y[3]

x[1, 4] + x[2, 4] + x[3, 4] + x[4, 4] + x[5, 4] + x[6, 4] + x[7, 4] + x[8, 4] + x[9, 4] + x[10, 4] + x[11, 4] + x[12, 4] + x[13, 4] + x[14, 4] + x[15, 4] + x[16, 4] + x[17, 4] + x[18, 4] + x[19, 4] + x[20, 4] <= 7*y[4]

x[1, 5] + x[2, 5] + x[3, 5] + x[4, 5] + x[5, 5] + x[6, 5] + x[7, 5] + x[8, 5] + x[9, 5] + x[10, 5] + x[11, 5] + x[12, 5] + x[13, 5] + x[14, 5] + x[15, 5] + x[16, 5] + x[17, 5] + x[18, 5] + x[19, 5] + x[20, 5] <= 20*y[5]

x[1, 6] + x[2, 6] + x[3, 6] + x[4, 6] + x[5, 6] + x[6, 6] + x[7, 6] + x[8, 6] + x[9, 6] + x[10, 6] + x[11, 6] + x[12, 6] + x[13, 6] + x[14, 6] + x[15, 6] + x[16, 6] + x[17, 6] + x[18, 6] + x[19, 6] + x[20, 6] <= 5*y[6]

x[1, 7] + x[2, 7] + x[3, 7] + x[4, 7] + x[5, 7] + x[6, 7] + x[7, 7] + x[8, 7] + x[9, 7] + x[10, 7] + x[11, 7] + x[12, 7] + x[13, 7] + x[14, 7] + x[15, 7] + x[16, 7] + x[17, 7] + x[18, 7] + x[19, 7] + x[20, 7] <= 18*y[7]

Nonbids must be set to 0:

x[1, 1] + x[2, 1] + x[3, 1] + x[4, 1] + x[5, 1] + x[6, 1] + x[7, 1] + x[8, 1] + x[9, 1] + x[10, 1] = 0

x[1, 2] + x[11, 2] + x[12, 2] + x[13, 2] + x[15, 2] + x[16, 2] + x[17, 2] + x[18, 2] + x[19, 2] + x[20, 2] = 0

x[1, 3] + x[2, 3] + x[3, 3] + x[4, 3] + x[5, 3] + x[6, 3] + x[7, 3] + x[8, 3] + x[9, 3] + x[10, 3] = 0

x[1, 4] + x[2, 4] + x[3, 4] + x[4, 4] + x[5, 4] + x[6, 4] + x[13, 4] + x[14, 4] + x[15, 4] + x[16, 4] + x[17, 4] + x[19, 4] + x[20, 4] = 0

x[6, 6] + x[7, 6] + x[8, 6] + x[9, 6] + x[10, 6] + x[11, 6] + x[12, 6] + x[13, 6] + x[14, 6] + x[15, 6] + x[16, 6] + x[17, 6] + x[18, 6] + x[19, 6] + x[20, 6] = 0

x[2, 7] + x[4, 7] = 0

No more than three carriers

y[1] + y[2] + y[3] + y[4] + y[5] + y[6] + y[7] <= 3

Solution:	Total Cost = $436,512
Carrier 2:	assigned cities 2, 3, 4, 5, 6, and 9
Carrier 5:	assigned cities 7, 8, and 10–20
Carrier 6:	assigned city 1

b.

# Carriers	Cost	Carriers Chosen
1	$524,677	5
2	$452,172	2,5
3	$436,512	2,5,6
4	$433,868	2,4,5,6
5	$433,112	1,2,4,5,6
6	$432,832	1,2,3,4,5,6
7	$432,832	1,2,3,4,5,6,7

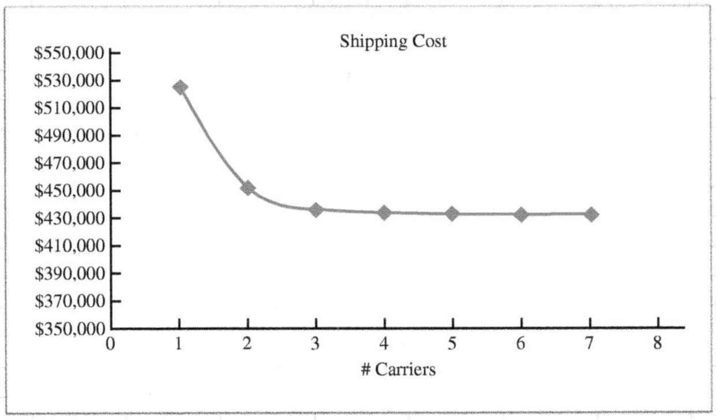

Shipping Cost

$550,000 $530,000 $510,000 $490,000 $470,000 $450,000 $430,000 $410,000 $390,000 $370,000 $350,000

0 1 2 3 4 5 6 7 8

Carriers

Given the incremental drop in cost, three seems like the correct number of carriers (the curve flattens considerably after three carriers). Notice that when seven carriers are allowed, only six carriers are actually assigned a city. That is, allowing a seventh carrier provides no benefit.

13. a. Add the following multiple-choice constraint to the problem:

$y_1 + y_2 = 1$

New optimal solution: $y_1 = 1, y_3 = 1, x_{12} = 10, x_{31} = 30, x_{52} = 10, x_{53} = 20$

Value = 940

b. Because one plant is already located in St. Louis, it is only necessary to add the following constraint to the model:

$y_3 + y_4 \leq 1$

New optimal solution: $y_4 = 1, x_{42} = 20, x_{43} = 20, x_{51} = 30$

Value = 860

14. a. Let 1 denote the Michigan plant
2 denote the first New York plant
3 denote the second New York plant
4 denote the Ohio plant
5 denote the California plant

It is not possible to meet needs by modernizing only one plant.

The following table shows the options which involve modernizing two plants.

Plant 1	2	3	4	5	Transmission Capacity	Engine Block Capacity	Feasible?	Cost
√	√				700	1300	No	
√		√			1100	900	Yes	60
√			√		900	1400	Yes	65
√				√	600	700	No	
	√	√			1200	1200	Yes	70
	√		√		1000	1700	Yes	75
	√			√	700	1000	No	
		√	√		1400	1300	Yes	75
		√		√	1100	600	No	
			√	√	900	1100	Yes	60

b. Modernize plants 1 and 3 or plants 4 and 5.

c. Let $x_i = \begin{cases} 1 & \text{if plant } i \text{ is modernized} \\ 0 & \text{if plant } i \text{ is not modernized} \end{cases}$

$$\begin{aligned} \text{Min} \quad & 25x_1 + 35x_2 + 35x_3 + 40x_4 + 25x_5 \\ \text{s.t.} \quad & \\ & 300x_1 + 400x_2 + 800x_3 + 600x_4 + 300x_5 \geq 900 \text{ Transmissions} \\ & 500x_1 + 800x_2 + 400x_3 + 900x_4 + 200x_5 \geq 900 \text{ Engine Blocks} \\ & x_1, x_2, x_3, x_4, x_5 \geq 0 \end{aligned}$$

d. Modernize plants 1 and 3.

16. a.

Min $105x_9 + 105x_{10} + 105x_{11} + 32y_9 + 32y_{10} + 32y_{11} + 32y_{12} + 32y_1 + 32y_2 + 32y_3$

$$\begin{aligned} x_9 + y_9 &\geq 6 \\ x_9 + x_{10} + y_9 + y_{10} &\geq 4 \\ x_9 + x_{10} + x_{11} + y_9 + y_{10} + y_{11} &\geq 8 \\ x_9 + x_{10} + x_{11} + y_9 + y_{10} + y_{11} + y_{12} &\geq 10 \\ x_{10} + x_{11} + y_{10} + y_{11} + y_{12} + y_1 &\geq 9 \\ x_9 + x_{11} + y_{11} + y_{12} + y_1 + y_2 &\geq 6 \\ x_9 + x_{10} + y_{12} + y_1 + y_2 + y_3 &\geq 4 \\ x_9 + x_{10} + x_{11} + y_1 + y_2 + y_3 &\geq 7 \\ x_{10} + x_{11} + y_2 + y_3 &\geq 6 \\ x_{11} + y_3 &\geq 6 \end{aligned}$$

$x_i, y_j \geq 0$ and integer for $i = 9, 10, 11$ and $j = 9, 10, 11, 12, 1, 2, 3$

b. Use all part-time employees.
Bring on as follows: 9:00 A.M.–6, 11:00 A.M.–2, 12:00 noon–6, 1:00 P.M.–1, 3:00 P.M.–6
Cost = $672

c. Same as in part (b)

d. New solution is to bring on one full-time employee at 9:00 A.M., four more at 11:00 A.M., and part-time employees as follows:
9:00 A.M.–5, 12:00 noon–5, and 3:00 P.M.–2

18. a. 52, 49, 36, 83, 39, 70, 79, 59

b. Thick crust, cheese blend, chunky sauce, medium sausage. Six of eight consumers will prefer this pizza (75%).

20. a. New objective function: Min $25x_1 + 40x_2 + 40x_3 + 40x_4 + 25x_5$
b. $x_4 = x_5 = 1$; modernize the Ohio and California plants
c. Add the constraint $x_2 + x_3 = 1$.
d. $x_1 = x_3 = 1$

22. $x_1 + x_2 + x_3 = 3y_1 + 5y_2 + 7y_3$
$y_1 + y_2 + y_3 = 1$

24. a. $x_{111}, x_{112}, x_{121}$
b. $x_{111} + x_{112} + x_{121} \leq 1$
c. $x_{531} + x_{532} + x_{533} + x_{541} + x_{542} + x_{543} + x_{551} + x_{552} + x_{561} \leq 1$
d. Only two screens are available.
e. $x_{222} + x_{231} + x_{422} + x_{431} + x_{531} + x_{532} + x_{533} + x_{631} + x_{632} + x_{633} \leq 2$

26. Let X_i = the amount (dollars) to invest in alternative i
$i = 1, 2, \ldots 10$
Y_i = 1 if Dave invests in alternative i, 0 if not
$i = 1, 2 \ldots 10$

Max $0.067X_1 + 0.0765X_2 + 0.0755X_3 + 0.0745X_4 + 0.075X_5 + 0.0645X_6 + 0.0705X_7 + 0.069X_8 + 0.052X_9 + 0.059X_{10}$

Subject to

$X_1 + X_2 + X_3 + X_4 + X_5 + X_6 + X_7 + X_8 + X_9 + X_{10} = 100{,}000$

Invest \$100,000

$X_i \leq 25{,}000Y_i \quad i = 1, 2, \ldots 10$

Invest no more than \$25,000 in any one fund

$X_i \geq 10{,}000Y_i \quad i = 1, 2, \ldots 10$

If invest in a fund, invest at least \$10,000 in a fund

$Y_1 + Y_2 + Y_3 + Y_4 \leq 2$

No more than 2 pure growth funds

$Y_9 + Y_{10} \geq 1$

At least 1 must be a pure bond fund

$X_9 + X_{10} \geq X_1 + X_2 + X_3 + X_4$

Amount in pure bonds must be at least that invested in pure growth funds

$X_i \geq 0 \qquad i = 1, 2, \ldots 10$

The optimal solution:

Fund	Amount Invested	Exp Return
1	\$ 0	\$ 0.00
2	\$ 12,500	\$ 956.25
3	\$ 0	\$ 0.00
4	\$ 0	\$ 0.00
5	\$ 25,000	\$ 1,875.00
6	\$ 0	\$ 0.00
7	\$ 25,000	\$ 1,762.50
8	\$ 25,000	\$ 1,725.50
9	\$0	\$0.00
10	\$ 12,500	\$ 737.50
	\$100,000	\$7,056.25

Chapter 12

2. a.

Min E
s.t.

$$wa + wb + wc + wd + we + wf + wg = 1$$
$$55.31wa + 37.64wb + 32.91wc + 33.53wd + 32.48we + 48.78wf + 58.41wg \geq 33.53$$
$$49.52wa + 55.63wb + 25.77wc + 41.99wd + 55.30we + 81.92wf + 119.70wg \geq 41.99$$
$$281wa + 156wb + 141wc + 160wd + 157we + 285wf + 111wg \geq 160$$
$$47wa + 3wb + 26wc + 21wd + 82we + 92wf + 89wg \geq 21$$
$$-250E + 310wa + 278.5wb + 165.6wc + 250wd + 206.4we + 384wf + 530.1wg \leq 0$$
$$-316E + 134.6wa + 114.3wb + 131.3wc + 316wd + 151.2we + 217wf + 770.8wg \leq 0$$
$$-94.4E + 116wa + 106.8wb + 65.52wc + 94.4wd + 102.1we + 153.7wf + 215wg \leq 0$$
$$wa, wb, wc, wd, we, wf, wg \geq 0$$

b. $E = 0.924$
$wa = 0.074$
$wc = 0.436$
$we = 0.489$
All other weights are zero.
c. D is relatively inefficient.
Composite requires 92.4 of D's resources.
d. 34.37 patient days (65 or older)
41.99 patient days (under 65)
e. Hospitals A, C, and E

4. a.

Min E
s.t.

$$wb + wc + wj + wn + ws = 1$$
$$3800wb + 4600wc + 4400wj + 6500wn + 6000ws \geq 4600$$
$$25wb + 32wc + 35wj + 30wn + 28ws \geq 32$$
$$8wb + 8.5wc + 8wj + 10wn + 9ws \geq 8.5$$
$$-110E + 96wb + 110wc + 100wj + 125wn + 120ws \leq 0$$
$$-22E + 16wb + 22wc + 18wj + 25wn + 24ws \leq 0$$
$$-1400E + 850wb + 1400wc + 1200wj + 1500wn + 1600ws \leq 0$$
$$wb, wc, wj, wn, ws \geq 0$$

b.

```
OPTIMAL SOLUTION

Objective Function Value =  0.960

 Variable          Value        Reduced Costs
-----------      ----------    -------------
     E              0.960           0.000
     wb             0.175           0.000
     wc             0.000           0.040
     wj             0.575           0.000
     wn             0.250           0.000
     ws             0.000           0.085
```

c. Yes; $E = 0.960$ indicates a composite restaurant can produce Clarksville's output with 96% of Clarksville's available resources.
d. More Output (Constraint 2 Surplus) \$220 more profit per week.

Less Input

Hours of Operation $110E = 105.6$ hours
FTE Staff $22 - 1.71$ (Constraint 6 Slack) $= 19.41$
Supply Expense $1400E - 129.614$ (Constraint 7 Slack) $= \$1214.39$

The composite restaurant uses 4.4 hours less operation time, 2.6 less employees, and $185.61 less supplies expense when compared to the Clarksville restaurant.

e. $wb = 0.175$, $wj = 0.575$, and $wn = 0.250$. Consider the Bardstown, Jeffersonville, and New Albany restaurants.

6. a. Flight Leg 1: $8 + 0 + 4 + 4 + 1 + 2 = 19$
Flight Leg 2: $6 + 3 + 2 + 4 + 2 + 1 = 18$
Flight Leg 3: $0 + 1 + 3 + 2 + 4 + 2 = 12$
Flight Leg 4: $4 + 2 + 2 + 1 + 6 + 3 = 18$

b. The calculation of the remaining demand for each ODIF is as follows:

ODIF	ODIF Code	Original Allocation	Seats Sold	Seats Available
1	PCQ	33	25	8
2	PMQ	44	44	0
3	POQ	45	18	27
4	PCY	16	12	4
5	PMY	6	5	1
6	POY	11	9	2
7	NCQ	26	20	6
8	NMQ	56	33	23
9	NOQ	39	37	2
10	NCY	15	11	4
11	NMY	7	5	2
12	NOY	9	8	1
13	CMQ	64	27	37
14	CMY	8	6	2
15	COQ	46	35	11
16	COY	10	7	3

c.

```
OPTIMAL SOLUTION

Objective Function Value =  15730.000

  Variable          Value          Reduced Costs
------------    ---------     ---------------
     PCQ            8.000             0.000
     PMQ            1.000             0.000
     POQ            3.000             0.000
     PCY            4.000             0.000
     PMY            1.000             0.000
     POY            2.000             0.000
     NCQ            6.000             0.000
     NMQ            3.000             0.000
     NOQ            2.000             0.000
     NCY            4.000             0.000
     NMY            2.000             0.000
     NOY            1.000             0.000
     CMQ            3.000             0.000
     CMY            2.000             0.000
     COQ            7.000             0.000
     COY            3.000             0.000
```

8. b. 65.7% small-cap growth fund
34.3% of the portfolio in a small-cap value
Expected return = 18.5%

c. 10% foreign stock
50.8% small-cap fund
39.2% of the portfolio in small-cap value
Expected return = 17.178%

10. Using LINGO or Excel Solver, the optimal solution is $X = 2$, $Y = -4$, for an optimal solution value of 0.

12. a. With $1000 being spent on radio and $1000 being spent on direct mail we can simply substitute those values into the sales function.

$$\begin{aligned} S &= -2R^2 - 10M^2 - 8RM + 18R + 34M \\ &= -2(2^2) - 10(1^2) - 8(2)(1) + 18(2) + 34(1) \\ &= -8 - 10 - 16 + 36 + 34 \\ &= 36 \end{aligned}$$

Sales of $36,000 will be realized with this allocation of the media budget.

b. Add a budget constraint to the sales function that is to be maximized.

$$\text{Max} \quad -2R^2 - 10M^2 - 8RM + 18R + 34M$$

s.t.

$$R + M \leq 3$$
$$R, M \geq 0$$

c. The optimal solution is to invest $2500 in radio advertising and $500 in direct mail advertising. The total sales generated will be $37,000.

14. a. The optimization model is

$$\text{Max} \quad 5L^{.25}C^{.75}$$

s.t.

$$25L + 75C \leq 75000$$
$$L, C \geq 0$$

b. The optimal solution to this is $L = 750$ and $C = 750$ for an optimal objective function value of 3750. If Excel Solver is used for this problem, we recommend starting with an initial solution that has $L > 0$ and $C > 0$.

16. a. Let OT be the number of overtime hours scheduled. Then the optimization model is

$$\text{Max} \quad -3x_1^2 + 42x_1 - 3x_2^2 + 48x_2 + 700 - 5OT$$

s.t.

$$4x_1 + 6x_2 \leq 24 + OT$$
$$x_1, x_2, OT \geq 0$$

b. The optimal solution is to schedule $OT = 8.66667$ overtime hours and produce $x_1 = 3.66667$ units of product 1 and $x_2 = 3.00000$ units of product 2 for a profit of 887.3333.

17. a. If X is the weekly production volume in thousands of units at the Dayton plant and Y is the weekly production volume in thousands of units at the Hamilton plant, then the optimization model is

$$\text{Min } X^2 - X + 5 + Y^2 + 2Y + 3$$

s.t.

$$X + Y = 8$$
$$X, Y \geq 0$$

b. Using LINGO or Excel Solver, the optimal solution is $X = 4.75$ and $Y = 3.25$ for an optimal objective value of 42.875.

18. Define the variables to be the dollars invested in the mutual fund. For example, IB = 500 means that \$500 is invested in the Intermediate-Term Bond fund. The LINGO formulation is

```
MIN = (1/5)*((R1 - RBAR)^2 + (R2 - RBAR)^2 +
      (R3 - RBAR)^2 + (R4 - RBAR)^2 + (R5 -
      RBAR)^2);

0.1006*FS + 0.1764*IB + 0.3241*LG
+ 0.3236*LV + 0.3344*SG + 0.2456*SV = R1;
0.1312*FS + 0.0325*IB + 0.1871*LG
+ 0.2061*LV + 0.1940*SG + 0.2532*SV = R2;
0.1347*FS + 0.0751*IB + 0.3328*LG
+ 0.1293*LV + 0.0385*SG - 0.0670*SV = R3;
0.4542*FS - 0.0133*IB + 0.4146*LG
+ 0.0706*LV + 0.5868*SG + 0.0543*SV = R4;
-0.2193*FS + 0.0736*IB - 0.2326*LG
- 0.0537*LV - 0.0902*SG + 0.1731*SV = R5;
FS + IB + LG + LV + SG + SV = 50000;
(1/5)*(R1 + R2 + R3 + R4 + R5) = RBAR;
RBAR > RMIN;
RMIN = 5000;

@FREE(R1);
@FREE(R2);
@FREE(R3);
@FREE(R4);
@FREE(R5);
```

The optimal solution to this model using LINGO is

```
Local optimal solution found.
  Objective value:                    6,784,038
  Total solver iterations:                   19

  Model Title: MARKOWITZ
```

Variable	Value	Reduced Cost
R1	9478.492	0.000000
RBAR	5000.000	0.000000
R2	5756.023	0.000000
R3	2821.951	0.000000
R4	4864.037	0.000000
R5	2079.496	0.000000
FS	7920.372	0.000000
IB	26273.98	0.000000
LG	2103.251	0.000000
LV	0.000000	208.2068
SG	0.000000	78.04764
SV	13702.40	0.000000
RMIN	5000.000	0.000000

Excel Solver will also produce the same optimal solution.

20. The optimal solution is $Q_1 = 52.223$, $Q_2 = 70.065$, $Q_3 = 37.689$, with a total cost of \$25,830.

22.

Model Title: MATCHING S&P INFO TECH RETURNS

Variable	Value	Reduced Cost
R1	−0.1526620	0.000000
R2	0.7916129	0.000000
R3	0.9403282	0.000000
R4	0.1694353	0.000000
R5	−0.5132641	0.000000
R6	−0.4379140	0.000000
R7	0.2329556	0.000000
R8	0.3760108E-03	0.000000
R9	0.1671686E-01	0.000000
AAPL	0.000000	1.624161
AMD	0.1014161	0.000000
ORCL	0.8985839	0.000000

24. a. Let:

FS = proportion of portfolio invested in the foreign stock mutual fund

IB = proportion of portfolio invested in the intermediate-term bond fund

LG = proportion of portfolio invested in the large-cap growth fund

LV = proportion of portfolio invested in the large-cap value fund

SG = proportion of portfolio invested in the small-cap growth fund

SV = proportion of portfolio invested in the small-cap value fund

$\overline{R}$ = the expected return of the portfolio

R_s = the return of the portfolio in years

Max $\overline{R}$

s.t.

$$\begin{aligned}
10.06FS + 17.64IB + 32.41LG + 32.36LV + 33.44SG + 24.56SV &= R_1\\
13.12FS + 3.25IB + 18.71LG + 20.61LV + 19.40SG + 25.32SV &= R_2\\
13.47FS + 7.51IB + 33.28LG + 12.93LV + 3.85SG - 6.70SV &= R_3\\
45.42FS - 1.33IB + 41.46LG + 7.06LV + 58.68SG + 5.43SV &= R_4\\
-21.93FS + 7.36IB - 23.26LG - 5.37LV - 9.02SG + 17.31SV &= R_5\\
FS + IB + LG + LV + SG + SV &= 1
\end{aligned}$$

$$\frac{1}{5}\sum_{s=1}^{5} R_s = \overline{R}$$

$$\frac{1}{5}\sum_{s=1}^{5} (R_s - \overline{R})^2 \le 30$$

$$FS, IB, LG, LV, SG, SV \ge 0$$

b. The optimal solution is (% are rounded to one place):

Foreign Stock	13.3%
Intermediate-Term Bond	49.6%
Large-Cap Growth	7.4%
Large-Cap Value	0.0%
Small-Cap Growth	0.0%
Small-Cap Value	29.8%

Maximum expected return = 10.45%

26. This is a nonlinear 0-1 integer programming problem. Let $X_{ij} = 1$ if tanker 1 is assigned loading dock j and 0 if not. The optimal solution to this model is 10000.00. Tanker 1 should be assigned to dock 2, tanker 2 to dock 1, and tanker 3 to dock 3. Depending on the starting point, Excel Solver will likely get stuck at a local optimum and not find the optimal solution that LINGO finds.

28. a.

Let X = the x coordinate of the tool bin
Y = the y coordinate of the tool bin

$$\text{Minimize } -(X-1)^2 + (Y-4)^2 + \sqrt{(X-1)^2 + (Y-2)^2} + \sqrt{(X-2.5)^2 + (Y-2)^2} + \sqrt{(X-3)^2 + (Y-5)^2} + \sqrt{(X-4)^2 + (Y-4)^2}$$

Solution: $X = 2.23$, $Y = 3.35$

b.

$$\text{Minimize } 12\sqrt{(X-1)^2 + (Y-4)^2} + 24\sqrt{(X-1)^2 + (Y-2)^2} + 13\sqrt{(X-2.5)^2 + (Y-2)^2} + 7\sqrt{(X-3)^2 + (Y-5)^2} + 17\sqrt{(X-4)^2 + (Y-4)^2}$$

Solution: $X = 1.91$, $Y = 2.72$

c.

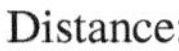

Distance:

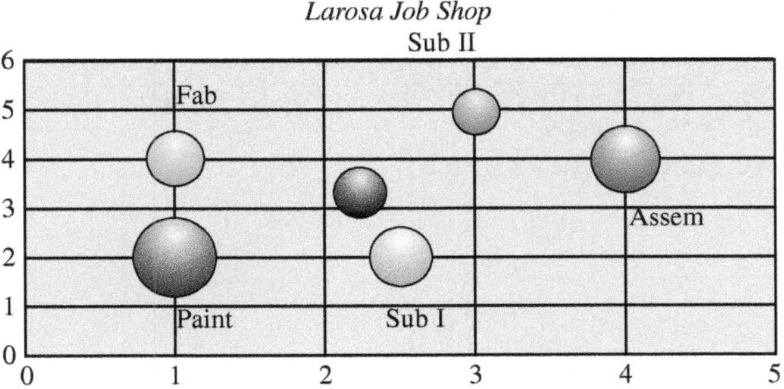

Demand-Weighted Distance

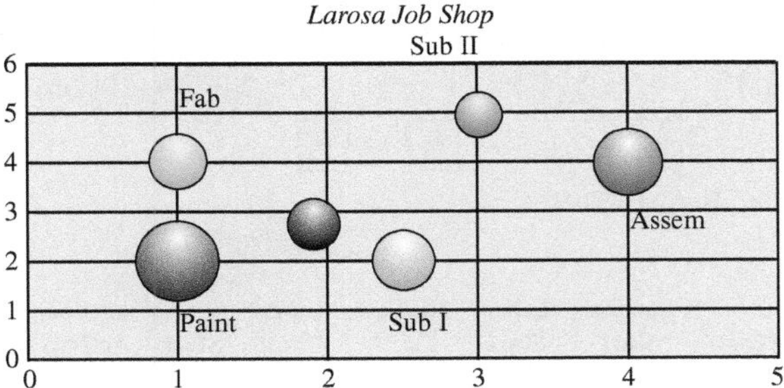

Using demand shifts the optimal location toward the paint cell (it has heavy demand).

30. Let X = the latitude of the optimal wedding location
Y = the longitude of the optimal wedding location

$$\text{Min } \sum_{i=1}^{15} R_i \left(69\sqrt{(X - \text{lat}_i)^2 + (Y - \text{long}_i)^2}\right)$$

where R_i = the number of relatives who are from the (lat_i, long_i) location. The optimal solution is $X = 40.204$, $Y = -75.214$, with an objective function value of 67,444.286.

Chapter 13

2.

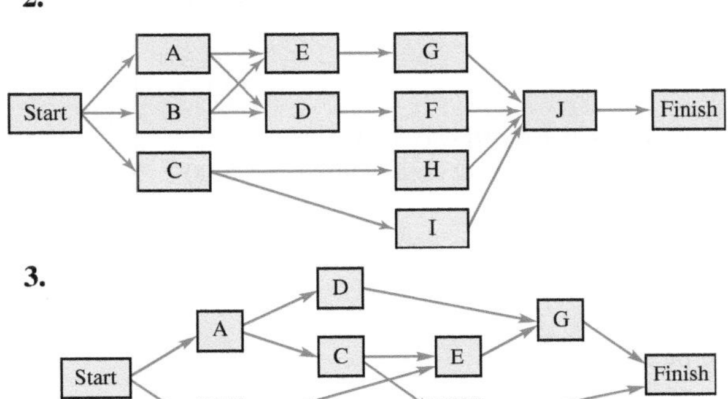

3.

4. a. A–D–G
b. No; Time = 15 months

6. a. Critical path: A–D–F–H
b. 22 weeks
c. No, it is a critical activity.
d. Yes, 2 weeks
e. Schedule for activity E:

Earliest start	3
Latest start	4
Earliest finish	10
Latest finish	11

8. a.

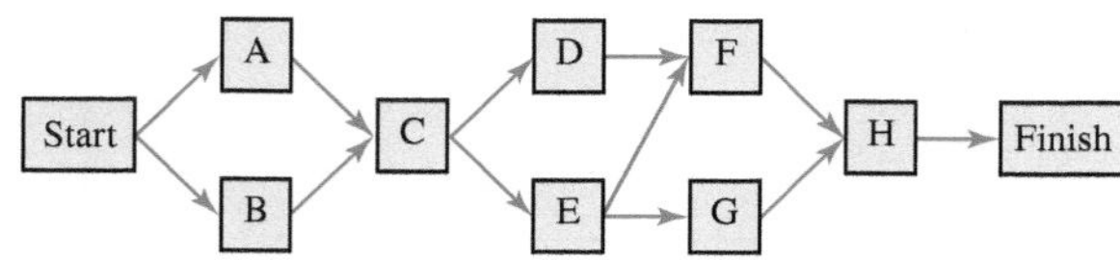

b. B–C–E–F–H
c.

Activity	Earliest Start	Latest Start	Earliest Finish	Latest Finish	Slack	Critical Activity
A	0	2	6	8	2	
B	0	0	8	8	0	Yes
C	8	8	20	20	0	Yes
D	20	22	24	26	2	
E	20	20	26	26	0	Yes
F	26	26	41	41	0	Yes
G	26	29	38	41	3	
H	41	41	49	49	0	Yes

d. Yes, time = 49 weeks

10. a.

Activity	Optimistic	Most Probable	Pessimistic	Expected Times	Variance
A	4	5.0	6	5.00	0.11
B	8	9.0	10	9.00	0.11
C	7	7.5	11	8.00	0.44
D	7	9.0	10	8.83	0.25
E	6	7.0	9	7.17	0.25
F	5	6.0	7	6.00	0.11

b. Critical activities: B–D–F
Expected project completion time: 9.00 + 8.83 + 6.00 = 23.83
Variance of projection completion time: 0.11 + 0.25 + 0.11 = 0.47

12. a. A–D–H–I
b. 25.66 days
c. 0.2578

13.

Activity	Expected Time	Variance
A	5	0.11
B	3	0.03
C	7	0.11
D	6	0.44
E	7	0.44
F	3	0.11
G	10	0.44
H	8	1.78

From Problem 6, A–D–F–H is the critical path, so $E(T) = 5 + 6 + 3 + 8 = 22$.
$\sigma^2 = 0.11 + 0.44 + 0.11 + 1.78 = 2.44$.

$$z = \frac{\text{Time} - E(T)}{\sigma} = \frac{\text{Time} - 22}{\sqrt{2.44}}$$

a. Time = 21: $z = -0.64$
Cumulative Probability = 0.2611
P(21 weeks) = 0.2611

b. Time = 22: $z = 0.00$
Cumulative Probability = 0.5000
P(22 weeks) = 0.5000

c. Time = 25: $z = +1.92$
Cumulative Probability = 0.9726
P(25 weeks) = 0.9726

14. a. A–C–E–G–H
b. 52 weeks (1 year)
c. 0.0174
d. 0.0934
e. 10 months—doubtful
13 months—very likely
Estimate 12 months (1 year)

16. a.

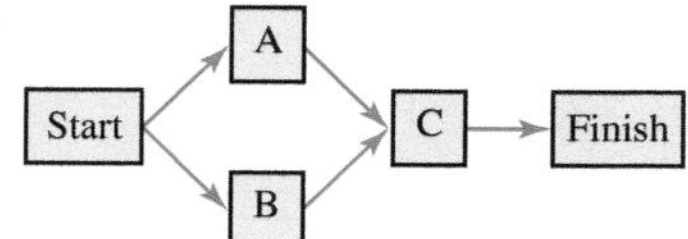

b. B–C

Activity	Expected Time	Variance
A	6.67	2.78
B	7.50	1.36
C	1.00	0.00

Expected Time = 7.5 + 1 = 8.5 weeks

$\sigma^2 = 1.36 + 0 = 1.36$

$$z = \frac{10 - 8.5}{\sqrt{1.36}} = 1.29$$

Cumulative probability = 0.90

c. A–C

Expected Time = 6.67 + 1 = 7.67 weeks

$\sigma^2 = 2.78 + 0 = 2.78$

$$z = \frac{10 - 7.67}{\sqrt{2.78}} = 1.40$$

Cumulative Probability = 0.92

P(Entire project completed) = 0.90 × 0.92 = 0.828

d. The probability estimate from (c) based on both paths is more accurate. Both paths must be completed for the entire project to be completed. These two paths only share one activity (C), which has no variability, and thus are effectively independent.

18. a.

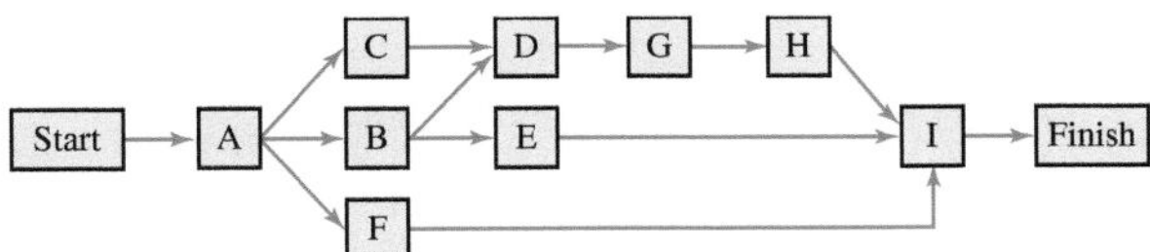

b.

Activity	Expected Time	Variance
A	1.17	0.03
B	6.00	0.44
C	4.00	0.44
D	2.00	0.11
E	3.00	0.11
F	2.00	0.11
G	2.00	0.11
H	2.00	0.11
I	1.00	0.00

Activity	Earliest Start	Latest Start	Earliest Finish	Latest Finish	Slack	Critical Activity
A	0.00	0.00	1.17	1.17	0.00	Yes
B	1.17	1.17	7.17	7.17	0.00	Yes
C	1.17	3.17	5.17	7.17	2.00	
D	7.17	7.17	9.17	9.17	0.00	Yes
E	7.17	10.17	10.17	13.17	3.00	
F	1.17	11.17	3.17	13.17	10.00	
G	9.17	9.17	11.17	11.17	0.00	Yes
H	11.17	11.17	13.17	13.17	0.00	Yes
I	13.17	13.17	14.17	14.17	0.00	Yes

c. A–B–D–G–H–I, 14.17 weeks

d. 0.0951, yes

20. a.

Activity	Maximum Crash	Crash Cost/Week
A	2	400
B	3	667
C	1	500
D	2	300
E	1	350
F	2	450
G	5	360
H	1	1000

Min $400Y_A + 667Y_B + 500Y_C + 300Y_D + 350Y_E + 450Y_F + 360Y_G + 1000Y_H$

s.t.

$x_A + y_A \geq 3 \quad x_E + y_E - x_D \geq 4 \quad x_H + y_H - x_G \geq 3$

$x_B + y_B \geq 6 \quad x_F + y_F - x_E \geq 3 \quad x_H \leq 16$

$x_C + y_C - x_A \geq 2 \quad x_G + y_G - x_C \geq 9$

$x_D + y_D - x_C \geq 5 \quad x_G + y_G - x_B \geq 9$

$x_D + y_D - x_B \geq 5 \quad x_H + y_H - x_F \geq 3$

Maximum Crashing:

$y_A \leq 2$

$y_B \leq 3$

$y_C \leq 1$

$y_D \leq 2$

$y_E \leq 1$

$y_F \leq 2$

$y_G \leq 5$

$y_H \leq 1$

All $x, y \geq 0$

b. Crash B(1 week), D(2 weeks), E(1 week), F(1 week), G(1 week)
Total cost = \$2427

c. All activities are critical.

21. a.

Activity	Earliest Start	Latest Start	Earliest Finish	Latest Finish	Slack	Critical Activity
A	0	0	3	3	0	Yes
B	0	1	2	3	1	
C	3	3	8	8	0	Yes
D	2	3	7	8	1	
E	8	8	14	14	0	Yes
F	8	10	10	12	2	
G	10	12	12	14	2	

Critical Path: A–C–E

Project completion time = $t_A + t_C + t_E = 3 + 5 + 6 =$ 14 days

b. Total cost = \$8400

22. a.

Activity	Max. Crash Days	Crash Cost/Day
A	1	600
B	1	700
C	2	400
D	2	400
E	2	500
F	1	400
G	1	500

Min $600Y_A + 700Y_B + 400Y_C + 400Y_D + 500Y_E + 400Y_F + 400Y_G$

s.t.

$X_A + Y_A \geq 3$

$X_B + Y_B \geq 2$

$-X_A + X_C + Y_C \geq 5$

$$
\begin{aligned}
-X_B + X_D + Y_D &\geq 5 \\
-X_C + X_E + Y_E &\geq 6 \\
-X_D + X_E + Y_E &\geq 6 \\
-X_C + X_F + Y_F &\geq 2 \\
-X_D + X_F + Y_F &\geq 2 \\
-X_F + X_G + Y_G &\geq 2 \\
-X_E + X_{FIN} &\geq 0 \\
-X_G + X_{FIN} &\geq 0 \\
X_{FIN} &\leq 12 \\
Y_A &\leq 1 \\
Y_B &\leq 1 \\
Y_C &\leq 2 \\
Y_D &\leq 2 \\
Y_E &\leq 2 \\
Y_F &\leq 1 \\
Y_G &\leq 1
\end{aligned}
$$

All $X, Y \geq 0$

b. Solution of the linear programming model in part (a) shows the following:

Activity	Crash	Crashing Cost
C	1 day	$400
E	1 day	500
	Total	$900

c. Total cost = Normal cost + Crashing cost
= $8400 + $900 = $9300

24. a.

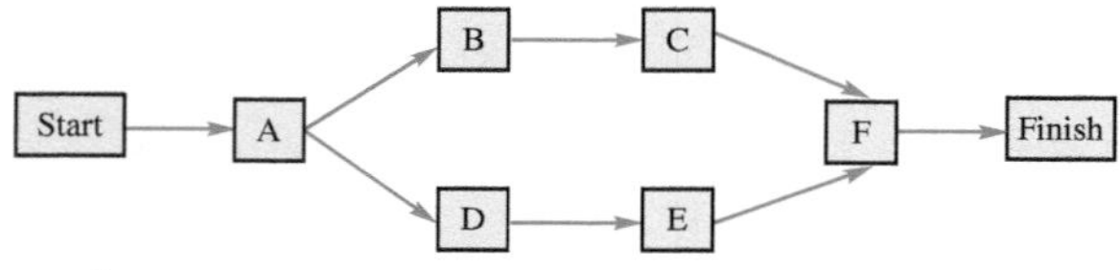

b.

Activity	Earliest Start	Latest Start	Earliest Finish	Latest Finish	Slack
A	0	0	10	10	0
B	10	10	18	18	0
C	18	18	28	28	0
D	10	11	17	18	1
E	17	18	27	28	1
F	28	28	31	31	0

c. A–B–C–F, 31 weeks

d. Crash A(2 weeks), B(2 weeks), C(1 week), D(1 week), E(1 week)

e. All activities are critical.

f. $112,500

Chapter 14

1. a. $Q^* = \sqrt{\dfrac{2DC_0}{C_h}} = \sqrt{\dfrac{2(3600)(20)}{0.25(3)}} = 438.18$

b. $r = dm = \dfrac{3600}{250}(5) = 72$

c. $T = \dfrac{250Q^*}{D} = \dfrac{250(438.18)}{3600} = 30.43$ days

d. $TC = \dfrac{1}{2}QC_h + \dfrac{D}{Q}C_0$

$= \dfrac{1}{2}(438.18)(0.25)(3) + \dfrac{3600}{438.18}(20) = \$328.63$

2. $164.32 for each; Total cost = $328.64

4. a. 1095.45

b. 240

c. 22.82 days

d. $273.86 for each; Total cost = $547.72

6. a. $Q^*_{pens} = \sqrt{\dfrac{2DC_0}{C_h}} = \sqrt{\dfrac{2(1500)(20)}{(1.50)(.10)}} = 632$ pens,

$T_{pens} = \dfrac{240Q^*}{D} = \dfrac{240(632)}{1500} = 101$ days

$Q^*_{pencils} = \sqrt{\dfrac{2DC_0}{C_h}} = \sqrt{\dfrac{2(400)(20)}{(4)(.10)}} = 200$ pencils,

$T_{pencils} = \dfrac{240Q^*}{D} = \dfrac{240(224)}{400} = 120$ days

$TC_{pens} = \dfrac{1}{2}Q_{pens}C_h + \dfrac{D}{Q_{pens}}C_0 = \dfrac{1}{2}(632)(.1)(1.5) + \dfrac{1500}{632}20 = \$94.87$

$TC_{pencils} = \dfrac{1}{2}Q_{pencils}C_h + \dfrac{D}{Q_{pencils}}C_0 = \dfrac{1}{2}(200)(.1)(4) + \dfrac{400}{200}20 = \$80$

Thus, the total cost is $94.87 + $80 = $174.87.

b. Setting the cycle times of pens and pencils equal:

$$\frac{240Q_{pens}}{D_{pens}} = \frac{240Q_{pencils}}{D_{pencils}}$$

which implies $Q_{pens} = 3.75Q_{pencils}$.

The total cost (for both pens and pencils) is:

$$TC = \frac{1}{2}Q_{pens}C_{h,\,pens} + \frac{D_{pens}}{Q_{pens}}C_{0,\,pens} + \frac{1}{2}Q_{pencils}C_{h,\,pencil} + \frac{D}{Q_{pencils}}C_{0,\,pencils}$$

Substituting $Q_{pens} = 3.75Q_{pencils}$ and combining like terms, we obtain

$$TC = \frac{1}{2} Q_{pencils} (3.75C_{h, pens} + C_{h, pencils}) + \frac{\frac{D_{pens} C_{0, pens}}{3.75} + D_{pencils} C_{0, pencils}}{Q_{pencils}}$$

We can solve for $Q_{pencils}$ by observing that this total cost equation is the same as

$$TC = \frac{1}{2} Q_{pencils} C_h' + \frac{(DC_0)'}{Q_{pencils}}$$

where $C_h' = 3.75C_{h, pens} + C_{h, pencils}$ and $(DC_0)' = \frac{D_{pens}C_{0, pens}}{3.75} + D_{pencils}C_{0, pencils}$.

Thus,

$$Q_{pencils} = \sqrt{\frac{2(DC_0)'}{C_h'}} = \sqrt{\frac{2\left(\frac{(1500)(15)}{3.75} + (400)(15)\right)}{3.75(.1)(1.5) + (.1)(4)}}$$

$= 158$ pencils

$Q_{pens} = 3.75(158) = 593$ pens

These quantities are ordered every T = (240)(593)/1500 = (240)(158)/400 = 95 days. The total cost (for both pens and pencils) is:

$$TC = \frac{1}{2}(593)(.1)(1.5) + \frac{1500}{593}(15) + \frac{1}{2}(158)(.1)(4) + \frac{400}{158}(15) = \$151.99.$$

Thus, the consolidated shipments result in annual savings of $174.87 − $151.99 = $22.88.

8. $Q^* = 11.73$, use 12
5 classes per year
$225,200

10. $Q^* = 1414.21$
$T = 28.28$ days
Production runs of 7.07 days

12. a. $$Q^* = \sqrt{\frac{2(6000)(2345)}{\left(1 - \frac{6000}{16000}\right)20}} = 1500$$

b. $D/Q^* = 6000/1500 = 4$ production runs
12 months/4 = 3-month cycle time

c. Current total cost using $Q = 500$ is as follows:

$$TC = \frac{1}{2}\left(1 - \frac{D}{P}\right) QC_h + \left(\frac{D}{C}\right)C_0 = \frac{1}{2}\left(1 - \frac{6000}{16000}\right)500(20) + \frac{6000}{500}(2345) = 3125 + 28140 = \$31,265$$

Proposed Total Cost using $Q^* = 1500$ is as follows:

$$TC = \frac{1}{2}\left(1 - \frac{6000}{16000}\right)1500(20) + \frac{6000}{1500}(2345)$$
$= 9375 + 9380 = \$18,755$

Change to $Q^* = 1500$
Savings = $31,265 − $18,755 = $12,510
12,510/31,265 = 40% savings over current policy

13. a. $$Q^* = \sqrt{\frac{2DC_0}{(1 - D/P)C_h}} = \sqrt{\frac{2(7200)(150)}{(1 - 7200/25,000)(0.18)(14.50)}} = 1078.12$$

b. Number of production runs $= \frac{D}{Q^*} = \frac{7200}{1078.12} = 6.68$

c. $T = \frac{250Q}{D} = \frac{250(1078.12)}{7200} = 37.43$ days

d. Production run length $= \frac{Q}{P/250} = \frac{1078.12}{25,000/250} = 10.78$ days

e. Maximum inventory $= \left(1 - \frac{D}{P}\right)Q = \left(1 - \frac{7200}{25,000}\right)(1078.12) = 767.62$

f. Holding cost $= \frac{1}{2}\left(1 - \frac{D}{P}\right)QC_h = \frac{1}{2}\left(1 - \frac{7200}{25,000}\right)(1078.12)(0.18)(14.50) = \$1001.74$

Ordering cost $= \frac{D}{Q}C_0 = \frac{7200}{1078.12}(150) = \$1001.74$

Total cost = $2003.48

g. $r = dm = \left(\frac{D}{250}\right)m = \frac{7200}{250}(15) = 432$

14. New $Q^* = 4509$

15. a. $$Q^* = \sqrt{\frac{2DC_0}{C_h}\left(\frac{C_h + C_b}{C_b}\right)} = \sqrt{\frac{2(12,000)(25)}{0.50}\left(\frac{0.50 + 5}{0.50}\right)} = 1148.91$$

b. $$S^* = Q^*\left(\frac{C_h}{C_h + C_b}\right) = 1148.91\left(\frac{0.50}{0.50 + 5}\right) = 104.45$$

c. Max inventory $= Q^* - S^* = 1044.46$

d. $T = \dfrac{250Q^*}{D} = \dfrac{250(1148.91)}{12{,}000} = 23.94$ days

e. Holding $= \dfrac{(Q - S)^2}{2Q} C_h = \$237.38$

Ordering $= \dfrac{D}{Q} C_0 = \$261.12$

Backorder $= \dfrac{S^2}{2Q} C_b = \$23.74$

Total cost $= \$522.24$

The total cost for the EOQ model in Problem 4 was \$547.72; allowing backorders reduces the total cost.

16. 135.55; $r = dm - S$; less than

18. 64, 24.44

20. $Q^* = 100$; Total cost $= \$3{,}601.50$

21. $Q = \sqrt{\dfrac{2DC_0}{C_h}}$

$Q_1 = \sqrt{\dfrac{2(500)(40)}{0.20(10)}} = 141.42$

$Q_2 = \sqrt{\dfrac{2(500)(40)}{0.20(9.7)}} = 143.59$

Because Q_1 is over its limit of 99 units, Q_1 cannot be optimal (see Problem 23); use $Q_2 = 143.59$ as the optimal order quantity.

Total cost $= \dfrac{1}{2}QC_h + \dfrac{D}{Q}C_0 + DC$

$= 139.28 + 139.28 + 4850.00 = \$5128.56$

22. $Q^* = 300$; Savings $= \$480$

24. a. Cost of overestimation, $c_o = \$9$

Cost of underestimation, $c_u = \$10 - \$9 - \$0.50 = \$0.50$

$P(\text{demand} \le Q^*) = \dfrac{c_u}{c_u + c_o} = \dfrac{0.5}{9.5} = 0.0526$

From the normal table, a cumulative probability of 0.0526 corresponds to $z = -1.62$.

Thus,

$Q^* = \mu - 1.62\sigma = 9000 - (1.62)(400) = 8352$ magazines

b. Cost of overestimation, $c_o = \$9 - \$8 = \$1$

Cost of underestimation, $c_u = \$10 - \$9 - \$0.50 = \$0.50$

$P(\text{demand} \le Q^*) = \dfrac{c_u}{c_u + c_o} = \dfrac{0.5}{1.5} = 0.3333$

From the normal table, a cumulative probability of 0.3333 corresponds to $z = -0.43$.

Thus,

$Q^* = \mu - 0.43\sigma = 9000 - (0.43)(400) = 8828$ magazines

25. a. $c_o = 80 - 50 = 30$

$c_u = 125 - 80 = 45$

$P(D \le Q^*) = \dfrac{c_u}{c_u + c_o} = \dfrac{45}{45 + 30} = 0.60$

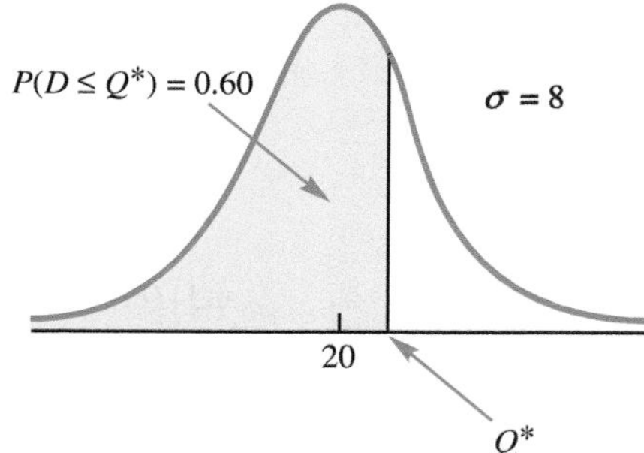

For the cumulative standard normal probability 0.60, $z = 0.25$;

$Q^* = 20 + 0.25(8) = 22$

b. $P(\text{Sell all}) = P(D \ge Q^*) = 1 - 0.60 = 0.40$

26. a. \$150

b. \$240 − \$150 = \$90

c. 47

d. 0.625

28. a. 440

b. 0.60

c. 710

d. $c_u = \$17$

29. a. $r = dm = (200/250)15 = 12$

b. $\dfrac{D}{Q} = \dfrac{200}{25} = 8$ orders/year

The limit of 1 stock-out per year means that $P(\text{Stock-out/cycle}) = 1/8 = 0.125$.

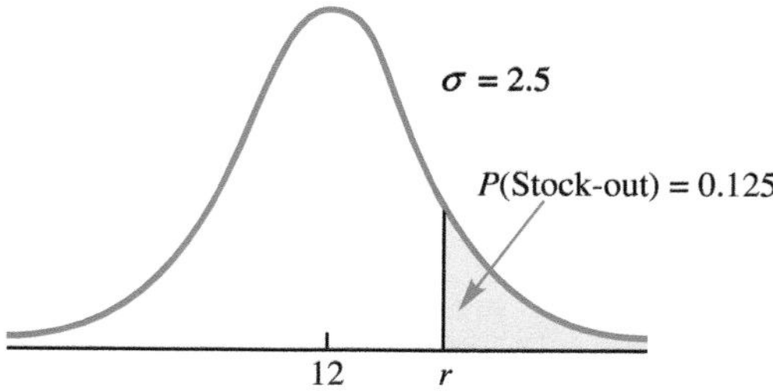

$P(\text{No stock-out/cycle}) = 1 - 0.125 = 0.875$

For cumulative probability 0.875, $z = 1.15$

Thus, $z = \dfrac{r - 12}{2.5} = 1.15$

$r = 12 + 1.15(2.5) = 14.875$ Use 15.

c. Safety stock = 3 units

Added cost $= 3(\$5) = \$15$/year

30. a. $Q^* = \sqrt{\dfrac{2DC_o}{C_h}} = \sqrt{\dfrac{2(52)\left(\dfrac{300}{100}\right)(15)}{(10)(.15)}} = 55.86$

≈ 56 boxes

b. $r = \mu + z\sigma = 300 + (2.33)(75) = 474.75 \approx 475$ cups.

32. a. 31.62

b. 19.8 (20); 0.2108

c. 5, $15

33. a. $1/52 = 0.0192$

b. $P(\text{No stock-out}) = 1 - 0.0192 = 0.9808$

For cumulative probability 0.9808, $z = 2.07$.

Thus, $z = \dfrac{M - 60}{12} = 2.07$

$M = \mu + z\sigma = 60 + 2.07(12) = 85$

c. $M = 35 + (0.9808)(85 - 35) = 84$

34. a. 243

b. 93, $54.87

c. 613

d. 163, $96.17

e. Yes, added cost would be only $41.30 per year.

f. Yes, added cost would be $4130 per year.

36. a. 40

b. 62.25; 7.9

c. 54

d. 36

Chapter 15

2. a. 0.4512

b. 0.6988

c. 0.3012

4.

n	P_n
0	0.3333
1	0.2222
2	0.1481
3	0.0988

$P(n > 3) = 1 - P(n <= 3) = 1 - 0.8024 = 0.1976$

5. a. $P_0 = 1 - \dfrac{\lambda}{\mu} = 1 - \dfrac{10}{12} = 0.1667$

b. $L_q = \dfrac{\lambda^2}{\mu(\mu - \lambda)} = \dfrac{10^2}{12(12 - 10)} = 4.1667$

c. $W_q = \dfrac{L_q}{\lambda} = 0.4167$ hour (25 minutes)

d. $W = W_q + \dfrac{1}{\mu} = 0.5$ hour (30 minutes)

e. $P_w = \dfrac{\lambda}{\mu} = \dfrac{10}{12} = 0.8333$

6. a. 0.3750

b. 1.0417

c. 0.8333 minutes (50 seconds)

d. 0.6250

e. Yes

8. 0.20, 3.2, 4, 3.2, 4, 0.80

Slightly poorer service

10. a. New: 1.3333, 2, 0.6667, 1, 0.6667

Experienced: 0.50, 1, 0.25, 0.50, 0.50

b. New $74; experienced $50; hire experienced

11. a. $\lambda = 2.5;\quad \mu = \dfrac{60}{10} = 6$ customers per hour

$L_q = \dfrac{\lambda^2}{\mu(\mu - \lambda)} = \dfrac{(2.5)^2}{6(6 - 2.5)} = 0.2976$

$L = L_q + \dfrac{\lambda}{\mu} = 0.7143$

$W_q = \dfrac{L_q}{\lambda} = 0.1190$ hours (7.14 minutes)

$W = W_q + \dfrac{1}{\mu} = 0.2857$ hours

$P_w = \dfrac{\lambda}{\mu} = \dfrac{2.5}{6} = 0.4167$

b. No; $W_q = 7.14$ minutes; firm should increase the service rate (μ) for the consultant or hire a second consultant.

c. $\mu = \dfrac{60}{8} = 7.5$ customers per hour

$L_q = \dfrac{\lambda^2}{\mu(\mu - \lambda)} = \dfrac{(2.5)^2}{7.5(7.5 - 2.5)} = 0.1667$

$W_q = \dfrac{L_q}{\lambda} = 0.0667$ hour (4 minutes)

The service goal is being met.

12. a. 0.25, 2.25, 3, 0.15 hours, 0.20 hours, 0.75

b. The service needs improvement.

14. a. 8

b. 0.3750

c. 1.0417

d. 12.5 minutes

e. 0.6250

f. Add a second consultant.

16. a. 0.50

b. 0.50

c. 0.10 hours (6 minutes)

d. 0.20 hours (12 minutes)

e. Yes, $W_q = 6$ minutes is most likely acceptable for a marina.

18. a. $L_q = \dfrac{(\lambda/\mu)^2\lambda\mu}{(k-1)!(2\mu-\lambda)^2}P_0$

$= \dfrac{(1.8)^2(5.4)(3)}{(2-1)!(6-5.4)^2}(0.0526) = 7.67$

$L = L_q + \lambda/\mu = 7.67 + 1.8 = 9.47$

$W_q = \dfrac{L_q}{\lambda} = \dfrac{7.67}{5.4} = 1.42$ minutes

$W = W_q + 1/\mu = 1.42 + 0.33 = 1.75$ minutes

$P_W = \dfrac{1}{k!}\left(\dfrac{\lambda}{\mu}\right)^k\left(\dfrac{k\mu}{k\mu-\lambda}\right)P_0$

$= \dfrac{1}{2!}(1.8)^2\left(\dfrac{6}{6-5.4}\right)0.0526 = 0.8526$

b. $L_q = 7.67$; Yes

c. $W = 1.75$ minutes

20. a. Use $k = 2$.
$W = 3.7037$ minutes
$L = 4.4444$
$P_w = 0.7111$

b. For $k = 3$
$W = 7.1778$ minutes
$L = 15.0735$ customers
$P_N = 0.8767$
Expand post office.

21. $L_q = \dfrac{\lambda^2}{\mu(\mu-\lambda)} = \dfrac{(2.5)^2}{7.5(7.5-2.5)} = 0.1667$

$L = L_q + \dfrac{\lambda}{\mu} = 0.50$

Total cost $= \$25L + \$16$
$= 25(0.50) + 16 = \$28.50$

Two channels: $\lambda = 2.5$; $\mu = 60/10 = 6$
With $P_0 = 0.6552$,

$L_q = \dfrac{(\lambda/\mu)^2\lambda\mu}{1!(2\mu-\lambda)^2}P_0 = 0.0189$

$L = L_q + \dfrac{\lambda}{\mu} = 0.4356$

Total cost $= 25(0.4356) + 2(16) = \$42.89$
Use one consultant with an 8-minute service time.

22.

Characteristic	A	B	C
a. P_0	0.2000	0.5000	0.4286
b. L_q	3.2000	0.5000	0.1524
c. L	4.0000	1.0000	0.9524
d. W_q	0.1333	0.0208	0.0063
e. W	0.1667	0.0417	0.0397
f. P_w	0.8000	0.5000	0.2286

The two-channel System C provides the best service.

24. a. $\mu = 1/2 = 0.5$

b. $W_q = W - 1/\mu = 10 - 1/0.5 = 8$ minutes

c. $L = \lambda W = 4(10) = 40$

26. a. 0.2668, 10 minutes, 0.6667

b. 0.0667, 7 minutes, 0.4669

c. \$25.33; \$33.34; one-channel is more economical

27. a. $2/8$ hours $= 0.25$ per hour

b. $1/3.2$ hours $= 0.3125$ per hour

c. $L_q = \dfrac{\lambda^2\sigma^2 + (\lambda/\mu)^2}{2(1-\lambda/\mu)}$

$= \dfrac{(0.25)^2(2)^2 + (0.25/0.3125)^2}{2(1-0.25/0.3125} = 2.225$

d. $W_q = \dfrac{L_q}{\lambda} = \dfrac{2.225}{0.25} = 8.9$ hours

e. $W = W_q + \dfrac{1}{\mu} = 8.9 + \dfrac{1}{0.3125} = 12.1$ hours

f. Same as $P_w = \dfrac{\lambda}{\mu} = \dfrac{0.25}{0.3125} = 0.80$

80% of the time the welder is busy.

28. a. 10, 9.6

b. Design A with $\mu = 10$

c. 0.05, 0.01

d.

Characteristic	Design A	Design B
P_0	0.5000	0.4792
L_q	0.3125	0.2857
L	0.8125	0.8065
W_q	0.0625	0.0571
W	0.1625	0.1613
P_w	0.5000	0.5208

e. Design B has slightly less waiting time.

30. a. $\lambda = 42$; $\mu = 20$

i	$(\lambda/\mu)^i/i!$
0	1.0000
1	2.1000
2	2.2050
3	1.5435
Total	6.8485

j	P_j
0	1/6.8485 = −0.1460
1	2.1/6.8485 = −0.3066
2	2.2050/6.8485 = −0.3220
3	1.5435/6.8485 = −0.2254
	1.0000

b. 0.2254
c. $L = \lambda/\mu(1 - P_k) = 42/20(1 - 0.2254) = 1.6267$
d. Four lines will be necessary; the probability of denied access is 0.1499.

32. a. 31.04%
b. 27.58%
c. 0.2758, 0.1092, 0.0351
d. 3, 10.92%

34. $N = 5$; $\lambda = 0.025$; $\mu = 0.20$; $\lambda/\mu = 0.125$

a.

n	$\dfrac{N!}{(N-n)}\left(\dfrac{\lambda}{\mu}\right)^n$
0	1.0000
1	0.6250
2	0.3125
3	0.1172
4	0.0293
5	0.0037
Total	2.0877

$P_0 = 1/2.0877 = 0.4790$

b. $L_q = N - \left(\dfrac{\lambda + \mu}{\lambda}\right)(1 - P_0)$

$= 5 - \left(\dfrac{0.225}{0.025}\right)(1 - 0.4790) = 0.3110$

c. $L = L_q + (1 - P_0) = 0.3110 + (1 - 0.4790) = 0.8321$

d. $W_q = \dfrac{L_q}{(N - L)\lambda} = \dfrac{0.3110}{(5 - 0.8321)(0.025)}$

$= 2.9854$ minutes

e. $W = W_q + \dfrac{1}{\mu} = 2.9854 + \dfrac{1}{0.20} = 7.9854$ minutes

f. Trips/day = (8 hours)(60 minutes/hour)(λ)
= (8)(60)(0.025) = 12 trips
Time at copier: 12 × 7.9854 = 95.8 minutes/day
Wait time at copier: 12 × 2.9854 = 35.8 minutes/day

g. Yes, five assistants × 35.8 = 179 minutes (3 hours/day), so 3 hours per day are lost to waiting.
(35.8/480)(100) = 7.5% of each assistant's day is spent waiting for the copier.

Chapter 16

Simulation results will vary. These results provide general guidance on the approximate output values.

2. a. Base case: Profit = (300 − 200) × 4000 − 300,000 = 100,000
Worst case: Profit = (300 − 240) × 0 − 300,000 = −300,000
Best case: Profit = (300 − 160) × 20,000 − 300,000 = 2,500,000

b. See Figure G16.2b. Average profit is approximately $108,681 with a probability of 0.54 of a loss. This project appears to be risky.

FIGURE G16.2b

	A	B	C	D	E	F	G
1	**Madeira Manufacturing Company**						
2							
3	**Parameters**						
4	Unit Selling Price	300					
5	Fixed Cost	300000					
6	Variable Cost	=RANDBETWEEN(B10,B11)					
7	Demand	=LN(RAND())*(–1*E10)					
8							
9	**Variable Cost (Uniform Distribution)**			**Demand (Exponential Distribution)**			
10	Smallest Value	160		Mean	4000		
11	Largest Value	240					
12							
13	**Model**						
14	Profit	=((B4–B6)*B7) – B5					
15							
16							
17	**Simulation Trial**	**Unit Variable Cost**	**Demand**	**Profit**		**Summary Statistics**	
18	1	=B6	=B7	=B14		Mean Profit	=AVERAGE(D18:D1017)
19	2	=TABLE(,D2)	=TABLE(,D2)	=TABLE(,D2)		Probability of Loss	=COUNTIF(D18:D1017,"<0")/COUNT(D18:D1017)
20	3	=TABLE(,D2)	=TABLE(,D2)	=TABLE(,D2)			
21	4	=TABLE(,D2)	=TABLE(,D2)	=TABLE(,D2)			
22	5	=TABLE(,D2)	=TABLE(,D2)	=TABLE(,D2)			
23	6	=TABLE(,D2)	=TABLE(,D2)	=TABLE(,D2)			
24	7	=TABLE(,D2)	=TABLE(,D2)	=TABLE(,D2)			
25	8	=TABLE(,D2)	=TABLE(,D2)	=TABLE(,D2)			
26	9	=TABLE(,D2)	=TABLE(,D2)	=TABLE(,D2)			
27	10	=TABLE(,D2)	=TABLE(,D2)	=TABLE(,D2)			

4. As the number of dice in the sum increases, the distribution becomes more bell-shaped. This demonstrates the central limit theorem.

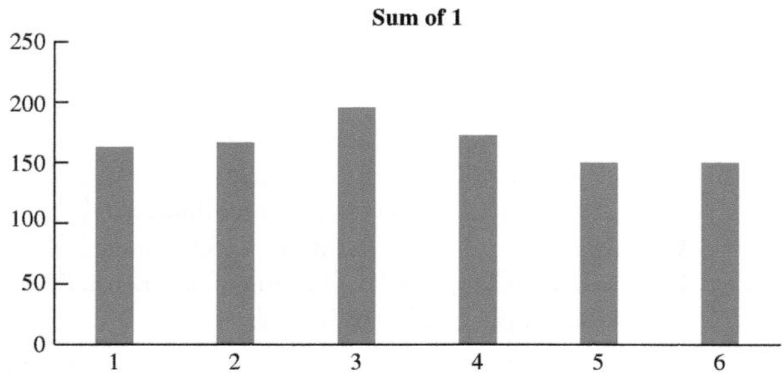

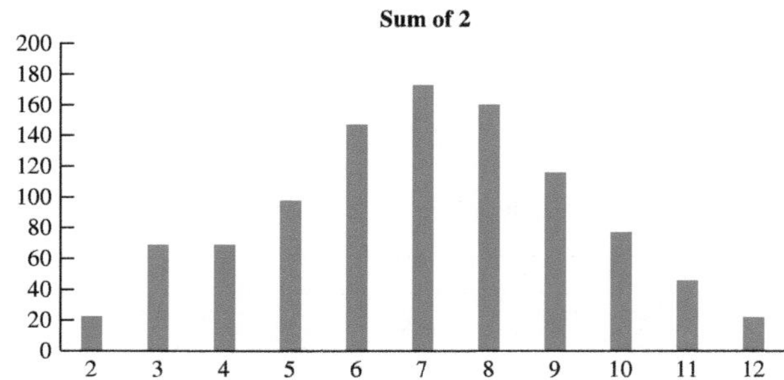

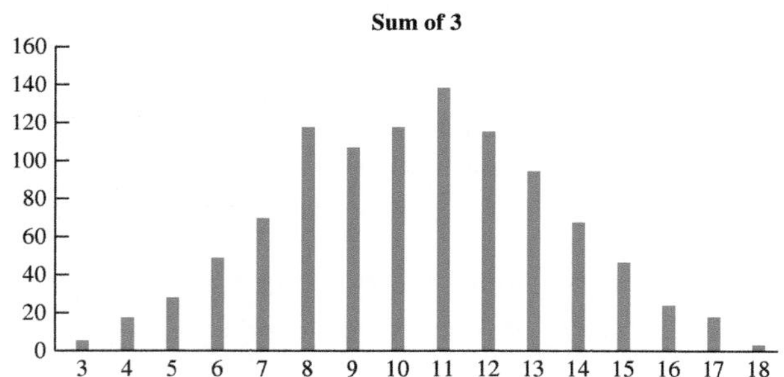

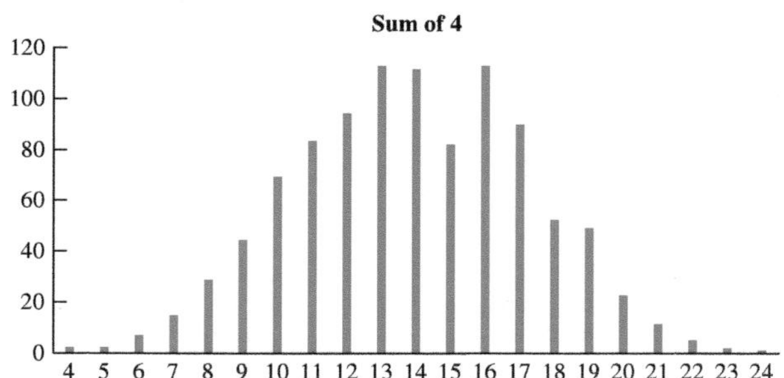

6. a.

	A	B	C	D	E	F
1	**Statewide**					
2						
3	**Parameters**					
4	Claims Payment	=VLOOKUP(RAND(),A8:C14,3,TRUE)				
5						
6	**Claims Payment**					
7	Lower End of Interval	Upper End of Interval	Payment	Probability		Squared Deviation From Mean
8	0	=D8+A8	0	0.83		=(C8-$F$17)^2
9	=B8	=D9+A9	500	0.06		=(C9-$F$17)^2
10	=B9	=D10+A10	1000	0.05		=(C10-$F$17)^2
11	=B10	=D11+A11	2000	0.02		=(C11-$F$17)^2
12	=B11	=D12+A12	5000	0.02		=(C12-$F$17)^2
13	=B12	=D13+A13	8000	0.01		=(C13-$F$17)^2
14	=B13	=D14+A14	10000	0.01		=(C14-$F$17)^2
15						
16	**Simulation Trial**	**Claims Payment**		**Summary Statistic**	**Simulation Estimate**	**Formulaic Computation**
17	1	=B4		Mean Payment	=AVERAGE(B17:B1016)	=SUMPRODUCT(C8:C14,D8:D14)
18	2	=TABLE(,H10)		Payment Standard Deviation	=STDEV.S(B17:B1016)	=SQRT(SUMPRODUCT(D8:D14,F8:F14))
19	3	=TABLE(,H10)				
20	4	=TABLE(,H10)				
21	5	=TABLE(,H10)				
22	6	=TABLE(,H10)				
23	7	=TABLE(,H10)				
24	8	=TABLE(,H10)				
25	9	=TABLE(,H10)				
26	10	=TABLE(,H10)				

b. The simulation-based estimates of the payment mean and standard deviation are \$513 and \$1736, respectively. Computing the mean and standard deviation directly from the distribution using the respective formulas, we obtain \$400 and \$1458, respectively. To reduce the discrepancy between the simulation-based estimates and the analytical computation, we can increase the number of simulation trials.

8. a.

	A	B	C	D	E	F	G	H
1	**New York Stock Exchange**							
2								
3	**Parameters**							
4	3-Month Stock Price Change	=VLOOKUP(RAND(),$A$11:$C$17,3,TRUE)						
5	3-Month Stock Price Change	=VLOOKUP(RAND(),$A$11:$C$17,3,TRUE)						
6	3-Month Stock Price Change	=VLOOKUP(RAND(),$A$11:$C$17,3,TRUE)						
7	3-Month Stock Price Change	=VLOOKUP(RAND(),$A$11:$C$17,3,TRUE)						
8								
9	**3-Month Stock Price Change**							
10	Lower End of Interval	Upper End of Interval	Change	Probability				
11	0	=D11+A11	−2	0.05				
12	=B11	=D12+A12	−1	0.1				
13	=B12	=D13+A13	0	0.25				
14	=B13	=D14+A14	1	0.2				
15	=B14	=D15+A15	2	0.2				
16	=B15	=D16+A16	3	0.1				
17	=B16	=D17+A17	4	0.1				
18	**Model**							
19	Current Stock Price	39						
20	Stock Price in 3 Months	=B19+B4						
21	Stock Price in 6 Months	=B20+B5						
22	Stock Price in 9 Months	=B21+B6						
23	Stock Price in 12 Months	=B22+B7						
24								
25	**Simulation Trial**	Stock Price in 3 Months	Stock Price in 6 Months	Stock Price in 9 Months	Stock Price in 12 Months		**Summary Statistics**	
26	1	=B20	=B21	=B22	=B23		Mean Stock Price in 12 Months	=AVERAGE(E26:E1025)
27	2	=TABLE(,G35)	=TABLE(,G35)	=TABLE(,G35)	=TABLE(,G35)		St. Dev. Stock Price in 12 Months	=STDEV.S(E26:E1025)
28	3	=TABLE(,G35)	=TABLE(,G35)	=TABLE(,G35)	=TABLE(,G35)			
29	4	=TABLE(,G35)	=TABLE(,G35)	=TABLE(,G35)	=TABLE(,G35)			
30	5	=TABLE(,G35)	=TABLE(,G35)	=TABLE(,G35)	=TABLE(,G35)			
31	6	=TABLE(,G35)	=TABLE(,G35)	=TABLE(,G35)	=TABLE(,G35)			
32	7	=TABLE(,G35)	=TABLE(,G35)	=TABLE(,G35)	=TABLE(,G35)			
33	8	=TABLE(,G35)	=TABLE(,G35)	=TABLE(,G35)	=TABLE(,G35)			
34	9	=TABLE(,G35)	=TABLE(,G35)	=TABLE(,G35)	=TABLE(,G35)			
35	10	=TABLE(,G35)	=TABLE(,G35)	=TABLE(,G35)	=TABLE(,G35)			

b. The mean stock price after 12 months is \$43.51, and the standard deviation is \$3.27.

c. The lowest stock price that is possible after 12 months is \$31, resulting from four consecutive three-month changes of −\$2. The highest stock price that is possible after 12 months is \$55, resulting from four consecutive three-month changes of +\$4. To model a wider range of outcomes, an unbounded distribution for the three-month change could be used. The normal distribution or skewed normal distribution may be two choices.

10. See Figure G16.10.

a. Expected project length is 33.91 weeks with a standard deviation of 2.81 weeks.

b. Probability of completing project in 35 weeks or less is 0.729.

FIGURE G16.10

	A	B	C	D	E	F	G	H	I
1	**Project**								
2									
3	**Parameters**								
4	Activity A Duration	=VLOOKUP(RAND(),A11:C14,3,TRUE)							
5	Activity B Duration	=VLOOKUP(RAND(),F11:H13,3,TRUE)							
6	Activity C Duration	=VLOOKUP(RAND(),A18:C22,3,TRUE)							
7	Activity D Duration	=VLOOKUP(RAND(),F18:H19,3,TRUE)							
8									
9	**Activity A**					**Activity B**			
10	Lower End of Interval	Upper End of Interval	Duration	Probability		Lower End of Interval	Upper End of Interval	Duration	Probability
11	0	-D11+A11	5	0.25		0	=I11+F11	3	0.2
12	=B11	=D12+A12	6	0.35		=G11	=I12+F12	5	0.55
13	=B12	=D13+A13	7	0.25		=G12	=I13+F13	7	0.25
14	=B13	=D14+A14	8	0.15					
15									
16	**Activity C**					**Activity D**			
17	Lower End of Interval	Upper End of Interval	Duration	Probability		Lower End of Interval	Upper End of Interval	Duration	Probability
18	0	=D18+A18	10	0.1		0	=I18+F18	8	0.6
19	=B18	=D19+A19	12	0.25		=G18	=I19+F19	10	0.4
20	=B19	=D20+A20	14	0.4					
21	=B20	=D21+A21	16	0.2					
22	=B21	=D22+A22	18	0.05					
23									
24	**Model**								
25	Project Length	=SUM(B4:B7)							
26									
27	**Simulation Trial**	**Activity A**	**Activity B**	**Activity C**	**Activity D**	**Project Length**		**Summary Statistics**	
28	1	=B4	=B5	=B6	=B7	=B25		Mean Project Length	=AVERAGE(F28:F1027)
29	2	=TABLE(,H33)	=TABLE(,H33)	=TABLE(,H33)	=TABLE(,H33)	=TABLE(,H33)		St. Dev. Project Length	=STDEV.S(F28:F1027)
30	3	=TABLE(,H33)	=TABLE(,H33)	=TABLE(,H33)	=TABLE(,H33)	=TABLE(,H33)		P(Project Length <36)	=COUNTIF(F28:F1027,"<36")/COUNT(F28:F1027)
31	4	=TABLE(,H33)	=TABLE(,H33)	=TABLE(,H33)	=TABLE(,H33)	=TABLE(,H33)			
32	5	=TABLE(,H33)	=TABLE(,H33)	=TABLE(,H33)	=TABLE(,H33)	=TABLE(,H33)			
33	6	=TABLE(,H33)	=TABLE(,H33)	=TABLE(,H33)	=TABLE(,H33)	=TABLE(,H33)			
34	7	=TABLE(,H33)	=TABLE(,H33)	=TABLE(,H33)	=TABLE(,H33)	=TABLE(,H33)			
35	8	=TABLE(,H33)	=TABLE(,H33)	=TABLE(,H33)	=TABLE(,H33)	=TABLE(,H33)			
36	9	=TABLE(,H33)	=TABLE(,H33)	=TABLE(,H33)	=TABLE(,H33)	=TABLE(,H33)			
37	10	=TABLE(,H33)	=TABLE(,H33)	=TABLE(,H33)	=TABLE(,H33)	=TABLE(,H33)			

12. a. Average net profit is $5,165.

b. There is a .039 probability that the overbooking strategy will result in less than $5000 net profit (the net profit resulting from no overbooking).

	A	B	C	D	E	F
1	**South Central Airlines**					
2						
3	**Parameters**					
4	**Capacity**	50				
5	**Number of Reservations**	52				
6	**Passengers Showing Up**	=VLOOKUP(RAND(),A10:C14,3,TRUE)				
7						
8	**Passengers Showing Up**					
9	Lower End of Interval	Upper End of Interval	Cost	Probability		
10	0	=D10+A10	48	0.05		
11	=B10	=D11+A11	49	0.25		
12	=B11	=D12+A12	50	0.5		
13	=B12	=D13+A13	51	0.15		
14	=B13	=D14+A14	52	0.05		
15						
16	**Marginal Profit**	100				
17	**Marginal Overbooking Cost**	150				
18						
19	**Model**					
20	**Profit from Reservations**	=B5*B16				
21	**Overbooked Passengers**	=IF(B6>B4,B6–B4,0)				
22	**Total Overbooking Cost**	=B17*B21				
23	**Net Profit**	=B20–B22				
24						
25	**Simulation Trial**	**Passengers Showing Up**	**Net Profit**		**Summary Statistics**	
26	1	=B6	=B23		Mean Profit per Unit	=AVERAGE(C26:C1025)
27	2	=TABLE(,J26)	=TABLE(,J26)		P(Profit < $5000)	=COUNTIF(C26:C1025,"<5000")/COUNT(C26:C1025)
28	3	=TABLE(,J26)	=TABLE(,J26)			
29	4	=TABLE(,J26)	=TABLE(,J26)			
30	5	=TABLE(,J26)	=TABLE(,J26)			
31	6	=TABLE(,J26)	=TABLE(,J26)			
32	7	=TABLE(,J26)	=TABLE(,J26)			
33	8	=TABLE(,J26)	=TABLE(,J26)			
34	9	=TABLE(,J26)	=TABLE(,J26)			
35	10	=TABLE(,J26)	=TABLE(,J26)			

c. The same spreadsheet design can be used to simulate other overbooking strategies, including accepting 51, 53, and 54 passenger reservations. In each case, South Central would need to estimate the distribution of the number of passengers showing up and rerun the simulation model. This would enable South Central to evaluate the other overbooking alternatives and determine the most beneficial overbooking policy.

Alternatively, the distribution of passengers showing up for the flight could be modeled as a binomial random variable in which n = the reservation limit and p = probability of an individual passenger showing up for a flight.

14. See Figure G16.14.

a. We win the bid about 64% of the time with a bid of $750,000.

FIGURE G16.14

	A	B	C	D	E	F	G	H
1	**Contractor Bidding**							
2								
3	**Parameters**							
4	Contractor A Bid	=B8+(B9–B8)*RAND()						
5	Contractor B Bid	=NORM.INV(RAND(),E8,E9)						
6								
7	**Contractor A (Uniform Distribution)**			**Contractor A (Normal Distribution)**				
8	Minimum Value	600000		Mean	700000			
9	Maximum Value	800000		Standard Deviation	50000			
10								
11	**Model**							
12	Our Bid	750000						
13	Winning Bid	=MAX(B4,B5,B12)						
14	Winning Contractor	=IF(B12>MAX(B4:B5),"US",IF(B4>B5,"A","B"))						
15								
16	**Simulation Trial**	Contractor A's Bid	Contractor B's Bid	Winning Bid	Winning Contractor		**Summary Statistics**	
17	1	=B4	=B5	=B13	=B14		P(We Win Bid)	=COUNTIF(E17:E1016,"=US")/COUNTA(E17:E1016)
18	2	=TABLE(,I8)	=TABLE(,I8)	=TABLE(,I8)	=TABLE(,I8)			
19	3	=TABLE(,I8)	=TABLE(,I8)	=TABLE(,I8)	=TABLE(,I8)			
20	4	=TABLE(,I8)	=TABLE(,I8)	=TABLE(,I8)	=TABLE(,I8)			
21	5	=TABLE(,I8)	=TABLE(,I8)	=TABLE(,I8)	=TABLE(,I8)			
22	6	=TABLE(,I8)	=TABLE(,I8)	=TABLE(,I8)	=TABLE(,I8)			
23	7	=TABLE(,I8)	=TABLE(,I8)	=TABLE(,I8)	=TABLE(,I8)			
24	8	=TABLE(,I8)	=TABLE(,I8)	=TABLE(,I8)	=TABLE(,I8)			
25	9	=TABLE(,I8)	=TABLE(,I8)	=TABLE(,I8)	=TABLE(,I8)			
26	10	=TABLE(,I8)	=TABLE(,I8)	=TABLE(,I8)	=TABLE(,I8)			

b. Bidding $765,000 results in winning approximately 75% of the time. Bidding $775,000 results in winning approximately 82% of the time. Thus, to ensure at least an 80% chance of winning the bid, we must bid $775,000.

16. See Figure G16.16. Estimates possess non-neglible variability.

FIGURE G16.16

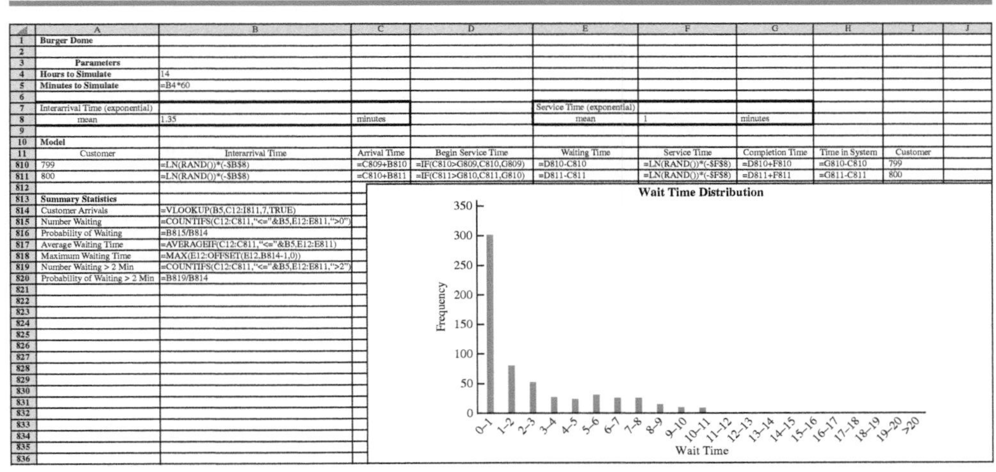

	A	B	C	D	E	F	G	H	I	J
1	**Burger Dome**									
2										
3	**Parameters**									
4	**Hours to Simulate**	14								
5	**Minutes to Simulate**	=B4*60								
6										
7	Interarrival Time (exponential)				Service Time (exponential)					
8	mean	1.35	minutes		mean	1	minutes			
9										
10	**Model**									
11	Customer	Interarrival Time	Arrival Time	Begin Service Time	Waiting Time	Service Time	Completion Time	Time in System	Customer	
810	799	=LN(RAND())*(-$B$8)	=C809+B810	=IF(C810>G809,C810,G809)	=D810-C810	=LN(RAND())*(-$F$8)	=D810+F810	=G810-C810	799	
811	800	=LN(RAND())*(-$B$8)	=C810+B811	=IF(C811>G810,C811,G810)	=D811-C811	=LN(RAND())*(-$F$8)	=D811+F811	=G811-C811	800	
812										
813	**Summary Statistics**									
814	Customer Arrivals	=VLOOKUP(B5,C12:I811,7,TRUE)								
815	Number Waiting	=COUNTIFS(C12:C811,"<="&B5,E12:E811,">0")								
816	Probability of Waiting	=B815/B814								
817	Average Waiting Time	=AVERAGEIF(C12:C811,"<="&B5,E12:E811)								
818	Maximum Waiting Time	=MAX(E12:OFFSET(E12,B814-1,0))								
819	Number Waiting > 2 Min	=COUNTIFS(C12:C811,"<="&B5,E12:E811,">2")								
820	Probability of Waiting > 2 Min	=B819/B814								

a. Average wait time is approximately 2.29 minutes.

b. The longest wait time varies, but 15.0 is a representative value.

c. There is an estimated probability of 0.4037 of a customer waiting more than 2 minutes.

d. See Figure G16.16.

e. It is not appropriate to increase the number of trials because Burger Dome is trying to model the waiting line behavior during its 14-hour work day (and each day begins with no customers in the system from the previous day).

18. Estimates possess considerable variability, but adding a second employee results in a reduced average wait time (0.16 minutes), decreased maximum wait time (5.1 minutes), and decreased probability of waiting more than 2 minutes (0.0180). Burger Dome needs to evaluate whether these improvements are worth the cost of the second employee.

20. See Figure G16.20.

FIGURE G16.20

	A	B	C	D	E
1	**Blackjack**				
2					
3	**Parameters**				
4	End Value of Dealer's Hand	=VLOOKUP(RAND(),A9:C14,3,TRUE)			
5	End Value of Your Hand	=VLOOKUP(RAND(),A18:C23,3,TRUE)			
6					
7	**End Value of Dealer's Hand**				
8	Lower End of Interval	Upper End of Interval	Value	Probability	
9	0	=D9+A9	17	0.1654	
10	=B9	=D10+A10	18	0.1063	
11	=B10	=D11+A11	19	0.1063	
12	=B11	=D12+A12	20	0.1017	
13	=B12	=D13+A13	21	0.0972	
14	=B13	=D14+A14	0	0.4231	
15					
16	**End Value of Your Hand**				
17	Lower End of Interval	Upper End of Interval	Value	Probability	
18	0	=D18+A18	17	0.0769	
19	=B18	=D19+A19	18	0.0769	
20	=B19	=D20+A20	19	0.0769	
21	=B20	=D21+A21	20	0.0769	
22	=B21	=D22+A22	21	0.0769	
23	=B22	=D23+A23	0	0.6155	
24					
25	**Model**				
26	Winner	=IF(B5=0,"Dealer",IF(B4>B5,"Dealer",IF(B4=B5,"Push","You")))			
27					
28	**Simulation Trial**	**Winner**		**Summary Statistics**	
29	1	=B26		P(Dealer Win)	=COUNTIF(B29:B1028,"=Dealer")/COUNTA(B29:B1028)
30	2	=TABLE(,G20)		P(Push)	=COUNTIF(B29:B1028,"=Push")/COUNTA(B29:B1028)
31	3	=TABLE(,G20)		P(You Win)	=COUNTIF(B29:B1028,"=You")/COUNTA(B29:B1028)
32	4	=TABLE(,G20)			
33	5	=TABLE(,G20)			
34	6	=TABLE(,G20)			
35	7	=TABLE(,G20)			
36	8	=TABLE(,G20)			
37	9	=TABLE(,G20)			

c. When the dealer has a 6 and you have a 16 and you decide to hit, you have about a 24.8% chance of winning, 3.9% chance of tying, and 71.3% chance of losing to the dealer.
d. When the dealer has a 6 and you have a 16 and you stay on 16, you have about a 43.5% chance of winning, 0% chance of tying, and 56.5% chance of losing to the dealer.

Chapter 17

2. **a.** 0.81
b. $\pi_1 = 0.5, \pi_2 = 0.5$
c. $\pi_1 = 0.6, \pi_2 = 0.4$

3. **a.** 0.10 as given by the transition probability
b. $\pi_1 = 0.90\pi_1 + 0.30\pi_2$ (1)
$\pi_2 = 0.10\pi_1 + 0.70\pi_2$ (2)
$\pi_1 + \pi_2 = 1$ (3)
Using (1) and (3),

$$0.10\pi_1 - 0.30\pi_2 = 0$$
$$0.10\pi_1 - 0.30(1 - \pi_1) = 0$$
$$0.10\pi_1 - 0.30 + 0.30\pi_1 = 0$$
$$0.40\pi_1 = 0.30$$
$$\pi_1 = 0.75$$
$$\pi_2 = (1 - \pi_1) = 0.25$$

4. **a.** $\pi_1 = 0.92, \pi_2 = 0.08$
b. $85

6. **a.** Given the opposing player last chose Rock, the transition matrix shows that she is most likely to choose Paper next (with probability 0.42). Therefore, you should choose Scissors (because Scissors beats Paper).
b.

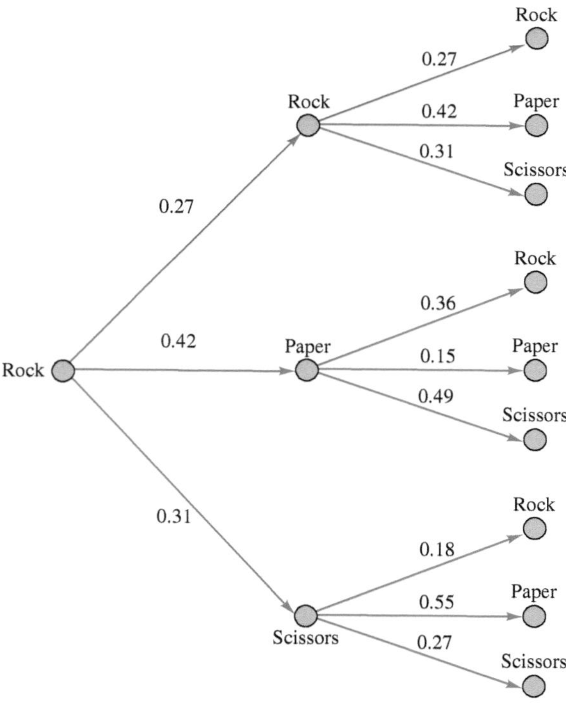

c. The one step probability matrix is

$$P = \begin{bmatrix} 0.27 & 0.42 & 0.31 \\ 0.36 & 0.15 & 0.49 \\ 0.18 & 0.55 & 0.27 \end{bmatrix}$$

The probability your opponent will choose Paper two rounds from now given she chose Rock last round is given by $\pi_2(2)$. This can be found from $\Pi(2)$ by first finding $\Pi(1)$ as follows:

$$\Pi(1) = [1 \quad 0 \quad 0] \begin{bmatrix} 0.27 & 0.42 & 0.31 \\ 0.36 & 0.15 & 0.49 \\ 0.18 & 0.55 & 0.27 \end{bmatrix}$$
$$= [0.27 \quad 0.42 \quad 0.31]$$

$$\Pi(2) = [0.27 \quad 0.42 \quad 0.31] \begin{bmatrix} 0.27 & 0.42 & 0.31 \\ 0.36 & 0.15 & 0.49 \\ 0.18 & 0.55 & 0.27 \end{bmatrix}$$
$$= [0.28 \quad 0.35 \quad 0.37]$$

So, $\pi_2(2)$ is 0.35.

8. **a.** $\pi_1 = 0.85\pi_1 + 0.20\pi_2 + 0.15\pi_3$ (1)
$\pi_2 = 0.10\pi_1 + 0.75\pi_2 + 0.10\pi_3$ (2)
$\pi_3 = 0.05\pi_1 + 0.05\pi_2 + 0.75\pi_3$ (3)
$\pi_1 + \pi_2 + \pi_3 = 1$ (4)

Using (1), (2), and (4) provides three equations with three unknowns; solving provides $\pi_1 = 0.548$, $\pi_2 = 0.286$, and $\pi_3 = 0.166$.
b. 16.6% as given by π_3
c. Quick Stop should take

	667 − 0.548(1000) =	119 Murphy's customers
and	333 − 0.286(1000) =	47 Ashley's customers
	Total	166 Quick Stop customers

10. $\pi_1 = 0.80\pi_1 + 0.05\pi_2 + 0.40\pi_3$ (1)
$\pi_2 = 0.10\pi_1 + 0.75\pi_2 + 0.30\pi_3$ (2)
$\pi_3 = 0.10\pi_1 + 0.20\pi_2 + 0.30\pi_3$ (3)
also
$\pi_1 + \pi_2 + \pi_3 = 1$ (4)

Using equations 1, 2, and 4, we have $\pi_1 = 0.442$, $\pi_2 = 0.385$, and $\pi_3 = 0.173$.

The Markov analysis shows that Special B now has the largest market share. In fact, its market share has increased by almost 11%. The MDA brand will be hurt most by the introduction of the new brand, T-White. People who switch from MDA to T-White are more likely to make a second switch back to MDA.

12. $(I - Q) = \begin{bmatrix} 1 & 0 \\ 0 & 1 \end{bmatrix} - \begin{bmatrix} 0.4 & 0.3 \\ 0.1 & 0.5 \end{bmatrix} = \begin{bmatrix} 0.6 & -0.3 \\ -0.1 & 0.5 \end{bmatrix}$

$$N = (I - Q)^{-1} = \begin{bmatrix} 1.85 & 1.11 \\ 0.37 & 2.22 \end{bmatrix}$$

$$NR = \begin{bmatrix} 1.85 & 1.11 \\ 0.37 & 2.22 \end{bmatrix} \begin{bmatrix} 0.2 & 0.1 \\ 0.2 & 0.2 \end{bmatrix} = \begin{bmatrix} 0.59 & 0.41 \\ 0.52 & 0.48 \end{bmatrix}$$

0.59 probability state 3 units end up in state 1;
0.52 probability state 4 units end up in state 1.

13. $I = \begin{bmatrix} 1 & 0 \\ 0 & 1 \end{bmatrix} \quad Q = \begin{bmatrix} 0.25 & 0.25 \\ 0.05 & 0.25 \end{bmatrix}$

$$(I - Q) = \begin{bmatrix} 0.75 & -0.25 \\ -0.05 & 0.75 \end{bmatrix}$$

$$N = (I - Q)^{-1} = \begin{bmatrix} 1.3636 & 0.4545 \\ 0.0909 & 1.3636 \end{bmatrix}$$

$$NR = \begin{bmatrix} 1.3636 & 0.4545 \\ 0.0909 & 1.3636 \end{bmatrix} \begin{bmatrix} 0.5 & 0.01 \\ 0.5 & 0.5 \end{bmatrix} = \begin{bmatrix} 0.909 & 0.091 \\ 0.727 & 0.273 \end{bmatrix}$$

$$BNR = [4000 \quad 5000] \begin{bmatrix} 0.909 & 0.091 \\ 0.727 & 0.273 \end{bmatrix} = [7271 \quad 1729]$$

Estimate $1729 in bad debts.

14. 3580 will be sold eventually; 1420 will be lost.

16. **a.** The Injured and Retired states are absorbing states.

b. Rearrange the transition probability matrix to the following:

	Injured	Retired	Backup	Starter
Injured	1	0	0	0
Retired	0	1	0	0
Backup	0.1	0.1	0.4	0.4
Starter	0.15	0.25	0.1	0.5

$$(I - Q) = \begin{bmatrix} 0.6 & -0.4 \\ -0.1 & 0.5 \end{bmatrix}$$

$$N = (I - Q)^{-1} = \begin{bmatrix} 1.923 & 1.538 \\ 0.385 & 2.308 \end{bmatrix}$$

$$NR = \begin{bmatrix} 0.423 & 0.577 \\ 0.385 & 0.615 \end{bmatrix}$$

38.5% of Starters will eventually be Injured and 61.5% will be Retired.

c. $BNR = [8 \quad 5] \begin{bmatrix} 0.423 & 0.577 \\ 0.385 & 0.615 \end{bmatrix}$

$= [5.308 \quad 7.691]$

We expect that 5.308 players will end up injured and 7.691 will retire.

Appendix A

2. =F6*$F$3

4.

	A	B	C	D
1	**Nowlin Plastics**			
2				
3	**Fixed Cost**	$3,000.00		
4				
5	**Variable Cost Per Unit**	$2.00		
6				
7	**Selling Price Per Unit**	$5.00		
8				
9	**Capacity**	1500		
10				
11	**Forecasted Demand**	1200		
12				
13	**Model**			
14				
15	**Production Volume**	1200		
16				
17	**Total Cost**	$5,400.00		
18				
19	**Total Revenue**	$6,000.00		
20				
21	**Total Profit (Loss)**	$600.00		
22				

	A	B	C
1	**Nowlin Plastics**		
2			
3	**Fixed Cost**	3000	
4			
5	**Variable Cost Per Unit**	2	
6			
7	**Selling Price Per Unit**	5	
8			
9	**Capacity**	1500	
10			
11	**Forecasted Demand**	1200	
12			
13	**Model**		
14			
15	**Production Volume**	=IF(B11<B9,B11,B9)	
16			
17	**Total Cost**	=B3+B5*B15	
18			
19	**Total Revenue**	=B7*B15	
20			
21	**Total Profit (Loss)**	=B19-B17	
22			

6. a.

	A	B	C	D	E
1	**Cox Electric Breakeven Analysis**				
2	**Parameters**				
3	Revenue per Unit	$0.65			
4				–$5,200.00	
5	Fixed Costs	$10,000.00	0	0	
6			10,000	–$6,000.00	
7	Material Cost per Unit	$0.15	20,000	–$2,000.00	
8			30,000	$2,000.00	
9	Labor Cost per Unit	$0.10	40,000	$6,000.00	
10			50,000	$10,000.00	
11			60,000	$14,000.00	
12	**Model**		70,000	$18,000.00	
13			80,000	$22,000.00	
14	Production Volume	12,000	90,000	$26,000.00	
15			100,000	$30,000.00	
16	Total Revenue	$7,800.00			
17					
18	Material Cost	$1,800.00			
19	Labor Cost	$1,200.00			
20	Fixed Cost	$10,000.00			
21	Total Cost	$13,000.00			
22					
23	Profit	–$5,200.00			
24					

Data Table
Row input cell:
Column input cell: $B$14
OK Cancel

Breakeven appears in the interval of 20,000 to 30,000 units.

b.

	A	B	C	D	E
1	**Cox Electric Breakeven Analysis**				
2					
3	Revenue per Unit	$0.65			
4					
5	Fixed Costs	$10,000.00			
6					
7	Material Cost per Unit	$0.15			
8					
9	Labor Cost per Unit	$0.10			
10					
11					
12	**Model**				
13					
14	Production Volume	25,000			
15					
16	Total Revenue	$16,250.00			
17					
18	Material Cost	$3,750.00			
19	Labor Cost	$2,500.00			
20	Fixed Cost	$10,000.00			
21	Total Cost	$16,250.00			
22					
23	Profit	$0.00			
24					

Goal Seek
Set cell: $B$23
To value: 0
By changing cell: $B$14
OK Cancel

8. a.

	A	B	C	D	E
1	OM 455				
2	Section 001				
3	Course Grading Scale Based on Course Average:				
4		**Lower**	**Upper**	**Course**	
5		**Limit**	**Limit**	**Grade**	
6		0	59	F	
7		60	69	D	
8		70	79	C	
9		80	89	B	
10		90	100	A	
11					
12		Midterm	Final	Course	Course
13	Lastname	Score	Score	Average	Grade
14	Benson	70	56	63.0	D
15	Chin	95	91	93.0	A
16	Choi	82	80	81.0	B
17	Cruz	45	78	61.5	D
18	Doe	68	45	56.5	F
19	Honda	91	98	94.5	A
20	Hume	87	74	80.5	B
21	Jones	60	80	70.0	C
22	Miranda	80	93	86.5	B
23	Murigami	97	98	97.5	A
24	Ruebush	90	91	90.5	A
25					
26					
27					
28			Grade	Count	
29			A	4	
30			B	3	
31			C	1	
32			D	2	
33			F	1	

	C	D
28	Grade	Count
29	A	=COUNTIF ($E$14:$E$24,C29)
30	B	=COUNTIF ($E$14:$E$24,C30)
31	C	=COUNTIF ($E$14:$E$24,C31)
32	D	=COUNTIF ($E$14:$E$24,C32)
33	F	=COUNTIF ($E$14:$E$24,C33)

b.

A	3
B	2
C	2
D	1
F	3

10. **a.** A portion of the spreadsheet is shown below.
b. See column I below.

	A	B	C	D	E	F	G	H	I	J
1	Order	Quantity	Price per Roll	Revenue						
2	1	86	$195	$16,770		Quantity Ordered				
3	2	452	$155	$70,060		From	To	Price per Roll		
4	3	492	$155	$76,260		1	50	$215		
5	4	191	$175	$33,425		51	100	$195		
6	5	356	$155	$55,180		101	200	$175		
7	6	148	$175	$25,900		201	and up	$155		
8	7	342	$155	$53,010						
9	8	382	$155	$59,210						
10	9	276	$155	$42,780						
11	10	118	$175	$20,650		Total Revenue	$7,107,505			
12	11	464	$155	$71,920						
13	12	188	$175	$32,900						
14	13	25	$215	$5,375		From	To	Price per Roll	Number Orders	% of Orders
15	14	427	$155	$66,185		1	50	$215	13	7.6%
16	15	30	$215	$6,450		51	100	$195	15	8.7%
17	16	111	$175	$19,425		101	200	$175	37	21.5%
18	17	161	$175	$28,175		201	and up	$155	107	62.2%
19	18	314	$155	$48,670				Total:	172	100.0%
20	19	442	$155	$68,510						

	A	B	C	D	E	F	G	H	I	J
1	Order	Quantity	Price per Roll	Revenue						
2	1	86	=VLOOKUP(B2,$F$4:$H$7,3)	=B2*C2		Quantity Ordered				
3	2	452	=VLOOKUP(B3,$F$4:$H$7,3)	=B3*C3		From	To	Price per Roll		
4	3	492	=VLOOKUP(B4,$F$4:$H$7,3)	=B4*C4		1	50	215		
5	4	191	=VLOOKUP(B5,$F$4:$H$7,3)	=B5*C5		51	100	195		
6	5	356	=VLOOKUP(B6,$F$4:$H$7,3)	=B6*C6		101	200	175		
7	6	148	=VLOOKUP(B7,$F$4:$H$7,3)	=B7*C7		201	and up	155		
8	7	342	=VLOOKUP(B8,$F$4:$H$7,3)	=B8*C8						
9	8	382	=VLOOKUP(B9,$F$4:$H$7,3)	=B9*C9						
10	9	276	=VLOOKUP(B10,$F$4:$H$7,3)	=B10*C10						
11	10	118	=VLOOKUP(B11,$F$4:$H$7,3)	=B11*C11		Total Revenue	=SUM(D2:D173)			
12	11	464	=VLOOKUP(B12,$F$4:$H$7,3)	=B12*C12						
13	12	188	=VLOOKUP(B13,$F$4:$H$7,3)	=B13*C13						
14	13	25	=VLOOKUP(B14,$F$4:$H$7,3)	=B14*C14		=F3	=G3	=H3	Number Orders	% of Orders
15	14	427	=VLOOKUP(B15,$F$4:$H$7,3)	=B15*C15		=F4	=G4	=H4	=COUNTIF($C$2:$C$173,H15)	=I15/$I$19
16	15	30	=VLOOKUP(B16,$F$4:$H$7,3)	=B16*C16		=F5	=G5	=H5	=COUNTIF($C$2:$C$173,H16)	=I16/$I$19
17	16	111	=VLOOKUP(B17,$F$4:$H$7,3)	=B17*C17		=F6	=G6	=H6	=COUNTIF($C$2:$C$173,H17)	=I17/$I$19
18	17	161	=VLOOKUP(B18,$F$4:$H$7,3)	=B18*C18		=F7	=G7	=H7	=COUNTIF($C$2:$C$173,H18)	=I18/$I$19
19	18	314	=VLOOKUP(B19,$F$4:$H$7,3)	=B19*C19				Total:	=SUM(I15:I18)	=SUM(J15:J18)
20	19	442	=VLOOKUP(B20,$F$4:$H$7,3)	=B20*C20						

12. Error #1: The formula in cell C17 is =SUMPRODUCT(C8:G11,B22:F25) but should be =SUMPRODUCT (C8:F11,B22:F25)

Error #2: The formula in cell G22 is =SUM(B22:E22) but should be =SUM(B22:F22)

Index

D

E

F

N

O

P

Q

R

S

T

U

V

W

Z